CME PROJECT

Geometry

PEARSON

Boston, Massachusetts
Glenview, Illinois
Shoreview, Minnesota
Upper Saddle River, New Jersey

Education Development Center, Inc.
Center for Mathematics Education
Newton, Massachusetts

Acknowledgments appear on page T776, which constitutes an extension of this copyright page.

Copyright © 2009 by Education Development Center, Inc. Published by Pearson Education, Inc., or its affiliates. All rights reserved. Printed in the United States of America. This publication is protected by copyright, and permission should be obtained from the publisher prior to any prohibited reproduction, storage in a retrieval system, or transmission in any form or by any means, electronic, mechanical, photocopying, recording, or likewise. For information regarding permission(s), write to Pearson School Rights and Permissions Department, One Lake Street, Upper Saddle River, New Jersey 07458.

Prentice Hall® and **Pearson Prentice Hall™** are trademarks, in the U.S. and/or in other countries, of Pearson Education, Inc., or its affiliate(s).

ExamView® and *LessonView®* are registered trademarks of FSCreations, Inc.

TI-Nspire™ is a trademark of Texas Instruments Incorporated.

PEARSON

13-digit ISBN 978-0-13-350022-6
10-digit ISBN 0-13-350022-5

1 2 3 4 5 6 7 8 9 10   11 10 09 08 07

Geometry
Teacher's Edition Contents

Student Edition With Teacher Notes

Math Symbols

Formulas

Measures

Properties of Real Numbers

The Center for Mathematics Education Project was developed at Education Development Center, Inc. (EDC) within the Center for Mathematics Education (CME), with partial support from the National Science Foundation.

Education Development Center, Inc.
Center for Mathematics Education
Newton, Massachusetts

This material is based upon work supported by the National Science Foundation under Grant No. ESI-0242476, Grant No. MDR-9252952, and Grant No. ESI-9617369. Any opinions, findings, and conclusions or recommendations expressed in this material are those of the author(s) and do not necessarily reflect the views of the National Science Foundation.

CME Project Development Team

Jean Benson, Al Cuoco, Nancy Antonellis D'Amato, Daniel Erman, Anna Baccaglini-Frank, Andrew Golay, Jane Gorman, Brian Harvey, Wayne Harvey, C. Jud Hill, Bowen Kerins, Doreen Kilday, Stephen Maurer, Melanie Palma, Mark Saul, Sarah Sword, Brett Thomas, Audrey Ting, and Kevin Waterman

Others who contributed include

Daniel Bennett, Steve Benson, Paul D'Amato, Robert Devaney, Eric Karnowski, Helen Lebowitz, Joseph Leverich, Darryl Ricard, and Tonya Walker.

13-digit ISBN 978-0-13-350017-2
10-digit ISBN 0-13-350017-9

1 2 3 4 5 6 7 8 9 10   11 10 09 08 07

Introduction to the CME Project

CME PROJECT

The CME Project, developed by EDC's Center for Mathematics Education, is a new NSF-funded high school program, organized around the familiar courses of algebra 1, geometry, algebra 2, and precalculus. The CME Project provides teachers and schools with a third alternative to the choice between traditional texts driven by basic skill development and more progressive texts that have unfamiliar organizations. This program gives teachers the option of a problem-based, student-centered program, organized around the mathematical themes with which teachers and parents are familiar. Furthermore, the tremendous success of NSF-funded middle school programs has left a need for a high school program with similar rigor and pedagogy. The CME Project fills this need.

The goal of the CME Project is to help students acquire a deep understanding of mathematics. Therefore, the mathematics here is rigorous. We took great care to create lesson plans that, while challenging, will capture and engage students of all abilities and improve their mathematical achievement. Independent research confirms that we achieved this goal in diverse classrooms around the country.

The Program's Approach

The organization of the CME Project provides students the time and focus they need to develop fundamental mathematical ways of thinking. Its primary goal is to develop in students robust mathematical proficiency.

- The program employs innovative instructional methods, developed over decades of classroom experience and informed by research, that help students master mathematical topics.

- One of the core tenets of the CME Project is to focus on developing students' Habits of Mind, or ways in which students approach and solve mathematical challenges.

- The program builds on lessons learned from high-performing countries: develop an idea thoroughly and then revisit it only to deepen it; organize ideas in a way that is faithful to how they are organized in mathematics; and reduce clutter and extraneous topics.

- It also employs the best American models that call for grappling with ideas and problems as preparation for instruction, moving from concrete problems to abstractions and general theories, and situating mathematics in engaging contexts.

- The CME Project is a comprehensive curriculum that meets the dual goals of mathematical rigor and accessibility for a broad range of students.

About CME

EDC's Center for Mathematics Education, led by mathematician and teacher **Al Cuoco,** brings together an eclectic staff of mathematicians, teachers, cognitive scientists, education researchers, curriculum developers, specialists in educational technology, and teacher educators, internationally known for leadership across the entire range of K–16 mathematics education. We aim to help students and teachers in this country experience the thrill of solving problems and building theories, understand the history of ideas behind the evolution of mathematical disciplines, and appreciate the standards of rigor that are central to mathematical culture.

Contributors to the CME Project

National Advisory Board The National Advisory Board met early in the project, providing critical feedback on the instructional design and the overall organization. Members include

Richard Askey, University of Wisconsin

James Madden, Louisiana State University, Baton Rouge

Edward Barbeau, University of Toronto

Jacqueline Miller, Education Development Center

Hyman Bass, University of Michigan

James Newton, University of Maryland

Carol Findell, Boston University

Robert Segall, Greater Hartford Academy of Mathematics and Science

Arthur Heinricher, Worcester Polytechnic Institute

Roger Howe, Yale University

Glenn Stevens, Boston University

Barbara Janson, Janson Associates

Herbert Wilf, University of Pennsylvania

Kenneth Levasseur, University of Massachusetts, Lowell

Hung-Hsi Wu, University of California, Berkeley

Teacher Advisory Board The Teacher Advisory Board for the CME Project was essential in helping us create an effective format for our lessons that embodies the philosophy and goals of the program. Their debates about pedagogical issues and how to develop mathematical topics helped to shape the distinguishing features of the curriculum.

> **Jayne Abbas, Charles Garabedian, Richard Coffey, Dennis Geller, Eileen Herlihy, Doreen Kilday, Gayle Masse, Hugh McLaughlin, Nancy McLaughlin, Allen Olsen, Kimberly Osborne, Brian Shoemaker,** and **Benjamin Sinwell**

Development Team The CME Project development team includes teachers, teacher educators, and mathematicians with many connections to the classroom, professional development in mathematics education, and education policy.

> **Jean Benson, Al Cuoco, Nancy Antonellis D'Amato, Daniel Erman, Anna Baccaglini-Frank, Andrew Golay, Jane Gorman, Brian Harvey, Wayne Harvey, C. Jud Hill, Bowen Kerins, Doreen Kilday, Stephen Maurer, Melanie Palma, Mark Saul, Sarah Sword, Brett Thomas, Audrey Ting,** and **Kevin Waterman**

Field-Test Teachers Our field-test teachers gave us the benefit of their classroom experience by teaching from our draft lessons and giving us extensive, critical feedback that shaped the drafts into realistic, teachable lessons. They shared their concerns and questions, and challenges and successes and kept us focused on the real world. Some of them even welcomed us into their classrooms as co-teachers to give us the direct experience with students that we needed to hone our lessons. Working with these expert professionals has been one of the most gratifying parts of the development—they are "highly qualified" in the most profound sense.

Algebra 1 or *Algebra 2* **California Calvin Baylon** and **Jaime Lao,** Bell Junior High School, San Diego; **Colorado Rocky Cundiff,** Ignacio High School, Ignacio; **Illinois Jeremy Kahan, Tammy Nguyen,** and **Stephanie Pederson,** Ida Crown Jewish Academy, Chicago; **Massachusetts Chris Martino** and **Kent Werst,** Arlington High School, Arlington; **Joe Bishop** and **Carol Rosen,** Lawrence High School, Lawrence; **Maureen Mulryan,** Lowell High School, Lowell; **New Hampshire Jayne Abbas** and **Terin Voisine,** Cawley Middle School, Hooksett; **New Mexico Mary Andrews,** Las Cruces High School, Las Cruces; **Ohio James Stallworth,** Hughes Center, Cincinnati; **Texas Arnell Crayton,** Bellaire High School, Bellaire; **Utah Troy Jones,** Waterford School, Sandy; **Washington Dale Erz, Kathy Greer, Karena Hanscom,** and **John Henry,** Port Angeles High School, Port Angeles; **Wisconsin Annette Roskam,** Rice Lake High School, Rice Lake.

Geometry **California Barney Martinez,** Jefferson High School, Daly City; **Massachusetts Jim Barnes,** Revere High School, Revere; **Larry Davidson,** Boston University Academy, Boston; **Carol Haney,** Revere High School, Revere; **Felisa Honeyman,** Newton South High School, Newton Centre; **Carol Martignette,** Arlington High School, Arlington

This Pacing Guide is provided to help you customize your course.

It accounts for 154 standard class periods. This allows an average of about three periods per chapter for assessments and other activities should you want to cover every lesson. A Daily Planner precedes each chapter and gives you lesson-by-lesson suggestions for that chapter.

Chapter 1 *An Informal Introduction to Geometry* — 21 Days

DAY	LESSON	DAY	LESSON
1	1.0 Habits of Mind	12	1.8 Drawings vs. Constructions
2	1.1 Getting Started	13	1.9 Drawing UnMessUpable Figures—Day 1
3	1.2 Drawing 3-D Objects	14	1.9 Drawing UnMessUpable Figures—Day 2
4	1.3 Drawing and Describing Shapes	15	1.10 Getting Started
5	1.4 Drawing From a Recipe	16	1.11 Numerical Invariants In Geometry—Day 1
6	1.5 Getting Started—Day 1	17	1.11 Numerical Invariants In Geometry—Day 2
7	1.5 Getting Started—Day 2	18	1.11 Numerical Invariants In Geometry—Day 3
8	1.6 Compasses, Angles, and Circles—Day 1	19	1.12 Spatial Invariants—Day 1
9	1.6 Compasses, Angles, and Circles—Day 2	20	1.12 Spatial Invariants—Day 2
10	1.7 Getting Started—Day 1	21	1.12 Spatial Invariants—Day 3
11	1.7 Getting Started—Day 2		

Chapter 2 *Congruence and Proof* — 25 Days

DAY	LESSON	DAY	LESSON
1	2.1 Getting Started	14	2.10 What Does a Proof Look Like?—Day 2
2	2.2 Length, Measure, and Congruence	15	2.11 Analyzing the Statement to Prove
3	2.3 Corresponding Parts	16	2.12 Analysis of a Proof—Day 1
4	2.4 Triangle Congruence—Day 1	17	2.12 Analysis of a Proof—Day 2
5	2.4 Triangle Congruence—Day 2	18	2.13 The Reverse List
6	2.5 Getting Started	19	2.14 Practicing Your Proof-Writing Skills
7	2.6 Deduction and Proof	20	2.15 Getting Started
8	2.7 Parallel Lines—Day 1	21	2.16 General Quadrilaterals
9	2.7 Parallel Lines—Day 2	22	2.17 Properties of Quadrilaterals
10	2.8 The Parallel Postulate—Day 1	23	2.18 Parallelograms—Day 1
11	2.8 The Parallel Postulate—Day 2	24	2.18 Parallelograms—Day 2
12	2.9 Getting Started	25	2.19 Classifying Parallelograms
13	2.10 What Does a Proof Look Like?—Day 1		

Chapter 3 Dissections and Area — 23 Days

DAY	LESSON	DAY	LESSON
1	3.1 Getting Started—Day 1	13	3.8 Parallelograms, Triangles, and Trapezoids—Day 3
2	3.1 Getting Started—Day 2	14	3.9 Getting Started
3	3.2 Do the Cuts Really Work?—Day 1	15	3.10 Proof by Dissection: The Pythagorean Theorem—Day 1
4	3.2 Do the Cuts Really Work?—Day 2	16	3.10 Proof by Dissection: The Pythagorean Theorem—Day 2
5	3.3 Cutting Algorithms	17	3.11 Pick-a-Proof (optional lesson)—Day 1
6	3.4 Checking an Algorithm and Justifying the Cuts—Day 1	18	3.11 Pick-a-Proof (optional lesson)—Day 2
7	3.4 Checking an Algorithm and Justifying the cuts—Day 2	19	3.12 Getting Started
8	3.5 The Midline Theorem	20	3.13 Surface Area of Prisms and Pyramids
9	3.6 Getting Started	21	3.14 Surface Area of Cylinders and Cones—Day 1
10	3.7 What is Area, Anyway?	22	3.14 Surface Area of Cylinders and Cones—Day 2
11	3.8 Parallelograms, Triangles, and Trapezoids—Day 1	23	3.15 Volume of Solids
12	3.8 Parallelograms, Triangles, and Trapezoids—Day 2		

Chapter 4 Similarity — 23 Days

DAY	LESSON	DAY	LESSON
1	4.1 Getting Started	13	4.10 Nested Triangles—Day 1
2	4.2 Scale Factors—Day 1	14	4.10 Nested Triangles—Day 2
3	4.2 Scale Factos—Day 2	15	4.11 Proving the Side-Splitter Theorems
4	4.3 What is a Well-Scaled Drawing?	16	4.12 The Side-Splitter Theorems (continued)
5	4.4 Testing For Scale	17	4.13 Getting Started
6	4.5 Checking for Scaled Copies—Day 1	18	4.14 Similar Figures
7	4.5 Checking for Scaled Copies—Day 2	19	4.15 Tests for Similar Triangles—Day 1
8	4.6 Getting Started	20	4.15 Tests for Similar Triangles—Day 2
9	4.7 Making Scaled Copies	21	4.15 Tests for Similar Triangles—Day 3
10	4.8 Ratio and Parallel Methods—Day 1	22	4.16 Areas of Similar Polygons—Day 1
11	4.8 Ratio and Parallel Methods—Day 2	23	4.16 Areas of Similar Polygons—Day 2
12	4.9 Getting Started		

Chapter 5 *Circles*   18 Days

DAY	LESSON	DAY	LESSON
1	5.1 Getting Started	10	5.8 Arcs and Central Angles—Day 1
2	5.2 Area and Perimeter of Blobs and Circles—Day 1	11	5.8 Arcs and Central Angles—Day 2
3	5.2 Area and Perimeter of Blobs and Circles—Day 2	12	5.9 Chords and Inscribed Angles—Day 1
4	5.3 Connecting Area and Circumference—Day 1	13	5.9 Chords and Inscribed Angles—Day 2
5	5.3 Connecting Area and Circumference—Day 2	14	5.10 Secants and Tangents
6	5.4 Getting Started	15	5.11 Power of a Point
7	5.5 An Area Formula for Circles	16	5.12 Getting Started
8	5.6 Circumference	17	5.13 Probability as a Ratio of Areas
9	5.7 Getting Started	18	5.14 Sets of Measure 0

Chapter 6 *Using Similarity*   13 Days

DAY	LESSON	DAY	LESSON
1	6.1 Getting Started	8	6.8 Finding Triangle Areas
2	6.2 An Inequality of Means	9	6.9 Extend the Pythagorean Theorem
3	6.3 Similarity in Ancient Greece	10	6.10 Getting Started
4	6.4 Concurrence of Medians	11	6.11 Cavalieri's Principle
5	6.5 Getting Started	12	6.12 Proving Volume Formulas
6	6.6 Some Special Triangles	13	6.13 Volume of a Sphere
7	6.7 Some Special Ratios		

Chapter 7 *Coordinates and Vectors*   15 Days

DAY	LESSON	DAY	LESSON
1	7.1 Getting Started	9	7.8 Perpendicular Lines
2	7.2 Reflections	10	7.9 Coordinates in Three Dimensions
3	7.3 Translations	11	7.10 Getting Started
4	7.4 Rotations	12	7.11 Introduction to Vectors—Day 1
5	7.5 Getting Started	13	7.11 Introduction to Vectors—Day 2
6	7.6 Midpoint and Distance Formulas—Day 1	14	7.12 The Vector Equation of a Line
7	7.6 Midpoint and Distance Formulas—Day 2	15	7.13 Using the Vector Equation of a Line
8	7.7 Parallel Lines and Collinear Points		

Chapter 8 *Optimization*   16 Days

DAY	LESSON	DAY	LESSON
1	8.1 Getting Started	9	8.9 Contour Lines and Functions
2	8.2 Finding the Shortest Path	10	8.10 Revisiting the Burning Tent
3	8.3 Reflecting to Find Shortest Paths	11	8.11 Getting Started
4	8.4 Getting Started	12	8.12 Reasoning by Continuity
5	8.5 Maximizing Areas, Part I	13	8.13 Proving Rich's Function Is Constant
6	8.6 Maximizing Areas, Part 2	14	8.14 The Isoperimetric Problem
7	8.7 Getting Started	15	8.15 The Question of Existence
8	8.8 Drawing Contour Plots	16	8.16 Solving the Isoperimetric Problem

1 An Informal Introduction to Geometry

2 Congruence and Proof

③ Dissections and Area

4 Similarity

5 Circles

x

Geometry

6 Using Similarity

7 Coordinates and Vectors

8 Optimization

CME Project
Student Handbook

What Makes CME Different

Welcome to the CME Project! The goal of this program is to help you develop a deep understanding of mathematics. Throughout this book, you will engage in many different activities to help you develop that deep understanding. Some of these instructional activities may be different from ones you are used to. Below is an overview of some of these elements and why they are an important part of the CME Project.

The Habits of Mind Experience

Mathematical Habits of Mind are the foundation for serious questioning, solid thinking, good problem solving, and critical analysis. These Habits of Mind are what will help you become a mathematical thinker. Throughout the CME Project, you will focus on developing and refining these Habits of Mind.

Lesson 1.0 is an introduction to Habits of Mind. This lesson consists of experiments that allow you to tinker with the mathematical ideas that you will formalize throughout the course.

Developing Habits of Mind

Develop thinking skills. This feature provides you with various methods and approaches to solving problems.

You will develop, use, and revisit specific Habits of Mind throughout the course. These include

- **Process** (how you work through problems)
- **Visualization** (how you "picture" problems)
- **Representation** (what you write down)
- **Patterns** (what you find)
- **Relationships** (what you find or use)

Developing good habits will help you as problems become more complicated.

Habits of Mind

Think. These special margin notes highlight key thinking skills and prompt you to apply your developing Habits of Mind.

You can find Developing Habits of Mind **on pages** 45, 55, 91, 106, 153, 198, 241, 243, 291, 325, 331, 332, 340, 426, 428, 448, 490, 548, 575, 585, 589, 603, 633, 650, 666, and 699.

Minds in Action

Discussion of mathematical ideas is an effective method of learning. The Minds in Action feature exposes you to ways of communicating about mathematics.

Join Sasha, Tony, Derman, and others as they think, calculate, predict, and discuss their way towards understanding.

Minds in Action / prologue

Sasha, Tony, and Derman have just skimmed through their CME Project Geometry book.

Sasha   Did you notice the student dialogs throughout the book?

Derman   Sure did!

Tony   They talk and think just the way we do.

Sasha   I know! And they even make mistakes sometimes, just the way we do.

Tony   But I like how they help each other to learn from those mistakes. I bet they use the Habits of Mind I saw all over the book, too.

Sasha   That's great! They should help a lot.

You can find Minds in Action on pages 27, 75, 92, 148, 175, 181, 206, 240, 266, 269, 275, 281, 310, 338, 358, 369, 392, 407, 414, 424, 428, 447, 454, 459, 469, 481, 504, 512, 520, 549, 555, 567, 575, 580, 600, 608, 632, 647, 667, 671, and 673.

Exploring Mathematics

Throughout the CME Project, you will engage in activities that extend your learning and allow you to explore the concepts you learn in greater depth . Two of these activities are In-Class Experiments and Chapter Projects.

In-Class Experiment

In-Class Experiments allow you to explore new concepts and apply the Habits of Mind.

You will explore math as mathematicians do. You start with a question and develop answers through experimentation.

You can find In-Class Experiments on pages 5, 6, 7, 16, 19, 51, 52, 53, 83, 144, 152, 205, 219, 249, 268, 283, 308, 317, 330, 338, 360, 367, 393, 400, 401, 406, 413, 421, 458, 465, 474, 499, 537, 541, 556, 566, 573, 579, 601, 604, 610, 613, 663, 666, 672, and 682.

Chapter Projects

Chapter Projects allow you to apply your Habits of Mind to the content of the chapter. These projects cover many different topics and allow you to explore and engage in greater depth.

Chapter Projects
Using Mathematical Habits

Here is a list of the Chapter Projects and page numbers.

Geometry

Using your CME Book

To help you make the most of your CME experience, we are providing the following overview of the organization of your book.

Focusing your Learning

In *Geometry*, there are 8 chapters, with each chapter devoted to a mathematical concept. With only 8 chapters, your class will be able to focus on these core concepts and develop a deep understanding of them.

Within each chapter, you will explore a series of Investigations. Each Investigation focuses on an important aspect of the mathematical concept for that chapter.

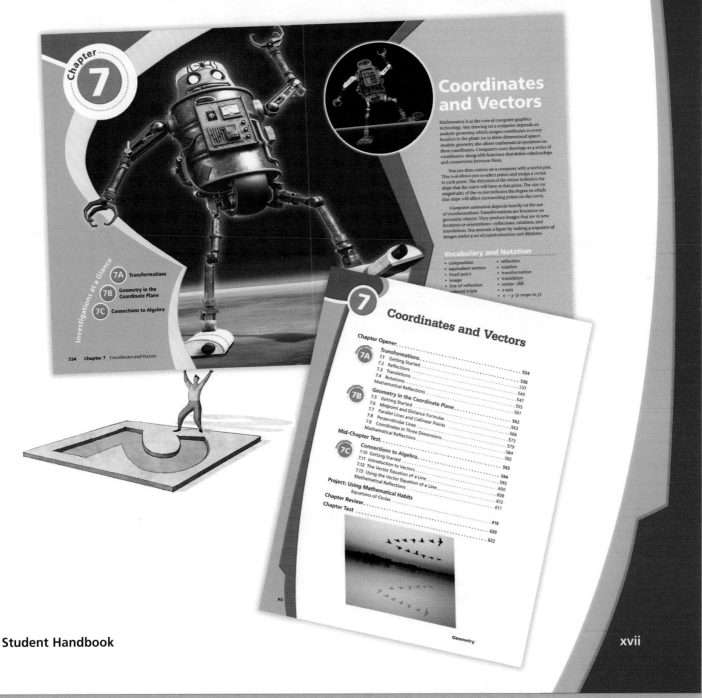

The CME Investigation

The goal of each mathematical Investigation is for you to formalize your understanding of the mathematics being taught. There are some common instructional features in each Investigation.

Getting Started

You will launch into each Investigation with a Getting Started lesson that activates prior knowledge and explores new ideas. This lesson provides you the opportunity to grapple with ideas and problems. The goal of these lessons is for you to explore—not all your questions will be answered in these lessons.

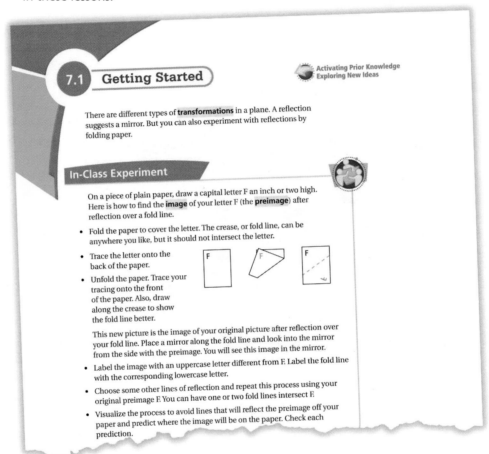

Learning the Mathematics

You will engage in, learn, and practice the mathematics in a variety of ways. The types of learning elements you will find throughout this course include

- **Worked-Out Examples** that model how to solve problems
- **Definitions and Theorems** to summarize key concepts
- **In-Class Experiments** to explore the concepts
- **For You to Do** assignments to check your understanding
- **For Discussion** questions to encourage communication
- **Minds in Action** to model mathematical discussion

Communicating the Mathematics

Student dialogs

By featuring dialogs between characters, the CME Project exposes you to a way of communicating about mathematics. These dialogs will then become a real part of your classroom!

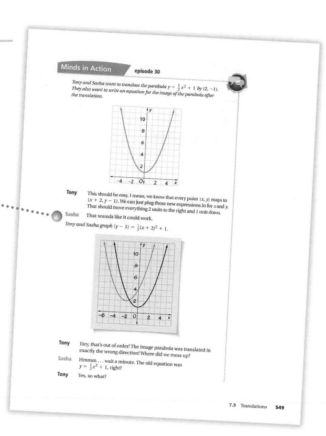

Minds in Action episode 30

Tony and Sasha want to translate the parabola $y = \frac{1}{2}x^2 + 1$ by $(2, -1)$. They also want to write an equation for the image of the parabola after the translation.

Tony This should be easy. I mean, we know that every point (x, y) maps to $(x + 2, y - 1)$. We can just plug those new expressions in for x and y. That should move everything 2 units to the right and 1 unit down.

Sasha That sounds like it could work.

Tony and Sasha graph $(y - 1) = \frac{1}{2}(x + 2)^2 + 1$.

Tony Hey, that's out of order! The image parabola was translated in exactly the wrong direction! Where did we mess up?

Sasha Hmmm . . . wait a minute. The old equation was $y = \frac{1}{2}x^2 + 1$, right?

Tony Yes, so what?

7.3 Translations **549**

Reflecting on the Mathematics

At the end of each Investigation, Mathematical Reflections give you an opportunity to put ideas together. This feature allows you to demonstrate your understanding of the Investigation and reflect on what you learn.

Practice

The CME Project views extensive practice as a critical component of a mathematics curriculum. You will have daily opportunities to practice what you learn.

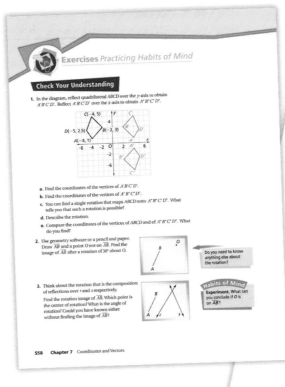

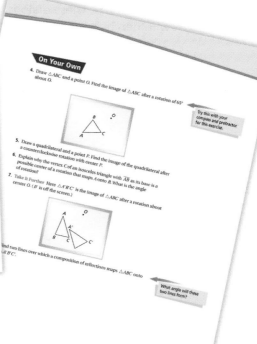

Check Your Understanding
Assess your readiness for independent practice by working through these problems in class.

On Your Own
Practice and continue developing the mathematical understanding you learn in each lesson.

Maintain Your Skills
Review and reinforce skills from previous lessons.

Also Available
An additional Practice Workbook is available separately.

Go Online

Throughout this book, you will find links to the Prentice Hall Web site. Use the Web Codes provided with each link to gain direct access to online material. Here's how to Go Online.

1 Go to PHSchool.com.

2 Enter the Web Code.

3 Click Go!

Go Online Lesson Web Codes

Additional Practice Web Codes: For every lesson, (except Getting Started lessons) there is additional practice online. Access this additional practice using the Web Code format at the right.

Additional Practice
Web Code format: bea-0203
02 = Chapter 2 03 = Lesson 3

Go Online Chapter Web Codes

Chapter	Vocabulary Quizzes	Mid-Chapter Test	Chapter Test	Chapter Project Information
1	bej-0151	bea-0152	bea-0153	bed-0161
2	bej-0251	bea-0252	bea-0253	bed-0261
3	bej-0351	bea-0352	bea-0353	bed-0361
4	bej-0451	bea-0452	bea-0453	bed-0461
5	bej-0551	bea-0552	bea-0553	bed-0561
6	bej-0651	bea-0652	bea-0653	bed-0661
7	bej-0751	bea-0752	bea-0753	bed-0761
8	bej-0851	bea-0852	bea-0853	bed-0861

Go Online Additional Web Codes

Video Tutor
Use Web Code: bee-0775 to access engaging online instructional videos that help bring math concepts to life. See page 74.

Interesting Links
Use Web Code: bee-9031 to access Web links to sites containing interesting facts related to the mathematics. See page 108.

Math Background
Use Web Code: bee-8031 to find additional information about certain Historical Perspectives. See page 111.

Chapter 1
An Informal Introduction to Geometry

This chapter sets an important mathematical perspective for the whole book, and, in fact, for the entire CME Project series. In this perspective, the methods mathematicians use to obtain results are just as important as the results themselves. Chapter 1 gives students a chance to experience some of these mathematical habits of mind as they preview many of the topics that the course covers.

Schools teach geometry for several reasons: as an introduction to deductive reasoning, as a way to develop important geometric formulas (such as the formulas for area), and as an arena in which to apply algebra. All of these purposes are important, but it is also a great place for students to experiment in mathematics and to see the interplay between experiment and deduction. In this chapter, students are not diving in to achieve mastery—they are getting their feet wet.

Chapter Overview

- Investigation 1A, *Picturing and Drawing*, requires students to visualize and draw objects.

- Investigation 1B, **Constructing**, has students discover the difference between drawing and constructing.

- Investigation 1C, **Geometry Software**, introduces the use of geometry software.

- Investigation 1D, *Invariants*, has students look for numerical, geometric, and spatial invariants.

For more information on the investigations, see

- Chapter Road Map, pp. 2 and 3
- Investigation Road Maps, pp. 8, 24, 36, 48

PROJECT The Project near the end of the chapter is optional. You can assign the Project at any time during the chapter depending on how often and how long you feel students should work on it.

Pacing Suggestions and Materials

Investigation 1A *Picturing and Drawing*

DAY	LESSON	HOMEWORK
1	1.1 *Getting Started* Core: 1, 2, 3, 4 Optional: none	Core: 5, 6, 7 Optional: 8, 9, 10, 11
2	1.2 *Drawing 3-D Objects* Core: 1, 2, 4 Optional: 3	Core: 5, 6, 8, 9, 10 Optional: 11, 12; Extension: 7
3	1.3 *Drawing and Describing Shapes* Core: 1, 2, 3 Optional: none	Core: 4, 5, 6, 13 Optional: 7, 8, 9, 10, 11, 12
4	1.4 *Drawing from a Recipe* Core: 1, 2, 3, 4 Optional: none	Core: 5, 7, 8, 9 Optional: 6, 10, 11, 12, 13

Investigation 1B *Constructing*

DAY	LESSON	HOMEWORK
1	1.5 *Getting Started*—Day 1 Core: 1, 2, 3, 4 Optional: none	Core: 7 Optional: none
2	1.5 *Getting Started*—Day 2 Core: 5, 6 Optional: none	Core: 8, 9, 10 Optional: 11, 12, 13
3	1.6 *Compasses, Angles, and Circles*—Day 1 Core: 1, 4, 5, 6, 9 Optional: 2, 3	Core: 10, 11 Optional: none
4	1.6 *Compasses, Angles, and Circles*—Day 2 Core: 7 Optional: 8	Core: 13, 14, 15, 16 Optional: 12, 17

NOTES	MATERIALS
	• flashlights or lamps • Blackline Master 1.1 • scissors • stiff paper or cardboard
	• straightedges
	• modeling clay • overhead projector
Have students do Exercises 2–4 in pairs or groups.	• compasses • protractors • straightedges

NOTES	MATERIALS
	• protractors • rulers
Review any conjectures that were made while completing Problems 1–4 before students complete the Getting Started exercises.	• protractors • rulers
Work through the For Discussion problems on the first day of this lesson.	• compasses • rulers • straightedges • Blackline Masters 1.6A, 1.6B
Begin the second day of this lesson with the Example.	• compasses • straightedges • Blackline Masters 1.6A, 1.6B

Mathematics Background

One consequence of the style of this book is that in addition to the standard content of a standard Geometry course, you also will be teaching your students the mathematical habits of mind that will help them investigate, understand, and explain mathematics. These habits are an essential part of the content of this course, and what follows is a description of the most common habits.

VISUALIZING It is not a coincidence that the words "I see" can also mean "I understand." Students will make mental pictures, drawings, and computer sketches of geometric objects and situations. They will change characteristics and analyze the effects of the changes. For example, imagine unfolding a paper cube to make a "net" for the cube. In one In-Class Experiment, students identify shapes that are nets of the cube, find as many different nets for the cube as they can, and decide when they have found all of them. As the course continues, they also extend their understanding of nets to other solids and use nets to compute surface area.

REASONING BY CONTINUITY Geometric reasoning is often closely connected with the mathematical habits used in calculus and analysis. In particular, you can approach many problems in geometry through *reasoning by continuity*—thinking about a continuously varying system and making an intuitive appeal to the intermediate value theorem. For example, is there a line that cuts the area of this blob exactly in half? Does the existence of such a line depend on the shape of the blob?

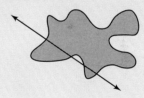

LOOKING FOR INVARIANTS As important as thinking about how things change through some action or choice is the habit of *looking for invariants*—noticing what does not change. For example, when you connect the midpoints of the sides of a quadrilateral in order, you make what looks like a parallelogram.

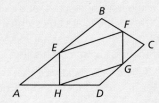

Students will prove that this midpoint quadrilateral *EFGH* is, in fact, a parallelogram no matter how you change the original quadrilateral *ABCD*. In other words, some of the properties of the midpoint quadrilateral are invariant.

This kind of thinking is also related to the habit of *looking for patterns,* because some of the attributes that *do* change, will do so in a patterned way that can allow students to see relationships and predict behavior.

Pacing Suggestions and Materials

Investigation 1C *Geometry Software*

DAY	LESSON	HOMEWORK
1	1.7 *Getting Started*—Day 1 Core: 1, 2 Optional: none	Core: none Optional: none
2	1.7 *Getting Started*—Day 2 Core: 3, 4 Optional: none	Core: 5, 6, 7 Optional: 8
3	1.8 *Drawings vs. Constructions* Core: 1, 2, 3 Optional: none	Core: 5, 6, 7 Optional: 4, 8
4	1.9 *Drawing UnMessUpable Figures*—Day 1 Core: 1, 2, 3, 4 Optional: none	Core: 10, 11, 12, 14 Optional: none
5	1.9 *Drawing UnMessUpable Figures*—Day 2 Core: 5, 6 Optional: 7; Extension: 8, 9	Core: 13 Optional: 15, 16, 17

Investigation 1D *Invariants*

DAY	LESSON	HOMEWORK
1	1.10 *Getting Started* Core: 1, 2 Optional: none	Core: 3, 4 Optional: 5, 6, 7
2	1.11 *Numerical Invariants in Geometry*—Day 1 In-Class Experiments	Core: 8 Optional: none
3	1.11 *Numerical Invariants in Geometry*—Day 2 In-Class Experiments	Core: 9 Optional: none; Extension: 10
4	1.11 *Numerical Invariants in Geometry*—Day 3 Core: 1, 2, 3, 7 Optional: 4, 5, 6	Core: 12 Optional: 11, 13
5	1.12 *Spatial Invariants*—Day 1 Core: 1, 2 Optional: none	Core: 7, 8 Optional: none
6	1.12 *Spatial Invariants*—Day 2 Core: 3, 4 Optional: none	Core: none Optional: 9
7	1.12 *Spatial Invariants*—Day 3 Core: 5, 6 Optional: none	Core: none Optional: 11; Extension: 10

NOTES	MATERIALS
Give students two class periods to explore the problems.	• geometry software
Exercise 8 requires geometry software.	• geometry software
Exercises 8 and 9 require geometry software.	• geometry software
The exercises in this lesson will most likely take two class periods to work through.	• geometry software • Blackline Master 1.9
	• geometry software • Blackline Master 1.9

NOTES	MATERIALS
Exercises 5–7 require geometry software.	• calculators • geometry software
The In-Class Experiments will most likely take two class periods to complete.	• geometry software • Blackline Master MC1
Give students class time to write up their results from the experiments or assign this as homework.	• geometry software • Blackline Master MC1
After students complete the In-Class Experiments, provide class time for them to work on the Check Your Understanding exercises.	• geometry software
	• geometry software • Blackline Masters MC1, 1.12
	• geometry software • Blackline Masters MC1, 1.12
Have students work in groups. Have each group do one of the Exercises 3–6.	• geometry software • Blackline Masters MC1, 1.12

ALGORITHMIC THINKING This course emphasizes *algorithmic thinking*—designing a recipe for carrying out a construction or some other task. The design of an algorithm is also connected to deductive *reasoning,* because students must give increasingly precise justifications that their algorithms do, in fact, accomplish what they claim.

For example, cut the parallelogram on the dotted line. Then rearrange the pieces as shown. The new shape appears to be a rectangle.

Can you be certain that the two "glued together" edges actually match up? Can you be certain that the angles fit together so that the new side isn't "bent"?

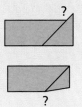

TINKERING It is also important for students to learn how to tinker with problems. Just as you can come to know cylinders better by recognizing and tinkering with their independent attributes, you also can come to know a problem better by looking for its independent attributes, changing them, and seeing what results. In this course, students may need to re-examine in one dimension or three, a problem posed in two dimensions. Encourage your students to play with problems and to distinguish between productive tinkering and random experimentation.

Developing Students' Mathematical Habits

In order to teach your students to develop and value new habits of mathematical thinking, you will need to give them many opportunities to examine how they are thinking and solving problems in your course. Try to foster a lively culture of mathematical investigation, one that values deep thinking about mathematical problems, and gives students the time and space to do such thinking alone and with others. Encourage them to articulate their ideas clearly, give precisely reasoned arguments, and discuss and refine their ideas with other students.

To develop curiosity and playfulness, as well as the confidence to stick with hard problems and discuss them with others, students need to feel safe to expose their initial thinking and admit their puzzlement. They need constructive feedback as they learn what constitutes a well-reasoned proof. Reward good, solid thinking and partial results as well as final solutions. Encourage students to present alternative approaches and strategies. And take some chances yourself! Students can learn a great deal about how to think mathematically if you are explicit about your own problem-solving process.

Chapter 1

Investigations at a Glance

1A Picturing and Drawing

1B Constructing

1C Geometry Software

1D Invariants

Chapter Road Map

INVESTIGATION 1A, *Picturing and Drawing,* requires students to visualize objects and to draw two-dimensional and three-dimensional objects. Students draw figures by being given a set of directions (a recipe) or by naming the features of the objects (parallel lines, right angles, symmetry).

INVESTIGATION 1B, *Constructing,* has students discover the difference between a drawing and a geometric construction. They construct triangles and look for invariants in their angle measures, construct perpendicular bisectors to reflect points over a line, and perform many other constructions both with compass and straightedge and with paper folding.

INVESTIGATION 1C, *Geometry Software,* introduces the use of geometry software. There are many instances where this book utilizes geometry software. This investigation gives students a chance to become familiar with all the features of the software, as well as to learn about features of many geometric figures.

An Informal Introduction to Geometry

A valuable geometry skill is being able to recognize what relationships between the parts or the measures of geometric figures stay the same while other elements associated with the figures change.

Here are some simple examples:
- The radius of a circle stays the same while you turn the circle about its center.
- The height of a triangle stays the same while you move a vertex of the triangle parallel to the triangle's base.
- The diagonals of a parallelogram bisect each other while you move the sides of the parallelogram.

Recognizing such invariants is a mathematical *habit of mind*. There are many others. And they are a focus of this book. The ways you think about mathematics—your habits of mind—are among the invaluable life applications that you will take from this course.

Vocabulary and Notation

- altitude
- angle bisector
- collinear points
- concurrent lines
- congruent
- constant
- construction
- disc
- equidistant
- equilateral
- invariant
- line of symmetry
- line segment
- median
- midline
- midpoint
- parallel lines
- parallel planes
- perpendicular bisector
- prism
- symmetric
- theorem
- ∠ACB (angle ACB)
- $\overleftrightarrow{CD}$ (line CD)
- $\overline{AB}$ (segment AB)

INVESTIGATION 1D, *Invariants,* focuses on invariants. Students look for numerical, geometric, and spatial invariants and make conjectures about parallel lines, angles in a triangle, angles in polygons, concurrence of lines, and collinearity of points.

Chapter Vocabulary and Notation

The following list gives key vocabulary and notation used in the chapter. Selected new vocabulary and notation items are shown in boldface on the student page.

- adjacent, p. 42
- altitude, p. 31
- angle bisector, p. 31
- chord, p. 55
- circumference, p. 51
- collinear points, p. 61
- concurrent lines, p. 59
- congruent, p. 42
- constant, p. 51
- construction, p. 27
- cross section, p. 7
- diagonal, p. 5
- diameter, p. 20
- disc, p. 61
- equidistant, p. 29
- equilateral, p. 20
- invariant, p. 49
- isosceles triangle, p. 31
- line, p. 37
- line of symmetry, p. 9
- line segment, p. 12
- median, p. 31
- midline, p. 31
- midpoint, p. 29
- net, p. 6
- octahedron, p.6
- parallel, p. 39

- parallel lines, p. 12
- parallel planes, p. 12
- parallelogram, p. 43
- perpendicular, p. 18
- perpendicular bisector, p. 29
- perspective, p. 45
- prism, p. 12
- radius, p. 20
- ratio, p. 25
- ray, p. 37
- reflect, p. 33
- regular polygon, p. 62
- rhombus, p. 44
- segment, p. 37
- symmetric, p. 9
- tangent, p. 19
- tetrahedron, p. 6
- theorem, p. 29
- ∠ACB (angle ACB), p. 38
- $\overleftrightarrow{CD}$ (line CD), p. 30
- $\overline{AB}$ (segment AB), p. 30

Chapter Technology

The CME Project assumes students perform calculator procedures on graphing calculators. Support for the use of technology is available in the Technology Handbook. See p. 712.

INVESTIGATION 1C *Geometry Software*

- **LESSON 1.7** Learn to construct figures; explore constructions by moving points, p. 37. Place points to make a 90° angle, p. 38.
- **LESSON 1.8** Construct a rotating windmill, p. 39. Move and trace points in a construction, p. 41.
- **LESSON 1.9** Construct UnMessUpable figures, pp. 43–44. Construct a house in perspective, p. 45. Construct iterations of Sierpinski's Triangle, p. 46.

INVESTIGATION 1D *Geometry Software*

- **LESSON 1.10** Draw parallel lines and search for invariants; find invariants in the diagonals of a square, p. 50.
- **LESSON 1.11** Find numerical invariants in the measurements of figures, pp. 51–57.
- **LESSON 1.12** Explore the concurrence of the perpendicular bisectors of a triangle, p. 59. Explore figures to find lines that are concurrent, pp. 61–63.

Lesson Overview

GOALS
- Warm up to the ideas behind the CME Project.
- Work experientially to begin developing mathematical habits of mind.

This lesson introduces students to one of the significant developmental objectives of the CME Project, namely, building sound habits of mind. The exploratory experience of this lesson is a feature of the Getting Started lesson in each investigation.

Instead of having each student perform all five experiments, you may wish to assign small groups an experiment to work on for one class period. Then have them present their results to the whole class. Alternatively, you could have the class work through all the experiments as a group. Then you could have whole=class discussions about each experiment.

MATERIALS
- clay
- dental floss
- number cubes
- rods
- rulers
- scissors
- Blackline Masters MC1, MC2, MC4, 1.1, MC9, 1.0A, 1.0B

VOCABULARY
- cross section
- diagonal
- net
- octahedron
- regular polygon
- tetrahedron

Launch

Start this lesson by assigning each small group one of the five experiments and any materials they will need. If your class is large enough, assign the Model the Problem Experiment to two groups. This way, students can collect much more data.

Explore

LOOK FOR PATTERNS There are three strategies for answering Problem 1. The first strategy, trying to determine how the answer is affected when one more person enters the room, is the essence of a powerful technique known as *mathematical induction,* which is useful in many counting problems.

In the second strategy, students get up, shake hands with everyone else, and count the number of times that they, personally, shake hands. Students may think that they can get the number of handshakes by multiplying the number of handshakes they count $(n - 1)$ by the number of people counting n.

If you watch college sports on television, you may have seen this message from the National Collegiate Athletic Association (NCAA).

> There are over 380,000 student-athletes, and just about every one of them will go pro in something other than sports.

For practitioners of mathematics (mathletes), a similar message could say

> There are over 30,000,000 student-mathletes in this country, and just about every one of them will go pro in something other than mathematics.

So, why play sports? Why study mathematics? Simple. In either venture, the habits you learn have value for the rest of your life. Compare these lists.

Habits of Body	Habits of Mind
Athletics	**Mathematics**
Take care of the body.	Take care of the mind.
Think ahead.	Think ahead.
Build strength.	Build mental agility.
Take a chance.	Take a chance.
Develop conditioning.	Develop persistence.
Respect the rules.	Respect the rules.
Practice mental toughness.	Practice mental discipline.
Visualize perfection.	Visualize relationships.
Plan strategies.	Plan strategies.
Have confidence.	Have confidence.
Model the opponent.	Model the problem.
Study styles.	Look for patterns.
Work as a team.	Work with others.
and many more . . .	**and many more . . .**

To get you started this year, try some of the following activities. As you proceed (and throughout the course), think about how you are thinking. Pay attention to your habits of mind!

There are over 380,000 student-athletes, and just about every one of them will go pro in something other than sports.

Answers

1. Check students' work.

2. 2; 5; 9; 14; 20;
$$d(n) = (n - 1) + (n - 2) + \ldots + 2 + 1, \text{ or } d(n) = \frac{n(\ -3)}{2}, \text{ or}$$
$$d(n) = \int_{d(n-1)+(n-2),\ n>3}^{0}{}_{,\ n=3}$$

3. Counting handshakes is like counting all the sides and all the diagonals of a polygon.

4. 14; there are 9 one-by-one-squares, 4 two-by-two squares, and 1 three-by-three square.

5. 20; in addition to the 14 squares from Exercise 4, there are 6 additional squares shown here.

In-Class Experiment

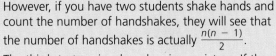

Look for Patterns

1. Since this is early in the class year, it is time for introductions. If everyone in a class shakes hands with everyone else, how many handshakes will there be?

2. How many diagonals are in a square? In a pentagon? In a hexagon? In a heptagon? In an octagon? Write a formula that relates the number of diagonals of *any* regular polygon to the number of sides.

> If *penta-*, *hexa-*, *hepta-*, and *octa-* mean 5, 6, 7, and 8, and *poly-* means "many," what does *-gon* mean?

Definitions

A **regular polygon** is a closed figure with sides all equal in length and angles all equal in measure. A **diagonal** of a polygon is a segment that joins two nonconsecutive vertices.

3. How is counting handshakes similar to counting diagonals? Explain.

In-Class Experiment

Build Mental Agility

Consider the question "How many squares are in the figure at the right?"

Many people would quickly answer "four," but, in fact, there are five squares in the figure, four small squares and one large square.

4. How many squares are in the figure at the left below? Explain how you got your answer.

5. Copy the dot pattern at the right below. How many squares can you make using the dots for vertices? Draw diagrams to support your answer.

6. **a.** This is not a net for a cube. There is no top or bottom square.

   b. This is not a net for a cube. There are only 5 squares in the net, while a cube has 6 faces.

   c. This is a net for a cube. If you cut it out and fold it, you get a cube.

   d. This is a net for a cube. If you cut it out and fold it, you get a cube.

7. 11; two nets are different when you cannot turn one into the other by rotating or flipping.

8.

9. Answers may vary. Sample:

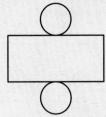

The circumference of the circles and the lengths of the sides of the rectangle they touch should be the same.

However, if you have two students shake hands and count the number of handshakes, they will see that the number of handshakes is actually $\frac{n(n-1)}{2}$.

The third strategy involves drawing a picture. If there are *n* people in the room, then you can model the handshakes by a regular *n*-gon with all the diagonals drawn in; that is, every person corresponds to a vertex, and every vertex is connected to every other vertex exactly once. This makes a nice connection to Problem 2.

PROBLEM 2 You may wish to provide students with Blackline Masters MC1 and 1.1 to help them find the number of diagonals in various regular polygons. This problem is essentially a pictorial variation of the handshake problem from Problem 1.

There are many ways to write rules for the number of diagonals of a regular polygon. Here is one theorem for the number of diagonals: *An n-gon has* $\frac{n(n-1)}{2} - n$, or equivalently, $\frac{n(n-3)}{2}$, *diagonals.* Here is another rule for the number of diagonals: For an *n*-sided polygon, find the sum of $n - 3$ terms in the series $2 + 3 + 4 + 5 + 6 + \ldots$

Students can derive a similar rule by experimenting with a polygon in a systematic way and noting the pattern. For octagon *ABCDEFGH,* students can draw five diagonals from vertex *A* and five additional diagonals from vertex *B.*

ERROR PREVENTION Watch for students who start with two adjacent vertices of the octagon when drawing its diagonals. These students may assume that five diagonals originate from each vertex, but this is not the case. The number of diagonals that originates from each remaining vertex is one less than the number that originates from the previous vertex.

To find the total number of diagonals, find the sum of the number of diagonals that originates from each vertex, $5 + 5 + 4 + 3 + 2 + 1$. If you combine the first and last terms of this expression, you get $6 + 5 + 4 + 3 + 2$.

You can generalize the rule as this theorem: *If n is the number of sides of the polygon, then the number of diagonals is* $2 + 3 + 4 + \cdots + (n - 2)$.

BUILD MENTAL AGILITY You may wish to provide students with Blackline Masters MC9 and 1.0A to use with this experiment.

Problem 4 you may wish to point out to students that some squares are tilted.

PLAN STRATEGIES You may wish to provide students with copies Blackline Master MC2, scissors, and tape to make the nets for Problems 4 and 5.

Students should see that since a cube has six square faces, a net of a cube must contain six squares. No more than four of these squares can be in a single straight strip. Starting from a strip of four squares,

continued on p.6

continued from p. 5

you can attach the last two squares as top and the bottom to any square in the strip.

GOING FURTHER Ask students how many different six-square nets are possible, even if the nets do not form a cube. This may lead students to see that two nets are actually equivalent if you can rotate, flip, or slide them so that they exactly coincide. In Chapter 2, this is a congruence test for two-dimensional figures.

PROBLEM 8 You may want to have a 3-D model of a tetrahedron for students to look at if they are unfamiliar with the term. Also, point out that this problem refersto a regular tetrahedron—all faces must be congruent.

VISUALIZE RELATIONSHIPS Provide students with various materials, such as gelatin or clay to help them explore these problems.

Students must first cut their material into several cubes. They need not be perfect cubes, but they should be close. Dental floss works better than knives for making planar slices through clay.

PROBLEM 12 There are no other possible shapes, except other types of triangles. As an extension, ask students whether it is possible to form every type of triangle as a cross section of a cube. This is a difficult question. Students may find it difficult to see how to get an obtuse triangle by cutting a cube.

This experiment with cross sections might offer a good opportunity to discuss the terms *parallel, perpendicular,* and *skew.* You may need to refine students' intuitions about these relationships between lines.

The usual definition of *parallel lines* states that they are coplanar and do not intersect. But many students think of parallel lines as lines that "point in the same direction". The first definition is the more mathematical one. The second requires a prior definition of the word *direction.* Students can often identify parallel lines, but do not visualize the plane that contains the parallel lines. It is useful to ask students to visualize this plane, for example, for pairs of parallel edges of a cube that are not on the same face.

It is possible for two lines to not intersect and to not be parallel. Such lines—called skew lines—do not lie in the same plane.

As a classroom exercise, have students identify pairs of edges of a cube as parallel, perpendicular, or skew. As an extension, ask them to count the numbers of such pairs.

Many students intuit perpendicular lines as lines that are vertical and horizontal, but they need not be. Have students describe two perpendicular lines that are neither vertical nor horizontal. If the students describe the diagonals of a face of a cube as a pair of such

6 Chapter 1 An Informal Introduction to Geometry

 In-Class Experiment

Plan Strategies

Think about unfolding a cube and laying out its faces as a set of squares attached at their edges. The figure that results from unfolding a three-dimensional solid is called a **net.** There are many nets for a cube.

6. Which of the following are nets for cubes? How do you know?

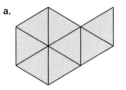

a.   b.   c.   d.

7. How many *different* nets for a cube can you make? What does it mean for nets to be different?

8. Find all the possible nets for a regular tetrahedron.

9. Draw a net for a cylinder. It should include the top and bottom circular faces. In your drawing, what lengths should be the same?

10. The three-dimensional figure made from eight triangular faces is an **octahedron.** Here are four drawings of eight congruent triangles connected in some way. Decide whether each is a net for a regular octahedron. What other nets can you find for regular octahedrons?

a.   b.

c.   d.

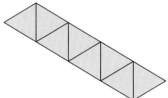
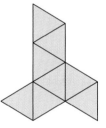

 Habits of Mind

Visualize. Continue to unfold the cube in your mind.

A **tetrahedron** is a three-dimensional solid with four triangular faces.

Answers

10. Parts (b) and (c) are nets of an octahedron. There are 11 possible nets, which are shown below.

11. See back of book.

12. no

13. It is not possible to make an octagon. The maximum number of sides a shape made by slicing a cube can have is 6 because a cube has only 6 faces.

14. **a.** a circle
    b. a circle, and ellipse, a rectangle, end section of an ellipse, middle section of an ellipse

15. Check students' work.

In-Class Experiment

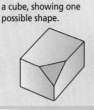

Visual Relationships

A **cross section** is the face you get when you make one slice through an object. These questions ask you to visualize the insides of solid objects.

a square	an equilateral triangle
a rectangle that is not a square	a triangle that is not equilateral
a pentagon	a hexagon
an octagon	a trapezoid
a parallelogram that is not a rectangle	

Here is an example of a cross section of a cube, showing one possible shape.

11. What cross-sectional shapes can you make by slicing a cube? Record which shapes above you can make, and describe how to make them.

12. Can you produce any shapes that are not listed above? Draw and name any other cross sections you can make.

13. If you think any of the shapes on the list above are impossible to make by slicing a cube, explain what makes them impossible.

14. What cross sections can you construct from the following shapes?

   a. a sphere   **b.** a cylinder

In-Class Experiment

Model the Problem

For this experiment, you need three number cubes and eighteen rods—three rods of each length, 1 unit through 6 units.

Roll the number cubes and pick three corresponding rods. For example, if you roll 5, 3, 5, pick two rods of size 5 and one of size 3. Try to make a triangle using the three rods as the sides of the triangle. Some sets of three rods will work, and others will not.

15. Repeat the experiment several times. Keep a table of your results. For the combinations that do not work, write an explanation of what went wrong when you tried to make a triangle.

16. **Write About It** Your experiments dealt only with side lengths from 1 to 6 and not with noninteger lengths, such as $4\frac{1}{2}$ or 3.14159. Write a rule that explains how you can tell if *any* three segments will actually fit together to make a triangle. Some sets of three lengths just do not work. Explain why they do not and how to predict which ones do not from the lengths involved.

17. Which of the following sets of three lengths will make a triangle? Explain.

   a. 1 cm, 6 cm, 6 cm   **b.** 2 cm, 4 cm, 6 cm
   c. 1 cm, 1 cm, 1 cm   **d.** 2.1 cm, 4 cm, 6 cm
   e. 0.99 cm, 0.99 cm, 2 cm

16. You can make a triangle with three given lengths only when the sum of any two of the lengths is greater than the third. If this is not the case, the two shorter cannot meet to form a triangle.

17. a. These lengths can make a triangle because 6 cm + 6 cm > 1 cm, and 6 cm + 1 cm > 6 cm.

b. These lengths cannot make a triangle because 2 cm + 4 cm = 6 cm.

c. These lengths can make a triangle because 1 cm + 1 cm > 1 cm.

d. These lengths can make a triangle because
6 cm + 2.1 cm > 4 cm,
4 cm + 6 cm > 2.1 cm, and
4 cm + 2.1 cm > 6 cm.

e. These lengths cannot make a triangle because
0.99 cm + 0.99 cm < 2 cm.

---

lines, have them draw a cube with an orientation so that the diagonals of a face are horizontal and vertical.

GOING FURTHER Challenge students to determine whether pairs of "body diagonals" of a cube (the diagonals that do not lie on a face) are perpendicular and give a good argument in defense of their answer.

PROBLEM 13 It is impossible to make any polygonal cross section with more than 6 sides from a cube, because doing so would require the plane to intersect more than six faces. This cannot happen because a cube has only six faces.

This argument is an example of how to prove that something is impossible. Students find it easy to see that some situations are not possible, especially in geometry. But they usually have trouble constructing an argument to show that a particular situation is not possible. Such arguments usually involve a proof by contradiction, which is not easy for students to intuit. The "little" argument above is an appropriate and relatively easy example to build on for later understanding.

PROBLEM 14 introduces the ellipse. While recognizing the ellipse and knowing its name are important, naming the other conic sections is optional at this point.

MODEL THE PROBLEM Before beginning the experiment, students may have to set some rules as to how the rods meet at the corners.

A powerful strategy for determining what triples will make a triangle is to keep one side constant and fit different-sized rods with it. Some students may have difficulty organizing their work. Entering their results in a table might help. You may wish to copy and distribute Blackline Master 1.0B for students to use.

Some students may develop the strategy of starting with the longest side, and seeing whether the two shorter sides fit with it to form a triangle. This strategy does in fact work, but you should make it explicit for students by asking them to explain why it works. Listening carefully to their explanations might give clues about their level of understanding of logic and the nature of proof.

This experimentation leads to a theorem that students will formally prove in Lesson 2.14, the Triangle Inequality Theorem: *In a triangle, the length of one side is less than the sum of the lengths of the other two sides.*

Wrap Up

Once groups have complete their assigned experiment, collect data, and come to any conclusions or generalizations, have them report their findings to the whole class.

Investigation Overview

This investigation asks students to use visualization skills to analyze pictures and to draw objects. Students will need to picture both the visible and invisible—a very important habit of mind.

You may wish to assign Questions 1–3 for students to think and write about during the investigation.

Learning Goals

- Visualize mental images in order to analyze their parts.
- Analyze visual scenes in order to draw them.
- Develop clear language to describe shapes.

Habits and Skills

- Write and follow careful directions.
- Identify and represent parallels.
- Use names, features, and algorithms to describe shapes accurately and precisely.

Investigation 1A

Picturing and Drawing

In *Picturing and Drawing*, you will learn the importance of pictures. Many problems are solved or made easier by drawing pictures. The pictures can be on paper, on a computer, or in your head. Even when your goal is to draw a picture on paper, mental pictures are important. Visualizing clear and detailed pictures in your head can help you draw better.

By the end of this investigation, you will be able to answer questions like these.

1. What is a line of symmetry?

2. What is a prism?

3. What should you keep in mind when you give traveling directions to someone or tell someone how to draw a figure or complete a task?

You will learn how to

- visualize mental images in order to analyze their parts
- analyze visual scenes in order to draw them
- develop clear language to describe shapes

You will develop these habits and skills:

- Write and follow careful directions.
- Identify and represent parallels.
- Use names, features, and algorithms to describe shapes accurately and precisely.

The roof of the Pantheon in Rome is a dome with a round opening (oculus) 29 ft in diameter. Describe the shadow cast by the roof of the Pantheon on the inside of the building.

Investigation Road Map

LESSON 1.1, *Getting Started,* introduces students to finding lines of symmetry as well as visualizing shadows cast by various objects.

LESSON 1.2, *Drawing 3-D Objects,* has students follow an algorithm for transforming a 2-dimensional figure into a 3-dimensional solid. This lesson introduces terms such as *prism, line segment, parallel lines,* and *parallel planes.*

LESSON 1.3, *Drawing and Describing Shapes,* challenges students to describe objects either by the name of the object, a recipe for making that object, or specific features of that object (such as a shadow it can cast).

LESSON 1.4, *Drawing from a Recipe,* requires students to follow an algorithm for drawing an object and to eventually write their own directions that someone else will follow for drawing an object.

Activating Prior Knowledge
Exploring New Ideas

For artists to draw realistic scenes, they must be able to draw shadows.

For You to Explore

1. Visualize a square casting a shadow on a floor or wall. Can the shadow be nonsquare? Nonrectangular? In other words, can the measures of the shadow's angles be other than 90°?

2. What kinds of shadows can an equilateral triangle cast? Can its shadow be circular?

Definition

When you can fold a figure in half so that the two halves fit exactly on top of each other, the shape is **symmetric**. The line that contains the fold is a **line of symmetry**.

For example, the vertical line through the first letter T below is a line of symmetry. The horizontal line through the second T is not a line of symmetry even though it divides the T into two identical parts. If you fold the T along the horizontal line, the two halves will not fit exactly on top of each other.

vertical line of symmetry

3. Which other letters are symmetric? Which letters are both horizontally symmetric and vertically symmetric?

4. Describe the lines of symmetry of a circle.

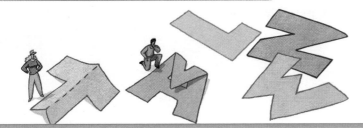

Answers

For You to Explore

1. yes; yes

2. Assuming a light source with parallel rays, the shadow of an equilateral triangle can be any kind of triangle or a segment; the shadow of a circle can be a circle, an ellipse, or a segment.

3. Answers may vary. Sample: The following letters have a horizontal or vertical line of symmetry (depending on how they are drawn): A, B, C, c, D, E, H, I, i, K, l, M, O, o, T, U, V, v, W, w, X, x and Y. The uppercase letters H, I, O, o, X, and x have both horizontal and vertical lines of symmetry. (The letters O, o, Q, X, and x may have a diagonal line of symmetry, if you draw them simply enough.)

4. any line through the center of the circle

Lesson Overview

GOALS

- Warm up to the ideas of the investigation.

- Use a visual approach to develop mathematical habits of mind.

This lesson gives students a taste of each visualizing and analyzing techniques they will use in this investigation. For many students, this may be the first time they have analyzed 2- and 3-dimensional shapes so closely. They need to see, hold, and manipulate shapes whenever possible. Do not ask students to visualize, unless there is no alternative. Students who have trouble visualizing a figure need you to help them see it, so that in the future, they can visualize objects on their own. The lesson also introduces the term *line of symmetry* for use in Problems 3 and 4. This term will come up again Lessons 1.2 and 1.3.

FOR YOU TO EXPLORE
- Core: 1, 2, 3, 4

MATERIALS
- flashlights or lamps
- scissors
- stiff paper or cardboard
- Blackline Master 1.1

HOMEWORK
- Core: 5, 6, 7
- Optional: 8, 9, 10, 11

VOCABULARY
- symmetric
- line of symmetry

Launch

Before you assign Problems 1 and 2, launch the lesson by leading the following demonstration. Drape a cloth over the overhead projector. Then use different shapes (circles, triangles, pentagons, and so on) to make a variety of shadows for each shape. Ask students to decide which shape casts each shadow. Before students get too involved in the demonstration, have them complete Problems 1 and 2. Provide students with their own light sources, such as flashlights. Encourage them to explain their answers.

You may wish to break for a class discussion about symmetry before assigning Problems 3 and 4.

Explore

For You to Explore

PROBLEMS 1 AND 2 Some students will cut figures out of paper to try to make the shadows. Encourage them to explain how they have to position the square relative to the light in order to change the side lengths and angle measures of the shadow.

A square pyramid made from clay provides a very nice model for Problem 1. You can think of the vertex as a source of light, the square base as a shadow, and the cross sections as the shapes (and

continued on p. 10

continued from p. 9

their orientations relative to the light) that cast the shadows. Do not forget a nonright pyramid!

You may want to ask students why it is impossible for a square to cast a circular shadow or any type of curved shadow. An exploration of this question can lead to the insight that if three points are collinear, then their projections (their shadows) are also collinear. In other words, collinearity is a projective invariant.

PROBLEM 3 Encourage students to try to find the longest symmetric word they can, such as KICKBOX (horizontally symmetric).

PROBLEM 4 A cardboard circle with a diameter that can rotate 360° is a good model.

Wrap Up

Review the term *line of symmetry* with your class. You may wish to demonstrate how figures can have horizontal, vertical, or rotational lines of symmetry. Exercise 6 deals with several quadrilaterals. Before assigning it for homework, you may wish to review the definitions of these quadrilaterals.

Exercises

HOMEWORK
- Core: 5, 6, 7
- Optional: 8, 9, 10, 11

Answers

Exercises

5. Shapes 1, 2, and 8 can cast square shadows if the beams of light are parallel. Shapes 6 and 7 can cast square shadows if the beams of light are from a nearby point source; Explanations: Check students' work.

6. 1 line of symmetry:

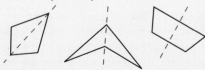

2 lines of symmetry:

Exercises *Practicing Habits of Mind*

On Your Own

5. Which of the shapes below can cast a square shadow? Which ones cannot? Explain.

6. Classify each quadrilateral below by the number of lines of symmetry it has. Draw the lines of symmetry of each quadrilateral. Look for various kinds of lines of symmetry.

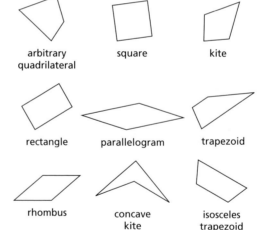

arbitrary quadrilateral   square   kite

rectangle   parallelogram   trapezoid

rhombus   concave kite   isosceles trapezoid

Go Online
Video Tutor
PHSchool.com

Web Code: **bee-0775**

Go Online
PHSchool.com

For more information about lines of symmetry, go to Web Code: **bee-9031**

---

4 lines of symmetry:

All others have no lines of symmetry.

7. The triangle and its shadow have the same shape, but the shadow is bigger.

8.

7. Suppose a light shines directly down on a triangle that is parallel to the ground. What properties of the triangle and its shadow are the same? What properties are different?

Maintain Your Skills

A grid polygon is a polygon that has all of its sides on the grid lines of graph paper. Three of the four figures below are grid polygons. Two of the grid polygons, B and D, are the same except for their positions.

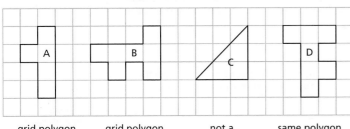

| grid polygon (encloses 5 grid squares) | grid polygon (encloses 7 grid squares) | not a grid polygon | same polygon as polygon B |

For Exercises 8–11, draw as many different grid polygons as you can that

- enclose the given number of grid squares
- have at least two lines of symmetry

Show all the lines of symmetry in each polygon.

8. 4 grid squares

9. 5 grid squares

10. 6 grid squares

11. 7 grid squares

On Your Own

EXERCISES 5 AND 6 These exercises begin to introduce the notion of a geometric transformation: a set of rules for changing a geometric figure. One very useful way to think of geometry is as the study of what changes and what remains the same when you apply a given set of transformations. Exercise 5 looks at a set of transformations called *central projections,* while Exercise 6 involves line reflections.

EXERCISE 6 Extends the idea of symmetry beyond horizontal and vertical symmetry. The solution to this exercise introduces the idea of rotational symmetry about a point. You may wish to use Blackline Master 1.1 with this exercise.

Some students have trouble distinguishing line symmetry from point symmetry. For example, small children often write the letter S backwards. They seem to know that the letter has symmetry, but they cannot distinguish the point symmetry from the line symmetry they know from other figures. So they do not distinguish the letter S from its image when reflected in a line. (They do not make this mistake as often with the letter E, for example, because the letter E has no point symmetry to confuse them.)

If you encounter this problem, it might be worthwhile to the students to draw a line of symmetry for the letters S or N, then for a parallelogram, and carefully show that, for each figure, the reflection image is different from the original figure.

9.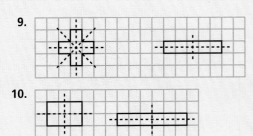

10.

11.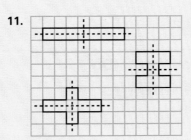

Lesson Overview

GOALS

- Write and follow careful directions.
- Identify and represent parallels.

This lesson uses many new vocabulary terms, but students do not have to understand each term before they begin the lesson. You can develop and explain the terms as necessary as students work through the problems and exercises. Or, if they work in groups, students can help each other understand and make sense of the new terms.

CHECK YOUR UNDERSTANDING

- Core: 1, 2, 4
- Optional: 3

MATERIALS

- straightedges

HOMEWORK

- Core: 5, 6, 8, 9, 10
- Optional: 11, 12
- Extension: 7

VOCABULARY

- prism
- line segment
- parallel lines
- parallel planes

Launch

In the For You to Do section, the definitions of several vocabulary terms are given. Students will use these definitions to make a block letter or a three-dimensional figure in the recipe that follows.

Explore

As a class, discuss the vocabulary terms from the For You to Do section. Then give students time to read the recipe that follows and draw a Three-dimensional figure of their own.

Have you ever tried to write your name in letters that have a three-dimensional look?

You can use the recipe on the next page to turn "flat" letters like these

into "solid" letters like these

For You to Do

1. The steps of the recipe on the next page use special terms, such as *prism*, *parallel*, and *line segment*. Read the definitions of these terms. Then follow the steps of the recipe.

Definitions

A **prism** is a solid formed by translating a given base shape into the third dimension along a line. You can think of a prism as the trail of the base shape as you slide the base shape through space.

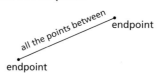

If the base shape has two or more corners, the prism has two or more side edges that are parallel.

A **line segment** is part of a line that contains two endpoints and all the points between the two endpoints.

all the points between
endpoint
endpoint

Parallel lines are lines in the same plane that do not intersect.

Parallel planes are planes in space that do not intersect.

two parallel lines

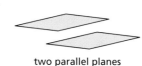

two parallel planes

a plane (for example, a piece of paper)

Answers

For You to Do

1. Check students' work.

Sample Recipe

Step 1 Choose a letter or other shape. Draw it in your notebook. This shape is the base of the prism that you will draw. The example at the right shows two bases. One is an L-shaped hexagon and the other is a house-shaped pentagon. If you like, you can rotate the base of your prism into the third dimension, as shown at the right.

Step 2 A prism needs two parallel bases, so draw a copy of your base shape near the first. Take care to make the line segments of the copy parallel to (and the same size as) the corresponding line segments of the first base. Note that the word *base* does not necessarily mean the bottom or the top of the solid. It can mean the front or the back, as shown at the right.

Step 3 Now connect the corresponding corners of the two bases. The result is called a wire-frame drawing.

Step 4 Wire-frame drawings can be visually confusing. Erasing the back lines may help the eye make sense of the picture. (It is usually easier to start with the wire-frame drawing and then erase the back lines, than it is to draw the correct view from scratch.) Go ahead and erase the appropriate lines in your picture.

Step 5 Shading can also help the eye make sense of the drawing. Shade all the visible parallel faces in your drawing. In general, you should shade the visible parallel faces in the same way.

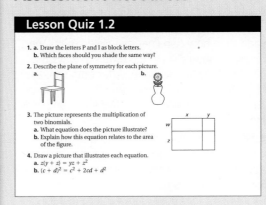

Now that the pentagonal prism looks like a house, the term *base* may be especially confusing. The *house's* base is the bottom rectangular face of the solid. The *prism's* bases are the front and back faces of the house.

Exercises Practicing Habits of Mind

Check Your Understanding

1. **Write About It** In each wire-frame drawing above, the segments that connect the two bases are parallel. Convince yourself that this is true. Then use a convincing argument to explain why.

Wrap Up

Have students share their 3-D figures or letters with the class and point out parallel planes, bases, edges, and so on. You may want to complete Exercise 1 as a class discussion. Then you can use Exercise 4 to test students' understanding.

Assessment Resources

Lesson Quiz 1.2

1. a. Draw the letters P and I as block letters.
   b. Which faces should you shade the same way?

2. Describe the plane of symmetry for each picture.
   a.   **b.**

3. The picture represents the multiplication of two binomials.
   a. What equation does the picture illustrate?
   b. Explain how this equation relates to the area of the figure.

4. Draw a picture that illustrates each equation.
   a. $z(y + z) = yz + z^2$
   b. $(c + d)^2 = c^2 + 2cd + d^2$

Exercises

1. Answers may vary. Sample: Since the two bases are the same distance apart at all points, the connecting lines appear to be the same length. Since the points on the second base are translated in the same direction from the corresponding points on the first base, the connecting segments take on the same slope. This makes them appear parallel.

Exercises

HOMEWORK
- Core: 5, 6, 8, 9, 10
- Optional: 11, 12
- Extension: 7

On Your Own

EXERCISE 6 Encourage students to set up an experiment. First, they should look at the figures given in the exercise—how one line divides the plane and then how two lines can divide the plane. Next, students should draw the different ways that three lines can divide the plane. After doing so, they should be able to visualize how four lines can divide the plane and then think of how five lines can divide the plane.

EXERCISE 7 is very difficult. You may wish to assign it as a long term project, or as a class project that you work on a little bit at a time. A good introductory exercise is to extend the faces of a cube and ask students into how many regions its faces divide space. Then do the same for the faces of a tetrahedron. These exercises solve the problem for $n = 4$, where n is the number of planes in space

EXERCISES 9–11 Students who have had experience in algebra may find these visual proofs quite enlightening. For students who have not had enough experience in algebra to understand the equations, you may adapt the exercises by using numbers, instead of variables.

2. **a.** In the block letters that you drew by following the recipe in the lesson, which faces are parallel?

   b. Why would you normally shade parallel faces the same way? Under what conditions, if any, would you shade them differently?

3. Pictures that can be seen in more than one way can play tricks on the eye. Try to draw each figure at the right. What confuses you?

4. Choose a letter. Draw a 2-in. block version of it. Use the technique shown in this section. Shade a base of the prism. Explain why you chose this shape as the base.

On Your Own

5. Three-dimensional solids can also have symmetry. A *plane of symmetry* of a three-dimensional figure divides it into two identical pieces. If you think of replacing the plane with a mirror, the half of the figure that is reflected in the mirror looks the same as the half that is hidden behind the mirror. Find five different symmetrical objects around your house, such as tissue boxes, cans of soup, and so on. Describe the planes of symmetry of each. You may include drawings of your descriptions.

6. A plane is infinite. Any line in a plane divides the plane into two regions.

Remember...
What does the term *infinite* mean?

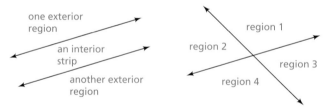

one region

the other region

Two lines may divide a plane into three or four regions, depending on how you place the lines.

one exterior region

an interior strip

another exterior region

region 1

region 2

region 3

region 4

With five lines, what is the maximum number of regions into which you can divide a plane?

Answers

2. **a.** Check students' work.
   b. Light hits parallel faces at the same angle; Answers may vary. Sample: Different shading on parallel faces would be necessary if other objects affect the light that the parallel faces receive.

3. Answers may vary. Sample: The darkest regions sometimes appear to be upper parts of a three-dimensional figure. Then they suddenly switch to be right-hand parts of a different figure.

4. Check students' work.

5. Check students' work.

6. 16

7. 15; 26

8. A

9. The figure on the left is a square whose top side and left side have each been divided into segments of lengths a and b. This allows you to divide the large rectangle into an a-by-a square, two a-by-b rectangles, and a b-by-b square. The area of the largest square is $(a + b)^2$. The areas of the four parts are a^2, ab, ab, and b^2. The area of the largest square is equal to the sum of the areas of the parts, so $(a + b)^2 = a^2 + 2ab + b^2$. The figure on the right is a rectangle divided into four smaller rectangles. The area of the largest rectangle is $(a + b)(c + d)$. This is equal to the sum of the areas of the parts. So $(a + b)(c + d) = ac + ad + bc + bd$.

7. Take It Further Space is infinite. Any plane in space divides space into two regions. Two planes may divide space into three or four regions, depending on how you place the planes. Three planes divide space into as few as four or as many as eight regions. What is the maximum number of regions into which you can divide space with four planes? With five planes?

This is the three-dimensional version of Exercise 6, but it is hard to picture. Experienced mathematicians can puzzle for weeks over the questions asked here.

8. Standardized Test Prep The Soma Cube is a cube with three units on each side. You can construct the cube 240 different ways from six shapes called tetracubes and one shape called a tricube. One of the tetracubes, shown at the right, is a branch or corner piece that is made of four cubes. One cube has one face of each of the other cubes attached to it. (The Soma Cube was invented by Piet Hein. www.piethein.com)

How many planes of symmetry does this tetracube have?

A. 1   **B.** 2   **C.** 3   **D.** 4

Sometimes pictures help you visualize and understand quantities or relationships between quantities.

9. Write About It What does each picture below tell you about the multiplication of binomials? Give reasons for each answer.

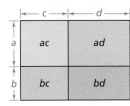

$(a + b)^2 = a^2 + 2ab + b^2$ $(a + b)(c + d) = ac + ad + bc + bd$

10. Write About It The first figure above shows $(a + b)^2 = a^2 + 2ab + b^2$. Explain how the figure at the right shows the same equation.

11. Draw a picture that illustrates the equation $d(c + f) = dc + df$.

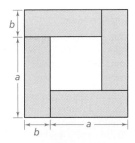

Maintain Your Skills

12. Make a list of all block letters that have lines of symmetry. Draw a three-dimensional representation of each letter. What kinds of symmetry do you see?

Go Online
PHSchool.com

For additional practice, go to Web Code: bea-0102

Additional Resources

PRINTED RESOURCES
- Solution Manual
- Practice Workbook
- Assessment Resources
- Teaching Resources

TECHNOLOGY
- Interactive Textbook
- TeacherExpress CD-ROM
- **Exam**View CD-ROM
- **PHSchool.com**
  - Additional Practice
  - Mid-Chapter and Chapter Tests
  - Video Tutors
  - Vocabulary Puzzles

Additional Practice

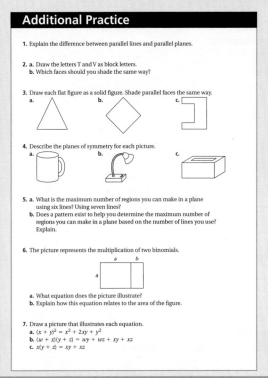

1. Explain the difference between parallel lines and parallel planes.

2. a. Draw the letters T and V as block letters.
   b. Which faces should you shade the same way?

3. Draw each flat figure as a solid figure. Shade parallel faces the same way.
   a.   b.   c.

4. Describe the planes of symmetry for each picture.
   a.   b.   c.

5. a. What is the maximum number of regions you can make in a plane using six lines? Using seven lines?
   b. Does a pattern exist to help you determine the maximum number of regions you can make in a plane based on the number of lines you use? Explain.

6. The picture represents the multiplication of two binomials.

   a. What equation does the picture illustrate?
   b. Explain how this equation relates to the area of the figure.

7. Draw a picture that illustrates each equation.
   a. $(x + y)^2 = x^2 + 2xy + y^2$
   b. $(w + x)(y + z) = wy + wz + xy + xz$
   c. $x(y + z) = xy + xz$

Practice: For Lesson 1.2, assign Exercises 1–7.

10. The area of the entire figure is $(a + b)^2$. The length of each side of the white square is $a - b$, so the area of the white square is $(a - b)^2$. Each shaded rectangle has area ab. The area of the entire figure equals the sum of the areas of the parts, so $(a + b)^2 = 4ab + (a - b)^2$.

11.

	c	f
d	dc	df

12. The block capital letters that have symmetry are A, B, C, D, E, H, I, K, M, O, T, U, V, W, X, and Y. For each line of symmetry of the 2-dimensional letter, there is a corresponding plane of symmetry for the 3-dimensional letter. Each of these planes of symmetry contains the corresponding line of symmetry and is perpendicular to the plane of the 2-dimensional letter. Since each of the 3-dimensional letters is like a prism, there is also a plane of symmetry that passes through the midpoints of the lateral edges of the prism.

Lesson Overview

GOALS

- Visualize mental images in order to analyze their parts.
- Analyze visual scenes in order to draw them.
- Develop clear language to describe shapes.

This lesson is about describing shapes in different ways. Students will need to use precise vocabulary so that other people can follow and clearly understand the algorithms they write for drawing shapes.

CHECK YOUR UNDERSTANDING
- Core: 1, 2, 3

MATERIALS
- modeling clay
- overhead projector

HOMEWORK
- Core: 4, 5, 6, 13
- Optional: 7, 8, 9, 10, 11, 12

VOCABULARY
- perpendicular

Launch

Read through the descriptions of *Names, Features,* and *Recipes* with your class before assigning the In-Class Experiment.

Explore

In-Class Experiment

The In-Class Experiment asks students to discover what objects look like given only information about the shadows they cast. Provide students with clay, sponges, dough, or other modeling material so they can make the objects and test their conjectures.

You can use an overhead projector to demonstrate the shadows cast by various objects in these problems.

HINTS FOR STUDENTS FOR PROBLEM 3

- For very difficult problems like this, it helps to think of only one shadow at a time, or to think of how you can combine the objects from Problems 1 and 2 into a single object.
- There is a common household tool that has this shape.

It is often important to describe shape and other spatial information accurately with words.

You can describe shapes in many ways.

Names Some shapes have special names, such as *circle* or *square*. One name may be enough to describe a shape. When a shape looks like another shape that has a special name, you may use some extra words to describe the original shape. For instance, you may say, "like an upside-down L," "like a house lying on its side," or "saddle-shaped."

Features Often you may not know the shape of a figure or solid. You must determine the shape from some set of features. Scientists face this situation when they try to deduce the shape of a molecule from what they know about the atoms that form the molecule or from how the molecule scatters light or X-rays.

Recipes Sometimes, describing how a picture looks is not as helpful as describing how to draw it. For example, suppose you give someone traveling directions. You would more likely say to walk two blocks north, turn left, and walk another block than describe the path as an upside-down L. The recipes you use in mathematics are often called *algorithms* or *constructions*.

You will practice using each of these three ways to describe shapes. Then you will be better prepared to combine them in whatever manner best suits your purpose.

As you proceed, try to notice whether you use *names, features,* or *recipes* to describe pictures or to draw pictures from descriptions.

In-Class Experiment

Casting Shadows

The shape of an object's shadow usually depends on how light hits the object. In the problems below, you will think about solids and the shadows they cast. You will also deduce the properties of a solid based on its shadows.

1. A solid casts a circular shadow on the floor. When the solid is lit from the front, it casts a square shadow on the back wall. What solid might it be? Try to make a model out of clay, sponge, dough, or other material. Describe the solid in words as well as you can. Then try to draw a picture of it.

> Objects under the midday sun on a clear day generally cast the most distinct and least distorted shadows.

Answers

In-Class Experiment

1. Answers may vary. Sample: a cylinder

2. Answers may vary. Sample: a cone

3.

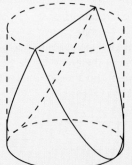

2. A solid casts a circular shadow on the floor. When the solid is lit from the left, it casts a triangular shadow on the right wall. What solid might it be? Try to make a model out of clay, sponge, dough, or other material. Describe the solid in words as well as you can. Then try to draw a picture of it.

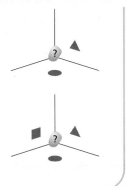

3. Suppose a solid casts a circular shadow on the floor, a triangular shadow when lit from the left, and a square shadow when lit from the front. What solid might it be? Try to make a model out of clay, sponge, dough, or other material. Describe the solid in words as well as you can. Then try to draw a picture of it.

Exercises *Practicing Habits of Mind*

Check Your Understanding

1. Read the following directions.

Face north. Walk four feet. Turn right. Walk six feet. Turn right again. Walk four feet. Turn right again and walk six feet. Turn right again.

Suppose you follow these directions.

a. What shape will your path form?

b. In what direction will you be facing when you finish?

c. The direction *turn right* does not specify how far to turn. Yet you probably made an assumption. What was your assumption? What makes it seem reasonable?

2. Pick a simple shape.

a. Describe it by name.

b. Describe it with a recipe that you can use to draw it.

3. Read the following recipe.

Draw two segments that are perpendicular at their midpoints. Connect the four endpoints in order.

a. Draw a shape that the recipe above describes.

b. Does the recipe describe only one shape? Explain.

Exercises

1. a. a rectangle

b. north

c. The assumption is that the right turn is a 90° right turn. This is reasonable because in 90° turns are common in everyday experience.

2. a–b. Answers may vary. Samples are given.

a. a square with sides 5 cm

b. Draw a segment 5 cm long. At each endpoint of this segment, draw another segment. The two new segments should be perpendicular to the first, should each be 5 cm long, and should be on the same side of the original segment. Connect the other two endpoints of the two new segments to form a closed figure.

3. a. Check students' work. The students' figures should be rhombuses or squares.

b. No; although the shape will have to be a rhombus, it can be any rhombus, or even a square.

Wrap Up

Assign the Check Your Understanding exercises for classwork and have students share their answers.

Assessment Resources

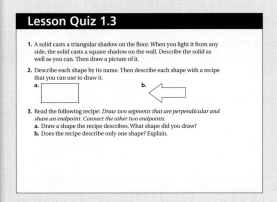

Lesson Quiz 1.3

1. A solid casts a triangular shadow on the floor. When you light it from any side, the solid casts a square shadow on the wall. Describe the solid as well as you can. Then draw a picture of it.

2. Describe each shape by its name. Then describe each shape with a recipe that you can use to draw it.

a. **b.**

3. Read the following recipe: *Draw two segments that are perpendicular and share an endpoint. Connect the other two endpoints.*
a. Draw a shape the recipe describes. What shape did you draw?
b. Does the recipe describe only one shape? Explain.

Exercises

HOMEWORK

- Core: 4, 5, 6, 13
- Optional: 7, 8, 9, 10, 11, 12

Check Your Understanding

EXERCISES 1–3 Any geometric recipe, just like any cooking recipe, assumes that the person following the recipe has some knowledge. For example, a cooking recipe that calls for a cup of flour assumes that the reader knows to use an 8-oz measuring cup, instead of a teacup.

To encourage class discussion, you might ask, "When is it reasonable to interpret such nonspecific statements such as *turn right* to mean *turn 90° right*?" You may want to draw students' attention to the fact that the way you give and receive directions has a lot to do with your previous experiences and with the context at hand.

Maintain Your Skills

EXERCISES 7–13 introduce students to some simple commands of Turtle Geometry. Students should find the patterns in these exercises and be able to predict the paths that similar commands make.

Additional Resources

PRINTED RESOURCES
- Solution Manual
- Practice Workbook
- Assessment Resources
- Teaching Resources

TECHNOLOGY
- Interactive Textbook
- TeacherExpress CD-ROM
- ExamView CD-ROM
  - Additional Practice
  - Mid-Chapter and Chapter Tests
  - Video Tutors
  - Vocabulary Puzzles

Additional Practice

1. Suppose you follow these directions: Face south. Drive south for 2 blocks. Turn left. Drive 5 blocks. Turn left again. Drive 2 blocks. Turn left again. Drive 5 more blocks.
   a. What shape will your path form?
   b. Describe your final location. In what direction will you be facing?

2. Describe each shape by its name. Then describe each shape with a recipe that you can use to draw it.
   a. **b.** **c.**

3. Read the following recipe: *Draw two parallel segments. Connect the endpoints in order.*
   a. Draw a shape the recipe describes.
   b. Can you follow this recipe to draw a different shape? Explain.

4. **a.** Draw a triangle that has only one line of symmetry.
   b. Can you draw other triangles that fit this description? What do they have in common?

5. A certain 3-dimensional solid has a vertical cross section that is a rectangle and a horizontal cross section that is a circle. Name and draw the 3-dimensional solid.

6. Write directions that describe how to draw the letters in the word CAT.

7. Draw a square. Draw a circle inside the square so that the circle touches each side of the square at one point. Draw a segment connecting the center of the circle to the bottom right corner of the square. Erase the sides of the square. What letter have you drawn?

8. Write directions that describe how to draw each figure.
   a. **b.**

Practice: For Lesson 1.3, assign Exercises 1, 2, 6, and 8.

On Your Own

4. Read the two recipes below.

   Recipe 1: Draw two perpendicular segments that share one endpoint. Make one segment 3 cm long and the other segment 6 cm long. Connect the other two endpoints.

   Recipe 2: Draw a right triangle with legs of length 3 cm and 6 cm.

   a. Do the two recipes describe the same shape?

   b. Draw the shapes that each recipe describes.

5. A quadrilateral has horizontal, vertical, and diagonal lines of symmetry.

   a. Draw a quadrilateral that fits this description.

   b. Is there only one quadrilateral that fits the description? Explain.

6. What three-dimensional solid has a circle as every cross section?

Maintain Your Skills

The exercises below use commands from Turtle Geometry. Turtle Geometry is a computer language that moves a cursor (the turtle) forward or backward. The programmer tells the cursor how many steps to move and in what direction. The command *FD 2* means "move forward 2 steps." *RT 90* means "turn to the right 90°." *Repeat 6* means "repeat the given command 6 times."

Follow the commands below. Use a computer or a pencil and protractor to trace out a path.

7. FD 2 RT 90, FD 2 RT 90, FD 2 RT 90, FD 2 RT 90

8. Repeat 6 [FD 2 RT 45]

9. Repeat 6 [FD 2 RT 60]

10. Repeat 8 [FD 2 RT 45]

11. Repeat 8 [FD 2 RT 30]

12. Repeat 12 [FD 2 RT 30]

13. **Standardized Test Prep** Amina entered the following commands into her Turtle Geometry program.

    RT 30 FD 20, RT 60 FD 30, RT 60 FD 20, RT 120 FD 50, RT 120 FD 20

    Which figure did the program draw for her?

    A. an irregular pentagon   **B.** an open figure

    C. a triangle   **D.** an isosceles trapezoid

For additional practice, go to **Web Code: bea-0103**

Answers

4. **a.** yes   **b.**

3 cm
6 cm

5. **a.**

   b. Yes; the figure must be a square, though the size of the square can vary.

6. a sphere

7.

8.

9.

As you translate words into drawings and drawings into words, you will meet more geometry ideas. Many of them will be familiar to you. You may want to talk about others with classmates or your teacher. To talk about the new ideas, you will need to recall more terminology.

If you carefully follow the instructions in the recipe below, you will get a certain picture. Compare your picture to your classmates' pictures. Are they they same?

In-Class Experiment

Drawing From a Recipe

Step 1 Draw a horizontal line segment.

Step 2 Above the segment, draw two circles that are the same size and tangent to the segment. *Tangent* means "just touching." Leave some space between the two circles—a space roughly the size of the circles' diameter.

Step 3 Draw a line segment above the two circles and tangent to them. It should extend slightly beyond the two circles. Label this segment's left endpoint L and its right endpoint R.

Step 4 From L, draw a segment upward that is perpendicular to $\overline{LR}$ and about half the length of $\overline{LR}$. Label its top endpoint B. From R, draw another segment in the same way. Label its top endpoint F.

Step 5 Draw $\overline{BF}$.

Step 6 Use a pencil to lightly extend $\overline{BF}$ about two thirds of its length to the right. Label the endpoint of the new segment X.

Step 7 Use a pencil to lightly draw a segment downward from X that is perpendicular to $\overleftrightarrow{LR}$. This segment should be roughly the length of $\overline{FR}$. Find the midpoint of this new segment. Label it M.

Step 8 Draw $\overline{MR}$. Then erase the construction lines from Steps 6 and 7. What does your picture look like?

The two figures are tangent here, but not here.

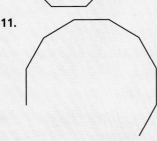

10.

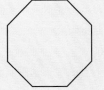

11.

12.

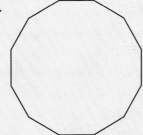

13. D

In-Class Experiment

Check students' work; a wagon.

GOALS

• Analyze visual scenes in order to draw them.

• Develop clear language to describe shapes.

This lesson allows students to draw from a recipe, using whatever tools and methods they prefer. Any difficulties students encounter will motivate them to learn more sophisticated construction methods later. The next investigation introduces more formal hand construction tools such as a ruler, a protractor, or a compass.

CHECK YOUR UNDERSTANDING

• Core: 1, 2, 3, 4

MATERIALS

• straightedges
• compasses
• protractors
• rulers

HOMEWORK

• Core: 5, 7, 8, 9
• Optional: 6, 10, 11, 12, 13

VOCABULARY

• tangent
• equilateral
• arc
• diameter
• radius

Launch

Before assigning the In-Class Experiment, you may want to review any unfamiliar vocabulary terms with your class.

Explore

In-Class Experiment

Give students ample time to work on this construction and compare their finished products with each other.

CLASSROOM ACTIVITY Have students sit back-to-back in pairs. One student describes a shape while the other draws it. The student drawing the shape may not ask questions of the student giving directions. Then have students exchange roles. For this activity, it is best to make cards with various shapes on them. Letters or polygons might be too easy, because they have simple names. Combinations of either are more effective. You may be able to find, in an art supply or museum store, packs of cardboard squares that are divided into eight isosceles right triangles with various combinations of white and black shading.

Wrap Up

Assign the Check Your Understanding exercises for classwork. You can assign one of the exercises from Exercises 2–4 to pairs or small groups.

Assessment Resources

Exercises

HOMEWORK
• Core: 5, 7, 8, 9
• Optional: 6, 10, 11, 12, 13

Check Your Understanding

EXERCISE 1 asks students to draw the three medians of a triangle. These three medians meet at the *centroid.* You may or may not wish to introduce this vocabulary term now—it will come up again in future activities.

Students who draw freehand often do not draw the medians with enough accuracy to be sure that the medians concur. But in this chapter, it is enough simply to raise the question of concurrence and have students think about how they can resolve the question without relying on the accuracy of a drawing.

Students using geometry software will immediately see that the medians of a triangle are concurrent. Again, this circumstance might start a discussion about the need to prove concurrency, instead of relying on experimentation with software.

EXERCISES 2–4 Students should understand the terms *midpoint, equilateral, radius, tangent, perpendicular,* and *diameter.*

Exercises *Practicing Habits of Mind*

Check Your Understanding

1. Use a pencil and straightedge to draw a large triangle. Find and label the midpoint of each side. Connect each midpoint to the opposite vertex. Label the points where these three segments intersect.

   Exercises 2–4 describe how to draw certain letters of the alphabet. Use the descriptions to draw the letters. The descriptions are fairly good, but you may have to guess what some parts of the descriptions mean. Check whether your results make sense.

2. Draw an equilateral triangle with 2-inch sides and a horizontal base. Find and connect the midpoints of the two nonhorizontal sides. Erase the base of the original triangle. What letter did you draw?

> The prefix *equi-* means "equal." *Lateral* means "side." **Equilateral** means "sides with equal length."

3. Draw a circle with a $\frac{1}{2}$-inch radius. Draw a slightly larger circle directly below and tangent to the first circle. Draw the vertical segment that connects the centers of the circles. Draw the horizontal diameter of each circle. In the top circle, erase the bottom right 90° section of the circle. In the bottom circle, erase the top left 90° section of the circle. Then erase the vertical and horizontal segments that you sketched. What letter did you draw?

4. Draw a circle. Draw two diameters that are about 45° from vertical and are perpendicular to each other. Erase the 90° section of the circle on the right side of the circle. Then erase the diameters. What letter did you draw?

On Your Own

5. Write directions that describe how to draw your initials. Use precise language. Some letters are complicated to draw, so take advantage of any geometry terms that will make your directions more clear.

6. Write careful directions that describe how to walk from the door of your math classroom to the main office of your school.

Answers

Exercises

1.

2. A

3. S

4. C

5–6. Check students' work.

7. Write directions that describe how to draw the figure below. Then have three classmates draw the figure following your directions. If any of the three pictures differs from the figure below, explain what you think caused the difference.

8. Standardized Test Prep Enrique has a system he uses to draw regular polygons inscribed in a circle.

Step 1 He draws a large circle. Then he draws a line tangent to the circle.

Step 2 For a polygon with m congruent sides, he divides $360°$ by $2m$ to get y.

Step 3 He then draws an angle with measure $y°$ such that the following statements are true.

- The point of tangency is the vertex of the angle.
- The tangent line is one side of the angle.
- The other side of the angle passes through the circle.

Step 4 Next, he draws a line segment from the point of tangency to the point where the other side of the angle intersects the circle.

Step 5 Finally, he uses a compass to construct $(m - 1)$ segments with endpoints on the circle such that the following are true:

- The $(m - 1)$ segments are congruent to the first segment.
- The m segments form a regular polygon.

If Enrique wants to draw a regular nonagon, or nine-sided polygon, inscribed in a circle, what number of degrees will he use for his angle with the tangent?

A. $10°$ **B.** $20°$ **C.** $40°$ **D.** $80°$

The more difficult the task, the clearer the directions must be.

7. Check students' work.

8. B

On Your Own

EXERCISE 5 asks students to write directions that describe how to draw their initials. If one of their initials is A, S, or C, ask them to write a recipe different from the ones given in Exercises 2–4. When you review these exercises as a class, you can ask students to exchange their directions and test them.

EXERCISE 9 The construction leads to this conjecture: *The radius of a circle is perpendicular to the line tangent to the circle at the endpoint of the radius.* It is not necessary that students know this fact now, but you can point this out as you review this exercise.

Maintain Your Skills

EXERCISES 10–13 give students some practice giving precise directions for drawing a geometric figure. The figures are iterations of Sierpinski's Triangle, beginning with an equilateral triangle. "Sierpinski's Triangle," or "Sierpinski's Gasket," is named for the Polish mathematician Waclaw Sierpinski and is one of the simplest examples of a fractal. It begins with an equilateral triangle. Each iteration contains new triangles you make by connecting the midpoints of the sides of the other triangles. If you color the odd numbers in Pascal's Triangle, Sierpinski's Triangle will emerge.

As a hint to the structure of this object, and of the directions students might write, you might give them permission to use the answer to each exercise in their solution to the next exercise. This will make them aware of the recursive nature of the construction. For this reason, it is important for each student or group to do all these exercises in order, rather than dividing the exercises among different students or groups.

Additional Resources

PRINTED RESOURCES
- Solution Manual
- Practice Workbook

- Assessment Resources
- Teaching Resources

TECHNOLOGY
- Interactive Textbook
- TeacherExpress CD-ROM
- ExamView CD-ROM
- PHSchool.com
  - Additional Practice
  - Mid-Chapter and Chapter Tests
  - Video Tutors
  - Vocabulary Puzzles

Additional Practice

1. Suppose you follow these directions: Face south. Drive south for 2 blocks. Turn left. Drive 5 blocks. Turn left again. Drive 2 blocks. Turn left again. Drive 5 more blocks.
   a. What shape will your path form?
   b. Describe your final location. In what direction will you be facing?

2. Describe each shape by its name. Then describe each shape with a recipe that you can use to draw it.
   a. b. c.

3. Read the following recipe: *Draw two parallel segments. Connect the endpoints in order.*
   a. Draw a shape the recipe describes.
   b. Can you follow this recipe to draw a different shape? Explain.

4. a. Draw a triangle that has only one line of symmetry.
   b. Can you draw other triangles that fit this description? What do they have in common?

5. A certain 3-dimensional solid has a vertical cross section that is a rectangle and a horizontal cross section that is a circle. Name and draw the 3-dimensional solid.

6. Write directions that describe how to draw the letters in the word CAT.

7. Draw a square. Draw a circle inside the square so that the circle touches each side of the square at one point. Draw a segment connecting the center of the circle to the bottom right corner of the square. Erase the sides of the square. What letter have you drawn?

8. Write directions that describe how to draw each figure.
   a. b.

Practice: For Lesson 1.4, assign Exercises 3–5 and 7.

---

9. Carefully read and follow the recipe below.

   Step 1 Draw a circle. Label the center of the circle point *A*.

   Step 2 Draw a radius of the circle. Label its endpoint on the circle point *B*.

   Step 3 Draw a segment that is tangent to the circle at *B*. The segment should be longer than the diameter of the circle.

   Step 4 Draw a second radius of the circle that is perpendicular to $\overline{AB}$. Label the point where it touches the circle point *D*.

   Step 5 Draw a segment that is tangent to the circle at *D*. The segment should be longer than the diameter of the circle.

   Step 6 Label the intersection of the two tangent segments point *C*.

   a. What kind of quadrilateral is *ABCD*?

   b. Make a conjecture. In a circle, what is the measure of the angle formed by a radius and a line that is tangent to the circle at the endpoint of the radius?

Maintain Your Skills

Write directions that describe how to draw each figure.

10. 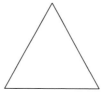 11.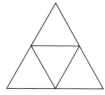

12. 13.

Go Online
PHSchool.com

For additional practice, go to Web Code: bea-0104

Answers

9. a. square
   b. a right angle

10. Answers may vary. Sample: Draw an equilateral triangle.

11. Answers may vary. Sample: Draw an equilateral triangle. Mark the midpoints of the sides of the triangle. Connect the midpoints with segments.

12. Answers may vary. Sample: Repeat the procedure used for Exercise 11 for all the triangles in Exercise 11 except the center triangle.

13. Answers may vary. Sample: Start with the figure you obtained in Exercise 12. That figure contains three groups of triangles similar to the group of triangles for Exercise 12. Repeat the procedure used for Exercise 12 on each of these groups of small triangles.

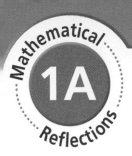

1A Mathematical Reflections

In this investigation, you learned the importance of pictures. You found lines of symmetry. You also learned to draw three-dimensional solids. The following questions will help you summarize what you have learned.

1. Name three kinds of shapes that can cast a circular shadow. Name a shape that cannot cast a circular shadow. Explain your reasoning.

2. Draw a three-dimensional block version of the figure at right. Label the base. Shade any visible parallel faces.

3. How many lines of symmetry does a square have? How many lines of symmetry does a rectangle have? Can a rectangle ever have the same number of lines of symmetry as a square? Explain.

4. Read the following recipe.

   Draw two horizontal parallel segments that are the same length. Connect the two left endpoints. Connect the two right endpoints.

   a. Draw a shape described by this recipe.

   b. Does this recipe describe only one shape? Explain.

5. Write careful directions that describe how to draw the number 5. Use any geometry terms that might make your directions more clear.

6. What is a line of symmetry?

7. What is a prism?

8. What should you keep in mind when you give traveling directions to someone or tell someone how to draw a figure or complete a task?

Vocabulary

In this investigation, you learned these terms. Make sure you understand what each one means and how you use it.

- equilateral
- line of symmetry
- line segment
- parallel lines
- parallel planes
- prism
- symmetric

The shadow of the roof of the Pantheon covers the entire inside of the building except for one spot of sunlight.

Mathematical Reflections

EXERCISES 6–8 At the start of the investigation, you may have assigned these as Questions 1–3 for students to think and write about.

Mathematical Reflections

1. Answers may vary. Sample: A circle or an ellipse can cast a circular shadow. A square cannot cast a circular shadow. Its edges are straight, but a circle is curved.

2. See back of book.

3. 4; 2; only if the rectangle is a square

4. **a.** Answers may vary. Sample:

   b. No; the recipe describes a variety of parallelograms.

5–8. See back of book.

Investigation Overview

In this investigation, students construct various shapes by describing features and using hand construction tools, including paper folding, which is an often-overlooked construction tool. The symmetry of folds provides an ideal way to construct midpoints and angle bisectors. Paper folding also allows you to make right angles by bisecting a segment. This investigation introduces any vocabulary terms in the context of constructions.

You may wish to assign Questions 1–3 for students to think and write about during the investigation

Learning Goals

- Use hand construction tools.
- Know that points on the perpendicular bisector of a line segment are equidistant from its endpoints.
- Know about special segments that are associated with triangles.
- Explain the difference between a construction and a drawing.

Habits and Skills

- Use hand construction tools.
- Choose the right tool for a construction (including paper folding).
- Identify invariants—values or relationships that stay the same while other values or relationships change.

Investigation 1B Constructing

In *Constructing,* you will construct geometric figures. For many figures, you will have to deduce the recipes—how to construct each figure—on your own. Life often presents problems in this way. You know what you need, but not how to make it. Such problems have always inspired creative, inventive thinking. The solutions—the how-to parts—always depend on what tools are available.

By the end of this investigation, you will be able to answer questions like these.

1. What is the difference between drawing a figure and constructing a figure?
2. What is invariant about the measures of the angles in a triangle?
3. How can you construct the perpendicular bisector of a segment?

You will learn

- to use hand construction tools
- that points on the perpendicular bisector of a line segment are equidistant from its endpoints
- about special segments that are associated with triangles

You will develop these habits and skills:

- Use hand construction tools.
- Choose the right tool for a construction (including paper folding).
- Identify invariants—values or relationships that stay the same while other values or relationships change.

Follow construction steps carefully and you get a desired result.

Investigation Road Map

LESSON 1.5, *Getting Started,* asks students to use their knowledge of the Triangle Inequality to experiment and make conjectures about the sides and angles of triangles.

LESSON 1.6, *Compasses, Angles, and Circles,* has students follow a dialog between Tony and Sasha about constructing a triangle using only rulers. Then students see an example of constructing a midpoint that uses two different construction methods. One method uses a compass and straightedge, and the other method uses paper folding.

Measurements are approximations. However, very careful measurements can suggest exact relationships.

For You to Explore

For the problems below, use whatever tools seem best. Keep track of your answers, as well as *how* you solved each problem—what tools you used and how you used them.

Use these sets of lengths for Problems 1–4.

3 in., 5 in., 7 in.	3 in., 5 in., 4 in.
3 in., 8 in., 4 in.	2 in., 3 in., 3 in.

1. For each set of lengths given above, construct a triangle with those side lengths. If a triangle is not possible, explain why.

2. For each triangle you constructed in Problem 1, do the following.

   a. Measure the angles.

   b. Compare your triangle to someone else's triangle. Are the two triangles identical? Do the angles of the two triangles match exactly?

   c. Summarize and explain what you observe.

3. For each triangle you constructed in Problem 1, find the sum of the measures of its angles. Are the sums invariant?

4. The triangles you constructed in Problem 1 may have an invariant, but you only tested a few triangles.

   a. Do you believe that your invariant holds for all triangles or only for some triangles? Explain.

   b. What will convince you that the sum of the measures of the angles of any triangle is invariant?

Use these sets of angle measures for Problems 5 and 6.

40°, 60°, 80°	60°, 70°, 80°	120°, 30°, 30°
30°, 60°, 90°	90°, 90°, 90°	

5. For each set of angle measures given above, construct a triangle with those angle measures. If a triangle is not possible, explain why.

6. For each triangle you constructed in Problem 5, do the following.

   a. Measure the lengths of the sides (in inches or centimeters, whichever is more convenient).

   b. Find the ratio of the longest side to the shortest side (divide the longest side by the shortest side).

   c. Compare your triangle to someone else's triangle. Are the two triangles identical? Are the ratios from part (b) equal?

   d. Summarize and explain what you observe.

Habits of Mind

Look for a relationship. In one of the triangles you constructed, exactly two sides are the same length. Why do you think this is true?

Answers

For You to Explore

1.

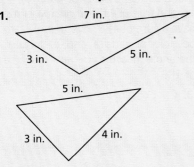

A triangle with side lengths 3 in., 8 in., and 4 in. is not possible since sides of 3 in. and 4 in. would not reach each other if they are connected to each end of an 8 in. side.

continued on p. 26

Lesson Overview

GOALS

- Warm up to the ideas of the investigation.
- Use a hands-on approach to develop mathematical habits of mind.

These problems lead students to a conjecture about the sum of the measures of the angles of a triangle. You can complete this lesson in one day, or you can take two days to complete this lesson and discuss the conjecture.

FOR YOU TO EXPLORE	**HOMEWORK**
• Core: 1, 2, 3, 4, 5, 6	• Core: 7, 8, 9, 10
	• Optional: 11, 12, 13
MATERIALS	
• protractors	**VOCABULARY**
• rulers	• ratio

Launch

Assign Problems 1–4 to pairs or small group of students. Several of the problems require students to compare their results with others'.

Explore

For You to Explore

PROBLEM 2 previews SSS triangle congruence. Discuss with students what it means for two triangles to be "identical." Ask students if it matters whether one triangle is "right side up" while another is "upside down."

PROBLEMS 3 AND 4 lead to this theorem: *The sum of the measures of the angles of a triangle in the plane is an invariant. Regardless of the triangle, the angle sum is* 180°. Students will see a proof of this theorem later.

PROBLEM 5 By using the Triangle Angle-Sum Theorem, students should be able to rule out the 60-70-80 set and the 90-90-90 set because the sum of the angle measures is greater than 180°. Drawing the remaining triangles may be more difficult than drawing the triangles in Problem 1. Make sure students spend time comparing the triangles they draw, as it is possible to construct more than one triangle with the given sets of angle measures.

You cannot draw a 90-90-90 triangle in a plane, but you *can* draw it on a sphere. Let vertex A be on the equator. Let vertex B be on the equator $\frac{1}{4}$ of the way around the globe from A. Let the third vertex be at the North Pole.

Wrap Up

Have a class discussion to summarize what students learned about triangles while completing these problems. You can use Exercise 9 for this discussion.

Exercises

HOMEWORK
- Core: 7, 8, 9, 10
- Optional: 11, 12, 13

Maintain Your Skills

EXERCISES 11–13 require students to construct triangles that meet the given conditions. In each exercise, the sum of the is two given angle measures is 90°. The measure of the third angle of each triangle is 90°. The three triangles in each exercise must be similar.

continued from p. 25

Answers

2. **a.** 3 in., 5 in., 7 in.: 120°, 22°, 38°;
   3 in., 4 in., 4 in.: 90°, 37°, 53°;
   2 in., 3 in., 3 in.: 70.5°, 70.5°, 39°
   b. All students should get triangles that are the same size and shape. The angles should match exactly.
   c. Check students' work.

3. Yes, the sum is always 180°.

4. **a.** This invariant holds for all triangles.
   b. Check students' work.

5. See back of book; triangles with angles 60°, 70°, and 80° or 90°, 90°, and 90° are not possible since the sum of the angles would be greater than 180°.

6. See back of book.

Exercises *Practicing Habits of Mind*

On Your Own

7. Choose a triangle you constructed for Problem 1. Without measuring, construct a new triangle with sides that are half the length of each side of your original triangle.

8. In Problems 1 and 5, some of the triangles were impossible to construct. Which ones were they? Explain what went wrong when you tried to construct each triangle.

9. In Problems 2 and 6, you used given side lengths and angle measures to construct triangles. Then you compared your results with those of classmates. Now compare the two experiments. In what ways, if any, are the results different?

   After you completed Problems 1– 3, you probably came to the following conclusion:

Conjecture 1.1 *Triangle Angle-Sum Conjecture*

> The sum of the measures of the angles of a triangle is an invariant. Regardless of the triangle, the angle sum is 180°.

You will prove this later.

10. Assume that the Triangle Angle-Sum Conjecture is true. Explain whether it is possible to construct a triangle with each of the given angle measures.
    a. 50°, 50°, 50°   **b.** 60°, 60°, 60°
    c. 45°, 45°, 90°   **d.** 72°, 72°, 36°
    e. two 90° angles and a third angle

Go Online
Video Tutor
PHSchool.com

Web Code: bee-0775

Maintain Your Skills

In each exercise below, construct three different triangles that meet the given condition.

11. one 30° angle and one 60° angle

12. one 40° angle and one 50° angle

13. one 20° angle and one 70° angle

Exercises

7. Check students' work.

8. The third triangle in Problem 1 is impossible to construct because 3 + 4 < 8. The second and fourth triangles in Problem 5 are impossible to construct because their angle sums would be greater than 180°.

9. Comparing the results from Problem 6 shows that equal angle measures yield triangles that have the same shape, though the triangles may be different sizes. Comparing results from Problem 2 shows that equal side lengths yield triangles that are both the same shape and same size.

10. Triangles are possible for parts (b), (c), and (d) since the angle measures have a sum of 180°. No triangles are possible for parts (a) and (e) because the angle measures do not have a sum of 180°.

11–13. Check students' work.

Compasses, Angles, and Circles

Geometers distinguish between a drawing and a construction. You make a drawing to aid memory, thought, or communication. A rough sketch serves this purpose quite well. On the other hand, a **construction** is a guaranteed recipe. A construction shows how, in principle, to accurately draw a figure with a specified set of tools.

In your study of geometry you will probably use both hand construction tools and computer tools. The computer tools are introduced in the next investigation.

> Drawings are aids to problem solving. Constructions are solutions to problems.

Hand Construction Tools

Compass A compass is any device—even a knotted piece of string—that allows you to move a pencil a fixed distance around a certain point. A compass allows you to copy distances and to construct circles of any size that you can place anywhere.

Straightedge An object with a straight edge—even a piece of paper—helps you draw a segment to look straight. In general, a straightedge is unmarked and you cannot use it to measure distances. You can use a straightedge to draw a line through, or a segment between, two points. You can also use a straightedge to extend a drawing of a line.

Measuring devices Rulers and protractors are measuring devices. You can use a ruler to measure the length of a segment or the distance between two points. You can use a protractor to measure an angle.

> **Remember...**
> You use a ruler to draw straight segments and to measure distances. You can also use a ruler as a straightedge, ignoring its markings.

Paper Paper is not just a surface on which to write and draw. You can use the symmetries formed by folding paper to construct geometric figures creatively. You can also use dissection—the process of cutting paper figures and rearranging their parts—as a powerful aid to reasoning.

String You can use string and tacks to build devices that you can use to construct circles, ellipses, spirals, and other curves.

Minds in Action   episode 1

Sasha and Tony are trying to draw a triangle with side lengths 3 in., 4 in., and 5 in.

Sasha   I'm going to use three rulers to draw this triangle.

Tony   Why *three* rulers?

Sasha   Watch and learn, Tony. First, I'll draw a segment that is one of the given lengths, say the 5-inch segment. Then I'll use the other two rulers to represent the other two sides of the triangle and swing them toward each other until they meet. I'll connect the point

---

Lesson Overview

GOALS

- Use hand construction tools.
- Explain the difference between a construction and a drawing.
- Know the statement of the triangle inequality.
- Know that points on the perpendicular bisector of a line segment are equidistant from its endpoints.

Students use many different construction methods in this lesson. As you go over the different methods, be sure to emphasize to students the protocols for what you expect their work to look like when they use each method. For instance, when students use a compass, do you expect them to label intersection points? Erase or keep construction lines? When students use paper folding, do you expect them to identify the folds? Explain the steps they took?

CHECK YOUR UNDERSTANDING
- Core: 1, 4, 5, 6, 7, 9
- Optional: 2, 3, 8

MATERIALS
- compasses
- rulers
- straightedges
- Blackline Masters 1.6A, 1.6B

HOMEWORK
- Core: 10, 11, 13, 14, 15, 16
- Optional: 12, 17

VOCABULARY
- altitude
- angle bisector
- construction
- equidistant
- isosceles triangle
- median
- midline
- midpoint
- perpendicular bisector
- reflect
- theorem
- $\overleftrightarrow{CD}$ (line CD)
- $\overline{AB}$ (segment AB)

Launch

Place all the tools available to students at the front of your room. Write a list of four or five simple shapes—circle, square, line, 45° angle—and ask students which tools they can use to construct. The goal is to construct each shape with each tool. Then, have students share tools and discuss how to use each tool.

Have students read the dialog between Tony and Sasha and try to re-do their constructions. Students can do this individually or you can have one student show the class Tony's construction and another student show Sasha's construction.

where the two rulers meet to each end of the 5-inch segment. That gives me my triangle.

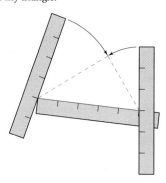

Tony   Very nice, but I bet I can do the same thing with only one ruler.

Sasha   Let's see!

Tony   Okay. First I'll start just like you did and draw the 5-inch segment. Then I'll put the ruler at one end of the 5-inch segment, mark off 4 inches, and swing the ruler around with my pencil to sketch an arc.

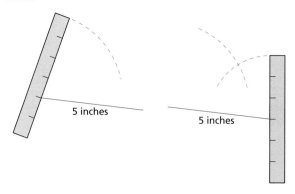

5 inches

5 inches

Then I'll put the ruler at the other end of the 5-inch segment, mark off the 3-inch side, and swing the ruler around to make another arc. And, voilà, there's my triangle!

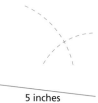

5 inches

1. Do you see Tony's triangle? Explain how you know his triangle has the correct side lengths.

2. The title of this lesson is *Compasses, Angles, and Circles*, but this lesson has not yet mentioned compasses, angles, and circles. How do Sasha's and Tony's ruler tricks both imitate a compass?

3. How can a compass make a geometric construction easier?

Example

Problem Draw a line segment. Without measuring, construct its midpoint. A **midpoint** is the point on a segment that is halfway between the two endpoints.

Solution The simplest approach is to use symmetry by folding. Fold the segment so that its endpoints lie on top of each other. This matches its two halves exactly. The point that separates the two halves is the midpoint.

In fact, all points on the fold line are equidistant from the two endpoints of the segment. This is easier to see when the paper is folded. Any point on the fold is the same distance from each of the two original endpoints, because the endpoints are now at the same place.

> **Equidistant** means "the same distance."

The fold line is also perpendicular to the segment. You can show this by

- matching angles around the bisector to show they are congruent
- showing that the sum of the measures of the adjacent angles is 180°

Therefore, the fold line is the perpendicular bisector of the segment. The **perpendicular bisector** of a segment is a line that is perpendicular to a segment at the segment's midpoint.

Theorem 1.1 Perpendicular Bisector Theorem

Each point on the perpendicular bisector of a segment is equidistant from the two endpoints of the segment.

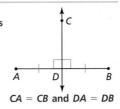

$CA = CB$ and $DA = DB$

> A **theorem** is a statement that has been proven. Although you will not prove the Perpendicular Bisector Theorem or its converse until Chapter 2, you can use both as theorems now.

Explore

For Discussion

Use these questions to check students' understanding of Tony and Sasha's constructions. Students should see that Tony and Sasha are using their rulers instead of a compass in these constructions.

Some students may not see understand immediately how to copy distances with a compass. Show these students a simpler example.

Euclid thought a compass was incapable of transferring lengths in this way. His compass was an instrument that collapsed when taken off the paper, so it could only draw a circle with a given radius.

Example

Ask the class: How can you find the midpoint of a line segment? If no one suggests folding the paper, read through the Example.

Have students try the construction of the perpendicular bisector using a compass and straightedge on the same paper they used for the paper folding construction. The Perpendicular Bisector Theorem is useful for various constructions in this investigation and future investigations.

The activities in this section mostly avoid the delicate issue of the converse of the Perpendicular Bisector Theorem: the statement that each point that is equidistant from the endpoints of a line segment lies on the perpendicular bisector. Students will deal with this statement and the notion of converses later in the course.

Answers

For Discussion

1. The first side was drawn with the correct side length. The other two sides are radii of circles where the radii are equal to each of the other two side lengths.

2. The rulers are used to construct arcs of circles, just as a compass does.

3. Compasses are designed to construct circles and arcs easily.

Wrap Up

Review the construction techniques from this lesson. Work through Exercise 5 as a whole class. This exercise uses the Perpendicular Bisector Theorem.

Assessment Resources

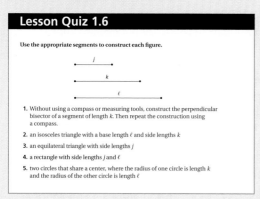

Lesson Quiz 1.6

Use the appropriate segments to construct each figure.

j

k

ℓ

1. Without using a compass or measuring tools, construct the perpendicular bisector of a segment of length *k*. Then repeat the construction using a compass.
2. an isosceles triangle with a base length *ℓ* and side lengths *k*
3. an equilateral triangle with side lengths *j*
4. a rectangle with side lengths *j* and *ℓ*
5. two circles that share a center, where the radius of one circle is length *k* and the radius of the other circle is length *ℓ*

Exercises

HOMEWORK
- Core: 10, 11, 13, 14, 15, 16
- Optional: 12, 17

Answers

Exercises

1. a. Mark two points, *A* and *B*, on the given line. Construct the perpendicular bisector of $\overline{AB}$.
   b. Use the procedure from part (a) to construct a line perpendicular to the perpendicular bisector from part (a).

2. Make a diagonal fold and crease the paper so that one corner of the sheet falls on the opposite long edge. Cut off the narrow rectangular strip of excess paper.

3. a. Fold the square to make the left side match the right side. Fold the resulting rectangle so that the top side matches the bottom side.
   b. Open the folded sheet from part (a). Fold the corners of the large square inward to meet at the point of intersection of the crease lines. The new crease lines form a square with half the area of the large square.

The converse of the Perpendicular Bisector Theorem is also true. Each point that is equidistant from the two endpoints of a segment is on the perpendicular bisector of the segment.

You can use the converse of the Perpendicular Bisector Theorem to find the midpoint of a segment using a compass and a straightedge. From each segment endpoint, swing an arc with radius *r*. Make sure that *r* is greater than half the length of the original segment.

The two points of intersection of the arcs are both *r* units from each endpoint of the segment. The line through the two points is the perpendicular bisector of the segment. All points on the perpendicular bisector are equidistant from the endpoints of the segment. This includes the point of intersection of the perpendicular bisector and the segment, namely the midpoint of the segment.

To see this, fold the paper along the perpendicular bisector. You superimpose the two endpoints of the segment in this way. You also superimpose the two line segments from any point on the fold to each endpoint of the segment. This means that the distances from any point on the perpendicular bisector to the endpoints of the segment must be the same.

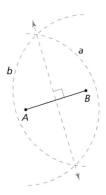

Exercises *Practicing Habits of Mind*

Check Your Understanding

For each construction described, do the construction and then tell how you did it. Use any hand construction tools *except* rulers, protractors, or other measurement tools. Do not forget paper folding. Some exercises are harder than others. If you have trouble with an exercise, skip it. Come back to it later. When you return to it, you will have more experience and knowledge.

1. Draw a line. Then construct a line with the given property.
   a. perpendicular to the given line
   b. parallel to the given line

> To distinguish a line from a segment, show an arrowhead at each end of a line diagram. Show a small dot at each end of a segment diagram.

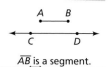

$\overleftrightarrow{AB}$ is a segment.

---

4. Check students' work. To construct the angle bisector of an angle, fold through the vertex so that the sides of the angle coincide.

5. a. Answers may vary. Sample: Construct a circle centered at one endpoint of the segment and having the segment as a radius. Draw another radius, not collinear with the first. Draw the segment that connects the endpoints on the circle.
   b. Answers may vary. Sample: Fold the segment in half. Mark a point on the crease line (but not the

midpoint of the original segment), and draw segments from that point to the endpoints of the segment.
   c. Answers may vary. Sample: Open the compass to the length of the segment. Use that radius and construct the two circles that have centers at the endpoints of the segment. Select a point where the circles intersect and draw segments from that point to the endpoints of the segment.
   d. Answers may vary. Sample: Construct perpendicular lines

2. Start with a sheet of paper ($8\frac{1}{2}$ in. by 11 in.). Use paper folding and scissors to construct the largest square possible.

3. Start with the largest square you can construct from an $8\frac{1}{2}$ in.-by-11 in. sheet of paper (you may want to make a few of them). Then do the following:

   a. Construct a square with exactly one fourth the area of your original square.

   b. Construct a square with exactly one half the area of your original square.

4. Draw an angle. Then construct its bisector.

5. For each construction below, start with a new segment. Then use the segment to construct the given shape.

   a. an isosceles triangle with each congruent side also congruent to your segment

   b. an isosceles triangle with base congruent to your segment

   c. an equilateral triangle with each side congruent to your segment

   d. a square with each side congruent to your segment

6. Illustrate each definition below with a sketch. The first is done for you as an example.

> An **angle bisector** is a ray that divides an angle exactly in half, making two congruent angles.

↑ angle bisector

Definitions

a. A triangle has three *altitudes*.

An **altitude** is a perpendicular segment from a vertex of a triangle to the line that contains the opposite side.

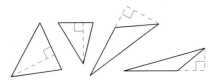

b. A triangle has three medians.

A **median** is a segment that connects a vertex of a triangle to the midpoint of the opposite side.

c. A triangle has three *midlines*.

A **midline** is a segment that connects the midpoints of two sides of a triangle.

Check Your Understanding

Some students may want to use scissors in their constructions.

EXERCISE 1 The Example showed part (a) of this exercise. Part (b) is a little more difficult. Students must construct a perpendicular to the perpendicular.

EXERCISE 2 Students may have some experience making a square from an $8\frac{1}{2}$ in.-by-11 in. piece of paper. But explaining why this is the largest square possible require some thought.

EXERCISE 3 In part (b), the Solution Manual explains why the result has half the area of the original square. If you also care to prove that the result is a square, the easiest argument is probably by symmetry. Regardless of how you rotate the creased figure, all of its parts (including the angles) will match up, because you made them in the same way from a set of original parts that are all identical.

This problem implicitly asks students to construct the length $\sqrt{2}$. What about the constructability of irrational lengths? You may encourage students to think about this issue now by asking them: "Compared to the original square, what is the length of the sides of the new square?" Let the length of a side of the original square be 2 units; then the legs of the corner triangles (outside the half-sized square) are 1 unit long. The Pythagorean Theorem then says that the length of the hypotenuse is $\sqrt{2}$. You can also prove this using area. If the length of the original square's sides are 2 units each, its area is 4 square units. The half-sized square's area is therefore 2 square units, so its side must be $\sqrt{2}$ units.

continued on p. 32

---

through the endpoints of the given segment. Construct a circle with one of the endpoints as its center that passes through the other endpoint. Construct a line parallel to the original segment through one of the points of intersection of the circle and the line perpendicular to the original segment.

6. **b.**   **c.**

continued from p. 31

Now you have a method of constructing one irrational length. You cannot, however, construct all irrational lengths. The proof of this fact is also the proof of the impossibility of squaring the circle and many other classic impossible constructions.

EXERCISE 4 Paper folding is probably the easiest way for students to construct the bisector of an angle. The following theorem helps explain how to construct an angle bisector with a straightedge and compass. Theorem: *All points on the bisector of an angle are equidistant from the two sides of the angle.*

EXERCISES 8 AND 9 You may wish to use Blackline Master 1.6A with these exercises. In Exercise 9, students will need to know the Perpendicular Bisector Theorem to help them construct a circle that passes through all three vertices of a triangle. Point out that this method works for any three noncollinear points.

On Your Own

EXERCISE 12 If students have trouble with this exercise, you can give them a hint by challenging them to construct a rhombus using the techniques they learned in this lesson. To do so, they will need to construct two equilateral triangles that share one side.

EXERCISE 13 For some students, the fact that any three noncollinear points lie on a unique circle is counter-intuitive. Usually, it is the case of three points that form an obtuse triangle that gives them doubts. This exercise serves to make evident the fact that the center of a circle may be outside the triangle formed by the three points. For most students, you can postpone talking about the uniqueness of the circle.

7. Draw four triangles. Use one triangle for each construction below.

   a. Construct the three medians of the triangle.

   b. Construct the three midlines of the triangle.

   c. Construct the three angle bisectors of the triangle.

   d. **Take It Further** Construct the three altitudes of the triangle.

   e. Compare your constructions in parts (a)–(d) to other students' constructions. What are the similarities and differences? Write any conjectures you have.

8. Start with a square. Construct its diagonals. Study the resulting figure. Write what you observe about the diagonals (lengths, angles formed, regions formed, and so on).

9. Start with an equilateral triangle. Construct a circle that passes through the three vertices of the triangle.

Construct—, do not draw.

On Your Own

10. Copy this segment onto a sheet of paper.

   Use a straightedge and a compass to construct two different isosceles triangles, each with two sides that are the same length as this segment.

11. Use a compass to construct two circles, such that one circle has a radius that is the same length as the diameter of the other circle.

12. Construct a quadrilateral with at least one 60° angle and all sides that are the same length.

13. Draw several different triangles. For each triangle, construct a circle that passes through all three vertices. For what kinds of triangles is the circle's center in the following locations?

   a. inside the triangle

   b. on the triangle

   c. outside the triangle

Answers

7–8. See back of book.

9. Answers may vary. Sample: Construct the perpendicular bisectors of two sides of the equilateral △ABC. The perpendicular bisectors intersect at a point X. Construct the circle that has center X and radius XA.

10. Answers may vary. Sample: Construct a circle with center A and radius AC. Pick a point B on the circle that is not collinear with

A and C. Construct segments $\overline{AB}$ and $\overline{BC}$.

11. Answers may vary. Sample: Construct a circle. Draw a line through the center of the circle. Call the points of intersection A and B. Construct a circle with center A and radius AB.

12. Answers may vary. Sample: Construct an equilateral triangle. Construct another equilateral triangle with one of the sides of the first triangle as its base. The vertices of the two triangles are the vertices of the required quadrilateral.

14. Standardized Test Prep Mr. Mendoza's geometry class came up with four conjectures about the medians and the altitudes of triangles. Which of the following conjectures is NOT correct?

A. A median of a triangle divides the triangle into two smaller triangles of equal area.

B. The intersection of the three medians of a triangle is always inside the triangle.

C. In a right triangle, the altitudes intersect at the vertex of the largest angle.

D. In an obtuse triangle, exactly one of the altitudes lies outside the triangle.

15. Salim planted three new saplings. He wants to install a rotating sprinkler to water the three saplings. Where should he install the sprinkler to make sure that all three saplings get the same amount of water?

a. Trace the saplings onto your paper.

b. Show where Salim should install the sprinkler.

c. Explain your answer.

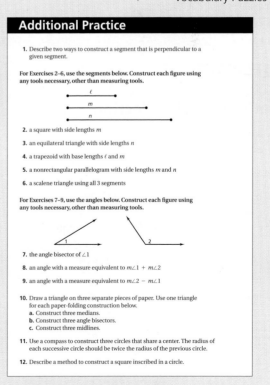

This is Salim's garden.

16. To reflect a point over a line, do the following:

- Construct a perpendicular line from the given point A to the given line ℓ.

- On the perpendicular, mark point A' on the other side of ℓ from A so that A' and A are the same distance from ℓ.

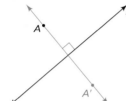

a. On your own, draw a point and then draw a line that does not pass through that point.

b. Follow the directions above to reflect the point over the line. Think of the line as a mirror. In the figure above, A' is the reflection of A in the mirror. A and A' are the same distance from and in the same position relative to the mirror.

Maintain Your Skills

17. Copy points A and B onto a sheet of paper. Then construct 15 different points that are equidistant from A and B.

Go Online
PHSchool.com

For additional practice, go to **Web Code: bea-0106**

13. a. acute triangles
   b. right triangles
   c. obtuse triangles

14. D

15. a. Check students' work.
   b. Construct the perpendicular bisectors of two of the sides of the triangle that has the bases of the saplings as vertices. Place the sprinkler at the point of intersection of the perpendicular bisectors.

   c. Answers may vary. Sample: The point of intersection of the perpendicular bisectors of the triangle the three saplings form is the center of the circle that passes through the three saplings. If you place the sprinkler at this point of intersection, the sprinkler is equidistant from the three saplings.

16. a–b. Check students' work.

17. Check students' work.

EXERCISE 15 Some students may ask, or the teacher may ask, what would happen if Salim planted a fourth tree. The answer to this question is not simple as the answer to Exercise 15 and might lead to some interesting class discussion. If the new tree is on the circle through the three original trees, then the sprinkler will remain in the same position. If not, there is no place to put the sprinkler so that the trees are equally watered. You may wish to use Blackline Master 1.6B with this exercise.

EXERCISE 16 introduces reflection and asks students to follow steps to construct the reflection of a point over a line. This uses the Perpendicular Bisector Theorem.

Maintain Your Skills

EXERCISE 17 requires students to construct the perpendicular bisector of a segment, and then remember that any point on the perpendicular bisector of a segment is equidistant from the endpoints of the segment.

Additional Resources

PRINTED RESOURCES
- Solution Manual
- Practice Workbook
- Assessment Resources
- Teaching Resources

TECHNOLOGY
- Interactive Textbook
- TeacherExpress CD-ROM
- **Exam**View CD-ROM
- **PHSchool.com**
  – Additional Practice
  – Mid-Chapter and Chapter Tests
  – Video Tutors
  – Vocabulary Puzzles

Additional Practice

1. Describe two ways to construct a segment that is perpendicular to a given segment.

For Exercises 2–6, use the segments below. Construct each figure using any tools necessary, other than measuring tools.

2. a square with side lengths m

3. an equilateral triangle with side lengths n

4. a trapezoid with base lengths ℓ and m

5. a nonrectangular parallelogram with side lengths m and n

6. a scalene triangle using all 3 segments

For Exercises 7–9, use the angles below. Construct each figure using any tools necessary, other than measuring tools.

7. the angle bisector of $\angle 1$

8. an angle with a measure equivalent to $m\angle 1 + m\angle 2$

9. an angle with a measure equivalent to $m\angle 2 - m\angle 1$

10. Draw a triangle on three separate pieces of paper. Use one triangle for each paper-folding construction below.
   a. Construct three medians.
   b. Construct three angle bisectors.
   c. Construct three midlines.

11. Use a compass to construct three circles that share a center. The radius of each successive circle should be twice the radius of the previous circle.

12. Describe a method to construct a square inscribed in a circle.

Practice: For Lesson 1.6, assign Exercises 1–12.

Mathematical Reflections

EXERCISES 6–8 At the start of the investigation, you may have assigned these as Questions 1–3 for students to think and write about.

Mathematical Reflections 1B

In this investigation, you learned the difference between a rough drawing or sketch and a geometric construction. You made the Triangle Angle-Sum Conjecture and learned about the Perpendicular Bisector Theorem. The following questions will help you summarize what you have learned.

1. Describe each shape below using its features. Each description should be specific enough that no other shape can be confused with the given shape.

   a. isosceles trapezoid
   b. isosceles triangle
   c. rhombus
   d. regular octagon

2. Draw an angle and construct its bisector. Describe each step of your construction.

3. Copy $\overline{AC}$ at the right onto a sheet of paper. Then construct a square such that $\overline{AC}$ is one of its diagonals.

4. Write the steps that describe how to construct the circle that passes through points A, B, and C below.

5. Is it possible to construct a triangle with angles that measure 30°, 60°, and 90°? If you think it is possible, construct such a triangle.

6. What is the difference between drawing a figure and constructing a figure?

7. What is invariant about the measures of the angles in a triangle?

8. How can you construct the perpendicular bisector of a segment?

Vocabulary and Notation

In this investigation, you learned these terms and symbols. Make sure you understand what each one means and how you use it.

- altitude
- angle bisector
- construction
- equidistant
- median
- midline
- midpoint
- perpendicular bisector
- theorem
- $\overleftrightarrow{CD}$ (line CD)
- $\overline{AB}$ (segment AB)

Different constructions give different results.

Answers

Mathematical Reflections

1. **a–d.** Answers may vary. Samples are given.
   a. a quadrilateral with exactly one pair of parallel sides and the other pair of sides of equal length
   b. a triangle with at least two sides of equal length
   c. a quadrilateral with four sides of equal length
   d. an octagon with all sides of equal length and all angles of equal measure

2. Answers may vary. Sample: Use the vertex of the angle as a center and draw an arc that intersects the sides of the angle at points M and N. Construct the perpendicular bisector of $\overline{MN}$. This line bisects the angle.

3. Answers may vary. Sample: Construct the perpendicular bisector of $\overline{AC}$. Use the midpoint M of $\overline{AC}$ as center and draw the circle with radius MC. Points A and C and the two points where the perpendicular bisector intersects the circle are the vertices of the desired square.

4. Answers may vary. Sample: Construct the perpendicular bisectors of any two of the segments $\overline{AB}$ and $\overline{BC}$. Call the intersection of the two perpendicular bisectors O. Construct a circle with center O and radius $\overline{AB}$.

5. Check students' work. One possible construction involves constructing an equilateral triangle and the perpendicular bisector of one side of the triangle.

6. Unlike a sketch or freehand drawing, a construction uses reliable tools, such as a straightedge and compass, and a recipe that always works.

7. the sum of the angle measures (180°)

8. Answers may vary. Sample: Open the compass to the length of the segment. Construct two circles that use this radius and have the endpoints of the segment as centers. Construct the line through the two points where the circles intersect.

Mid-Chapter Test

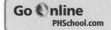

Go Online
PHSchool.com

For a mid-chapter test,
go to Web Code: bea-0152

Multiple Choice

1. How many lines of symmetry does the figure have?

   A. 1   **B.** 2
   C. 3   **D.** 4

2. The plane is horizontal. What best describes the shape of the cross section?

   A. rectangle

   B. rhombus

   C. square

   D. trapezoid

3. The following directions describe how to draw a certain letter of the alphabet.

   Draw a 2-in. vertical segment. Construct the midpoint of the segment. From the midpoint, draw a $\frac{3}{4}$-in. horizontal segment to the right. From each endpoint of the vertical segment, draw a 1-in. horizontal segment to the right.

   If you follow the directions, which letter of the alphabet will you draw?

   A. B   **B.** E
   C. F   **D.** H

Open Response

4. Construct each shape that is described below. Then name the shape.

   a. a quadrilateral with four 90° angles

   b. a closed figure with three sides, each 5 centimeters long

   c. a quadrilateral with two pairs of congruent sides

   d. the set of points that are equidistant from a given point

5. Fifty chalkboard designers attend the National Chalkboard Designers meeting in St. Johnsbury, Vermont. Each designer greets and exchanges business cards with each of the other designers. How many business card exchanges are there?

6. Tell whether each statement below is true. If a statement is not true, explain why.

   a. A square can cast a square shadow.

   b. A square can cast a circular shadow.

   c. A circle can only cast a circular shadow.

   d. All sides of a figure are shown by its shadow.

7. Use a compass and straightedge to construct an equilateral triangle. Describe each step of your construction.

8. Construct a triangle that meets each of the following specifications. If a triangle cannot be constructed, explain why.

   a. side lengths: 3 cm, 4 cm, 6 cm

   b. side lengths: 3 cm, 3 cm, 6 cm

   c. angle measures: 40°, 40°, 110°

   d. angle measures: 30°, 60°, 90°

9. Copy $\overline{AB}$ onto a sheet of paper. Then construct three different isosceles triangles such that $\overline{AB}$ is one of the congruent sides of each triangle.

   A  B

Mid-Chapter Test

Assessment Resources

> **Mid-Chapter Test**
>
> 1. Tell whether each statement is *true* or *false*. If the statement is false, explain why.
>   **a.** A triangle can cast a triangular shadow.
>   **b.** A rectangle can cast a circular shadow.
>   **c.** A pyramid can cast a square shadow.
>   **d.** A square can only cast a square shadow.
>
> 2. Use a compass and straightedge to construct a right triangle. Describe your steps.
>
> 3. **a.** Do any of the letters in the word MATH have symmetry? Explain.
>   **b.** Does the word MATH have symmetry? Explain.
>
> 4. Follow the recipe below to create a picture. Describe the picture you create.
>   • Draw a horizontal segment.
>   • Find the midpoint of the segment.
>   • From the midpoint, draw a vertical segment below the horizontal segment.
>   • At the lower endpoint of the vertical segment, draw the curved part of the letter J.
>   • Draw the top half of a circle, using the original segment as the horizontal diameter of the circle.
>
> 5. Construct the reflection of point *G* over line ℓ.
>
> 6. Construct each triangle to meet the following specifications. If you cannot construct the triangle, explain why.
>   **a.** side lengths: 4 cm, 6 cm, 3 cm
>   **b.** side lengths: 4 in., 4 in., 8 in.
>   **c.** angle measures: 120°, 50°, 20°
>   **d.** angle measures: 60°, 60°, 60°

Also available: Form B

Mid-Chapter Test

1. D   **2.** A   **3.** B

4. Check students' work.
   a. rectangle
   b. equilateral triangle
   c. parallelogram or kite
   d. circle

5. 1225

6. **a.** true
   b. False; segments cannot cast curved shadows.
   c. False; the shadow might be elliptical.
   d. False; a closed, flat shape whose plane is perpendicular to the ground will cast a line-segment shadow.

7. Draw $\overline{AB}$. Construct a circle with center A and radius $\overline{AB}$, and a circle with center B and radius $\overline{AB}$. Construct segments from one of the points of intersection of the two circles to A and B.

8. **a.** Check students' work.
   b. not constructible; 3 cm + 3 cm = 6 cm
   c. Not constructible; the sum of the angle measures is greater than 180°.
   d. Check students' work.

9. Answers may vary. Sample: Construct the circle with center A and radius $\overline{AB}$. Pick three points C, D, and E on the circle and not on $\overleftrightarrow{AB}$. $\triangle ABC$, $\triangle ABD$, and $\triangle ABE$ are the required triangles.

Investigation Overview

You can directly compare geometry software constructions to constructions on paper with ruler and compass. Geometry software constructions can often use the same algorithms. However, the software usually has more tools and more usable strategies available.

You may wish to assign Questions 1–3 for students to think and write about during the investigation.

Learning Goals

- Use geometry software to construct figures.
- Explain the difference between a construction and a drawing.
- Construct familiar shapes (such as squares, parallelograms, etc.) from their required characteristics.

Habits and Skills

- Use geometry software to construct figures.
- Choose the right tool for a construction.
- Use geometry software to find invariants in familiar figures.
- Identify essential properties of rectangles, squares, parallelograms, equilateral triangles, and rhombuses.

Investigation 1C

Geometry Software

In *Geometry Software*, you will make moving pictures of geometric figures. You will construct figures so that required features are built in. Then you will vary other features to experiment with the figures. For instance, you will build a square so that it will stay a square while you rotate it or resize it in any way you please.

By the end of this investigation, you will be able to answer questions like these.

1. How can you use geometry software to construct figures with specific features?

2. How can you use geometry software to test for invariants?

3. How can you use geometry software to illustrate the difference between *drawing* a figure and *constructing* a figure?

You will learn how to

- use geometry software to construct figures

- explain the difference between a construction and a drawing

You will develop these habits and skills:

- Use geometry software to construct figures.

- Choose the right tool for a construction.

- Use geometry software to find invariants in familiar figures.

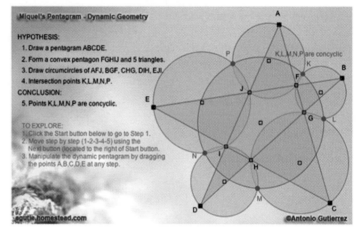

What changes when you drag any of the star-tips *A*, *B*, *C*, *D*, or *E*?

Investigation Road Map

LESSON 1.7, *Getting Started,* has students explore the tools of their geometry software. The problems are an introduction to the software features that students will use most often in this investigation.

LESSON 1.8, *Drawings vs. Constructions,* shows students the consequences of drawing (instead of constructing) features of a figure with geometry software.

LESSON 1.9, *Drawing UnMessUpable Figures,* challenges students to use geometry software to construct figures that are "UnMessUpable". For example, a square will stay a square no matter how you drag it around the computer screen—angle measures will stay 90°, and sides will stay congruent to each other.

Activating Prior Knowledge
Exploring New Ideas

Every geometry software program has geometric construction tools, labeling tools, and movement tools.

For You to Explore

1. Use geometry software. Explore and ask questions until you can do the following.

   - Use line segments to draw a triangle.
   - Draw two circles. Connect them with a line segment. The segment's endpoints should be on the circles.
   - Move a point, segment, or circle in each of the first two drawings.
   - Draw a ray.
   - Draw a line.
   - Draw a point that travels *only* along a segment.

A bit of everything

2. **a.** Use the point tool to place two points on your screen as shown below on the left. Then use only the circle tool to complete the picture below on the right. Make sure that your picture does not contain more than four points.

   b. Now move each point around and describe the effect on the drawing. It may help to label the points.

3. Construct a triangle with two vertices that can be moved about freely and one vertex that can only be moved on a circle.

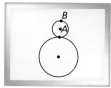

4. Draw two lines. Construct a triangle. Fix one vertex on one of the lines. Place the other vertices so that you can move both of them, but only along the other line.

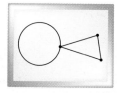

Answers

For You to Explore

1–4. Check students' work.

Lesson Overview

GOALS

- Warm up to the ideas of the investigation.
- Use a hands-on approach to develop mathematical habits of mind.

There may be a lot of startup involved at the beginning of this investigation. Spend at least two days allowing your students to complete the problems and exercises in this lesson. You might want to start with a whole-class reading and discussion of the introductory pages so that students get the point of the software they will use. There can be difficulty in starting up the software, accidentally closing windows, finding the right tools, etc. After the first two days, however, students will be more comfortable, and things will move more quickly.

Throughout this lesson, encourage comparisons to constructions made with compass, ruler, and protractor.

FOR YOU TO EXPLORE	HOMEWORK
• Core: 1, 2, 3, 4	• Core: 5, 6, 7
MATERIALS	• Optional: 8
• geometry software	**VOCABULARY**
	• line
	• perpendicular
	• ray
	• segment

Launch

Before assigning the For You to Explore problems, spend some time setting your students up at their computers (individually or in pairs) and tell them a little bit about the software they will be using. Starting up the software and setting up a blank palette will take some instruction the first time.

Assign Problem 1 and give students ample time to find the needed tools. Circulate among them to watch for troubles.

Explore

Once students are comfortable with the basic tools of the geometry software, have them work on Problems 2–4. Since this is probably your students' first time using this software, these problems may take some time to complete. Walk around and randomly test your students' constructions. For example, if a point is supposed to be stuck to a segment, try to drag it off. It may take students a couple of tries to correctly construct the figures.

Wrap Up

Review construction techniques with your students such as

- constructing a segment
- constructing points
- placing a point on a segment
- constructing a circle

You may want to assign Exercise 5 in class and have students share their work.

Exercises

HOMEWORK
- Core: 5, 6, 7
- Optional: 8

On Your Own

EXERCISE 6 illustrates a common mistake that students can make when constructing figures using geometry software—free-floating points. It may have come up as you were testing students' constructions. This occurs when students draw a segment on top of a point instead of placing a point on a segment.

EXERCISE 7 It is important that students understand that segments that are perpendicular do not necessarily touch. While constructing with geometry software, students may need to draw a segment off to the side as a reference.

They can construct things perpendicular to this segment, but it will not show up in the final figure.

Maintain Your Skills

EXERCISE 8 While it is likely that students have seen the notation ∠ACB before, note that this is the first time that it appears in this book.

In this exercise, students will use several features of the geometry software:

- drawing segments
- naming points
- measuring lengths
- measuring angle measure

Exercises *Practicing Habits of Mind*

On Your Own

5. **Write About It** Write directions for drawing the figures in Problems 2–4. Include directions for how to get a point to "stick" to a line or circle.

6. Buddy made the following sketch. He intended to fix one vertex on one line. He also wanted to place the other vertices so that he could move both of them, but only along the other line.

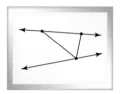

When the teacher checked Buddy's sketch, she selected a point and moved it to a new position, as shown below.

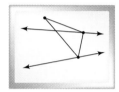

a. What mistake did Buddy make?

b. How can he fix his mistake?

7. If a line is perpendicular to $\overline{BC}$, must the line intersect $\overline{BC}$?

Maintain Your Skills

8. Use geometry software. Place two points A and B on your screen, as shown. Find positions for point C such that the measure of ∠ACB is 90°.

The notation ∠ACB ("angle ACB") means the angle formed by $\overrightarrow{CA}$ and $\overrightarrow{CB}$.

Answers

Exercises

5. Answers may vary. Sample: To construct the figure in Exercise 2, use the circle tool to construct a circle centered at A that passes through B, then construct a circle with an arbitrary center that passes through a point on the first circle. To construct the figure in Exercise 3, draw a circle first using the circle tool. Place a point on the circle and construct a triangle with the segment tool using this point as one of the vertices. To construct the figure in Exercise 4, draw two lines then place one point on one line and two points on the other line using the point tool. Connect all three points using the segment tool.

6. a. Buddy did not construct the vertex on the line.

   b. Draw the lines first, then construct each vertex on the lines.

Drawings vs. Constructions

To construct a figure that stays the way you want when you move one of its parts, you must build in the required features. If a point must be on a line or circle, you cannot place the point first and then adjust it to look right. You must actually place the point *on* the line or *on* the circle.

When you build in the required properties with geometry software, you can move one part of a figure and all the other parts will adjust accordingly. For instance, parallel lines will remain parallel. The midpoint of a segment will remain the midpoint.

Example

Constructing a Windmill

Step 1 Open a new sketch page on your computer.

Step 2 Place point *A* on your screen. Then construct $\overline{BC}$. Your screen should now show four objects: three points, *A*, *B*, and *C*, and one segment, $\overline{BC}$.

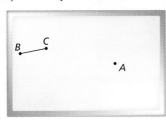

> Due to software settings, labels for points may not appear automatically. Also, the labels for your points may be different from the labels shown here. Labels for points depend on the order in which you place the points.

Step 3 Use the appropriate tool to construct a line through *A* that is perpendicular to the line containing $\overline{BC}$. The line should stay perpendicular to $\overline{BC}$ no matter how you move *A*, *B*, or *C*.

Step 4 Construct a line through *A* that is parallel to $\overline{BC}$.

Step 5 Construct a circle centered at *A* with radius $\overline{BC}$. If you stretch or shrink $\overline{BC}$, the circle should stretch or shrink, accordingly. Again, you need a special tool for this construction. (Keep this sketch for Exercise 1.)

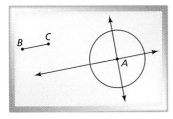

> *Radius of a circle* usually refers to a segment from the circle's center to a point on the circle. *Radius of the circle* usually refers to the length of a radius.

7. no

8. Any point on the circle that has $\overline{AB}$ as a diameter, other than *A* and *B* themselves, yields the required angle.

Lesson Overview

GOALS

- Use geometry software to construct figures.
- Explain the difference between a construction and a drawing.
- Construct familiar shapes (such as a square, parallelogram, and so on) from their required characteristics.

In this lesson, students learn techniques for using software to construct moveable shapes. In the process of doing this, it may be important for students to label, or relabel, objects. This is a good way for students to learn how to use the labeling feature of the software.

CHECK YOUR UNDERSTANDING	HOMEWORK
• Core: 1, 2, 3	• Core: 5, 6, 7
	• Optional: 4, 8
MATERIALS	**VOCABULARY**
• geometry software	• parallel

Launch

After reading the introductory paragraph with your class, work through the Example and have students follow along on their computers.

Explore

Example

Lead your students through the five steps in this Example, helping them find the appropriate construction tools. Help them save this sketch so they can use it for Exercise 1.

Wrap Up

Use the For Discussion as a way to summarize what students have just constructed. If they constructed all the objects according to their definitions, then the circle will move along with *A* as students drag point *A*. The size of the circle and the slopes of the two lines through it will adjust to match the size and slope of segment $\overline{BC}$.

Assessment Resources

Exercises

HOMEWORK

- Core: 5, 6, 7
- Optional: 4, 8

Check Your Understanding

EXERCISES 1 AND 2 Before students can complete these exercises, they will need to add to the construction completed in the Example. Make sure students *hide* the construction lines and do not *delete* them. This is a very common mistake.

For Discussion

1. What happens when you use the selection tool to move A, B, and C?

Sometimes you need to use a line or a circle to construct a figure, but you may not want to see these construction lines in the finished product.

When you used construction lines to construct a figure by hand, you later erased them. When you use geometry software to construct a figure, you must not erase, or delete, the construction lines. You can, however, *hide* them. Find out how to use your software to hide parts of a construction.

Exercises *Practicing Habits of Mind*

Check Your Understanding

In the Example you constructed a windmill. Follow Steps 1–3 below to clean up the construction. Refer to the diagram in Step 5 of the Example. You will use the windmill in Exercises 1 and 2.

Step 1 Place points where the circle intersects the two lines.

Step 2 Construct segments from the center of the circle to each intersection point.

Step 3 Hide (do not delete) the circle and the lines. Do not hide the segments.

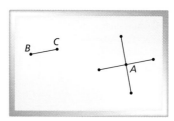

1. **a.** Describe what happens to the segments when you rotate $\overline{BC}$.
   b. Describe what happens to the segments when you stretch or shrink $\overline{BC}$.

Answers

For Discussion

1. Answers may vary. Sample: As you drag B or C, the length of $\overline{BC}$ changes, and hence the size of the circle changes. The two lines remain perpendicular to each other, although they will rotate around A. When you move A, the circle and lines move with it.

Exercises

1. **a.** The other two segments rotate. One of them remains perpendicular to $\overline{BC}$ and the other parallel to $\overline{BC}$. The position of point A does not change.
   b. The segments that intersect at A also stretch or shrink. Their lengths are equal to BC.

2. The four points trace paths that result in a figure that has rotational symmetry.

2. Most geometry software allows you to trace the position of an object as you move it. Activate the Trace feature for the four points at the end of your windmill. Then move point *B* and watch what happens. Describe the effect.

3. Use geometry software to draw two intersecting segments. Move them until they look about the same length and perpendicular to each other at their midpoints. Move one of the endpoints. How is your sketch affected when you move this point, compared to how your construction is affected when you move point *B*?

On Your Own

4. **Write About It** Compare the tools used for hand constructions (paperfolding, compass, straightedge) to the basic tools of geometry software. How are they similar? How are they different? Do you think you can do more with one set of tools than with the other? Explain.

5. In Step 4 of the windmill construction (see the Example), why was it necessary to *construct* the line parallel to $\overline{BC}$ rather than *draw* it parallel to $\overline{BC}$?

6. Why did you need the circle to construct the windmill?

7. **Standardized Test Prep** Naima is frustrated. Her geometry software does not have a command that constructs a line tangent to a given circle. Which of the following methods can Naima use to construct a line that is tangent to a circle with center *O* so that point *P* on the circle is the point of tangency?

A. Construct the perpendicular bisector of $\overline{OP}$.

B. Construct the line that is perpendicular to $\overline{OP}$ at point *O*. Let *Q* be one point where this line intersects the circle. Construct $\overleftrightarrow{PQ}$.

C. Construct a line through *P* that is parallel to a diameter of the circle and that intersects the circle in two points.

D. Construct the line through *P* that is perpendicular to $\overline{OP}$.

Maintain Your Skills

Use geometry software.

8. a. Draw any triangle. Label it △*ABC*.

 b. Construct *M*, the midpoint of $\overline{AB}$.

 c. Through *M*, construct a line parallel to $\overline{AC}$. Let *N* be the point where this line intersects $\overline{BC}$.

 d. Hide the line. Then draw $\overline{MN}$.

 e. Drag one of the vertices of △*ABC*. Then compare *MN* and *AC*.

Go Online
PHSchool.com

For additional practice, go to **Web Code: bea-0108**

---

3. Because the two segments have no constructed relationship to each other, they move independently. When you stretch or shrink one, the other does not change at all.

4. Answers may vary. Sample: Geometry software allows you to do all the constructions that hand tools permit. The software has special tools that make many constructions very fast and accurate. Geometry software also gives you a large region in which to operate since you can scroll from left to right and from top to bottom on the computer screen.

5. Drawing the line parallel to $\overline{BC}$ fails to link the behavior of the line to changes in $\overline{BC}$. As a result, the segments that intersect at *A* will not act like arms of a windmill.

6. The circle keeps the arms of the windmill the same length as $\overline{BC}$.

7. D

8. a–d. Check students' work.
 e. *MN* is always half of *AC*.

Maintain Your Skills

EXERCISE 8 allows students to practice using the tools of their geometry software and gives a preview of the Midline Theorem. This exercise requires the use of software so it may be more suitable for in-class work, rather than homework.

Additional Resources

PRINTED RESOURCES
• Solution Manual
• Practice Workbook
• Assessment Resources
• Teaching Resources

TECHNOLOGY
• Interactive Textbook
• TeacherExpress CD-ROM
• **Exam***View* CD-ROM
• **PHSchool.com**
 – Additional Practice
 – Mid-Chapter and Chapter Tests
 – Video Tutors
 – Vocabulary Puzzles

Additional Practice

Use the appropriate tools of a geometry software program.

1. Draw a scalene triangle and label each vertex.
 a. Move a vertex. Then move a different vertex. Which parts of the triangle change and which parts stay the same?
 b. Move a side. Which parts of the triangle change and which parts stay the same?
 c. Adjust the triangle so it again looks scalene. Construct a segment anywhere. Make it a reflection line. Select the entire triangle and reflect it. Label each new vertex.
 d. Move a vertex of the original triangle. Then move a side. What changes take place?
 e. Construct segments that connect the vertices of the original triangle to the corresponding vertices of its image. What seems to be the relationship between these segments? Does this relationship change if you move a side or an angle?

2. Draw a quadrilateral and label each vertex.
 a. Construct the midpoints of each side.
 b. Connect the midpoints to form a smaller quadrilateral. Label each of these vertices.
 c. Measure the length and the slopes of the sides of the smaller quadrilateral. What kind of quadrilateral does it seem to be?
 d. Measure the angles of the smaller quadrilateral. Do the measurements confirm your conjecture about the quadrilateral's type?
 e. Move a vertex and then move a side of the larger quadrilateral. Does your conjecture about the smaller quadrilateral remain the same?

3. Draw a triangle of any size.
 a. Construct a median of the triangle.
 b. Measure and record the lengths of the sides and the median, the measures of the angles, and the perimeter of the triangle.
 c. Change the scale of the triangle and remeasure each part in part (b).
 d. Compare the measures of the two triangles. Describe the ratios of corresponding parts.

Practice: For Lesson 1.8, assign Exercises 1–3.

Lesson Overview

GOALS

- Use geometry software to construct figures.
- Explain the difference between a construction and a drawing.
- Construct familiar shapes (such as a square, parallelogram, and so on) from their required characteristics.

Your job during this lesson is to test students' constructions. When students think they have completed their construction, try to "mess up" their UnMessUpable figure. If you cannot, they have succeeded!

<table>
<tr><td>CHECK YOUR UNDERSTANDING</td><td>HOMEWORK</td></tr>
</table>

CHECK YOUR UNDERSTANDING
- Core: 1, 2, 3, 4, 5, 6
- Optional: 7
- Extension: 8, 9

MATERIALS
- geometry software
- Blackline Master 1.9

HOMEWORK
- Core: 10, 11, 12, 13, 14
- Optional: 15, 16, 17

VOCABULARY
- adjacent
- congruent
- parallelogram
- perspective
- rhombus

Launch

Discuss the term *UnMessUpable Figure* with your class before you lead them through the two constructions that the Example presents.

Explore

Example

Ask students to consider how they can use the software to construct a square. Then, once students have thought about it, have them share their results. If you can, demonstrate the steps on an overhead screen or large monitor so students can see the steps in action. Once students have shared their ideas, read through the Example. See if they have any new ideas in the For Discussion.

1.9 Drawing UnMessUpable Figures

Here is one way to think about the difference between a construction and a drawing. Think about which properties of a figure remain unchanged when you move a point or other part of the figure.

If you *draw* (not *construct*) a square, you are guaranteed to have a quadrilateral at best. The figure may happen to look like a square at certain moments, but you can change it into a nonsquare quadrilateral by dragging a vertex or side. Its squareness is not guaranteed—it is not UnMessUpable, you could say.

Example

Problem Construct a square.

Solution Below are two possible solutions. Other solutions are possible as well.

Two adjacent congruent sides, four right angles Construct $\overline{AB}$. Construct a perpendicular to $\overline{AB}$ at each of points A and B. Construct the circle centered at A with radius $\overline{AB}$ to locate point C. Construct the line through C that is perpendicular to $\overline{AC}$ (or parallel to $\overline{AB}$) to locate point D. *ABDC* is the constructed square.

> **Congruent** sides are sides that are equal in length.

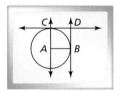

Three congruent sides with right angles between them Construct $\overline{AB}$. Construct a perpendicular to $\overline{AB}$ at each of points A and B. Construct two circles—one centered at A and one centered at B, each with radius $\overline{AB}$—to locate points C and D. *ABDC* is the constructed square.

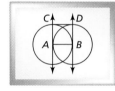

For Discussion

1. Describe other ways to construct a square.

Answers

For Discussion

1. Answers may vary. Sample: Draw a line. Construct a perpendicular to the line. Construct a circle with a center at the intersection of the two lines. Construct the segments connecting the intersections of the circle and the lines.

Exercises *Practicing Habits of Mind*

Check Your Understanding

In the exercises below, your mission is to construct figures that are guaranteed UnMessUpable. No one should be able to change what is required for your figure by dragging a point or moving a segment. Work to construct the figure that is specified, not just a figure that looks like it.

1. Construct a parallelogram that will remain a parallelogram even if you move its vertices.

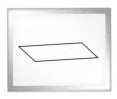 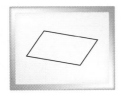

> A *parallelogram* is a quadrilateral with two pairs of parallel sides. Note that rectangles, rhombuses, and squares are all special types of parallelograms.

2. Construct two circles so that each circle passes through the center of the other circle. If you change the size of one circle, the size of the other circle should change with it.

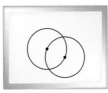

3. Construct three circles so that each circle passes through the centers of the other two circles. As you change the size of one circle, the sizes of the other two circles should also change.

4. Construct an equilateral triangle that remains an equilateral triangle when you change its size and orientation.

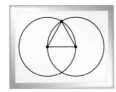

> Why are the three points in this figure exactly the same distance from one another?

Exercises

1–5. Check students' work.

Wrap Up

Blackline Master 1.9 offers a scavenger hunt for students to test their knowledge of the geometry software as well as poke around the menus to find some features they may not yet have discovered.

Assessment Resources

Lesson Quiz 1.9

Using a compass and straightedge, construct each UnMessUpable figure.

1. an isosceles triangle that you can adjust in size but that remains isosceles
2. two circles that are tangent to each other and one of which has a radius twice as long as the other
3. a rhombus that will always remain a rhombus
4. the letter I that you can adjust in size but that remains an I

Exercises

HOMEWORK
- Core: 10, 11, 12, 13, 14
- Optional: 15, 16, 17

Check Your Understanding

Assign these exercises to individuals or pairs to work on in class. It may take a couple of class periods to complete all of these, but make sure students complete at least Exercises 1–5.

EXERCISE 1 Review the definition of parallelogram with your students.

EXERCISES 2–4 You can point out to your students that these three constructions are related, and one construction may help them with the others.

EXERCISE 6 Students may not know what a rhombus is, so review the definition with them. Some students may make a rhombus by connecting the intersection points and centers of two congruent circles, as in the figure below.

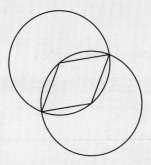

Such a rhombus will always have angles of 120° and 60°. Consider this a real solution, but challenge students to make a rhombus that is less limited. For example, another two-circle solution appears below.

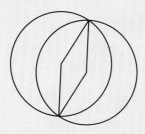

EXERCISE 8 Ask students, "Can you set up both pairs of opposite sides to be equal in length but not parallel?" In fact, there is no such ordinary quadrilateral, but there are other 4-sided figures with this property. In a cross-quadrilateral, for example, this is possible. The diagonals and two nonparallel sides of an isosceles trapezoid form such a cross-quadrilateral. (In plane geometry, a cross-quadrilateral is not generally considered a quadrilateral: polygons are conventionally defined to prevent self-intersection, and quadrilaterals are 4-sided polygons.)

5. Construct the letter T with the following requirements. The top of the T is to remain perpendicular to and centered on the stem when you move points or segments of the T.

> Can you construct your T so it always stays upright?

6. Find two different ways to construct a guaranteed UnMessUpable rhombus with geometry software. Write clear directions for each construction. If either construction guarantees only a certain type of rhombus, explain why.

> A *rhombus* is a quadrilateral with four congruent sides.

7. **a.** Construct two rectangles that

   • share one vertex

   • have two sides lined up

   • have one diagonal lined up, as shown, no matter how you move the vertices or sides

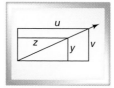

   b. Your software has a feature that computes the ratio of the lengths of two segments. Use that feature to compare the two ratios $\frac{z}{y}$ and $\frac{u}{v}$.

8. **Take It Further** Construct a quadrilateral that you can distort in all sorts of ways but that will *always* have one pair of opposite sides equal in length.

Answers

6. Answers may vary. Sample:
   Method 1: Construct a circle with center C. Construct two noncollinear radii of the circle, $\overline{CX}$ and $\overline{CY}$. Construct a line through X parallel to $\overline{CY}$. Construct a line through Y parallel to $\overline{CX}$. Let P be the point where these two lines intersect. The required parallelogram is CXPY.

   Method 2: Construct $\overline{AB}$. Construct the perpendicular bisector of $\overline{AB}$. Construct a circle with its center at the midpoint of $\overline{AB}$. Mark the points D and E where the perpendicular bisector intersects the circle. The required parallelogram is ADBE.

7. **a.** Check students' work.
   b. The ratios are equal.

9. Take It Further Use geometry software to construct a house in perspective. When you are done, your construction should have these features:

- You should be able to adjust the points on its near end so that the corresponding points on its far end adjust automatically.

- Your picture should include a *drag* point. Move the drag point to see what the house looks like from different perspectives.

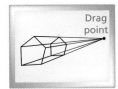

Developing Habits of Mind

Make a model. For the house you drew in Lesson 1.2, the following statements are true.

- Its two bases are identical.
- The segments that connect the bases are all parallel.
- The corresponding sides of the bases are parallel.

On the other hand, in the perspective construction of the house, the following statements are true.

- The bases of the house are not identical (what mathematicians call "congruent"). They are, however, the same shape (what mathematicians call "similar").
- The segments that connect the bases are not parallel. Instead, they converge to a single point.
- The corresponding sides of the bases are parallel.

These facts suggest one way to construct a house in perspective. Sketch the near end of the house. Place a drag point (also called a vanishing point in both mathematics and art) on your screen. Connect the vertices of the house's near end to the vanishing point. Then construct the house's far end. Make sure each segment of the house's far end is parallel to the corresponding segment of the near end.

8–9. Check students' work.

EXERCISE 11 Here are some ideas that are important, and possibly new.

CONSTRUCTION VS. DRAWING A construction is a method of building that, if you execute it correctly, guarantees that the desired properties are built in. A drawing, however accurate it may be, is a picture in which you use a method that cannot, in general, guarantee the right properties.

EXTENDING OR NARROWING DEFINITIONS Students who know the definition of *perpendicular* to often overlook the fact that segments can be perpendicular to one another without touching. Similarly, *radius* is both a segment and a measure. A circle can have a radius of *BC* without touching segment *BC*. *Quadrilateral, vertex,* and even *point* may have acquired new refinements to their definitions.

MINIMAL DEFINING/UNIQUELY DETERMINING PROPERTIES What properties uniquely determine a line? (Answer: two points or a point and a slope) What properties uniquely determine a circle? (Answer: center and radius or center and point on circle) What properties define a rectangle? A square? A parallelogram? A quadrilateral?

PARTICULAR CONSTRUCTIONS These include square, rectangle, parallelogram, equilateral triangle, midpoints, and angle bisectors.

EXERCISE 12 gives students an opportunity to make connections to what they have learned about graphing lines in algebra. In particular, the point-slope form for the equation of a line indicates that these two features—a point and a slope (parallel or perpendicular to a given line)—are enough to uniquely determine a line.

Maintain Your Skills

EXERCISES 15–17 require student to make three iterations of Sierpinski's Triangle using geometry software. Sierpinski's Triangle also appears in Exercises 10–13 from Lesson 1.4.

Additional Resources

PRINTED RESOURCES
- Solution Manual
- Practice Workbook
- Assessment Resources
- Teaching Resources

TECHNOLOGY
- Interactive Textbook
- TeacherExpress CD-ROM
- **Exam**View CD-ROM
- **PHSchool.com**
  - Additional Practice
  - Mid-Chapter and Chapter Tests
  - Video Tutors
  - Vocabulary Puzzles

Additional Practice

Using a compass and a straightedge, construct each UnMessUpable figure.

1. a rectangle that will always remain a rectangle

2. two circles that share a center and have radii in a ratio of 2 : 1

3. three circles that are the same size and tangent to each other

4. a. Construct a square that you can adjust in size and orientation, but that remains a square.
  b. How can you make sure that the quadrilateral you construct is a square?

5. Find two different ways to construct an equilateral triangle with geometry software. Write clear directions for each construction.

6. Construct a segment *AB*. Construct points *X* and *Y* on segment *AB* so that *AX* = *XY* = *YB*.

7. Construct a regular hexagon inscribed in a circle that will remain a regular hexagon as the radius of the circle changes.

Practice: For Lesson 1.9, assign Exercises 1–7.

On Your Own

10. Standardized Test Prep The students in Ms. Lau's Geometry class used geometry software to construct a specific type of quadrilateral that keeps its required features if someone drags one of the vertices.

- Jeremy's group constructed a parallelogram with congruent consecutive sides.
- Amy's group constructed a quadrilateral with diagonals that bisect the quadrilateral's angles.
- Alexandra's group constructed a quadrilateral with four congruent sides.
- Sang's group constructed a quadrilateral with diagonals that are perpendicular to each other at their midpoints.

Which type of quadrilateral did each group construct?

A. a rectangle   **B.** a square

C. a rhombus   **D.** a trapezoid

11. Write About It As you learned to use geometry software, you probably also did some geometric thinking. List some geometric ideas, terminology, or techniques that you learned, relearned, polished up, or invented.

12. No geometry software allows you to construct a line that is perpendicular to another line or segment unless you first identify both a line (or a segment) *and* a point. Why is this a sensible restriction?

13. Write About It Select one of the UnMessUpable figures you constructed in Exercises 1–8. Write detailed directions that describe the construction process. To test your directions, switch with a partner. Do you both get the predicted results?

14. Look back at Exercise 4. How do you make sure that the triangle you construct is equilateral? Describe what features of the construction or the resulting figure guarantee that the triangle has three congruent sides.

Maintain Your Skills

Use geometry software to construct the following figures. Describe required features that remain unchanged if you drag a vertex.

Go Online
PHSchool.com

For additional practice, go to **Web Code: bea-0109**

15.

16.

17.
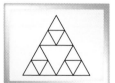

Answers

10. C

11. Check students' work.

12. There are infinitely many lines perpendicular to any given line or segment. Specifying a point makes it possible to tell the software which of these infinitely many lines you want.

13–17. Check students' work.

Mathematical Reflections

1. Tony neglected to construct all three vertices of the triangle on the circle.

2. Check students' work.

3. Answers may vary. Sample: Construct $\overline{AB}$ and lines perpendicular to $\overline{AB}$ at *A* and *B*. Pick a point *C* on the perpendicular through *B* and construct the line through *C* perpendicular to $\overleftrightarrow{BC}$.

In this investigation, you learned the difference between drawing and constructing with geometry software. You used software to construct figures that retained specific features no matter how you moved around their parts. The following questions will help you summarize what you have learned.

1. Tony had to construct a triangle inscribed in a circle. He drew the picture on the left. Sasha selected a vertex. She moved it and made the picture on the right. Explain Tony's mistake.

2. Construct an UnMessUpable square with a side length of 5 cm.

3. List steps that tell how to construct a rectangle with geometry software. The figure must remain a rectangle for any movement of its vertices.

4. Use geometry software to construct an equilateral triangle with side lengths that vary when you drag a point of the construction.

5. What feature do you have to make invariant in a parallelogram so that it is always a rhombus, no matter how you drag its vertices?

6. How can you use geometry software to construct figures with specific features?

7. How can you use geometry software to test for invariants?

8. How can you use geometry software to illustrate the differences between *drawing* a figure and *constructing* a figure?

Vocabulary and Notation

In this investigation, you learned this term and this symbol. Make sure you understand what each one means and how you use it.

- **congruent**
- **∠ACB** (angle *ACB*)

Drag any of the star-tips *A*, *B*, *C*, *D*, or *E*, and the points *K*, *L*, *M*, *N*, and *P* remain concyclic (on the same circle)!

Miquel's Pentagram - Dynamic Geometry

HYPOTHESIS:
1. Draw a pentagram ABCDE.
2. Form a convex pentagon FGHIJ and 5 triangles.
3. Draw circumcircles of AFJ, BGF, CHG, DIH, EJI.
4. Intersection points K,L,M,N,P.

CONCLUSION:
5. Points K,L,M,N,P are concyclic.

K,L,M,N,P are concyclic

TO EXPLORE:
1. Click the Start button below to go to Step 1.
2. Move step by step (1-2-3-4-5) using the Next button (located to the right of Start button.
3. Manipulate the dynamic pentagram by dragging the points A,B,C,D,E at any step.

agutie.homestead.com   ©Antonio Gutierrez

Mathematical Reflections

EXERCISES 6–8 At the start of the investigation, you may have assigned these as Questions 1–3 for students to think and write about.

Let *D* be the point where this line intersects the perpendicular through *A*. The quadrilateral *ABCD* is the required rectangle.

4. Check students' work.

5. Answers may vary. Sample: Two adjacent sides are congruent.

6. Answers may vary. Sample: Geometry software allows you to construct objects that have geometrical relationships with each other that do not change as you alter other elements of the construction.

7. Answers may vary. Sample: Geometry software lets you measure angles and segments and observe geometric properties that are invariant as you move or change elements of the construction.

8. Answers may vary. Sample: Geometric relationships that you construct using geometry software are invariant regardless of how you otherwise alter the construction, whereas relationships that are merely drawn in are not preserved.

Investigation Overview

There are many In-Class Experiments (many require geometry software) for students to perform, so this investigation can take up to eight days to complete. Although there are many conjectures and theorems that come out of Lesson 1.12 while students are looking for concurrences and collinearities, you can skip this lesson if you are pressed for class time.

This investigation introduces students to the hunt for numerical invariants (constant measure, sum, product, ratio, and difference) and spatial invariants (shape, collinearity, and concurrence).

You may wish to assign Questions 1–3 for students to think and write about during the investigation.

Learning Goals

- Explain that invariants can be numbers, relationships between numbers, shapes, and relationships between shapes.
- Search for numerical invariants, such as constant sums, products, differences, or ratios.
- Describe various types of invariants in geometry.
- Identify the invariant relationships for the sums of the measures of the angles of polygons.
- Identify the invariant relationship that exists when a line parallel to one side of a triangle cuts the other two sides of the triangle proportionally.
- Search for geometric invariants, such as points of concurrency (particularly among perpendicular bisectors and angle bisectors in a triangle) and collinearity of points.

Habits and Skills

- Search for numerical invariants.
- Search for spatial invariants.
- Make conjectures.
- Use software to tinker with geometric models.

Investigation 1D
Invariants

In *Invariants*, you will use geometry software to experiment with figures. You will stretch and squash parts of a figure to get a feel for how the parts work together, which patterns exist, and which values or relationships stay the same, even when others change.

Some of the invariants that you discover will lead to useful theorems. As you proceed, visualize, draw pictures, and make calculations. Do whatever helps you make an educated guess.

By the end of this investigation, you will be able to answer questions like these.

1. What is an invariant? What kinds of invariants should you look for in geometry?

2. What invariant relationship exists when a line parallel to the base of a triangle intersects the other sides of that triangle?

3. What shape do you form when you connect the consecutive midpoints of a quadrilateral?

You will learn how to

- describe various types of invariants in geometry
- identify the invariant relationships for the sums of the measures of the angles of polygons
- identify the invariant relationship that exists when a line parallel to one side of a triangle cuts the other two sides of the triangle proportionally
- search for geometric invariants, such as points of concurrency and collinearity of points

You will develop these habits and skills:

- Search for numerical invariants.
- Search for spatial invariants.
- Make conjectures.
- Use software to tinker with geometric models.

Pop-up book artists are experts on how parts of a figure work together.

Investigation Road Map

LESSON 1.10, *Getting Started,* has students work on two problems—one that asks them to look for numerical invariants, and one that asks them to look for spatial invariants.

LESSON 1.11, *Numerical Invariants in Geometry,* has students work through three In-Class Experiments to search for invariants in figures, including parallelism, angle measure, constant sums and differences, and constant products and ratios.

LESSON 1.12, *Spatial Invariants,* introduces students to three spatial invariants: shape, concurrence, and collinearity.

Getting Started

 **Activating Prior Knowledge**
Exploring New Ideas

Something that is true for each member of a collection is an **invariant** for the collection.

For You to Explore

1. Study the three different collections below.

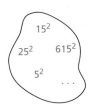
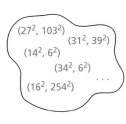
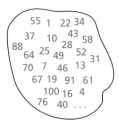

a. In the first set, each number before squaring ends in 5. Evaluate the squares. What invariants do you find?

b. The second set contains pairs of square numbers. In each pair, the two numbers before squaring end in digits that add to 10. Evaluate all the squares. What invariants do you find?

c. The third set contains 1, 4, 7, 10, 13, and so on. Explain whether 301 is in the set. Choose pairs of numbers from the set and find their products. What seems to be true about their products? What seems to be true about the sums of four numbers chosen from the set? What seems to be true about the differences of any two numbers?

2. Draw two polygons like quadrilateral *ABCD* and △*EFG* below. On each side, draw two points that roughly divide the sides into thirds. Connect each vertex to two points on different sides to form the largest angle possible. The connecting segments surround a region. The two diagrams here suggest

- the region has eight sides when the original shape has four sides
- the region has six sides when the original shape has three sides

Is this a reliable pattern? In other words, does the inside region always have twice the number of sides as the original shape when you connect vertices to "third points" in this way? Explain.

> **Remember...**
> An invariant over a set is something that is the same for every member of the set.

> To make the angle with vertex at *B*, connect *B* to the point on $\overline{AD}$ that is closer to *A*, and to the point on $\overline{CD}$ that is closer to *C*.

Lesson Overview

GOALS
- Warm up to the ideas of the investigation.
- Search for numerical invariants, such as constant sums, products, differences, or ratios.

FOR YOU TO EXPLORE • Core: 1, 2	**HOMEWORK** • Core: 3, 4 • Optional: 5, 6, 7
MATERIALS • geometry software • graphing calculators	**VOCABULARY** • invariant

Launch

Before assigning the For You to Explore problems, review the term *invariant* with your class.

Explore

For You to Explore

There are only two problems in this lesson, but each will take students some time to work through. Students can use geometry software or pencil and paper for Problem 2.

PROBLEM 1 A calculator might be helpful for use in searching for numerical invariants.

PROBLEM 2 The pattern this problem suggests is not a reliable one. Make sure students experiment with other polygons to test the pattern.

Answers

For You to Explore

1. a–c. Answers may vary. Samples are given.

a. All of the squares end in 25.

b. If the units digits of a pair of whole numbers have a sum of 10, then the squares of the numbers have the same units digits.

c. Yes; the product of any two numbers in the set is also in the set; the sum of any four numbers in the set is also in the set; the difference of two numbers in the set is 1 less than some number in the set.

2. The triangle seems always to produce a hexagon, but the quadrilateral does not always produce an octagon. This can be verified by dragging the vertices of the quadrilateral to various positions.

Wrap Up

If there is time, assign Exercise 3 for work in class. Students can then share their tables with a classmate to see if they have the required invariant.

Exercises

HOMEWORK
- Core: 3, 4
- Optional: 5, 6, 7

Maintain Your Skills

EXERCISES 5–7 require the use of geometry software. You may want to assign these exercises in class. They provide a good introduction to spatial invariants, while also providing additional practice on constructing with geometry software.

On Your Own

3. The table at the right shows pairs of numbers. An invariant for the table is 4 because $\frac{r}{q} = 4$ for each pair. Make three different tables like the one at the right so that the invariant for each table is 8. Use a different operation to build each table.

q	r
$\frac{1}{8}$	$\frac{1}{2}$
4	16
8	32
100	400

4. Draw a quadrilateral. Construct the midpoints of its sides. Then connect the consecutive midpoints.

   a. Explain why the figure formed must be a quadrilateral.

   b. Can the figure formed be *any* kind of quadrilateral, or are certain kinds of quadrilaterals not possible? Explain.

   > In other words, besides the number of sides, what other invariants, if any, exist?

Maintain Your Skills

5. a. Use geometry software to construct a figure like the one at the right, in which lines ℓ and m are parallel. Then drag a point or one of the lines to change the appearance of the figure. Lines ℓ and m should remain parallel.

   b. List some invariants that you find.

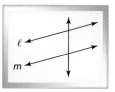

6. a. Use geometry software to construct a square like the one at the right.

   b. Drag some points. List some invariants that you find.

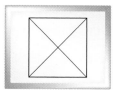

7. a. Use geometry software. Construct a line ℓ and a point P that is not on ℓ. (Do not place P too far away from ℓ.) Choose a point Q on line ℓ. Draw $\overline{PQ}$. Construct the circle with $\overline{PQ}$ as a diameter. Keep P and ℓ fixed. Place three or four more points on ℓ. Connect each of these new points to P with a line segment. Draw a circle with this segment as its diameter.

   b. List some invariants that you find.

> **Habits of Mind**
>
> **Visualize.** If $\overline{PQ}$ is a diameter, where is the center of the circle?

Answers

Exercises

3. Answers may vary. Sample:

$\frac{z}{w} = 8$

w	z
2	16
3	24
4	32
5	40

$g + h = 8$

g	h
0	8
2	6
4	4
6	2

$m - n = 8$

m	n
10	2
20	12
30	22
40	32

4. a. The figure formed by joining the midpoints has four vertices, no three of which are collinear, and when you connect the midpoints in order, the resulting figure will not cross itself.

   b. Quadrilaterals that are not parallelograms are impossible.

5. a. Check students' work.

   b. Answers may vary. Sample:

   The measures of ∠1, ∠3, ∠6, and ∠8 are equal. The measures of ∠2, ∠4, ∠5, and ∠7 are equal.

6. a. Check students' work.

   b. Answers may vary. Sample: The diagonals have equal lengths. The diagonals are perpendicular. The area of each small triangle is $\frac{1}{4}$ the area of the square.

7. a. Check students' work.

   b. Answers may vary. Sample: All the circles pass through the point where the line through P perpendicular to ℓ intersects ℓ. The centers of the circles all lie on the same line.

Numerical Invariants in Geometry

Positions of points, intersections of lines, lengths of segments, measures of angles, and even sums or ratios of these measurements may be invariant.

A numerical invariant is called a **constant.** In this section, these two words mean the same thing.

For the problems in the following In-Class Experiments, do each of the following tasks.

- Draw and measure the objects with geometry software.
- Drag parts of the figure. Watch what changes and what remains the same.
- Make conjectures that seem likely. Then find a way to test them.
- Organize and record your results.

In-Class Experiment

Geometric Objects

1. Use geometry software to construct a circle and one of its diameters. Find the circumference, the length of the diameter, and the area of the circle. Also calculate the ratio of each pair of these measurements. Which ratios, if any, seem invariant as you change the size of the circle?

2. Construct two parallel lines that are a fixed distance apart. Construct △DEF such that points D, E, and F are on the lines, as shown.

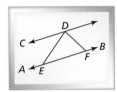

In parts (a)–(e), which measures seem invariant in △DEF as D moves along $\overleftrightarrow{CD}$?

a. the measure of ∠EDF   b. DE + DF

c. the perimeter of △DEF   d. the area of △DEF

e. the sum of the measures of ∠D, ∠E, and ∠F

f. Can you find any other invariants?

3. Study your construction from Problem 2 as D moves along $\overleftrightarrow{CD}$.

a. Find two angles that have equal measure, no matter where D is located on $\overleftrightarrow{CD}$.

b. Find pairs or groups of angles that have an invariant sum of 180°.

c. Can you find two angles such that the measure of one is always greater than the measure of the other? Explain.

In-Class Experiment

1. The ratio $\frac{\text{circumference}}{\text{diameter}}$ is invariant. It is equal to π, or about 3.14.

2. **a.** no   **b.** no   **c.** no

   d. yes   **e.** yes

   f. Answers may vary. Sample: the distance between the midpoints of $\overline{DE}$ and $\overline{DF}$

3. **a.** $m\angle CDE = m\angle DEF$

   b. Answers may vary. Sample:
   $m\angle AED + m\angle DEF = 180°$;
   $m\angle CDE + m\angle EDF + m\angle EFD$
   $= 180°$

   c. $m\angle EFD < m\angle AED$;
   $m\angle FED < m\angle BFD$

Launch

It is a good idea to have some pre-made sketches handy on your computer. These can be time-savers for students who, after repeatedly trying, are unsuccessful constructing the sketches required in the In-Class Experiments, or for students who lose previously saved sketches. All students should attempt to make the sketches.

Explore

In-Class Experiment

Make sure students *construct* the diameter, rather than just draw a segment that looks right.

PROBLEM 6 You may wish to use Blackline Master MC1 with this problem.

---

4. Draw △*ABC*. Construct the midpoint *D* of $\overline{BC}$. Construct median $\overline{AD}$. As you stretch and distort △*ABC*, what is invariant? (Be sure that *D* remains the midpoint of $\overline{BC}$!)

  a. Find two segments such that their lengths are a constant ratio.

  b. Are there any invariant areas? Invariant ratios of areas?

  c. Find at least one other invariant. Provide a chart or table of measurements and some sketches to show the measures or ratios that do not change.

Remember...

A median of a triangle is a line segment that connects one of the triangle's vertices to the midpoint of the opposite side.

In-Class Experiment

Constant Sum and Difference

You may be convinced that the sum of the angle measures of a triangle is invariably 180°. What do you think about the sums of the angle measures of other kinds of polygons? Are they also 180°? Or do different kinds of polygons—quadrilaterals, pentagons, hexagons, and so on—have their own special fixed numbers? If so, is it possible to predict the sum of the angle measures of a given polygon?

5. Experiment with the sums of the angle measures of quadrilaterals, pentagons, hexagons, and so on. Be sure to test both regular and irregular shapes. Which types of polygons, if any, have constant sums of angle measures?

6. You can divide a polygon with *n* sides into (*n* − 2) triangles. How might this help you find a rule that describes the sum of the measures of the angles of a polygon?

Habits of Mind

Generalize. Trying this for a few simple polygons may suggest what you can do for any polygon. Once you get the general idea, try to make a convincing argument that applies to every polygon.

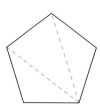

Three triangles form a pentagon.

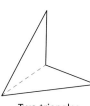

Two triangles form a quadrilateral.

Six triangles form an octagon.

7. Assume that the sum of the angle measures of a triangle is invariant. Write an argument that shows that the sum of the angle measures of an *n*-sided polygon is also invariant. Find a rule that will tell you the angle sum if you know *n*, the number of sides.

Answers

4. a. $\overline{BD}$ and $\overline{DC}$

  b. no; yes

  c. Answers may vary. Sample: The ratio of the area of △*ABD* to the area of △*ABC* is always $\frac{1}{2}$.

In-Class Experiment

5. all convex polygons having the same number of sides

6. The sum of the angle sums of the triangles is the sum of the measures of the interior angles of the polygon.

7. Since you can dissect any polygon with *n* sides into (*n* − 2) triangles, and since the vertex of each triangle lies at a vertex of the polygon, then the sum of the interior angle measures of the polygon is the sum of the angle sums of all the triangles. If the polygon has *n* sides, then the sum of the interior angle measures is (*n* − 2)180°.

Constant Product and Ratio

Use geometry software to draw a triangle. Construct and connect the midpoints of two sides. Your construction will look something like the construction below. Point D is the midpoint of $\overline{AC}$, and E is the midpoint of $\overline{AB}$.

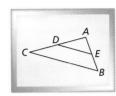

8. Move one of the triangle's vertices. As you distort the triangle, look for invariants.

9. Measure the lengths of $\overline{DE}$ and $\overline{BC}$. Compare these lengths as you drag one of the vertices.

You know about the following invariants because you deliberately built them into your triangle.

- $CD = DA$ (because D is the midpoint of $\overline{AC}$)
- $AE = EB$ (because E is the midpoint of $\overline{AB}$)
- $\frac{AD}{AC} = \frac{1}{2}$
- $\frac{AE}{AB} = \frac{1}{2}$

You may not have listed this next invariant because it is almost too obvious. It is built into the software, and it is important.

- As you drag one vertex of the triangle, the other two vertices do not move. Therefore, the length of the side opposite the vertex you move does not change.

The remaining invariants were not built in by anyone. They are natural consequences of the invariants listed above.

- As $\overline{CB}$ gets longer, so does $\overline{DE}$. In fact, $\frac{DE}{CB} = \frac{1}{2}$.
- $\frac{\text{area}(\triangle ABC)}{\text{area}(\triangle AED)} = 4$
- $\overline{DE}$ is parallel to $\overline{CB}$.

The results of the In-Class Experiment suggest the following conjecture.

Conjecture 1.2 Midline Conjecture

A segment connecting the midpoints of two sides of a triangle is parallel to the third side and is half its length.

Go Online
PHSchool.com

For more information about invariants, go to Web Code: bee-9031

You will prove the Midline Conjecture in Chapter 2.

In-Class Experiment

8. Check students' work. Some interesting invariants are $\frac{AD}{AC}$, $\frac{DE}{BC}$, and $\frac{\text{area } \triangle AED}{\text{area } \triangle ABC}$.

9. Check students' work.

In-Class Experiment

Spend some time reviewing all of the invariants listed. Conclude this experiment by posting the Midline Conjecture on the board.

Wrap Up

Your students have done a lot of work searching for invariants in these three In-Class Experiments. Before sending them off on their own with the Check Your Understanding exercises, take some time to review any conjectures that students made and any new vocabulary they came across. Make a list of any unanswered questions that you may want to come back to at a later date.

Assessment Resources

Lesson Quiz 1.11

1. **a.** In your own words, define *numerical invariant*.
   b. Give an example of a numerical invariant.

2. In the picture, $\triangle ABC$ is equilateral and D is the midpoint of $\overline{AC}$. Which of the following are invariant as B moves along line n?
   a. the perimeter of $\triangle ABC$
   b. the ratio of $\frac{AB}{BC}$
   c. the area of $\triangle ABC$
   d. $m\angle ADB$

3. In the picture, $\overline{BC}$ is the diameter of circle A, and D is a point on circle A. Which of the following are invariant as D moves around circle A?
   a. $m\angle BDC$
   b. the area of $\triangle BCD$
   c. AD
   d. the sum of $\angle BDC + \angle DCA + \angle ABD$

Exercises

HOMEWORK
- Core: 8, 9, 12
- Optional: 11, 13
- Extension: 10

Check Your Understanding

EXERCISE 1 has students construct a 90° angle inscribed in a circle. If students do not recall the Pythagorean Theorem, they may not consider the invariant $AD^2 + DB^2 = AB^2$.

EXERCISE 2 Make sure that students construct this rectangle with angles that remain 90° but with sides that can vary their lengths. It should be "UnMessUpable" as a rectangle, but should be able to change dimensions.

EXERCISE 3 Students should be sure that point D is stuck to the ray when they construct this figure with geometry software.

Exercises *Practicing Habits of Mind*

Check Your Understanding

1. Use geometry software to construct a circle and one of its diameters. Place a point on the circle away from an endpoint of the diameter. Then complete the triangle as shown in the third figure below.

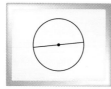 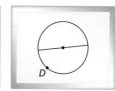 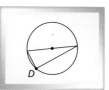

   a. Move D around the circle. What measures or relationships are invariant as D moves? Look at angles, lengths, sums, and ratios.

   b. Leave D in one place and stretch the circle. What measures or relationships are invariant as the size of the circle changes?

2. Construct a rectangle $ABCD$ so that you can stretch its length and width. Which of the following are invariants?

   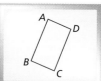

   a. the length-to-width ratio: $\frac{AB}{AD}$

   b. the ratio of the lengths of the opposite sides: $\frac{AB}{DC}$

   c. the perimeter of rectangle $ABCD$

   d. the ratio of the lengths of the diagonals: $\frac{AC}{BD}$

   e. the ratio of the perimeter of rectangle $ABCD$ to its area

3. In the figure below, C is fixed on $\overline{AB}$, but D is not fixed. Move C and D. Find two sums related to the figure that are constant.

   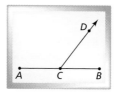

4. Use geometry software to draw two parallel lines m and n. Fix points A and B on line m. Place point C on line n. Draw $\triangle ABC$. Now move point C along n. Look at the area and perimeter of the triangle. What invariants do you notice?

Answers

Exercises

1. Call the endpoints of the diameter A and B.

   a. Answers may vary. Sample: $m\angle ADB$ is always 90°. In $\triangle ADB$, $\overline{AB}$ is the longest side and $\angle D$ is the largest angle. $m\angle A + m\angle B$ is always 90°. The length of $\overline{AB}$ does not change.

   b. Answers may vary. Sample: $\angle D$ is the largest angle, and $\overline{AB}$ is the longest side. $m\angle D$ is 90°, as is $m\angle A + m\angle B$. The ratio of any two sides is constant. The ratio of the circumference of the circle to the diameter of the circle is constant. The ratio of the area of $\triangle ABD$ to the area of the circle is constant.

2. b and d

3. $AC + CB$, $m\angle ACD + m\angle DCE$

4. the area of $\triangle ABC$

Use geometry software to construct a circle. Place a point C anywhere inside the circle. Place point D on the circle. Construct the line through D and C to meet the circle a second time at point E. Then hide $\overleftrightarrow{DC}$. Construct $\overline{DC}$, $\overline{EC}$, and $\overline{DE}$. As you move D along the circle, $\overline{DE}$ will pivot about C.

5. Measure $\overline{CE}$ and $\overline{CD}$. When the chord pivots about C, do CE and CD change in opposite ways (one increases while the other decreases) or in the same way? Use that information to help you find a numerical invariant.

6. The number you found does not depend on the location of D. You can move D, and the number remains fixed. But the number does *not* remain fixed when C is moved. For which location of C inside the circle is the number greatest? Explain.

7. Draw $\triangle ABC$.

Draw $\triangle ABC$. Place a point D arbitrarily on $\overline{AC}$. Through D, construct the line that is parallel to $\overline{CB}$. Use that line to construct $\overline{DE}$. Then hide $\overleftrightarrow{DE}$. Your construction should resemble your construction from the Constant Product and Ratio In-Class Experiment earlier in the lesson. This time, D and E are movable points rather than midpoints.

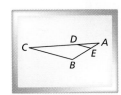

As D moves along $\overline{AC}$, $\overline{DE}$ moves with it. Look at different lengths and areas. Try to find some invariants. Record your conjectures and appropriate supporting evidence.

A *chord* of a circle is a segment with endpoints that are on the circle.

$\overline{AB}$ is a chord of the circle.

Developing Habits of Mind

Experiment. Exercise 7 is a good example of how you get different results when you slightly change a problem. You know from earlier work that certain ratios are invariant when D is the midpoint of $\overline{AC}$. When D is fixed on $\overline{AC}$ but is *not* its midpoint, are those ratios still invariant? Or does their invariance depend on D being the midpoint?

When you move D, are the ratios constant? If so, the ratios are again invariant. If not, perhaps a relationship exists between two or more of the ratios.

EXERCISES 5 AND 6 are an informal exploration of the power of a point. Students will explore the power of a point more thoroughly in Lesson 5.11.

EXERCISE 7 refers to the Constant Product and Ratio In-Class Experiment. The ratio $\frac{DA}{CA}$ is invariant as you drag A or C. This is not a geometric theorem but an invariant built deliberately into the software. For some students, it may be worth pursuing the following question: How can you tell whether a discovered result is a fact of geometry or an artifact of the software?

The ratios $\frac{AE}{AD}$, $\frac{DE}{AD}$, and $\frac{AE}{DE}$ are invariant as D moves. That fact makes their sums, differences, products, squares, and so on, invariant as D moves. The actual values of these invariants, however, depend on the shape of (which is to say, the angles in) $\triangle ABC$.

5. opposite ways; $CE \cdot CD$

6. The product $CE \cdot CD$ is greatest when C is at the center of the circle.

7. Answers may vary. Sample:
$$\frac{AD}{DC} = \frac{AE}{EB}, \frac{\text{Area}(\triangle ADE)}{\text{Area}(\triangle ACB)} = \left(\frac{DE}{CB}\right)^2;$$
To support these observations, use the software to measure the lengths and areas, and calculate the quantities in the equations.

On Your Own

EXERCISE 10 is an investigation of the golden ratio. It requires significant algebraic manipulation, including the use of the quadratic formula.

EXERCISE 11 asks students to investigate perimeters and areas of triangles, squares, and circles. This is a preview of the work they will do with area in Chapter 3.

8. Tennis balls are sold in cans of three. Which is greater—the height of the can or the circumference of the can?

9. In the figure below, $\overleftrightarrow{CD} \parallel \overleftrightarrow{AB}$. How can you construct a right triangle that has the same area as $\triangle EFG$?

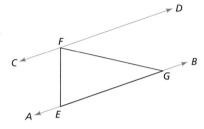

10. **Take It Further**

    a. Use geometry software to construct a rectangle. Then divide the rectangle into a square and a smaller rectangle.

    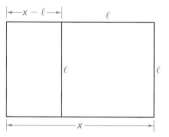

    a rectangle

    the rectangle divided into a square and a smaller rectangle

    Find the length-to-width ratio in each rectangle. What do you notice about the two ratios?

    b. The figure at the right illustrates a special invariant ratio in geometry. Start with a particular rectangle. Divide the rectangle into a square and a smaller rectangle. In the two rectangles, the length-to-width ratios are equal. In fact, you can divide the smaller rectangle into a square and an even smaller rectangle. The length-to-width ratio of the smaller rectangle is the same as the length-to-width ratio of the first two rectangles. What is the numerical value of this ratio?

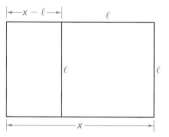

Answers

8. the circumference

9. Construct the line through F perpendicular to $\overleftrightarrow{EG}$. Let H be the point where the perpendicular intersects $\overleftrightarrow{EG}$. Construct a segment $\overline{HK}$ on $\overleftrightarrow{EG}$ that has the same length as $\overline{EG}$. $\triangle FHK$ has the same area as $\triangle EFG$.

10. a. They are equal.

    b. $\dfrac{1 + \sqrt{5}}{2}$

11. Decide whether each ratio in parts (a)–(c) is constant, even if you stretch the given figure. Justify each answer.

    a. The square remains square. Is the ratio $\dfrac{\text{area of triangle}}{\text{area of square}}$ invariant? If so, what is the ratio?

    b. The circle remains a circle. The square remains a square. Each side of the square outside the circle is fixed to a radius. Is the ratio $\dfrac{\text{area of circle}}{\text{area of square}}$ invariant? If so, what is the ratio?

    c. The triangle remains a triangle. You can reshape it in any way. Is the ratio $\dfrac{\text{perimeter of triangle}}{\text{area of triangle}}$ invariant? If so, what is the ratio?

12. Standardized Test Prep Maya constructed a regular hexagon inside a circle. The hexagon consists of six equilateral triangles. To compute the sum of the measures of the angles of the regular hexagon, she found the sum of the measures of the angles of the six triangles. From that sum, she subtracted the measure of each angle with a vertex at the center of the circle.

What is the sum of the measures of the angles of Maya's regular hexagon?

A. 360°   **B.** 540°   **C.** 720°   **D.** 1080°

> **Go Online**
> PHSchool.com
>
> For additional practice,
> go to Web Code: bea-0111

Maintain Your Skills

13. Find five cylindrical objects. Measure the diameter and the circumference of each. What is the $\dfrac{\text{circumference}}{\text{diameter}}$ ratio for each object?

> **Go Online**
> **Video Tutor**
> PHSchool.com
>
> Web Code: bee-0775

Maintain Your Skills

EXERCISE 13 has students investigate the invariant ratio of circumference to diameter of any cylindrical object. This is likely an exercise students have completed in an earlier mathematics class.

Additional Resources

PRINTED RESOURCES
- Solution Manual
- Practice Workbook
- Assessment Resources
- Teaching Resources

TECHNOLOGY
- Interactive Textbook
- TeacherExpress CD-ROM
- **Exam**View CD-ROM
- **PHSchool.com**
  - Additional Practice
  - Mid-Chapter and Chapter Tests
  - Video Tutors
  - Vocabulary Puzzles

Additional Practice

Use the appropriate tools of a geometry software program.

1. Construct scalene triangle *ABC*. Find the midpoints of $\overline{AB}$ and $\overline{BC}$.
  a. Construct $\overline{DE}$ to connect the midpoints.
  b. Measure the length of $\overline{DE}$ and the length of $\overline{AC}$. What is the relationship between the lengths of these two segments?
  c. Move vertex *B*. What is the effect on the relationship between the lengths of $\overline{DE}$ and $\overline{AC}$?
  d. List two other measures or relationships that are invariant as *B* moves.

2. Construct parallelogram *ABCD* that can be stretched to any length or width. Which of the following are invariant?
  a. the ratio of the lengths of the opposite sides, $\frac{AB}{CD}$
  b. the perimeter of parallelogram *ABCD*
  c. the ratio of the lengths of the diagonals, $\frac{AC}{BD}$
  d. the ratio of the perimeter of parallelogram *ABCD* to its area

3. Construct a triangle. Find the midpoints of each side.
  a. Construct the three medians of the triangle. Then measure the medians.
  b. Label the point at which the medians intersect. This point is called the *centroid* of the triangle.
  c. Construct a segment from each vertex to the *centroid*. Measure the lengths of these three segments.
  d. Move a vertex and a side of the triangle. Does an invariant relationship exist between each median and its corresponding segment that you constructed in part (c)? Explain.

4. Construct a triangle. Construct the bisector of each angle.
  a. Label the point at which the angle bisectors intersect. This point is called the *incenter* of the triangle.
  b. Construct a perpendicular segment from the *incenter* to each side of the triangle. Measure the length of each of these segments. What do you notice?
  c. Manipulate any part of the triangle. Does an invariant relationship exist between the three perpendicular segments? Explain.
  d. Make a conjecture about the *incenter* of a triangle.

Practice: For Lesson 1.11, assign Exercises 1–4.

11. a. yes; $\frac{1}{2}$
    b. yes; π (or about 3.14)
    c. no

12. C

13. Check students' work. If the objects are true cylinders, the ratio should be approximately 3.14.

Lesson Overview

GOALS

- Explain that invariants can be numbers, relationships between numbers, shapes, and relationships between shapes.
- Describe various types of invariants in geometry.
- Search for geometric invariants, such as points of concurrency (particularly among perpendicular bisectors and angle bisectors in a triangle) and collinearity of points.

The notion of shape is a difficult one to define precisely. In this lesson, students use two notions of shape.

1. Two polygons have the same shape if they have the same number of sides.

2. Two figures have the same shape if the ratios of corresponding line segment lengths are equal.

Since this is an exploration, you do not have to distinguish between these two notions. Students should merely notice what is invariant as they move the figures they construct.

CHECK YOUR UNDERSTANDING
- Core: 1, 2, 3, 4, 5, 6

MATERIALS
- geometry software
- Blackline Masters MC1, 1.12

HOMEWORK
- Core: 7, 8
- Optional: 9, 11
- Extension: 10

VOCABULARY
- angle bisector
- collinear points (collinearity)
- concurrent lines (concur)
- disc
- perpendicular bisector

Launch

Begin by reviewing Exercise 2 from Lesson 1.10. Give students some time to make these figures with geometry software and investigate this exercise further before going on to the For Discussion questions.

1.12 Spatial Invariants

Shape: A Geometric Invariant

Invariants do not have to be numbers or relationships between numbers. Invariants can be shapes or relationships between shapes, as well. In Lesson 1.10, you searched for shape invariants in the figures below.

It appears that when the outside shape has four sides, the inside shape has eight. When the outside shape has three sides, the inside shape has six. It turns out that, in the case of a triangle, the figure formed on the inside is always a hexagon. Otherwise, the strict doubling pattern is not reliable.

Investigate these figures further. Learn or invent a way to divide a segment accurately into thirds. For this investigation, however, it is acceptable to divide the segment by estimating or by measuring.

Geometry software preserves proportions along a segment when you stretch or shrink the segment. So, your estimated thirds will stay fixed throughout the experiment, unless you deliberately change them.

For Discussion

What *can* happen is often as useful as what *must* happen.

1. If the outside polygon has n sides, can the inside polygon ever have more than $2n$ sides? If so, what is the greatest number of sides the inside polygon can have?

2. Can the inside polygon ever have fewer than $2n$ sides? If so, what is the fewest number of sides the inside polygon can have?

3. Can the inside polygon ever be regular? Explain.

Answers

For Discussion

1. no; $2n$

2. yes; $2n - 2$

3. No; the inner polygon must have an even number of sides, and the opposite sides can never be parallel, as in a regular polygon.

Concurrence: A Geometric Invariant

You may recognize the picture below from one of the experiments you performed earlier.

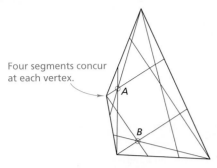

Four segments concur at each vertex.

At each vertex of the outside quadrilateral, four segments intersect or concur. That is no surprise. It was intentional.

Definition

Three or more lines that meet or intersect at one point are concurrent lines.

Lines ℓ, m, and n are concurrent lines.

In the first figure above, three *inside* segments are also concurrent. Two such concurrences are at points A and B. These concurrences were not deliberately built in. They are something of a surprise. If you move the vertices of the quadrilateral, you will see that these concurrences are not invariant.

When concurrence is an invariant for a given figure, a special relationship exists.

For You to Do

4. Use geometry software to draw a triangle. Construct the perpendicular bisector of each side. Can you adjust the triangle so that the three perpendicular bisectors are concurrent?

5. Hide the perpendicular bisectors. Construct the angle bisectors of your triangle. Can you adjust the triangle so that the three angle bisectors are concurrent?

6. Under which circumstances, if any, are the three perpendicular bisectors and the three angle bisectors of a triangle concurrent?

For You to Do

4. yes

5. yes

6. when the triangle is equilateral

Explore

SHAPE: A GEOMETRIC INVARIANT You may wish to use Blackline Master MC1 here.

CONCURRENCE: A GEOMETRIC INVARIANT Review the definition of concurrence by investigating the diagram. Then let students investigate concurrencies in triangles by having them complete the three For You to Do problems.

Take some time to review the two theorems about concurrency in triangles before going on to the collinearity section.

COLLINEARITY: A GEOMETRIC INVARIANT Review the definition of *collinear* with your class. You may wish to give students Blackline Master 1.12 for use in the For You to Do. Since students will need several different sized discs, they can cut out all of the discs from the blackline master, or join up with other students who cut out different sized discs.

It may surprise you that the perpendicular bisectors in a triangle are concurrent. If you analyze the situation, though, it becomes less surprising.

Refer to Theorem 1.1 in Lesson 1.6.

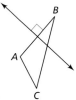

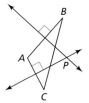

All the points on the perpendicular bisector of $\overline{AB}$ are the same distance from *A* and *B*.

All the points on the perpendicular bisector of $\overline{AC}$ are the same distance from *A* and *C*.

Point *P* is constructed so that it is equidistant from *A* and *B* and equidistant from *A* and *C*. So *P* is also equidistant from *B* and *C*. *P* must lie on the perpendicular bisector of $\overline{BC}$.

Theorem 1.2 Concurrence of Perpendicular Bisectors

In any triangle, the perpendicular bisectors of the sides are concurrent.

In △ *ABC*, the perpendicular bisectors of $\overline{AB}$, $\overline{BC}$, and $\overline{AC}$ are concurrent at *G*.

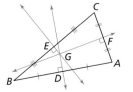

You can make a similar argument for the angle bisectors of a triangle. Any point on the bisector of ∠*ABC* is the same distance from $\overline{AB}$ and $\overline{BC}$. Any point on the bisector of ∠*CAB* is the same distance from $\overline{AC}$ and $\overline{AB}$. The point of intersection of the two angle bisectors is the same distance from $\overline{AC}$ and $\overline{BC}$. That puts it on the bisector of ∠*ACB* as well.

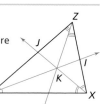

Theorem 1.3 Concurrence of Angle Bisectors

In any triangle, the angle bisectors are concurrent.

In △ *XYZ*, the angle bisectors of ∠*X*, ∠*Y*, and ∠*Z* are concurrent at *K*.

Collinearity

It is noteworthy when three lines intersect at the same point. It is also noteworthy when three apparently unrelated points lie on the same line.

Definition

Three or more points that are on the same line are **collinear points.**

For You to Do

Step 1 Trace a circle onto a sheet of paper.

Step 2 Poke a small hole through the paper at the center of the circle.

Step 3 Carefully cut out your **disc** (the circle and its interior).

Step 4 Work with three or four classmates who made discs of different sizes. Draw two points on a large sheet of paper. Place them close enough together that the smallest disc can touch both.

Step 5 Place one of your discs on the large sheet. Move it so that the edge of the disc touches both points.

Step 6 Mark the center of the circle on the large sheet.

Step 7 Remove the disc. Repeat Steps 5 and 6 with the other discs.

Step 8 After using all your discs, look at the circles' center marks. What is invariant about their positions?

Step 9 Draw two new points. Without using your discs, draw the figure that would be formed by a large number of circle center marks.

Exercises *Practicing Habits of Mind*

Check Your Understanding

1. Use geometry software. Place five points on your screen. Connect them with segments so that you have an arbitrary convex pentagon. Construct the perpendicular bisector of each side of your pentagon. See the diagram and answer the questions on the next page.

Answers

For You to Do

Check students' work.

For You to Do

You may wish to complete this activity as a whole class exploration with the overhead. Distribute one overhead transparency to each student and instruct him or her to draw one accurate circle and its center on the transparency. Make sure that circle sizes vary across the class. On an overhead projection screen, mark two points and then have students come up one-by-one to lay their circles onto the screen so that their circle's circumference touches the two points. When all of the transparencies are laid one on top of the other, the centers of the circles will lie on a line.

You can also use geometry software for this activity.

Wrap Up

Make a list of new vocabulary, conjectures, and theorems on the board for reference.

Assessment Resources

Exercises

HOMEWORK
- Core: 7, 8
- Optional: 9, 11
- Extension: 10

Check Your Understanding

EXERCISES 1 AND 2 are about the perpendicular bisectors and angle bisectors of pentagons. These two exercises are difficult. You may want to ask questions about the point of concurrence. In each case, what might be special about that point? For the perpendicular bisectors, it must be equidistant from all five vertices, so it must be the center of the circumcircle. For the angle bisectors, the point of concurrence must be equidistant from all of the sides. This is the center of the incircle.

continued on p. 62

continued on p. 61

EXERCISES 3–6 You may want pairs of students to choose one of these exercises and present the results to the class. If every student were to complete all four problems, you would need at least three days.

a. In the diagram at the left below, is there a point at which three or more perpendicular bisectors are concurrent?

b. If not, is it possible to adjust the vertices of the pentagon so that at least three bisectors are concurrent?

c. Is it possible to adjust the vertices of the pentagon so that all five bisectors are concurrent?

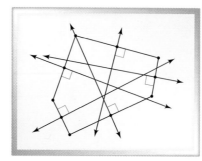 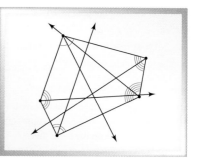

2. Try the same kind of experiment with the angle bisectors of a pentagon. See the diagram at the right above. Start with an arbitrary pentagon. Construct the angle bisector of each angle. Is it possible to adjust the vertices of the pentagon so that all five angle bisectors are concurrent?

It is a good habit to start an investigation with a special case. It simplifies what you have to look at. It can also suggest what to look for in other cases. Among polygons, the triangle is special because it is the simplest. Exercises 3–6 suggest other special cases.

3. Regular polygons are a very special case. Is concurrence of perpendicular bisectors an invariant for regular polygons? Experiment. Be sure to experiment with regular quadrilaterals (squares), regular pentagons, and regular hexagons. What do your experiments suggest? Explain.

4. Is concurrence of angle bisectors an invariant for regular polygons? Experiment, describe a conjecture, and explain the result.

5. Use geometry software to construct a circle. Place five points on the circle. Connect the points to form an irregular pentagon. Check the angle bisectors and perpendicular bisectors of the pentagon for concurrence. Do you observe any invariants? Explain.

6. Draw a circle. Construct an irregular polygon outside the circle so that all the sides of the polygon are tangent to the circle. Perform the two concurrence experiments. Do you observe any invariants? Explain.

Answers

Exercises

1. a. Check students' work.
b. yes
c. yes

2. yes

3. Experimentation suggests that concurrence of perpendicular bisectors is an invariant of regular polygons. Check students' work.

4. Experimentation suggests that concurrence of angle bisectors is an invariant of regular polygons. Check students' work.

5. The five perpendicular bisectors are concurrent at the center of the circle. The five angle bisectors are not concurrent.

6. The five angle bisectors are concurrent at the center of the circle. The five perpendicular bisectors are not concurrent.

7. The medians are concurrent.

On Your Own

7. Construct several different triangles. Then construct their medians. Describe any concurrence or collinearity you find.

8. **Standardized Test Prep** Triangle *ABC* is an isosceles triangle. $\overline{AD}$, $\overline{BE}$, and $\overline{CF}$ are altitudes. $\overline{AD}$, $\overline{BG}$, and $\overline{CH}$ are angle bisectors. Points *D*, *I*, and *J* are the midpoints of $\overline{BC}$, $\overline{AC}$, and $\overline{AB}$, respectively.

Which of the following statements may NOT be true?

A. The concurrences of the altitudes, angle bisectors, and medians are collinear.

B. $\overline{CI} \cong \overline{CD}$

C. $\overline{AD}$ is a median.

D. $\angle BCH \cong \angle HCA$

9. Use a piece of paper or geometry software to build an arbitrary quadrilateral. On one side, place an arbitrary point. Connect the point to the two opposite vertices of the quadrilateral. Do the same on the opposite side.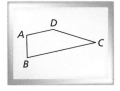

Finally, draw the diagonals of the quadrilateral. Find two obvious collinearities. Find one surprising collinearity.

10. **Take It Further** Consider this statement: In any hexagon, there can be at most one concurrence of three diagonals. Is this statement true or false? Explain your reasoning.

Maintain Your Skills

11. Construct trapezoid *ABCD* such that you can drag its vertices and sides.

a. Construct the diagonals and their point of intersection. Then construct the midpoints of the two parallel sides.

b. Find two collinearities that are intentionally built in. Find one collinearity that is not intentionally built in. Experiment to determine whether that collinearity is invariant.

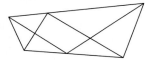

Go Online
PHSchool.com

For additional practice, go to **Web Code: bea-0112**

Additional Practice

Use the appropriate tools of a geometry software program.

1. Randomly place six points. Connect the points with segments so that you have an arbitrary convex hexagon. Construct the perpendicular bisector of each side of the hexagon.
   a. Is there a point at which three or more perpendicular bisectors are concurrent? If not, is it possible to adjust one or more vertices to make such a point?
   b. Is it possible to adjust the vertices so that all six bisectors concur at a single point?
   c. Construct all six angle bisectors. Is it possible to adjust the vertices so that all of the angle bisectors are concurrent?

2. Construct a circle.
   a. Place six points on the circle and connect them to form an irregular hexagon.
   b. Check the perpendicular bisectors of the sides for concurrence. Do you observe any invariants? Explain.

3. Construct an arbitrary trapezoid.
   a. On one side, place an arbitrary point. Connect the point to the two opposite vertices of the trapezoid. Do the same on the opposite side.
   b. Draw the diagonals of the trapezoid. Describe a surprising collinearity.

4. Construct a triangle.
   a. Construct the three medians of the triangle.
   b. Construct the three midlines of the triangle.
   c. Are any of these six segments concurrent? Is it possible to adjust the vertices so that all six segments concur at a single point?
   d. Do you observe any invariants? Explain.

5. Is the concurrence of altitudes an invariant for triangles? Experiment with several different triangles. What do your experiments suggest?

Practice: For Lesson 1.12, assign Exercises 1–5.

---

8. B

9. Two nonsurprising collinearities are those built into the figure by placing the arbitrary points on the sides of the quadrilateral. A surprising collinearity is the two intersections of the segments drawn in the figure and the intersection of the diagonals.

10. True; suppose a convex hexagon has three diagonals concurrent at point *P* inside the polygon. The diagonals that give the concurrency at point *P* join the diametrically opposite vertices. Every interior point of concurrency of three diagonals will necessarily result in this same set of diametrically opposite connections and hence will result in this same point of concurrency *P*.

11. a. Check students' work.

b. The midpoints of the parallel segments are constructed to be collinear with the endpoints of the segment, but they turn out to be collinear with the intersection of the diagonals as well.

Mathematical Reflections

EXERCISES 6–8 At the start of the investigation, you may have assigned these as Questions 1–3 for students to think and write about.

Mathematical
1D
Reflections

In this investigation you studied invariants—things that are the same for every member of a collection. You explored numerical invariants and spatial invariants, including concurrence and collinearity. The following questions will help you summarize what you have learned.

1. What is the sum of the measures of the angles of a pentagon? Of a hexagon?

2. In △ABC, D and E are the midpoints of $\overline{BC}$ and $\overline{AC}$, respectively. The lengths of some segments are marked. Find $\frac{CD}{CB}$ and $\frac{CF}{CH}$. Explain your reasoning.

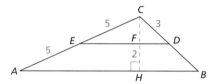

3. Draw a circle. Place and label two fixed points on the circle. Then place and label a third point on the circle that is not fixed. Join it to the two fixed points. What invariant(s) do you notice in your construction?

4. Are the medians of an equilateral triangle concurrent? Explain.

5. What invariants can you think of for a regular hexagon? List as many as you can.

6. What is an invariant? What kinds of invariants should you look for in geometry?

7. What invariant relationship exists when a line parallel to the base of a triangle intersects the other sides of that triangle?

8. What shape do you form when you connect the consecutive midpoints of a quadrilateral?

Vocabulary

In this investigation, you learned these terms. Make sure you understand what each one means and how you use it.

- **collinear points**
- **concurrent lines**
- **constant**
- **disc**
- **invariant**

What remains invariant when you open the pop-up book?

Answers

Mathematical Reflections

1. 540°; 720°

2. $\frac{CD}{CB} = \frac{1}{2}$ and $\frac{CF}{CH} = \frac{1}{2}$; Since D is the midpoint of $\overline{CB}$, CB = 6. Since $\overline{ED}$ is a midline of △ABC, F is the midpoint of $\overline{CH}$. Therefore CF = 2 and CH = 4.

3. The points A and B divide the circle into two arcs. The angle at point C is invariant wherever you place C within each of these two arcs, though the angle for each arc will be different, unless A and B are two ends of a diameter of a circle.

4. Yes; the medians of an equilateral triangle are also altitudes of the triangle, and since altitudes of an equilateral triangle are concurrent, so are its medians.

5. Answers may vary. Sample: angle measures, symmetric about the lines that pass through opposite vertices, symmetric about any line that passes through the midpoints of opposite sides

6. An invariant is a feature of a figure that does not change as other features change; Answers may vary. Sample: numerical measures and relationships, relationships involving collinearity or concurrency

7. Answers may vary. Sample: The lengths of corresponding sides are proportional, as are the lengths of corresponding medians and altitudes.

8. a parallelogram

Project: Using Mathematical Habits

Folding Squares

Project

You could assign this project to small groups to work on. Give groups some time to experiment in class. Then you could plan a day for groups to present to the whole class.

The good news is that there are several ways to use paper folding to solve each problem below. The challenge is to find one way!

You can use all that you know from previous courses about squares, their sides and angles, and their areas. You cannot, however, make any measurements with a ruler.

Materials:

square sheets of paper

Begin with several sheets of square paper.

1. Select a square. Use folding to construct a square with area $\frac{3}{4}$ the area of your original square. Remember, no rulers are allowed. Explain your construction.

2. Select another square and another fraction of the form $\frac{m}{n}$. Use folding. Try to construct a square with area $\frac{m}{n}$ times the area of the original square. For what fractions $\frac{m}{n}$ can you do this? Explain.

3. Construct a small square on a sheet of paper. Use folding to construct a second square with area exactly twice the area of your small square. Explain how you did it.

4. The paper below has been folded so that square *BGJH* has area equal to that of rectangle *ABCD*. This is called "squaring the rectangle." Explain how to square a rectangle using paper folding. Explain why the folding works. (*Hint:* Use Fold 0 to make rectangle *ABCD*.)

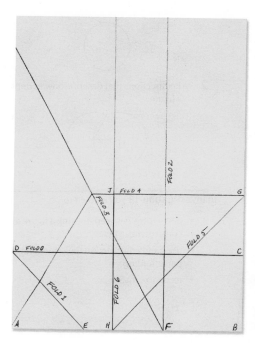

Project

1–2. See back of book.

3. Answers may vary. Sample: Construct the first square in one corner of the square sheet of paper. If not already done, extend each side of the square to the edge of the paper by folding along its sides. Construct the diagonal that does not intersect the shared corner of the small square and the square sheet of paper by folding one corner of the small square to its opposite corner. Construct lines through the two vertices on the sides of the paper that are perpendicular to the constructed diagonal of the smaller square. Connect with a fold the two points where these perpendiculars intersect the lines you constructed as extensions of the sides of the smaller square.

4. See back of book.

Answers

Chapter Review

1.

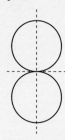

2. Answers may vary. Sample: Construct a circle and mark its center. Then, using the same radius, construct another circle centered at any point on the first circle. The two circles intersect at two points. Choose either point of intersection and construct the triangle determined by that point and the centers of the two circles.

3. a. Check students' work.
   b. not possible

4. a. Check students' work.
   b. not possible

5. The sum of the angle measures is 360°; The sum of the angle measures is $(n - 2)180°$.

6. Check students' work.

7. Check students' work; All sides must be the same length.

8. no; Choose two points A and B at random on one of the lines and one point C at random on the second line. On the second line, choose a point whose distance from C is equal to AB. The four points are the vertices of a parallelogram.

Go Online
PHSchool.com
For vocabulary review, go to Web Code: bej-0151

In **Investigation 1A** you learned to

- visualize geometric objects well enough to draw them
- use clear language to describe shapes
- write and follow careful directions

The following questions will help you check your understanding.

1. Copy the figure. Draw all of its lines of symmetry.

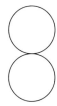

2. Write directions that describe how to draw this figure.

In **Investigation 1B** you learned to

- distinguish between drawing a figure and constructing a figure
- use hand construction tools, including paper folding
- recognize invariants

The following questions will help you check your understanding.

3. If possible, construct a triangle with the given angle measures.
   a. 60°, 40°, 80°   **b.** 100°, 20°, 45°

4. If possible, construct a triangle with the given side lengths.
   a. 4 cm, 5 cm, 6 cm   **b.** 3 in., 2 in., 6 in.

5. What is invariant about the angles of a quadrilateral? About a polygon with n sides?

In **Investigation 1C** you learned to

- use geometry software tools to construct UnMessUpable figures
- use geometry software to test for invariants

The following questions will help you check your understanding.

6. Construct an UnMessUpable square with side length 4 cm.

7. Use geometry software. Construct an UnMessUpable rectangle. Which invariant would you have to build into your rectangle to make the figure an UnMessUpable square?

8. The two lines below are parallel. If you choose any four points on the lines and connect them, will the result be a parallelogram? To get a parallelogram, which points can you choose randomly, and how do you have to choose the others?

In **Investigation 1D** you learned to

- apply the Midline Conjecture
- search for numerical and spatial invariants
- make conjectures and use software to experiment with geometric models

The following questions will help you check your understanding.

9. What is the definition of a perpendicular bisector? Explain why the three perpendicular bisectors of the sides of a triangle are concurrent.

10. Decide whether each ratio below is constant, even if the given figure is stretched. Justify each answer.

a. The rectangle remains a rectangle. Points E and F remain the midpoints of $\overline{AB}$ and $\overline{DC}$, respectively. Is the ratio

$$\frac{\text{area of } AEFD}{\text{area of } ABCD}$$

invariant? If so, what is the ratio?

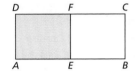

b. The two arcs below remain centered at A and B and have radius AB. You can stretch $\overline{AB}$. Is the ratio

$$\frac{\text{area of } AEBF}{\text{area of circle centered at } A}$$

invariant? If so, what is the ratio? (Recall, the area of a circle is πr^2, where r is the radius of the circle.)

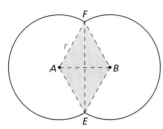

c. You can stretch the sides of the regular hexagon below. Is the ratio

$$\frac{\text{area of hexagon}}{\text{perimeter of hexagon}}$$

invariant? If so, what is the ratio?

9. The perpendicular bisector of a segment is the line perpendicular to the segment at its midpoint. A point is on the perpendicular bisector of a segment if and only if it is equidistant from the endpoints of the segment. In a triangle ABC, the perpendicular bisectors of $\overline{AB}$ and $\overline{AC}$ intersect at some point D, since $\angle A$ is not a straight angle. Since $DA = DB$ and $DA = DC$, it follows that $DB = DC$. Therefore D is on the perpendicular bisector of $\overline{BC}$.

10. a. yes; $\frac{1}{2}$ **b.** yes; $\frac{\pi\sqrt{3}}{2}$ **c.** no

Chapter Test

Assessment Resources

Chapter Test   Form A   page 1

1. In your own words, describe the meaning of *invariant*.

2. Use the segment below. Construct a square with diagonals of length *d*.

   d

3. Construct each triangle to meet the specifications. If you cannot construct the triangle, explain why.
   a. side lengths: 3 cm, 4 cm, 6 cm
   b. side lengths: 3 in., 3 in., 6 in.
   c. angle measures: 40°, 40°, 110°
   d. angle measures: 30°, 60°, 90°

4. Use the table.
   a. Describe the invariant relationship between *x* and *y* in the table.
   b. List three more pairs of numbers (*x*, *y*) that fit this invariant relationship.
   c. Can *x* or *y* have a negative value in this relationship? Explain.
   d. Can *x* = 0 in this relationship? Can *y* = 0 in this relationship? Explain.

x	y
70	20
28	62
35	55

5. Use the figure below. Describe any concurrences and collinearities. Then describe the triangle and segments. For example, what type of triangle is this? What are $\overline{CY}$, $\overline{BX}$, and $\overline{AZ}$?

   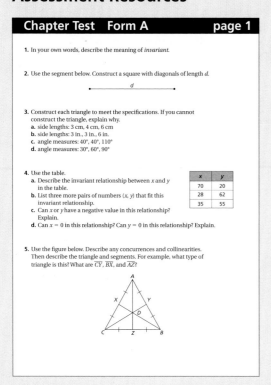

Also available: Form B

Answers

Chapter Test

1. C   **2.** C   **3.** B

4. A   **5.** B   **6.** D

7. A   **8.** B   **9.** B

10. Answers may vary. Sample: the sum of the angle measures of a triangle, concurrency of the perpendicular bisectors of the sides of a triangle, the type of figure you get if you connect the midpoints of a quadrilateral in order

11. a. yes; a tetrahedron
   b. no
   c. yes; a rectangular box
   d. yes; a tetrahedron
   e. no
   f. yes; a cylinder
   g. no

Go Online
PHSchool.com

For a chapter test, go to
Web Code: bea-0153

Multiple Choice

1. Which type of cross section can you NOT form by intersecting a plane and a right circular cone?

   A. an ellipse   **B.** a triangle

   C. a rectangle   **D.** a circle

2. Which figure has exactly two lines of symmetry?
   A. regular pentagon   **B.** circle
   C. square   **D.** rectangle

3. Which figure could be the intersection of two different planes?
   A. point   **B.** line
   C. line segment   **D.** plane

4. Which block letter has a vertical line of symmetry?

   A.   **B.**

   C.   **D.**

5. Which name best describes a parallelogram with four right angles?
   A. square   **B.** rectangle
   C. trapezoid   **D.** rhombus

6. Which method describes how to divide a segment into four congruent segments?
   A. Construct the midpoint of the segment.
   B. Construct the perpendicular bisector of the segment.
   C. Construct a square with each side congruent to the original segment.
   D. Construct the perpendicular bisector of the segment. Then construct the perpendicular bisector of each of the new segments.

7. Which word or phrase best completes the following sentence?

   The point of concurrency of the medians of a triangle is always __?__ the triangle.

   A. inside   **B.** on a vertex of
   C. on a side of   **D.** outside

8. The figures below show how to construct a type of segment associated with a triangle. What is constructed?
   A. altitude   **B.** median
   C. midline   **D.** angle bisector

9. Which method describes how to construct an altitude of a triangle?
   A. Construct the midpoint of one side of the triangle. Then construct the segment from that midpoint to the opposite vertex.
   B. Construct the perpendicular from a vertex to the opposite side.
   C. Construct the midpoint of two sides of the triangle. Then construct the segment connecting those two midpoints.
   D. Construct the angle bisector of one angle of the triangle.

---

12. To say that two or more lines, segments, or rays are concurrent means that they all have a single point in common. The perpendicular bisectors of the sides are concurrent. So are the medians, and so are the angle bisectors.

13. a. 90°
   b. 45°
   c. 120°

14. Answers may vary. Sample: Construct a circle. Use the same radius and construct a circle with center on the first circle. Mark one of the points where the circles intersect. Use this point and the centers of the circles as the vertices of an equilateral triangle.

15. Answers may vary. Sample:

m	n
2	12
24	1
6	4
-3	-8
48	0.5

Open Response

You will need a compass and straightedge to complete these problems.

10. Give three examples of geometric invariants that you learned in this chapter. Think about lengths, angle measures, areas (and ratios of those quantities), collinearity, concurrence, shape, and so on. Describe each invariant carefully. Include pictures with each descriptions.

11. Which of the figures below can you fold into a closed solid? For each one, name the solid or describe its features.

a.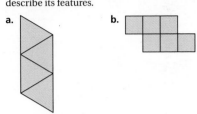

b.

c.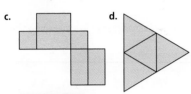

d.

e.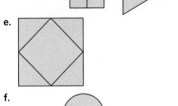

f.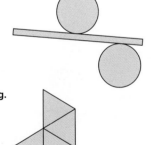

g.

12. Describe what the term *concurrence* means. Then give three examples of concurrences in triangles. Draw a figure to represent each. Explain which segments in each drawing are concurrent.

13. Angle *NMA* is inscribed in circle *T* in the following ways. In each case, what is the measure of ∠*NMA*?

  a. ∠*NMA* is inscribed in a semicircle.

  b. ∠*NMA* is inscribed in a $\frac{3}{4}$ circle.

  c. ∠*NMA* is inscribed in a $\frac{1}{3}$ circle.

14. Use a compass and straightedge to construct an equilateral triangle. Describe how you completed this construction.

15. Make a table that shows the following invariant relationship: *m* and *n* are numbers such that their product *mn* is invariant. (Choose a specific value of *mn*.)

16. a. To construct a parallel line with geometry software, which two pieces of information do you need? Explain.

  b. To construct a circle with geometry software, which two pieces of information do you need? Explain.

17. Explain why the angle bisectors of a triangle are concurrent.

18. Imagine that you construct △*ABC* using geometry software so that *A* and *B* are fixed. You can move *C*, but $\overline{AC}$ remains congruent to $\overline{BC}$. (*Hint:* Along what path can you move *C*?)

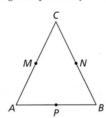

The midpoints of the sides of △*ABC* are *M*, *N*, and *P*. Connect them and shade △*MNP*. Find the ratio $\frac{\text{area } \triangle MNP}{\text{area } \triangle ABC}$. Is this ratio invariant?

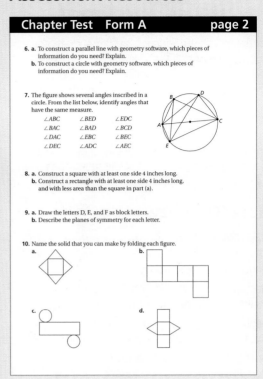
16. a. You need a line and a point. There are infinitely many lines parallel to a given line ℓ, so in addition to the line ℓ you need information that allows you to settle on one particular line parallel to ℓ.

  b. The center point and the radius. There are infinitely many circles that have a given point as center. The radius allows you to settle on a particular one of these.

17. A point inside a triangle is on the bisector of an angle of the triangle if and only if it is equidistant from the sides of the angle. The bisectors of two angles of the triangle must intersect. The point of intersection of the two bisectors is therefore equidistant from the sides of all three angles and therefore is on the bisector of the third angle.

18. $\frac{1}{4}$; yes

Chapter 2
Congruence and Proof

This chapter is an introduction to formal mathematical proof centered around the idea of congruence. Students come to understand what congruence is, how you define it, and the conditions that are necessary to prove congruence. They construct proofs of congruence under various conditions. It is important for students to understand the congruence relationship. It is even more vital that they understand deductive reasoning, which is at the heart of a proof.

Chapter Overview

- Investigation 2A, *The Congruence Relationship,* introduces the definition of congruence and the symbol that represents it.

- Investigation 2B, *Proof and Parallel Lines,* centers around the idea of proving statements.

- Investigation 2C, *Writing Proofs,* presents several ways of writing and coming up with a proof.

- Investigation 2D, *Quadrilaterals and Their Properties,* allows students to apply their knowledge of proofs to properties of quadrilaterals.

For more information on the investigations, see
- Chapter Road Map, pp. 70, 71
- Investigation Road Maps, pp. 72, 88, 114, 142

PROJECT The project near the end of the chapter is optional. You can assign the Project at any time during the chapter depending on how often and how long you feel students should work on it.

Pacing Suggestions and Materials

Investigation 2A *The Congruence Relationship*

DAY	LESSON	HOMEWORK
1	2.1 Getting Started Core: 1, 2, 3, 4 Optional: none	Core: 5, 6 Optional: 8, 9, 10, 11, 12; Extension: 7
2	2.2 Length, Measure, and Congruence Core: 1, 2, 3, 4, 5, 6 Optional: none	Core: 8, 9 Optional: 7, 14; Extension: 10, 11, 12, 13
3	2.3 Corresponding Parts Core: 1, 2, 3 Optional: 4	Core: 5, 6, 7, 9 Optional: 8, 10, 11
4	2.4 Triangle Congruence—Day 1 Core: 1 Optional: none	Core: 2 Optional: none
5	2.4 Triangle Congruence—Day 2 Core: 3, 4, 6, 7 Optional: 5	Core: 8, 9, 10, 11, 12, 13, 14, 16 Optional: 17; Extension: 15

Investigation 2B *Proof and Parallel Lines*

DAY	LESSON	HOMEWORK
1	2.5 Getting Started Core: 1, 2 Optional: none	Core: 4, 5, 6 Optional: 3, 7, 8, 9
2	2.6 Deduction and Proof Core: 1, 2 Optional: none	Core: 3, 4, 5, 6 Optional: 7
3	2.7 Parallel Lines—Day 1 Core: 1 Optional: none	Core: 5, 6 Optional: none
4	2.7 Parallel Lines—Day 2 Core: 2, 3, 4 Optional: none	Core: 7, 8, 9 Optional: 10, 11, 12
5	2.8 The Parallel Postulate—Day 1 Core: 1 Optional: 2	Core: 8, 9 Optional: none
6	2.8 The Parallel Postulate—Day 2 Core: 4, 5, 6 Optional: 3, 7	Core: 11, 12 Optional: 13,15 Extension: 10,14

NOTES	MATERIALS
	• protractors (optional) • rulers (optional) • Blackline Master 2.2 (optional)
	• protractors • rulers • Blackline Masters 2.3A–B
If you choose to complete this lesson in two days, stop after the For You to Do.	• protractors • rulers
An optional activity is outlined later in these notes as a way to give students additional practice.	

NOTES	MATERIALS
	• geometry software • protractors • rulers
	• protractors • Blackline Master 2.6
If you choose to spend two days on this lesson, work through the whole lesson once on the first day and assign the suggested homework.	• Blackline Master 2.7
If this is the second day for this lesson, give students a chance to read through the whole lesson again before working on the remaining exercises.	
Work through the For You to Do on the first day.	• geometry software
Have students re-read what you were able to get through on day 5 and go on to prove the triangle angle sum theorem.	• geometry software

Mathematics Background

EXPERIENCE BEFORE FORMALIZATION For centuries, the development of geometry in school has followed the Euclidean tradition. Geometry is presented as a system in which you deduce results through a long chain of reasoning, starting from a few axioms. Proofs appear in a polished form, after you have done the work. This serves to mask the techniques mathematicians use to devise proof.

In fact, many students think that the way to write a proof is to state the given, leave a few spaces, and state the conclusion. Then, fill in the spaces with seemingly arbitrary statements and reasons (which students probably think they have to memorize). They need help to understand from where the logical argument of a completed proof comes. This is the goal of this chapter.

CME Project—Geometry adopts a somewhat different organization in which students experience ideas before they formalize them. Students tinker with the conditions described in a theorem and use some specific strategies, such as working backwards or making a flow chart, to gain the insights that allow them to come up with the reasoning necessary for the formal proof. This is faithful to the practice of mathematics where the conception of a proof is separate from its presentation. Students learn several techniques for making the logical connections needed to come up with a proof. Then, they consider the much easier task of presenting their arguments.

WHY ARE PROOFS NECESSARY? Proof is central to mathematics, but not just because it is traditional. You cannot solve some problems in any other way, such as a question about an infinite class of objects. It is impossible to check each case that every angle inscribed in a semicircle is a right angle. Similarly, it does not make sense to check that every instance of the statement "the sum of two odd integers is even" is true.

A proof shows more than the fact that something happens. It shows *why* it happens, in the sense that it shows how it follows from other established results.

The search for proof often leads to new insights and new results. For instance, connecting in order the midpoints of a quadrilateral produces a parallelogram. The proof of this fact can lead to the understanding of when that parallelogram will be a rhombus.

THE ROLE OF AXIOMS Mathematics today is a vast enterprise. It is next to impossible in one person's lifetime to develop the background needed to master every specialty and every research area. Most mathematicians concentrate on one circle of ideas (sometimes for a decade or more) and then move to another. Each subspecialty has its own traditions, style, and often, special sets of axioms. Of course, you can apply the results in one area to other areas.

continued on page 70c

continued from page 70b

In fact, this is often how breakthroughs arise. This means that axioms need to be consistent.

High school mathematics has small areas in which students can specialize, too. Students can experience what it is like to work in a small axiom system. One such area is the theory of congruent triangles. A related area is the theory of parallel lines. This chapter develops both of these theories.

Pacing Suggestions and Materials

Investigation 2C *Writing Proofs*

DAY	LESSON	HOMEWORK
1	2.9 Getting Started Core: 1, 2, 3, 4 Optional: none	Core: 5, 6, 7 Optional: 8a–c; Extension: 8d
2	2.10 What Does a Proof Look Like?—Day 1 Core: 1 Optional: none	Core: 5, 6, 7 Optional: none
3	2.10 What Does a Proof Look Like?—Day 2 Core: 2, 3, 4 Optional: none	Core: 8, 9, 11 Optional: 10, 12
4	2.11 Analyzing the Statement to Prove Core: 1, 2 Optional: none	Core: 3, 4, 5, 6, 7, 8, 9 Optional: 10
5	2.12 Analysis of a Proof—Day 1 Core: 1 Optional: none	Core: 4, 5 Optional: 6
6	2.12 Analysis of a Proof—Day 2 Core: 2, 3 Optional: none	Core: 7, 8, 9 Optional: 10, 11
7	2.13 The Reverse List Core: 1, 2 Optional: none	Core: 3, 4, 5, 6, 7, 9 Optional: 10; Extension: 8
8	2.14 Practicing Your Proof-Writing Skills Core: 1, 2, 6 Optional: 3, 4, 5	Core: 8, 9, 10, 11, 14, 15 Optional: 7, 12, 13, 18, 19; Extension: 16, 17

Investigation 2D *Quadrilaterals and Their Properties*

DAY	LESSON	HOMEWORK
1	2.15 Getting Started Core: 1, 2, 3 Optional: none	Core: 4, 5, 6, 7, 8 Optional: 10, 11, 12; Extension: 9
2	2.16 General Quadrilaterals Core: 1, 2, 3 Optional: none	Core: 4, 5, 6, 7 Optional: 9; Extension: 8
3	2.17 Properties of Quadrilaterals Core: 1, 2, 3, 4, 5, 6, 7, 8, 9, 10, 11 Optional: none	Core: 18, 19, 20 Optional: 12, 13, 14, 15, 16, 17, 21, 22, 23, 24
4	2.18 Parallelograms—Day 1 Core: 6, 7 Optional: none; Extension: 8	Core: 29, 31, 32 Optional: none; Extension: 30
5	2.18 Parallelograms—Day 2 Core: 1, 2, 3, 4, 5 Optional: none	Core: 15,16, 17 Optional: 9, 10, 11, 12, 13, 14, 18, 19, 20, 21 23, 24, 25, 26, 27, 28, 33, 34, 35, 36, 37
6	2.19 Classifying Parallelograms Core: 1, 2, 7, 8, 9 Optional: 3, 4, 5, 6, 10, 11, 12, 13	Core: 14, 15, 16, 17, 21, 22 Optional: 18, 19, 20, 23, 24, 25

NOTES	MATERIALS
	• protractors • rulers
If you choose to complete this lesson over two days, carefully review the homework exercises (5 and 6) and give students ample time to work on the remaining exercises in class.	
	• Blackline Master 2.11
Work through the Example, For You to Do and For Discussion about Visual Scan on the first day.	• protractors • rulers
After reviewing the homework exercises, present the Flow Chart method.	• Blackline Master 2.12
Working through these problems may take two days.	• compasses • protractors • rulers

NOTES	MATERIALS
	• compasses • protractors • rulers
On the first day of this lesson, work through Theorem 2.8.	• geometry software • scissors • Blackline Master MC5
	• Blackline Master 2.19

Developing Students' Mathematical Habits

Key habits in this chapter include mixing experiment with deduction, looking for invariants, and performing thought experiments. While teaching, reinforce these techniques:

- Use insights gained from experiment and explicit techniques used by mathematicians to build the ideas behind proofs.
- Develop a theory of congruent triangles to prove that two triangles are congruent and list the consequences when you know triangles are congruent.
- Develop a theory of parallel lines to prove that two lines are parallel and list the consequences when you know lines are parallel.
- "Work backwards" from a conclusion to a hypothesis as a thought experiment to write a proof.

Chapter **2**

Investigations at a Glance

2A The Congruence Relationship

2B Proof and Parallel Lines

2C Writing Proofs

2D Quadrilaterals and Their Properties

Chapter Road Map

INVESTIGATION 2A, *The Congruence Relationship,* introduces students to the notion of congruence and the symbol that represents it. Students learn about the importance of using correct notation when comparing two congruent figures. The last lesson in this investigation develops the triangle congruence postulates and introduces the idea that congruent parts of congruent triangles are congruent, or CPCTC.

INVESTIGATION 2B, *Proof and Parallel Lines,* stresses the important difference between experimentation and proof. Leading up to the statement of the Parallel Postulate, students prove two important theorems. The Alternate Interior Parallel Theorem (AIP Theorem) states that if two lines are cut by a transversal and the alternate interior angles formed are congruent, then the lines are parallel. The Parallel Alternate Interior Theorem (PAI Theorem) states that if parallel lines are cut by a transversal, then the alternate interior angles are congruent.

Congruence and Proof

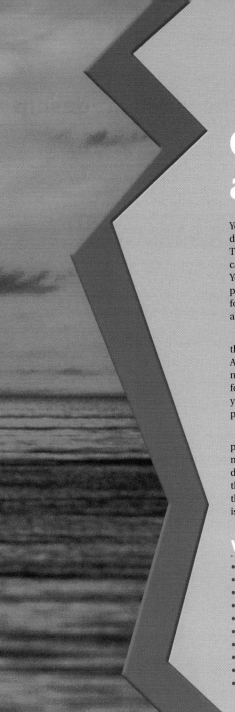

You may have heard the saying, "Red sky at night, sailor's delight. Red sky at morning, sailors take warning." Through years of experience, sailors learned that they can use this saying, within limits, to predict the weather. You can use your own experiences, as well, to make predictions or conjectures. After you complete the following activity, you will be able to make a conjecture about the sum of the measures of the angles of a triangle.

Draw a large triangle on paper and cut it out. Tear off the angles. Place the vertices of the three angles together. Arrange the sides of the angles edge to edge, so there are no gaps. One edge of your new figure should appear to form a straight angle, which measures 180°. But how can you be sure? You can measure the three angles with a protractor, but measurement is not exact.

For problems like this, you can use mathematical proof to verify your results. Mathematical proof is a method that relies on certain assumptions, precise definitions, and logical deductions to prove new facts. In this chapter, you will prove, among many other results, that the sum of the measures of the angles of a triangle is 180°.

Vocabulary and Notation

- alternate interior angles
- consecutive angles
- corresponding angles
- equiangular
- exterior angle
- isosceles triangle
- isosceles trapezoid
- kite
- parallelogram
- quadrilateral
- rhombus
- scalene triangle
- supplementary angles
- transversal
- trapezoid
- vertical angles
- ≅ (is congruent to)
- ∥ (is parallel to)
- ⊥ (is perpendicular to)
- AB (the length of $\overline{AB}$)

Chapter Vocabulary and Notation

The following list gives key vocabulary and notation used in the chapter. Selected new vocabulary and notation items are shown in boldface on the student page.

- alternate interior angles, p. 99
- assumption, p. 84
- base angles, p. 149
- bases, p. 147
- closed figure, p. 144
- concave quadrilaterals, p. 145
- conclusion, p. 123
- congruent, ≅, p. 73
- consecutive angles, p. 99
- converse, p. 105
- corollary, p. 100
- corresponding angles, p. 99
- corresponding parts, p. 79
- counterexample, p. 122
- diagonal, p. 143
- equiangular, p. 124
- exterior angle, p. 90
- hypothesis, p. 123
- isosceles trapezoid, p. 149
- isosceles triangle, p. 120
- kite, p. 147
- legs, p. 120
- parallel lines, ∥, pp. 98, 99
- parallelogram, p. 151
- postulate, p. 84
- proof, p. 115
- quadrilateral, p. 144
- rectangle, p. 157
- rhombus, p. 157
- scalene triangle, p. 136
- self-intersecting figure, p. 145
- side, p. 144
- skew quadrilateral, p. 145
- square, p. 157
- supplementary angles, p. 102
- transversal, p. 89
- trapezoid, p. 147
- trisected, p. 155
- vertex angle, p. 120
- vertex/vertices, p. 144
- vertical angles, p. 99
- AB (the length of segment AB), p. 75
- ≇ (is not congruent to), p. 106
- ⊥ (is perpendicular to), p. 77
- $\overline{JK}$ (segment with endpoints J and K), p. 75

Chapter Technology

Support for the use of technology is available in the Technology Handbook. See p. 172.

INVESTIGATION 2B *Geometry Software*

- **LESSON 2.5** Construct a pair of parallel lines and a transversal, construct a pair of intersecting lines and a transversal, and study the angle relationships, p. 89. Draw a line and a point not on the line, and study the properties of parallel and perpendicular lines, p. 90.

- **LESSON 2.8** Construct two parallel lines and a moveable transversal, and look for invariants in the measures of the angles formed, p. 105.

INVESTIGATION 2C *Geometry Software*

- **LESSON 2.14** Show that the perimeter of the parallelogram formed by drawing lines from a point along the base parallel to the congruent sides of an isosceles triangle is invariant, p. 137.

INVESTIGATION 2D *Geometry Software*

- **LESSON 2.18** Construct and compare the properties of the diagonals of parallelograms, p. 152.

INVESTIGATION 2C, *Writing Proofs,* presents several ways of writing a proof, and more importantly, several ways to come up with a proof. There are many exercises for students to work through in this investigation, so it is the lengthiest in this chapter. Many of these exercises are core exercises. Perhaps the most important of these exercises is a formal proof of the statement that the sum of the measures of the angles of a triangle is 180°.

INVESTIGATION 2D, *Quadrilaterals and Their Properties,* has students apply their skills of analysis and exposition to the proof of some important properties of quadrilaterals. At the same time, students will deepen their understanding of the relationship between a statement and its converse.

Investigation Overview

This investigation introduces the notion of congruence as meaning "same shape and size." Students learn standard mathematical notation that they can use to communicate about congruent figures.

The following two questions are the focus of this investigation.

- If two figures are congruent, what do you know about the measures of their corresponding parts?
- If two figures have certain measures that are equal, are the figures congruent?

You may wish to assign Questions 1–3 for students to think and write about during the investigation.

Learning Goals

- Define congruence.
- Interpret statements about congruent figures and use the correct notation to write statements.
- Test for congruence in triangles.

Habits and Skills

- Name corresponding parts of congruent figures.
- Use triangle congruence postulates to show that two triangles are congruent.
- Make logical inferences to draw conclusions about congruence.

Investigation 2A

The Congruence Relationship

In *The Congruence Relationship*, you will study congruent figures—figures that are the same shape and the same size. To understand mathematics or the arts, history or psychology, science or social relationships, you look at how things differ and also at how they are the same. Mathematics looks at quantities, relationships in space, ways to classify items, and certain processes that are used. The focus of this investigation is shape and what it means when two shapes are the same.

By the end of this investigation, you will be able to answer questions like these.

1. What does it mean to say that two figures are congruent?

2. Why is it important to keep track of corresponding parts in congruent figures?

3. What are some ways to prove that two triangles are congruent?

You will learn how to

- define congruence

- interpret statements about congruent figures and use the correct notation to write statements

- test for congruence in triangles

You will develop these habits and skills:

- Name corresponding parts of congruent figures.

- Use triangle congruence postulates to show that two triangles are congruent.

- Make logical inferences to draw conclusions about congruence.

Some houses in master-planned developments are the same shape and size.

Investigation Road Map

LESSON 2.1, *Getting Started,* introduces the concept of congruence. Students think about how to decide whether two figures are congruent. They also practice using correct notation and translating mathematical statements into English sentences.

LESSON 2.2, *Length, Measure, and Congruence,* has students describe geometric objects in more than one way. Students distinguish between different descriptions, and decide which way is best in a given situation.

LESSON 2.3, *Corresponding Parts,* introduces the tick mark as a way to indicate corresponding parts of figures. Students also learn that corresponding parts of congruent figures are congruent.

LESSON 2.4, *Triangle Congruence,* explores corresponding parts of congruent triangles. Students investigate triangle congruence postulates.

Mathematical language is clear and precise. Each word has exactly one meaning. Sometimes you invent new words. Sometimes you modify the meanings of familiar words. In either case, everyone must agree on which words to use and what those words mean.

For You to Explore

1. As a class, decide what you will mean by this statement: "These two figures are the same."

   To make a wise decision about the meaning of the statement, you might consider some specific cases. For example, look at the four figures below. Decide which figures you would call the same.

   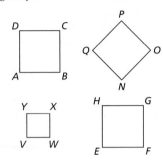

2. In some ways, all of the objects above are the same. Explain.

3. In some ways, they are all different. Explain.

   Mathematical language uses several words to describe two figures that are the same. For a start, we say that two figures are **congruent** if they have the same shape and the same size, regardless of location or orientation. But size and shape are not very precise terms, so we will develop a better definition.

   △*ABC* is congruent to △*A'B'C'*, but they have different orientations. If you walk from *A* to *B* to *C* to *A*, you turn *left* twice. If you walk from *A'* to *B'* to *C'* to *A'*, you turn *right* twice.

   Congruence is such an important mathematical relationship that it has its own symbol, ≅. In Problem 1 above, squares *ABCD* and *EFGH* are congruent. You write □*ABCD* ≅ □*EFGH*.

4. You can think of the congruence symbol as composed of two parts: = and ~. What aspects of congruence might these two parts represent?

Answers

For You To Explore

1. Answers may vary. Sample: Two figures are the same if they have the same shape and the same size.

2. All are squares.

3. Answers may vary. Sample: They have different locations and labels.

4. Answers may vary. Sample: = means same size, and ~ means same shape.

Lesson Overview

GOALS
- Warm up to the ideas of the investigation.
- Define congruence.

This lesson emphasizes that mathematical language is clear and precise. Students discuss what it means to say that "two figures are the same." They think about how to decide whether two figures are the same. They learn that when two figures have the same shape and the same size, the figures are congruent. Students also learn the notation used to express congruence, and they see notation used in mathematical statements.

FOR YOU TO EXPLORE	VOCABULARY
• Core: 1, 2, 3, 4	• congruent
• Optional: none	• ≅

HOMEWORK
- Core: 5, 6
- Optional: 8, 9, 10, 11, 12
- Extension: 7

Launch

Complete Problem 1 as a class. Have students study the figures. Lead a discussion about the ways in which the figures are the same and the ways in which they are different.

Explore

Work on the For You to Explore problems as a class. The goal is to have students experience some of the important concepts that they will learn later in this investigation. This lesson starts students thinking about mathematical language and teaches them that a slight difference in notation can have a big impact on the meaning of a statement.

For You To Explore

PROBLEMS 1–4 explore the idea that congruence describes a relationship among figures. That is, it groups figures in sets in which the members are related. They are related by being congruent. Certain properties do not have to be the same in order for figures to be congruent. Here are some examples:

- Figures may be in different locations and still be congruent.
- Figures may be in different positions (upside down, turned, and so on) and still be congruent.
- You may draw figures in different colors, and they are still congruent.

Congruent does not mean *exactly the same*. It means *the same in certain aspects*. Exploring congruence in this way develops students' intuitions about the meaning of size and shape. They are the two properties that congruent figures share.

Wrap Up

Write the word *congruence* and the symbol that represents it on the board. Discuss the definition of congruence in the student text and have your class explain the definition in its own words.

Exercises

HOMEWORK
- Core: 5, 6
- Optional: 8, 9, 10, 11, 12
- Extension: 7

Maintain Your Skills

EXERCISES 8–12 use symbols that students should become familiar with. These symbols include ≅ (congruent), ∠ (angle), and △ (triangle).

Exercises *Practicing Habits of Mind*

On Your Own

You can use *congruent* to describe figures in any number of dimensions. Here are some examples.

- 1 dimension: two line segments that are the same length
- 2 dimensions: two triangles that are the same shape and same size
- 3 dimensions: two spheres with the same radius, or two tetrahedrons that are the same shape and same size

Go Online
Video Tutor
PHSchool.com
Web Code: bee-0775

5. **Write About It** Assume you can use any tool or method. Describe how you can decide whether a pair of each of the following are congruent: line segments; angles; triangles; rectangular solids (boxes); cones; and cylinders.

One class chose the following test for congruence. Given two shapes drawn on paper, if you can cut out one and fit it exactly on top of the other shape (nothing hanging over above or sticking out below), then the two shapes are congruent. Or, two figures are congruent if they differ only in position.

6. Can you use this test to determine whether two line segments are congruent?

7. **Take It Further** How can you adapt the test so that you can use it to determine whether three-dimensional objects such as spheres or rectangular boxes are congruent?

> The word *congruence* comes from the Latin word *congruens*, which means "to meet together." If you superimpose one figure on another and they meet edge to edge, then they are congruent.

Maintain Your Skills

Translate these congruence statements into English sentences.

8. △*TRL* ≅ △*MTV*

9. $\overline{TO}$ ≅ $\overline{BE}$

10. □*BARK* ≅ □*MEOW*

11. △*LMO* ≅ △*L'M'O'*

12. ∠*ABC* ≅ ∠*ABD*

Are these two gloves congruent?

Answers

Exercises

5. See back of book.

6. yes

7. Answers may vary. Sample: For spheres, cut through their centers with a straight slice and then compare the radii of the cross sections. For rectangular boxes, make a net that wraps perfectly around each box.

8. Triangle *TRL* is congruent to triangle *MTV*.

9. Segment *TO* is congruent to segment *BE*.

10. Square *BARK* is congruent to square *MEOW*.

11. Triangle *LMO* is congruent to triangle *L'M'O'*.

12. Angle *ABC* is congruent to angle *ABD*.

Length, Measure, and Congruence

You can describe a single geometric object in more than one way. For example, you can refer to a line segment by its name or by its length. In the coordinate plane, you can also refer to a line segment by its slope. In geometry, it is important to make the distinction between a geometric object, such as a point or a segment or a circle, and a numerical value that describes it.

Symbols are designed to help make these distinctions. For example, the symbol $\overline{JK}$, with an overbar, represents the line segment with endpoints J and K. The symbol JK, without the overbar, represents the length of $\overline{JK}$.

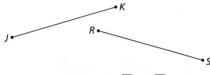

two segments: $\overline{JK}$ and $\overline{RS}$

You can compare two shapes to determine whether they are congruent. You can also compare two numbers to determine whether they are equal. You cannot, however, compare a shape to a number.

Minds in Action   episode 2

Sasha and Tony discuss the seven statements below that seem to describe the two segments at the right.

- $JK \cong RS$
- $\overline{JK} \cong \overline{RS}$
- $JK = RS$
- $\overline{JK} = \overline{RS}$
- $JK = 1$ inch
- $\overline{JK} = 1$
- $\overline{JK} \cong 1$ inch

Sasha The sentence $JK \cong RS$ makes no sense!

Tony What do you mean?

Sasha Well, $\cong$ is the symbol for *congruent*, right?

Tony Yes.

Sasha So, when you use that symbol you're supposed to be comparing objects. Without the little line over them, JK and RS aren't segments. They're just lengths.

Tony That's being a little picky, don't you think?

Sasha No, not really. You have to make a distinction between things that are *equal*, like the lengths JK and RS, and things that are *congruent*, like $\overline{JK}$ and $\overline{RS}$.

Tony So, the statement $JK = RS$ is correct, right? Because it says that the two *measurements* are equal, and numbers can be equal.

Sasha Yes.

Lesson Overview

GOAL

- Interpret statements about congruent figures and write statements using the correct notation.

This lesson highlights the importance in notation when writing mathematical statements. Students should practice using the correct notations consistently from the beginning. This will help ensure that they not only write accurate statements, but that they understand what the notation represents. The difference between a figure and a figure's measurement and the difference between congruence and equality are significant.

CHECK YOUR UNDERSTANDING	HOMEWORK
• Core: 1, 2, 3, 4, 5, 6	• Core: 8, 9
• Optional: none	• Optional: 7, 14
	• Extension: 10, 11, 12, 13

MATERIALS	VOCABULARY
• protractors	• JK
• rulers	• $\overline{JK}$
• Blackline Master 2.2 (optional)	• $\perp$

Launch

Discuss the difference between writing JK and $\overline{JK}$ with your students. Then, have them read the dialog between Sasha and Tony. It emphasizes the importance of using correct notation.

Explore

Use For Discussion Problems 1 and 2 to summarize the dialog and check for understanding.

Minds in Action

The statement $JK \cong RS$ does not make sense. JK and RS refer to lengths, while the congruence symbol applies only to shapes. The statement $\overline{JK} \cong \overline{RS}$ is correct. It means that two line segments are congruent. The statement $JK = RS$ is also correct. It is correct that two numbers are equal. This statement means that the length of $\overline{JK}$ equals the length of $\overline{RS}$.

Many students will say that the statement $\overline{JK} = \overline{RS}$ is incorrect. Their reasoning is that two line segments cannot be equal; they can only be congruent. You may want to assign a more subtle meaning to this statement. Line segments are sets of points, and two sets of points (or of anything) are equal if they contain exactly the same elements. So this statement can mean that line segments $\overline{JK}$ and $\overline{RS}$ are the same set of points. Statements like this may be too advanced for students learning elementary geometry.

The statement $JK = 1$ inch means that the length of $\overline{JK}$ is 1, or that the distance from J to K is 1. This is a valid statement. The statement $\overline{JK} = 1$, however, is not valid. The statement $\overline{JK} = 1$ inch is incorrect because 1 inch indicates a measurement. A segment cannot be congruent to a measurement.

For Discussion

PROBLEM 1 uses the fact that all segments have the same shape. So, if they have the same length, you can superimpose one onto the other. Therefore, segments with the same length are congruent. By the definition of congruence, if two segments are congruent, they have the same length. Note that Problem 2 is the converse of Problem 1.

For Discussion

State whether each of the statements that Sasha and Tony discussed is correct. If a statement is *not* correct, explain why.

1. If two segments are the same length, are they congruent? Explain.

2. If two segments are congruent, are they the same length? Explain.

The symbols for an angle and its measure are different from the symbols for a segment and its length, but the distinction is the same. An angle is a geometric object. Its measure is a number.

In the figure at the right, write $\angle NPQ$, $\angle QPN$, or $\angle P$ to refer to the first angle. Write $m\angle NPQ$ to refer to its measure.

$$\angle NPQ \cong \angle RST$$
or
$$m\angle NPQ = m\angle RST$$

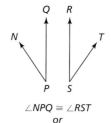

Exercises Practicing Habits of Mind

Check Your Understanding

1. Decide whether each statement below describes geometric objects or numbers. If a statement describes geometric objects, state whether points, segments, or other objects are explicitly mentioned.

   a. $JK = RS$

   b. $\overline{JK} \cong \overline{RS}$

   c. $\overline{JK}$ and $\overline{RS}$ are the same length.

   d. The distance from J to K is the same as the distance from R to S.

2. **a.** Explain why the following statement is incorrect: $\angle NPQ = 56.6°$

   b. Write the following statement symbolically: Angle NPQ has a measure of 56.6 degrees.

3. If $m\angle NPQ = m\angle RST$, are the two angles congruent? Explain.

4. If $\angle NPQ \cong \angle RST$, are the measures of the two angles equal? Explain.

5. Explain whether the following statement is true or false: If two triangles are both congruent to the same triangle, then they are congruent to each other.

Answers

For Discussion

1–2. The answer to both questions is *yes*. Congruence of segments and equality of their measures are equivalent.

Exercises

1. **a.** numbers
   b. segments
   c. segments and numbers
   d. points and numbers

2. **a.** $\angle NPQ$ is a geometric figure, and 56.6° is a numerical measure.
   b. $m\angle NPQ = 56.6°$

3. Yes; if two angles have equal measures, then you can place one angle on top of the other so that they fit exactly.

4. Yes; if you can put one angle on top of another to get a perfect match, then the protractor positions can also be matched exactly when you measure them.

6. In $\triangle ABD$ at the right, $AD = BD$, $\overline{DC}$ is an altitude (that is, $\overline{DC} \perp \overline{AB}$), and F and E are midpoints. Decide whether each of the following statements is *true*, *false*, or *nonsensical*. Justify your answers. You may use measuring tools if you want.

Remember...
The symbol $\perp$ means "is perpendicular to."

a. $FD = DE$

b. $\overline{FD} = \overline{DE}$

c. $\overline{FD} = 1.5$ cm

d. $\angle ACD = 90°$

e. $\triangle DFB = \triangle DEA$

f. $\angle ACD$ is a right angle.

g. $\overline{FA} \cong \overline{BE}$

h. $\overline{FA} \cong \overline{BD}$

i. $\angle ADC = \angle BDC$

j. $m\angle ADC = m\angle BDC$

k. $m\angle DFB \cong m\angle DEA$

l. $\angle DFB \cong \angle DEA$

m. $\triangle DCA \cong \angle DCB$

n. $\triangle DCA \cong \angle EAD$

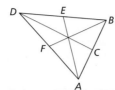

On Your Own

7. Define the following words or symbols.

a. congruent   **b.** $\cong$ **c.** $\perp$

8. Standardized Test Prep Anna has a simple rule for deciding which symbol to use.

Objects are congruent. Measurements of objects are equal.

Which of the following statements is NOT written correctly according to Anna's rule?

A. $\overline{DF} \cong \overline{RT}$

B. $m\angle CSD \cong m\angle BSL$

C. $\angle ADF \cong \angle WZM$

D. $AC = FH$

9. Are all equilateral triangles congruent? Explain.

Polyominoes are shapes that are made of squares. The sides of polyominoes meet edge to edge with no gaps or overlaps. The three shapes on the left are polyominoes. The three shapes on the right are not polyominoes, because the squares do not meet edge-to-edge.

polyominoes   not polyominoes

Congruent polyominoes that have different orientations are not different polyominoes.

---

5. Yes; if two triangles are congruent to the same triangle, then they can all be superimposed onto one another so that they fit exactly.

6. a–n. See back of book.

7. a. A pair of figures are congruent if they have exactly the same size and shape.

b. The symbol $\cong$ means "is congruent to."

c. The symbol $\perp$ means "is perpendicular to."

8. B

9. No; equilateral triangles are not congruent if their side lengths are different.

Wrap Up

Before assigning the Check Your Understanding exercises, make sure students understand the difference between comparing two objects and comparing two measures.

Assessment Resources

Lesson Quiz 2.2

1. Explain whether the following statement is true or false. If two angles are each congruent to the same angle, then they are congruent to each other.

2. Complete the following statements given $m\angle DBE = m\angle EBC$ and B is the midpoint of $\overline{AC}$.

a. $\angle DBE \cong$ _____

b. $AB =$ _____

c. $m\angle ABD + m\angle$ _____ $= 180°$

d. $\frac{1}{2}m\angle DBC = m\angle$ _____

3. Are all right triangles congruent? Explain.

Exercises

HOMEWORK
- Core: 8, 9
- Optional: 7, 14
- Extension: 10, 11, 12, 13

Check Your Understanding

EXERCISE 6 is a good indicator of whether students understand the difference between comparing two objects and comparing two measures.

On Your Own

EXERCISE 9 Students must know the properties of equilateral triangles for this exercise.

EXERCISES 10–13 involve combinatorial geometry, the counting of sets of geometric objects. The point of the discussion, however, is not really the number of sets. It is the question of when two objects are "the same."

Technically, the definition of *polyomino* should state that these are planar figures. If students consider shapes not lying in a single plane, then many more polyominoes are possible. The question about tetrominoes will bring up the question of leaving the plane for space quite naturally.

EXERCISE 11 There are only two trominoes. One tromino consists of three squares in a row, and the other forms an "L" shape.

continued on p. 78

continued from p. 77

EXERCISE 12 The difficult tetromino for most students is the one in which you can flip one tetromino to the position of another tetromino. Are these tetrominoes the same? In this course, and in most work in elementary geometry, you consider two figures congruent that differ only in orientation.

Maintain Your Skills

EXERCISE 14 Students must judge whether several pairs of figures are congruent. Students may choose to measure the figures, or you can provide them with a copy of Blackline Master 2.2 so they can cut out one figure to see whether they can lay it on top of the other figure with no overlap.

Additional Resources

PRINT RESOURCES
• Solution Manual
• Practice Workbook
• Assessment Resources
• Teaching Resources

TECHNOLOGY
• Interactive Textbook
• TeacherExpress CD-ROM
• **Exam***View* CD-ROM
• **PHSchool.com**
  – Additional Practice
  – Mid-Chapter and
    Chapter Tests
  – Video Tutors
  – Vocabulary Puzzles

Additional Practice

Given triangle *JLK*, decide whether the following statements are *true, false,* or *nonsensical.*

1. *m∠KLJ* = 90°	2. *JM* ≅ *MK*
3. *JM* = *MK*	4. *∠JML* ≅ *LMK*
5. *m∠MJL* = *m∠MLJ*	6. *LK* ≅ *LM*
7. *m∠LMK* = *m∠LKJ*	8. *∠J* ≅ *∠KLJ*

For Exercises 9 and 10, use the congruent triangles below.

9. List all the corresponding parts.

10. Write three correct congruence statements.

11. Explain the difference between congruency and equality when comparing two figures.

12. Are all squares congruent? Explain.

13. Draw triangles *PIN* and *MAT* so that △*PIN* ≅ △*MAT*. Mark congruent corresponding parts.

Practice: For Lesson 2.2, assign Exercises 1–8.

---

10. **Dominoes:** How many different polyominoes can you make with two squares?

11. **Trominoes:** How many different polyominoes can you make with three squares?

12. **Tetrominoes:** How many different polyominoes can you make with four squares?

13. Combine the T tetromino (polyomino with 4 squares) at the right with another tetromino to make an eight-square polyomino. How many tetromino shapes can you combine with the T tetromino to get this shape?

Maintain Your Skills

14. Assume you can use any tool or method. Describe how you can decide whether the figures in each pair are congruent.

a.
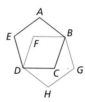
two circles

b.

two artists

c.

two pentagons,
ABCDE and *BGHDF*

d.

two bent arrows

e.

two stars

f.
two snowflakes

Go Online
PHSchool.com

For additional practice,
go to **Web Code: bea-0202**

Answers

10. one

11. two

12. five

13. Check students' work.

14. Answers may vary. Samples are given.
    a. Measure the radii of the circles.
    b. Fold along the vertical line halfway between the two figures to see if they match.

c. Fold along the line through *B* and *D* to see if the figures match.

d. Trace the left arrow onto a piece of paper. Rotate the traced figure and slide it on top of the one on the right.

e. Trace the left star onto a piece of paper. Slide the traced figure on top of the one on the right.

f. Trace the left snowflake onto a piece of paper. Rotate the traced figure and slide it on top of the one on the right.

2.3 Corresponding Parts

It is difficult to draw congruent figures by hand. It is also difficult to decide whether two given figures are congruent. You may not have the tools necessary. Or you may not want to take the time to use those tools. For these reasons, tick marks are very useful.

The picture below shows nine segments, with eight of the segments forming four angles. Like markings indicate which segments are congruent and which angles are congruent. For example, $\overline{ON} \cong \overline{BC}$ and $\angle GHI \cong \angle ABC$.

The small box that marks $\angle DEF$ indicates that $\angle DEF$ is a right angle.

Habits of Mind

Compare. Are two segments that have different numbers of tick marks not congruent?

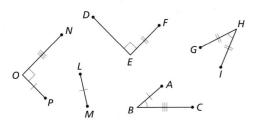

For You to Do

1. What other relationships are indicated in the above diagram?

A congruence statement communicates a large amount of information. The congruence statement $\triangle QRS \cong \triangle XYZ$ tells you that the two triangles are congruent. The orders in which the vertices are written also tells you that

$$\overline{QR} \cong \overline{XY}, \overline{RS} \cong \overline{YZ}, \text{ and } \overline{QS} \cong \overline{XZ},$$

and that

$$\angle Q \cong \angle X, \angle R \cong \angle Y, \text{ and } \angle S \cong \angle Z.$$

You can summarize this matching of parts in a congruence statement by saying that corresponding parts of congruent figures are congruent.

Remember...

For triangles, *parts* means "sides" and "angles".

The sails are congruent. So are their corresponding parts.

For You to Do

1. $\overline{ON} \cong \overline{BC} \cong \overline{GH} \cong \overline{HI}$,
   $\overline{OP} \cong \overline{LM} \cong \overline{AB}, \angle E \cong \angle O$,
   $m\angle O = 90°$

GOAL

• Understand the meaning of corresponding parts.

This lesson shows students how to use tick marks to indicate relationships among parts of figures. Students practice interpreting tick marks on figures. They also write and comprehend congruence statements in mathematical notation. This lesson also emphasizes the importance of paying close attention to the notation.

CHECK YOUR UNDERSTANDING

• Core: 1, 2, 3
• Optional: 4

MATERIALS

• protractors
• rulers
• Blackline Masters 2.3A–B (optional)

HOMEWORK

• Core: 5, 6, 7, 9
• Optional: 8, 10, 11

VOCABULARY

• corresponding parts

Launch

Draw the figures on the board without the tick marks. Have students point out corresponding parts. Draw the tick marks in the appropriate places as students identify them. You may wish to provide copies of Blackline Master 2.3A for students to use.

Explore

You may want students to work together on Problem 1. Watch out for students who might not realize that parts of figures can be congruent even if the figures are not congruent. For example, $\overline{LM} \cong \overline{OP}$ even though $\overline{LM}$ stands alone while $\overline{OP}$ forms an angle with another segment. You may wish to provide copies of Blackline Master 2.3A for students to use.

Wrap Up

End your discussion about corresponding parts by talking about how important the order of vertices is when you name figures in congruence statements. For example, $\triangle ABC \cong \triangle DEF$ may not be the same as $\triangle ABC \cong \triangle DFE$. Ask students if they can think of a case when the order of vertices does not matter. This is the case when you are comparing two triangles that are congruent equilateral triangles.

Assessment Resources

Exercises

HOMEWORK
- Core: 5, 6, 7, 9
- Optional: 8, 10, 11

Check Your Understanding

EXERCISE 4 has a student draw two congruent figures so another student can write the appropriate congruence statement. You might choose to have students repeat this exercise several times.

On Your Own

EXERCISE 7 shows students overlapping triangles and asks them to write congruence statements for triangles they think are congruent. Students probably will not be able to prove any of these congruence statements yet.

Exercises *Practicing Habits of Mind*

Check Your Understanding

1. The two triangles at the right are congruent. Decide whether each congruence statement below is correct. Explain your reasoning.

   a. $\triangle DFA \cong \triangle GCE$ **b.** $\triangle DFA \cong \triangle EGC$

   c. $\triangle DFA \cong \triangle CEG$ **d.** $\triangle DFA \cong \triangle ECG$

   e. $\triangle DFA \cong \triangle GEC$ **f.** $\triangle DFA \cong \triangle CGE$

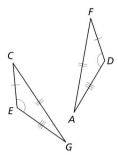

2. Even though only one of the statements above is correct, there are other correct congruence statements for these two triangles. Write two more congruence statements.

3. **Write About It** Explain the meaning of the statement "corresponding parts of congruent figures are congruent." It may help to draw a picture.

4. On a single sheet of paper, draw and label two congruent triangles. Your triangles should be oriented differently. Use marks to indicate congruent segments and congruent angles. Exchange papers with a classmate. Write a congruence statement for your classmate's triangles.

On Your Own

5. Assume $\triangle CAT \cong \triangle DOG$. List all the corresponding parts.

6. **Standardized Test Prep** You are given that $\triangle DFG \cong \triangle CHK$. Which of the following statements is true by "corresponding parts of congruent figures are congruent"?

   A. $m\angle FGD = m\angle CKH$ **B.** $\overline{CH} \cong \overline{DG}$

   C. $DF = HK$ **D.** $\angle FGD \cong \angle KCH$

7. Use the figure below. Some pairs of triangles are *certainly not* congruent. List any pairs of triangles that appear to be congruent.

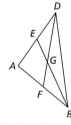

Answers

Exercises

1. Only part (d) is a correct statement. The hash marks in the diagram tell us which segments are known to be congruent. Part (d) is consistent with that information, and the others are not.

2. Answers may vary. Sample: $\triangle DAF \cong \triangle EGC$, $\overline{DF} \cong \overline{EC}$

3. Answers may vary. Sample: If you can place one figure on top of another so that they match perfectly, then the figures are congruent and the parts that match are congruent.

4. Check students' work.

5. $\angle C \cong \angle D$, $\angle A \cong \angle O$, $\angle T \cong \angle G$, $\overline{CA} \cong \overline{DO}$, $\overline{AT} \cong \overline{OG}$, and $\overline{CT} \cong \overline{DG}$

6. A

7. $\triangle AFD \cong \triangle AEB$, $\triangle FBD \cong \triangle EDB$, $\triangle EGD \cong \triangle FGB$

8. You can compare figures in many different ways. Congruence is a *shape* comparison. Area is a *quantitative* comparison. Use what you know about area to answer the following questions.

> Similarity is another shape comparison. Perimeter is another quantitative comparison.

   a. If two polygons are congruent, must they have the same area? Explain.

   b. If two polygons have the same area, must they be congruent? Explain.

9. The figure below contains three congruent triangles.

   a. Write a correct congruence statement for each pair of congruent triangles.

   b. On your own sketch, mark congruent corresponding parts.

   c. In quadrilateral *ABDC*, which triangle is congruent to $\triangle ABC$?

   d. In $\triangle BCE$, which triangle is congruent to $\triangle ECD$?

10. The figure at the right is not drawn to scale. The markings indicate which pairs of segments and which pairs of angles are congruent. Segments that appear to be straight are meant to be.

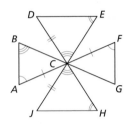

   a. Assume $m\angle F = 80°$, $m\angle H = 50°$, and $m\angle B = 40°$. What are the measures of $\angle A$, $\angle E$, and $\angle D$?

   b. Use a ruler and protractor to draw the figure to scale. Draw each angle with the correct angle measure. Draw congruent segments so that they are actually congruent.

Maintain Your Skills

11. Think about two congruent irregular pentagons. How many pairs of corresponding parts do they have? Draw and label your pentagons. Write a congruence statement. List all corresponding congruent parts.

Go Online
PHSchool.com

For additional practice, go to **Web Code: bea-0203**

Additional Practice

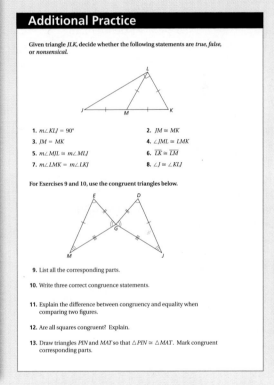

Given triangle *JLK*, decide whether the following statements are *true, false,* or *nonsensical.*

1. $m\angle KLJ = 90°$ **2.** $JM \cong MK$

3. $JM = MK$ **4.** $\angle JML \cong \angle LMK$

5. $m\angle MJL \cong m\angle MLJ$ **6.** $\overline{LK} \cong \overline{LM}$

7. $m\angle LMK = m\angle LKJ$ **8.** $\angle J \cong \angle KLJ$

For Exercises 9 and 10, use the congruent triangles below.

9. List all the corresponding parts.

10. Write three correct congruence statements.

11. Explain the difference between congruency and equality when comparing two figures.

12. Are all squares congruent? Explain.

13. Draw triangles *PIN* and *MAT* so that $\triangle PIN \cong \triangle MAT$. Mark congruent corresponding parts.

Practice: For Lesson 2.3, assign Exercises 9–13.

---

8. a. Yes; if two polygons are congruent, then one can be made to fit exactly on top of the other. What is inside the polygons will match, too, and area is a numerical measure of the inside.

   b. No; for example, a 4 in.-by-4 in. square has the same area as a 2 in.-by-8 in. rectangle, but they are not congruent.

9. See back of book.

10. See back of book.

11. See back of book.

Lesson Overview

GOALS

- Understand the meaning of corresponding parts.
- Test for congruence in triangles.

The activities in this lesson may take two days to complete. See the Daily Planner for suggestions on how to split up the exercises in this lesson. Students investigate triangle congruence to determine when two triangles are congruent. Two triangles are congruent if their corresponding sides and corresponding angles are also congruent. They also explore the converse of this statement.

CHECK YOUR UNDERSTANDING
- Core: 1, 3, 4, 6, 7
- Optional: 5

MATERIALS
- protractors
- rulers

VOCABULARY
- assumption
- postulate

HOMEWORK
- Core: 2, 8, 9, 10, 11, 12, 13, 14, 16
- Optional: 17
- Extension: 15

Launch

Begin this lesson by reading the introductory paragraphs with your class and answering the For Discussion problems. You may wish to draw students' attention to the margin note about writing the converse of a statement. This text does not formally address logic statements (except for a brief treatment of converse in Investigation 2D), but students should be aware of terms such as *hypothesis, conclusion,* and *converse.*

Explore

For Discussion

PROBLEM 1 will get students thinking about whether there are any shortcuts when testing two triangles for congruence. Is it necessary to test all three corresponding pairs of angles and all three corresponding pairs of sides? One easy suggestion is that you do not need to check the third pair of corresponding angles when the other two pairs of angles are congruent. In this case, the sums of the two pairs of corresponding angles are equal. The measure of the third angle in each triangle will be 180° minus the sum of the other two angles.

Discuss combinations that students name in the For You to Do and the list of abbreviations in the table before going on to the In-Class Experiment.

Triangle Congruence

You know that corresponding parts of congruent figures are congruent. For triangles, you say that corresponding parts of congruent triangles are congruent. In other words, if two triangles are congruent, then their corresponding sides and corresponding angles are also congruent.

The converse of this statement is also true. If the corresponding sides and corresponding angles of two triangles are congruent, then the triangles are congruent. This gives an exact method for proving triangles are congruent, but checking the six pairs of corresponding parts is a great deal of work.

> You can abbreviate *corresponding parts of congruent triangles are congruent* as CPCTC.

> **Remember...**
> How do you form the converse of a statement?

For Discussion

1. Can you check fewer than six pairs of corresponding parts to determine whether two triangles are congruent? For instance, if the three angles in one triangle are congruent to the three angles in another triangle, are the two triangles congruent? Or if the three sides in one triangle are congruent to the three sides of another triangle, are the two triangles congruent?

2. Discuss the meaning of the following statement. *Information that is enough to specify one triangle is also enough to ensure that two triangles are congruent.* Is the statement true? Explain.

Classifying Your Information

You can *sometimes* determine whether two triangles are congruent when three parts of one triangle are congruent to three parts of another triangle. But not any three pairs of congruent parts guarantee that two triangles are congruent. For example, two triangles that have congruent corresponding angles are not necessarily congruent.

Which three pairs of congruent parts guarantee that two triangles are congruent? To answer that question, first make a list of the possible combinations of three parts in one triangle. For example, $\triangle ABC$ has six parts: three sides and three angles.

three sides: $\overline{AB}$, $\overline{BC}$, and $\overline{AC}$
three angles: $\angle A$, $\angle B$, and $\angle C$

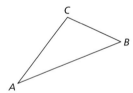

For You to Do

3. List the possible combinations of three parts of $\triangle ABC$. Here are two examples.

- $\angle A$, $\angle B$, $\angle C$
- $\overline{AB}$, $\angle A$, $\angle B$

Answers

For Discussion

1. It turns out that in certain cases all you need are three pairs of congruent parts to know that two triangles are congruent.

2. The statement is true. If you have enough information to specify one triangle, you can then compare it to another one to see if they are congruent.

For You to Do

3. • $\angle A$, $\angle B$, $\overline{AB}$
$\angle A$, $\angle B$, $\overline{BC}$
$\angle A$, $\angle B$, $\overline{AC}$
$\angle A$, $\angle C$, $\overline{AB}$
$\angle A$, $\angle C$, $\overline{BC}$
$\angle A$, $\angle C$, $\overline{AC}$
$\angle B$, $\angle C$, $\overline{AB}$
$\angle B$, $\angle C$, $\overline{BC}$
$\angle B$, $\angle C$, $\overline{AC}$

You can classify your combinations in many ways. Here is a scheme that people have found useful. Note that this is *not* a list of ways to show two triangles are congruent.

Three Parts	Abbreviation Triplet	Meaning for a Triangle	Example for △ABC
Three angles	AAA	Three angles of the triangle	$\angle A$, $\angle B$, $\angle C$
Two angles, one side	ASA	Two angles and the side between them	$\angle A$, $\overline{AB}$, $\angle B$
	AAS	Two angles and a side not between the angles	$\angle A$, $\angle B$, $\overline{BC}$
Two sides, one angle	SAS	Two sides and the angle between them	$\overline{AC}$, $\angle A$, $\overline{AB}$
	SSA	Two sides and an angle not between the sides	$\overline{AC}$, $\overline{AB}$, $\angle B$
Three sides	SSS	Three sides of the triangle	$\overline{AC}$, $\overline{AB}$, $\overline{BC}$

ASA should be read as "angle-side-angle."

Order is important. SAS is not the same as SSA. Also, ASA is not the same as AAS.

Which of these triplets can you use to prove that two triangles are congruent? You can investigate this question. Try to build two noncongruent triangles that share a given triplet. If you can, then the triplet does not guarantee triangle congruence. If you cannot, then there is a good chance that the triplet does guarantee congruence.

In-Class Experiment

Work with a partner or in a small group to determine which of the triplets below guarantee triangle congruence. For each triplet, try to build two noncongruent triangles with the given angle measures and side lengths.

4. **ASA** angles with measures 40° and 70°; a side of length 2 in. that is between them

5. **AAS** angles with measures 40° and 70°; a side of length 2 in. that is not between them

6. **SAS** sides of lengths 2 in. and 3 in.; an angle with measure 60° that is between them

7. **SSA** sides of lengths 2 in. and 4 in.; an angle with measure 20° that is not between them

8. **SSS** sides of lengths 2 in., 3 in., and 4 in.

- $\overline{AB}$, $\overline{BC}$, $\overline{AC}$
  $\overline{AB}$, $\overline{BC}$, $\angle A$
  $\overline{AB}$, $\overline{BC}$, $\angle B$
  $\overline{AB}$, $\overline{BC}$, $\angle C$
  $\overline{AB}$, $\overline{AC}$, $\angle A$
  $\overline{AB}$, $\overline{AC}$, $\angle B$
  $\overline{AB}$, $\overline{AC}$, $\angle C$
  $\overline{BC}$, $\overline{AC}$, $\angle A$
  $\overline{BC}$, $\overline{AC}$, $\angle B$
  $\overline{BC}$, $\overline{AC}$, $\angle C$

In-Class Experiment

4. not possible

5. not possible

6. not possible

7. See back of book.

8. not possible

In-Class Experiment

Students should complete this experiment in pairs or small groups. They will need rulers and protractors to draw the triangles. Ask students which triangles they could build. Their answers should correspond to the list of Triangle Congruence Postulates in the Assumption.

Wrap Up

Before assigning the Check Your Understanding exercises, you may wish to use this activity to give students practice in identifying congruent triangles.

OPTIONAL ACTIVITY Give each student a note card with three pieces of information about a triangle on it. Design each note card so that some cards list sets of three angles (AAA), some list three sides (SSS), and some list a combination of sides and angles. Make sure you make duplicates of some cards (such as the SSA and AAA cards) so students have a chance to see that not all clues will give information to draw a unique triangle.

Have students draw the triangle from the clues on their note cards. If they think that the triangle they drew is the only possibility, then they can label their set of clues "unique." If they cannot draw a triangle based on the card, or if they can draw more than one triangle, then they should label the set of clues "not unique." Have students work together to decide if they agree whether the triangles described on the cards are unique.

Here are some examples of possible clues for cards.

$AB = 4\,cm$, $BC = 6\,cm$, $AC = 5.5\,cm$

$AB = 4$, $BC = 6$, $m\angle B = 64°$

$m\angle A = 76°$, $m\angle B = 64°$, $m\angle C = 40°$

$AC = 5.5\,cm$, $BC = 6\,cm$, $m\angle B = 64°$

$m\angle A = 76°$, $m\angle C = 40°$, $AC = 5.5\,cm$

$BC = 6\,cm$, $AC = 5.5\,cm$, $m\angle A = 76°$

$m\angle B = 64°$, $m\angle C = 40°$, $AC = 5.5\,cm$

When an activity depends on drawing, it is not unusual for students to draw incorrectly, or simply not be able to visualize alternative ways of drawing. All students can easily conclude incorrectly, on the basis of their figures, that SSA will determine only one triangle and is a triangle congruence postulate. Plan ahead for ways to deal with this possibility.

Conclude this activity by reviewing the triangle congruence postulates.

Exercises

HOMEWORK
- Core: 2, 8, 9, 10, 11, 12, 13, 14, 16
- Optional: 17
- Extension: 15

Check Your Understanding

Many of these exercises require students to prove statements. For now, accept a reasonable argument as proof. Students will gain more practice with formal proofs in upcoming lessons.

EXERCISE 4 gives students two triangles with three congruent pieces (two sides and a nonincluded angle). In Investigation 2C, students will use the Isosceles Triangle Theorem to show that these two triangles are definitely congruent.

The results of the In-Class Experiment suggest the following assumption.

Postulate *The Triangle Congruence Postulates*

If two triangles share the following triplets of congruent corresponding parts, then the triangles are congruent.

- ASA
- SAS
- SSS

What can you do with the AAS triplet? You can prove that this triplet guarantees triangle congruence if you assume that the other triangle congruence postulates are true. You also have to assume that the sum of the measures of the angles of a triangle is 180°.

And what can you do with the SSA triplet? In Exercise 7, you will show why this triplet does not guarantee triangle congruence.

> **Remember...**
> Another word for assumption is *postulate*. A **postulate** is a statement that is accepted without proof.

> Mathematicians like to make as few assumptions and to prove as many theorems as possible.

Exercises Practicing Habits of Mind

Check Your Understanding

For Exercises 1 and 2, do each of the following:

a. Construct △ABC with the given angle measures and given side lengths.

b. Compare results with a classmate. Are your triangles congruent?

c. If your triangles are not congruent, what additional information will guarantee that the triangles are congruent?

1. $m\angle A = 36°$, $m\angle B = 72°$, $m\angle C = 72°$

2. $m\angle A = 60°$, $AB = 8$ cm, $BC = 7$ cm

In Exercises 3 and 4, is △ABC ≅ △ADC? If the two triangles are congruent, state which triangle congruence postulate helped you decide.

3. 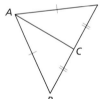   4.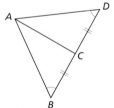

Answers

Exercises

1. **a.** Check students' work.
   b. not necessarily
   c. one of the side lengths

2. **a.** Check students' work.
   b. not necessarily
   c. Answers may vary. Sample: the length of the third side

3. yes; SSS

4. yes, though you would need to first deduce that $\overline{AB} \cong \overline{AD}$; SAS

EXERCISES 6 AND 7 show that SSA is not a triangle congruence postulate.

5. Show in two different ways that a diagonal of a square divides the square into two congruent triangles. Use a different triangle congruence postulate each time.

Remember...

A *square* is a quadrilateral with four congruent sides and four right angles.

6. You and a friend are making triangular pennants. Your friend says that each pennant should have a 30° angle, a 14-inch side, and an 8-inch side. Explain why this information does not guarantee that all the pennants will be congruent.

7. The diagram at the right proves, without words, that the SSA triplet does not guarantee triangle congruence. Explain the proof.

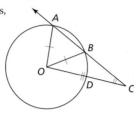

Note that point *O* is the center of the circle. Why use a circle in this proof without words?

On Your Own

For Exercises 8–12, do each of the following:

a. Tell whether the given information is enough to show that the triangles are congruent. The triangles are not necessarily drawn to scale.

b. If the given information is enough, list the pairs of corresponding vertices of the two triangles. Then state which triangle congruence postulate guarantees that the triangles are congruent.

8.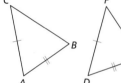

9.

10.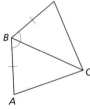

11.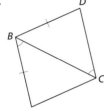

12.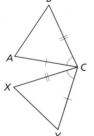

5. Let the square be *ABCD*, and choose the diagonal $\overline{BD}$. All sides of a square are congruent, and all angles of a square are right angles and hence congruent. The sides $\overline{BA}$ and $\overline{DA}$ and their included right angle in △*BAD* are congruent, respectively, to sides $\overline{BC}$ and $\overline{DC}$ and their included right angle in △*BCD*. So △*BAD* ≅ △*BCD* by SAS. Also, $\overline{BD}$ ≅ $\overline{BD}$, so △*BAD* ≅ △*BCD* by SSS.

6. Answers may vary. Sample: SSA is not a valid test for congruence.

7. If SSA were a valid way to prove congruence, then △*COA* ≅ △*COB*. But it is obvious from the figure that these triangles are not congruent.

8. no

9. yes; △*ABC* ≅ △*DEF*; SSS

10. yes; △*ABC* ≅ △*DBC*; SAS

11. No

12. yes; △*ABC* ≅ △*YXC*; SAS

On Your Own

EXERCISE 14 Students must know what a perpendicular bisector is in order to show that the two triangles in this exercise are congruent using SAS.

EXERCISE 15 builds on the work done in Exercise 14.

Additional Resources

PRINT RESOURCES
- Solution Manual
- Practice Workbook
- Assessment Resources
- Teaching Resources

TECHNOLOGY
- Interactive Textbook
- TeacherExpress CD-ROM
- **Exam***View* CD-ROM
- **PHSchool.com**
  - Additional Practice
  - Mid-Chapter and Chapter Tests
  - Video Tutors
  - Vocabulary Puzzles

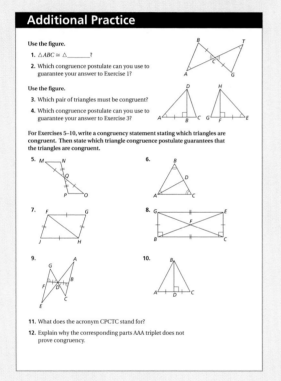

Additional Practice

Use the figure.

1. △*ABC* ≅ △_____?

2. Which congruence postulate can you use to guarantee your answer to Exercise 1?

Use the figure.

3. Which pair of triangles must be congruent?

4. Which congruence postulate can you use to guarantee your answer to Exercise 3?

For Exercises 5–10, write a congruency statement stating which triangles are congruent. Then state which triangle congruence postulate guarantees that the triangles are congruent.

5.

6.

7.

8.

9.

10.

11. What does the acronym CPCTC stand for?

12. Explain why the corresponding parts AAA triplet does not prove congruency.

Practice: For Lesson 2.4, assign Exercises 1–12.

---

13. **Standardized Test Prep** In △*ABC*, $\overline{CD}$ is the bisector of ∠*ACB*. Which of the following conjectures is true?

   A. There is not sufficient evidence to prove that △*ACD* ≅ △*BCD*.

   B. △*ACD* ≅ △*BCD* is true by the Angle-Side-Angle postulate. In each triangle, the side between the two angles is $\overline{CD}$.

   C. △*ACD* ≅ △*BCD* is true by the Side-Angle-Side postulate. Angle *ACD* and ∠*BCD* are the congruent angles that are between the two pairs of congruent sides.

   D. △*ACD* ≅ △*BCD* is true by the Side-Side-Side postulate.

14. In the figure at the right, $\overline{BD}$ is the perpendicular bisector of $\overline{AC}$. Based on this statement, which two triangles are congruent? Prove that they are congruent.

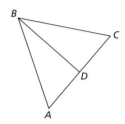

15. **Take It Further** In the figure at the right, $\overline{AD}$ is the perpendicular bisector of $\overline{BC}$. Based on this information, two triangles in the figure are congruent.

   Assume each additional piece of information in parts (a)–(c) is also true. For each part, determine which two additional triangles, if any, are congruent. Then tell which triangle congruence postulate guarantees their congruence.

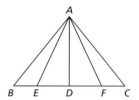

   a. *AB* = *AC*

   b. $\overline{AD}$ is the perpendicular bisector of $\overline{EF}$.

   c. ∠*EAD* ≅ ∠*FAD*

16. Assume you know that the sum of the measures of the angles in a triangle is 180°.

   a. In △*ABC* and △*DEF*, *m*∠*A* = *m*∠*D* = 72°, *m*∠*B* = *m*∠*E* = 47°, and *AC* = *DF* = 10 in. Is △*ABC* ≅ △*DEF*? Explain.

   b. Explain why the AAS triplet guarantees triangle congruence.

For additional practice, go to **Web Code: bea-0204**

Maintain Your Skills

17. Does a diagonal of a rectangle divide the rectangle into two congruent triangles? Can you say the same for the diagonals of a parallelogram? For the diagonals of a trapezoid? For the diagonals of a kite? Explain.

Remember...
What are some good definitions for *rectangle*, *parallelogram*, *trapezoid*, and *kite*?

Answers

13. B

14. △*ABD* and △*CBD*; since $\overline{BD}$ is the perpendicular bisector of $\overline{AC}$, $\overline{AD} ≅ \overline{CD}$ and ∠*ADB* ≅ ∠*CDB*. $\overline{BD}$ is common to the two triangles. Therefore, △*ABD* ≅ △*CBD* by SAS.

15. See back of book.

16. See back of book.

17. A diagonal of a rectangle divides it into two congruent triangles. (Opposite sides of a rectangle are congruent, and a diagonal divides it into two triangles that have the diagonal as a common side, so SSS applies.) A diagonal of a parallelogram divides it into two congruent triangles. (Use the same reasoning as for rectangles.) A diagonal of a trapezoid divides it into two noncongruent triangles. One diagonal of a kite will divide it into two congruent triangles; the other diagonal usually will not. The only kites for which both diagonals give two congruent triangles are kites with four congruent sides.

Mathematical 2A Reflections

In this investigation, you studied congruent figures—figures that are the same shape and size. You determined whether two figures were congruent based on relationships between their parts. You also learned postulates that you can use to prove two triangles are congruent.

1. **a.** Name the triangle congruence postulates.

   b. Explain what each one means.

   c. Draw a picture to illustrate each postulate.

2. Tell whether each statement below makes sense. If a statement does not make sense, explain why. Then rewrite the statement so that it does make sense.

   a. $MA \cong FL$ **b.** $m\angle A = m\angle L$

   c. $MT = FO$ **d.** $\overline{TA} \cong \overline{LO}$

   e. $\angle AMT = \angle LFO$

3. Triangle ABC and $\triangle DEF$ are isosceles. $\overline{AC} \cong \overline{BC}$ and $\overline{DF} \cong \overline{EF}$. If $\angle ACB \cong \angle DFE$ and $\overline{CB} \cong \overline{FD}$, can you determine whether the two triangles are congruent? Explain.

4. Draw $\triangle ABC$. Find the midpoint of $\overline{BC}$. Call it point O. Draw $\overrightarrow{AO}$. Mark point D on $\overrightarrow{AO}$ so that $\overline{OD} \cong \overline{OA}$. Look for congruent triangles in your figure. (*Hint:* $\angle DOB \cong \angle AOC$ and $\angle AOB \cong \angle DOC$.) Explain why $\overline{BD} \cong \overline{AC}$. Explain why $\overline{CD} \cong \overline{AB}$.

5. In the figure at the right, $\overrightarrow{OD}$ is the angle bisector of $\angle AOB$. $\overline{OA} \cong \overline{OB}$. Explain why $\overline{AD} \cong \overline{BD}$.

6. What does it mean to say that two figures are congruent?

7. Why is it important to keep track of corresponding parts in congruent figures?

8. What are some ways to prove that two triangles are congruent?

Vocabulary and Notation

In this investigation, you learned this term and these symbols. Make sure you understand what each one means, and how to use it.

- postulate
- $\cong$ (is congruent to)
- *JK* (length of $\overline{JK}$)
- $\perp$ (is perpendicular to)

These two houses are the same shape and size.

Mathematical Reflections

EXERCISES 6–8 At the start of the investigation, you may have assigned these as Questions 1–3 for students to think and write about.

Mathematical Reflections

1. See back of book.

2. See back of book.

3. From the given information, it follows that $\overline{AC}$, $\overline{BC}$, $\overline{DF}$, and $\overline{EF}$ are all congruent. Since $\angle ACB \cong \angle DFE$, the triangles are congruent by SAS.

4. See back of book.

5. Since $\overrightarrow{OD}$ bisects $\angle AOB$, the angles $\angle AOD$ and $\angle BOD$ are congruent.

Therefore $\triangle AOD \cong \triangle BOD$ by SAS. Hence $\overline{AD} \cong \overline{BD}$ by CPCTC.

6. Answers may vary. Sample: The figures have the same shape and size.

7. Answers may vary. Sample: Knowing which parts are corresponding parts tells you which parts have the same size.

8. Answers may vary. Sample: Show that there is a way to match their sides and their angles so that all corresponding parts have the same measure. You could also use ASA, SAS, SSS, or AAS.

Investigation Overview

In this investigation, students study a basic geometric object, the line. They will discover different relationships among lines that intersect, and even relationships among lines that do not intersect. They explore the angles formed by intersecting lines, including the angles within a triangle.

You may wish to assign Questions 1–3 for students to think and write about during the investigation.

Learning Goals

- Identify pairs of congruent angles when parallel lines are cut by a transversal.
- Make assumptions and write proofs in order to understand the need for proof in mathematics.
- Prove that the sum of the angle measures in any triangle is 180°.

Habits and Skills

- Develop and present a deductive proof.
- Search for invariants.
- Visualize key elements of a problem situation.

Investigation 2B

Proof and Parallel Lines

In *Proof and Parallel Lines,* you will study one of the basic objects in geometry, the line. Some distinct lines in a plane intersect, while others do not. When lines intersect, they form angles. These angles have special relationships. You will prove some of these relationships in this investigation. When lines do not intersect, there are also provable consequences. As you investigate parallel lines and angle measures, you will gather what you need to prove that the sum of the angles in a triangle is 180 degrees.

By the end of this investigation, you will be able to answer questions like these.

1. Why is proof so important in mathematics?

2. What are some invariant angle relationships when parallel lines are cut by a transversal?

3. What is the sum of the measures of the interior angles of any triangle?

You will learn how to

- identify pairs of congruent angles when parallel lines are cut by a transversal

- make assumptions and write proofs in order to understand the need for proof in mathematics

- prove that the sum of the angle measures in any triangle is 180°

You will develop these habits and skills:

- Develop and present a deductive proof.

- Search for invariants.

- Visualize key elements of a problem situation.

As parallel lines, the E, F, G, R, and V trains form congruent alternate exterior angles with the Shea Stadium train.

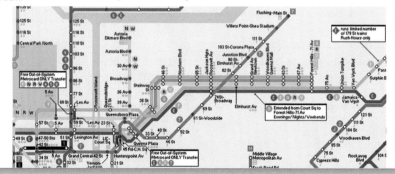

Investigation Road Map

LESSON 2.5, *Getting Started,* has students use geometry software to investigate angle measures, including when a transversal cuts a pair of parallel lines.

LESSON 2.6, *Deduction and Proof,* is an introduction to mathematical proofs. Students see the difference between experimentation and proof.

LESSON 2.7, *Parallel Lines,* has students learn the names of the special angle pairs they investigated in Lesson 2.6. The lesson presents the AIP Theorem, which states that if two lines form congruent alternate interior angles with a transversal, then the two lines are parallel.

LESSON 2.8, *The Parallel Postulate,* introduces the Parallel Postulate and has students prove the converse of the AIP Theorem. They also prove that the sum of the measures of the interior angles of any triangle is 180°.

Activating Prior Knowledge
Exploring New Ideas

You met mathematical proof when you learned the Triangle Congruence Postulates. Now you will use geometry software to discover some important geometric relationships. Ultimately, you will prove some of these relationships.

For You to Explore

Use geometry software to complete Problems 1 and 2.

1. Construct a pair of parallel lines cut by a transversal. Measure the angles.

   a. Move the transversal while the parallel lines remain fixed. Which angles stay congruent? Move one of the parallel lines while keeping them parallel. Which angles stay congruent?

   b. Which sums of angle measures are invariant?

2. Construct a pair of intersecting lines cut by a transversal. Measure the angles.

   a. Move the transversal while the intersecting lines remain fixed. What invariants can you find? Move one of the intersecting lines while the transversal remains fixed. What invariants can you find?

   b. How do the angle measures compare to the angle measures in Problem 1? How do the sums of angle measures compare to the sums of angle measures in Problem 1?

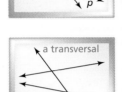

Remember...

A **transversal** is a line that intersects two or more lines.

a transversal

Exercises *Practicing Habits of Mind*

On Your Own

3. Construct a triangle. Draw its three midlines. Consider the side lengths, angle measures, and areas of the figures formed. List your observations. If you know each of the following, what else can you determine about the triangle?

   a. the length of one midline   b. the area of the original triangle

Remember...

A **midline** (or **midsegment**) connects the midpoints of two sides of a triangle.

Answers

For You To Explore

1. See back of book.

2. See back of book.

Exercises

3. a. The length of a midline is half the length of the side that it does not intersect.

   b. The area of the original triangle is four times the area of the triangle formed by the midlines.

Lesson Overview

GOALS

- Warm up to the ideas of the investigation.
- Identify pairs of congruent angles when a transversal cuts parallel lines.

Students use geometry software to explore intersecting lines, angles, and parallel lines.

FOR YOU TO EXPLORE	**HOMEWORK**
• Core: 1, 2	• Core: 4, 5, 6
• Optional: none	• Optional: 3, 7, 8, 9
MATERIALS	**VOCABULARY**
• geometry software	• exterior angle
• protractors	• transversal
• rulers	

Launch

As an introduction to the process of proof, present the following summary of a mathematical investigation that searches for invariants, or elements that do not change.

EXPERIMENT using hand or computer drawings to visualize the situation and gather data.

RECORD YOUR EXPERIMENT explaining the process and any unanswered questions.

SUMMARIZE YOUR WORK with a brief description. Include questions for further exploration.

Explore

For You to Explore

PROBLEMS 1 AND 2 Lesson 2.6 formally states the Vertical Angles Theorem. Lesson 2.7 introduces alternate interior angles.

Wrap Up

Summarize information and conjectures. For example, when a transversal cuts a pair of parallel lines, it forms several pairs of congruent angles; vertical angles are congruent; a triangle that you form by connecting the endpoints of a circle's diameter to another point on the circle is a right triangle; the measures of the interior angles of a triangle sum to 180°.

Exercises

HOMEWORK
- Core: 4, 5, 6
- Optional: 3, 7, 8, 9

On Your Own

EXERCISE 3 Note that each midline is parallel to the side it does not intersect, and its length is half the length of that side. Students will prove this in Exercise 32 in Lesson 2.18.

The four triangles that you form by drawing three midlines are all similar to the original triangle. The similarity ratio is $\frac{1}{2}$ for all of them. Therefore, they are congruent and have the same area, which is $\frac{1}{4}$ the area of the original triangle.

EXERCISE 4 is noteworthy because you can write a proof without using properties of parallel lines. However, a proof using the fact that the angle measurements of a triangle sum to 180° is circular. The sum of the angle measures of a triangle depends on properties of parallel lines, as does the property that if a pair of corresponding angles are congruent, then the lines are parallel. Discuss circular logic.

EXERCISE 5 Explain that students can prove the Exterior Angle Theorem without the Triangle Angle Sum Theorem by using the fact that an angle that sits inside another angle has a smaller measure. Proving the Exterior Angle Theorem without the Triangle Angle Sum Theorem is essential.

The figure in Exercise 4 shows $\overline{AM}$ extended to R. You need this to prove the Exterior Angle Theorem used in the proof of the AIP Theorem in Lesson 2.7.

Maintain Your Skills

EXERCISES 7–9 preview the Parallel Postulate in Lesson 2.9.

GOING FURTHER In Exercise 8, advanced students may investigate analogous problems in 3 dimensions. You cannot, however, easily use software.

- There is still only one line parallel to a given line, through a given point. There are, however, many lines that are skew to the original line.

- There is a unique plane parallel to a given line through a given point.

- There is still only one line perpendicular to a given line from a point outside, because the given line and the point determine the plane in which you must draw the perpendicular.

- Starting with a point on the line, lots of perpendiculars form a pinwheel that is the unique plane perpendicular to the line at the given point.

- After developing a definition of perpendicularity, students may ask how many planes pass through a line perpendicular to a given plane if the line is itself perpendicular to the given plane? Oblique to the given plane? Parallel to the given plane?

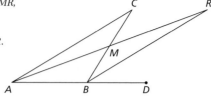

4. In this figure, $\angle CMA \cong \angle BMR$, M is the midpoint of $\overline{BC}$, and $AM = MR$. Prove that $m\angle C = m\angle CBR$.

5. A common problem in geometry involves a triangle with one side extended. In the figure below, $\angle CBD$ is an **exterior angle** of $\triangle ABC$.

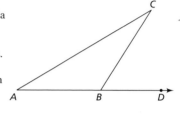

One form of the Exterior Angle Theorem states that the measure of a triangle's exterior angle is greater than the measures of either of the triangle's two remote interior angles. The remote interior angles are nonadjacent to the exterior angle. In this case, $m\angle CBD$ is greater than either $m\angle A$ or $m\angle C$. How can you prove the Exterior Angle Theorem?

> In order to actually *prove* the Exterior Angle Theorem, you must show that the measure of any exterior angle is greater than the measures of either remote interior angle in any triangle.

6. Use the figure at the right. Find the measures of $\angle BDA$, $\angle ADQ$, and $\angle CDQ$ for the following conditions.

   a. $m\angle BDC = 62°$
   b. $m\angle BDC = 72°$
   c. $m\angle BDC = 55°$
   d. $m\angle BDC = x°$

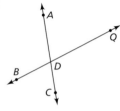

Maintain Your Skills

Use geometry software. Draw a line ℓ. Draw a point P not on line ℓ.

7. How many lines will the software allow you to construct parallel to ℓ through P? How many lines exist that are parallel to ℓ through P?

8. How many lines will the software allow you to construct perpendicular to ℓ through P? How many lines exist that are perpendicular to ℓ through P?

9. a. Construct a line through P that is perpendicular to ℓ. Label it n.
   b. Construct a line through P that is perpendicular to n. Label it m.
   c. What happens when you use the software to determine the intersection of ℓ and m?

Answers

4. See back of book.

5. See back of book.

6. a. $m\angle BDA = 118°$,
      $m\angle ADQ = 62°$,
      $m\angle CDQ = 118°$
   b. $m\angle BDA = 108°$,
      $m\angle ADQ = 72°$,
      $m\angle CDQ = 108°$
   c. $m\angle BDA = 125°$,
      $m\angle ADQ = 55°$,
      $m\angle CDQ = 125°$

   d. $m\angle BDA = 180° - x°$,
      $m\angle ADQ = x°$,
      $m\angle CDQ = 180° - x°$

7. one; one

8. one; one

9. a–b. Check students' work.
   c. There is no intersection point.

Deduction and Proof

How do you know the length of a segment or the measure of an angle? One way is to measure using a ruler or protractor, respectively. But measurement has some drawbacks.

- Measurement is not exact. No matter how precise your ruler or protractor is, neither will provide an exact measurement.

- Certain measurements are difficult or impossible to determine. For instance, the distance between two cities is difficult to find directly. The distance between Earth and the moon is impossible to measure directly.

- A measurement is only reliable if it holds true for an infinite number of cases.

The Developing Habits of Mind section below illustrates the third point. You will also learn more about it in Chapter 5.

> In many real-life cases, estimation is sufficient. In mathematics, however, exactness is necessary to eliminate error.

Developing Habits of Mind

Use a Deductive Process. In Lesson 2.5, you explored the angle measures in the figure below.

You may have noticed that, no matter where P is on the circle, the measure of $\angle P$ seems to be 90°. How can you prove that this is true? You can measure $\angle P$ when P is at various points until you grow tired of it. Suppose you do this 100 times. Will you know for sure that $m\angle P$ is always 90°? You may be very convinced, but you cannot be certain. Mathematicians establish certainty by proving a statement is true using the deductive method.

You could check all these angles.

You can prove statements using the deductive method by showing that a simple statement leads to a desired conclusion based on logical reasoning. Important conclusions are called theorems. Conclusions that are accepted without proof are called postulates, axioms, or assumptions. Once you prove a theorem, you can use it as an assumption to prove other theorems.

Lesson Overview

GOAL

- Make assumptions and write proofs to understand the need for proof in mathematics.

Students think about other ways than measuring to find the length of a segment or the measure of an angle. They use deductive reasoning to prove statements true for an infinite number of cases and discuss why proving statements can be helpful in mathematics.

CHECK YOUR UNDERSTANDING
- Core: 1, 2
- Optional: none

MATERIALS
- protractors
- Blackline Master 2.6

HOMEWORK
- Core: 3, 4, 5, 6
- Optional: 7

VOCABULARY
- deduction
- theorem
- postulate
- axiom
- assemption
- vertical angles

Launch

Before discussing the deductive method of proof, have your students read the lesson through Minds in Action. Ask students to summarize what they have read. You may ask, "Why do you think that mathematicians need to prove statements?"

Explore

Assign For You to Do to complete individually or with a partner.

You may wonder where ideas for new theorems come from or who gets to decide what statements are assumed without proof. Ideas from theorems often come from experiments. The postulates that are assumed depend on what information is necessary and what is already known.

One reason to prove results in geometry is to check measurements. For example, if you know from a theorem that two segments should be equal, then the measurements of those segments should be the same. Measurements are subject to error in a way that logical deduction is not.

Habits of Mind

Reason logically.
New results come from reasoning about things that must follow logically from what is already known or assumed. The mixing of deduction and experiment is one of the distinguishing features of mathematical research.

Minds in Action   episode 3

Sasha and Ivan are making triangular pennants for the school's sports teams. Ivan made a pennant with two 14-in. sides and a 30° angle between those two sides.

Ivan I measured the other two angles of my triangle. One is 73 degrees and the other is 77 degrees.

Sasha But they should both be the same. Measure more carefully.

So Ivan did.

Ivan This time, they are 74.3 degrees and 75.7 degrees.

Sasha Close. But they should both be the same.

Ivan What do you mean? How do you know they should both be the same? My protractor says they are a little off. The bottom one is always a little bigger than the top one.

Sasha They should both be the same. Look. Draw a median. The two triangles are congruent.

Ivan Okay, I see. Yeah.

Sasha And the two angles you are measuring are corresponding angles in the congruent triangles. So they have to be congruent.

Ivan I guess I'll get a better protractor.

Remember...

A *median* of a triangle is a line segment drawn from one of the triangle's vertices to the midpoint of the opposite side.

For Discussion

1. Ivan agrees that the two triangles formed by Sasha's median are congruent. Do you? Explain.

2. How do you know that the two angles that Ivan measured are corresponding parts of the two triangles formed by the median?

$\overline{AM}$ is a median of △ABC.

Answers

For Discussion

1. The two triangles formed by drawing the median are congruent by SSS. The two angles that Ivan measures are congruent by CPCTC.

2. Both angles are opposite the median.

For You to Do

The result of the experiment below may lead to a theorem.

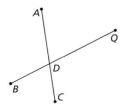

two intersecting segments

> Angles such as ∠ADB and ∠CDQ are called *vertical angles.*

Suppose that $\overline{AC}$ and $\overline{BQ}$ intersect so that $m\angle BDC = 72°$. What is the measure of each angle below?

3. $m\angle BDA$ **4.** $m\angle ADQ$ **5.** $m\angle QDC$

> You may find it helpful to look back at Exercise 6 in Lesson 2.5.

You should notice that some of the angle measures are the same. Now suppose that $m\angle ADB = 125°$. What are the measures of the other angles?

Each time you repeat this experiment, you should find that the two pairs of opposite angles have the same measure. Your measurements may lead you to believe that the statement below is true.

Theorem 2.1   *The Vertical Angles Theorem*

In the figure below, $m\angle ADB = m\angle CDQ$ and $m\angle BDC = m\angle ADQ$.

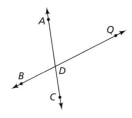

How can you prove this theorem true without using measurement? Since angle measures are numbers, you can use algebra. Use guess-check-generalize to show that the theorem is true for certain angle measures. Do not forget to keep track of your steps. For instance, the steps shown on the following page are for the case in which $m\angle ADB = 125°$.

For You to Do

Refer students to Exercise 7 in Lesson 2.5 if they need help with Problems 3–5. The experiment in For You to Do should lead students to Theorem 2.1, the Vertical Angles Theorem.

Lead students through finding the other angle measures when $m\angle ADB = 125°$. Then have them repeat the experiment when $m\angle ADB$ equals some other measure.

Point out that this work only shows that the theorem is true for a few angle measures. Remind students that this does not prove that the statement is true for all angle measures. Then lead them through the general proof, which will probe the theorem for all angle measures.

For You to Do

3. 118°

4. 62°

5. 118°

Step 1 Suppose that $m\angle ADB = 125°$.

Step 2 You know that $m\angle ADB + m\angle ADQ = 180°$. Therefore, you know that $125° + m\angle ADQ = 180°$.

Step 3 So, $m\angle ADQ = 180° - 125° = 55°$.

Step 4 You also know that $m\angle ADQ + m\angle CDQ = 180°$. Therefore, you know that $55° + m\angle CDQ = 180°$.

Step 5 Then, $m\angle CDQ = 180° - 55° = 125°$.

Step 6 So, $m\angle ADB = m\angle CDQ$ because they both have the same measure, $125°$.

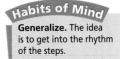

Habits of Mind

Generalize. The idea is to get into the rhythm of the steps.

If you repeat this process with several different angle measures, you may convince yourself that the steps will always work. To present a more convincing argument, repeat this process with a generic value for the measure of $\angle ADB$. Simply use a variable to represent $m\angle ADB$.

Step 1 Suppose that $m\angle ADB = x°$.

Step 2 You know that $m\angle ADB + m\angle ADQ = 180°$. Therefore, $x° + m\angle ADQ = 180°$.

Step 3 So, $m\angle ADQ = 180° - x°$.

Step 4 You also know that $m\angle ADQ + m\angle CDQ = 180°$. Therefore, $(180° - x°) + m\angle CDQ = 180°$.

Step 5 So $m\angle CDQ = 180° - (180° - x°) = 180° - 180° + x° = x°$.

Step 6 Then $m\angle ADB = m\angle CDQ$ because they both measure $x°$.

This argument is convincing, but it is not a mathematical proof. In a mathematical proof, each statement is supported with a reason. A reason is an assumption or theorem that you already know is true. Below is an incomplete two-column mathematical proof of the Vertical Angles Theorem.

Statement	Reason
1. Suppose $m\angle ADB = x°$.	The variable x represents any number.
2. You know that $m\angle ADB + m\angle ADQ = 180°$, so $x° + m\angle ADQ = 180°$.	
3. Similarly, $m\angle ADQ = 180° - x°$.	Basic rules of algebra
4. You know that $m\angle ADQ + m\angle CDQ = 180°$, so $(180° - x°) + m\angle CDQ = 180°$.	
5. Then, $m\angle CDQ = 180° - (180° - x°)$ $= 180° - 180° + x° = x°$.	Basic moves and rules of algebra
6. So, $m\angle ADB = m\angle CDQ$.	If the measures of two angles are equal to the same value, then two measures of the two angles are equal.

6. As a class, choose a reason to support statements 2 and 4 in the proof. Your reason should be an assumption or theorem that you can accept without proof.

7. The reasons for statements 3 and 5 in the proof on the previous page come from algebraic reasoning. What basic rules of algebra are used in these steps?

Exercises *Practicing Habits of Mind*

Check Your Understanding

1. Use the figure below. ∠COA and ∠DOB are right angles.

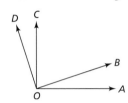

a. If $m\angle BOA = 25°$, find $m\angle COB$ and $m\angle COD$.

b. If $m\angle COB = 63°$, find $m\angle BOA$ and $m\angle COD$.

c. If $m\angle DOC = 31°$, find $m\angle COB$ and $\angle BOA$.

d. If $m\angle DOC = 31°$, find $m\angle DOA$.

e. If $m\angle AOB = x°$, find $m\angle COB$ and $m\angle COD$.

2. Use the figure below. ∠COA and ∠DOB are right angles. Prove that $m\angle BOA = m\angle COD$.

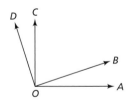

> When you write a proof, be sure to state explicitly any assumptions you make.

Wrap Up

Work on For Discussion Problems 6 and 7 as a class. Have students help you come up with justifications for each step.

Assessment Resources

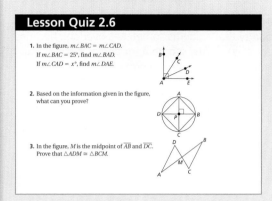

Lesson Quiz 2.6

1. In the figure, $m\angle BAC = m\angle CAD$.
   If $m\angle BAC = 25°$, find $m\angle BAD$.
   If $m\angle CAD = x°$, find $m\angle DAE$.

2. Based on the information given in the figure, what can you prove?

3. In the figure, M is the midpoint of $\overline{AB}$ and $\overline{DC}$. Prove that $\triangle ADM \cong \triangle BCM$.

Exercises

HOMEWORK
- Core: 3, 4, 5, 6
- Optional: 7

Check Your Understanding

EXERCISE 1 Remind students about the definition of *complementary*. This exercise will help with the next exercise.

EXERCISE 2 Emphasize the fact that this is a generic calculation. Students should be able to justify each step in the calculation using their knowledge of algebra.

Answers

For Discussion

6. Answers may vary. Sample: If two angles have a common side and their noncommon sides form a line, then the sum of their measures is 180°.

7. Step 3 uses the fact that you can subtract the same number from both sides of an equation without changing the solution. Step 5 uses the any-order, any-grouping principle.

Exercises

1. a. $m\angle COB = 65°$,
      $m\angle COD = 25°$
   b. $m\angle BOA = 27°$,
      $m\angle COD = 27°$
   c. $m\angle COB = 59°$,
      $m\angle BOA = 31°$
   d. $m\angle DOA = 121°$
   e. $m\angle COB = 90° - x°$,
      $m\angle COD = x°$

2. See back of book.

On Your Own

EXERCISE 4 Students have seen this figure in Exercise 10 of Lesson 2.4. There they decided whether the two triangles were congruent. Now they will write the reasons for each step proving that $\overline{AC} \cong \overline{DC}$. You may wish to provide copies of Blackline Master 2.6 for students to use.

EXERCISES 4 AND 5 The proofs in these exercises use a property that students sometimes overlook because it is so obvious. Any segment, or angle, is congruent to itself. This is the reflexive property.

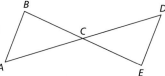
3. **Standardized Test Prep** $\overline{BE}$ bisects $\overline{AD}$ at C. Point C is the midpoint of $\overline{BE}$. Fill in the missing reason in the following proof.

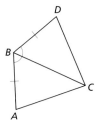

Statements	Reasons
1. $\overline{BE}$ bisects $\overline{AD}$ at C. Point C is the midpoint of $\overline{BE}$.	1. Given
2. $\overline{AC} \cong \overline{DC}$	2. Definition of bisects
3. $\overline{BC} \cong \overline{EC}$	3. Definition of midpoint
4. $\angle BCA \cong \angle ECD$	4. ?
5. $\triangle ABC \cong \triangle DEC$	5. SAS triangle congruence postulate

A. Supplementary angles are congruent.

B. Corresponding angles are congruent.

C. Opposite angles are congruent.

D. Vertical angles are congruent.

4. Use the figure below. $\overline{AB} \cong \overline{DB}$ and $m\angle ABC = m\angle DBC$.

Provide the missing reasons in the proof to show that $\overline{AC} \cong \overline{DC}$.

Statements	Reasons
a. $\overline{AB} \cong \overline{BD}$	Given
b. $m\angle ABC = m\angle DBC$	?
c. $\overline{BC} \cong \overline{BC}$	?
d. $\triangle ABC \cong \triangle DBC$	?
e. $\overline{AC} \cong \overline{DC}$	?

Answers

3. D

4. **b.** given
   c. Every figure is congruent to itself.
   d. SAS
   e. CPCTC

5. In this figure, $\overline{PL} \cong \overline{RQ}$ and $\overline{PQ} \cong \overline{RL}$. Prove each of the following.

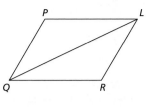

a. $\triangle QPL \cong \triangle LRQ$

b. $\angle P \cong \angle R$

6. Use the figure below.
$m\angle DCB = m\angle ECA$. Points E, C, and D are collinear. $\overline{FC} \perp \overline{ED}$.

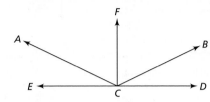

a. Based on the given information, what can you prove?

b. Prove your conjecture from part (a).

Maintain Your Skills

7. Use the figure below. Suppose that $m\angle 1 + m\angle 6 = 90°$, and $m\angle 7 = 140°$.

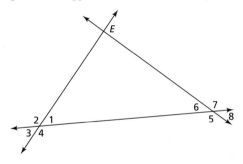

a. Find the measure of each numbered angle.

b. Assume you know that the sum of the measures of the angles in a triangle is 180°. Find the measure of each angle around point E.

Go Online
PHSchool.com

For additional practice, go to Web Code: bea-0206

In Lesson 2.8, you will prove that the sum of the measures of the angles in a triangle is 180°.

Additional Practice

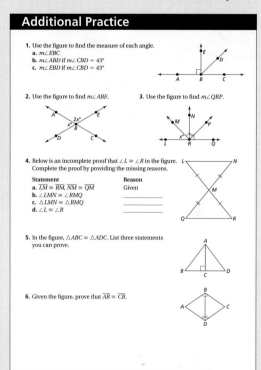

1. Use the figure to find the measure of each angle.
 a. $m\angle EBC$
 b. $m\angle ABD$ if $m\angle CBD = 43°$
 c. $m\angle EBD$ if $m\angle CBD = 43°$

2. Use the figure to find $m\angle ABE$.
3. Use the figure to find $m\angle QRP$.

4. Below is an incomplete proof that $\angle L \cong \angle R$ in the figure. Complete the proof by providing the missing reasons.

Statement	Reason
a. $\overline{LM} \cong \overline{RM}, \overline{NM} \cong \overline{QM}$	Given
b. $\angle LMN \cong \angle RMQ$	___
c. $\triangle LMN \cong \triangle RMQ$	___
d. $\angle L \cong \angle R$	___

5. In the figure, $\triangle ABC \cong \triangle ADC$. List three statements you can prove.

6. Given the figure, prove that $\overline{AB} \cong \overline{CB}$.

Practice: For Lesson 2.6, assign Exercises 1–6.

---

5. a. Since $\overline{PL} \cong \overline{RQ}$, $\overline{PQ} \cong \overline{RL}$, and $\overline{QL} \cong \overline{QL}$, you can conclude $\triangle QPL \cong \triangle LRQ$ by SSS.

b. Because $\triangle QPL \cong \triangle LRQ$, $\angle P \cong \angle R$ by CPCTC.

6. a. Answers may vary. Sample:
$m\angle FCA = m\angle FCB$

b. $\overline{FC} \perp \overline{ED}$ (given).
$m\angle FCD = 90°$ and $m\angle FCE = 90°$ (definition of perpendicular lines).
$m\angle ACE + m\angle FCA = m\angle FCE$ and $m\angle BCD + m\angle FCB = m\angle FCD$ (the measure

of an angle is the sum of the measures of its parts).
$m\angle ACE + m\angle FCA = m\angle BCD + m\angle FCB$ (properties of equality). But $m\angle ACE = m\angle DCB$ (given), so $m\angle FCA = m\angle FCB$ (basic rules of equations).

7. a. $m\angle 1 = 50°$, $m\angle 2 = 130°$, $m\angle 3 = 50°$, $m\angle 4 = 130°$, $m\angle 5 = 140°$, $m\angle 6 = 40°$, $m\angle 7 = 140°$, $m\angle 8 = 40°$

b. 90°

Lesson Overview

GOAL

- Identify pairs of congruent angles when a transversal cuts parallel lines.

You may choose to spend two days on this lesson. Students need time to read and digest the mathematics. This lesson contains information that is necessary for Lesson 2.8, in which students learn the Parallel Postulate. This lesson also contains definitions of special pairs of angles and proofs of theorems using these definitions.

CHECK YOUR UNDERSTANDING
- Core: 1, 2, 3, 4
- Optional: none

MATERIALS
- Blackline Master 2.7

HOMEWORK
- Core: 5, 6, 7, 8, 9
- Optional: 10, 11, 12

VOCABULARY
- alternate interior angles
- consecutive angles
- corresponding angles
- corollary
- parallel lines
- supplementary angles
- vertical angles
- ∥

Launch

Begin the lesson by asking students for a definition of parallel lines. Then review the definition in the margin notes.

Developing Habits of Mind

Read to understand. This lesson is different from many of the others in this book. You will need to read and comprehend a set of ideas. These mathematical principles have been studied for centuries. Some of them took generations to solve or prove. An important part of mathematics is the ability to read and understand the mathematical writing of others. To understand a new idea, sometimes you may need to read it more than once. You will practice these skills in this lesson.

You see parallel lines in your everyday life. You have probably studied them in previous mathematics courses. Parallel lines will be the focus of this lesson and the following lesson. You will address these questions.

1. How can you determine whether two lines are parallel?
2. What information can you draw from parallel lines?

Here is the definition of parallel lines given in Chapter 1.

Definition

Parallel lines are lines in the same plane that do not intersect.

This seems like a simple definition. However, if you need to determine whether two given lines are parallel, the definition is not very helpful. You can't graph both lines forever in each direction to check that they never intersect. In this lesson, you will develop several simple tests that involve measuring angles to determine if lines are parallel.

First, you need to be familiar with the vocabulary on the next page.

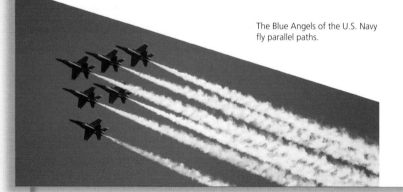

The Blue Angels of the U.S. Navy fly parallel paths.

> **Remember...**
> You have studied the equations of parallel lines. How can you determine whether two lines are parallel from their equations?

> **Remember...**
> You can also say that parallel lines are everywhere equidistant. *Everywhere equidistant* means "the same distance apart at every point."

Facts and Notation

The pairs of angles that are formed when a transversal intersects two lines have special names based on their positions.

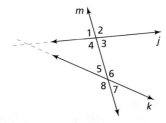

- Pairs of angles such as ∠3 and ∠5, or ∠4 and ∠6, are **alternate interior angles.**

- Pairs of angles such as ∠1 and ∠5, or ∠4 and ∠8, are **corresponding angles.**

- Pairs of angles such as ∠2 and ∠4, or ∠5 and ∠7, are **vertical angles.**

- Angles on the same side of the transversal and between the lines (for example, ∠3 and ∠6) are called **consecutive angles.**

For You to Do

1. Use the figure at the right. Suppose you have three sticks. The sticks represent lines ℓ, m, and n. The sticks ℓ and n are fixed together to form a 62° angle at point A. The sticks representing m and n intersect at P. You can pivot the stick representing m about point P.

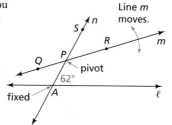

Habits of Mind

Experiment. This is a thought experiment. You can turn it into a physical experiment by building a model with sticks.

How can you adjust the angles at P to ensure that line ℓ is parallel to line m (ℓ ∥ m)? Explain.

The result of the experiment above suggests several theorems that allow you to say that two lines are parallel.

Theorem 2.2   The AIP Theorem

If two lines form congruent alternate interior angles with a transversal, then the two lines are parallel.

AIP stands for "alternate interiors parallel." You can think of the *AI* as the hypothesis of the theorem, and the *P* as the conclusion.

Explore

For You to Do

Draw the figure in the Facts and Notation on the board or overhead, or provide students with copies of Blackline Master 2.7. Review the names of the special pairs of angles that the transversal and the lines form. You can also review Theorem 2.1, the Vertical Angles Theorem.

For You to Do is a good opportunity to use geometry software. This is a preview of Theorem 2.2, the Alternate Interior Parallel Theorem. The proof of the AIP Theorem is a proof by contradiction. This type of proof can be a bit tricky to follow. Sketch the figures on the board or overhead and lead students through the proof. This is also a good opportunity for a demonstration using geometry software.

Theorems 2.2 and 2.3 use the abbreviations AIP and PAI. This should help students keep the theorems straight. Students may not appreciate the shortcut name for the AIP Theorem until they see the PAI Theorem and need some way to tell them apart.

For Discussion

The proof of the Exterior Angle Theorem requires that you find the midpoint M of $\overline{BC}$ and extend $\overline{AM}$ through M twice the distance of $\overline{AM}$ to make $\overline{BA'}$, as in the figure shown. You can prove triangles AMC and $A'MB$ congruent using SAS. $\angle C$ and $\angle A'BC$ are congruent. Therefore, you can show that $m\angle DBA' + m\angle A'BC$ must be larger than $m\angle C$.

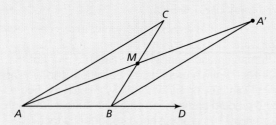

Ask your class to come up with assumptions based on the proof of the Exterior Angle Theorem. Record this list. It might include the following statements.

- Each segment has a midpoint M.

- $\overline{AMA'}$ is a straight line and forms vertical angles with $\overline{CMB}$.

- You can add $m\angle CBA'$ and $m\angle A'BC$ to get $m\angle CBD$.

- $m\angle CBD$ is larger than each of the two angles that form $\angle CBD$.

Wrap Up

Make a connection between Exercise 7 in Lesson 2.6 and the Exterior Angle Theorem in Problem 2 before assigning the exercises.

Assessment Resources

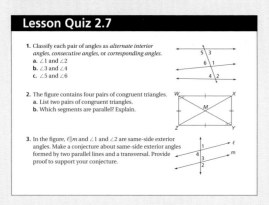

The AIP Theorem on the previous page is illustrated in the figure below.

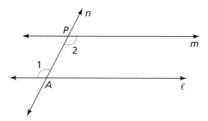

Proof Assume that $m\angle 1 = m\angle 2$. You need to show that $\ell \parallel m$. The proof of this fact is indirect. Begin by supposing the lines are not parallel and then prove the theorem by contradiction.

Suppose lines ℓ and m are not parallel. Then they must intersect somewhere. Suppose they intersect at a point R like this.

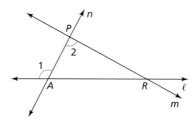

A triangle, $\triangle ARP$, is formed. By the Exterior Angle Theorem, $m\angle 1 > m\angle 2$. But this contradicts our assumption that $m\angle 1 = m\angle 2$. Therefore, point R cannot exist. This implies that lines ℓ and m do not intersect. So, $\ell \parallel m$.

The AIP Theorem and the corollaries that you will soon investigate allow you to use certain angle measures to determine whether two lines are parallel. This is much easier than checking whether two lines intersect.

A **corollary** is a consequence that logically follows from a theorem.

For Discussion

2. The proof of the AIP Theorem depends on the Exterior Angle Theorem shown here.

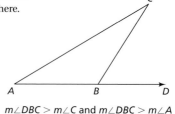

$$m\angle DBC > m\angle C \text{ and } m\angle DBC > m\angle A$$

The Exterior Angle Theorem also depends on some basic assumptions. Discuss these assumptions.

Answers

For Discussion

2. Answers may vary. Sample: Every segment has a midpoint; you can arbitrarily extend segments to a known length.

Exercises *Practicing Habits of Mind*

Check Your Understanding

1. Give a precise definition for each term listed below. Illustrate each with a diagram.

   a. alternate interior angles
   b. alternate exterior angles
   c. corresponding angles
   d. consecutive angles

2. Use the figure below. The tick marks indicate congruent segments.

   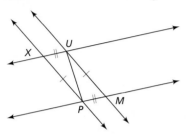

   > These types of angles are formed when two lines are cut by a transversal. The two lines may or may not be parallel.

   a. Which triangles, if any, are congruent? Explain.
   b. Which angles, if any, are congruent? Explain.
   c. Which lines, if any, are parallel? Explain.

3. Use the figure below. The tick marks indicate congruent segments.

   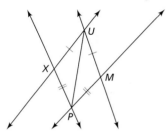

   a. Which triangles, if any, are congruent? Explain.
   b. Which angles, if any, are congruent? Explain.
   c. Which lines, if any, are parallel? Explain.

Exercises

HOMEWORK

- Core: 5, 6, 7, 8, 9
- Optional: 10, 11, 12

Check Your Understanding

EXERCISE 1 In part (b), students will be writing their own definitions of *alternate exterior angles* based on their understanding of alternate interior angles.

EXERCISE 2 You can prove the triangles in this exercise congruent by SSS. Since corresponding parts of congruent triangles are congruent, students can understand that alternate interior angles *XUP* and *MPU* are congruent and therefore $\overleftrightarrow{XU} \parallel \overleftrightarrow{PM}$. It should not be too hard for students to show that $\overleftrightarrow{PX} \parallel \overleftrightarrow{MU}$. Showing that corresponding angles are congruent may be more challenging for them.

EXERCISES 2 AND 3 At this point, be sure that students are not using the PAI Theorem. They should not assume that angles are congruent because lines are parallel.

Exercises

1. See back of book.

2. See back of book.

3. a. $\triangle XUP \cong \triangle MUP$; SSS

    b. All the vertical angles are congruent. (There are two pairs of vertical angles at each of the points *X*, *U*, *M*, and *P*.) Also, $\angle XPU \cong \angle MPU$, $\angle XUP \cong \angle MUP$, and $\angle UXP \cong \angle UMP$ by CPCTC.

    c. None are necessarily parallel; the conditions that let you use the AIP Theorem are not present.

EXERCISE 4 will really test your students' understanding of the different angle pairs they have
encountered so far. Encourage them to draw
diagrams as they complete this exercise to help
them understand the statements.

4. Decide whether each statement below is true. Prove why or why not.

   a. If two lines form congruent corresponding angles with a transversal,
      then the two lines are parallel.

   b. If two lines form congruent alternate exterior angles with a transversal,
      then the two lines are parallel.

   c. If two lines form congruent consecutive angles with a transversal, then
      the two lines are parallel.

   d. If two lines form supplementary alternate exterior angles with a
      transversal, then the two lines are parallel.

   e. If two lines form supplementary consecutive angles with a transversal,
      then the two lines are parallel.

Each statement that is
true is a corollary of
the AIP Theorem.

Remember...

Two angles are
supplementary angles
if the sum of their
measures is 180°.

On Your Own

5. Suppose two lines are perpendicular to the same line. Are the two lines
   parallel? Explain.

6. Two lines in the same plane either intersect or are parallel. Explain. Is the
   statement true of two lines in space? Explain.

   In Exercises 7 and 8, use the given information to determine which
   segments in each figure must be parallel. For each exercise, provide a proof
   to support your answer.

7. Point O is the midpoint of both $\overline{NP}$ and $\overline{MQ}$.

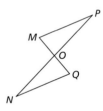

8. The diagonals of quadrilateral MPQN intersect
   at point O. MO = PO and NO = QO.

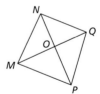

Answers

4. **a–e.** See back of book.

5. yes, if the two lines are in the same
   plane; possibly not, if they are not
   in the same plane

6. Two lines either do or do not
   intersect, and, by definition, parallel
   lines are lines in the same plane
   that do not intersect. In space,
   it is possible for nonintersecting
   lines to be nonparallel, because
   the noninteresecting lines may not
   lie in the same plane. The lines

determined by the edges of a
rectangular box provide examples.

7. $\overleftrightarrow{MP} \parallel \overleftrightarrow{NQ}$; since O is the midpoint
   of $\overline{MQ}$ and $\overline{NP}$, $\overline{MO} \cong \overline{QO}$, and
   $\overline{NO} \cong \overline{PO}$. The vertical angles
   that have vertex O are congruent.
   Hence, $\triangle PMO \cong \triangle NQO$ by
   SAS, and $\angle N \cong \angle P$ by CPCTC.
   Therefore, $\overleftrightarrow{MP} \parallel \overleftrightarrow{NQ}$ by the AIP
   Theorem.

8. See back of book.

9. Standardized Test Prep In the figure below, $\overrightarrow{BG}$ intersects $\overline{AC}$ at point B. $\overrightarrow{BG}$ intersects $\overline{DF}$ at point E. Angle ABG and $\angle GEF$ are supplementary.

Choose the correct reason for step number 8 in the proof below.

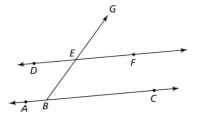

Statements	Reasons
1. $\overline{BG}$ intersects $\overline{AC}$ and $\overline{DF}$ at points B and E, respectively.	**1.** Given
2. $\angle ABG$ and $\angle GEF$ are supplementary.	**2.** Given
3. $m\angle ABG + m\angle GEF = 180°$	**3.** definition of supplementary angles
4. $\angle GEF \cong \angle DEB$	**4.** Vertical angles are congruent.
5. $m\angle GEF = m\angle DEB$	**5.** definition of congruent angles
6. $m\angle ABG + m\angle DEB = 180°$	**6.** substitution property of equality
7. $\angle ABG$ and $\angle DEB$ are supplementary angles.	**7.** definition of supplementary angles
8. $\overleftrightarrow{AC} \parallel \overleftrightarrow{DF}$	**8.** ___?___

A. If corresponding angles are congruent, then the lines are parallel.

B. If consecutive interior angles are supplementary, then the lines are parallel.

C. If alternate interior angles are congruent, then the lines are parallel.

D. If consecutive exterior angles are supplementary, then the lines are parallel.

10. In the figure below, $m\angle DEG + m\angle HFI = 180°$, and $m\angle FGE = m\angle HFI$.

Find the lines in the figure that must be parallel, if there are any. Prove what you find.

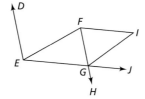

9. B

10. $\overline{FI} \parallel \overline{EJ}$ and $\overline{DE} \parallel \overline{FH}$; it is given that $m\angle FGE = m\angle HFI$, so $\overline{FI} \parallel \overline{EJ}$ by the AIP Theorem. $\angle DEG$ is supplementary to $\angle HFI$ and hence is supplementary to the congruent angle $\angle FGE$. From what was proved in Exercise 4 (e), it follows that $\overline{DE} \parallel \overline{FH}$.

Additional Resources

PRINT RESOURCES
- Solution Manual
- Practice Workbook
- Assessment Resources
- Teaching Resources

TECHNOLOGY
- Interactive Textbook
- TeacherExpress CD-ROM
- **Exam**View CD-ROM
- **PHSchool.com**
  - Additional Practice
  - Mid-Chapter and Chapter Tests
  - Video Tutors
  - Vocabulary Puzzles

Additional Practice

1. Classify each pair of angles as *alternate interior angles, consecutive angles,* or *corresponding angles.*
   a. ∠4 and ∠2
   b. ∠3 and ∠4
   c. ∠1 and ∠5

2. In the figure, $a \parallel b$.
   a. Find $m\angle 1$.
   b. Find $m\angle 2$.

3. In the figure, $m \parallel n$ and $r \parallel s$.
   a. Which angles are congruent? Explain.
   b. Which triangles are congruent? Explain.
   c. Which segments are congruent? Explain.

4. List the parallel lines or segments in each figure.
   a.   **b.**

5. Find the value of x in each figure.
   a.   **b.**

6. In the figure, H is the midpoint of both $\overline{GI}$ and $\overline{LK}$. Prove that $\overline{LG} \parallel \overline{KI}$.

Practice: For Lesson 2.7, assign Exercises 1–3.

Maintain Your Skills

11. Use the figure below. For each statement, find all the missing angle measures.

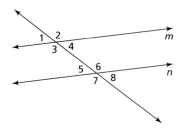

a. $m\angle 1 = 58°$ and $m\angle 5 = 58°$ **b.** $m\angle 1 = 58°$ and $m\angle 6 = 125°$
c. $m\angle 4 = 55°$ and $m\angle 6 = 125°$ **d.** $m\angle 7 = 125°$ and $m\angle 3 = 125°$
e. $m\angle 7 = 125°$ and $m\angle 1 = 55°$

> **Go Online**
> **Video Tutor**
> PHSchool.com
> Web Code: bee-0775

12. Decide whether each statement below guarantees that $m \parallel n$.

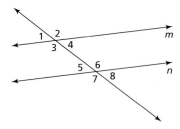

a. $m\angle 1 = 58°$ and $m\angle 5 = 58°$ **b.** $m\angle 1 = 58°$ and $m\angle 6 = 125°$
c. $m\angle 4 = 55°$ and $m\angle 6 = 125°$ **d.** $m\angle 7 = 125°$ and $m\angle 3 = 125°$
e. $m\angle 7 = 125°$ and $m\angle 1 = 55°$ **f.** $m\angle 7 = m\angle 6$
g. $m\angle 7 = m\angle 2$ **h.** $m\angle 7 + m\angle 3 = 180°$
i. $m\angle 4 + m\angle 6 = 180°$

> **Go Online**
> PHSchool.com
> For additional practice,
> go to Web Code: bea-0207

Answers

11. a. $m\angle 2 = 122°$, $m\angle 3 = 122°$,
$m\angle 4 = 58°$, $m\angle 6 = 122°$,
$m\angle 7 = 122°$, $m\angle 8 = 58°$
b. $m\angle 2 = 122°$, $m\angle 3 = 122°$,
$m\angle 4 = 58°$, $m\angle 5 = 55°$,
$m\angle 7 = 125°$, $m\angle 8 = 55°$
c. $m\angle 1 = 55°$, $m\angle 2 = 125°$,
$m\angle 3 = 125°$, $m\angle 5 = 55°$,
$m\angle 7 = 125°$, $m\angle 8 = 55°$
d. $m\angle 1 = 125°$, $m\angle 2 = 55°$,
$m\angle 4 = 125°$, $m\angle 5 = 125°$,
$m\angle 6 = 55°$, $m\angle 8 = 125°$
e. $m\angle 2 = 55°$, $m\angle 3 = 55°$,
$m\angle 4 = 125°$, $m\angle 5 = 125°$,
$m\angle 6 = 55°$, $m\angle 8 = 125°$

12. a. yes
b. no
c. yes
d. yes
e. yes
f. no
g. yes
h. no
i. yes

The Parallel Postulate

Suppose you have a line ℓ and a point P that is not on line ℓ. How many lines through P can you draw that are parallel to ℓ? The experiments in this book and your common sense suggest that there is only one. People tried for centuries to prove this from simpler statements, and they had no success. The concept that there exists only one line parallel to a given line through a point not on the given line cannot be proved. In this course, it is accepted that no proof exists, and it is assumed true.

Postulate   The Parallel Postulate

If a point P is not on a line ℓ, exactly one line through P exists that is parallel to ℓ.

Remember...

In this case, the word *exists* means that there is a parallel line.

Now that you have assumed that a parallel to a given line through a point exists and is unique, you can answer the second question from the beginning of Lesson 2.7: What information can you draw from parallel lines? In Lesson 2.7, you used certain angle measures to determine whether lines were parallel. Now you can work in the other direction and determine the measures of certain angles when two parallel lines are cut by a transversal.

For You to Do

1. Use geometry software to construct two parallel lines and a moveable transversal. Measure all the angles and note any two angles that have the same measure and any two angles with measures that add to 180°.

   Move the transversal. Check which of the equalities found above is invariant. Is there a state of the sketch in which all the angles have the same measure?

This activity leads to the converse of the AIP Theorem.

Theorem 2.3   The PAI Theorem

If two parallel lines are cut by a transversal, then the alternate interior angles are congruent.

To form the **converse** of an *if-then* statement, interchange the *if* and *then* clauses. So the PAI Theorem is the converse of the AIP Theorem.

For You to Do

1. All the vertical angles have equal measures. So do alternate interior angles, alternate exterior angles, and corresponding angles. Consecutive angles have measures with a sum of 180°. So do pairs of exterior angles on the same side of the transversal, all pairs of adjacent angles, and a pair consisting of an interior angle and the angle that is vertical to the interior angle that forms a consecutive pair with the first interior angle. All eight angles are congruent if the transversal is perpendicular to the parallel lines.

Lesson Overview

GOALS

- Identify pairs of congruent angles when a transversal cuts parallel lines.
- Prove that the sum of the angle measures in any triangle is 180°.

This is another lesson where students will need ample time to read and understand the mathematics, so you may want to teach this lesson over two days. This lesson covers the Parallel Postulate, the PAI Theorem and its proof, and the Triangle Angle Sum Theorem and its proof. There is also a significant amount of historical information about parallel lines.

CHECK YOUR UNDERSTANDING
- Core: 1, 4, 5, 6
- Optional: 2, 3, 7

MATERIALS
- geometry software

HOMEWORK
- Core: 8, 9, 11, 12
- Optional: 13, 15; Extension: 10, 14

VOCABULARY
- converse

Launch

Begin by asking students to read the text at the beginning of the lesson, up to For You to Do. Then work on the For You to Do problem as a class. Students will need computers with geometry software or you can set this up as a class demonstration.

Explore

For You to Do

Students should notice that the angle pairs they encountered in the last lesson (alternate interior angles, corresponding angles, vertical angles) are congruent. This provides evidence that the converse of the AIP theorem is true. The one case in which all of the angle pairs are congruent is when the transversal is perpendicular to the parallel lines. The proof of the PAI Theorem is, again, a proof by contradiction. It relies on the Parallel Postulate.

You can prove the PAI Theorem with an indirect proof.

Proof Suppose parallel lines n and ℓ are cut by a transversal t, as shown in the figure below.

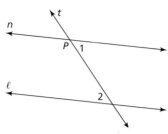

You want to prove that $\angle 1 \cong \angle 2$. Since this is an indirect proof, suppose that $\angle 1 \not\cong \angle 2$ and show that this leads to something that is impossible. Construct a line m through P so that the intersection of m and t form an $\angle 3$ that *is congruent* to $\angle 2$.

> The symbol $\not\cong$ means "is not congruent to."

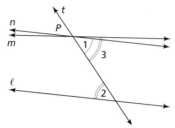

By the AIP Theorem, you can conclude that $m \parallel \ell$. However, you originally assumed that $n \parallel \ell$. So there are two distinct lines through P that are parallel to ℓ. This contradicts the Parallel Postulate. So you can conclude that $\angle 1 \cong \angle 2$. Therefore, if two parallel lines are cut by a transversal, then the alternate interior angles are congruent.

Developing Habits of Mind

Use a different process to get the same result. You can prove the PAI Theorem in a more direct way. Without assuming that $\angle 1 \not\cong \angle 2$, construct line m as you did above so that $\angle 3 \cong \angle 2$. By the AIP Theorem, $m \parallel \ell$. Since there is only one line parallel to ℓ through P, m and n must be the same line. Therefore, $\angle 1$ and $\angle 3$ must be the same angle, so $\angle 1 \cong \angle 2$.

Answers

For Discussion

2. Answers may vary. Sample: n is parallel to ℓ; you can draw a line m so that it forms an angle with the same measure as $\angle 2$; there is only one line through P parallel to ℓ (the Parallel Postulate).

For You to Do

3. $m\angle 1 = 70°$, $m\angle 2 = 110°$, $m\angle 3 = 115°$, $m\angle 4 = 65°$, $m\angle 5 = 115°$, $m\angle 6 = 70°$, $m\angle 7 = 110°$, $m\angle 8 = 70°$, $m\angle 9 = 45°$, $m\angle 10 = 65°$, $m\angle 11 = 70°$, $m\angle 12 = 65°$

4. Answers may vary. Sample: Use PAI to get $m\angle 10 = 65°$. Use vertical angles to get $m\angle 12 = m\angle 10 = 65°$. Use the fact that $\angle 11$, the angle labeled 45°, and $\angle 12$ form a straight angle to get $m\angle 11 = 70°$. Use vertical angles to get $m\angle 8 = 70°$ and $m\angle 9 = 45°$. Use PAI to get $m\angle 6 = 70°$. For the angles with vertices on line m, all pairs

For Discussion

2. What assumptions do you need to make in this argument?

For You to Do

3. Use the figure below. Lines *n* and *m* are parallel, as indicated by the red arrowhead on each line. Find the measures of all the numbered angles.

4. Explain how you found each angle measure.

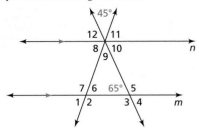

For Discussion

5. You already have overwhelming evidence that the sum of the angle measures in a triangle is 180°. You have used this idea to support other arguments. You may even know several different ways to explain why it is true. Use the diagram below to write an argument that proves that the sum of the angle measures in any triangle is 180°.

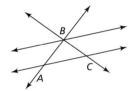

You can state the result of this discussion as a theorem.

Theorem 2.4   The Triangle Angle-Sum Theorem

The sum of the measures of the angles of a triangle is 180°.

$$m\angle A + m\angle B + m\angle C = 180°$$

For Discussion

PROBLEM 2 Here are a few assumptions.

- $n \parallel \ell$
- The transversal is a straight line that cuts through both *n* and *ℓ*.
- You can draw a line *m* so that it forms an angle with the same measure as $\angle 2$.
- There is only one line through *P* parallel to *ℓ* (Parallel Postulate).

For Discussion

PROBLEM 5 Stress that the sum of the measures of the angles of a triangle is 180° is a theorem. The proof of the Triangle Angle Sum Theorem using the PAI Theorem follows.

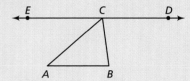

Draw a line $\overleftrightarrow{ED}$ through C that is parallel to $\overline{AB}$, the base of the triangle. Angles *ECA* and *BAC* are congruent and angles *DCB* and *ABC* are congruent because of the PAI Theorem.

If you add the measure of angles *DCB* and *BCA*, you get the measure of angle *DCA*.

If you add the measures of angles *ECA* and *DCA*, you get 180°.

If you add the measures of angles *ECA*, *BCA*, and *DCB*, you also get 180°.

So, $m\angle BAC + m\angle ABC + m\angle BCA = 180°$.

Wrap Up

Have students read the Historical Perspective. Discuss how scientists use careful experiments instead of logical connections. Have students find a situation when the scientific method would be better than deductive reasoning. Find a situation when logical reasoning might be better.

---

of angles that have a common side are supplementary. It follows that $m\angle 2 = m\angle 7 = 110°$, $m\angle 1 = 70°$, $m\angle 3 = 115°$, $m\angle 4 = 65°$, and $m\angle 5 = 115°$.

For Discussion

5. Let $\triangle ABC$ be any triangle. Draw the line *m* through *B* parallel to $\overline{AC}$. Label the angles as shown.

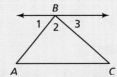

It follows from the PAI Theorem that $m\angle A = m\angle 1$ and $m\angle C = m\angle 3$. But $m\angle 1 + m\angle 2 + m\angle 3 = 180°$, since the numbered angles at *B* form a straight angle. Therefore, by substituting, $m\angle A + m\angle 2 + m\angle C = 180°$.

Exercises

HOMEWORK
- Core: 8, 9, 11, 12
- Optional: 13, 15; Extension: 10, 14

Check Your Understanding

EXERCISES 2 AND 3 Students will need computers with geometry software to complete these exercises.

 Exercises *Practicing Habits of Mind*

Check Your Understanding

1. Use the figure below. Assume $m \parallel n$.

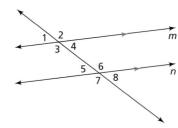

Go Online
PHSchool.com

For more information about parallel lines cut by a transversal, go to
Web Code: bee-9031

Find the measure of each numbered angle for the following conditions.

a. $m\angle 6 = 108°$ b. $m\angle 8 = 46°$

c. $m\angle 4 = x°$ d. $2m\angle 4 = m\angle 7$

e. $m\angle 7 = 2x$ and $m\angle 4 = x$

2. Use geometry software to construct two parallel lines a and b. Then construct two transversals c and d that each intersect a and b. See the figure below.

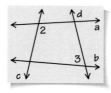

In this figure, lines a and b were drawn carelessly. They are clearly *not* parallel.

a. Move the lines so that $\angle 2 \cong \angle 3$. Do lines c and d have any special relationship? Is this relationship invariant or is it dependent on the congruence of $\angle 2$ and $\angle 3$?

b. Move the lines so that $c \parallel d$. Are the measures of $\angle 2$ and $\angle 3$ equal or are they dependent on lines a and b also being parallel?

c. How would your answers to parts (a) and (b) differ if lines a and b were not parallel?

Answers

Exercises

1. See back of book.

2. a. Yes, $c \parallel d$; yes.
   b. If $m\angle 2 = m\angle 3$, then $c \parallel d$.
   c. The relationships in parts (a) and (b) would not hold.

3. Use geometry software to construct a pair of parallel lines so that point *A* is on one line and point *B* is on the other. Place a moveable point *P* between the parallel lines. Construct $\overline{PA}$ and $\overline{PB}$, as shown in the figure below. What invariants can you find?

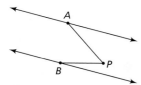

How does the angle formed by the two bungee cords compare to the angles they form at the poles?

4. The following theorem is an important consequence of the Triangle Angle-Sum Theorem.

Theorem 2.5   *The Unique Perpendicular Theorem*

If a point *P* is not on line ℓ, there is exactly one line through *P* that is perpendicular to ℓ.

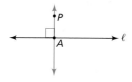

$\overleftrightarrow{PA}$ is unique.

Prove this theorem. (*Hint:* You may want to prove the theorem by contradiction. What would happen if there were more than one line through *P* that was perpendicular to ℓ?)

5. Is the sum of the measures of the angles of a quadrilateral invariant? Explain.

6. **Write About It** Explain the difference between the AIP and PAI Theorems.

7. Use geometry software to construct $\overrightarrow{AD}$ and $\overrightarrow{AE}$. Place point *B* on $\overrightarrow{AD}$ and point *C* on $\overrightarrow{AE}$. Then construct $\overline{BC}$, $\overline{CD}$, and $\overline{DE}$, as shown in the figure below. Move the parts so that $\overline{BC} \cong \overline{CD} \cong \overline{DE}$.

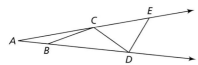

a. What conjectures can you make about the angles in the figure? Describe any invariant relationships you find.

b. Is it possible to make $\overline{BC}$ and $\overline{DE}$ parallel *and* congruent? Explain.

EXERCISE 5 You may wish to give your students a hint that dividing a figure into triangles, or triangulating a figure, can help find the sum of the measures of the interior angles of the figure. This is helpful because they already know the sum of the measures of the interior angles of a triangle.

EXERCISE 11 Students may need to refer to their work in Lesson 2.5 to review AAS.

3. Answers may vary. Sample: The measure of $\angle P$ is the sum of the measures of the acute angles at *A* and *B*.

4. Suppose the exterior angle is at vertex *C* of $\triangle ABC$. Since the exterior angle is supplementary to $\angle BCA$, $m(\text{exterior angle}) + m\angle BCA = 180°$. But by the Triangle Angle-Sum Theorem, $m\angle A + m\angle B + m\angle BCA = 180°$. It follows by algebra that $m(\text{exterior angle}) = m\angle A + \angle B$.

5. Yes; a diagonal of a quadrilateral divides it into two triangles. The sum of the measures of the angles of the quadrilateral is equal to the sum of the angle measures of the triangles, which is $180° + 180°$, or $360°$.

6. Answers may vary. Sample: One is the converse of the other.

7. See back of book.

On Your Own

EXERCISE 14 This theorem is critical for many proofs later in the course. For example, students will find the distance from a point to a line by dropping a perpendicular from the point to the line. The distance is equal to the measure of the segment whose endpoints are the point and the intersection of the perpendicular and the original line. Since there is a unique perpendicular line to measure, there is a unique distance between a point and a line.

On Your Own

8. **Standardized Test Prep** In the figure at the right, $\overleftrightarrow{AB} \parallel \overleftrightarrow{EF}$. The measure of $\angle BCD = 25°$. The measure of $\angle ABD$ is 125°. What is the measure of $\angle BDC$?

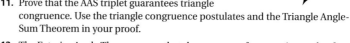

   A. 55° **B.** 80°

   C. 100° **D.** 125°

9. In the figure at the right, lines p and t are parallel.

   a. Why is $\angle 1 \cong \angle 2$?

   b. Why is $\angle 2 \cong \angle 3$?

   c. Why is $\angle 1 \cong \angle 3$?

10. **Take It Further** Prove that two lines that are both parallel to a third line are parallel to each other.

11. Prove that the AAS triplet guarantees triangle congruence. Use the triangle congruence postulates and the Triangle Angle-Sum Theorem in your proof.

12. The Exterior Angle Theorem says that the measure of an exterior angle of a triangle is greater than the measure of either of the two remote interior angles. You can take this one step further. Prove that the measure of an exterior angle of a triangle is equal to the sum of the measures of the two remote interior angles.

> Why do you think we did not prove this originally?

13. For each polygon listed below, prove that the sum of the measures of its angles is invariant. Then find the sum of the measures of the angles for each polygon. Justify your answers.

   a. pentagon (five-sided polygon) **b.** hexagon (six-sided polygon)

14. **Take It Further** Use your knowledge of parallel lines. Decide whether each of the constructions (a)–(d) is possible. Explain.

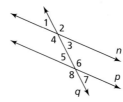 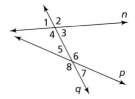

   a. Lines n and p are not parallel and $m\angle 3 + m\angle 6 = 180°$.

   b. Line n is parallel to line p and $m\angle 4 = m\angle 6$.

   c. Line n is parallel to line p and $m\angle 2 = m\angle 5$.

   d. $m\angle 4 + m\angle 5 > m\angle 2 + m\angle 7$

Answers

8. C

9. **a.** PAI Theorem
   b. Vertical Angles Theorem
   c. $\angle 1 \cong \angle 2$ by part (a), and $\angle 2 \cong \angle 3$ by part (b), so $\angle 1 \cong \angle 3$.

10. See back of book.

11. See back of book.

12. See back of book.

13. See back of book.

14. Suppose there are two lines perpendicular to ℓ through P, and that they intersect ℓ at M and N. The triangle MNP has two right angles at M and N. These together with the angle at P would give the triangle an angle sum greater than 180°. Therefore there is only one such perpendicular.

EXERCISE 15 In the diagram, $m\angle 5$ is always 90°.

Maintain Your Skills

15. In the figure at the right, lines m and n are parallel. $\overline{PR}$ bisects $\angle WPQ$. $\overline{QR}$ bisects $\angle XQP$.

   In parts (a)–(f), use each angle measure given to find the measure of the remaining numbered angles.

   a. $m\angle 1 = 64°$ **b.** $m\angle 1 = 68°$

   c. $m\angle 3 = 130°$ **d.** $m\angle 8 = 60°$

   e. $m\angle 7 = 140°$ **f.** $m\angle 2 = x°$

Habits of Mind

Look for invariants. Which angle measures are invariant? What conjecture, if any, can you make?

Historical Perspective

Around 300 B.C., Euclid and other Greek mathematicians tried to formalize the system of mathematical proof. They wanted to start with a few basic facts that everyone agreed were true. These facts allowed them to derive statements that were not as obvious and that could not be checked by physical experiment. These mathematicians wrote a series of books called *Elements*.

   Much of *Elements* is about numbers, arithmetic, and what we now call algebra. There is also a detailed treatment of geometry. *Elements* formed the basis of how geometry has been taught and learned for centuries.

   The Euclidean tradition of deducing new results from simple assumptions and other established results is the "gold standard" in mathematics. Mathematicians discover results, solve problems, and get insights in a variety of ways. Many of these methods are very complex. But when mathematicians present their results to others, their claims are accepted only when they can justify them with a logical deductive proof.

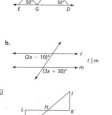

α
β
λ

$\alpha \| \lambda$ $\beta \| \lambda$

Additional Resources

PRINT RESOURCES
- Solution Manual
- Practice Workbook
- Assessment Resources
- Teaching Resources

TECHNOLOGY
- Interactive Textbook
- TeacherExpress CD-ROM
- **Exam**View CD-ROM
- **PHSchool.com**
  - Additional Practice
  - Mid-Chapter and Chapter Tests
  - Video Tutors
  - Vocabulary Puzzles

Additional Practice

1. Classify each pair of angles as *alternate interior angles, consecutive angles,* or *corresponding angles.*
   a. $\angle 4$ and $\angle 2$
   b. $\angle 3$ and $\angle 4$
   c. $\angle 1$ and $\angle 5$

2. In the figure, $a \| b$.
   a. Find $m\angle 1$.
   b. Find $m\angle 2$.

3. In the figure, $m \| n$ and $r \| s$.
   a. Which angles are congruent? Explain.
   b. Which triangles are congruent? Explain.
   c. Which segments are congruent? Explain.

4. List the parallel lines or segments in each figure.
   a. **b.**

5. Find the value of x in each figure.
   a. **b.**

6. In the figure, H is the midpoint of both $\overline{GI}$ and $\overline{LK}$. Prove that $\overline{LG} \| \overline{KI}$.

Practice: For Lesson 2.8, assign Exercises 4–6.

15. a. $m\angle 1 = 64°$, $m\angle 2 = 64°$, $m\angle 3 = 52°$, $m\angle 4 = 128°$, $m\angle 5 = 90°$, $m\angle 6 = 26°$, $m\angle 7 = 52°$, $m\angle 8 = 26°$

   b. $m\angle 1 = 68°$, $m\angle 2 = 68°$, $m\angle 3 = 44°$, $m\angle 4 = 136°$, $m\angle 5 = 90°$, $m\angle 6 = 22°$, $m\angle 7 = 44°$, $m\angle 8 = 22°$

   c. $m\angle 1 = 25°$, $m\angle 2 = 25°$, $m\angle 3 = 130°$, $m\angle 4 = 150°$, $m\angle 5 = 90°$, $m\angle 6 = 65°$, $m\angle 7 = 130°$, $m\angle 8 = 65°$

   d. $m\angle 1 = 30°$, $m\angle 2 = 30°$, $m\angle 3 = 120°$, $m\angle 4 = 60°$, $m\angle 5 = 90°$, $m\angle 6 = 60°$, $m\angle 7 = 120°$, $m\angle 8 = 60°$

   e. $m\angle 1 = 20°$, $m\angle 2 = 20°$, $m\angle 3 = 140°$, $m\angle 4 = 40°$, $m\angle 5 = 90°$, $m\angle 6 = 70°$, $m\angle 7 = 140°$, $m\angle 8 = 70°$

   f. $m\angle 1 = x°$, $m\angle 2 = x°$, $m\angle 3 = 180° - 2x°$, $m\angle 4 = 2x°$, $m\angle 5 = 90°$, $m\angle 6 = 90° - x°$, $m\angle 7 = 180° - 2x°$, $m\angle 8 = 90° - x°$

Mathematical Reflections

EXERCISES 5–7 At the start of the investigation, you may have assigned these as Questions 1–3 for students to think and write about.

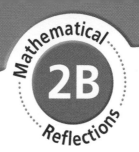

2B Mathematical Reflections

In this investigation, you studied lines and angles. You learned about the types of angles formed when two lines intersect and the types of angles formed when two parallel lines are intersected by a transversal. You also learned about mathematical proof—a logical way to move from a simple statement to a desired conclusion.

1. Use the figure at the right. Find the measure of each numbered angle. Lines m and n are parallel.

2. Two lines are intersected by a transversal. The measures of the consecutive angles that are formed are $103°$ and $75°$. Are the two lines parallel? Explain.

3. Draw two segments $\overline{AB}$ and $\overline{CD}$ that intersect at point O so that $\overline{AO} \cong \overline{OB}$ and $\overline{CO} \cong \overline{OD}$. Prove that $\overline{AC} \cong \overline{BD}$.

4. Use the figure at the right. Explain how to draw a line through P that is parallel to ℓ.

5. Why is proof so important in mathematics?

6. What are some invariant angle relationships when parallel lines are cut by a transversal?

7. What is the sum of the measures of the interior angles of any triangle?

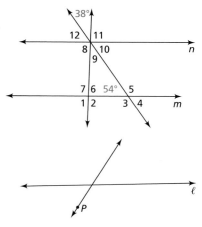

Vocabulary and Notation

In this investigation, you learned these terms and symbols. Make sure you understand what each one means and how to use it.

- alternate interior angles
- consecutive angles
- converse
- corollary
- corresponding angles
- exterior angle
- parallel lines
- supplementary angles
- transversal
- vertical angles
- $\not\cong$ (is not congruent to)
- $\parallel$ (is parallel to)

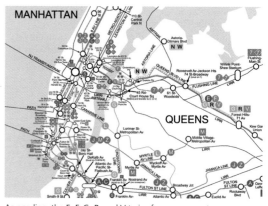

As one line, the E, F, G, R, and V trains form congruent vertical angles with the Shea Stadium train.

Answers

Mathematical Reflections

1. $m\angle 1 = 88°$, $m\angle 2 = 92°$, $m\angle 3 = 126°$, $m\angle 4 = 54°$, $m\angle 5 = 126°$, $m\angle 6 = 88°$, $m\angle 7 = 92°$, $m\angle 8 = 88°$, $m\angle 9 = 38°$, $m\angle 10 = 54°$, $m\angle 11 = 88°$, $m\angle 12 = 54°$

2. No; the consecutive angles are not supplementary.

3. $\angle AOC \cong \angle BOD$ (vertical angles). It follows by SAS that $\triangle AOC \cong \triangle BOD$, so $\overline{AC} \cong \overline{BD}$ by CPCTC.

4. See back of book.

5. Answers may vary. Sample: A proof makes it clear why a statement is true in general rather than in just a few specific cases.

6. Answers may vary. Sample: Alternate interior angles are congruent. Corresponding angles are congruent. Alternate exterior angles are congruent. Consecutive angles are supplementary.

7. $180°$

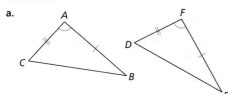

For a mid-chapter test, go to Web Code: bea-0252

Mid-Chapter Test

1. The triangles in each pair below are congruent. Use the tick marks to write correct congruence statements.

a.

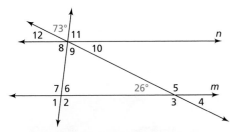

b.

c.

2. In the figure below, lines m and n are parallel. Find the measure of each numbered angle.

3. Suppose $\triangle CAT \cong \triangle PIG$.

   a. Name five pairs of congruent parts.

   b. Construct two such triangles. Use tick marks to mark the corresponding congruent parts.

4. Suppose that two students both construct a triangle based on the information given. Can you be sure that the students' triangles are congruent? Explain.

   a. $AB = 3$ cm, $BC = 4$ cm, $m\angle C = 40°$

   b. $XY = 1$ cm, $YZ = 2$ cm, $XZ = 1.5$ cm

   c. $m\angle T = 30°$, $m\angle O = 20°$, $m\angle M = 130°$

5. Determine whether you have enough information to prove that the triangles in each pair are congruent. If you do have enough information, state which triangle congruence theorem or postulate guarantees that they are congruent. The triangles are not necessarily drawn to scale.

   a.

   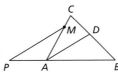

   b.

   c.   d.

6. In the figure below, $\overline{AD}$ bisects $\angle CAB$ and $\overline{PM} \parallel \overline{AD}$. Prove that $\triangle APM$ is isosceles.

7. Find x, y, and z.

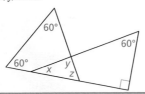

Assessment Resources

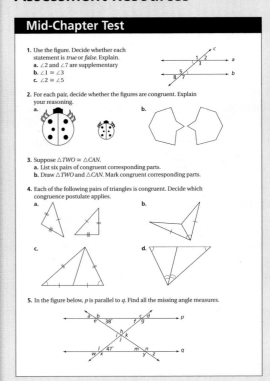

Also available: Form B

Mid-Chapter Test

1. **a–b.** Students' answers may have letters permuted. Samples are given.

   a. $\triangle ABC \cong \triangle FED$

   b. $\triangle ISO \cong \triangle GRT$ or $\triangle ISO \cong \triangle GTR$

   c. $\triangle NMA \cong \triangle ZYX$

2. $m\angle 1 = 81°$, $m\angle 2 = 99°$, $m\angle 3 = 154°$, $m\angle 4 = 26°$, $m\angle 5 = 154°$, $m\angle 6 = 81°$, $m\angle 7 = 99°$, $m\angle 8 = 81°$, $m\angle 9 = 73°$, $m\angle 10 = 26°$, $m\angle 11 = 81°$, $m\angle 12 = 26°$

3. **a.** any five of the following:
   $\overline{CA} \cong \overline{PI}$,
   $\overline{AT} \cong \overline{IG}$, $\overline{CT} \cong \overline{PG}$, $\angle C \cong \angle P$,
   $\angle A \cong \angle I$, $\angle T \cong \angle G$

   b. Check students' work.

4. **a.** No; SSA is not a valid congruence test.

   b. Yes; SSS guarantees congruence.

   c. No; AAA is not a valid congruence test.

5. See back of book.

6. See back of book.

7. $x = 30°$, $y = 90°$, $z = 60°$

Investigation Overview

In this investigation, students construct both mathematical and nonmathematical arguments. As they move toward reading and writing more formal proofs, students learn there are many correct ways to prove the same fact. There are also many ways to present a proof, and the working proof may look different from the final proof. Because there are so many proofs for students to work through in this investigation, it may take longer than others in this chapter.

You may wish to assign Questions 1–3 for students to think and write about during the investigation.

Learning Goals

- Use a variety of ways to write and present proofs.
- Identify the hypothesis and conclusion of a given statement.
- Write simple triangle congruence proofs.
- Use the Perpendicular Bisector Theorem and the Isosceles Triangle Theorem to prove that two parts of a figure are congruent.

Habits and Skills

- Identify the hypothesis and conclusion of a statement.
- Use different methods to write a proof.
- Choose an appropriate way to present a proof.
- Recognize the difference between experimentation and deduction.

Investigation 2C
Writing Proofs

In *Writing Proofs,* you will study mathematical proof. A proof is a logical argument that explains a new observation using facts you already know. You start with statements that everyone agrees with. Then you use logic that everyone agrees with to convince yourself and others that other statements have to follow. Your proof must be clear, so that alternate interpretations or counterexamples are not possible.

By the end of this investigation, you will be able to answer questions like these.

1. What are the different ways to organize and analyze a proof?
2. What is the Perpendicular Bisector Theorem?
3. In the statement "All trees are green," what is the hypothesis and what is the conclusion?

You will learn how to

- use a variety of ways to write and present proofs
- identify the hypothesis and conclusion of a given statement
- write simple triangle congruence proofs
- use the Perpendicular Bisector Theorem and the Isosceles Triangle Theorem to prove that corresponding parts of a figure are congruent

You will develop these habits and skills:

- Identify the hypothesis and conclusion of a statement.
- Use different methods to write a proof.
- Choose an appropriate way to present a proof.
- Recognize the difference between experimentation and deduction.

The triangle formed by this ski bridge has congruent legs and congruent base angles.

Investigation Road Map

LESSON 2.9, *Getting Started,* prepares students for more formal proof writing.

LESSON 2.10, *What Does a Proof Look Like?,* presents samples of a proof written in several styles.

LESSON 2.11, *Analyzing the Statement,* provides an explanation of hypothesis and conclusion.

LESSON 2.12, *Analysis of a Proof,* presents two proof writing methods, the visual scan and the flow chart.

LESSON 2.13, *The Reverse List,* presents another proof method.

LESSON 2.14, *Practicing Your Proof-Writing Skills,* explains the Perpendicular Bisector Theorem and the Isosceles Triangle Theorem.

2.9 Getting Started

In previous lessons, you used assumptions and theorems to informally prove that triangles are congruent and lines are parallel. In this lesson, you will write more informal **proofs,** or convincing arguments, in preparation for writing formal mathematical proofs.

> How is the term *argument* used differently in mathematics than in everyday language?

For You to Explore

1. Draw a square and divide it into four equal parts. Write an argument that convinces a classmate that each part has the same area. Share your argument with a classmate. Is your argument convincing?

2. Draw a square and divide it into five equal parts. Write an argument that shows that each of the five parts has the same area. Make sure that your argument is convincing.

3. If you find the sum of an odd number and an even number, is the result an odd number or an even number? Write a convincing argument to prove that your result is correct for each of the following audiences.

   a. fourth graders

   b. algebra students

4. You know that the sum of the measures of the angles in a triangle is 180°. Use this fact to show that the sum of the measures of the angles in a quadrilateral is 360°.

Exercises *Practicing Habits of Mind*

On Your Own

5. Use the figure at the right. Ruth claims that $\triangle ABC \cong \triangle DBC$.

   Her argument states the following.
   - The triangles share side $\overline{BC}$.
   - $\angle ACB \cong \angle DCB$ because they are both right angles.
   - The diagram tells us that $\overline{AC} \cong \overline{DC}$.

   Does Ruth's argument support her claim? What triangle congruence postulate should she use to conclude that $\triangle ABC \cong \triangle DBC$? Explain.

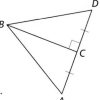

Answers

For You to Explore

1. Answers may vary. Sample: Start with a square with sides of length a. Its area is a^2. Connect midpoints of opposite sides. The result is four small squares, each with side length $\frac{a}{2}$. The area of each small square is $\frac{a^2}{4}$, and the sum of the areas of all the small squares is $4\left(\frac{a^2}{4}\right)$, or a^2.

2–3. See back of book.

4. Answers may vary. Sample: Draw a diagonal of the quadrilateral to divide it into two triangles. The sum of the angle measures of the quadrilateral is equal to the sum of the angle measures of the two triangles. By the Triangle Angle-Sum Theorem, this latter sum is 180° + 180°, or 360°.

Exercises

5. yes; SAS

Lesson Overview

GOALS
- Warm up to the ideas of the investigation.
- Use a variety of ways to write and present proofs.

Students draw and divide a square into 4 and then 5 equal parts. They write an argument that convinces a classmate that they have divided the square evenly. Then, students decide whether the sum of an even and odd number is even or odd, and write two arguments. They write one argument for a 4th grader, and the other for an algebra student. Finally, students argue that the angles of a quadrilateral add up to 360°.

FOR YOU TO EXPLORE	HOMEWORK
• Core: 1, 2, 3, 4	• Core: 5, 6, 7
• Optional: none	• Optional: 8a–c
MATERIALS	• Extension: 8d
• protractors	**VOCABULARY**
• rulers	• proof

Launch

Discussion the term *argument* and how its meaning differs in a mathematical context.

Explore

Students may have trouble differentiating between an argument appropriate for a 4th grader and an argument appropriate for an algebra student. You might lead a discussion about the use of variables and how to represent even and odd numbers.

For You to Explore

PROBLEMS 1 AND 2 ask students to divide a square into equal parts and write convincing arguments to show that the parts are truly equal.

PROBLEM 3 requires students to write two convincing arguments—one that a child would understand and one that requires algebra.

Wrap Up

Assign On Your Own exercises for homework. Point out that Exercises 5 and 6 require that students critique someone else's proof—a good preparation for writing proofs.

Exercises

HOMEWORK
- Core: 5, 6, 7
- Optional: 8a–c
- Extension: 8d

Maintain Your Skills

EXERCISE 8 Students write some algebraic proofs about odd and even numbers. They will need to understand how to represent odd and even numbers algebraically.

---

6. **What's Wrong Here?** Ruth was asked to make a conjecture about the figure below and then prove it. The given information is $\angle ABC \cong \angle ACB$ and $\overline{BE} \cong \overline{CD}$.

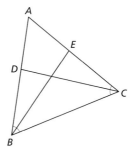

Ruth decided that $\triangle BDC \cong \triangle CEB$. She used the following argument.
- The triangles share side $\overline{BC}$.
- This, with the given information, shows that $\triangle BDC \cong \triangle CEB$ by SAS.

Explain what is wrong with Ruth's argument.

7. Write an argument to show that the measure of one of a triangle's exterior angles is equal to the sum of the measures of the two opposite interior angles. Use the figure below to show that $m\angle DAB = m\angle B + m\angle C$.

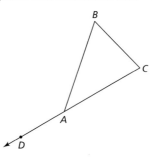

Maintain Your Skills

8. Prove each of the following statements using algebra.

   a. The sum of two even numbers is even.

   b. The sum of two odd numbers is even.

   c. The product of an even number and another number is even.

   d. **Take It Further** The product of two odd numbers is odd.

In this stained glass suncatcher, which is greater, $m\angle C$ or $m\angle J$? Give a convincing argument.

Answers

6. The pair of congruent angles is not an included pair.

7. See back of book.

8. **a.** Two even numbers can be written as $2a$ and $2b$. Their sum is $2a + 2b = 2(a + b)$, which is an even number.

   b. Two odd numbers can be written as $2a + 1$ and $2b + 1$. Their sum is $2a + 1 + 2b + 1 = 2a + 2b + 2 = 2(a + b + 1)$, which is an even number.

   c. An even number can be written as $2a$. The other number can be written as b (we don't know if it is even or odd). The product is $(2a)b = 2(ab)$, which is an even number.

   d. Two odd numbers can be written as $2a + 1$ and $2b + 1$. Their product is $(2a + 1)(2b + 1) = 4ab + 2a + 2b + 1 = 2(2ab + a + b) + 1$, which is an odd number.

.10 What Does a Proof Look Like?

As you might imagine, the way that you make your argument in a proof can vary. The rules of reasoning govern the logic of the proof, no matter who writes it. However, the way the proof looks depends on the customs and culture of the country where you study. Schools in China, Israel, France, or Russia sometimes teach ways to present proofs that are quite different from the methods taught in most American schools.

Following the diagram below are four different proofs that $\triangle ABE \cong \triangle DCE$. The given information is $\overline{AB} \parallel \overline{CD}$, and E is the midpoint of $\overline{AD}$.

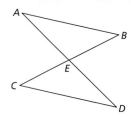

Two-Column Statement-Reason Proof

In the two-column statement-reason proof below, a set of true statements, logically ordered, appears in the left column. The given information usually appears first in the left column. The last statement shows what you are trying to prove.

The right column explains why each statement in the left column is true. You usually state the reasons as assumptions, theorems, or definitions, or as "givens." Givens are statements that one assumes are true for the proof.

Statements	**Reasons**
1. $\overline{AB} \parallel \overline{CD}$	1. given
2. $\angle ABE \cong \angle DCE$	2. Parallel lines form congruent alternate interior angles with a transversal.
3. $\angle BAE \cong \angle CDE$	3. Parallel lines form congruent alternate interior angles with a transversal.
4. E is the midpoint of $\overline{AD}$.	4. given
5. $\overline{AE} \cong \overline{DE}$	5. The midpoint is defined as the point that divides a segment into two congruent parts.
6. $\triangle ABE \cong \triangle DCE$	6. AAS

Lesson Overview

GOAL

• Use a variety of ways to write and present proofs.

This lesson uses one simple proof to show that you can present proofs in a variety of ways. It presents the paragraph proof, two-column statement-reason proof, and outline-style proof.

CHECK YOUR UNDERSTANDING
• Core: 1, 2, 3, 4
• Optional: none

HOMEWORK
• Core: 5, 6, 7, 8, 9, 11
• Optional: 10, 12

VOCABULARY
• counter example
• isosceles triangle
• legs
• vertex angle

Launch

Read the examples as a class and then use For Discussion as a summary.

Explore

For Discussion

PROBLEM 1 All of the proofs use the same methods to apply the AAS postulate: the parallel lines produce two pairs of alternate interior angles, and the midpoint produces two congruent line segments. In each proof, the writer carefully gives the reason for every deduction.

PROBLEM 2 Here are some advantages and disadvantages you might give for each proof style.

PARAGRAPH PROOF

- looks more like an actual explanation as opposed to a structured mathematical device
- less intimidating
- may be difficult to read without the notation displayed separately

TWO-COLUMN PROOF

- very organized; no need for a lot of writing
- rigid structure could be intimidating
- may be difficult to decide in what order to list the steps

OUTLINE STYLES

- organized, but not as harshly as the two-column proof
- less writing
- *because* and *therefore* notation confusing
- does not give all the details

Wrap Up

Before assigning the Check Your Understanding exercises, discuss the difference between *deduction* and *experimentation* with your students. In the first four exercises, students compare results from experimentation with a deductive proof.

Assessment Resources

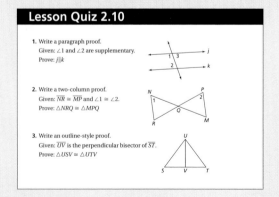

Lesson Quiz 2.10

1. Write a paragraph proof.
Given: ∠1 and ∠2 are supplementary.
Prove: $j \parallel k$

2. Write a two-column proof.
Given: $\overline{NR} \cong \overline{MP}$ and ∠1 ≅ ∠2.
Prove: △NRQ ≅ △MPQ

3. Write an outline-style proof.
Given: $\overline{UV}$ is the perpendicular bisector of $\overline{ST}$.
Prove: △USV ≅ △UTV

Paragraph Proof

In the paragraph proof below, a series of sentences fit together logically to establish that the two triangles are congruent. The sentences are written in paragraph form.

Because $\overline{AB} \parallel \overline{CD}$, the alternate interior angles are congruent. So ∠ABE ≅ ∠DCE and ∠BAE ≅ ∠CDE. Also, because E is the midpoint of $\overline{AD}$, $\overline{AE} \cong \overline{DE}$. Therefore, △ABE ≅ △DCE by AAS.

> Notice that a paragraph proof consists of several sentences that contain both words and mathematical symbols.

Outline-Style Proof

Students who study in China may use an outline-style proof. You can use the symbol ∵ meaning *because* to indicate the given information. The symbol ∴ means *therefore*. It indicates that the information follows from the given information. You write the important reasons inside the parentheses.

∵ $\overline{AB}$ is parallel to $\overline{CD}$.

∴ ∠ABE ≅ ∠DCE (alternate interior angles)

∴ ∠BAE ≅ ∠CDE (alternate interior angles)

∵ E is the midpoint of $\overline{AD}$.

∴ $\overline{AE} \cong \overline{ED}$ (definition of midpoint)

∴ △ABE ≅ △DCE (AAS)

Students who study in Russia may use another type of outline-style proof. The proof below illustrates this type of proof. You make an outline of the written statements and justify each statement.

Given that $\overline{AB}$ is parallel to $\overline{CD}$ and E is the midpoint of $\overline{AD}$, △ABE ≅ △DCE by AAS because

1. ∠ABE ≅ ∠DCE (PAI Theorem)
2. ∠BAE ≅ ∠CDE (PAI Theorem)
3. $\overline{AE} \cong \overline{DE}$ (definition of midpoint)

For Discussion

1. Each of the four proofs above uses the AAS triangle congruence postulate to show that △ABE ≅ △DCE. What else do the four proofs have in common?

2. What are the advantages and disadvantages of each type of proof?

You have just learned several different ways to present a mathematical proof. However, you may still be wondering, "Why bother doing a proof at all?" This is a surprisingly complex question. The need for proof is a result of tradition, necessity, and culture.

Mathematicians are experimenters performing thought experiments. They build models, gather data, and use data to make conjectures. To reach a valid conclusion, mathematicians rely on deduction and proof. New insights, or results, come from reasoning about things that must follow logically from what they already know or assume.

Answers

For Discussion

1. Answers may vary. Sample: They all flow logically from hypothesis to conclusion, using postulates and previously established theorems to make deductions.

2. Answers may vary. Sample: Two-column statement-reason proofs are very organized and you don't need to do a lot of writing, but it may be difficult to decide in what order to list the steps. Outline-style proofs are also very structured, but may be hard to understand if all the details are not given. Paragraph proofs are more like ordinary writing and can be less intimidating, but they are less structured.

The combination of deduction and experimentation is one of the distinguishing characteristics of mathematical research. The results of mathematical research do not hold true because they are *observed* to hold true. Instead, mathematicians derive results logically from some very simple assumptions.

Early in your geometry course, you prove that two triangles are congruent for two reasons. Triangle concepts are important, and the structure of these proofs is relatively simple. In most of the proofs that follow, you can follow a straightforward plan.

- Determine which parts of the two triangles are congruent.
- Determine whether you have enough information to prove that the triangles are congruent. Which triangle congruence postulate (SSS, SAS, ASA, or AAS) can you use to prove that they are congruent?
- Organize the information. Then write the proof.

Exercises *Practicing Habits of Mind*

Check Your Understanding

1. Use the following conjecture to answer parts (a) and (b). The sum of the measures of the interior angles of an n-gon is $(n - 2) \cdot 180$.

   a. Describe an experiment you can perform to test this conjecture.

   b. Write a deductive proof to prove the conjecture.

> An n-gon is a polygon with n sides, where n is a whole number greater than or equal to 3.

For Exercises 2–4, use each figure and the given information to write a proof. Use a proof style described in this lesson.

2. **Given** $\overline{AB} \cong \overline{CB}$ and $\overline{BD} \cong \overline{BE}$

   Prove $\triangle ABD \cong \triangle CBE$

Answers

Exercises

1. **a.** Answers may vary. Sample: Use geometry software to draw convex polygons with different numbers of sides. Use the measurement and calculate features of the software to find the sum of the measures of the angles of each polygon. Check that the sums are the ones predicted by the expression $(n - 2)180°$.

   b. Answers may vary. Sample: Suppose you start with an n-gon. If you select a vertex and draw all the diagonals from that vertex, you get $(n - 2)$ triangles. The sum of the angles of the n-gon is equal to the sum of the angles of all these triangles, or $(n - 2)180°$.

2. $\angle ABD \cong \angle CBE$ by the Vertical Angles Theorem. Since $\overline{AB} \cong \overline{BC}$ and $\overline{BD} \cong \overline{BE}$, it follows by the SAS Postulate that $\triangle ABD \cong \triangle CBE$.

Check Your Understanding

EXERCISE 1 is another chance for students to devise an experiment and write a proof about a geometric fact.

Most students will not think of the case of nonconvex polygons, but if this does arise, here is a treatment for a nonconvex figure.

By drawing a diagonal, any pentagon is split into a triangle and a quadrilateral.

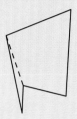

The sum of the measures of the angles of the pentagon is equal to the sum of the measures of the angles of the quadrilateral (360°) and the triangle (180°), which is 540°. You must be sure that the diagonal you draw lies entirely within the figure. The following figure shows a diagonal that does not lie entirely within the pentagon.

You need to prove that there is a diagonal in any (possibly nonconvex) pentagon that lies entirely within the figure. Take any vertex of the pentagon and call it P. There are two vertices of the pentagon (call them A and B) that are joined to this vertex by sides, and two other "remote" vertices. Choose the remote vertex closest to P. If it lies inside $\triangle PAB$, then it is the endpoint of a diagonal from P that lies inside the pentagon. If it lies outside $\triangle PAB$, then $\overline{AB}$ is a diagonal that lies inside the pentagon.

For a hexagon, the argument is slightly trickier. Using the same argument, show that any hexagon has a diagonal that lies entirely inside the figure. This diagonal divides the hexagon into two quadrilaterals, or a pentagon and a triangle. In either case, the sum of the measures of the angles is 720°.

You can handle the general case (n sides, not necessarily convex) by a strong induction based on the argument above.

3. Given $\overline{SV} \cong \overline{UT}$ and $\overline{ST} \cong \overline{UV}$

Prove $\triangle STV \cong \triangle UVT$

4. Given *SEBW* is a square.

Prove $\triangle SWB \cong \triangle EBW$

On Your Own

5. Standardized Test Prep In the figure below, $\triangle ABC$ is an isosceles triangle with $\angle A \cong \angle B$. $\overline{CD}$ is a median of $\triangle ABC$. $\overline{CE}$ bisects $\angle ACD$. $\overline{CF}$ bisects $\angle BCD$. Which of the following is a correct way to prove that $\triangle ACE \cong \triangle BCF$?

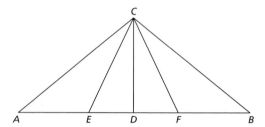

A. It is *not* possible to prove that $\triangle ACE \cong \triangle BCF$ based on the information given.

B. $\triangle ACD \cong \triangle BCD$ by SSS. This implies $\angle ACD \cong \angle BCD$ by CPCTC. So $m\angle ACD = m\angle BCD$. Because $\overline{CE}$ and $\overline{CF}$ are angle bisectors, $m\angle BCF = \frac{1}{2}m\angle BCD = \frac{1}{2}m\angle ACD = m\angle ACE$. So $\angle BCF \cong \angle ACE$. Because $\triangle ABC$ is an isosceles triangle with $\angle A \cong \angle B$, the sides opposite those angles are congruent. So $\overline{AC} \cong \overline{BC}$. Then $\triangle ACE \cong \triangle BCF$ by ASA.

> **Remember...**
>
> An **isosceles triangle** is a triangle with at least two congruent sides. You call the congruent sides **legs**. The **vertex angle** is the angle formed by the two legs.

Answers

3. It is given that $\overline{SV} \cong \overline{TU}$ and $\overline{ST} \cong \overline{VU}$. Since every segment is congruent to itself, $\overline{VT} \cong \overline{VT}$. Therefore, $\triangle STV \cong \triangle UVT$ by SSS.

4. Since all sides of a square are congruent, $\overline{SW} \cong \overline{EB}$. $\overline{WB} \cong \overline{BW}$ since a segment is congruent to itself. The angles of a square are right angles and are congruent, so $\angle SWB \cong \angle EBW$. Therefore, $\triangle SWB \cong \triangle EBW$ by SAS.

5. B

C. Because $\triangle ABC$ is an isosceles triangle with $\angle A \cong \angle B$, the sides opposite those angles are congruent. So $\overline{AC} \cong \overline{BC}$. Point D is the midpoint of $\overline{AB}$, so $\overline{AD} \cong \overline{BD}$. Then $\triangle ACD \cong \triangle BCD$ by SAS and $\overline{AE} \cong \overline{FB}$ by CPCTC. This implies $\triangle ACE \cong \triangle BCF$ by SAS.

D. Since $\overline{CD}$ is a median of $\triangle ABC$, D is the midpoint of $\overline{AB}$. So $\overline{AD} \cong \overline{BD}$. Because $\overline{CE}$ and $\overline{CF}$ are angle bisectors, they divide $\overline{AD}$ and $\overline{BD}$, respectively, into two congruent segments. So $\overline{AE} \cong \overline{ED}$ and $\overline{BF} \cong \overline{FD}$. Because $\triangle ABC$ is an isosceles triangle with $\angle A \cong \angle B$, the sides opposite those angles are congruent. So $\overline{AC} \cong \overline{BC}$. Since $\overline{AE} \cong \overline{BF}$, $\triangle ACE \cong \triangle BCF$ by SAS.

6. Draw an isosceles triangle and the bisector of its vertex angle. Prove that the two smaller triangles formed are congruent.

7. In $\triangle XMY$, $\overline{XE}$ is a median, and $\overline{XY} \cong \overline{XM}$. The bulleted list below is a sketch of a proof that $\triangle XEM \cong \triangle XEY$. Study the list. Then write the proof in either two-column, paragraph, or outline style.

- $\overline{XE}$ is a median, so E is the midpoint of $\overline{MY}$.
- $\overline{XY} \cong \overline{XM}$ is given.
- The two triangles share $\overline{XE}$.
- The triangles have three pairs of congruent sides.

8. What's Wrong Here? Below is a proof that shows that any two lines are parallel. Explain what is wrong with the proof.

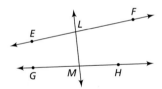

Suppose $\overleftrightarrow{EF}$ and $\overleftrightarrow{GH}$ are lines. Draw transversal $\overleftrightarrow{LM}$.

$\because \angle ELM$ and $\angle HML$ are alternate interior angles.

$\therefore \angle ELM \cong \angle HML$

$\therefore \overleftrightarrow{EF} \parallel \overleftrightarrow{GH}$ (AIP Theorem)

6. Suppose in $\triangle ABC$, $\overline{AC} \cong \overline{AB}$ and $\overline{AD}$ bisects $\angle CAB$. By the definition of an angle bisector, $\angle CAD \cong \angle BAD$. Every segment is congruent to itself, so $\overline{AD} \cong \overline{AD}$. Therefore, $\triangle ACD \cong \triangle ABD$ by SAS.

7. Answers may vary. Sample: It is given that $\overline{XE}$ is a median of $\triangle XMY$. Hence E is the midpoint of $\overline{MY}$, and consequently $\overline{ME} \cong \overline{YE}$. It is given that $\overline{XY} \cong \overline{XM}$.

A segment is congruent to itself, so $\overline{XE} \cong \overline{XE}$. Therefore, $\triangle XEM \cong \triangle XEY$ by SSS.

8. There is no basis for asserting that $\angle ELM \cong \angle HML$.

EXERCISE 10 Students need to understand the use of a counterexample to prove that a statement is incorrect.

EXERCISE 11 uses the definition of a circle to prove that triangles are congruent.

Additional Resources

PRINT RESOURCES
- Solution Manual
- Practice Workbook
- Assessment Resources
- Teaching Resources

TECHNOLOGY
- Interactive Textbook
- TeacherExpress CD-ROM
- **Exam**View CD-ROM
- **PHSchool.com**
  - Additional Practice
  - Mid-Chapter and Chapter Tests
  - Video Tutors
  - Vocabulary Puzzles

Additional Practice

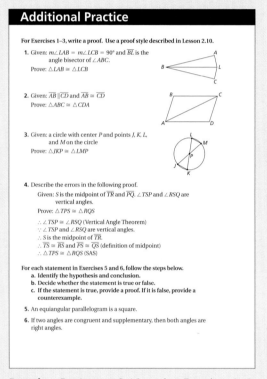

For Exercises 1–3, write a proof. Use a proof style described in Lesson 2.10.

1. Given: $m\angle LAB = m\angle LCB = 90°$ and $\overline{BL}$ is the angle bisector of $\angle ABC$.
Prove: $\triangle LAB \cong \triangle LCB$.

2. Given: $\overline{AB} \parallel \overline{CD}$ and $\overline{AB} \cong \overline{CD}$
Prove: $\triangle ABC \cong \triangle CDA$

3. Given: a circle with center P and points $J, K, L,$ and M on the circle
Prove: $\triangle JKP \cong \triangle LMP$

4. Describe the errors in the following proof.
Given: S is the midpoint of $\overline{TR}$ and $\overline{PQ}$. $\angle TSP$ and $\angle RSQ$ are vertical angles.
Prove: $\triangle TPS \cong \triangle RQS$

$\therefore \angle TSP \cong \angle RSQ$ (Vertical Angle Theorem)
$\because \angle TSP$ and $\angle RSQ$ are vertical angles.
$\therefore S$ is the midpoint of $\overline{TR}$.
$\therefore \overline{TS} \cong \overline{RS}$ and $\overline{PS} \cong \overline{QS}$ (definition of midpoint)
$\therefore \triangle TPS \cong \triangle RQS$ (SAS)

For each statement in Exercises 5 and 6, follow the steps below.
  a. Identify the hypothesis and conclusion.
  b. Decide whether the statement is true or false.
  c. If the statement is true, provide a proof. If it is false, provide a counterexample.

5. An equiangular parallelogram is a square.

6. If two angles are congruent and supplementary, then both angles are right angles.

Practice: For Lesson 2.10, assign Exercises 1–4.

---

9. In the figure at the right, $\overleftrightarrow{AB} \parallel \overleftrightarrow{ED}$ and $\overline{AB} \cong \overline{ED}$.

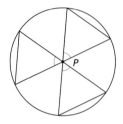

  a. Timothy uses this information to prove that $\triangle ABF \cong \triangle DEF$. Explain why his paragraph proof is incorrect.

  It is given that $\overleftrightarrow{AB} \parallel \overleftrightarrow{ED}$, so $\angle DEB \cong \angle ABE$ because parallel lines form congruent alternate interior angles with a transversal. And $\angle AFB \cong \angle DFE$ because they are vertical angles, and vertical angles are congruent. It is also given that $\overline{AB} \cong \overline{ED}$, so $\triangle ABF \cong \triangle DEF$ by ASA.

  b. Is it possible to prove that $\triangle ABF \cong \triangle DEF$? If so, write a correct proof.

10. To show that a statement is true, mathematicians require deductive proof. Explain how you can convince someone that the statement "All horses are the same color" is *not* true.

11. Use circle P below to prove that the three triangles are congruent. Point P is the center of the circle.

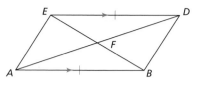

Maintain Your Skills

12. Use this conjecture about prime numbers. "Choose a whole number and square it. Then find the sum of the original whole number, its square, and 41. The sum is a prime number." For each value of n in parts (b)–(i) below, determine whether the sum is a prime number.

  a. What is a prime number?

  b. $n = 1$ **c.** $n = 2$ **d.** $n = 3$ **e.** $n = -1$

  f. $n = -2$ **g.** $n = -10$ **h.** $n = 15$ **i.** $n = 100$

  j. Determine whether the conjecture is true. If it is true, prove it. If it is not true, find a counterexample.

Go Online
PHSchool.com

For additional practice, go to Web Code: bea-0210

Remember...
A counterexample is an example that makes the statement false.

Answers

9. a. The wrong congruence postulate was used.

  b. Yes; change the congruence test used in Timothy's proof from ASA to AAS.

10. Exhibit two horses of different colors.

11. The angles marked in the diagram are given to be congruent. The segments that determine these angles are all congruent because they are radii of the same circle. Therefore, the three triangles are congruent by SAS.

12. a. A prime number is a whole number that has only two factors, 1 and itself.

  b–i. yes

  j. Not true; sample counterexample: $n = 41$ gives 1763, which is not prime (divisible by 1, 41, and 43).

Analyzing the Statement to Prove

Usually, statements that you prove are not expressed in the following Given-Prove form.

Given isosceles triangle *ABC* with *AB* = *BC*
Prove ∠*A* ≅ ∠*C*

Instead, you may make statements about things that you suspect are true, such as the results of an experiment. Most likely, you use English sentences to make these statements. For instance, you might say, "Vertical angles are congruent," or "Base angles of an isosceles triangle are congruent," or "If it rains this afternoon, then practice will be canceled."

In the above statements, how do you know what to prove? You can break each sentence into two parts, a hypothesis and a conclusion. In the sentence "Vertical angles are congruent," the hypothesis is "The angles are vertical angles." The conclusion is "The angles are congruent." Then you can rewrite the sentence "Vertical angles are congruent." You can write, "If two angles are vertical angles, then they are congruent."

Here are two rules of thumb that may help you recognize each part of a sentence.

- If a sentence appears in *if-then* form, the clause beginning with *if* is the hypothesis. The clause beginning with *then* is the conclusion.
- If a sentence does not appear in *if-then* form, the subject of the sentence is the hypothesis. The predicate of the sentence is the conclusion.

The fact that a sentence states a conclusion does not necessarily mean that the conclusion is true. Carefully read the table below before beginning the exercises.

> **Remember...**
> The **hypothesis** is what you are assuming is true. The **conclusion** states what you need to prove.

> Sometimes the word *then* is not stated. For example, "If it is raining this afternoon, practice will be canceled."

Sentence	Hypothesis	Conclusion
If two parallel lines are cut by a transversal, the alternate interior angles are congruent.	Two parallel lines are cut by a transversal.	The alternate interior angles are congruent.
The base angles of an isosceles triangle are congruent.	Two angles are base angles of an isosceles triangle.	These two angles are congruent.
Two triangles with the same area are congruent.	Two triangles have the same area.	The two triangles are congruent.
Congruent triangles have the same area.	Two triangles are congruent.	They have the same area.
People with large hands have large feet.	Certain people have large hands.	These people have large feet.
Out of sight, out of mind.	Something is out of sight.	It is also out of mind.

Lesson Overview

GOAL
- Identify the hypothesis and conclusion of a given statement.

Students write if-then statements to recognize the hypothesis and conclusion.

CHECK YOUR UNDERSTANDING
- Core: 1, 2
- Optional: none

MATERIALS
- Blackline Master 2.11

HOMEWORK
- Core: 3, 4, 5, 6, 7, 8, 9
- Optional: 10

VOCABULARY
- conclusion
- equiangular
- hypothesis

Launch

Before using the terms *hypothesis* and *conclusion*, present statement such as:
- Vertical angles are congruent.
- If you are hungry, then you have a snack.

These statements are either true or false. They have two parts, a hypothesis and conclusion.

Explore

Discuss identifying hypotheses and conclusions and review the chart.

Wrap Up

You may have students work on proofs from On Your Own.

Assessment Resources

Lesson Quiz 2.11

Rewrite each statement in if-then form. Then identify the hypothesis and the conclusion.

1. Odd integers less than 10 are prime.
2. An isosceles triangle has two congruent sides.

For each statement, follow the steps below.
  a. Draw a picture to illustrate the hypothesis.
  b. Decide whether the statement is *true* or *false.*
  c. If the statement is true, provide a proof. If it is false, provide a counterexample.

3. If a polygon is a pentagon, then the sum of the measures of its interior angles is 540°.
4. If two angles are supplementary, then one of the angles is obtuse and the other angle is acute.

Exercises

HOMEWORK
- Core: 3, 4, 5, 6, 7, 8, 9
- Optional: 10

Check Your Understanding

EXERCISE 1 Students determine which statements in the table are not necessarily true. If they determine a statement is not necessarily true, they should provide a counterexample.

EXERCISE 2 You may wish to provide copies of Blackline Master 2.11.

On Your Own

EXERCISES 4–9 Students decide whether the statements are true. If they decide the statement is not true, they should provide a counterexample. Students will need to know the following terms: *perpendicular*, *bisect*, *equilateral*, and *equiangular*.

Additional Resources

PRINT RESOURCES
- Solution Manual
- Practice Workbook
- Assessment Resources
- Teaching Resources

TECHNOLOGY
- Interactive Textbook
- TeacherExpress CD-ROM
- **Exam**View CD-ROM
- **PHSchool.com**
  - Additional Practice
  - Mid-Chapter and Chapter Tests
  - Video Tutors
  - Vocabulary Puzzles

Additional Practice

For Exercises 1–3, write a proof. Use a proof style described in Lesson 2.10.

1. Given: $m\angle LAB = m\angle LCB = 90°$ and $\overline{BL}$ is the angle bisector of $\angle ABC$.
   Prove: $\triangle LAB \cong \triangle LCB$

2. Given: $\overline{AB} \parallel \overline{CD}$ and $\overline{AB} \cong \overline{CD}$
   Prove: $\triangle ABC \cong \triangle CDA$

3. Given: a circle with center P and points $J, K, L,$ and M on the circle
   Prove: $\triangle JKP \cong \triangle LMP$

4. Describe the errors in the following proof.
   Given: S is the midpoint of $\overline{TR}$ and $\overline{PQ}$. $\angle TSP$ and $\angle RSQ$ are vertical angles.
   Prove: $\triangle TPS \cong \triangle RQS$

   ∴ $\angle TSP \cong \angle RSQ$ (Vertical Angle Theorem)
   ∵ $\angle TSP$ and $\angle RSQ$ are vertical angles.
   ∴ S is the midpoint of $\overline{TR}$.
   ∴ $\overline{TS} \cong \overline{RS}$ and $\overline{PS} \cong \overline{QS}$ (definition of midpoint)
   ∴ $\triangle TPS \cong \triangle RQS$ (SAS)

For each statement in Exercises 5 and 6, follow the steps below.
   a. Identify the hypothesis and conclusion.
   b. Decide whether the statement is true or false.
   c. If the statement is true, provide a proof. If it is false, provide a counterexample.

5. An equiangular parallelogram is a square.

6. If two angles are congruent and supplementary, then both angles are right angles.

Practice: For Lesson 2.11, assign Exercises 5 and 6.

Exercises *Practicing Habits of Mind*

Check Your Understanding

1. Which of the statements in the table on the previous page are not necessarily true? Explain.

2. In each sentence below, identify the hypothesis and conclusion.
   a. If two lines form congruent alternate interior angles with a transversal, then the lines are parallel.
   b. If n is any whole number, $n^2 + n + 41$ is prime.
   c. Two triangles are congruent if three sides of one triangle are congruent to three sides of the other triangle.
   d. Two lines that are parallel to a third line are also parallel to each other.

Go Online
Video Tutor
PHSchool.com

Web Code: bee-0775

On Your Own

3. **Standardized Test Prep** Which is the hypothesis of the following statement? If two angles are congruent, then they have the same measure.
   A. Two angles are congruent.   **B.** They have the same measure.
   C. Two angles are not congruent.   **D.** They do not have the same measure.

For Exercises 4–9, draw a picture that illustrates the hypothesis. Then determine whether the statement is true. If a statement is true, give a proof. If a statement is not true, give a counterexample.

4. Two lines that are perpendicular to the same line are parallel to each other.

5. A line that bisects an angle of a triangle also bisects the side that is opposite the angle.

6. Equilateral quadrilaterals are **equiangular.**

7. If a triangle has two congruent angles, it is isosceles.

8. Equiangular triangles are equilateral.

9. Equiangular quadrilaterals are equilateral.

Maintain Your Skills

10. A right triangle has legs $\overline{AB}$ and $\overline{AC}$ such that $AB = \frac{1}{2} AC$. Write a conjecture that relates CB to both AB and AC. Then prove that $(CB)^2 = 5(AB)^2$.

Go Online
PHSchool.com

For additional practice, go to **Web Code: bea-0211**

Answers

Exercises

1. The third statement is false; a right triangle with legs of length 1 and 4 has the same area as a right triangle with leg lengths 2 and 2, but they are not congruent. The fifth statement is false; there are people with large hands who do not have large feet. The sixth statement is false; you can keep things in mind even when they are not visible.

2. See back of book.

3. A

4. See back of book.

5. False; the sketch of the hypothesis shown here provides a counterexample.

6–10. See back of book.

12

Analysis of a Proof

You have had some practice writing proofs. However, the real question is, how do you come up with a proof in the first place? Coming up with a proof is sometimes called the "analysis of the proof."

Analysis is always necessary before writing a proof. Sometimes analysis is very brief and occurs almost without you noticing it. If you readily find the logic underlying the proof, then writing the proof is just a matter of expressing the logic clearly.

How can you begin a proof if you do not yet understand the logic? Suppose that you have many facts and clues, but none of them points to a solution. In this chapter, you will learn three techniques for analyzing proofs.

- visual scan
- flowchart
- reverse list

You may find that a single method makes the most sense to you and becomes your main tool for analysis. However, to be skilled at analysis, you will need to use all three techniques. In fact, if you are having trouble understanding a proof using one method, it can be quite helpful to switch from one technique to another.

The Visual Scan

A visual scan is a strategy that involves careful examination of the figures in the proof. First, you can mark a sketch of the figure to show all of the known congruent parts. Next, you can mark additional parts that you conclude are congruent. Finally, study the figure and a strategy for writing the proof may become clear.

> The visual-scan strategy may be the simplest way to analyze a proof. The strategy is similar to doing mental math. You simply see what you have to do.

A basketball player visually scans the court before passing the ball.

Lesson Overview

GOALS

- Use a variety of ways to write and present proofs.
- Write simple triangle congruence proofs.

You may wish to spend two days on this lesson. This lesson and the lessons that follow have many exercises for students to work on. See the Daily Planner at the beginning of the chapter for options. Students learn how to analyze a proof. They learn to start a proof by employing one of several analysis techniques: a visual scan, flowchart, or reverse list.

CHECK YOUR UNDERSTANDING
- Core: 1, 2, 3
- Optional: none

MATERIALS
- protractors
- rulers
- Blackline Master 2.12

HOMEWORK
- Core: 4, 5, 7, 8, 9
- Optional: 6, 10, 11

Launch

Give students time to express frustrations that they have coming up with a proof. Some students find this very difficult. Then read about the two techniques that this lesson presents. The more examples students see, the more comfortable they will become with beginning and writing proofs.

Explore

Have students read about the visual scan and lead them through Example 1. Students can use the outline that For You to Do provides to prove that the base angles of an isosceles triangle are congruent. For Discussion extends this proof to equilateral triangles.

For Discussion

In For You to Do, students proved that the base angles of an isosceles triangle are congruent. Think of an equilateral triangle as an isosceles triangle with any pair of sides serving as the two congruent ones. Apply the earlier proof twice to show that all three angles are congruent.

Now read through the flow chart in Example 2 with your students. Allow pairs of students to work on For You to Do Problem 3.

Example 1

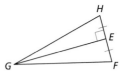

Given *E* is the midpoint of $\overline{HF}$. $\overline{EG} \perp \overline{HF}$.

Prove $\overline{HG} \cong \overline{FG}$

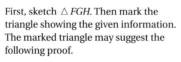

First, sketch △*FGH*. Then mark the triangle showing the given information. The marked triangle may suggest the following proof.

- Show that △*HEG* ≅ △*FEG* by SAS.
- Then conclude that $\overline{HG} \cong \overline{FG}$ because they are corresponding parts of congruent triangles.

You can use this strategy to write the proof below.

Proof Point *E* is the midpoint of $\overline{HF}$. So $\overline{HE} \cong \overline{FE}$. $\overline{EG}$ is the perpendicular bisector of $\overline{HF}$. So $m\angle GEF = m\angle GEH = 90°$. It follows that $\angle GEF \cong \angle GEH$. Triangle *HEG* and △*FEG* share $\overline{EG}$. So △*HEG* ≅ △*FEG* by SAS. Since corresponding parts of congruent triangles are congruent, $\overline{HG} \cong \overline{FG}$.

For You to Do

1. Use the visual-scan strategy. Prove that the base angles of an isosceles triangle are congruent. Below is an outline for your proof.

   - First sketch an isosceles triangle. Label its vertices.
   - Construct the bisector of the vertex angle. Label the point where the bisector intersects the base of the triangle.
   - Show that the two triangles formed by the bisector are congruent.
   - Conclude that the base angles of the isosceles triangle are congruent.

For Discussion

2. How can you use a proof like the one above to prove that an equilateral triangle is equiangular?

In the proofs above, you used the CPCTC strategy to prove that corresponding sides or corresponding angles of two triangles are congruent. To show that two segments or angles are congruent, you can use this strategy:

> This strategy is simple and direct. Can you only use it with triangles, though?

- First, find two triangles that contain the segments or the angles that you are trying to prove congruent. Prove that the triangles are congruent.
- Then, conclude that the segments or the angles are congruent, because they are corresponding parts of congruent triangles.

   Keep the CPCTC strategy in mind as you work on this lesson. Notice how often you use it.

Answers

For You to Do

1.

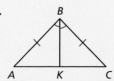

We are given isosceles △*ABC* with $\overline{AB} \cong \overline{CB}$ and with $\overline{BK}$ bisecting ∠*ABC*, where *K* is on $\overline{AC}$. By the definition of an angle bisector, ∠*ABK* ≅ ∠*CBK*. Since a segment is congruent to itself, $\overline{BK} \cong \overline{BK}$.

Hence △*ABK* ≅ △*CBK* by SAS. Therefore, ∠*A* ≅ ∠*C* by CPCTC.

For Discussion

2. Assume all three sides of △*XYZ* are congruent. Since *XY* = *ZY*, it follows from what was proved above that ∠*X* ≅ ∠*Z*. Likewise, since *YZ* = *XZ*, it follows that ∠*X* ≅ ∠*Y*. Since congruence is transitive, all three angles are congruent.

The Flowchart

The flowchart strategy is a "top-down" analysis technique. For instance, at the top of the flowchart you write statements about what you know is true. Below each statement you write conclusions based on the statement. You continue to write statements, moving down in the flowchart, until you reach the desired conclusion. An example of a flowchart is shown in Example 2.

Example 2

Given isosceles $\triangle ABC$ with $\overline{AB} \cong \overline{CB}$ and $\overline{AE} \cong \overline{CD}$

Prove $\angle BDE \cong \angle BED$

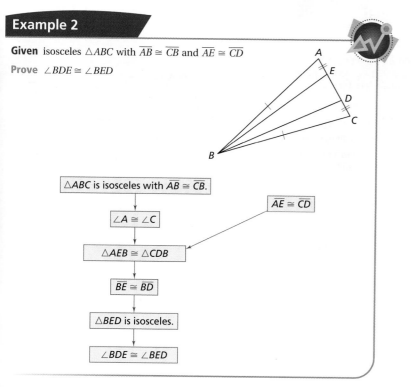

```
┌─────────────────────────────────────┐
│ △ABC is isosceles with AB ≅ CB.     │
└─────────────────────────────────────┘
               │
               ▼
        ┌──────────┐         ┌──────────┐
        │ ∠A ≅ ∠C  │         │ AE ≅ CD  │
        └──────────┘         └──────────┘
               │                  │
               ▼                  │
        ┌──────────────┐ ◄────────┘
        │ △AEB ≅ △CDB  │
        └──────────────┘
               │
               ▼
        ┌──────────┐
        │ BE ≅ BD  │
        └──────────┘
               │
               ▼
        ┌────────────────────┐
        │ △BED is isosceles. │
        └────────────────────┘
               │
               ▼
        ┌────────────────┐
        │ ∠BDE ≅ ∠BED    │
        └────────────────┘
```

For You to Do

3. Write the proof that is outlined in the flowchart above.

Habits of Mind

Be concise. When you write a proof, leave out any unnecessary information. A well-written proof takes the most direct route through the flowchart.

A flowchart strategy has several advantages. When a flowchart is complete, it forms an outline for writing the actual proof. A flowchart also gives you a way to investigate and organize what you know, even if the entire proof is still unclear. You may also write any extra information in the flowchart. This information may help you generate alternate ways to write the proof.

For You to Do

3. $AB = BC$ (given), so $\overline{AB} \cong \overline{BC}$. It follows by the reasoning in the Problem 1 that $\angle A \cong \angle C$. Since $AE = BC$ (given), $\overline{AE} \cong \overline{BC}$ and thus $\triangle AEB \cong \triangle CDB$ by SAS. By CPCTC, $\overline{BE} \cong \overline{BD}$. Again use the reasoning in Problem 1 to conclude that in $\triangle BED$ you have $\angle BDE \cong \angle BED$.

Wrap Up

Discuss the benefits of the two techniques that the lesson presents. Then assign Check Your Understanding exercises as in-class work.

Assessment Resources

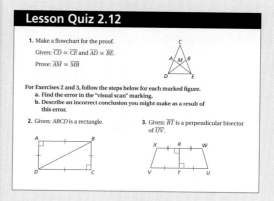

Lesson Quiz 2.12

1. Make a flowchart for the proof.

   Given: $\overline{CD} \cong \overline{CE}$ and $\overline{AD} \cong \overline{BE}$.

   Prove: $\overline{AM} \cong \overline{MB}$

   For Exercises 2 and 3, follow the steps below for each marked figure.
   a. Find the error in the "visual scan" marking.
   b. Describe an incorrect conclusion you might make as a result of this error.

2. Given: $ABCD$ is a rectangle.

3. Given: $\overline{RT}$ is a perpendicular bisector of $\overline{UV}$.

Exercises

HOMEWORK
* Core: 4, 5, 7, 8, 9
* Optional: 6, 10, 11

Check Your Understanding

EXERCISE 1 is a review of the visual scan technique. Students find the error in the markings on the given figure.

EXERCISE 2 is a review of the flow chart technique. Students make a flow chart for the given proof.

EXERCISE 3 Students write a proof based on a flow chart. You may wish to provide copies of Blackline Master 2.12 for students to use.

Exercises *Practicing Habits of Mind*

Check Your Understanding

1. **What's Wrong Here?** Kenneth is given the following problem.

   Given that $\overline{AC}$ and $\overline{BH}$ bisect each other and that $\overline{AB} \cong \overline{CH}$, show that $m\angle ABC = m\angle AHC$. What type of quadrilateral is *ABCH*?

   Kenneth uses the visual-scan strategy and marks the figure at the right.

   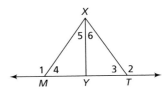

   a. What marking error did Kenneth make?

   b. What incorrect conclusion in a proof might result from his marking error?

2. Use the figure and the given information. Make a flowchart for the proof without writing the actual proof.

   Given $\angle 1 \cong \angle 2$. $\overline{XY}$ bisects $\angle MXT$.

   Prove $\overline{MY} \cong \overline{YT}$

   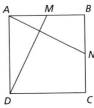

3. In the figure at the right, *ABCD* is a square. Points *M* and *N* are the midpoints of $\overline{AB}$ and $\overline{BC}$, respectively.

   a. The flowchart below outlines a proof that shows $\overline{AN} \cong \overline{DM}$. Copy and complete the flowchart.

   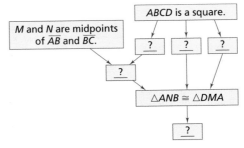

   b. Use the completed flowchart to write the proof.

Answers

Exercises

1. a. The halves of $\overline{AC}$ may not be congruent to the halves of $\overline{BH}$.

   b. The original markings would allow you to conclude that *ABCH* is a rectangle.

2. See back of book.

3. a.

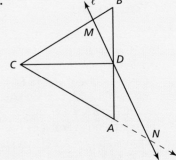

4. Standardized Test Prep $\triangle ABC$ is an isosceles triangle with $\overline{AB} \cong \overline{AC}$. $\overline{AE}$, $\overline{BF}$, and $\overline{CD}$ are medians.

The flowchart below outlines a proof that shows that $\overline{FB} \cong \overline{DC}$. Which of the statements below best completes the flowchart?

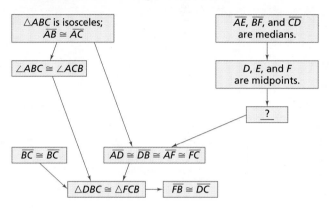

A. $\angle ABF \cong \angle FBC$

B. $\overline{AD} \cong \overline{DB}$; $\overline{AF} \cong \overline{FC}$; $\overline{BE} \cong \overline{EC}$

C. $\overline{AE} \cong \overline{AE}$

D. $\triangle ABE \cong \triangle ACE$

For Exercise 5, use the visual scan strategy to analyze the proof. Copy the figure onto a separate piece of paper, and mark the given information. Then write an outline for the proof.

5. Given $\overline{HJ} \cong \overline{HL}$ and $\overline{JK} \cong \overline{LK}$
Prove $\triangle HJM \cong \triangle HLM$

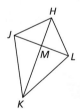

b. Because $ABCD$ is a square, all its sides are congruent. So $\overline{AB} \cong \overline{BC}$ and $\overline{AB} \cong \overline{DA}$. Also, all its angles are congruent. So $\angle MAD \cong \angle NBA$. Since $\overline{AB} \cong \overline{BC}$ and M and N are the midpoints of $\overline{AB}$ and $\overline{BC}$, respectively, it follows that $\overline{AM} \cong \overline{BN}$. Hence $\triangle ABN \cong \triangle DAM$ by SAS. By CPCTC, $\overline{AN} \cong \overline{DM}$.

4. B

5. Check students' diagrams. Proof outlines may vary. Sample:
- $\overline{HL} \cong \overline{HL}$ and $\overline{JK} \cong \overline{LK}$ (given)
- $\overline{HK}$ is congruent to itself.
- $\triangle JHK \cong \triangle LHK$ (SSS)
- $\angle JHM \cong \angle LHM$ (CPCTC)
- $\overline{HM}$ is congruent to itself.
- $\triangle HJM \cong \triangle HLM$ (SAS)

On Your Own

All of these exercises are important.

EXERCISE 6 Students do not need to use a triangle congruence postulate. They use the fact that perpendicular segments form 90° angles.

EXERCISE 7 is less straightforward. Students add angles to make new congruent angles, and then prove that two overlapping triangles are congruent.

EXERCISE 8 involves overlapping triangles and making two new congruent angles. Remind students that all equilateral triangles have three 60° angles.

EXERCISE 9 Students use the fact that isosceles triangles have congruent base angles. They must know the definition of median.

EXERCISE 10 Use congruent triangles to prove that a point on the perpendicular bisector of a segment is equidistant from the endpoints of that segment.

Additional Resources

PRINT RESOURCES
- Solution Manual
- Practice Workbook
- Assessment Resources
- Teaching Resources

TECHNOLOGY
- Interactive Textbook
- TeacherExpress CD-ROM
- **Exam**View CD-ROM
- **PHSchool.com**
  – Additional Practice
  – Mid-Chapter and Chapter Tests
  – Video Tutors
  – Vocabulary Puzzles

Additional Practice

For Exercises 1 and 2, follow the steps below for each marked figure.
   a. Find the error in the "visual scan" marking.
   b. Describe an incorrect conclusion you might make as a result of this error.

1. Given: $\overline{LK} \cong \overline{MN}$ and $\overline{LK} \perp \overline{KN}$.

2. Given: $\overline{QS} \cong \overline{RS}$ and $\angle Q \cong \angle R$.

3. Make a flowchart for the proof.
   Given: $\overline{DC}$ is the perpendicular bisector of $\overline{AB}$.
   Prove: $\overline{DA} \cong \overline{DB}$

4. Use a visual scan to analyze the proof. Then write an outline for the proof.
   Given: $\overline{AC}$ bisects $\angle BCD$, and $\angle 1 \cong \angle 2$.
   Prove: $\triangle BAC \cong \triangle DAC$

Prove each statement. Use a reverse list to write the proof.

5. If a point is on the bisector of an angle, then it is equidistant from the sides of the angle.

6. If a point is equidistant from the endpoints of a segment, then it is on the bisector of the segment.

7. If a triangle is a right triangle, then the acute angles are complementary.

Practice: For Lesson 2.12, assign Exercises 1–4.

---

6. **Given** $\overleftrightarrow{GF} \perp \overleftrightarrow{GH}$ and $\overleftrightarrow{GJ} \perp \overleftrightarrow{GK}$
   Prove $\angle JGF \cong \angle KGH$

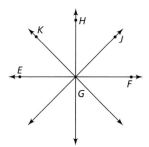

7. **Given** $FACG$ and $DABE$ are squares.
   Prove $\triangle FAB \cong \triangle CAD$

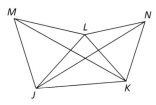

8. **Given** $\triangle LJM$ and $\triangle LKN$ are equilateral.
   Prove $\overline{MK} \cong \overline{NJ}$

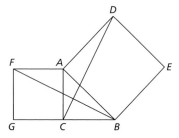

9. **Given** $\triangle QRT$ is an isosceles triangle. $\overline{QT} \cong \overline{TR}$. $\overline{VR}$ and $\overline{UQ}$ are medians.
   Prove $VR = UQ$

10. **Given** Point P is on the perpendicular bisector of $\overline{LM}$.
    Prove $PL = PM$

Go Online
PHSchool.com

For additional practice,
go to Web Code: **bea-0212**

Maintain Your Skills

11. Draw a coordinate plane. Plot points $O(0, 0)$ and $A(6, 0)$. Choose and label point B on the line $x = 3$ such that B is *not* on the x-axis. Prove that $\triangle AOB$ is an isosceles triangle.

Habits of Mind

Visualize. Before you write the proof, sketch a coordinate plane. Draw $\triangle AOB$ and the line $x = 3$. Then use the visual-scan strategy.

Answers

6. Since $\overleftrightarrow{GF} \perp \overleftrightarrow{GH}$, $m\angle HGJ + m\angle JGF = 90°$. Since $\overleftrightarrow{GJ} \perp \overleftrightarrow{GK}$, $m\angle KGH + m\angle HGJ = 90°$. By the basic moves of equations, it follows that $m\angle JGF = m\angle KGH$. Therefore, $\angle JGF \cong \angle KGH$.

7. Since $FACG$ and $DABE$ are squares, $\overline{FA} \cong \overline{CA}$, $\overline{AD} \cong \overline{AB}$, and $\angle FAC \cong \angle DAB$. Since $\angle FAC \cong \angle DAB$, $m\angle FAC + m\angle BAC = m\angle DAB + m\angle BAC$. Hence $m\angle FAB = m\angle CAD$. Therefore, by SAS, $\triangle FAB \cong \triangle CAD$.

8. It follows from the Triangle Angle-Sum Theorem that each angle of an equilateral triangle has a measure of 60°. Therefore the parts of $\angle MLK$ are congruent to the parts of $\angle JLN$, which implies $\angle MLK \cong \angle JLN$. Sides of an equilateral triangle are congruent, so $\overline{ML} \cong \overline{JL}$ and $\overline{LK} \cong \overline{LN}$. So by SAS, $\triangle MLK \cong \triangle JLN$. Hence $\overline{MK} \cong \overline{JN}$ by CPCTC.

9–11. See back of book.

The Reverse List

When you use the visual-scan strategy or the flowchart strategy, you start with what you know and work toward the final conclusion that you want to prove. The reverse-list strategy works in the opposite direction. You start with the information that you want to prove and work backward. You repeatedly ask yourself, "What information do I need?" and "What strategy can I use to prove that?"

Habits of Mind

Different Approaches
The reverse-list strategy is a bottom-up strategy rather than a top-down strategy.

Make a reverse list.

Below is an analysis of a proof that uses the reverse-list strategy.

Given $TUVW$ is a rectangle. X is the midpoint of $\overline{TU}$.

Prove $\triangle XWV$ is isosceles.

You need to prove that $\triangle XWV$ is an isosceles triangle.

Habits of Mind

Draw a diagram.
When you use the reverse-list strategy, how do you know which sides, angles, or triangles to try to prove congruent? A careful sketch often helps.

Need $\triangle XWV$ is an isosceles triangle.
Use A triangle is isosceles if two of its sides are congruent.

Need $\overline{VX} \cong \overline{WX}$
Use CPCTC

Need congruent triangles: $\triangle WXT \cong \triangle VXU$
Use SAS

Need two congruent sides: $\overline{TW} \cong \overline{UV}$
Use Opposite sides of a rectangle are congruent.

Need $TUVW$ is a rectangle.
Use given information

Need two congruent angles: $\angle T \cong \angle U$
Use Each angle in a rectangle is a right angle. So the four angles in a rectangle are congruent.

Need $TUVW$ is a rectangle.
Use given information

Need two congruent sides: $\overline{TX} \cong \overline{UX}$
Use The midpoint of a segment divides the segment into two congruent segments.

Need X is the midpoint of $\overline{TU}$.
Use given information

A complete reverse-list analysis outlines the proof in reverse order. Below is the proof that is outlined in the reverse list above.

Proof Point X is the midpoint of $\overline{TU}$. So $\overline{TX} \cong \overline{UX}$. $TUVW$ is a rectangle. So its opposite sides are congruent, and its four right angles are congruent. So $\overline{TW} \cong \overline{UV}$ and $\angle T \cong \angle U$. Therefore $\triangle WXT \cong \triangle VXU$ by SAS. So $\overline{VX} \cong \overline{WX}$ by CPCTC. This tells us that $\triangle XWV$ is an isosceles triangle.

Lesson Overview

GOALS

- Use a variety of ways to write and present proofs.
- Write simple triangle congruence proofs.

This lesson presents the third method of analysis. It is the reverse list. You start with the statement you want to prove and work backward.

CHECK YOUR UNDERSTANDING
- Core: 1, 2
- Optional: none

HOMEWORK
- Core: 3, 4, 5, 6, 7, 9
- Optional: 10
- Extension: 8

Launch

Begin by describing the reverse list process. Then slowly explain the example in the text.

Explore

Stress the need to ask the questions: "What do I need? What can I use to prove that?"

If students keep these questions in mind, the reverse list is easier to make. Since the text presents only one example of a proof using this technique, you may wish to complete a Check Your Understanding exercise in class.

Wrap Up

As a class, review the four points to remember located at the end of the lesson. Then assign Check Your Understanding exercises as in-class work.

Assessment Resources

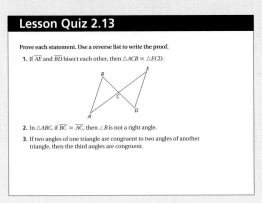

Lesson Quiz 2.13

Prove each statement. Use a reverse list to write the proof.

1. If $\overline{AE}$ and $\overline{BD}$ bisect each other, then $\triangle ACB \cong \triangle ECD$.

2. In $\triangle ABC$, if $\overline{BC} \cong \overline{AC}$, then $\angle B$ is not a right angle.

3. If two angles of one triangle are congruent to two angles of another triangle, then the third angles are congruent.

How do you decide which strategies to use when you write a reverse list? There is no foolproof method. However, there is a straightforward way to narrow down the number of strategies.

What results prove the needed conclusion?

Look back through your notes or back in your book. Find all the previously established results that you have used to prove a needed conclusion. For example, in the reverse list above, you needed to show that $\overline{TX} \cong \overline{UX}$. This is your needed conclusion. So you should look for previously established results with the conclusion "congruent segments." At this point, you have only used a few.

- The legs of an isosceles triangle are congruent.
- The corresponding sides of congruent triangles are congruent.
- The two segments formed by the midpoint of a segment are congruent.

Which results relate to what I know?

Once you narrow down your list, you go through the results one by one. Decide which result you can really use to prove your conclusion. How do you choose? You decide whether a relationship exists between the conclusion you need and each result. In this case, you can go down the list of results and ask a question for each one.

- Are $\overline{TX}$ and $\overline{UX}$ the sides of an isosceles triangle? No; $\overline{TX}$ and $\overline{UX}$ are not sides of the same triangle.
- Are $\overline{TX}$ and $\overline{UX}$ the corresponding sides of two congruent triangles? $\overline{TX}$ and $\overline{UX}$ are the corresponding sides of $\triangle WXT$ and $\triangle VXU$. The reason you want to prove that $\overline{TX} \cong \overline{UX}$ in the first place is so you can prove that $\triangle WXT \cong \triangle VXU$.
- Are $\overline{TX}$ and $\overline{UX}$ two segments that are formed by the midpoint of a segment? Yes; you know from the given information that X is the midpoint of $\overline{TU}$.

When you use the reverse-list strategy to analyze a proof, here are some points to remember:

- Use the given information to prove a needed result when possible.
- Use CPCTC to prove that corresponding sides or corresponding angles of congruent triangles are congruent.
- Right now, you have four ways to prove that two triangles are congruent: SSS, SAS, ASA, and AAS.
- The reverse-list strategy almost always works.

You may go down some dead ends before you hit the right path.

Answers

Exercises

1. a–b. Answers may vary. Samples are given.

  a. Let the intersection of the perpendicular bisector and $\overline{AB}$ be C.

   Need: $\triangle APB$ is isosceles.

   Use: Isosceles triangles have two congruent sides.

   Need: $\overline{AP} \cong \overline{PB}$

Use: CPCTC

Need: $\triangle APC \cong \triangle BPC$

Use: SAS

Need: $\overline{PC} \cong \overline{PC}$

Use: The triangles share this side.

Need: $\angle PCB \cong \angle PCA$

Use: Both are right angles because $\overrightarrow{PC}$ is a perpendicular bisector.

Need: $\overline{AC} \cong \overline{BC}$

Use: C is a midpoint because $\overrightarrow{PC}$ is a perpendicular bisector.

Exercises Practicing Habits of Mind

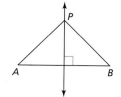

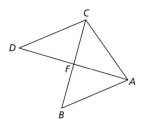

Check Your Understanding

1. In the figure at the right, P is a point on the perpendicular bisector of $\overline{AB}$.

   a. Make a reverse list that you can use to prove that $\triangle APB$ is an isosceles triangle.

   b. Write a proof that shows $\triangle APB$ is an isosceles triangle. Use your reverse list from part (a).

2. In the figure at the right, $\overline{AD}$ is the perpendicular bisector of $\overline{BC}$.

   a. Which triangles must be congruent?

   b. Write a proof that shows that the two triangles in part (a) are congruent.

On Your Own

In Exercises 3–8, prove each statement. Use a reverse list to write each proof.

3. If a triangle is isosceles, then the medians from its legs to the vertices of its base angles are congruent.

4. If a triangle is isosceles, then the bisectors of its base angles are congruent.

5. If two altitudes of a triangle are congruent, then the triangle is isosceles.

6. If a triangle is isosceles, then the altitudes drawn to its legs are congruent.

7. In isosceles triangle ABC, $\overline{AC} \cong \overline{BC}$. Point M is the midpoint of $\overline{AC}$. Point N is the midpoint of $\overline{CB}$. Prove that $\triangle CMN$ is an isosceles triangle.

8. **Take It Further** In the two triangles at the right, $\overline{AC} \cong \overline{DF}$ and $\overline{CB} \cong \overline{FE}$. $\overline{AM}$ and $\overline{DN}$ are congruent medians. Show that $\triangle ABC \cong \triangle DEF$.

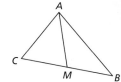

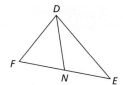

Exercises

HOMEWORK
- Core: 3, 4, 5, 6, 7, 9
- Optional: 10
- Extension: 8

Check Your Understanding

EXERCISE 1 Students can use the proof that they wrote for Exercise 9 in Lesson 2.12 to help them with the reverse list and proof for this exercise.

EXERCISE 2 does not state that you must use a reverse list, but it encourages students to practice the technique.

On Your Own

Students will need to draw their own diagrams for these exercises.

When students have completed these exercises, post a class list of the proven facts. Encourage students to also keep this list in their notebooks.

EXERCISES 3–8 contain important facts for students to prove, so assigning each of these exercises is a good idea. If this is too much for one night's homework, choose a couple of the exercises for students to complete in class.

---

b. Since $\overrightarrow{PC}$ is a perpendicular bisector of $\overline{AB}$, C is the midpoint of $\overline{AB}$ and hence $\overline{AC} \cong \overline{BC}$. Also, since $\overrightarrow{PC}$ is a perpendicular bisector of $\overline{AB}$, $m\angle PCB = m\angle PCA = 90°$. Since $\triangle ACP$ and $\triangle BCP$ share side $\overline{PC}$, these triangles are congruent by SAS. Also, by CPCTC, $\overline{AP} \cong \overline{PB}$. Thus $\triangle APB$ has two congruent sides and is isosceles.

2. a. $\triangle AFC$ and $\triangle AFB$

   b. $\overline{CF} \cong \overline{BF}$ ($\overline{AD}$ bisects $\overline{BC}$). $\overline{AF} \cong \overline{AF}$ (every segment is congruent to itself). $\angle AFC \cong \angle AFB$ ($\overline{AD}$ and $\overline{BC}$ are perpendicular). Therefore, $\triangle AFC \cong \triangle AFB$ by SAS.

3. See the proof for Exercise 9 of Lesson 2.12.

4–8. See back of book.

PRINT RESOURCES
- Solution Manual
- Practice Workbook
- Assessment Resources
- Teaching Resources

TECHNOLOGY
- Interactive Textbook
- TeacherExpress CD-ROM
- **Exam**View CD-ROM
- PHSchool.com
  - Additional Practice
  - Mid-Chapter and
    Chapter Tests
  - Video Tutors
  - Vocabulary Puzzles

Additional Practice

For Exercises 1 and 2, follow the steps below for each marked figure.
  a. Find the error in the "visual scan" marking.
  b. Describe an incorrect conclusion you might make as a result of this error.

1. Given: $\overline{LK} \cong \overline{MN}$ and $\overline{LK} \perp \overline{KN}$.

2. Given: $\overline{QS} \cong \overline{RS}$ and $\angle Q \cong \angle R$.

3. Make a flowchart for the proof.
Given: $\overline{DC}$ is the perpendicular bisector of $\overline{AB}$.
Prove: $\overline{DA} \cong \overline{DB}$

4. Use a visual scan to analyze the proof. Then write an outline for the proof.
Given: $\overline{AC}$ bisects $\angle BCD$, and $\angle 1 \cong \angle 2$.
Prove: $\triangle BAC \cong \triangle DAC$

Prove each statement. Use a reverse list to write the proof.

5. If a point is on the bisector of an angle, then it is equidistant from the sides of the angle.

6. If a point is equidistant from the endpoints of a segment, then it is on the bisector of the segment.

7. If a triangle is a right triangle, then the acute angles are complementary.

Practice: For Lesson 2.13, assign Exercises 5–7.

---

9. Standardized Test Prep Triangle ABC at the right is an isosceles triangle with $\angle ABC \cong \angle ACB$. $\overline{CD}$ is the bisector of $\angle ACB$. $\overline{BE}$ is the bisector of $\angle ABC$. Suppose you want to prove that $\overline{EF} \cong \overline{DF}$.

Which of the statements and reasons below complete the following reverse list?

Need	$\overline{EF} \cong \overline{DF}$
Use	CPCTC
Need	I
Use	I
Need	II
Use	II
Need	III
Use	III
Need	$\triangle BCE \cong \triangle CBD$
Use	ASA
Need	$\overline{BC} \cong \overline{BC}$
Use	The two triangles share the side.
Need	$\angle ACD \cong \angle DCB \cong \angle ABE \cong \angle EBC$
Use	definition of congruent angles
Need	$m\angle ACD = m\angle DCB = m\angle ABE = m\angle EBC$
Use	definition of angle bisector
Need	$\overline{CD}$ is the bisector of $\angle ACB$. $\overline{BE}$ is the bisector of $\angle ABC$.
Use	given
Need	$\frac{1}{2}m\angle ABC = \frac{1}{2}m\angle ACB$
Use	multiplication property of equality
Need	$m\angle ABC = m\angle ACB$
Use	definition of congruent angles
Need	$\angle ABC \cong \angle ACB$
Use	given

A. I. $\triangle BDF \cong \triangle CEF$; AAS
  II. $\angle CFE \cong \angle BFD$; the Vertical Angle Theorem
  III. $\overline{CE} \cong \overline{BD}$; CPCTC

B. I. $\triangle ADC \cong \triangle AEB$; SAS
  II. $\overline{AB} \cong \overline{AC}$; definition of isosceles triangle
  III. $\overline{BE} \cong \overline{CD}$; CPCTC

C. I. $\triangle ADC \cong \triangle AEB$; AAS
  II. $\overline{AB} \cong \overline{AC}$; definition of isosceles triangle
  III. $\angle A \cong \angle A$; the two triangles share this angle.

D. I. $\triangle BDF \cong \triangle CEF$; ASA
  II. $\angle BDF \cong \angle CEF$; CPCTC
  III. $\overline{BE} \cong \overline{CD}$; CPCTC

Maintain Your Skills

10. In $\triangle ABC$, $m\angle CAB = 90°$. To conclude that each statement listed below is true, what additional information do you need about the *angles* of $\triangle ABC$? About the *sides*?

  a. $\triangle ABC$ is half of an equilateral triangle.

  b. $\triangle ABC$ is half of a square.

  c. $\triangle ABC$ is half of an isosceles triangle.

Go Online
PHSchool.com

For additional practice,
go to **Web Code: bea-0213**

Answers

9. A

10. a. The other two angles measure 60° and 30°; one of the sides is half as long as $\overline{BC}$.

  b. $m\angle ABC = m\angle CBA = 45°$; $\overline{AC} \cong \overline{AB}$

  c. No additional conditions are needed.

Practicing Your Proof-Writing Skills

Below are some general guidelines for you to follow as you work on a mathematical investigation.

- *Explore* the problem. Use hand or computer drawings to help you understand the statement of the problem.

- *Explain* what you observe. If you can, justify your observations with a proof. If you cannot write a complete proof, describe the information you have. Then say what information is missing from your proof.

- *Summarize* your work. Include drawings, conjectures that you made, a list of important vocabulary words, theorems, rules or ideas that you discovered, and questions that require further exploration.

Below is the Perpendicular Bisector Theorem again, along with its proof.

Theorem 1.1 *Perpendicular Bisector Theorem*

Each point on the perpendicular bisector of a segment is equidistant from the two endpoints of the segment.

Proof Suppose $\overline{PC}$ is the perpendicular bisector of $\overline{AB}$. Then C is the midpoint of $\overline{AB}$. So $\overline{AC} \cong \overline{BC}$.

Also, because $\overline{PC}$ is the perpendicular bisector of $\overline{AB}$, $m\angle PCA = m\angle PCB = 90°$.

Triangle PCA and $\triangle PCB$ share $\overline{PC}$, so $\triangle PCA \cong \triangle PCB$ by SAS.

Since $\triangle PCA \cong \triangle PCB$, $\overline{AP} \cong \overline{BP}$ by CPCTC.

A similar argument proves that $\overline{AP} \cong \overline{BP}$ for any point P on $\overline{PC}$.

Therefore, any point on the perpendicular bisector of a line segment is equidistant from the endpoints of the line segment.

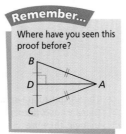

For You to Do

1. State and prove the converse of the Perpendicular Bisector Theorem.

Remember...
Where have you seen this proof before?

The measures of the angles in a triangle are related to the lengths of the triangle's sides. For example, suppose a triangle has two congruent sides. Then it must also have two congruent angles.

Proof Suppose $\triangle ABC$ is an isosceles triangle, with $\overline{AB} \cong \overline{AC}$. Construct the median from A. Call the point where the median intersects $\overline{BC}$ point D. Point D is the midpoint of $\overline{BC}$. So $\overline{BD} \cong \overline{CD}$.

Triangle ADB and $\triangle ADC$ share side $\overline{AD}$. So $\triangle ADB \cong \triangle ADC$ by SSS. Then, by CPCTC, $\angle B \cong \angle C$.

For You to Do

1. If a point is equidistant from the endpoints of a segment, then it lies on the perpendicular bisector of that segment. Proof: The only point on $\overline{AB}$ that is equidistant from A and B is the midpoint of $\overline{AB}$; it lies on the perpendicular bisector of $\overline{AB}$. Now consider a point P not on $\overline{AB}$ that is equidistant from A and B. Draw $\overline{PC}$. $\overline{PC} \cong \overline{PC}$ (every segment is congruent to itself). Also, $\overline{PA} \cong \overline{PB}$ and $\overline{AC} \cong \overline{BC}$. Hence $\triangle PCA \cong \triangle PCB$ (SSS).

Hence $\angle PCA$ and $\angle PCB$ are right angles. Thus $\overleftrightarrow{PC}$ is the perpendicular bisector of $\overline{AB}$, and P is on the perpendicular bisector.

Wrap Up

Your students now have multiple strategies for coming up with a proof, as well as a variety of methods for presenting a proof. Encourage them to use past examples as references as they complete the Check Your Understanding exercises in class.

Assessment Resources

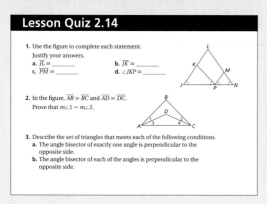
Exercises

HOMEWORK
- Core: 8, 9, 10, 11, 14, 15
- Optional: 7, 12, 13, 18, 19
- Extension: 16, 17

Check Your Understanding

EXERCISE 1 uses the Perpendicular Bisector Theorem to show that two triangles within a figure are congruent, and thus, two of their corresponding parts are congruent.

EXERCISE 2 asks students to investigate the Hinge Theorem: If two sides of one triangle are congruent to two sides of another triangle, and the included angle of the first is larger than the included angle of the second, then the third side of the first is longer than the third side of the second.

Theorem 2.6 *Isosceles Triangle Theorem*

The base angles of an isosceles triangle are congruent.

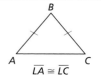

$$\overline{LA} \cong \overline{LC}$$

For You to Do

2. State and prove the converse of the Isosceles Triangle Theorem.

3. Can a scalene triangle have two angles the same size? Develop a conjecture that you can use to identify the largest, smallest, and middle-sized angles in a triangle. How can you prove your conjecture?

Remember...
A **scalene triangle** has no sides that are the same length.

Exercises *Practicing Habits of Mind*

Check Your Understanding

1. Use the figure below. $\overleftrightarrow{ST}$ is the perpendicular bisector of $\overline{RQ}$. Prove that $\angle SRT \cong \angle SQT$.

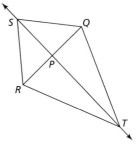

2. The SAS postulate implies that if two sides and the included angle of one triangle are congruent to two sides and the included angle of another triangle, then the third sides of the two triangles are also congruent.

   Suppose, instead, that two sides of one triangle are congruent to two sides of another, but that the included angle in the first triangle is larger than the included angle in the second triangle. What can you conclude about the third sides of the two triangles?

This result is sometimes called the Hinge Theorem. Can you think of a reason why?

Answers

For You to Do

2. If two angles of a triangle are congruent, then the triangle is isosceles, with two congruent sides opposite the two congruent angles. Proof: First note that both congruent angles must have measures less than 90°, otherwise the sum of the measures of all three angles would be greater than 180°. This ensures that the altitude from the third side lies entirely within the triangle. This altitude divides the triangle into two smaller triangles that are congruent to each other by AAS. Then you can conclude that the sides opposite the congruent angles are themselves congruent by CPCTC.

3. No; the largest angle of a scalene triangle is opposite the longest side, and the smallest angle is opposite the smallest side.

   It is enough to prove that if $\triangle ABC$ has $AB > BC$, then $m\angle BCA > m\angle BAC$. Use the figure below.

For Exercises 3–5, do each of the following.

- Draw the figure described.
- Use your drawing. Explain what the statement says about the figure.
- Write what you know about the figure. Then make and explain conjectures about what you think might be true.
- Try to prove the last sentence. Use any method.

3. Draw square *ABCD*. Construct rays $\overrightarrow{AB}$, $\overrightarrow{BC}$, $\overrightarrow{CD}$, and $\overrightarrow{DA}$. Choose point *E* on $\overrightarrow{AB}$, point *F* on $\overrightarrow{BC}$, point *G* on $\overrightarrow{CD}$, and point *H* on $\overrightarrow{DA}$ such that $\overline{BE} \cong \overline{CF} \cong \overline{DG} \cong \overline{AH}$. Quadrilateral *EFGH* is a square.

4. Draw a quadrilateral with congruent diagonals and one pair of opposite sides that are congruent. At least one of the four triangles into which the quadrilateral is divided is isosceles.

5. Draw an isosceles triangle. Pick any point along the base. From this point, draw lines parallel to the congruent sides, forming a parallelogram. The perimeter of the parallelogram is fixed, regardless of which point is picked along the base.

> **Remember...**
>
> In order to *prove* that a quadrilateral is a square, you need to show that its sides are all congruent and its angles are all congruent.

> You can do this exercise with geometry software.

6. The four statements below describe this figure.

- △*ABC* is isosceles with base $\overline{AB}$.
- $\overline{CD}$ is a median.
- $\overline{CD}$ is an altitude.
- $\overline{CD}$ is the angle bisector of ∠*ACB*.

Show that if any two of the statements are given, you can prove the other two statements. For example,

Given statements 1 and 2
Prove statements 3 and 4

Continue writing proofs until you have used two of the statements to prove the remaining two for all but one case. How many theorems do you have?

Write up your work for this exercise. Organize your sketches, notes, questions, ideas, and proofs. Prepare a page on which you will write the proof for the one remaining case. Write and hand in that proof when you know you have the information needed.

On Your Own

7. Refer to the diagram for Exercise 6. Write one new statement, either about △*ABC* or about △*ADC* and △*BDC*, that guarantees that all four of the statements in Exercise 6 are true.

8. Describe the set of triangles that meets each of the following conditions.

   a. The perpendicular bisector of exactly one side passes through the opposite vertex.

EXERCISES 3–5 have students make a drawing of the figure. Make conjectures about what is true about this figure and try to prove the given statement. Students can use geometry software.

EXERCISE 6 The directions state, "Show that if any two of the statements are given, you can prove the other two statements." This exercise requires six proofs. Clarify that students must identify all of the combinations before they begin. You may wish to split the class up into small groups and have each group tackle one of the proofs. Alternately, each group member can complete one proof.

On Your Own

EXERCISE 7 is a summary of Exercise 6.

EXERCISE 8 Students investigate triangles where the perpendicular bisector of a side passes through the opposite vertex. Note that it is possible for one side to have this property (an isosceles triangle). It is also possible for all three sides to have this property (an equilateral triangle). It is not possible for exactly two sides to have this property.

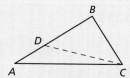

Since *AB* > *BC*, you can mark point *D* on $\overline{AB}$ so that *BD* = *BC*. Draw $\overline{DC}$. Clearly *m*∠*BCA* > *m*∠*BCD*. The Isosceles Triangle Theorem implies *m*∠*BCA* = *m*∠*BDC*. So *m*∠*BCA* > *m*∠*BDC*. But *m*∠*BDC* > *m*∠*BAC* by the Exterior Angle Theorem. Therefore *m*∠*BCA* > *m*∠*BAC*.

Exercises

1. Answers may vary. Sample: Since $\overleftrightarrow{ST}$ is the perpendicular bisector of $\overline{RQ}$, it follows from the Perpendicular Bisector Theorem that $\overline{SR} \cong \overline{SQ}$ and $\overline{TR} \cong \overline{TQ}$. Since $\overline{ST} \cong \overline{ST}$, △*SRT* ≅ △*SQT* (SSS). Therefore, ∠*SRT* ≅ ∠*SQT*.

2. The side opposite the included angle for the first triangle is longer than the side opposite the included angle for the second triangle.

3–8 See back of book.

EXERCISE 9 Students must use the Perpendicular Bisector Theorem to explain how to construct the center of a circle.

b. The perpendicular bisector of each of exactly two of the sides passes through the opposite vertex.

c. The perpendicular bisector of each of the sides passes through the opposite vertex.

You may find it helpful to construct some triangles that meet each condition and some triangles that do not. Explain what you find.

9. Use a cup or glass to trace a circle on a sheet of paper. Explain how to find the center of the circle.

10. **Standardized Test Prep** Brittany found a piece of broken pottery that looks like part of a circular dinner plate. She wants to determine the radius of the plate, but she has less than half of the plate. First, she traces the outline of the outer edge of the pottery on a sheet of paper. Then she draws two line segments with endpoints that are on different parts of the curve. Next, she constructs the perpendicular bisector of each line segment. She extends the perpendicular bisectors until they intersect. Finally, she measures the distance from the point of intersection of the perpendicular bisectors to a point on the curve. Why does this procedure guarantee that she has found the radius of the plate?

A. A line that is perpendicular to the tangent of a circle will always go through the center of the circle. Each bisected line segment is tangent to the circle.

B. The perpendicular bisector of a chord divides the arc associated with the chord into two congruent arcs. The length of each arc is equal to the radius of the circle.

C. A point on the perpendicular bisector of a segment is equidistant from the endpoints of the segment. The distance from the intersection of the perpendicular bisectors to a point on a circle is the radius of the circle.

D. The point of intersection of the perpendicular bisectors, along with the midpoints of the perpendicular bisectors, determine an isosceles triangle. The segment that connects the midpoints of the perpendicular bisectors is the base of the isosceles triangle. The radius of the circle is the length of one of the legs of the isosceles triangle.

11. Describe an algorithm that you can use to construct a circle that passes through the vertices of a given triangle.

12. A circular saw blade shattered. All you can find is a piece that looks like the figure below. Explain how to find the diameter of the blade so you can buy a new one.

How can you make a model of the original plate if you find only this piece?

Remember...
What does the term *algorithm* mean?

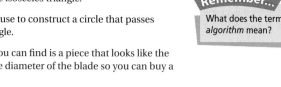

Answers

9. Answers may vary. Sample: Mark three points *A*, *B*, and *C* on the circle. Draw $\overline{AB}$, $\overline{BC}$, and their perpendicular bisectors. The point of intersection of the bisectors is the center of the circle.

10. C

11. Construct the perpendicular bisectors of two of the sides of the triangle. The point of intersection of these two bisectors is the center

of the circle that passes through all 3 vertices.

12. Pick three points *A*, *B*, and *C* on the rim of the blade. Draw the perpendicular bisectors of $\overline{AB}$ and $\overline{BC}$. They will intersect at a point *P*. Measure $\overline{PA}$ to get the radius of the blade. Double the radius to find the diameter.

13. Yes, the perpendicular bisectors of the sides of a triangle always meet at a single point. Suppose $\triangle ABC$ is any triangle and that ℓ, *m*, and *n* are the perpendicular

13. Show that if the hypotenuse and a leg of one right triangle are congruent to the hypotenuse and a leg of another right triangle, then the triangles are congruent.

This test for right-triangle congruence is sometimes called "hypotenuse-leg" and is abbreviated HL.

14. Draw several triangles. In each triangle, construct the perpendicular bisector of each side. Notice that the perpendicular bisectors in each triangle intersect in one point. Is this true for all triangles? Provide a proof or a counterexample.

Habits of Mind

Be efficient. If you use geometry software, you can make one construction and just drag it around.

15. Perform the paper-folding construction shown at the right. Start with a rectangular sheet of paper.

Fold *A* onto *B*, and crease along the dotted line.

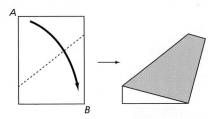

Then fold *C* onto *D*, and crease along the dotted line.

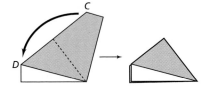

Unfold the paper. The creases should look like this.

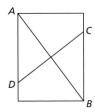

Prove that any point on $\overline{CD}$ is the same distance from *A* as from *B*.

EXERCISE 13 is an application of the conclusions found in Exercises 9 and 11.

EXERCISE 14 has students prove the Hypotenuse-Leg Theorem. This is a core exercise, since upcoming proofs use the Hypotenuse-Leg Theorem.

EXERCISE 15 Students must use a paper-folding experiment to show that one crease is a perpendicular bisector of the other crease.

bisectors of $\overline{AB}$, $\overline{BC}$, and $\overline{AC}$, respectively. Lines ℓ and m intersect in some point P. By the Perpendicular Bisector Theorem, P is equidistant from A and B and also equidistant from B and C. Hence it is equidistant from A and C. In the For You to Do that comes immediately after the proof of the Perpendicular Bisector Theorem, we proved the converse of the Perpendicular Bisector Theorem. It follows that P also lies on the perpendicular bisector of $\overline{AC}$.

14. Match up two triangles along the congruent leg so that the two right angles form a straight angle. The resulting triangle is isosceles, meaning the base angles are congruent. Therefore the two right triangles are congruent by AAS.

15. Because of the way the folds were made, $\overline{CD}$ is perpendicular to $\overline{AB}$ at the midpoint of $\overline{AB}$. Thus $\overline{CD}$ is the perpendicular bisector of $\overline{AB}$, and it follows from the Perpendicular Bisector Theorem that each point on $\overline{CD}$ is equidistant from A and B.

PRINT RESOURCES
- Solution Manual
- Practice Workbook
- Assessment Resources
- Teaching Resources

TECHNOLOGY
- Interactive Textbook
- TeacherExpress CD-ROM
- **Exam**View CD-ROM
- **PHSchool.com**
  – Additional Practice
  – Mid-Chapter and Chapter Tests
  – Video Tutors
  – Vocabulary Puzzles

Additional Practice

1. In the figure, *ABCD* is a rhombus. Prove that $\overleftrightarrow{AC}$ bisects $\angle A$ and $\angle C$.

2. In the figure, $\overline{BF}$ is a perpendicular bisector of $\overline{AC}$, and $\overline{BF}$ bisects $\angle DBE$. Prove that $\overline{BD} \cong \overline{BE}$.

3. Cut three scalene triangles out of a piece of paper. Use one triangle for each set of folding instructions.
   a. Fold one vertex to another vertex. Make a conjecture about the folded line you form.
   b. Fold one side to another side. Make a conjecture about the folded line you form.
   c. Fold so that a side overlaps itself and the fold contains a vertex. Make a conjecture about the folded line you form.

4. Use a cup or glass to trace a circle on a piece of paper. Fold the circle in half twice, vertically and horizontally. Describe the angles you form. Make a conjecture about the number of degrees in a circle.

Use the HL test for right triangles in each proof.

5. Given: $\triangle JKL$ is an isosceles triangle with base $\overline{JL}$ and $\overline{KM} \perp \overline{JL}$.
   Prove: $\triangle JKM \cong \triangle LKM$

6. Given: $\overline{DH} \perp \overline{FD}$, $\overline{DH} \perp \overline{GH}$, and $\overline{FH} \cong \overline{GD}$.
   Prove: $\angle F \cong \angle G$

Practice: For Lesson 2.14, assign Exercises 1–6.

There is no SSA triangle postulate. Two sides and a nonincluded angle of one triangle can be congruent to two sides and the corresponding nonincluded angle of another triangle without the two triangles being congruent.

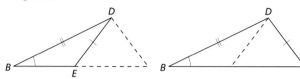

16. **Take It Further** Could there be an SS**A** postulate? Suppose you know that the nonincluded angle is the *largest* angle in each triangle. That is, suppose that the two sides and the largest nonincluded angle of one triangle are congruent to the corresponding two sides and largest angle of the other triangle. Can you conclude that the triangles are congruent? Explain.

> If SS**A** does guarantee triangle congruence, it is a generalization of HL. Explain.

17. **Take It Further** And is there an SSa postulate? Suppose you know that the nonincluded angle is the *smallest* angle in each triangle. Can you conclude that the triangles are congruent? Explain.

Maintain Your Skills

18. Use the figure at the right. $\overline{AD} \cong \overline{BC}$. $\overline{AB} \parallel \overline{DC}$. Point *E* is the intersection of $\overleftrightarrow{AD}$ and $\overleftrightarrow{BC}$. Prove that $\triangle ABE$ is isosceles.

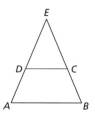

19. Here are two quite plausible statements.

In a triangle,
- the longest side is opposite the largest angle
- the shortest side is oposite the smallest angle

You may assume that both statements are theorems. Use one or both of the statements to help you prove the Triangle Inequality Theorem:

In a triangle, the length of one side is less than the sum of the lengths of the other two sides.

In other words, in $\triangle ABC$, prove that $AB < AC + CB$ (*Hint:* Use the figure at the right to write a reverse list.)

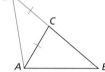

16–18. See back of book.

19. Answers may vary. Sample: If the longest side of a triangle is opposite the largest angle, and the shortest side is opposite the smallest angles, then the "middle" side is opposite the "middle" angle. So for any $\triangle ABC$, if $m\angle A < m\angle B < m\angle C$, then $BC < AC < AB$. In the diagram, $m\angle D = m\angle DAC$ because $\triangle ACD$ is isosceles. Since $m\angle DB = m\angle DAC + m\angle CAB = m\angle D + m\angle CAB$, you can conclude

that $m\angle DAB > m\angle D$, and hence $DB > AB$. But since $DB = AC + CB$, you also have $AC + CB > AB$.

Mathematical Reflections

2C

In this investigation, you studied mathematical proof. You learned different ways to think about and analyze the proof-writing process. You also learned several ways to write and organize a mathematical proof. You used these skills to practice and improve your own proof-writing techniques.

1. In the figure at the right, △ABC is isosceles with base $\overline{AB}$. $\overleftrightarrow{CP}$ is the bisector of ∠ACB. Point P is on this angle bisector.

   Prove that △APB is isosceles.

2. The hypotenuse and one of the acute angles of a right triangle are congruent to the hypotenuse and one of the acute angles of another right triangle. Prove that the two triangles are congruent or give a counterexample.

3. In the figure at the right, △ABC is isosceles with base $\overline{AB}$. $\overline{EA} \cong \overline{FB}$ and $\overline{AS} \cong \overline{BT}$. Prove that △AES ≅ △BFT.

4. The base and the angle opposite the base in one isosceles triangle are congruent to the base and the angle opposite the base in another isosceles triangle. Prove that the two triangles are congruent or provide a counterexample.

5. Write a reverse list for this statement about the figure at the right.

   If $\overline{TA} \cong \overline{TC} \cong \overline{TB}$, then △ABC is a right triangle.

   Then use the list to prove the statement.

6. What are the different ways to organize and analyze a proof?

7. What is the Perpendicular Bisector Theorem?

8. In the statement "All trees are green," what is the hypothesis and what is the conclusion?

Vocabulary

In this investigation, you learned these terms. Make sure you understand what each one means and how to use it.

- conclusion
- equiangular
- hypothesis
- isosceles triangle
- legs
- proof
- scalene triangle
- vertex angle

The steel cables form congruent angles with the roadway, so the triangle is isosceles.

EXERCISES 6–8 At the start of the investigation, you may have assigned these as Questions 1–3 for students to think and write about.

Mathematical Reflections

1. △APC ≅ △BPC by SAS, so $\overline{AP} \cong \overline{BP}$ by CPCTC. Therefore △APB is isosceles.

2. Since △ABC is isosceles, with $\overline{AC} \cong \overline{BC}$, it follows that ∠EAS ≅ ∠FBT. Therefore, △AES ≅ △BFT by SAS.

3. By AAS, it follows immediately that the triangles are congruent.

4. The triangles are congruent. Since the triangles are isosceles, the base angles in each are congruent. Since the angles opposite the bases of the triangles are congruent top each other, it follows from the Triangle Angle-Sum Theorem that the base angles in one triangle are congruent to the base angles in the other. Therefore the two triangles are congruent by ASA.

5–8. See back of book.

Investigation Overview

This investigation introduces quadrilaterals as planar and convex shapes, with four sides that intersect each other only at the endpoints. Students learn about quadrilaterals with specific properties, such as kites and trapezoids. Finally, students characterize the class of quadrilaterals called parallelograms. They study parallelograms through the converses of statements that have been proved.

You may wish to assign Questions 1–3 for students to think and write about during the investigation.

Learning Goals

- Define and classify quadrilaterals.
- Understand the meaning of converse and write the converse of a conditional statement.
- Understand the meaning of *always, never, sometimes* in mathematics.

Habits and Skills

- Characterize sets in a given class.
- Understand that the converse of a statement is not automatically true when the initial statement is true.
- Reason by continuity.

Investigation 2D

Quadrilaterals and Their Properties

In *Quadrilaterals and Their Properties*, you will explore four-sided figures. Chances are you already know a great deal about quadrilaterals. From the earliest elementary grades, you have constructed, measured, cut, and folded squares and rectangles. Now you will use this practical experience as you begin a more formal study of quadrilaterals. All of the properties of these shapes are important in understanding what makes each one unique.

By the end of this investigation, you will be able to answer questions like these.

1. What are some special properties of parallelograms? Of kites? Of trapezoids?

2. Are all squares also considered parallelograms? Are all parallelograms also considered squares?

3. If a statement is true, must its converse also be true?

You will learn how to

- define and classify quadrilaterals
- write the converse of a conditional statement
- understand the meaning of *always, never,* and *sometimes* in mathematics

You will develop these habits and skills:

- Characterize sets in a given class.
- Understand that the converse of a statement is not automatically true when the initial statement is true.
- Reason by continuity.

a nonconformist use of quadrilaterals

Investigation Road Map

LESSON 2.15, *Getting Started*, has students construct both a square and a rectangle with diagonals. Students list as many properties as possible.

LESSON 2.16, *General Quadrilaterals,* explores closed, skew, concave, and planar quadrilaterals.

LESSON 2.17, *Properties of Quadrilaterals,* introduces kites and trapezoids. Students also learn the mathematical meaning of *always, sometimes,* and *never* in the context of the properties of quadrilaterals.

LESSON 2.18, *Parallelograms,* introduces properties of parallelograms. Students also learn about converses.

LESSON 2.19, *Classifying Parallelograms,* further explores rectangles and squares, and introduces the rhombus.

Activating Prior Knowledge
Exploring New Ideas

You will use your basic knowledge of squares and rectangles to discover additional properties and characteristics of quadrilaterals.

For You to Explore

1. Use any method you choose to construct a square and a rectangle.

2. List as many properties as you can of the sides, angles, and diagonals of the square and of the rectangle.

3. Can you find a property of the rectangle that is not a property of the square?

Remember...
A diagonal is a segment that connects two non-consecutive vertices of a polygon.

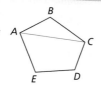

 **Exercises** *Practicing Habits of Mind*

On Your Own

4. Draw a quadrilateral with four congruent sides that is not a square. What do you call this type of quadrilateral?

5. Draw a quadrilateral with two congruent diagonals that is not a rectangle.

6. Draw a quadrilateral with four congruent angles. Must it be a rectangle?

7. Construct a rectangle with perpendicular diagonals that are 4 cm.

8. Write another description for the figure you constructed in Exercise 7. Use a different name for the quadrilateral.

9. **Take It Further** Without using a ruler to measure, fold a nonsquare sheet of paper into a square. How do you know that the figure you folded is a square?

Remember...
A polygon with exactly four sides is called a *quadrilateral*.

Maintain Your Skills

Find the area of each figure.

10.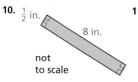
$\frac{1}{2}$ in.
8 in.
not to scale

11.
4 cm

12.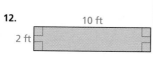
10 ft
2 ft

Go Online
Video Tutor
PHSchool.com
Web Code: bee-0775

Answers

For You to Explore

1. Check students' work.

2. Answers may vary. Sample: All sides are congruent, opposite sides are parallel, and adjacent sides are perpendicular, diagonals are congruent, diagonals are perpendicular, all angles are right angles

3. no

Exercises

4. rhombus

5. Check students' work.

6. yes

7. Check students' work.

8. square

9. See back of book.

10. 20 ft²

11. 16 cm²

12. 4 in.²

Lesson Overview

GOALS

- Define and classify quadrilaterals.

- Classify parallelograms.

Students list properties of the diagonals of a square and of a rectangle.

FOR YOU TO EXPLORE	HOMEWORK
• Core: 1, 2, 3	• Core: 4, 5, 6, 7, 8
• Optional: none	• Optional: 10, 11, 12
	• Extension: 9
MATERIALS	
• compasses	**VOCABULARY**
• protractors	• diagonal
• rulers	

Launch

Ask students to explain why their construction results in a square or a rectangle. Since they have no formal definitions of these figures, the explanations may not be precise.

Explore

This investigation explores statements such as the following:

- Every square is a rectangle.

- Not every rectangle is a square.

The underlying notion is the relation between a statement and its converse.

Wrap Up

Although students do not see a formal presentation of area until Chapter 3, they should have prior knowledge that will help them with these problems and exercises. The markings on the figures will allow them to differentiate squares and rectangles.

Exercises

HOMEWORK

- Core: 4, 5, 6, 7, 8
- Optional: 10, 11, 12
- Extension: 9

Lesson Overview

GOAL

- Define and classify quadrilaterals.

Students explore the definition of quadrilaterals, and discover quadrilaterals that are skew, self-intersecting, or concave.

CHECK YOUR UNDERSTANDING

- Core: 1, 2, 3
- Optional: none

HOMEWORK

- Core: 4, 5, 6, 7
- Optional: 9
- Extension: 8

VOCABULARY

- closed figure
- concave
- quadrilateral
- self-intersecting
- side
- skew
- vertex (vertices)

Launch

Assign the In-Class Experiment for students to work on individually. Point out the margin note that describes a closed figure.

Explore

In-Class Experiment

The point of this experiment is to explore the nature of a precise definition. The problems encourage students to carefully read and dissect the definition. Many students will quickly read the description given here and assume that they must draw a convex, plane quadrilateral that does not intersect itself. In fact, this task implies none of these properties. It is often the case that no student will draw a nonconvex, or non-planar, or self-intersecting quadrilateral. In this case, you should give such an example and challenge the class to tell what is wrong. In fact, nothing is wrong, as the ensuing discussion shows.

Wrap Up

Students may draw their figures on the board or overhead. Read the examples of self-intersecting, skew, and concave quadrilaterals.

It is difficult to write a precise definition. There is one more subtlety to discuss. If you draw a triangle and choose a point on one of its sides (not an endpoint), you can think of this figure as consisting of four line segments, two of which are collinear. It then qualifies as a quadrilateral according to the definition. You probably do not want to consider this figure a quadrilateral, and so should technically add something to the definition to that effect.

You have already explored some properties and characteristics of familiar quadrilaterals, such as squares and rectangles. Now, you are going to take a look at some less-common quadrilaterals.

In-Class Experiment

On a separate sheet of paper, sketch several figures that each have the following properties.

- The figure is made of four segments.
- The segments intersect at their endpoints.
- Each endpoint is shared by exactly two segments.

Answer the following questions about each of your figures.

1. Is your figure closed? Can you draw a figure with the three properties listed above that is not closed?

2. Must your figure lie on a plane? Can you show a figure with the three properties listed above that does not lie on a plane?

3. Does your figure intersect itself? Explain.

> A figure is **closed** if you can "walk" its outer edges and get back to where you started.

The following definition is not new to you, but here it is stated formally.

Definition

A **quadrilateral** is a figure that consists of four segments called its **sides**. The sides intersect at their endpoints, called the quadrilateral's **vertices**, so that each vertex is the endpoint of exactly two sides.

> The plural of *vertex* is *vertices*.

Are these figures quadrilaterals?

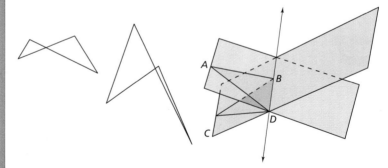

Answers

In-Class Experiment

1–3. Check students' work.

The definition of quadrilateral does not say that the sides of a quadrilateral are only connected to each other at their endpoints. The first two figures on the previous page have points in common in addition to their endpoints. You call such figures self-intersecting quadrilaterals.

The definition of a quadrilateral also does not say that the quadrilateral must lie in one plane. The last figure on the previous page does not. You call it a **skew quadrilateral.**

The two figures below are also quadrilaterals, but it is often inconvenient to include them in a discussion. You call them **concave** (or nonconvex) quadrilaterals. A concave quadrilateral has at least one diagonal outside the quadrilateral.

A figure is **self-intersecting** if you "walk" its outer edges and go through the same point more than once before you get back to where you started.

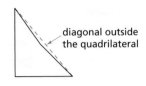

diagonal outside the quadrilateral

diagonal outside the quadrilateral

In this book, the term *quadrilateral* does not include self-intersecting, skew, or concave quadrilaterals, unless mentioned specifically.

Exercises *Practicing Habits of Mind*

Check Your Understanding

1. A figure is closed if you can walk its outer edges and get back to where you started. The definition of *quadrilateral* does not say that a quadrilateral must be closed. Can you draw a quadrilateral that satisfies the definition, but is not closed?

2. A figure is *planar* if all its points lie in the same plane. The definition of *quadrilateral* does not say that a quadrilateral must be planar. Can you draw a quadrilateral that satisfies the definition but is not planar?

3. Explain why each figure below is not a quadrilateral.

a. b. c. d.

While this issue is valid mathematically, it is unlikely that students will raise it, or get confused because you do not.

Assign the Check Your Understanding exercises for in-class work.

Assessment Resources

Exercises

HOMEWORK
- Core: 4, 5, 6, 7
- Optional: 9
- Extension: 8

Exercises

1. no

2. yes

3. a. The four segments do not intersect at their endpoints.

   b. Some endpoints are not shared by exactly two segments.

   c. There are only three segments in the figure.

   d. Some endpoints are not shared by exactly two segments.

On Your Own

EXERCISE 6 For a self-intersecting quadrilateral, the diagonals both lie outside the figure and the sum of its angles need not be 360°. However, a self-intersecting quadrilateral cannot have an angle-sum greater than 360°.

EXERCISE 7 For a skew quadrilateral, *inside* and *outside* are difficult to clearly define. The proof is quite involved.

Additional Resources

PRINT RESOURCES
- Solution Manual
- Practice Workbook
- Assessment Resources
- Teaching Resources

TECHNOLOGY
- Interactive Textbook
- TeacherExpress CD-ROM
- **Exam**View CD-ROM
- **PHSchool.com**
  - Additional Practice
  - Mid-Chapter and Chapter Tests
  - Video Tutors
  - Vocabulary Puzzles

Additional Practice

For Exercises 1 and 2, use the given true statement about polygons.
  a. Describe how the statement differs from the definition of a quadrilateral.
  b. Based on the statement, are all quadrilaterals also polygons? Explain.

1. A polygon is a closed plane figure with at least three sides.

2. The sides of a polygon intersect only at their endpoints and no adjacent sides are collinear.

3. Prove that the sum of the measures of the angles of a convex quadrilateral is always 360°. Include a drawing.

4. A trapezoid is a quadrilateral with exactly one pair of parallel sides.
  a. Can a trapezoid have 2 congruent sides? 3 congruent sides?
  b. Justify your answers with examples.
  c. Can a trapezoid have exactly one right angle? Two or three right angles? Justify your answers with examples.

5. A kite is a quadrilateral in which two pairs of adjacent sides are congruent.
  a. Can a kite have 3 congruent sides? 4 congruent sides? Justify your answers with examples.
  b. Can a kite have exactly one right angle? More than one right angle? Justify your answers with examples.

6. In the figure, △ABC is isosceles and $\overline{BD}$ is the perpendicular bisector of $\overline{AC}$. Write an outline for a proof that ABCD is a kite.

For Exercises 7–10, complete each statement with *always, sometimes,* or *never* to make the statement true. Justify your answer with a proof or examples.

7. The bases of a trapezoid are _____ congruent.

8. One diagonal of a kite _____ forms two isosceles triangles.

9. One pair of adjacent angles of a trapezoid is _____ congruent.

10. The sum of the measures of the angles of an isosceles trapezoid is _____ 360°.

Practice: For Lesson 2.16, assign Exercises 1–3.

On Your Own

4. **Standardized Test Prep** Which of the following statements is NOT true about a quadrilateral in a plane?

  A. Except for its endpoints, all the points on at least one of a quadrilateral's diagonals lie in the interior of the quadrilateral.

  B. At least one diagonal of a quadrilateral divides the quadrilateral into two triangles.

  C. The sum of the measures of the interior angles of a quadrilateral is 360°.

  D. The four vertices of every quadrilateral lie on a unique circle.

Review the following triangle theorems. Then complete Exercises 5–8.

- The sum of the measures of the angles of a triangle is 180°.
- The sum of the lengths of any two sides of a triangle is greater than the length of the third side.

5. The sum of the measures of the angles of a quadrilateral is always 360°. Explain why this is true.

6. Is the sum of the measures of the angles of a self-intersecting quadrilateral always 360°?

7. Is the sum of the measures of the angles of a skew quadrilateral always 360°?

8. **Take It Further** Prove that the sum of the lengths of any three sides of a quadrilateral is greater than the length of the fourth side. Determine whether your proof works for each type of quadrilateral listed below.

- concave
- self-intersecting
- skew

If your proof does not work for one or more types of the quadrilaterals listed above, can you write a different proof that will hold? Or does the proof fail because the property is not a characteristic of that type of quadrilateral?

> How would you define the angles of a self-intersecting quadrilateral?

Maintain Your Skills

9. Two angles of a quadrilateral both measure $x°$. The other two angles both measure $2x°$.

  a. Find the value of x.

  b. Find the measure of each angle.

  c. Can you determine the shape of the quadrilateral? Is more than one type of quadrilateral possible?

Go Online PHSchool.com

For additional practice, go to Web Code: bea-0216

Answers

4. D

5. You can dissect a concave quadrilateral into two triangles just like you can with a convex quadrilateral. The two triangles have angle sums of 180° each, and their combined angle sum is 360°.

6. no

7. no

8. Let ABCD be a convex quadrilateral. Draw diagonal $\overline{BD}$. By the Triangle Inequality Theorem, $b + BD > a$ and $c + d > BD$. It follows that $b + c + d > a$.

  a. The proof still works for concave quadrilaterals since points B, C, and D and points A, B, and D are all vertices of triangle.

  b. The same proof works for self-intersecting quadrilaterals because any three vertices determine a triangle.

  c. The same proof works for skew quadrilaterals because any three vertices determine a triangle.

9. See back of book.

Certain quadrilaterals have properties and characteristics that distinguish them from other quadrilaterals. For example, a square is the only quadrilateral that has four congruent sides and four congruent angles.

You can use the special properties of certain quadrilaterals to prove additional properties. You will do this in the exercises.

Below are the definitions of two special types of quadrilaterals.

Definition

A **trapezoid** is a quadrilateral with exactly one pair of parallel sides. The two parallel sides are called the **bases** of the trapezoid.

bases

Definition

A **kite** is a quadrilateral in which two adjacent sides are congruent, and the other two adjacent sides are congruent as well.

Habits of Mind

More than one meaning A trapezoid is sometimes defined as a quadrilateral with *at least* one pair of parallel sides. According to this definition, a parallelogram is a special type of trapezoid.

Example

Prove that one of the diagonals of a kite divides it into two congruent triangles.

First you must determine which diagonal appears to divide the kite into two congruent triangles. Unless your kite is a square, only one of its diagonals will divide the kite into two congruent triangles. This diagonal is sometimes called the *symmetry diagonal*.

Given kite *ABCD* with diagonal $\overline{BD}$
Prove $\triangle DAB \cong \triangle DCB$

Proof Because *ABCD* is a kite, $\overline{AB} \cong \overline{CB}$ and $\overline{AD} \cong \overline{CD}$. Triangle *DAB* and $\triangle DCB$ share $\overline{BD}$. So $\triangle DAB \cong \triangle DCB$ by SSS.

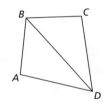

What is so special about the diagonals of a square?

Lesson Overview

GOALS

- Define and classify quadrilaterals.
- Understand the meaning of *always, never,* and *sometimes* in mathematics.

Students explore special quadrilaterals such as kites and trapezoids.

CHECK YOUR UNDERSTANDING
- Core: 1, 2, 3, 4, 5, 6, 7, 8, 9, 10, 11
- Optional: none

HOMEWORK
- Core: 18, 19, 20
- Optional: 12, 13, 14, 15, 16, 17, 21, 22, 23, 24, 25

VOCABULARY
- base angles
- bases of a trapezoid
- isosceles trapezoid
- kite
- trapezoid

Launch

Have students record definitions of quadrilaterals. Display definitions and drawings.

Explore

Discuss the Example and answer the question in the margin note.

Wrap Up

Read Minds in Action in preparation for the exercises.

Assessment Resources

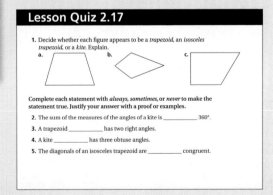

Lesson Quiz 2.17

1. Decide whether each figure appears to be a *trapezoid,* an *isosceles trapezoid,* or a *kite.* Explain.
   a.   b.   c.

Complete each statement with *always, sometimes,* or *never* to make the statement true. Justify your answer with a proof or examples.

2. The sum of the measures of the angles of a kite is _____ 360°.

3. A trapezoid _____ has two right angles.

4. A kite _____ has three obtuse angles.

5. The diagonals of an isosceles trapezoid are _____ congruent.

Exercises

HOMEWORK
- Core: 18, 19, 20
- Optional: 12, 13, 14, 15, 16, 17, 21, 22, 23, 24, 25

Check Your Understanding

EXERCISE 3 Students will see in Exercise 10, a trapezoid with congruent diagonals must have a pair of congruent sides (an isosceles trapezoid).

EXERCISE 5 The figure below shows an isosceles trapezoid in which one of the bases is congruent to the two legs.

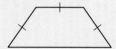

EXERCISE 6 One way to construct a trapezoid is to draw ∠*DAB* with a ray bisecting it and then draw a parallel to *AB* through *D*. The point where this parallel intersects the angle bisector can be chosen as a third vertex of the trapezoid, and almost any other point on $\overleftrightarrow{AB}$ can be the fourth vertex.

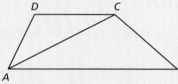

Or, use geometry software. Students can draw a trapezoid by taking parallel lines $\overleftrightarrow{AB}$ and $\overleftrightarrow{XY}$ (where *A* and *B* will be two vertices of the trapezoid).

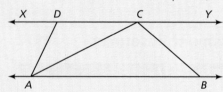

Choose point *C* on $\overleftrightarrow{XY}$ for a third vertex, and a point *D* on $\overleftrightarrow{XY}$ as a fourth vertex. Then, if they draw $\overline{AD}$, they can move *D* back and forth along $\overleftrightarrow{XY}$. If *D* is very close to *C*, then $m\angle CAD < m\angle DAB$. If *D* is very far from *C*, then $m\angle CAD > m\angle DAB$. Since geometric lengths vary continuously, there must be a position for *D* in between these extremes where $m\angle CAD = m\angle DAB$.

Note that this reasoning by continuity shows only that the figure in question exists. It does not tell you how to actually draw it.

EXERCISE 8 If one angle of a trapezoid is a right angle, then an angle consecutive to it must also be a right angle, since consecutive angles of parallel lines are supplementary. So if a trapezoid has one right angle, it must in fact have two right angles.

148 Chapter 2 Congruence and Proof

Minds in Action episode 4

Sasha and Tony are working on Exercises 2–8 in the Check Your Understanding section of this lesson.

Tony Here are the directions: Complete each sentence with *always*, *sometimes*, or *never* to make the statement true.

Sasha That's right. *Always* means you can prove it. So if we choose *always*, we have to be ready to write a proof.

Tony Proofs mean work. Let's try to answer *never*.

Sasha But for *never* we have to give a proof also—a proof that shows that the statement cannot be true.

Tony Well, maybe we can answer *sometimes*.

Sasha *Sometimes* means we have to show an example when the statement is true, and another example when the statement is false. We need two different examples!

Tony So these kinds of questions are like true-or-false questions. *Always* is the same as *true*.

Sasha Yeah, but *false* is divided into *sometimes* statements, which are sometimes true (and sometimes false), and *never* statements, which are never true.

Tony That's terrible—whatever we answer, we have to prove something!

Sasha Come on—proofs are fun!

Exercises *Practicing Habits of Mind*

Check Your Understanding

1. Which of the figures A–L, here and on the next page, appear to be trapezoids? Explain.

Answers

Exercises

1. *A*, *B*, *C*, *G*, *H*, *I*, *K*, and *L*

2. always

3. sometimes

4. sometimes

5. sometimes

6. sometimes

7. sometimes

8. never

9. Answers may vary. Sample: The distance between two parallel lines is the length of a segment perpendicular to both lines and with one endpoint on each line.

10. Let *ABCD* be an isosceles trapezoid with parallel bases $\overline{AB}$ and $\overline{CD}$ ($AB > BC$) and $\overline{BC} \cong \overline{AD}$. Draw lines through each of the four vertices perpendicular to the parallel lines. Let the intersection of $\overline{AB}$ and the perpendicular line through *D* be *X*, and let the intersection of $\overline{AB}$ and the

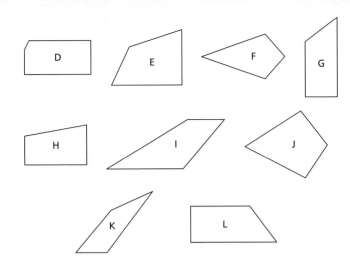

For Exercises 2–8, complete each sentence with *always*, *sometimes*, or *never* to make the statement true. Justify your answer with a proof or some examples.

2. The sum of the measures of the angles of a trapezoid is __?__ 360°.

3. The diagonals of a trapezoid are __?__ congruent.

4. Two sides of a trapezoid are __?__ congruent.

5. Three sides of a trapezoid are __?__ congruent.

6. One diagonal of a trapezoid __?__ bisects one of the trapezoid's angles.

7. Two angles of a trapezoid are __?__ right angles.

8. Exactly one angle of a trapezoid is __?__ a right angle.

9. Two parallel lines can be close to each other or far apart. So it is natural to refer to the distance between two parallel lines. Write a definition that describes the distance between parallel lines.

10. Read the following definition. Then prove that the base angles of an isosceles trapezoid are congruent.

Definition

An **isosceles trapezoid** is a trapezoid with opposite nonparallel sides that are congruent. Each pair of angles with vertices that are the endpoints of the same base are called **base angles**.

∠A and ∠B are base angles.
∠D and ∠C are base angles.

11. Prove that the diagonals of an isosceles trapezoid are congruent.

EXERCISE 9 This definition requires support from three propositions.

1. A line segment perpendicular to one of two parallel lines is perpendicular to the other. This is true because alternate interior angles formed by a transversal and parallel lines are congruent. So if one alternate interior angle is a right angle, so is the other.

2. The perpendicular distance is the shortest distance from a given point to a given line. Indeed, if you draw any other segment from the given point to a point on the line, this new segment is the hypotenuse of a right triangle, and so is longer than the perpendicular, which is a leg of the triangle.

3. Any two segments perpendicular to the same pair of parallel lines are congruent. Indeed, the two segments, together with the parallel lines, form a rectangle. Since a rectangle is a parallelogram, its opposite sides are congruent. This shows that the two perpendicular segments are congruent.

The proof that the base angles of an isosceles trapezoid are congruent (Exercise 10) uses this definition.

EXERCISES 10 AND 11 are important exercises. The definition of a trapezoid is oddly controversial. Some people define it as a quadrilateral with exactly two parallel sides, so that a parallelogram is not a type of trapezoid. Others use the definition in this text, which allows a trapezoid to have more than one pair of parallel sides, so that a parallelogram is a type of trapezoid.

At issue is the case of an isosceles trapezoid. If you define an isosceles trapezoid as a trapezoid with a pair of equal and opposite sides, then a parallelogram qualifies as an isosceles trapezoid. However, the theorem that the base angles of an isosceles trapezoid are congruent is false for a parallelogram, and you would have to reword this theorem in some clumsy way.

The authors have attempted to avoid this controversy in two ways:

- This text defines a trapezoid so that parallelograms (including rectangles, rhombuses, and squares) are types of trapezoids.
- This text defines an isosceles trapezoid as a trapezoid with one pair of equal and nonparallel sides. This excludes parallelograms (or rectangles, rhombuses, or squares) from being classified as isosceles trapezoids. By this definition, these figures are trapezoids, but not isosceles trapezoids.

In Exercise 11, students prove that the diagonals of an isosceles trapezoid are congruent.

perpendicular line through C be Y. Extend $\overline{CD}$ so that $\overleftrightarrow{CD}$ intersects the perpendicular line through A at M and the perpendicular line through B at N. *XAMD* and *BYCN* are rectangles. Opposite sides of rectangles are congruent. It follows by SSS that the four right triangles in the figure are congruent. By CPCTC, ∠ADX ≅ ∠CBY. And since ∠BCY ≅ ∠ADX by CPCTC, we have
$m\angle BCY + m\angle XDC = m\angle ADX + m\angle YCD$. Therefore, $m\angle BCD \cong \angle ADC$.

11. Let *ABCD* be an isosceles trapezoid with parallel bases $\overline{AB}$ and $\overline{CD}$ and $\overline{BC} \cong \overline{AD}$. Draw diagonals $\overline{AC}$ and $\overline{BD}$. Sides $\overline{AD}$ and $\overline{DC}$ in △ADC are congruent to sides $\overline{BC}$ and $\overline{CD}$ in △BCD. ∠ADC ≅ ∠BCD (by Exercise 10). Therefore △ADC ≅ △BCD, and $\overline{AC} \cong \overline{BD}$ by CPCTC.

Maintain Your Skills

Students will study converses in more depth in the next lesson. These exercises give a preview of the validity of statements and their converses.

Additional Resources

PRINT RESOURCES
- Solution Manual
- Practice Workbook
- Assessment Resources
- Teaching Resources

TECHNOLOGY
- Interactive Textbook
- TeacherExpress CD-ROM
- **Exam**View CD-ROM
- **PHSchool.com**
  - Additional Practice
  - Mid-Chapter and Chapter Tests
  - Video Tutors
  - Vocabulary Puzzles

Additional Practice

For Exercises 1 and 2, use the given true statement about polygons.
   a. Describe how the statement differs from the definition of a quadrilateral.
   b. Based on the statement, are all quadrilaterals also polygons? Explain.

1. A polygon is a closed plane figure with at least three sides.

2. The sides of a polygon intersect only at their endpoints and no adjacent sides are collinear.

3. Prove that the sum of the measures of the angles of a convex quadrilateral is always 360°. Include a drawing.

4. A trapezoid is a quadrilateral with exactly one pair of parallel sides.
   a. Can a trapezoid have 2 congruent sides? 3 congruent sides?
   b. Justify your answers with examples.
   c. Can a trapezoid have exactly one right angle? Two or three right angles? Justify your answers with examples.

5. A kite is a quadrilateral in which two pairs of adjacent sides are congruent.
   a. Can a kite have 3 congruent sides? 4 congruent sides? Justify your answers with examples.
   b. Can a kite have exactly one right angle? More than one right angle? Justify your answers with examples.

6. In the figure, △ABC is isosceles and $\overline{BD}$ is the perpendicular bisector of $\overline{AC}$. Write an outline for a proof that ABCD is a kite.

For Exercises 7–10, complete each statement with *always, sometimes,* or *never* to make the statement true. Justify your answer with a proof or examples.

7. The bases of a trapezoid are _____ congruent.

8. One diagonal of a kite _____ forms two isosceles triangles.

9. One pair of adjacent angles of a trapezoid is _____ congruent.

10. The sum of the measures of the angles of an isosceles trapezoid is _____ 360°.

Practice: For Lesson 2.17, assign Exercises 4–10.

On Your Own

12. Which of the following figures appear to be kites? Explain.

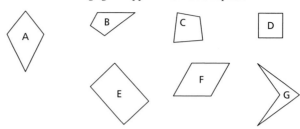

For Exercises 13–17, complete each sentence with *always, sometimes,* or *never* to make the statement true.

13. The sum of the measures of the angles of a kite is __?__ 360°.

14. The diagonals of a kite are __?__ perpendicular.

15. A kite __?__ has two congruent angles.   16. A kite __?__ has a right angle.

17. One diagonal of a kite __?__ bisects one of its angles.

18. **Standardized Test Prep** Which of the following statements is always true?

   I. A kite has at least one pair of congruent adjacent sides.

   II. A kite has at least one pair of congruent opposite angles.

   III. The diagonals of an isosceles trapezoid are congruent.

   A. I only   **B.** I and II only   **C.** I and III only   **D.** I, II, and III

19. Prove that the symmetry diagonal of a kite bisects two angles of the kite.

20. Prove that the diagonals of a kite are perpendicular.

Maintain Your Skills

Determine whether each statement is true or false. Provide a counterexample if the statement is false.

21. If you live in Canada, then you live in Montreal.

22. If you live in Montreal, then you live in Canada.

23. If a figure has an area of 16 square units, then it is a square.

24. All telephone numbers in Vermont have an area code of 802.

25. If your home telephone number area code is 802, then you live in Vermont.

For additional practice, go to **Web Code: bea-0217**

Answers

12. All are kites except Figure E. They all have two sets of adjacent congruent sides.

13. always

14. always

15. always

16. sometimes

17. always

18. All three statements are always true. The correct answer is D.

19. Let *ABCD* be a kite with $\overline{AB} \cong \overline{BC}$ and $\overline{CD} \cong \overline{DA}$. Draw the diagonal $\overline{BD}$. Since △*DAB* ≅ △*DCB* (SSS), the two parts of ∠*ABC* are congruent, and the two parts of ∠*CDA* are congruent (CPCTC). Therefore, the symmetry diagonal $\overline{BD}$ bisects these angles.

20–25. See back of book.

Parallelograms

You define special quadrilaterals, such as parallelograms, by their characteristics. You can probably guess the defining characteristic of a parallelogram, just from its name.

Definition

A **parallelogram** is a quadrilateral with two pairs of opposite parallel sides.

For You to Do

1. Which of the figures below appear to be parallelograms? Explain.

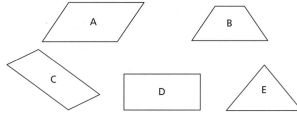

2. Notice that a rectangle is a parallelogram, according to the definition of *parallelogram* above. Which other common quadrilaterals fit the definition of *parallelogram*?

When you study any kind of quadrilateral, it is often useful to draw its diagonals. The following is an important theorem about the diagonals of a parallelogram.

Theorem 2.7

Each diagonal of a parallelogram divides the parallelogram into two congruent triangles.

Given   Parallelogram *ABCD* with diagonal $\overline{AC}$

Prove $\triangle ABC \cong \triangle CDA$

Proof   *ABCD* is a parallelogram. By definition, $\overline{BC} \parallel \overline{AD}$ and $\overline{BA} \parallel \overline{CD}$. From the PAI Theorem, it follows that $\angle BCA \cong \angle DAC$ and $\angle BAC \cong \angle DCA$. Triangle *ABC* and $\triangle CDA$ share $\overline{AC}$. So $\triangle ABC \cong \triangle CDA$ by ASA.

For You to Do

1. Figures A, C, and D; they have congruent and parallel opposite sides.

2. square, rhombus

Lesson Overview

GOALS

- Define and classify quadrilaterals.
- Classify parallelograms.
- Understand the meaning of converse and write the converse of a conditional statement.
- Understand the meaning of *always, never,* and *sometimes* in mathematics.

Students see the formal definition of *parallelogram* and explore properties involving the diagonals. This lesson also introduces the converse of a statement.

CHECK YOUR UNDERSTANDING
- Core: 1, 2, 3, 4, 5, 6, 7
- Optional: none
- Extension: 8

MATERIALS
- geometry software
- scissors
- Blackline Master MC5

HOMEWORK
- Core: 15, 16, 17, 29, 31, 32
- Optional: 9, 10, 11, 12, 13, 14, 18, 19, 20, 21, 22, 23, 24, 25, 26, 27, 28, 33, 34, 35, 36, 37
- Extension: 30

VOCABULARY
- parallelogram
- trisected

Launch

Have students add *parallelogram* to their list of quadrilateral definitions. Add it to your classroom list as well. Have students complete the problems in For You to Do that ask them to identify figures that are parallelograms and think of additional quadrilaterals that are parallelograms.

For You to Do

Most students will find these problems easy. The usual difficulty is that students confuse the definition of a parallelogram (the pairs of parallel sides) with other properties they observe in the figure. One theme of this lesson is that all other properties follow logically from the definition of a parallelogram.

Be sure that students include the defining characteristic of parallelograms: two pairs of parallel sides.

Explore

The remainder of this lesson presents several properties of parallelograms. The lesson provides one proof, but expects students to come up with the other proofs. You may choose to do this as a class. Remind students that *bisect* means "cut into two equal pieces."

In-Class Experiment

The In-Class Experiment addresses certain basic misconceptions that students often develop about parallelograms. The most basic misconception, at the root of all the others, is that a parallelogram has a line of symmetry. The most easily recognizable special parallelograms—rectangles, rhombuses, squares—are special exactly because they have lines of symmetry. So those parallelograms that are most familiar to students are the exceptions. This fact, together with the students' unfamiliarity with point symmetry (which every parallelogram has), tends to confuse them. You may wish to provide copies of Blackline Master MC5 for students to use.

Wrap Up

In the exercises, students will prove or disprove converses of statements about parallelograms. Wrap up this lesson by reading Developing Habits of Mind. Post the properties of parallelograms in your room and/or encourage students to write them in their notebooks.

For Discussion

3. Prove that $\overline{BD}$ also divides parallelogram $ABCD$ into two congruent triangles.

In-Class Experiment

4. Use geometry software. Construct several different parallelograms. Then construct the diagonals of each parallelogram. Compare the lengths of the two diagonals of each parallelogram.

5. The diagonals of a parallelogram divide each of the parallelogram's four angles into a pair of smaller angles. Find the measure of each angle in each pair. What invariant relationship, if any, exists between the measures of the two angles in each pair?

6. Cut a parallelogram out of paper. Try to fold the parallelogram in half. That is, try to find a line of symmetry that divides the parallelogram into two congruent pieces.

7. Use the parallelogram you cut out of paper. Draw its two diagonals. Call their point of intersection P. Fold the parallelogram so that the fold goes through P and is perpendicular to one of the diagonals. Which points, if any, coincide after you make the fold?

Discuss your results with the rest of the class.

> **Habits of Mind**
>
> **Check your work.** How can you be sure that the figure you cut out is a parallelogram?

For Discussion

8. Do you think the statement below is true or false?

The intersection point of the diagonals of a parallelogram is the midpoint of each diagonal.

Give a proof or find a counterexample.

You can prove that the statement is true. This important fact leads to the theorem below.

Theorem 2.8

The diagonals of a parallelogram bisect each other.

$AE = EC$ and $BE = ED$

Answers

For Discussion

3. Since $ABCD$ is a parallelogram, $\overline{BC} \parallel \overline{AD}$. $\angle CBD \cong \angle ADC$ and $\angle ABD \cong \angle CDB$ by PAI. Also, $\overline{BD}$ is congruent to itself. Hence, $\triangle ABD \cong \triangle CDB$ by ASA.

In-Class Experiment

4–7. Check students' work.

For Discussion

8. The statement is true. Let $ABCD$ be a parallelogram and let P be the intersection of its diagonals. Then $\triangle ABD \cong \triangle CDB$ by Theorem 2.7. This implies $\angle ADB \cong \angle CBD$ by CPCTC. Also by Theorem 2.7, $\triangle BAC \cong \triangle DCA$, which means $\angle BCA \cong \angle CAD$ and $\overline{BC} \cong \overline{AD}$, again by CPCTC. Therefore $\triangle APD \cong \triangle CPB$, and $\overline{BP} \cong \overline{PD}$ and $\overline{CP} \cong \overline{PA}$ by CPCTC.

You now know several things about parallelograms. If you know that a figure is a parallelogram, then all of the following statements are true:

1. Its opposite sides are parallel.

2. Its opposite sides are congruent.

3. Its opposite angles are congruent.

4. Its consecutive angles are supplementary.

5. Either diagonal divides the figure into two congruent triangles.

6. Its diagonals bisect each other.

Converses

Later you will investigate the converses of the statements listed above. What will the converses tell you? Well, for example, here is the converse of statement 6:

> If the diagonals of a quadrilateral bisect each other, then the quadrilateral is a parallelogram.

You can use converse statements that are true to classify quadrilaterals as parallelograms.

Developing Habits of Mind

Communicate a conditional situation. Statements of the form "if A, then B" are sometimes called conditional statements. One or more conditions are implied by the *if* part.

Some *if-then* statements are descriptions of elements of sets. You may see a statement like this one: "If an object belongs to set A, then it also belongs to set B."

For example, you can restate one of the corollaries to Theorem 2.7 this way:

> If a quadrilateral belongs to the set of parallelograms, then it also belongs to the set of quadrilaterals with opposite sides congruent.

> **Remember...**
> A corollary is a consequence of a main theorem.

The converse of this statement, also a conditional statement, is the following:

> If a quadrilateral belongs to the set of quadrilaterals with opposite sides congruent, then it also belongs to the set of parallelograms.

You can prove that the converse of the statement is also true. Start with a quadrilateral with opposite sides that are congruent. Draw the diagonals of the quadrilateral. By SSS, there is a pair of congruent triangles. Then by CPCTC, the alternate interior angles are congruent. By AIP, the sides of the figure are parallel.

In this example, the statement and its converse are both true, but this is not always the case. Sometimes the converse of a true conditional statement is false. For example, consider this statement: "If a person lives in Dallas, then that person lives in Texas." The converse of this statement is "If a person lives in Texas, then that person lives in Dallas." You can easily find a counterexample to the converse, such as "the person lives in Austin."

Assessment Resources

Lesson Quiz 2.18

For Exercises 1–3, decide whether each statement is *true* or *false*. If the statement is false, give a counterexample.

1. A parallelogram has two pairs of parallel and congruent sides.

2. Consecutive angles of a parallelogram are complementary.

3. The diagonals of all parallelograms are congruent.

4. Given: $ABCD$ is a parallelogram, and $\overline{AC}$ and $\overline{BD}$ intersect at point E.
   Prove: $\overline{AC}$ and $\overline{BD}$ bisect each other.

Exercises

HOMEWORK
- Core: 15, 16, 17, 29, 31, 32
- Optional: 9, 10, 11, 12, 13, 14, 18, 19, 20, 21, 22, 23, 24, 25, 26, 27, 28, 33, 34, 35, 36, 37
- Extension: 30

Check Your Understanding

EXERCISE 1 Some students may need to verbalize the fact that the goal of the proof is to show that both pairs of opposite sides are parallel. Then the quadrilateral satisfies the definition of a parallelogram.

EXERCISE 3 The converse theorems allow students to decide when a quadrilateral is a parallelogram. Usually, they have to know something about two pairs of sides or two pairs of angles. Theorem 2.10 uses only one pair of sides, but you must know two things about this pair.

Exercises *Practicing Habits of Mind*

Check Your Understanding

For Exercises 1–5, do the following.

- Write the converse of the statement.
- Decide whether the converse is true or false.
- If the converse is true, provide a proof.
- If the converse is false, give a counterexample.

1. If a quadrilateral is a parallelogram, then its opposite sides are congruent.

2. If a quadrilateral is a parallelogram, then its consecutive angles are supplementary.

3. If a quadrilateral is a parallelogram, then its opposite angles are congruent.

4. If a quadrilateral is a parallelogram, then each diagonal divides the parallelogram into two congruent triangles.

5. If a quadrilateral is a parallelogram, then its diagonals bisect each other.

6. The two angles at either end of a side in a parallelogram are called *consecutive angles*. State and prove a theorem about the consecutive angles of a parallelogram.

7. Prove the following corollaries of Theorem 2.7.
   a. Both pairs of opposite sides of a parallelogram are congruent.
   b. Both pairs of opposite angles of a parallelogram are congruent.

8. **Take It Further** A line that passes through the intersection point of a parallelogram's diagonals intersects the parallelogram in two points. Prove that the intersection point of the parallelogram's diagonals is the midpoint of the line segment that connects these points.

On Your Own

For Exercises 9–28, complete each sentence with *always*, *sometimes*, or *never* to make the statement true.

9. A parallelogram _?_ has two congruent sides.

10. A parallelogram _?_ has three congruent sides.

11. A parallelogram _?_ has exactly three congruent sides.

12. A parallelogram _?_ has four congruent sides.

13. A parallelogram _?_ has congruent diagonals.

14. A quadrilateral with congruent diagonals is _?_ a parallelogram.

Answers

Exercises

1. If a quadrilateral has its opposite sides congruent, then it is a parallelogram; true; let $ABCD$ be a quadrilateral with $\overline{AB} \cong \overline{DC}$ and $\overline{AD} \cong \overline{BC}$. Draw diagonal $\overline{AC}$. By SSS, $\triangle ADC \cong \triangle CBA$. Use AIP to conclude $\overline{AB} \parallel \overline{DC}$ and $\overline{AD} \parallel \overline{BC}$.

2. If a quadrilateral has each pair of consecutive angles supplementary, then it is a parallelogram; true; let $ABCD$ be a quadrilateral with each pair of consecutive angles supplementary. Since $\angle A$ and $\angle B$ are supplementary, $\overline{AD} \parallel \overline{BC}$. Since $\angle A$ and $\angle D$ are supplementary, $\overline{AB} \parallel \overline{DC}$.

3. If a quadrilateral has both pairs of opposite angles congruent, then it is a parallelogram; true; let $ABCD$ be a quadrilateral with $\angle A \cong \angle C$ and $\angle B \cong \angle D$. Hence $m\angle A + m\angle B + m\angle C + m\angle D = 2(m\angle A + m\angle B) = 360°$, or $m\angle A + m\angle B = 180°$.

15. If one diagonal of a quadrilateral divides it into two congruent triangles, then the quadrilateral is _?_ a parallelogram.

16. If two consecutive angles of a quadrilateral are supplementary, then the quadrilateral is _?_ a parallelogram.

17. A quadrilateral with one right angle is _?_ a parallelogram.

18. A quadrilateral with exactly one right angle is _?_ a parallelogram.

19. A quadrilateral with two right angles is _?_ a parallelogram.

20. A quadrilateral with exactly two right angles is _?_ a parallelogram.

21. A quadrilateral with exactly two right angles opposite each other is _?_ a parallelogram.

22. A quadrilateral with three right angles is _?_ a parallelogram.

23. A quadrilateral with diagonals that bisect each other is _?_ a parallelogram.

24. If the longer diagonal of a quadrilateral bisects the shorter diagonal, then the quadrilateral is _?_ a parallelogram.

Hint: Can a quadrilateral have exactly three right angles?

25. A quadrilateral with two congruent sides is _?_ a parallelogram.

26. A quadrilateral with three congruent sides is _?_ a parallelogram.

27. A quadrilateral with exactly three congruent sides is _?_ a parallelogram.

28. A quadrilateral with four congruent sides is _?_ a parallelogram.

29. Standardized Test Prep Which of the following statements is NOT true?

A. Every parallelogram has at least one line of symmetry.

B. The diagonals of a parallelogram always bisect each other.

C. Opposite angles of a parallelogram are congruent.

D. Consecutive angles of a parallelogram are supplementary.

30. Take It Further In the figure at the right, the sides of parallelogram *MNPQ* are trisected. Four of the trisection points form quadrilateral *STWX*.

A segment is **trisected** if it is divided into three congruent parts.

a. List some facts that you can prove about quadrilateral *STWX*.

b. What type of quadrilateral is *STWX*? Prove your conjecture.

c. Suppose you draw $\overline{SW}$ and $\overline{TX}$. What can you say about these two segments?

On Your Own

EXERCISES 9–28 It is not necessary for each student to complete all of these exercises. Some of them are core exercises, but you should feel free to assign all or some of them. You may want to assign a couple to each student and then have a class discussion.

Therefore, consecutive angles are supplementary, and, by Exercise 2, *ABCD* is a parallelogram.

4. If each diagonal of a quadrilateral divides it into two congruent triangles, then the quadrilateral is a parallelogram; true; match up any two congruent triangles along a congruent side. The opposite angles in the resulting quadrilateral are congruent, so, by Exercise 3, the quadrilateral is a parallelogram.

5. If a quadrilateral has diagonals that bisect each other, then it is a

parallelogram; true; the diagonals divide the parallelogram into four triangles. You can prove that pairs of these are congruent by SAS. Then you know that opposite sides of the quadrilateral are congruent. Therefore the quadrilateral is a parallelogram by Exercise 1.

6–30. See back of book.

EXERCISE 31 is a core exercise. It asks students to prove the Midline Theorem, which they will need in upcoming lessons.

Additional Resources

PRINT RESOURCES
- Solution Manual
- Practice Workbook
- Assessment Resources
- Teaching Resources

TECHNOLOGY
- Interactive Textbook
- TeacherExpress CD-ROM
- **Exam**View CD-ROM
- PHSchool.com
  - Additional Practice
  - Mid-Chapter and Chapter Tests
  - Video Tutors
  - Vocabulary Puzzles

Additional Practice

For Exercises 1–4, use the given statement about quadrilaterals.
  a. Write the converse of the statement.
  b. Decide whether the converse is true or false.
  c. If the converse is true, provide a proof. If the converse is false, give a counterexample.

1. If a quadrilateral has opposite sides parallel, then it is a parallelogram.

2. If a quadrilateral is equiangular, then it is a parallelogram.

3. If a quadrilateral has diagonals that bisect each other, then it is a parallelogram.

4. If a quadrilateral has diagonals that are perpendicular, then it is a parallelogram.

5. In the figure, *ABCD* and *DEFG* are parallelograms. Prove each statement.
  a. ∠*B* ≅ ∠*F*
  b. $\overline{BC} \| \overline{EF}$
  c. *m*∠*A* + *m*∠*F* = 180°

For Exercises 6–8, complete each statement with *always*, *sometimes*, or *never* to make the statement true.

6. A rectangle is _____ a square.

7. An equiangular parallelogram is _____ a rectangle.

8. A rhombus has diagonals that are _____ perpendicular bisectors.

9. *GHJK* is a rectangle with diagonals $\overline{GJ}$ and $\overline{HK}$. Decide whether each statement is true or false.
  a. ∠*JGH* ≅ ∠*GJK*
  b. ∠*GKH* ≅ ∠*JKH*
  c. △*HJK* ≅ △*KGH*
  d. $\overline{GH} \| \overline{KJ}$

10. In the figure, *ABCD* is a rhombus. Prove that $\overline{AC} \perp \overline{BD}$.

11. In the figure, *ABCD* is an isosceles trapezoid and *E*, *F*, *G*, and *H* are the midpoints of the sides. Is *EFGH* a parallelogram? Can you specify which type? Explain.

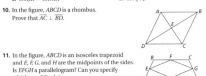

Practice: For Lesson 2.18, assign Exercises 1–5.

---

31. Prove the theorem below.

Theorem 2.9

If two opposite sides of a quadrilateral are congruent and parallel, then the figure is a parallelogram.

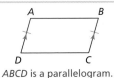

ABCD is a parallelogram.

32. In the figure at the right, *M* and *N* are midpoints of $\overline{AB}$ and $\overline{AC}$, respectively. Point *P* lies on the same line as *M* and *N*, and $\overline{MN} \cong \overline{NP}$.
  a. Prove that △*AMN* ≅ △*CPN*.
  b. What can you conclude about quadrilateral *MPCB*? Explain.
  c. Show that $MN = \frac{1}{2}BC$.
  d. What else can you conclude about the relationship between $\overline{MN}$ and $\overline{BC}$? Explain.

You can state the results of Exercise 32 as a theorem.

Theorem 2.10 Midline Theorem

The segment that joins the midpoints of two sides of a triangle is parallel to the third side and half the length of the third side.

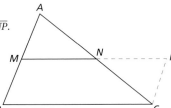

$\overline{EB} \| \overline{DC}; EB = \frac{1}{2}DC$

Remember...
You first saw this statement as Conjecture 1.2 in Chapter 1.

Maintain Your Skills

For Exercises 33–37, do each of the following.
  a. Rewrite each statement in *if-then* form.
  b. Decide whether the statement is true.
  c. Write the converse of the statement.
  d. Decide whether the converse is true.

33. People who live in New York City also live in New York State.

34. Every lizard is a reptile.

35. A bird is an animal with feathers.

36. All cowboys are from Texas.

37. Every piece of fruit is an apple.

Go Online
PHSchool.com
For additional practice, go to Web Code: bea-0218

Answers

31. Draw $\overline{AC}$. ∠*DAC* ≅ ∠*BCA* by PAI, and $\overline{AC} \cong \overline{AC}$. So △*ABC* ≅ △*CDA* by SAS. Therefore ∠*BAC* ≅ ∠*DCA* by CPCTC, and $\overline{AB}$ is parallel to $\overline{CD}$ by AIP. Both pairs of opposite sides of *ABCD* are parallel, so *ABCD* is a parallelogram.

32. a. △*AMN* and △*CPN* are congruent by SAS.

  b. *MPCB* is a parallelogram; ∠*AMN* ≅ ∠*CPN* by CPCTC,

so $\overline{PC} \| \overline{AB}$ by AIP. Also, $\overline{AM} \cong \overline{CP}$ by CPCTC. Since *M* is the midpoint of $\overline{AB}$, we know that $\overline{AM} \cong \overline{MB}$. From this it follows that $\overline{MB} \cong \overline{CP}$. *MPCB* is a parallelogram by Theorem 2.9.

  c. Since *MPCB* is a parallelogram, *MP* = *BC*. Since $\overline{MN} \cong \overline{NP}$, it follows that $MN = \frac{1}{2}BC$.

  d. $\overline{MN}$ is parallel to $\overline{BC}$ because *MPCB* is a parallelogram.

33–37. See back of book.

The different types of parallelograms are ordinary parallelograms, rectangles, rhombuses, and squares. Rectangles and rhombuses are special types of parallelograms. Squares are a special type of rectangle and a special type of rhombus.

You may be surprised that an ordinary rectangle is a type of parallelogram. This is probably because you more often think of a rectangle's four right angles than of its parallel sides.

Definitions

A **rectangle** is a parallelogram with four right angles.

A **rhombus** is a parallelogram with four congruent sides.

A common term for a rhombus is *diamond*.

A square is a special kind of rectangle with four congruent sides. A square is also a special kind of rhombus, with four congruent angles.

The definition for a square is given below.

A **square** is a rectangle with four congruent sides.

A square has all the properties of both a rectangle and a rhombus. Of course, a square also has the properties of a parallelogram and of a quadrilateral.

- The diagonals of a square are congruent because a square is a rectangle. (See Exercise 1.)

- The diagonals of a square are perpendicular because a square is a rhombus. (See Exercise 21.)

- The diagonals of a square bisect each other because a square is a parallelogram.

- The sum of the measures of the angles of a square is 360° because a square is a quadrilateral.

Assessment Resources

Lesson Quiz 2.19

For Exercises 1–3, write a proof.

1. Given: *ABCD* is a square.
   Prove: *ABCD* is a rhombus.

2. Given: *ABCD* is a rectangle.
   Prove: The diagonals of *ABCD* are congruent.

3. Given: *ABCD* is a square.
   Prove: The diagonals of *ABCD* form four congruent triangles.

4. Describe the difference between a kite and a rhombus. Is a rhombus a kite? Explain.

Exercises

HOMEWORK
- Core: 14, 15, 16, 17, 21, 22
- Optional: 18, 19, 20, 23, 24, 25

Check Your Understanding

EXERCISE 12 Some students may not immediately see that a square is a type of rhombus. Make sure to discuss this point.

For You to Do

Decide whether each statement is true.

1. All rectangles are parallelograms.

2. Some parallelograms are rhombuses.

3. All rectangles are squares.

4. Some squares are rectangles.

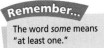
Remember...
The word *some* means "at least one."

Exercises Practicing Habits of Mind

Check Your Understanding

1. Prove that the diagonals of a rectangle are congruent.

2. Prove that a parallelogram with two congruent adjacent sides is a rhombus.

   For Exercises 3–13, complete each sentence with *always*, *sometimes*, or *never* to make the statement true.

3. A rhombus is __?__ a rectangle.

4. A square is __?__ a parallelogram.

5. A rectangle is __?__ a rhombus.

6. A square is __?__ a rectangle.

7. The opposite sides of a rectangle are __?__ congruent.

8. The diagonals of a rectangle are __?__ congruent.

9. If the diagonals of a quadrilateral are congruent, then the quadrilateral is __?__ a rectangle.

10. Two adjacent sides of a rectangle are __?__ congruent.

11. The diagonals of a rectangle __?__ bisect its angles.

12. A rhombus __?__ has a right angle.

13. Opposite sides of a rhombus are __?__ congruent.

Answers

For You to Do

1. true

2. true

3. false

4. true

Exercises

1. Let *ABCD* be a rectangle. Opposite sides of *ABCD* are congruent, so $\overline{AD} \cong \overline{BC}$. All angles of *ABCD* are right angles, so $\angle DAB \cong \angle CBA$. $\overline{AB}$ is congruent to itself. Hence $\triangle DAB \cong \triangle CBA$. Therefore, the diagonals $\overline{DB}$ and $\overline{CA}$ are congruent by CPCTC.

2. Let *ABCD* be a parallelogram with a pair of congruent adjacent sides. Opposite sides of a parallelogram are congruent, so all four sides of

14. **Standardized Test Prep** Which of the following statements is NOT true?

  A. A square is different from a rhombus because a square has four congruent sides.

  B. A rectangle is a parallelogram with four congruent angles.

  C. A square is a rectangle with four congruent sides.

  D. A rhombus is a parallelogram with four congruent sides.

15. Prove that a parallelogram with one right angle is a rectangle.

16. Prove that if the diagonals of a parallelogram are congruent, then the parallelogram is a rectangle.

17. What type of quadrilateral do you form when you connect the midpoints of a rectangle's sides? Prove your conjecture.

> In Exercises 17 and 18, make sure you do not assume that the quadrilateral is a parallelogram.

For Exercises 18–23, prove each statement.

18. If a quadrilateral has four congruent sides, then it is a rhombus.

19. Either diagonal of a rhombus divides the rhombus into two isosceles triangles.

20. The diagonals of a rhombus bisect the vertex angles of the rhombus.

21. The diagonals of a rhombus are perpendicular.

22. If the diagonals of a parallelogram are perpendicular, then the parallelogram is a rhombus.

23. If one diagonal of a parallelogram bisects two opposite angles of the parallelogram, then the parallelogram is a rhombus.

24. Draw a square and connect the midpoints of its sides. Prove that the figure formed is also a square.

Habits of Mind

Think it through.
To prove that a quadrilateral is a square, can you just prove that its four sides are congruent?

Maintain Your Skills

Rectangles, rhombuses, and squares are special types of quadrilaterals. You can show the relationships among these quadrilaterals with a Venn diagram. In a Venn diagram, a circle represents a set.

25. Copy and complete each Venn diagram with the correct type of quadrilateral.

Go Online
PHSchool.com

For additional practice, go to Web Code: bea-0219

a.

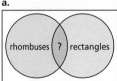

b.

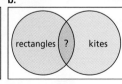

c.

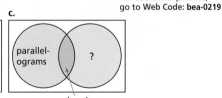

rhombuses

ABCD are congruent. Therefore, *ABCD* is a rhombus.

3. sometimes

4. always

5. sometimes

6. always

7. always

8. always

9. sometimes

10. sometimes

11. sometimes

12. sometimes

13. always

14. A

15. If a parallelogram has a right angle, then all its angles are right angles (consecutive angles of a parallelogram are supplementary). A parallelogram with four right angles is a rectangle.

16–25. See back of book.

Maintain Your Skills

EXERCISE 25 You may wish to provide copies of Blackline Master 2.19 for students to use.

Additional Resources

PRINT RESOURCES
- Solution Manual
- Practice Workbook
- Assessment Resources
- Teaching Resources

TECHNOLOGY
- Interactive Textbook
- TeacherExpress CD-ROM
- **Exam**View CD-ROM
- **PHSchool.com**
  - Additional Practice
  - Mid-Chapter and Chapter Tests
  - Video Tutors
  - Vocabulary Puzzles

Additional Practice

For Exercises 1–4, use the given statement about quadrilaterals.
  a. Write the converse of the statement.
  b. Decide whether the converse is true or false.
  c. If the converse is true, provide a proof. If the converse is false, give a counterexample.

1. If a quadrilateral has opposite sides parallel, then it is a parallelogram.

2. If a quadrilateral is equiangular, then it is a parallelogram.

3. If a quadrilateral has diagonals that bisect each other, then it is a parallelogram.

4. If a quadrilateral has diagonals that are perpendicular, then it is a parallelogram.

5. In the figure, *ABCD* and *DEFG* are parallelograms. Prove each statement.
  a. $\angle B \cong \angle F$
  b. $\overline{BC} \parallel \overline{EF}$
  c. $m\angle A + m\angle F = 180°$

For Exercises 6–8, complete each statement with *always, sometimes,* or *never* to make the statement true.

6. A rectangle is _____ a square.

7. An equiangular parallelogram is _____ a rectangle.

8. A rhombus has diagonals that are _____ perpendicular bisectors.

9. *GHJK* is a rectangle with diagonals $\overline{GJ}$ and $\overline{HK}$. Decide whether each statement is true or false.
  a. $\angle JGH \cong \angle GJK$ **b.** $\angle GKH \cong \angle JKH$
  c. $\triangle HJK \cong \triangle KGH$ **d.** $\overline{GH} \parallel \overline{KJ}$

10. In the figure, *ABCD* is a rhombus. Prove that $\overline{AC} \perp \overline{BD}$.

11. In the figure, *ABCD* is an isosceles trapezoid and *E, F, G,* and *H* are the midpoints of the sides. Is *EFGH* a parallelogram? Can you specify which type? Explain.

Practice: For Lesson 2.19, assign Exercises 6–11.

Mathematical Reflections

EXERCISES 6–8 At the start of the investigation, you may have assigned these as questions 1–3 for students to think and write about.

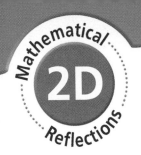

2D Mathematical Reflections

In this investigation, you studied different types of quadrilaterals, such as kites and trapezoids. You also studied the characteristics of the special types of parallelograms—rectangles, rhombuses, and squares.

1. Is a quadrilateral with perpendicular diagonals always a kite? Explain.

2. In the figure below, $\overline{ST} \cong \overline{RT}$, but the segments are not congruent to $\overline{TQ}$. All angles of $\triangle PTS$ and $\angle RTQ$ measure 60°. Prove that $PQRS$ is a trapezoid.

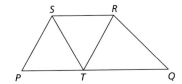

3. Describe the difference between a parallelogram and a rectangle.

4. Can a kite ever be a parallelogram? Explain.

5. Prove that a kite can be divided into two isosceles triangles by a single segment. Can this be done in more than one way? Explain.

6. List some special properties of each quadrilateral below.
   - parallelogram
   - kite
   - trapezoid

7. Are all squares also parallelograms? Are all parallelograms also squares? Explain.

8. If a statement is true, is its converse also true?

Vocabulary

In this investigation, you learned these terms. Make sure you understand what each one means and how to use it.

- base angles
- bases of a trapezoid
- closed figure
- concave
- isosceles trapezoid
- kite
- parallelogram
- quadrilateral
- rectangle
- rhombus
- self-intersecting figure
- side
- skew quadrilateral
- square
- trapezoid
- trisected
- vertex/vertices

Nonconformity stands out.

Answers

Mathematical Reflections

1. No; counterexample:

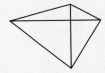

2. The measures of the three small angles with vertex T have a sum of 180°. You know that $m\angle PTS = m\angle QTR = 60°$, so $m\angle STR = 60°$ also. Since $\overline{ST} \cong \overline{TR}$, $\triangle STR$ is isosceles. The Triangle Angle-Sum Theorem implies that $m\angle TSR = 60°$, and so $\overline{SR} \parallel \overline{PQ}$ by AIP. $\angle P$ and $\angle RTQ$ are congruent corresponding angles for $\overline{PS}$ and $\overline{TR}$ and transversal $\overline{PQ}$, so $\overline{PS} \parallel \overline{TR}$. Since there is only one line through R parallel to $\overline{PS}$, it follows that $\overline{PS}$ and $\overline{RQ}$ are not parallel. Hence $PQRS$ has exactly one pair of opposite sides parallel and so is a trapezoid.

3–8. See back of book.

Project: Using Mathematical Habits

Dividing Into Congruent Pieces

Draw several different triangles. Try to divide your triangles into the following numbers of congruent pieces.

- two
- three
- four
- five

Margaret divided this triangle into two congruent pieces.

1. Into how many of the above numbers of congruent pieces can you always divide any triangle? Explain.

2. Dividing a triangle into certain of the above numbers of congruent pieces is possible only if you begin with special types of triangles. How are they special?

3. For which of the above numbers, if any, is it *impossible* to find a triangle that can be divided into that number of congruent pieces?

4. **Write About It** Explain why some of the numbers above require special triangles. (*Hint:* See Exercise 2.) For the number(s) you find, if any, explain why no triangle is possible.

5. **Write About It** Explain why any triangle can be divided into congruent pieces in infinitely many ways. (*Hint:* See Exercise 1.)

6. Draw five different squares. Try to divide the squares into the following number of congruent triangles.

- two
- three
- four
- five
- six

7. For what values of n is it easy to divide a square into n congruent triangles? Explain.

8. For what values of n, if any, can you give a convincing argument that it is impossible to divide a square into n congruent triangles? Explain.

A Noncongruent Challenge

9. Show how to divide a 13-by-15 rectangle into nine squares so that no two of the squares have a side completely in common. The squares are not necessarily congruent.

8. when n is odd
9. Check students' work.

Answers

Project

1. You can divide any triangle into 4 congruent triangles by constructing the three midlines of the triangle.

2. You can divide a triangle into two congruent triangles only if it is isosceles. You can divide a triangle into three congruent treiangles only if it is equilateral.

3. It is impossible to divide a triangle into five congruent pieces.

4. Check students' work.

5. Since you can divide any triangle into four congruent pieces by construting the midlines, you can continue dividing the larger triangle by diviiding each of the foud smaller triangles using the same method. This process can continue indefinitely.

6. Check students' work.

7. Answers may vary. Sample: When n is even; divide the square into $\frac{n}{2}$ congruent rectangles. Construct a diagonal of each rectangle to get n congruent triangles.

Answers

Chapter Review

1. By construction, $\angle ACB \cong \angle DCB$ and $\angle ABC \cong \angle DBC$. Also, $\overline{BC} \cong \overline{BC}$. Therefore $\triangle ABC \cong \triangle ABC$ by ASA.

2. By Exercise 1, $\triangle ABC \cong \triangle DBC$. By CPCTC, $\overline{AC} \cong \overline{DC}$. By construction, $\angle ACB \cong \angle DCB$. Also, $\overline{CP} \cong \overline{CP}$. Therefore $\triangle ACP \cong \triangle DCP$ by SAS, and $\overline{AP} \cong \overline{DP}$ by CPCTC.

3. By PAI, $\angle CAB \cong \angle DBA$ and $\angle ACD \cong \angle BDC$. By construction, $\overline{AC} \cong \overline{BD}$. So $\triangle ACE \cong \triangle BDE$ by ASA. Therefore $\overline{AE} \cong \overline{BE}$ by CPCTC.

4. 360°

5. $\ell \parallel m$

In **Investigation 2A** you learned to

- define congruence
- test for congruence in triangles
- use the correct language and notation to read and write statements about congruent figures

The following questions will help you check your understanding.

1. Use $\triangle ABC$. Draw point D so that $\overline{BC}$ is the angle bisector of $\angle ACD$ and of $\angle ABD$. Prove that $\triangle ABC \cong \triangle DBC$.

2. Use your drawing from Exercise 1. Choose a point P on $\overline{BC}$. Prove that $\overline{AP} \cong \overline{DP}$.

In **Investigation 2B** you learned to

- identify parallel lines by looking at pairs of angles that are formed when the lines are cut by transversals
- identify pairs of congruent angles when parallel lines are cut by transversals
- write and present a deductive proof
- prove that the sum of the angle measures of a triangle is 180°

The following questions will help you check your understanding.

3. Draw $\overline{AB}$. Draw two parallel lines—one through A and one through B. Choose a point C on the line through A. Choose a point D on the line through B. Choose C and D so that they are on opposite sides of $\overline{AB}$ and $\overline{AC} \cong \overline{BD}$. Draw $\overline{CD}$. Let E name the point where $\overline{AB}$ and $\overline{CD}$ intersect. Explain why E is the midpoint of $\overline{AB}$.

4. What is the sum of the measures of the angles of a quadrilateral?

5. Use the figure below. Suppose $\angle 1 \cong \angle 5$. What can you conclude about lines ℓ and m? Explain.

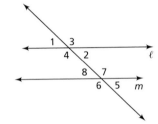

In **Investigation 2C** you learned to

- recognize the difference between experimentation and deduction
- write and present triangle congruence proofs
- use the Perpendicular Bisector Theorem
- apply the Isosceles Triangle Theorem to prove parts of a figure are congruent

The following questions will help you check your understanding.

6. Draw $\overline{AB}$ that is less than 4 cm long. Find a point R that is 2 cm from both A and B. Find a point S that is 3 cm from both A and B. Draw $\overleftrightarrow{RS}$. Prove that $\overleftrightarrow{RS} \perp \overline{AB}$.

7. Describe the type of triangle that has the given property.

a. The bisector of exactly one angle of the triangle contains the midpoint of the opposite side.

b. Each altitude of the triangle coincides with a perpendicular bisector of a side.

8. Use the figure below. $\triangle ABC \cong \triangle DCB$. Prove that $\triangle CTB$ is isosceles.

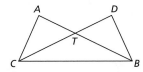

In **Investigation 2D** you learned to

- classify quadrilaterals
- understand the meaning of *converse*
- reason by continuity
- understand the meaning of *always, never,* and *sometimes* in mathematics

The following questions will help you check your understanding.

9. Write the converse of the following statement.

If a quadrilateral is a kite, then the diagonals of the quadrilateral intersect to form right angles.

Determine whether the converse is true. If it is true, provide a written proof. If it is not, provide a counterexample.

10. Write *always, sometimes,* or *never* to best complete each sentence.

a. A kite __?__ has four congruent sides.

b. The diagonals of a parallelogram __?__ bisect each other.

c. The diagonals of a rectangle are __?__ perpendicular.

d. A kite __?__ has exactly one pair of parallel sides.

6. Each point S and R is on the perpendicular bisector of $\overline{AB}$ by the converse of the Perpendicular Bisector Theorem. Hence $\overline{SR}$ is the perpendicular bisector of $\overline{AB}$.

7. a. nonequilateral isosceles triangles

b. equilateral triangles

8. $\overline{AC} \cong \overline{DB}$ and $\angle CAT \cong \angle BDT$ by CPCTC. Also, $\angle ATC \cong \angle DTB$ by the Vertical Angles Theorem. Therefore, $\triangle ATC \cong \triangle DTB$ by AAS, and $\overline{CT} \cong \overline{CB}$ by CPCTC.

9. If the diagonals of a quadrilateral are perpendicular, then the quadrilateral is a kite; false.

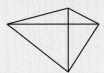

10. a. may

b. must

c. may

d. cannot

Chapter Test

Assessment Resources

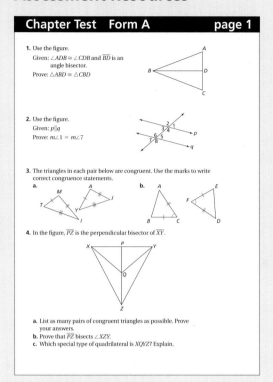
---

1. If △DEF ≅ △LMN, which of the following must be a correct congruence statement?

A. ∠D ≅ ∠N   **B.** ∠F ≅ ∠L
C. $\overline{EF}$ ≅ $\overline{MN}$ **D.** $\overline{DE}$ ≅ $\overline{NM}$

2. What other information do you need to prove that the two triangles are congruent by SSS?

A. $\overline{RS}$ ≅ $\overline{WU}$

B. ∠T ≅ ∠V

C. ∠S ≅ ∠U

D. no additional information needed

3. Lines f and g are parallel. Which statement can you deduce from this information?

A. ∠3 ≅ ∠8   **B.** ∠3 ≅ ∠4
C. ∠3 ≅ ∠7   **D.** ∠3 ≅ ∠5

4. The diagonals of a certain quadrilateral are perpendicular. What kind of quadrilateral must the figure be?

A. parallelogram   **B.** rhombus
C. rectangle   **D.** square

5. For each pair, decide whether the two figures are congruent. Explain your reasoning.

a.
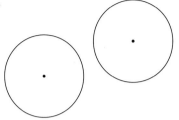

b.

circles

c.
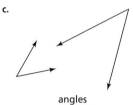
angles

d.

e.
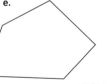
pentagons

Answers

Chapter Test

1. C

2. A

3. C

4. D

5. a. Not congruent; measurement shows that the wingspans are different.

b. Congruent; measurement shows that the circles have the same radius.

c. Congruent; measuring with a protractor shows that the angles are the same size.

d. Congruent; a tracing of the first picture fits exactly on top of the other picture.

e. Not congruent; a tracing of the first pentagon does not fit exactly on the second pentagon.

6. a. Since opposite sides of the parallelogram are parallel, ∠CAD ≅ ∠BCA and ∠DCA ≅ ∠BAC by PAI. Every segment is congruent to itself, so $\overline{AC}$ ≅ $\overline{AC}$. Hence △ABC ≅ △CDA by ASA.

b. The triangles are not congruent.

c. Since all three sides of △ABC are congruent and E and F are midpoints, $\overline{AE}$ ≅ $\overline{FC}$. △ABC ≅ △CBA (SSS), so ∠BAC ≅ ∠BCA (CPCTC). Therefore △EAC ≅ △FCA by SAS.

7. a. Answers may vary. Sample: A geometry software experiment, or construction and measurement by hand, provides evidence, but not proof, that the altitudes of an equilateral triangle are congruent.

b. An altitude of an equilateral triangle divides it into two congruent right triangles (by AAS). It follows that the altitude from any vertex of the equilateral triangle bisects the opposite side. Therefore, the six large right triangles determined by the altitudes are

6. For each diagram, use the given information. Determine whether the two triangles are congruent. If they are congruent, prove it using the triangle congruence postulates.

a. *ABCD* is a parallelogram. Is △*ABC* ≅ △*CDA*?

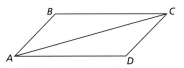

b. ∠*ADE* ≅ ∠*B* and ∠*AED* ≅ ∠*C*. Is △*ABC* ≅ △*ADE*?

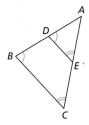

c. △*ABC* is an equilateral triangle. Points *E* and *F* are the midpoints of $\overline{AB}$ and $\overline{CB}$, respectively. Is △*EAC* ≅ △*FCA*?

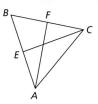

7. Recall the definition of an equilateral triangle.

a. Describe an experiment that would lead you to conjecture that the altitudes of an equilateral triangle are congruent.

b. Prove that the altitudes of an equilateral triangle are congruent.

8. Use the figure below. Lines *m* and *n* are parallel. Prove that *m*∠1 = *m*∠2.

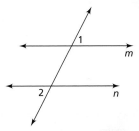

9. Decide whether each statement is true. If a statement is not true, provide a counterexample.

a. All rectangles are squares.

b. All trapezoids are parallelograms.

c. All rectangles are parallelograms.

d. All rhombuses are squares.

e. All squares are rhombuses.

f. All squares are kites.

g. All parallelograms are kites.

10. Write *always*, *sometimes*, or *never* to best complete each sentence.

a. The diagonals of a kite __?__ bisect each other.

b. The diagonals of a parallelogram __?__ bisect each other.

c. A median of a triangle is __?__ an altitude of the triangle.

d. The diagonals of a rhombus are __?__ perpendicular.

11. Write the converse of the following statement.

If an altitude of a triangle is the perpendicular bisector of one side of the triangle, then the triangle is equilateral.

If the statement is true, provide a written proof.

If the converse is true, provide a written proof.

---

all congruent and the altitudes themselves are all congruent.

altitude is perpendicular to the side to which it is drawn and therefore forms right angles with that side. The two right triangles into which the altitude divides the triangle are congruent. Hence the parts of the side to which the altitude is drawn are congruent, which means the altitude is the perpendicular bisector of the side.

8. The angles that form pairs of vertical angles with ∠1 and ∠2 are alternate interior angles for the parallel lines *m* and *n* and the transversal. These alternate interior angles are congruent by PAI. Since vertical angles are congruent, it follows that ∠1 ≅ ∠2.

9. a. false
   b. false
   c. true
   d. false
   e. true
   f. true
   g. false

10. a. sometimes
   b. always
   c. sometimes
   d. always

11. • If a triangle is equilateral, then the altitude to a side of the triangle is the perpendicular bisector of that side.

   • The original statement is not true.

   • An equilateral triangle is equiangular and has all its sides congruent. An

Cumulative Review

Assessment Resources

Cumulative Review

1. Draw the letters M, A, T, and H as block letters. Then describe the lines of symmetry of each letter.

2. Draw a picture that illustrates each equation.
   a. $(x + y)^2 = x^2 + 2xy + y^2$
   b. $(w + x)(y + z) = wy + wz + xy + xz$

3. Describe each shape by name. Then write directions that describe how to draw each shape.
   a.
   b.

4. Describe how to construct a midline of a triangle.

5. On a sheet of paper, copy line ℓ and point P. Then construct the line through P that is parallel to ℓ.

6. Construct an equilateral triangle with 2-in. sides.

7. Copy the angle onto a sheet of paper. Then construct its bisector.

8. Use geometry software to draw a triangle. Then construct one of its altitudes.

9. Construct each figure so that it is UnMessUpable. Write clear directions that describe each construction.
   a. a square
   b. a right triangle
   c. two congruent circles that pass through each other's centers

10. Construct two circles that share a center so that the ratio of their radii is 3 : 1.

11. Use geometry software to construct a rectangle *ABCD* that will remain a rectangle, even if you stretch it. Determine which of the following measures, if any, is an invariant.
    a. the ratio of the lengths of the opposite sides, $\frac{AB}{CD}$
    b. the perimeter of *ABCD*
    c. the ratio of the lengths of the diagonals, $\frac{AC}{BD}$
    d. the ratio of the perimeter of *ABCD* to the area of *ABCD*

12. Explain why you cannot use SSA to prove that two triangles are congruent.

13. Construct each of the following. Label each point of concurrency.
    a. an equilateral triangle and its three altitudes
    b. a right triangle and its three medians
    c. an obtuse triangle and its three perpendicular bisectors
    d. an isosceles triangle and its three angle bisectors

14. Complete each sentence with *always*, *sometimes*, or *never* to make the statement true.
    a. The concurrence of the altitudes of a regular polygon is _?_ invariant.
    b. The concurrence of the medians of a regular polygon is _?_ invariant.
    c. The concurrence of the angle bisectors of a regular polygon is _?_ invariant.

15. Explain the difference between the terms *congruent* and *equal*.

16. Are all right isosceles triangles congruent? Explain.

Answers

Cumulative Review

1. The letters M, A, T, and H all have vertical lines of symmetry. The letter H also has a horizontal line of symmetry.

2. a.

   b.

3. a. Rectangle; directions may vary. Sample: Draw a vertical segment 1.5 cm in length. From the endpoints of this segment, draw two horizontal segments 2.5 cm in length, each on the same side of the vertical segment. Finally, connect the other two endpoints of the horizontal segments.

   b. Five-pointed star; directions may vary. Sample: Draw a regular pentagon. Draw all the diagonals of the pentagon. Erase the original pentagon, and erase the smaller pentagon that resulted from drawing the diagonals.

4. Find the midpoint of two sides of a triangle and draw the segment connecting them.

5.

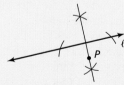

For Exercises 17 and 18, do the following. The triangles in each pair are congruent.

a. Write a congruence statement.

b. Tell which congruence postulate or theorem helped you decide.

17.

18.

19. In the figure below, M is the midpoint of $\overline{AB}$ and $\overline{CD}$. Prove that $\triangle ADM \cong \triangle BCM$.

20. If you and a classmate both construct $\triangle ABC$ so that $m\angle A = 53°$, $m\angle B = 39°$, and $m\angle C = 88°$, will your two triangles be congruent? Explain.

21. In the figure below, $f \parallel q$. Classify each pair of angles as *alternate interior angles, consecutive angles,* or *corresponding angles.*

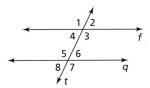

a. $\angle 4$ and $\angle 6$ b. $\angle 5$ and $\angle 4$

c. $\angle 3$ and $\angle 7$ d. $\angle 5$ and $\angle 1$

22. In the figure below, $m \parallel n$. Use the PAI Theorem to find $m\angle 1$ and $m\angle 2$.

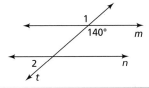

23. In the figure, H is the midpoint of $\overline{GI}$ and K is the midpoint of $\overline{GL}$. Prove that $\overleftrightarrow{HK} \parallel \overleftrightarrow{IL}$.

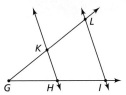

24. Given $\overline{AB} \parallel \overline{CD}$ and $\overline{AB} \cong \overline{CD}$

Prove $\triangle ABC \cong \triangle CDA$

For Exercises 25–27, do the following.

a. Identify the hypothesis and conclusion.

b. Draw a picture that illustrates the hypothesis.

c. Decide whether the statement is true.

d. If the statement is true, give a proof. If the statement is false, give a counterexample.

25. Two lines that are parallel to a third line are parallel to each other.

26. An equiangular parallelogram is a square.

27. If two angles are congruent and supplementary, then both angles are right angles.

28. Make a flowchart for the proof without writing the actual proof.

Given $\ell \perp \overline{AB}$, ℓ bisects $\overline{AB}$ at C, and P is on ℓ.

Prove $\overline{PA} \cong \overline{PB}$

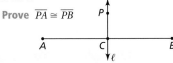

For Exercises 29 and 30, write a reverse list. Then prove each statement.

29. If a point is on the bisector of an angle, then the point is equidistant from the sides of the angle.

30. If a point is equidistant from the endpoints of a segment, then that point is on the bisector of the segment.

6.

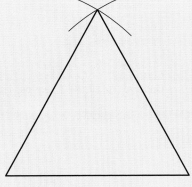

7.

8. Check students' work.

9. a–b. Answers may vary. Samples are given.

a. Draw a segment (call its endpoints A and B). Construct two lines perpendicular to the segment that pass through A and B. Construct a circle with center A and radius $\overline{AB}$. The circle intersects the line through A in two places. Pick one of them and call it D. Construct a line through D perpendicular to $\overleftrightarrow{AD}$. This line intersects the line through B. Call this the point of

intersection C. Draw $\overline{BC}$, $\overline{CD}$, and $\overline{AD}$. Quadrilateral $ABCD$ is an UnMessUpable square.

b. Draw a line. Place a point on the line and call it A. Construct a line through A perpendicular to the first line you drew. Place points B and C on the two lines, one per line. Draw segments $\overline{AB}$, $\overline{BC}$, and $\overline{AC}$. $\triangle ABC$ is an UnMessUpable right triangle.

c. Place a point on the screen. Call it A. Draw any circle with center A. Place a point on the circle. Call it B. Construct a circle with center B and radius $\overline{AB}$.

10. Check students' work.

11. a. invariant

b. not invariant

c. invariant

d. not invariant

12–30. See back of book.

Chapter 3
Dissections and Area

This chapter focuses on the mathematical topics of area and perimeter, the idea of dissecting one shape into another, and on the Pythagorean Theorem. It also includes a foray into three-dimensions with an investigation on volume and surface area.

Dissections and writing dissection algorithms provide a context for students to learn about area and perimeter and to get more experience with proofs. Students gain extensive experience using the Pythagorean Theorem and develop both an algebraic and a geometric understanding of the theorem. This chapter provides several dissection and area proofs of the theorem. It also introduces the topics of volume and surface area to give students some early experience. Students will justify the volume formulas more thoroughly in Chapter 6.

Chapter Overview

- Investigation 3A, *Cut and Rearrange,* has students cut and rearrange figures to make different figures with areas that are equal to those of the original figures. Students also analyze algorithms for the dissections they perform.
- Investigation 3B, *Area Formulas,* has students use their dissections to derive the area formulas for a parallelogram, a triangle, and a trapezoid.
- Investigation 3C, *Proof by Dissection,* focuses on proofs of the Pythagorean Theorem.
- Investigation 3D, *Measuring Solids,* has students find relationships between surface area and volume and relationships between special types of solids.

For more information on the investigations, see
- Chapter Road Map, pp. 168 and 169
- Investigation Road Maps, pp. 170, 194, 216, 230

PROJECT The Project near the end of the chapter is optional. You can assign the Project at any time during the chapter depending on how often and how long you feel students should work on it.

Mathematics Background

COMMENSURABILITY Even the simplest area formulas—such as the formula for the area of a rectangle—include a subtle application of limits. You can find the area of a rectangle without using limits if you can fill the rectangle exactly with a collection of congruent squares. Multiply the number of squares by the area of each square, and you have the area of the rectangle.

continued on p. 168b

DAILY PLANNER DAILY PLANNER DAILY P

Pacing Suggestions and Materials

Investigation 3A *Cut and Rearrange*

DAY	LESSON	HOMEWORK
1	3.1 Getting Started—Day 1 Core: 1, 2, 3 Optional: none	Core: 6 Optional: none
2	3.1 Getting Started—Day 2 Core: 4, 5 Optional: none	Core: 7 Optional: 8, 9
3	3.2 Do the Cuts Really Work?—Day 1 Core: 1, 2, 3 Optional: none	Core: 8, 9 Optional: none
4	3.2 Do the Cuts Really Work?—Day 2 Core: 4, 5 Optional: none; Extension: 6, 7	Core: 10, 12 Optional: 15, 16; Extension: 11, 13, 14
5	3.3 Cutting Algorithms Core: 1, 2, 3 Optional: none	Core: 4, 7 Optional: 5, 6, 8
6	3.4 Checking an Algorithm—Day 1 Core: 1 Optional: none	Core: 5, 6, 7, 8 Optional: none
7	3.4 Checking an Algorithm—Day 2 Core: 2, 3 Optional: 4	Core: 12, 13 Optional: 9, 10, 11, 14
8	3.5 The Midline Theorem Core: 1, 2, 3, 4 Optional: none	Core: 5, 6, 8, 9 Optional: 7, 11; Extension: 10

Investigation 3B *Area Formulas*

DAY	LESSON	HOMEWORK
1	3.6 Getting Started Core: 1, 2, 3 Optional: none	Core: 4, 5 Optional: 6
2	3.7 What is Area, Anyway? Core: 1, 2 Optional: none	Core: 3, 4, 5, 6, 7, 8, 9, 10 Optional: 11, 12, 13, 14
3	3.8 Area by Dissection—Day 1 Core: 1, 2 Optional: none	Core: 7, 9 Optional: none
4	3.8 Area by Dissection—Day 2 Core: 4, 5 Optional: none	Core: 10, 11 Optional: none
5	3.8 Area by Dissection—Day 3 Core: 6 Optional: 3	Core: 8, 12 Optional: 16, 17, 18; Extension: 13, 14, 15

NOTES	MATERIALS
This lesson can take 2 (or possibly 3) class periods to complete.	• rulers • scissors • Blackline Masters MC5, 3.1A–D (multiple copies for each student)
This may be a day for student presentations.	• rulers • scissors • Blackline Master 3.1E
	• geometry software • rulers • scissors • Blackline Masters MC5, 3.2A
	• geometry software • rulers • scissors • Blackline Masters 3.2A–D
	• Blackline Master 3.3
Students will be reviewing previously written algorithms throughout this lesson. Allot two days.	• Blackline Master 3.4

NOTES	MATERIALS
	• blank $8\frac{1}{2}$ in.-by-11 in. paper for Problem 2 • rulers • scissors
	• Blackline Master 3.7
	• rulers • scissors
	• geometry software • rulers • scissors
	• rulers • scissors • Blackline Masters 3.8A–B

continued from p. 168a

However, this is only possible if you can find a finite number of congruent squares that exactly fills the rectangle. For this to happen, the base and height of the rectangle must be *commensurable*. If the base and height are not commensurable, you have to use limits to determine the area instead of counting squares.

The idea of commensurability was very important to the ancient Greeks. Two line segments *a* and *b* are *commensurable* if and only if there exists some third segment *c* that you can lay end-to-end a whole number of times to produce a segment congruent to *a* and can also lay end-to-end, perhaps a different number of times, but still a whole number of times, to produce a segment congruent to *b*. Commensurability of *a* and *b* implies that $\frac{a}{b}$ is a rational number, and vice versa.

This relates to the idea of packing squares inside a rectangle to find the area of the rectangle. You need to be able to have some square that fits a whole number of times along both the length and width of the rectangle to be able to exactly fill the rectangle with congruent squares.

This distinction, however, may seem very unimportant to your students, because they have been working in a mathematical culture that completely accepts the existence of irrational numbers. However, if you want to use results that are *proven* only for rational numbers, you do have to extend those proofs to the real numbers through the use of limits. Your students will probably be completely unaware that there were any limits involved in proving these area formulas, but in other approaches, the use of limits is much more up front and, hence, less natural.

SCISSORS-CONGRUENCE Two-dimensional shapes are *scissors-congruent* if you can cut one shape into pieces and rearrange the pieces to form the other shape. The formal term for "scissors-congruent" is *equidecomposable*. Because you are working in two dimensions, you cannot overlap the pieces. In fact, one way to define area is as that quantity that is invariant under such a decomposition. This directly implies that if two shapes are scissors-congruent, they have the same area.

It seems that the converse of this idea is true, as well. In other words, if two shapes have equal areas, they must also be scissors-congruent. This result is true for simple polygons (polygons that do not cross themselves) in two dimensions by the Wallace-Bolyai-Gerwien Theorem.

You can prove this theorem in several steps. First, show that you can dissect any polygon into a finite number of triangles. You can do this by finding three consecutive vertices in your polygon and drawing the diagonal between the first and third of these vertices. This forms a triangle and a new polygon that has one fewer side than the original.

continued on p. 168c

Chapter 3 Dissections and Area **168b**

continued from p. 168b

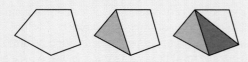

If you keep doing this, you eventually have only triangles left.

Then show that you can dissect any triangle into a rectangle. Find the midpoints of two sides and connect them. Then drop a perpendicular to this new segment to form two right triangles.

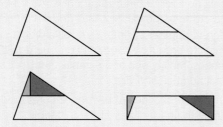

Then you can swing the two triangles down to form a rectangle.

Then, show that you can dissect any rectangle into a square. One way to do this dissection is to start with a rectangle and a square of equal areas. Then you can cut four congruent right triangles off of the two quadrilaterals, two triangles from each.

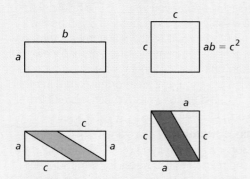

The parallelograms that remain must have equal areas, because they result from subtracting the same quantity of area from two quadrilaterals that had equal areas. They also have one pair of sides that are congruent because those sides are the hypotenuses of the congruent right triangles that you cut off. To show that you can dissect the darker parallelogram into the lighter one, envision placing the lighter one on top of the darker one with their bottom right vertices aligned.

continued on p. 168d

DAILY PLANNER DAILY PLANNER DAILY Pl

Pacing Suggestions and Materials

Investigation 3C *Proof by Dissection*

DAY	LESSON	HOMEWORK
1	3.9 Getting Started Core: 1 Optional: none	Core: 2, 3 Optional: 4
2	3.10 The Pythagorean Theorem—Day 1 Core: 1, 2 Optional: none	Core: 6, 7, 8 Optional: none
3	3.10 The Pythagorean Theorem—Day 2 Core: 3, 4, 5 Optional: none	Core: 9, 10, 11 Optional: 12
4	3.11 Pick a Proof (optional lesson)—Day 1 Core: 1 Optional: none	Core: 4, 5, 6 Optional: none
5	3.11 Pick a Proof (optional lesson)—Day 2 Core: 2, 3 Optional: none	Core: 7, 8, 9, 10, 11, 12, 13 Optional: 16; Extension: 14, 15

Investigation 3D *Measuring Solids*

DAY	LESSON	HOMEWORK
1	3.12 Getting Started Core: 1, 2, 3, 4 Optional: none	Core: 5, 6, 7, 8 Optional: 9, 10, 11, 12, 13; Extension: 14
2	3.13 Surface Area: Prisms and Pyramids Core: 1, 2, 3, 4 Optional: none	Core: 5, 6, 7, 8a–b, 9, 10 Optional: 11, 12, 13; Extension: 8c
3	3.14 Surface Area: Cylinders and Cones—Day 1 Core: 1 Optional: none	Core: 4a–b, 5 Optional: none
4	3.14 Surface Area: Cylinders and Cones—Day 2 Core: 2, 3 Optional: none	Core: 4c–d, 6, 7, 8, 9 Optional: 13, 14, 15; Extension: 10, 11, 12
5	3.15 Volumes of Solids Core: 1, 2, 3 Optional: none	Core: 4, 5, 6, 7, 8, 9 Optional: 11, 13, 14, 15, 16; Extension: 10,

NOTES	MATERIALS
Prepare a transparency of the proof in the In-Class Experiment.	• protractors • rulers
	• protractors • rulers
Students (or groups) choose one proof to analyze.	• Blackline Master 3.11
Students (or groups) present their proof explanations.	

NOTES	MATERIALS
	• models of solids
If you take two days to complete this lesson, begin by carefully reviewing students' work on prisms and pyramids and then work through the material on cylinders.	• models of solids • $8\frac{1}{2}$ in.-by-11 in. paper for Exercise 5
	• models of solids
	• cardstock • rice or dry sand • tape • Blackline Masters 3.15A and 3.15B

continued from p. 168c

The darker triangle that you can see sticking out behind the lighter parallelogram is the key to the dissection. The unshaded triangle in the middle figure represents that piece. You cut it off of one end of the darker parallelogram and paste it onto the opposite end to make a parallelogram congruent to the lighter one.

So where does this get you? You can dissect any polygon into triangles. Then you can dissect those triangles into rectangles and then squares. The dissection proofs of the Pythagorean Theorem that appear in this chapter can take any two of your squares and dissect them into a square that has area equal to the sum of their areas. Keep combining pairs of squares until you have a single square that has the same area as your original polygon. Now, since you can dissect *any* polygon into a square of equal area, you could dissect two different polygons that started out with equal areas and they would produce the same square. To dissect one of these polygons into the other, start at the first polygon and work until you have the single square. Then, following the steps for the dissection of the second polygon into the square in reverse, cut up the square and rearrange the pieces to form the second polygon.

What is even more interesting is that this result—that if two figures have the same area, you can always cut up one of them and rearrange the pieces to form the other figure—is *not* true in three dimensions. Max Dehn found a counterexample in 1901. He showed, through algebraic means, that it is impossible to cut a cube into a regular tetrahedron of equal volume.

Developing Students' Mathematical Habits

In this chapter, students use dissections to cut one type of polygon into pieces that they can then rearrange to form another type of polygon. Here are some key habits in this process:

- visualization, to predict the best cuts to make the dissection simple and reliable
- algorithmic thinking, to develop a procedure that will work in most cases and that does not depend on special properties (For example, a dissection of a triangle into a rectangle should not work only for right triangles unless the procedure also provides a dissection of any triangle into a right triangle.)
- deductive reasoning, to justify the steps of the algorithm (for example, proving that lines you say are straight are, in fact, straight)

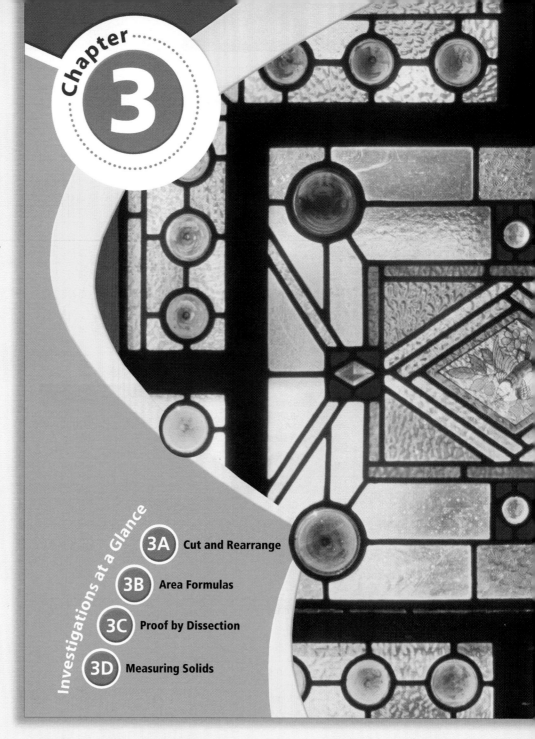

Chapter 3

Investigations at a Glance

3A Cut and Rearrange

3B Area Formulas

3C Proof by Dissection

3D Measuring Solids

Chapter Road Map

INVESTIGATION 3A, *Cut and Rearrange,* begins with students cutting and rearranging figures to make equal-area figures (or *scissors-congruent* figures). Students then analyze the algorithms they used for those dissections.

INVESTIGATION 3B, *Area Formulas,* has students use their dissections to derive the area formulas for a parallelogram, a triangle, and a trapezoid. Lesson 3.7 states some important assumptions about the areas of congruent figures that students will need to understand the derivations of the area formulas.

INVESTIGATION 3C, *Proof by Dissection,* focuses on the Pythagorean Theorem. Students have most likely seen or heard of the Pythagorean Theorem in previous courses, but they have a chance to review it here. Students also analyze several pictorial proofs of the theorem.

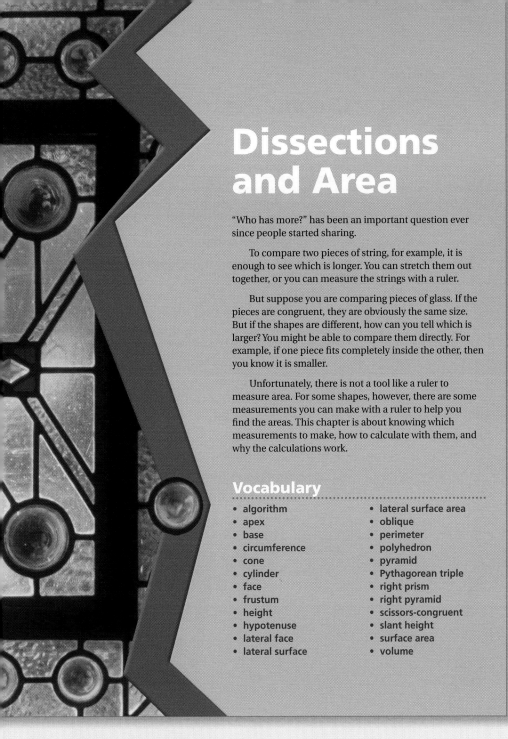

Dissections and Area

"Who has more?" has been an important question ever since people started sharing.

To compare two pieces of string, for example, it is enough to see which is longer. You can stretch them out together, or you can measure the strings with a ruler.

But suppose you are comparing pieces of glass. If the pieces are congruent, they are obviously the same size. But if the shapes are different, how can you tell which is larger? You might be able to compare them directly. For example, if one piece fits completely inside the other, then you know it is smaller.

Unfortunately, there is not a tool like a ruler to measure area. For some shapes, however, there are some measurements you can make with a ruler to help you find the areas. This chapter is about knowing which measurements to make, how to calculate with them, and why the calculations work.

Vocabulary

- algorithm
- apex
- base
- circumference
- cone
- cylinder
- face
- frustum
- height
- hypotenuse
- lateral face
- lateral surface
- lateral surface area
- oblique
- perimeter
- polyhedron
- pyramid
- Pythagorean triple
- right prism
- right pyramid
- scissors-congruent
- slant height
- surface area
- volume

Chapter Vocabulary and Notation

The following list gives key vocabulary and notation used in the chapter. Selected new vocabulary and notation items are shown in boldface on the student page.

- algorithm, p. 181
- apex, p. 237, 242
- base, pp. 208, 236, 237, 240, 242
- circumference, p. 241
- cone, p. 242
- cylinder, p. 240
- face, p. 235
- frustum, p. 246
- height, pp.205, 207, 208
- hypotenuse, p. 182
- lateral faces, pp. 236, 237
- lateral surface, pp. 240, 242
- lateral surface area, p. 237
- midline, p. 189
- oblique prism, p. 236
- oblique pyramid, p. 237
- parallelepiped, p. 232
- perimeter, p. 241
- pi, π, p. 241
- polyhedron, p. 235
- prism, p. 236
- pyramid, p. 237
- Pythagorean triple, p. 218
- right prism, p. 236
- right pyramid, p. 237
- scissors-congruent, p. 172
- slant height, p. 234
- surface area, p. 231
- tetrahedron, p. 232
- volume, p. 247

Chapter Technology

Support for the use of technology is available in the Technology Handbook. See p. 712.

INVESTIGATION 3A *Geometry Software*

- **LESSON 3.2** Draw triangles of equal area, p. 180.

INVESTIGATION 3B *Geometry Software*

- **LESSON 3.8** Dissect a parallelogram into a rectangle with the same base and height, p. 212.

INVESTIGATION 3D, *Measuring Solids,* helps students develop a concrete understanding of the surface area and the volume of a geometric solid. Students find relationships between surface area and volume and relationships between special types of solids. Whenever possible, students derive the formulas they use. When the mathematics for such a derivation is beyond the current reach of students, students find ways to estimate the measurements or make sense of a given formula.

Investigation Overview

The Daily Planner suggests that you spend at least two days on many of the lessons in this investigation. Students will need time to "play around" with the dissections and then to review and refine their algorithms.

To the casual visitor, your classroom might seem to be full of art students making collages. But as students solve and explain the exercises in this investigation, the mathematics involved will become clear and extensive.

To defend their solutions, students need to understand the properties of parallelograms, kites, trapezoids, rectangles, rhombuses, and squares. They will also develop general classifications for triangles and quadrilaterals. The following ideas will emerge: measure as a geometric invariant, dissection, and scissors-congruence.

You may wish to assign Questions 1–3 for students to think and write about during the investigation.

Learning Goals

- Devise and follow algorithms to dissect and rearrange one figure into an equal-area figure.
- Justify each cut in a dissection.
- Write general algorithms for dissections.
- Test algorithms with standard and extreme cases.

Habits and Skills

- Visualize ways to make equal-area figures through dissection.
- Write clear and precise algorithms.
- Reason by continuity to identify extreme cases.

Investigation 3A

Cut and Rearrange

In *Cut and Rearrange,* you will cut a given shape into parts. Then you will rearrange the parts to form a second shape. Cutting and rearranging will not convert a given shape into just any other imaginable shape. For example, you would not expect the resulting shape to have greater or lesser area. Chih-Han Sah was a mathematician who specialized in dissections of this sort. He called two figures that can be cut into each other scissors-congruent.

By the end of this investigation, you will be able to answer questions like these:

1. What is an algorithm?
2. Why is it important to justify each step in an algorithm?
3. What does the Midline Theorem say about the relationship between the midlines and the sides of a triangle?

You will learn how to

- devise and follow algorithms to dissect and rearrange one figure into an equal-area figure
- justify each cut in a dissection
- write general algorithms for dissections
- test algorithms with standard and extreme cases

You will develop these habits and skills:

- Visualize ways to make equal-area figures through dissection.
- Write clear and precise algorithms.
- Reason by continuity to identify extreme cases.

The total area remains the same no matter how you arrange the pieces.

Investigation Road Map

LESSON 3.1, *Getting Started,* has students cut and rearrange shapes to make new shapes that are scissors-congruent to the original shapes.

LESSON 3.2, *Do the Cuts Really Work?,* has students review the properties of various shapes to help explain the dissections they perform.

LESSON 3.3, *Cutting Algorithms,* has students write clear algorithms for the dissections they performed in the previous lessons.

LESSON 3.4, *Checking an Algorithm,* has students justify each step used in a dissection algorithm and encourages them to use nonstandard figures.

LESSON 3.5, *The Midline Theorem,* has students use the midlines of a triangle when solving dissection problems.

Geometric language helps you clearly describe how to move pieces to change one shape to another. Assume that you have a shape made of two right triangles. You can use three types of moves to change the shape into another.

In the figure at the upper left, two right triangles form a parallelogram. Moving clockwise, you can

- slide the gold triangle parallel to a base of the parallelogram to form a rectangle
- reflect the gold triangle across the dashed line to form a kite
- rotate the gold triangle about a vertex to form a triangle
- reflect the gold triangle across the dashed line to form the original parallelogram

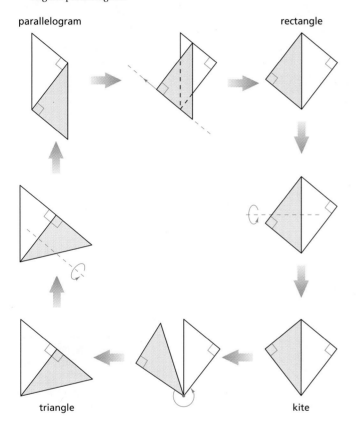

parallelogram   rectangle

triangle   kite

Lesson Overview

GOALS

- Explore ideas that are basic to the goals of this investigation.
- Use a hands-on approach to develop mathematical habits of mind.

The amount of time it takes to complete the problems and exercises in this lesson can vary greatly from class to class. It may take two or three days for students to complete and present the problems and exercises. The first day can be very frustrating to many students who do not know how to do these problems and exercises. But by Day 2 or Day 3, students should be more successful.

This lesson introduces *dissection*—cutting and rearranging geometric shapes to produce other shapes that are equal in area. The relation "equal in area" is a theme that dominates the remainder of this chapter, so it is important to have an initial discussion of what it means, as well as some agreement by the class about what term students will use to describe it. A more formal discussion of area comes in Investigation 3B.

FOR YOU TO EXPLORE
- Core: 1, 2, 3, 4, 5
- Optional: none

MATERIALS
- rulers
- scissors
- Blackline Masters MC5, 3.1A–E (multiple copies for each student)

HOMEWORK
- Core: 6, 7
- Optional: 8, 9

VOCABULARY
- scissors-congruent

Launch

Look at the three transformations shown in the diagram. Then divide the class into small groups to work on Problem 1 on the following page, cutting a parallelogram into a scissors-congruent rectangle.

Explore

Below are some things to remember as you teach this investigation:

- Many students will have no idea how to do the problems and exercises in this lesson, and they may begin by cutting almost randomly or with very awkward strategies. Do not give too many hints, though. The struggle pays off.
- Remind students that they must use all of the cut-up pieces to make the new shape so that the two figures will be scissors-congruent.

continued on p. 172

continued from p. 171

- While students are working in groups, ask a lot of questions, such as, "What do you think might work?" "How do you know that idea will *not* work?" "How do you know the shape you made is really a rectangle?" "Why did you make the cut right there?"

- At this point, if the solutions work for the particular figure given in the exercise, you should consider them correct. In Lessons 3.2, 3.3, and 3.4, students will formalize their solutions into general methods that will work in all cases.

Groups are likely to produce several correct solutions to Problem 1 fairly quickly. Have a few students share their solutions with the class. You can place cutouts directly on the overhead projector. Once students are reassured that these unusual problems really do have solutions and that there can be more than one correct answer, they should return to group work and try the rest of the Getting Started problems and exercises. Students are likely to discover a variety of different and creative solutions for these exercises. Be sure to ask, "Did anyone do the exercise in a different way?"

For You to Explore

PROBLEMS 1–5 Give students copies of Blackline Masters MC5, 3.1A–D. Have students cut up one figure and find a way to rearrange the pieces to form another figure:

- parallelogram to rectangle
- right triangle to rectangle
- scalene triangle to parallelogram
- scalene triangle to rectangle
- trapezoid to rectangle

Wrap Up

For Problems 1–5, have groups of students present their methods of dissection. You may wish to have students make a model of each method that you can display in your classroom.

Exercises

HOMEWORK
- Core: 6, 7
- Optional: 8, 9

On Your Own

EXERCISE 6 has students analyze three given dissections and describe how to perform the dissections and the rearranging.

For You to Explore

For Problems 1–5, start with the shape described. (Your teacher may give you copies of shapes to work with.) Cut this shape into pieces that you can rearrange to form the second shape described in the problem. The two shapes are **scissors-congruent.** Write a complete description of the cuts you made and how you moved the pieces.

1. Start with a parallelogram. Cut and rearrange to form a rectangle.

2. Start with a right triangle. Dissect and rearrange to form a rectangle.

3. Start with a (not right) scalene triangle. Cut and form a parallelogram.

4. Start with a (not right) scalene triangle. Cut and form a rectangle.

5. Start with a trapezoid. Dissect the trapezoid and form a rectangle.

> Each problem can be solved in more than one way. Work with classmates to find a few solutions. Then pick one that you like best. Save your written work. You will need it later.

> **Remember...**
> A scalene triangle has no two sides the same length.

Exercises *Practicing Habits of Mind*

On Your Own

6. Study each pair of figures below.

   Describe how to turn the first shape into the second shape by reflecting, rotating, or translating one or more of the pieces.

   a.

   b.

   c.

> **Go Online**
> **Video Tutor**
> PHSchool.com
> Web Code: bee-0775

Answers

Exercises

1–5. See back of book.

6. **a.** Answers may vary. Sample: Slide the triangle on the left side of the first figure to the right.

   b. Answers may vary. Sample: Rotate the top triangle in the first figure 180° about the top right vertex of the square. Then translate the other triangle to the right to fit.

   c. Answers may vary. Sample: Reflect the rightmost triangle in the first figure across the perpendicular bisector of the vertical segment.

7. **a.** Congruent; answers may vary. Sample: Reflect figure A about the horizontal line through the middle of the figure. Rotate the resulting figure 90° clockwise about the center point. Translate the resulting figure to the right.

   b. Not congruent; answers may vary. Sample: No side of figure B

7. Here is one definition of congruence.

   Two polygons are congruent if there is a transformation (reflection, rotation, translation, or combination of these) that maps one of the polygons onto the other.

   "Translation" is another way of saying *slide*.

   For example, polygons A and B are congruent. If you move A to the right and rotate it 90° clockwise, it will fit exactly on B.

   Decide whether the polygons in each pair below are congruent. If they are, describe a transformation that maps A onto B. If they are not, explain how you know.

   a.    **b.**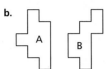

   c.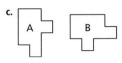

8. Combine two polygons shaped like the polygon at the right to form new polygons. For example, you can make a polygon like the one below.

   Form as many *different* polygons as you can. Polygons that are reflections, rotations, or translations of polygons you already have do not count as different. You may want to use graph paper.

9. Start with two congruent isosceles right triangles and a square. The sides of the square have the same length as each leg of the triangles. Put all three pieces together to form each figure.

   a. a trapezoid

   b. a right triangle

   c. a parallelogram that is not a rectangle

   d. a rectangle

   two isosceles right triangles

---

is as long as the longest side of figure A.

c. Congruent; rotate figure A 90° clockwise. Reflect the resulting figure about a vertical line and translate the result to get figure B. Finally, translate the figure to the right.

8. See back of book.

9. a.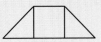

b.

c.

d.

Maintain Your Skills

EXERCISE 9 has students use two isosceles right triangles and a square to form different polygons. You may wish to provide students with Blackline Master 3.1E.

Lesson Overview

GOAL

- Devise and follow algorithms to dissect and rearrange one figure into an equal-area figure.

Students have now had some experience dissecting and rearranging figures. This lesson requires them to use the properties of various shapes to help explain why a cut works.

CHECK YOUR UNDERSTANDING
- Core: 1, 2, 3, 4, 5
- Optional: none
- Extension: 6, 7

HOMEWORK
- Core: 8, 9, 10, 12
- Optional: 15, 16
- Extension: 11, 13, 14

MATERIALS
- geometry software
- rulers
- scissors
- Blackline Masters MC5, 3.2A–D

Launch

Begin by reading the introduction to the lesson and Tony's description of dissecting a parallelogram into a rectangle. You may wish to have models of the pieces to tape to the board or to put on the overhead for demonstration. You may also wish to provide copies of Blackline Master MC5 for students to use.

Explore

Use Problems 1 and 2 in the first For Discussion section to check that students can justify the cuts that Tony made.

Then read through the Minds in Action section about how to dissect a triangle into a parallelogram. Both dissections in this lesson require students to understand properties of parallelograms.

Use Problems 3 and 4 in the second For Discussion section to help analyze Derman and Sasha's dissection.

Wrap Up

Assign the Check Your Understanding exercises. Ask students to present their solutions to the class. As students present their solutions, have them describe their methods of solving each exercise and explain why their methods work. Steer them away from vague statements, such as, "It looked right."

Students may be vague when they explain their solutions. For instance, they may say, "I cut in the

continued on p. 175

3.2 Do the Cuts Really Work?

Have you ever expected a dissection to work, but then discovered that the pieces did not quite fit? Or perhaps the pieces looked like they fit, but you found it difficult to be sure?

To understand why a dissection works, you must know properties of the shapes you are cutting. Here are some properties of parallelograms that you learned in Chapter 2.

- Parallelograms have exactly four sides.
- Opposite sides are parallel.
- Opposite sides are congruent.
- Opposite angles are congruent.
- Consecutive angles are supplementary.
- The diagonals bisect each other.

Habits of Mind

Confirm a process. If you can explain *why* a cut works, then you will know for sure that it does.
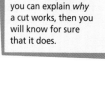

Here is Tony's method for dissecting a parallelogram into a rectangle.

Cut out the parallelogram. Make a fold through vertex *D* so that *A* lines up on the bottom, on $\overline{AB}$.

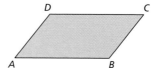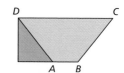

Then unfold and cut along the crease. Slide the triangular piece along $\overline{AB}$ so that $\overline{AD}$ matches up with $\overline{BC}$ and you have a rectangle.

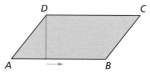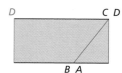

Tony cut two pieces: a triangle and a trapezoid. He then rearranged those pieces. But what guaranteed that the rearrangement had four sides? Here are two ways that his dissection might fail.

The newly glued edges might not match.   The new bottom edge might be crooked.

For Discussion

In Tony's method on the previous page, you slide the triangle to the opposite side of the trapezoid. Explain how the properties of parallelograms guarantee each of the following.

1. The two pieces fit together exactly.

2. The new bottom edge is straight.

Minds in Action   episode 5

Sasha and Derman are trying to dissect △ABC into a parallelogram.

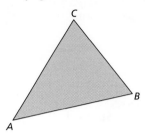

Sasha   First, cut out the triangle. Find the midpoint of $\overline{AC}$. Name it *M*. Find the midpoint of $\overline{BC}$. Name it *N*. Cut along $\overline{MN}$.

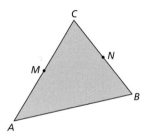 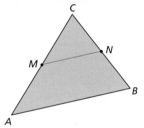

Derman   I see where you're going with this. You can rotate △*MCN*—the triangle you just cut off—around *M*, until $\overline{MC}$ matches up with $\overline{MA}$.

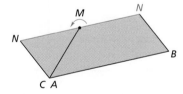

Sasha   Now we have a parallelogram, right?

---

continued from p. 174

middle...." You can ask clarifying questions, such as, "What do you mean by 'middle'? Do you mean at the midpoint?" Soon, the correct vocabulary will become part of the classroom culture for explaining solutions. Students will learn to communicate more clearly in order for you to understand them and for them to understand each other.

Assessment Resources

Lesson Quiz 3.2

1. Explain how the properties of rectangles guarantee each of the following dissections.
   a. a rectangle into an isosceles triangle
   b. a rectangle into a trapezoid

2. Explain how the properties of parallelograms guarantee each of the following dissections.
   a. a parallelogram into a rectangle
   b. a parallelogram into a triangle

3. Start with a rectangle. Dissect it into pieces you can rearrange to form two rhombuses. Describe your steps with diagrams.

4. Start with a parallelogram. Dissect it into pieces you can rearrange to form an isosceles trapezoid. Describe your steps with diagrams.

Answers

For Discussion

1. The pieces fit exactly because opposite sides of a parallelogram are congruent.

2. The new bottom edge is straight because consecutive angles of a parallelogram are supplementary.

Derman I guess we do, but what if it just *looks* like a parallelogram? What if our scissors techniques aren't accurate and the picture should really look like this?

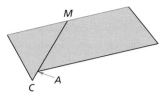

Sasha Good try Derman. But the steps we took *guarantee* that our figure only has four sides, and segments $\overline{MC}$ and $\overline{MA}$ are congruent.

See, since M is the midpoint of $\overline{AC}$ in the original triangle, MC must equal MA. So, sides $\overline{MC}$ and $\overline{MA}$ fit together exactly.

Derman Aaaahhh. It's a proof!

For Discussion

3. If the final figure is really a parallelogram, then the top edge must be straight. It must not look like the picture below. How does Sasha and Derman's method guarantee that it will be straight?

4. If the final figure is really a parallelogram, then it must be true that opposite sides are congruent. How does Sasha and Derman's method guarantee that $\overline{CN} \cong \overline{BN}$? That $\overline{AB} \cong \overline{NN}$?

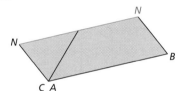

Later in this chapter you will see a more formal discussion about area. For now, assume that a polygon has area and that the area does not change when you dissect the polygon.

Answers

For Discussion

3. The top edge is straight because $m\angle CMN + m\angle AMN = 180°$.

4. $\overline{CN} \cong \overline{NB}$ because N is the midpoint of $\overline{CB}$ in the starting triangle. $\overline{AB} \cong \overline{NN}$ because $MN = \frac{1}{2}AB$, and $NN = 2MN = 2\left(\frac{1}{2}AB\right) = AB$.

Exercises

1. Answers may vary. Sample: Opposite sides are parallel and congruent. Diagonals bisect each other and are congruent.

2. a. Opposite sides of a rectangle are congruent.

b. Angles A and C are right angles, so they form a straight line when joined.

3. No; diagonals of a rectangles are congruent.

Exercises Practicing Habits of Mind

Check Your Understanding

1. **Write About It** List all the properties of rectangles that you can think of. Here is a start.

- Rectangles are parallelograms.
- Rectangles have exactly four sides.
- All angles measure 90°.

Here is Diego's method for turning a rectangle into an isosceles triangle. Use this for Exercises 2 and 3.

Start with a rectangle. Cut along a diagonal.

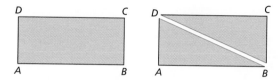

Slide $\triangle ABD$ to the right, along the bottom, so $\overline{AD}$ lines up with $\overline{BC}$. Then flip $\triangle ABD$ so you have a triangle instead of a parallelogram.

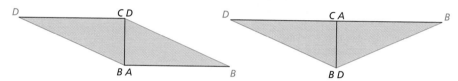

Diego's diagonal cut makes two triangles. Below are two ways that the dissection might fail.

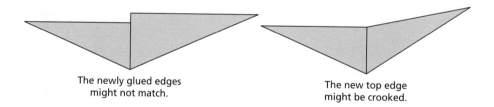

The newly glued edges might not match.

The new top edge might be crooked.

Exercises

Check Your Understanding

EXERCISES 1–4 You may wish to provide copies of Blackline Master 3.2A for students to use.

---

4. See back of book.

5. a. $\triangle DCN \cong \triangle PBN$ follows by AAS, since $\angle C \cong \angle PBN$ and $\angle CDN \cong \angle P$ by PAI, and $\overline{CN} \cong \overline{BN}$.

   b. $\overline{CD} \cong \overline{BP}$ by CPCTC.

   c. $\overline{MP} \| \overline{AP}$ and $MN = \frac{1}{2}AP$

   d. $MN = \frac{1}{2}(AB + CD)$

   e. $MN < AB;\ MN > CD$

6. See back of book.

7. Answers may vary. Sample: Suppose the original rectangle has side lengths b and h. Draw a segment connecting the midpoints of the sides of length b. Cut along this segment. Stack the pieces to get a rectangle with side lengths $2h$ and $\frac{b}{2}$. If $\frac{b}{2} \neq h$, you are done. If $\frac{b}{2} = h$, then go back to the original rectangle, and instead cut along the segment connecting the midpoints of the sides of length h. Stack the pieces to get a rectangle with side lengths $2b$ and $\frac{h}{2}$.

2. For Diego's method on the previous page, explain how the properties of rectangles guarantee the following.

   a. $\overline{AD}$ fits $\overline{BC}$ exactly.   **b.** The new top edge is straight.

3. If Diego cuts along the other diagonal, will he get a different triangle? Explain. Be sure to use what you know about rectangles.

4. Can you reverse a dissection process? Choose three shapes from the list below. For each shape, start with a rectangle and dissect it into pieces you can rearrange to form that shape.

   a. an isosceles triangle   **b.** a right triangle

   c. a nonrectangular parallelogram   **d.** a scalene triangle

   e. a trapezoid

5. For trapezoid *ABCD*, $\overline{MN}$ connects midpoint *M* of $\overline{AD}$ and midpoint *N* of $\overline{BC}$. Draw segment $\overline{DN}$. Then show the line through *D* and *N* and the line through *A* and *B* meeting at point *P*.

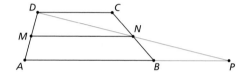

   a. Find two congruent triangles in the diagram. Prove they are congruent.

   b. Use these triangles to show that $\overline{CD} \cong \overline{BP}$.

   c. What does Theorem 2.10 (the Midline Theorem) say about $\overline{MN}$ and $\overline{AB}$?

   d. What can you say about $\overline{MN}$, $\overline{AB}$, and $\overline{CD}$?

   e. What else can you say about the relationship between $\overline{MN}$ and $\overline{AB}$? About the relationship between $\overline{MN}$ and $\overline{DC}$?

   You can state the result of Exercise 5 as Theorem 3.1.

Theorem 3.1

The segment joining the midpoints of the legs of a trapezoid is parallel to the bases. Its length is half the sum (the average) of the lengths of the bases.

The legs of a trapezoid are the two nonparallel sides.

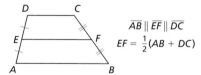

$\overline{AB} \parallel \overline{EF} \parallel \overline{DC}$

$EF = \frac{1}{2}(AB + DC)$

Answers

On Your Own

8. Check students' work.

9. Use dissection methods from the lesson. Dissect the given triangle into a parallelogram. Dissect the parallelogram into a rectangle. Finally, dissect the rectangle into a right triangle.

10. Cut along the diagonals of the square. Translate two adjacent triangles that result to form the desired rectangle.

11. See back of book.

12. C

13. Yes; cut along a diagonal to form two triangles and then use known dissection techniques to cut the triangles and rearrange them into rectangles that share a side, as shown below.

6. Take It Further Show how to dissect a parallelogram and rearrange the parts to form a rectangle that has one base that is congruent to a diagonal of the parallelogram.

7. Take It Further Start with a rectangle. Use dissection to make a rectangle with no sides congruent to the sides of the original figure.

On Your Own

8. Make a second copy of the trapezoid you used for Problem 5 in Lesson 3.1. Dissect it so that the pieces form a triangle.

9. Use a dissection argument. Show that △*ABC* is scissors-congruent to a right triangle.

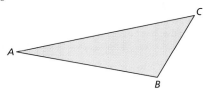

10. Cut a square into a rectangle that has a base congruent to one of the square's diagonals. Describe your steps.

11. Take It Further Start with an isosceles triangle with two sides of length *s*. Dissect it into two parts that you can rearrange to form a new isosceles triangle with two sides of length *s*. Are the two isosceles triangles congruent? Explain.

12. Standardized Test Prep *ACDF* is a trapezoid. *B* is the midpoint of $\overline{AC}$, and *E* is the midpoint of $\overline{DF}$. *CD* is 1.00 m. *BE* is 2.75 m. What is *AF*?

A. 1.875 m   **B.** 3.75 m

C. 4.50 m   **D.** 5.50 m

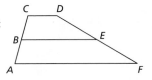

EXERCISE 6 has students show that you can dissect a parallelogram and rearrange the pieces to form a rectangle with one base that is congruent to a diagonal of the parallelogram. You may wish to provide copies of Blackline Master MC5 for students to use.

EXERCISE 7 has students dissect a rectangle and rearrange the pieces to form another rectangle with the same area but different dimensions.

On Your Own

There are many exercises in this lesson from which to choose. You may wish to assign some of them for homework and then have students present their results the next day. After presentations, assign more of the exercises for in-class work.

EXERCISE 8 has students dissect a trapezoid to form a triangle of equal area. This exercise presents a good opportunity to discuss and review *median*, *midline*, *altitude*, and *angle bisector*. As students provide explanations, encourage correct use of terminology, and ask them to prove some of their results.

EXERCISE 10 You may wish to provide copies of Blackline Master 3.2B for students to use.

EXERCISE 11 You may wish to provide copies of Blackline Master 3.2C for students to use.

13. (first figure)   (second figure)

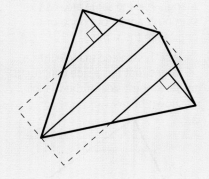
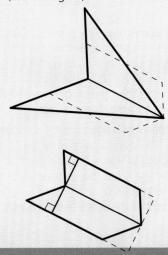

Maintain Your Skills

EXERCISE 15 Students must use the fact that two triangles with congruent bases and congruent heights have the same area.

Additional Resources

PRINT RESOURCES
- Solution Manual
- Practice Workbook
- Assessment Resources
- Teaching Resources

TECHNOLOGY
- Interactive Textbook
- TeacherExpress CD-ROM
- **Exam**View CD-ROM
- **PHSchool.com**
  - Additional Practice
  - Mid-Chapter and Chapter Tests
  - Video Tutors
  - Vocabulary Puzzles

Additional Practice

1. List all the properties of a square that you can think of. Can you think of a dissection that will turn the square into an isosceles triangle? Explain.

2. Use the figure. Suppose you slide △ABD to the right and flip it. Explain how the properties of squares guarantee each of the following.
   a. $\overline{AB}$ fits $\overline{CD}$ exactly.
   b. The new top edge is straight.

3. If you cut along the other diagonal in Exercise 2, will you get a different triangle? Explain.

4. Describe how to dissect a parallelogram into pieces that you can rearrange to form each shape.
   a. isosceles triangle
   b. right triangle
   c. trapezoid
   d. rectangle

5. In the figure, ACDF is an isosceles trapezoid, B is the midpoint of $\overline{AC}$, and E is the midpoint of $\overline{DF}$. Write an outline for a proof to show that $\overline{BE} \parallel \overline{CD}$ and $\overline{BE} \parallel \overline{AF}$.

6. Write specific and clear algorithms for each dissection.
   a. triangle to rectangle
   b. parallelogram to rectangle
   c. trapezoid to rectangle

7. Find a partner. Exchange the algorithms you wrote in Exercise 6.
   a. Follow your partner's algorithms. Do the algorithms work? Are the directions clear?
   b. Give your partner feedback on the algorithms you tried. Ask your partner for feedback on your algorithms. How can you improve your algorithms?

8. Write an algorithm for one part of your daily routine, such as making your bed or brushing your teeth. Describe how your algorithm might differ from a classmate's algorithm.

Practice: For Lesson 3.2, assign Exercises 1–5.

---

13. **Take It Further** Can you dissect any quadrilateral into a rectangle? Trace each figure. Then try to cut and rearrange it into a rectangle.

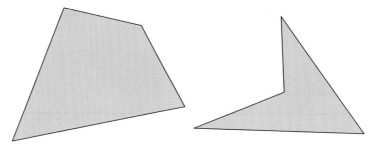

14. **Take It Further** If you suspect that two shapes have unequal areas, how could you show that one has greater area than the other?

Maintain Your Skills

15. Start with a scalene triangle. Think of a way to draw (by hand or with geometry software) another triangle of equal area that has no angles congruent to the angles of the original triangle.

16. Start with a scalene triangle. Find a way of dissecting it into a triangle with no sides congruent to the sides of the original. Justify your method.

Go Online
PHSchool.com

For additional practice, go to Web Code: bea-0302

AUSTRALIA

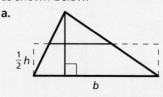

You can compare areas of irregular shapes by placing one shape over the other.

UNITED STATES (contiguous)

Answers

14. Answers may vary. Sample: Cut and rearrange one shape and try to fit it inside the other. If it does not entirely cover the second shape, then the second shape has a greater area than the first.

15. Construct a line through a vertex of the triangle parallel to the opposite side. Choose a point on the line other than the vertex of the triangle. Draw segments from that point to the other two vertices of the original triangle. The resulting triangle has the same area as the starting triangle, but none of the angles are the same.

16. Dissect the scalene triangle into a rectangle that has a side congruent to the longest side of the triangle, as shown below.

    a.

Cutting Algorithms

An **algorithm** is a process—a set of steps—that is completely determined. There is no unpredictability, no doubt what the steps will do each time you apply them. Many computer programs are algorithms, with every step precisely spelled out.

In Lesson 3.1, Problems 1–5 asked you to write a description of the cuts you made and how you moved the pieces. You may have written your descriptions as algorithms.

Now you will develop algorithms for successfully dissecting any triangle, trapezoid, or parallelogram into a rectangle. You will prove that your algorithms will always work. Remember that, for each problem, there may be many algorithms that work. However, there are others that do not work, or work only for special cases.

Later, you will use successful algorithms to develop formulas for the areas of triangles, parallelograms, and trapezoids.

> The word *algorithm* is a distorted transliteration of the name of a well-known mathematician who lived in Baghdad about 850. Abu-Ja'far Muhammad ibn Musa was known as al-Khwarizmi, which means "the one from Khwarazm." The Latin attempt at spelling al-Khwarizmi was Algorismi, which later became algorism and then algorithm.

Minds in Action   episode 6

Hannah draws the pictures below to show how to dissect a triangle into a rectangle. Darren studies her pictures. Then he tries to write complete and precise instructions for the cuts and rearrangements.

Hannah Darren, here's how I dissected a triangle into a rectangle.

I   II

III   IV

Darren Okay, let me see if I can figure out what you did. It looks like you first cut the triangle into two pieces.

Hannah Well, yes, but where did I make the cut? Be specific.

---

b.

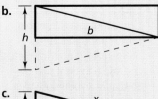

c.

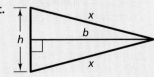

The ending triangle has side lengths h, x, and x. The side of length x is shorter than any side in the starting triangle because it is congruent to the altitude

of the original triangle. The two sides of length x are longer than any side of the original triangle, since the altitude of the ending triangle is congruent to the longest side of the starting triangle.

Lesson Overview

GOALS

- Devise and follow algorithms to dissect and rearrange one figure into an equal-area figure.
- Write general algorithms for dissection.

This lesson has students discover and use reliable algorithms for dissecting a parallelogram into a rectangle, a triangle into a rectangle, and a trapezoid into a rectangle.

Three main threads run through this lesson:

- Understand what algorithms are and learn to write them.
- Understand what is meant by a standard case and an extreme case and how these apply to the testing of algorithms.
- Continue to explore area and the determining properties of polygons.

This lesson aims to help students become more sophisticated in their understanding of the rigor involved in classifying shapes and in distinguishing between the general and the specific case.

CHECK YOUR UNDERSTANDING
- Core: 1, 2, 3
- Optional: none
- Extension: 6, 7

MATERIALS
- Blackline Master 3.3

HOMEWORK
- Core: 4, 7
- Optional: 5, 6, 8

VOCABULARY
- algorithm
- hypotenuse

Launch

Begin by reading the discussion about the definition of *algorithm* at the beginning of this lesson.

Explore

Use the Minds in Action section as an example of a dissection algorithm.

Use Problem 1 in the For Discussion section to emphasize the importance of using specific instructions and careful vocabulary when you write an algorithm.

Wrap Up

Assign the Check Your Understanding exercises to pairs or groups of students. Students must write algorithms, test them, rewrite them, discuss them, and then rewrite the algorithms one last time. Many students have had little experience with the sort of rigorous thinking this lesson requires. Such students may be content accepting a correct solution for one case as a correct solution for similar cases.

Assessment Resources

Exercises

HOMEWORK
- Core: 4, 7
- Optional: 5, 6, 8

Check Your Understanding

EXERCISE 1 has students go through a process of editing the algorithms they wrote in Lesson 3.1. You can save class time by assigning groups of students only one algorithm to edit. Then have each group share their results with the rest of the class.

Darren Picky, picky. I guess you found the midpoints of the two sides of the triangle and connected them. That guarantees that you have congruent edges when you move the pieces around.

Hannah Good. What did I do next?

Darren You drew this little segment to make two triangles.

I know, I need to be specific.

The segment must be the altitude from the vertex of the triangle to the midline. An altitude forms 90° angles, which you want for a rectangle.

Then you rotated each little right triangle around a midpoint. The hypotenuse of each lined up with the lower half of the side of the original triangle. Now you have a rectangle!

> In a right triangle, the **hypotenuse** is the side opposite the right angle.

For Discussion

1. Why is it important for Darren to "be specific" when he describes the cuts that Hannah made? What might happen if he were not as specific as Hannah apparently insisted?

Exercises *Practicing Habits of Mind*

Check Your Understanding

In Lesson 3.1, you wrote about how you dissected a parallelogram, a triangle, and a trapezoid into rectangles. Exercises 1–3 below ask you to edit these old descriptions (or write new ones). Be as clear and precise about the steps as you now can be.

1. Rewrite your algorithm for each dissection.
   - parallelogram to rectangle
   - triangle to rectangle
   - trapezoid to rectangle
   a. Draw pictures that show your steps.
   b. Describe the same steps precisely using words only.

Answers

For Discussion

1. If Darren is not specific about how the cuts are made, he cannot be sure that sides align properly, and that sides of the resulting figure are straight.

Exercises

1. **a.** Answers may vary. See back of book for sample answers.

b. • parallelogram to rectangle
   Cut along an altitude that passes through a vertex of the parallelogram. Translate the resulting right triangle so that its hypotenuse aligns with the opposite side of the parallelogram.

   • triangle to rectangle
   Cut along the midline parallel to the longest side of the triangle. Cut along the altitude to the longest side of the resulting smaller triangle. Rotate each of the smaller

2. Find a partner. Exchange the steps you wrote in Exercise 1 (but not the pictures) on how to dissect a parallelogram into a scissors-congruent rectangle.

  a. Follow your partner's directions exactly as written. Does the algorithm work? Are the directions clear? Are any directions confusing?

  b. Give your partner feedback on the algorithm you tried. Listen to your partner's feedback on yours. How can you refine the directions?

3. Work with a partner again in the same way. Refine your algorithm for dissecting a trapezoid into a rectangle.

On Your Own

4. Standardized Test Prep In $\triangle ABC$, E and F are midpoints. The area of $\triangle ABC$ is 30 cm². What is the area of parallelogram $ABIF$?

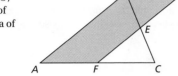

  A. 15 cm²   **B.** 20 cm²

  C. 30 cm²   **D.** 60 cm²

5. Write an algorithm for tying your shoelace. Be precise. Do not leave out any steps.

6. Write an algorithm for multiplying a three-digit number by a two-digit number.

7. Write final versions of dissection algorithms for the three dissections below. (See Exercise 1.) Be as clear as possible.

  a. Dissect a parallelogram into a rectangle.

  b. Dissect a triangle into a rectangle.

  c. Dissect a trapezoid into a rectangle.

> Assume you know how to multiply two one-digit numbers.

Maintain Your Skills

8. Describe a way to dissect each triangle into a rectangle that has the same base as the triangle.

Go Online
PHSchool.com
For additional practice, go to **Web Code: bea-0303**

---

right triangles 180° about the midpoints of the sides of the original triangle.

• trapezoid to rectangle
  Cut along the midline parallel to the bases of the trapezoid. Rotate one of the resulting smaller trapezoids 180° about one of the endpoints of the midline. Dissect the resulting parallelogram into a rectangle using the technique described above.

2–3. Check students' work.

On Your Own

4. C

5. Check students' work.

6. See back of book.

7. Check students' work.

Maintain Your Skills

8. Check students' work.

EXERCISE 2 has students exchange their descriptions for how to dissect a parallelogram into a scissors-congruent rectangle and then give feedback to one another about the algorithm.

EXERCISE 3 is similar to Exercise 2, but students critique a partner's algorithm for dissecting a trapezoid into a rectangle.

On Your Own

EXERCISE 7 has students write final versions of the dissection algorithms from Exercise 1.

Maintain Your Skills

EXERCISE 8 You may wish to provide copies of Blackline Master 3.3 for students to use.

Additional Resources

PRINT RESOURCES
• Solution Manual
• Practice Workbook
• Assessment Resources
• Teaching Resources

TECHNOLOGY
• Interactive Textbook
• TeacherExpress CD-ROM
• *ExamView* CD-ROM
• **PHSchool.com**
  – Additional Practice
  – Mid-Chapter and Chapter Tests
  – Video Tutors
  – Vocabulary Puzzles

Additional Practice

1. List all the properties of a square that you can think of. Can you think of a dissection that will turn the square into an isosceles triangle? Explain.

2. Use the figure. Suppose you slide $\triangle ABD$ to the right and flip it. Explain how the properties of squares guarantee each of the following.
  a. $\overline{AB}$ fits $\overline{CD}$ exactly.
  b. The new top edge is straight.

3. If you cut along the other diagonal in Exercise 2, will you get a different triangle? Explain.

4. Describe how to dissect a parallelogram into pieces that you can rearrange to form each shape.
  a. isosceles triangle
  b. right triangle
  c. trapezoid
  d. rectangle

5. In the figure, $ACDF$ is an isosceles trapezoid, B is the midpoint of $\overline{AC}$, and E is the midpoint of $\overline{DF}$. Write an outline for a proof to show that $\overline{BE} \parallel \overline{CD}$ and $\overline{BE} \parallel \overline{AF}$.

6. Write specific and clear algorithms for each dissection.
  a. triangle to rectangle
  b. parallelogram to rectangle
  c. trapezoid to rectangle

7. Find a partner. Exchange the algorithms you wrote in Exercise 6.
  a. Follow your partner's algorithms. Do the algorithms work? Are the directions clear?
  b. Give your partner feedback on the algorithms you tried. Ask your partner for feedback on your algorithms. How can you improve your algorithms?

8. Write an algorithm for one part of your daily routine, such as making your bed or brushing your teeth. Describe how your algorithm might differ from a classmate's algorithm.

Practice: For Lesson 3.3, assign Exercises 6–8.

Lesson Overview

GOALS

- Justify each cut in a dissection.
- Write general algorithms for dissection.
- Test algorithms with standard and extreme cases.

This lesson shows students how to test an algorithm to determine whether it works. There are at least two natural approaches to use when trying to find a special case or a counterexample. One is to study the given algorithm and see if you can find places where it might fail. This approach works well for Problem 1. You can see in the given triangle that the altitude must bisect the opposite side, and you can ask yourself if that is, in fact, true for all triangles.

Another approach is to study some extreme figures, instead of the standard ones. For example, in the For You to Do section, you can begin by drawing many different types of parallelograms, being sure to include some oddly-shaped ones. It is these unusual figures that might cause an algorithm to fail. For this reason, it is important for students to keep these figures in mind as they write their own algorithms.

CHECK YOUR UNDERSTANDING
- Core: 1, 2, 3
- Optional: 4

HOMEWORK
- Core: 5, 6, 7, 8, 12, 13
- Optional: 9, 10, 11, 14

MATERIALS
- Blackline Master 3.4

Launch

Have students read the introductory paragraph of the lesson.

Explore

Read through the first For Discussion section. Problem 1 shows one method of dissecting a triangle and rearranging it to form a rectangle. Students need to show why this method does not work for all triangles. They must explain what special features of this particular triangle allow the method to work.

There are two main difficulties with this algorithm. First, it assumes that you can pick any vertex of the triangle and draw an altitude from it to the opposite side. However, this is not true for an obtuse triangle because two of the three altitudes lie outside the triangle. You may want to draw on the board an obtuse triangle and its three altitudes to illustrate this fact.

3.4 Checking an Algorithm

How can you know whether an algorithm works?

- You can check that it works for all possible cases. (Why will this not work for the algorithms you just wrote?)
- You can check the justification for each step.
- You can look for a single counterexample—a case for which the algorithm fails.

For Discussion

1. **What's Wrong Here?** Steps 1–3 below dissect a triangle into a rectangle. Study the pictures and justifications for each step.

   a. Show why this method will not work for all triangles.

   b. What special features must a triangle have for this method to work? Explain.

   Step 1 Cut out the triangle. Draw an altitude from the top vertex to the base. This makes two right triangles because the altitude forms 90° angles.

   Step 2 Slide one of the triangles along the base.

   Step 3 Flip one of the triangles. Now two of the sides of the original triangle match up.

   The final shape is a rectangle because

   - the two vertical sides are congruent. They were made by the same cut.
   - two opposite angles are right angles. They were made by an altitude cut.

Answers

For Discussion

1. **a.** The altitude might not intersect the opposite base, and the two sides that make up the diagonal in Step 3 might not be congruent.

   b. The triangle must be isosceles, with the two congruent sides forming the top vertex angle. If the triangle is isosceles, the altitude divides the triangle into two smaller triangles, and the sides forming the diagonal of the rectangle are congruent.

For You to Do

2. Here is another algorithm. This one is for cutting a parallelogram into a rectangle. It also has a flaw, but the flaw is quite subtle. Although it seems to work perfectly, there are parallelograms for which it fails. Fix it.

Step 1 Draw the perpendicular bisector of one side of the parallelogram.

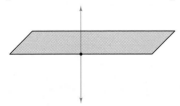

Step 2 Cut along the perpendicular bisector. This perpendicular cut guarantees right angles.

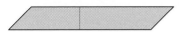

Step 3 Slide one piece parallel to the bisected side until the uncut ends match.

The sides *will* match. The properties of parallelograms guarantee that opposite sides are congruent. They also guarantee that the sum of measures of two consecutive angles is 180°.

There is a very natural pitfall in writing an algorithm. You may base the algorithm on a drawing or a situation that is too typical.

For example, most people tend to picture fairly symmetric figures, such as the first figure below.

But a less-symmetric figure is less special.

Most people also tend to picture a figure with one side horizontal, such as the second figure below, so that it looks as if it will not fall over. That can also be a pitfall. A rule that works well for an apparently stable figure may not work so well for a figure that looks "unbalanced", such as the third figure below.

This is why it is so important to have good strategies for checking and debugging a process.

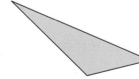

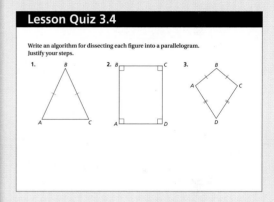
For You to Do

2. The perpendicular bisector of a parallelogram may not intersect the opposite side. If it does not, cut along the perpendicular bisector of an adjacent side.

Exercises

HOMEWORK
- Core: 5, 6, 7, 8, 12, 13
- Optional: 9, 10, 11, 14

Check Your Understanding

EXERCISE 1 requires students to review their dissection algorithms—checking standard and nonstandard cases—and revise them, if necessary.

For Discussion

Here is one way to find important special cases to test an algorithm. Stretch a definition to its extreme.

3. Discuss the difference between the definition of a trapezoid and your usual mental picture of a trapezoid.

4. With other students, find four trapezoids, quite different from each other, that are very atypical.

Exercises *Practicing Habits of Mind*

Check Your Understanding

1. **Write About It** Study your algorithms for dissecting parallelograms, triangles, and trapezoids into rectangles. Check some nonstandard figures for each algorithm. If there *are* figures for which your algorithm does not work, explain what features caused your algorithm to fail. Then revise the method and test it again.

2. **What's Wrong Here?** A student was asked to dissect a parallelogram and rearrange the pieces into a rectangle. The student gave the following argument.

 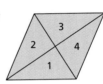 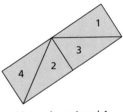

Draw the diagonals.   Move pieces 1 and 4.

a. What is wrong with this argument?

b. For which type(s) of parallelograms does this dissection work?

Answers

For Discussion

3. Check students' work.

4. Check students' work.

Exercises

1. Check students' work.

2. a. It does not work for all parallelograms.
   b. rhombuses

3. Check students' work.

4. a. The pieces match because the cuts are through the midpoint of the sides.

   b. yes

   c. The upper angles of the quadrilateral are right angles because the vertical cut in Step 1 is perpendicular to the horizontal cut. The bottom two angles both have one nonright angle of a right triangle meeting an angle congruent to the other nonright angle of the same right triangle.

3. Choose one of your cutting algorithms for dissecting parallelograms, scalene triangles, and trapezoids into rectangles. Justify each step to show why your algorithm reliably produces the desired result.

a. Why do pieces match?

b. Why are line segments straight?

c. Why are angles right angles?

d. Once more, pay close attention to whether your justification works in general, or only in certain cases.

4. Here is a way to turn a scalene triangle into a right triangle. Justify each step.

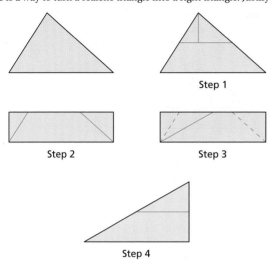

Step 1

Step 2   Step 3

Step 4

a. Why do pieces match up?

b. Are segments straight?

c. Why are there right angles?

d. Is this a specific case, or is it general enough for the algorithm to work for all scalene triangles?

On Your Own

5. Write an algorithm for dissecting a parallelogram into a triangle.

6. Justify each step you used in the dissection of the parallelogram into a triangle.

d. The algorithm is general enough to use for any triangle.

5. Answers may vary. Sample: Start with parallelogram *ABCD*. Let *M* be the midpoint of $\overline{BC}$. Draw $\overline{MD}$. Rotate $\triangle MCD$ 180° about *M*.

6. Answers may vary. Sample: $\overline{BM} \cong \overline{MC}$ since *M* is the midpoint of $\overline{BC}$. $\overline{AD}$ (in the triangle) is straight because $\angle B$ and $\angle C$ are supplementary (in the parallelogram). $\overline{AD}$ (in the triangle) is straight because $\angle B$ and $\angle C$ are supplementary (in the parallelogram). $\overline{DD'}$ (in the triangle) is straight because $\angle DMB$ and $\angle DMC$ are supplementary (in the parallelogram).

On Your Own

EXERCISES 10 AND 11 have students use previously written algorithms to perform new dissections.

Maintain Your Skills

EXERCISE 14 You may wish to provide copies of Blackline Master 3.4 for students to use.

Additional Resources

PRINT RESOURCES
- Solution Manual
- Practice Workbook
- Assessment Resources
- Teaching Resources

TECHNOLOGY
- Interactive Textbook
- TeacherExpress CD-ROM
- **Exam**View CD-ROM
- **PHSchool.com**
  – Additional Practice
  – Mid-Chapter and Chapter Tests
  – Video Tutors
  – Vocabulary Puzzles

Additional Practice

1. A student gave the following argument for dissecting a triangle into a parallelogram.

Find midpoint of base.   Move piece 2.

   a. What is wrong with this argument?
   b. For which type(s) of triangles does this dissection work?

2. **a.** Write an algorithm for dissecting an isosceles trapezoid into a rectangle.
   b. Justify each step of the algorithm.

3. **a.** Write an algorithm for dissecting a parallelogram into a triangle.
   b. Justify each step of the algorithm.

4. The length of one side of a triangle is 16. How long is the segment that joins the midpoints of the other two sides?

5. Use the figure.
   a. In what ways are △ACE and △BCD the same?
   b. In what ways are △ACE and △BCD different?
   c. Make a conjecture about △ACE and △BCD.

6. Use quadrilateral ABCD. The midpoints of the sides are E, F, G, and H. Explain why $\overline{HE}$ is congruent to $\overline{GF}$.

7. A kite has diagonals with lengths 10 and 18. You form a quadrilateral by joining the midpoints of the kite's sides.
   a. What is the perimeter of the inner quadrilateral?
   b. Describe the angles of the inner quadrilateral.

Practice: For Lesson 3.4, assign Exercises 1–3.

---

7. Write an algorithm for dissecting a triangle that is isosceles (but not equilateral) and rearranging it into a scalene triangle.

8. Justify each step you can use in the dissection of an isosceles triangle into a scalene triangle.

9. Suppose that Jane has an algorithm for dissecting a trapezoid into a rectangle. Explain how you could use Jane's steps to dissect a rectangle into a trapezoid.

10. Use your algorithms for dissecting a trapezoid into a rectangle and dissecting a rectangle into a nonrectangular parallelogram. Describe an algorithm for dissecting a trapezoid into a nonrectangular parallelogram.

11. Use your algorithms for dissecting a trapezoid into a rectangle and dissecting a triangle into a rectangle. Describe an algorithm for dissecting a trapezoid into a triangle.

12. The diagram suggests Noriko's method for cutting a trapezoid into a triangle.

    Answer the questions to help her justify her method.

    a. What point on $\overline{CD}$ does she need to find so that $\overline{CF}$ matches with $\overline{DF}$?

    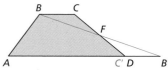

    b. Will the edge from B to B′ be straight? How do you know?

    c. Will the edge from A to B′ be straight? How do you know?

13. **Standardized Test Prep** What can you conclude from Noriko's method for dissection in Exercise 12?

    A. area of △ABB′ + area of △BCF + area of △FDB = area of △BCD

    B. area of △ABB′ = area of ABCD

    C. area of △BCF + area of ABFD − area of △FB′D = area ABCD

    D. area of △BCF + area of ABFD − area of △FB′D = area △ABB′

Maintain Your Skills

14. For each trapezoid below, apply Noriko's method (Exercise 12) for cutting a trapezoid into a triangle.

    a.   **b.** 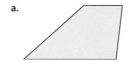   **c.**

Go Online
PHSchool.com

For additional practice, go to **Web Code: bea-0304**

Answers

7. Answers may vary. Sample: Use the algorithm from Exercise 4.

8. Answers may vary. Sample: The steps are justified in the answer to Exercise 4.

9. Perform Jane's algorithm in reverse.

10. First dissect the trapezoid into a rectangle. Then dissect the rectangle into a nonrectangular parallelogram.

11. First dissect the trapezoid into a rectangle. Then perform in reverse the algorithm for dissecting a triangle into a rectangle.

12. **a.** the midpoint
    b. Yes; ∠BFD and ∠DFB′ are supplementary.
    c. Yes; ∠FDB′ ≅ ∠BCF, and ∠BCF and ∠FDA are supplementary.

13. B

14. **a–c.** See back of book.

The Midline Theorem

One student used the following method to dissect a triangle into a parallelogram.

Start with a triangle. Cut between the midpoints of two sides.

Rotate the top triangle around one of the midpoints. The two segments will match because you cut at a midpoint.

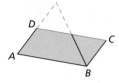

Quadrilateral *ABCD* is a parallelogram because the opposite sides are congruent. $\overline{AD} \cong \overline{BC}$ because they were made by cutting at a midpoint. $\overline{AB} \cong \overline{DC}$ because a midline cut makes a segment half as long as the base.

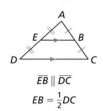

This student used an idea that you studied in Lesson 2.18.

Theorem 2.10 The Midline Theorem

The segment joining the midpoints of two sides of a triangle is parallel to the third side and is half as long as the third side.

$$\overline{EB} \parallel \overline{DC}$$
$$EB = \tfrac{1}{2}DC$$

Four horizontal cards are used on the floor, so two horizontal cards are needed halfway up.

Lesson Overview

GOALS

- Devise and follow algorithms to dissect and rearrange one figure into an equal-area figure.
- Test algorithms with typical and extreme cases.

This lesson has students use the Midline Theorem to prove one method for dissecting a triangle into a parallelogram.

CHECK YOUR UNDERSTANDING
- Core: 1, 2, 3, 4
- Optional: none

HOMEWORK
- Core: 5, 6, 8, 9
- Optional: 7, 11
- Extension: 10

Launch

Begin this lesson by reviewing the given dissection of a triangle into a parallelogram. Then review the Midline Theorem, which students first saw in Chapter 2.

Explore

Then discuss the formal proof in the Example section on the following page. For many students, this is best done as a class discussion, with the proof illustrated on the chalkboard or overhead projector.

Wrap Up

Assign the Check Your Understanding exercises for in-class work.

Assessment Resources

Lesson Quiz 3.5

1. *ABC* is an isosceles triangle with base $\overline{AC}$ and midline $\overline{DE}$.
   a. If $AC = 10$ and $AB = 16$, find *AD*, *BE*, and *DE*.
   b. If $AC = x - 10$ and $DE = 6$, find the value of *x*.

2. In quadrilateral *ABCD*, points *P, Q, R,* and *S* are the midpoints of the sides, and *PQRS* is a rectangle.
   a. Draw other quadrilaterals for which you can form a rectangle by connecting the midpoints of the sides.
   b. What must be true of quadrilateral *ABCD* if *PQRS* is a rectangle?

3. *RUST* is a parallelogram. If *X* is the midpoint of $\overline{RT}$ and *Y* is the midpoint of $\overline{US}$, what special type of quadrilateral is *XYST*? Prove your answer.

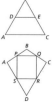

Exercises

HOMEWORK
- Core: 5, 6, 8, 9
- Optional: 7, 11
- Extension: 10

Example

Problem To prove the midline cut works, you need a slightly different construction. In $\triangle ABC$ below, D is the midpoint of $\overline{AC}$. E is the midpoint of $\overline{BC}$. You locate point F such that D, E, and F are collinear and $\overline{DE} \cong \overline{EF}$. Prove that $ABFD$ is a parallelogram.

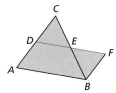

This setup makes DF twice DE. That is why you have to show only that $ABFD$ is a parallelogram.

Solution $\angle CED \cong \angle BEF$ because they are vertical angles. So, $\triangle DEC \cong \triangle FEB$ because of SAS. You can use CPCTC to conclude that $CD = BF$. Since D is the midpoint of $\overline{AC}$, you know that $CD = AD$. Therefore $AD = BF$.

Apply CPCTC again to see that $\angle CDE \cong \angle BFE$. These two angles are a pair of alternate interior angles formed by the transversal $\overline{DF}$ to $\overline{AD}$ and $\overline{BF}$. Therefore, $\overline{AD}$ and $\overline{BF}$ are parallel. Since $ABFD$ has two sides, $\overline{AD}$ and $\overline{BF}$, that are both congruent and parallel, $ABFD$ is a parallelogram.

Exercises *Practicing Habits of Mind*

Check Your Understanding

1. Find x, y, and z in the picture below. Assume segments that appear parallel are parallel.

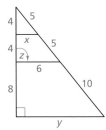

Answers

Exercises

1. $x = 3$, $y = 12$, $z = 90°$

For Exercises 2–4 use quadrilateral *ABCD*. The midpoints of the sides, points *E*, *F*, *G*, and *H*, are connected in order.

2. Explain why $\overline{EF}$ is congruent to $\overline{GH}$.

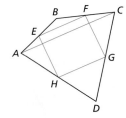

3. Explain why two other segments are congruent. (See Exercise 2.)

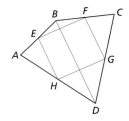

4. What kind of shape is *EFGH*? Prove it.

On Your Own

5. One side of a triangle has length 12.

   a. How long is the segment that joins the midpoints of the other two sides?

   b. How long would the segment joining the midpoints be if the side of the triangle had length 10? Length 18? Length 19?

6. A kite has diagonals with lengths 5 and 8. You form an inner quadrilateral by joining the midpoints of the kite's sides. What is the perimeter of the inner quadrilateral? Describe its angles.

7. The diagonals of a quadrilateral measure 12 and 8. You form an inner quadrilateral by joining the midpoints of the sides of the given quadrilateral. What is the perimeter of the inner quadrilateral?

8. What kind of quadrilateral do you get when you connect the midpoints of a kite? Feel free to experiment.

On Your Own

EXERCISES 6 AND 7 rely on the fact that the perimeter of the inner quadrilateral that you form by joining the midpoints of a given quadrilateral is the sum of the lengths of the diagonals of the original quadrilateral.

EXERCISE 8 has students experiment with a kite to determine what kind of quadrilateral you form when you connect the midpoints of its sides.

2. By the Midline Theorem, $EF = \frac{1}{2}$ AC and $GH = \frac{1}{2}AC$. So $EF = GH$, which implies $\overline{EF} \cong \overline{GH}$.

3. By the Midline Theorem, $EH = \frac{1}{2}$ BD and $FG = \frac{1}{2}BD$. So $EH = FG$, which implies $\overline{EH} \cong \overline{FG}$.

4. *EFGH* is a parallelogram, since both pairs of opposite sides are congruent.

5. a. 6
   b. 5; 9; 9.5

6. The perimeter of the inner quadrilateral is 13, and all angles are right angles.

7. 20

8. rectangle

EXERCISE 10 extends the idea of midline to quadrilaterals.

Additional Resources

PRINT RESOURCES
- Solution Manual
- Practice Workbook
- Assessment Resources
- Teaching Resources

TECHNOLOGY
- Interactive Textbook
- TeacherExpress CD-ROM
- **Exam**View CD-ROM
- PHSchool.com
  - Additional Practice
  - Mid-Chapter and Chapter Tests
  - Video Tutors
  - Vocabulary Puzzles

Additional Practice

1. A student gave the following argument for dissecting a triangle into a parallelogram.

Find midpoint of base.   Move piece 2.

   a. What is wrong with this argument?
   b. For which type(s) of triangles does this dissection work?

2. a. Write an algorithm for dissecting an isosceles trapezoid into a rectangle.
   b. Justify each step of the algorithm.

3. a. Write an algorithm for dissecting a parallelogram into a triangle.
   b. Justify each step of the algorithm.

4. The length of one side of a triangle is 16. How long is the segment that joins the midpoints of the other two sides?

5. Use the figure.
   a. In what ways are △ACE and △BCD the same?
   b. In what ways are △ACE and △BCD different?
   c. Make a conjecture about △ACE and △BCD.

6. Use quadrilateral *ABCD*. The midpoints of the sides are *E, F, G,* and *H*. Explain why $\overline{HE}$ is congruent to $\overline{GF}$.

7. A kite has diagonals with lengths 10 and 18. You form a quadrilateral by joining the midpoints of the kite's sides.
   a. What is the perimeter of the inner quadrilateral?
   b. Describe the angles of the inner quadrilateral.

Practice: For Lesson 3.5, assign Exercises 4–7.

---

9. **Standardized Test Prep** The lengths of the diagonals of a quadrilateral are 30 cm and 40 cm. What is the perimeter of the midline polygon of this quadrilateral?

   A. 25 cm   **B.** 50 cm   **C.** 70 cm   **D.** 100 cm

10. **Take It Further** You can generalize the idea of a midline (a segment joining midpoints of two sides of a triangle) to quadrilaterals. Here are some possible midlines for quadrilaterals.

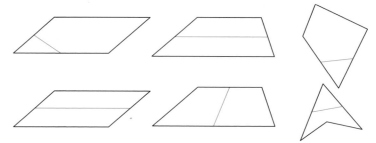

Experiment with the possible meanings of *midline* for a quadrilateral. Can you find any relationship between a midline and the sides of a quadrilateral? Between a midline and a diagonal? Answer the following questions.

   a. How do you define *midline* for a quadrilateral? Does it join any two midpoints? Two opposite midpoints? Two consecutive midpoints?
   b. With what kinds of quadrilaterals did you experiment?
   c. What did you find? Are there any special properties of a midline of a quadrilateral? Can you make any conjectures?

Maintain Your Skills

11. Draw a few quadrilaterals such that when you connect the midpoints of the sides you get a rhombus. Is there some way to tell whether a particular type of quadrilateral will have a midpoint quadrilateral that is a rhombus? Explain.

Go Online
PHSchool.com

For additional practice, go to **Web Code: bea-0305**

Answers

9. C

10. a. Answers may vary. Sample: A midline of a quadrilateral is a segment with endpoints that are midpoints of adjacent sides of the quadrilateral.

   b. Answers may vary. Sample: convex and concave, with and without parallel sides, with and without congruent sides

   c. Answers may vary. Sample: The midline quadrilateral is a parallelogram.

11. Yes, the inner quadrilateral will be a rhombus if and only if the outer quadrilateral is a rectangle. This is true because the outer quadrilateral will have congruent diagonals if and only if it is a rectangle.

Mathematical Reflections

1. Answers may vary. Sample: Cut along the perpendicular bisector of the longest side of the parallelogram. Slide one of the resulting pieces so that the smaller

Mathematical Reflections

3A

In this investigation, you used dissection to make scissors-congruent shapes. You also proved the Midline Theorem. These questions will help you summarize what you have learned.

1. Describe and justify each step in the dissection that turns any parallelogram into a rectangle.

2. Describe how you would dissect this rectangle into a right triangle. Justify each step. Draw pictures as needed.

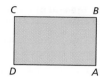

3. Is it possible to dissect each of these triangles into a parallelogram? If you think it is possible in either or both of the cases, describe the steps.

4. Copy and dissect the trapezoid at the right into a triangle.

5. Draw $\triangle ABC$. Join the midpoints of its three sides to form $\triangle DEF$. What is the ratio of the perimeter of $\triangle DEF$ to the perimeter of $\triangle ABC$?

6. What is an algorithm?

7. Why is it important to justify each step in an algorithm?

8. What does the Midline Theorem say about the relationship between a midline and the sides of a triangle?

Vocabulary

In this investigation, you learned these terms. Make sure you understand what each one means and how to use it.

- algorithm
- hypotenuse
- scissors-congruent

Some arrangements of parts make more sense than others.

Mathematical Reflections

EXERCISES 6–8 At the start of the investigation, you may have assigned these as Questions 1–3 for students to think and write about.

sides of the parallelogram coincide. The angles of the resulting shape are right angles because the cut was made perpendicular to the longer sides. Opposite sides of the resulting shape are congruent because one set of opposite sides was the result of a single cut, and the other set of opposite sides is identical to opposite sides of the original parallelogram.

2. Answers may vary. Sample: Draw $\overline{EA}$, where E is the midpoint of $\overline{BC}$. Rotate $\triangle ABE$ 180° about E. If the point A goes to A', then

$\triangle A'DA$ is the required right triangle. $\angle ACD$ is a straight angle because $\angle ACE$ and $\angle CDE$ are right angles. $\angle A'EA$ is a straight angle because it is the result of rotating $\overline{EA}$ 180° about E.

3. Yes; cut along the midline of the triangle. Then rotate the resulting smaller triangle 180° about one of the endpoints of the midline.

4. See back of book.

5. $\frac{1}{2}$

6–8. See back of book.

Investigation Overview

This investigation helps students understand the meaning of area and derive from their cutting algorithms the area formulas for parallelograms, triangles, and trapezoids. Students may already know some, if not all, of these formulas from previous coursework.

If students' past experience with formulas has been memorization and application, this investigation could be a real eye-opening experience because it may help them see from where the formulas come.

In this investigation, students assign variables to represent the base(s) and height of an uncut figure (a triangle, a parallelogram, or a trapezoid), cut and rearrange the pieces of the figure into a rectangle, and then express the base and height of the rectangle in terms of the dimensions of the original uncut figure. This requires a degree of abstraction that may be confusing and difficult for some students. Plan your teaching accordingly.

You may wish to assign Questions 1–3 for students to think and write about during the investigation.

Learning Goals

- Understand and apply basic assumptions about area.
- Identify critical measurements that can be used to find the areas of different types of polygons.
- Use dissection algorithms to develop area formulas for parallelograms, triangles, and trapezoids.

Habits and Skills

- Understand what area is and what kinds of transformations preserve area.
- Calculate areas of rectangles, parallelograms, triangles, and trapezoids.
- Reason by continuity to relate different area formulas and polygons.

Investigation 3B — Area Formulas

In *Area Formulas*, you will formalize the ideas of cutting and rearranging. You will derive and prove the area formulas for triangles, parallelograms, and trapezoids.

By the end of this investigation, you will be able to answer questions like these:

1. If two figures are scissors-congruent, do they have the same area? Explain.

2. Are all squares with the same area congruent?

3. What is the area formula for a parallelogram? For a triangle? For a trapezoid?

You will learn how to

- understand and apply basic assumptions about area

- identify critical measurements that can be used to find the areas of different types of polygons

- use dissection algorithms to develop area formulas for parallelograms, triangles, and trapezoids

You will develop these habits and skills:

- Understand what area is and what kinds of transformations preserve area.

- Calculate areas of rectangles, parallelograms, triangles, and trapezoids.

- Reason by continuity to relate different area formulas and polygons.

You can disassemble the tabletop and the table leaves. The total area remains the same.

Investigation Road Map

LESSON 3.6, *Getting Started,* asks students to informally explore the idea of the area of a rectangle.

LESSON 3.7, *What Is Area, Anyway?,* introduces students to what it means to find the area of a figure and what it means when two figures have the same area.

LESSON 3.8, *Area by Dissection,* has students use dissections to derive the area formulas for parallelograms, triangles, and trapezoids.

Getting Started

Activating Prior Knowledge
Exploring New Ideas

When you think of measurement, you probably think of feet or inches, or maybe centimeters or miles. These all are measures of length. Sometimes it is more important to know how much area a figure covers rather than how long or wide it is.

or You to Explore

1. **a.** What is the area formula for a rectangle?

   b. Draw several pictures of rectangles that have area 12 square units. How many are there in all?

2. Use half sheets of standard $8\frac{1}{2}$ in.-by-11 in. paper as your starting rectangle. Cut that rectangle into the following number of equal-area rectangles.

   a. two   **b.** four   **c.** five

3. Suppose you want to cut a rectangle into pieces having equal areas. Is there any number of pieces that is *not* possible? Explain your answer.

Exercises *Practicing Habits of Mind*

On Your Own

4. Make a parallelogram. Dissect it into a rectangle. Use an algorithm that you know will work with any parallelogram.

   a. Measure and record the length and width of the rectangle.

   b. Carefully rearrange your pieces into your original parallelogram. Note the measurements of the parallelogram that correspond to the rectangle's length and width.

5. Draw a triangle. Dissect it into a rectangle. Use an algorithm that you know will work with any triangle.

   a. Record the length and width of the rectangle.

   b. Carefully rearrange your pieces into your original triangle. Note how the rectangle's length and width relate to measurements of the triangle.

Go Online
Video Tutor
PHSchool.com
Web Code: bee-0775

Answers

For You to Explore

1. **a.** $A = \ell w$, where ℓ is the length of the rectangle and w is the width.

   b. infinitely many

2. **a–c.** Check students' work.

3. There is no number of pieces that is not possible, though eventually they will become too small to cut by hand.

Exercises

4. Check students' work.

5. Check students' work.

Lesson Overview

GOALS

- Warm up to the ideas of the investigation.
- Use a hands-on approach to develop mathematical habits of mind.

This lesson has students use drawings and dissections to help informally explore the idea of the area of a rectangle.

FOR YOU TO EXPLORE	HOMEWORK
• Core: 1, 2, 3	• Core: 4, 5
• Optional: none	• Optional: 6

MATERIALS
- rulers
- scissors

Launch

Have students explore the idea of an array of 1×1 units. They should understand that a 3×4 rectangle is the same as a 4×3 rectangle because one is just a rotation of the other.

Explore

Assign Problems 1–3 from the For You To Explore section for in-class work.

Wrap Up

Before assigning homework, allow students some time to discuss and summarize their findings.

For You to Explore

PROBLEM 1 Since the problem does not state that the lengths of the sides of a rectangle must be integers, students should give some examples of rectangles with noninteger side lengths. Here is an informal argument that justifies why ℓw is the correct formula:

If ℓ and w are integers, you can see that ℓw is the correct formula by dividing the rectangle into 1×1 squares. If the length or width of the rectangle is not an integer, however, you may have to divide the rectangle into smaller squares in order to fill the rectangle.

There are some rectangles that you cannot divide into squares, no matter how small the squares are.

The formula ℓw is still correct, but you need ideas from calculus to prove it.

PROBLEMS 2 AND 3 Use an $8\frac{1}{2}$ in.-by-11 in. rectangular sheet of paper to show that you can divide the rectangle into any number of equal-area rectangles. Dividing the rectangle into powers of 2 are easiest.

Exercises

HOMEWORK
- Core: 4, 5
- Optional: 6

On Your Own

EXERCISES 4 AND 5 preview the next lesson on the area of parallelograms, triangles, and trapezoids. Students will use their results from these exercises for the In-Class Experiment section in Lesson 3.7.

Maintain Your Skills

6. Use the rectangles shown below.

   a. Which of the rectangles have equal areas?

   b. Of the rectangles with equal areas, are any two congruent?

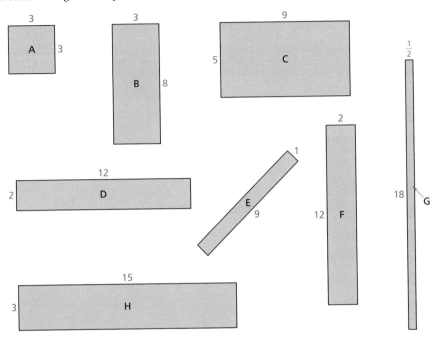

Answers

6. a. rectangles A, E, and G;
rectangles B, D, and F;
rectangles C and H

  b. yes, rectangles D and F

What Is Area, Anyway?

What is area? Someone might answer, "Area is what is inside a figure."

Attempts to make this answer more precise lead to statements such as "The area of a figure is the number of square units it contains." Square units could be square inches or square feet or square meters.

You choose a unit length (say, 1 inch) and construct a square with that side length—a square inch. Then you see how many of these squares fill the figure. A square that is 5 inches on a side will contain 25 square inches. A rectangle that is 5 feet by 3 feet will contain 15 square feet. (Why is that true?)

For areas of more complicated figures, counting squares gets out of hand. You cannot tile most shapes evenly with square units. You end up counting partial squares and making estimates. Sometimes an estimate is the best you can do. But for triangles, parallelograms, trapezoids, and other familiar figures, you can get exact formulas for area. They are given in terms of lengths and they are easy to calculate.

To get the formulas, you need to build a theory of area. Start with some basic assumptions that describe how you want area to behave. First, you assume that area is a function that assigns to each polygon a nonnegative real number. Then you make the following two postulates about the area function.

> It is possible that you can fill a figure with squares by two methods. It is also safe to assume that the numbers of squares needed by the two methods are the same.

blob covered by
unit squares

Postulate 3.1 The Congruence Postulate

Congruent figures have the same area.

Postulate 3.2 The Additivity Postulate

If two polygons P and Q do not intersect (except possibly at a point or along an edge), then the area of the union of P and Q is the sum of the areas of P and Q.

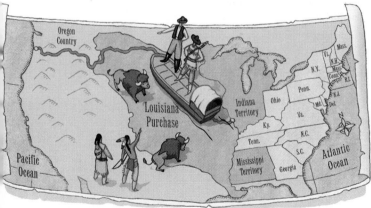

The Louisiana Purchase, in 1803, doubled the area of the United States.

Lesson Overview

GOAL

• Understand and apply basic assumptions about area.

This lesson introduces what the area of a figure represents. Students learn what it means for two figures to have the same area. They also derive a formula for area of a rectangle.

CHECK YOUR UNDERSTANDING	HOMEWORK
• Core: 1, 2 • Optional: none	• Core: 3, 4, 5, 6, 7, 8, 9, 10 • Optional: 11, 12, 13, 14

MATERIALS

• Blackline Master 3.7

Launch

Before your students read the text, ask them what they know about area. They may know some formulas, and they may even be able to describe area as the number of square units inside a figure. Then read and discuss the information at the beginning of the lesson. Write the two postulates on the board, and then discuss them. You may have to include an illustration for the Additivity Postulate.

Explore

Work through Example 1. Assign Problems 1–4 in the For You to Do section. The Developing Habits of Mind section introduces students to a method that they probably already know of finding the area of a rectangle—multiply its dimensions.

Wrap Up

Write the Rectangle and the Scissors-Congruent Postulates on the board, and then have students read through Example 2. Afterward, have students complete Problem 5 in the For You to Do section. Assign the Check Your Understanding exercises for in-class work.

Lesson Quiz 3.7

1. Which of the following triangles have equal areas?

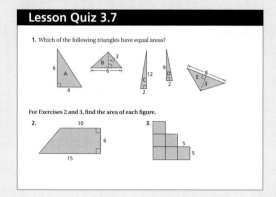

For Exercises 2 and 3, find the area of each figure.

2.

3.

Example 1

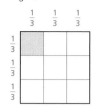

Problem What is the area of a square that measures $\frac{1}{3}$ on a side?

Solution A square that is $\frac{1}{3}$ on a side is the shaded portion of the unit square, or $\frac{1}{9}$ square unit.

The area of the small square is $\frac{1}{9}$ square unit.

For You to Do

Here are measurements for four rectangles. Find the area of each rectangle using only the definition of area and the area assumptions.

1. base 5 in. and height 2 in.

2. length 5 in. and width 1 in.

3. length 5.5 cm and width 2 cm

4. base $5\frac{1}{2}$ ft and width $2\frac{1}{4}$ ft

> You may know a formula for the area of a rectangle. Do not use it.

Developing Habits of Mind

Use Multiplication to Count. If you can divide the sides of a unit square and the sides of a rectangle into congruent segments, you can tile the rectangle with squares and find the area.

For example, you can fill a rectangle that measures $5\frac{1}{2}$ in. by $2\frac{1}{4}$ in. with squares $\frac{1}{4}$ in. on a side.

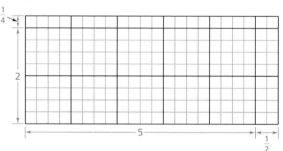

Answers

For You to Do

1. 10 in.^{2}

2. 5 in.^{2}

3. 11 cm^2

4. 12.375 ft^2

There will be 22 of these squares along the $5\frac{1}{2}$-in. side. There will be 9 such rows, so the rectangle contains

$$22 \cdot 9 = 198$$

squares, each $\frac{1}{4}$ in. on a side. But the area of each of these small squares is $\frac{1}{16}$ square inch. (Why?) So the area of the rectangle is

$$\frac{198}{16} = \frac{99}{8} = 12\frac{1}{2}$$

square inches.

But wait—there is another way to think about it: You have $2\frac{1}{4}$ rows of $5\frac{1}{2}$ squares. So you have

$$2\frac{1}{4} \cdot 5\frac{1}{2} = \frac{9}{4} \cdot \frac{11}{2} = \frac{99}{8} = 12\frac{1}{2}$$

unit squares altogether. To count the unit squares, you have only to multiply the dimensions—base times height—as you probably learned in previous courses.

The area model described above works for any rectangle with sides that you can divide into segments congruent to segments of a unit square. There are rectangles for which this cannot be done—one with side length $\sqrt{2}$, for example. The branch of mathematics called *analysis* shows that the method of multiplying length and width (or base and height) to find area works for all lengths. For now, you will assume that this is true.

Remember...

The fact that you cannot evenly divide the lengths 1 and $\sqrt{2}$ by the same number is the same as saying that $\sqrt{2}$ is irrational. You prove this fact in algebra.

Postulate 3.3 The Rectangle Postulate

The area of a rectangle with dimensions b and h (expressed in the same unit) is bh.

You need one more assumption about area that gets to the heart of this chapter. Dissecting one figure into another by cutting and rearranging the parts does not change what is inside the figure.

Postulate 3.4 The Scissors-Congruence Postulate

Two figures that are scissors-congruent have the same area.

This is all you will need to calculate areas of familiar shapes. By dissecting figures into rectangles and keeping track of the dimensions, you can find how many square units are in parallelograms, triangles, and trapezoids.

Example 2

Problem Find the area of this triangle.

Solution You can cut the triangle into a parallelogram.

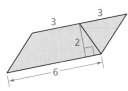

Then you can cut the parallelogram into a rectangle.

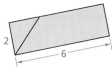

The area of the rectangle is 12. All of these dissections preserve area. So the area of the triangle is 12.

Habits of Mind

Be Intuitive. It seems plausible that the midline bisects the altitude. You use that idea here, but you have yet to justify it. See Exercise 1.

For You to Do

5. Find the area of this triangle by dissecting it into a rectangle.

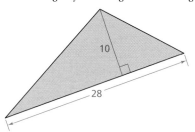

Answers

For You to Do

5. 140

Exercises *Practicing Habits of Mind*

Check Your Understanding

1. Here is a proof that a midline of a triangle cuts an altitude into two congruent parts. Fill in the missing reasons.

Given $\triangle ABC$ with midline $\overline{DE}$ and altitude $\overline{AF}$

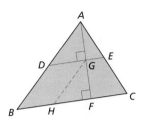

Prove $\overline{AG} \cong \overline{GF}$

Proof

Statement	Reason
Draw $\overline{HG} \parallel \overline{BA}$.	Parallel Postulate
$\overline{DE} \parallel \overline{BC}$	?
$BDGH$ is a parallelogram.	?
$\overline{BD} \cong \overline{DA}$	?
$\overline{HG} \cong \overline{BD}$	?
$\overline{HG} \cong \overline{DA}$	?
$\angle AGD \cong \angle GFH$	?
$\angle BAG \cong \angle HGF$	?
$\triangle DAG \cong \triangle HGF$	?
$\overline{AG} \cong \overline{GF}$	?

No matter how you climb, the line shows that you are halfway to the top.

Exercises

1. • Midline Theorem
   • Definition of parallelogram
   • Definition of midpoint
   • Opposite sides of a parallelogram are congruent.
   • Segments congruent to the same segment are congruent to each other.
   • Parallel lines and a transversal form congruent corresponding angles.

   • Parallel lines and a transversal form congruent corresponding angles.
   • AAS
   • CPCTC

Exercises

HOMEWORK
• Core: 3, 4, 5, 6, 7, 8, 9, 10
• Optional: 11, 12, 13, 14

Check Your Understanding

EXERCISE 1 is a core exercise. It gives students the opportunity to prove that a midline of a triangle divides in half one of the triangle's altitude. Students can use what they know about the corresponding, alternate interior, and vertical angles to explain why $\angle BAG \cong \angle HGF$. You may wish to provide copies of Blackline Master 3.7 for students to use.

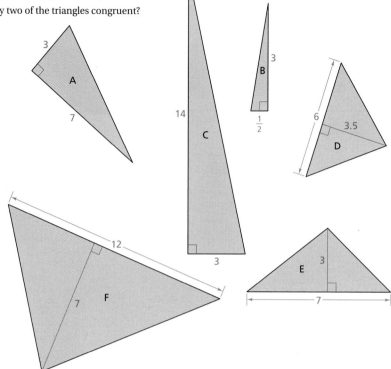

2. Use the triangles shown below.
    a. Which of the triangles have equal areas?
    b. Are any two of the triangles congruent?

On Your Own

For Exercises 3–8, find the area of each figure. Assume that sides that look parallel are parallel and angles that appear to be right angles are right angles.

3.

Answers:

2. **a.** A, D, and E
   b. no

3. 216

4.

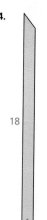

18

1

5.

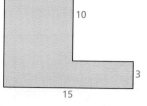

8

10

3

15

6.

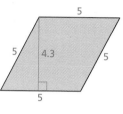

5

5

4.3

5

5

7.

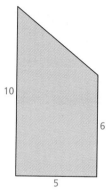

10

6

5

8.

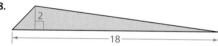

2

18

9. Standardized Test Prep What is the area of the shaded portion of the figure at the right?

A. 69 square units

B. 87 square units

C. 90 square units

D. 108 square units

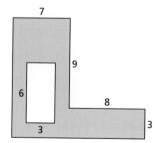

7

9

6

8

3

3

4. 18

5. 125

6. 21.5

7. 40

8. 18

9. A

Additional Resources

PRINT RESOURCES
- Solution Manual
- Practice Workbook
- Assessment Resources
- Teaching Resources

TECHNOLOGY
- Interactive Textbook
- TeacherExpress CD-ROM
- **Exam**View CD-ROM
- **PHSchool.com**
  - Additional Practice
  - Mid-Chapter and Chapter Tests
  - Video Tutors
  - Vocabulary Puzzles

Additional Practice

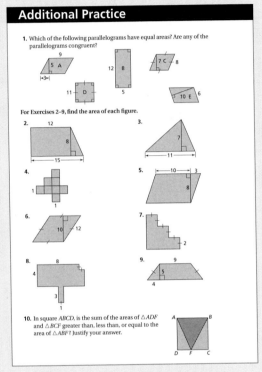

Practice: For Lesson 3.7, assign Exercises 1–10.

---

10. In rectangle *ABYX*, is the sum of the areas of △*ACX* and △*BCY* greater than, less than, or equal to the area of △*ABC*? Justify your answer.

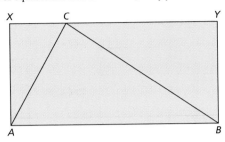

Maintain Your Skills

Find the areas of the two figures in each pair.

11. 3.5

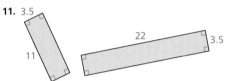

12.

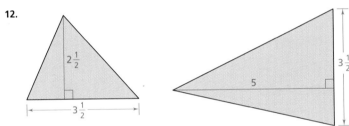

13.

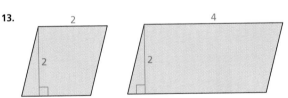

14. How does the area of a figure change if one dimension of the figure is doubled, as in Exercises 11–13?

Go Online
PHSchool.com

For additional practice, go to Web Code: bea-0307

Answers

10. Equal to; all three triangles have the same height. The area of △*ACB* is half the area of the rectangle, so the sum of the areas of △*AXC* and △*CYB* must be the same.

11. 38.5 and 77

12. $\frac{35}{8}$ and $\frac{35}{4}$

13. 4 and 8

14. The area doubles.

Area by Dissection

Sometimes you will need to find areas of figures that are not rectangles. If you can take these figures apart and rearrange them into rectangles you can use what you already know to find their areas.

In-Class Experiment

1. Discuss your answer to Exercise 4 from Lesson 3.7 with others. What conjectures can you make about measurements of a parallelogram compared with the dimensions of a scissors-congruent rectangle?

2. Discuss your answer to Exercise 8 from Lesson 3.7 with others. Write a conjecture about how measurements of a triangle compare with the dimensions of a scissors-congruent rectangle.

3. Draw a trapezoid (the more unusual its shape, the better). Trace at least two copies of it to dissect.

   a. Dissect the trapezoid into another figure—one with an area you know how to compute.

   b. Measure and record the dimensions that you will use to find its area.

   c. Carefully rearrange the parts into the original trapezoid.

   d. How do the measurements of the trapezoid compare to the dimensions of the new figure?

Name a pair of opposite sides of a parallelogram as its bases. The **height** of the parallelogram corresponding to the bases is the length of a perpendicular segment joining the bases.

> Does this definition agree with the image you have of the "height of a parallelogram"?

In each of the following figures, the length of the dashed red segment is the height corresponding to the bases shown in blue.

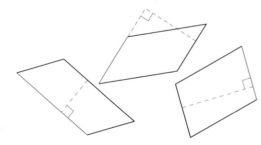

The height is not the same as the length of the other two sides, unless the parallelogram happens to be rectangular. Depending on your choice of the bases, you will sometimes have to measure the height outside, or partly outside, the parallelogram.

In-Class Experiment

1–3. Check students' work.

Lesson Overview

GOALS

- Identify critical measurements that can be used to find the areas of different types of polygons.

- Use dissection algorithms to develop area formulas for parallelograms, triangles, and trapezoids.

You will probably want to take two or three days to work through the development of the formulas and the problems and exercises in this lesson. Refer to the Daily Planner at the beginning of the chapter to determine which exercises to assign each day.

In this lesson, students use dissections to develop the area formulas for parallelograms, triangles, and trapezoids.

CHECK YOUR UNDERSTANDING	HOMEWORK
• Core: 1, 2, 4, 5, 6 • Optional: 3	• Core: 7, 8, 9, 10, 11, 12 • Optional: 16, 17, 18 • Extension: 13, 14, 15
MATERIALS	**VOCABULARY**
• geometry software • paper • rulers • scissors • Blackline Masters 3.8A–B	• base • height

Launch

Have students complete the In-Class Experiment, which encourages them to think about the different measurements in parallelograms, triangles, and trapezoids.

Explore

Discuss students' results to Problem 1 of the In-Class Experiment. Then read the definition of the height of a parallelogram and through the Minds in Action section. The For Discussion section that follows the Minds in Action dialog leads students to a formula for the area of a parallelogram.

Discuss students' results to Problem 2 of the In-Class Experiment. Then read the definition of the height of a triangle. Point out the many ways you can find the height of a triangle.

Discuss students' results to Problem 3 of the In-Class Experiment. Make sure you point out that there are several figures into which they can dissect a trapezoid, but a triangle or a parallelogram are the most helpful in terms of the development of the area formula.

Read the definition of the height of a trapezoid. Then read through the Example that follows, which shows how to dissect a trapezoid with bases a and b and height h into a triangle with base $a + b$ and

continued on p. 206

continued from p. 205

height $\frac{1}{2}h$. If some students dissect their trapezoid into a parallelogram, show them how they can derive the formula for the area of a trapezoid this way too. (The base of the parallelogram is $a + b$ and the height is $\frac{1}{2}h$, since they most likely cut the trapezoid at the midpoints of its legs to form the parallelogram.)

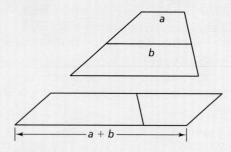

Wrap Up

To end the lesson, have students work on Problem 6 in the For Discussion section. If you wish, have students work in small groups.

Assessment Resources

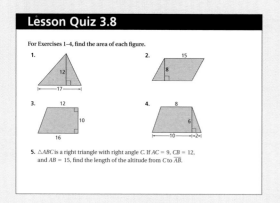

Lesson Quiz 3.8

For Exercises 1–4, find the area of each figure.

1.

2.

3.

4.

5. $\triangle ABC$ is a right triangle with right angle C. If $AC = 9$, $CB = 12$, and $AB = 15$, find the length of the altitude from C to $\overline{AB}$.

Derman sees a connection.

Derman   Tony, it seems that parallelograms and rectangles have something in common.

Tony   Well, they both have four sides.

Derman   Okay, that's true. But I think that they have the same area formula, too. Look what happens when I dissect this parallelogram into a rectangle.

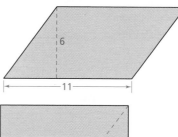

First I cut along the height of the parallelogram. Then I slide that piece over to make a rectangle.

Tony   So, how does that show that they have the same area formula?

Derman   Can't you see? I didn't throw away any part. Each figure has all of the same stuff. The rectangle has dimensions 6 by 11. Its area is 66. That means that the parallelogram's area is 66, too.

Tony   So the formula for the area of a parallelogram is *base* × *height*? Will that work for any parallelogram?

Slide the lower right triangular section to the left and up to form a rectangle.

For Discussion

Will Derman's method work for any parallelogram? Draw a new parallelogram. Label the base b and the corresponding height h.

4. Dissect the parallelogram and rearrange the parts into a rectangle.

5. Explain how your dissection ensures that the base and height of the rectangle are b and h.

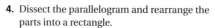

Does it matter which side of the parallelogram you call the base?

Answers

For Discussion

4–5. Check students' work.

Name a side of a triangle as its base. The altitude of the triangle corresponding to the base is the perpendicular segment from the line containing the base to the opposite vertex. The **height** of the triangle corresponding to the base is the length of the altitude.

In each of the following figures, the dashed red segment is the altitude corresponding to the base shown in blue. Depending on your choice of base, you may sometimes have to measure a height of a triangle outside the triangle.

Does this agree with how you normally picture the height of a triangle?

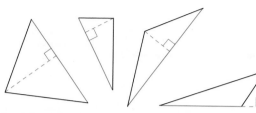

You already know that one way to dissect a triangle into a rectangle is to cut at a midline and rotate one part to form a parallelogram. The parallelogram then has base b and height $\frac{1}{2}h$.

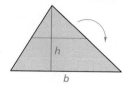 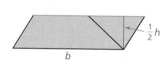

Next, you cut from a vertex of the parallelogram perpendicular to the opposite side as shown below. You slide one part to the opposite end of the parallelogram to form a rectangle. The rectangle has base b and height $\frac{1}{2}h$.

 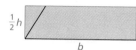

The original triangle and the rectangle are scissors-congruent. So the area of this rectangle, $\frac{1}{2}bh$, is the same as the area of the triangle.

The area formula for a triangle is

$$\text{area} = \tfrac{1}{2}(\text{base} \times \text{height})$$

Exercises

HOMEWORK
- Core: 7, 8, 9, 10, 11
- Optional: 16, 17, 18
- Extension: 13, 14, 15

Definitions

The two parallel sides (blue) of a trapezoid are its **bases**. The **height** of a trapezoid is the length of a perpendicular segment (red) between the bases.

> How do you normally picture the bases and height of a trapezoid?

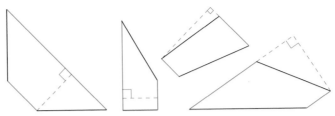

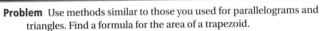

Example

Problem Use methods similar to those you used for parallelograms and triangles. Find a formula for the area of a trapezoid.

Solution Let a and b be the lengths of the bases of the trapezoid. Let h be the height of the trapezoid.

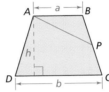
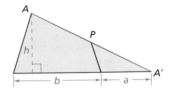

Use your method for dissecting a trapezoid into a triangle. Locate P, the midpoint of side $\overline{BC}$. Draw $\overline{AP}$ and rotate $\triangle ABP$ about P. The resulting triangle has base length $a + b$ and height h. Since the trapezoid and the triangle have the same area, you can conclude that the area of the trapezoid is given by

$$\text{area} = \tfrac{1}{2}(a + b)h = \tfrac{1}{2}h(a + b)$$

> Notice that the area of the trapezoid is its height times the average of its base lengths.

For Discussion

6. As a class, review the area formulas presented in this section. Make a poster or a special page in your notebook for the formulas and figures. Represent each formula using words and using symbols. Also show two diagrams representing different cases.

Answers

For Discussion

6. Check students' work.

Exercises *Practicing Habits of Mind*

Check Your Understanding

EXERCISES 1–3 give students a chance to practice using the formulas for areas of parallelograms, triangles, and trapezoids.

EXERCISES 4–6 Given a figure and some properties of that figure, students provide arguments that explain why the areas of two parts of the figure are equal.

Check Your Understanding

1. Find the area of each parallelogram.

a.
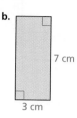
3 cm
3 cm   4 cm

b.
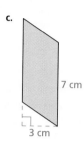
7 cm
3 cm

c.
7 cm
3 cm

2. Find the area of the given triangle.

a. △*LAU*   b. △*LUE*   c. △*LAE*

L
6
A   2   U   2   R   2   E

3. Find the area of each trapezoid.

a.
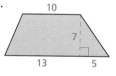
10
7
13   5

b.
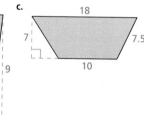
1
7
9
4   1

c.
18
7   7.5
10

Exercises

1. a. 21 cm^2

b. 21 cm^2

c. 21 cm^2

2. a. 6

b. 12

c. 18

3. a. 98

b. 27

c. 98

EXERCISE 7 has students decide whether two triangles have equal areas.

Students can use geometry software to experiment, to verify which statements appear to be true, and to construct counterexamples for the false statements. Then students can present their explanations on the computer rather than in writing.

ABCD is a square. *EHGD* is a square. *E, F,* and *G* are midpoints. In Exercises 4–6, show that two indicated areas are equal as follows. Find two large congruent shapes that have equal areas. Then subtract the same amount from each large area to end up with the desired smaller equal areas. Justify each step.

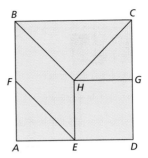

4. Show that *DEHG* has the same area as *EFBH*.

   a. Area of trapezoid *ABHE* = area of trapezoid *DEHC*. Explain.

   b. Area of △*AFE* = area of △*GHC*. Explain.

   c. So, area of *DEHG* = area of *EFBH*.

5. Show that △*BCH* has the same area as *EHGD*.

6. Show that △*BCH* has the same area as *EFBH*.

On Your Own

7. Decide whether each statement below is true for all cases. If you decide it is *not* generally true, do one of the following.

   • State that it is never true.

   • State that it can be true for special cases.

   Justify your answer with an explanation and examples.

   a. Cutting a triangle along a median forms two triangles of equal area.

   b. Cutting a triangle along an altitude forms two triangles of equal area.

   c. Cutting a triangle along an angle bisector forms two triangles of equal area.

   d. If two triangles have congruent angles and equal areas, they are congruent.

   e. If two triangles have equal side lengths, they have equal areas.

   f. If two triangles have equal areas, then they have equal side lengths.

   g. If two triangles have congruent angles, then they have equal areas.

Answers

4. a. The bases of the trapezoids are equal and the heights are equal.

   b. The triangles are congruent and therefore have equal areas.

   c. The area of each trapezoid is the sum of the areas of its parts, and the triangular parts have equal areas.

5. The trapezoids *BCGH* and *CDEH* have equal bases and equal heights and hence have equal areas. The area of each trapezoid is the sum of the areas of its parts, and △*HCG* is a common part for the trapezoids. So, area of △*BCH* = area of *EHGD*.

6. The trapezoids *BCGH* and *BAEH* have equal bases and equal heights and hence have equal areas. The area of each trapezoid is the sum of the areas of its parts. Since △*EAF* and △*CGH* are congruent by SAS, the remaining parts

△*BCH* and *EFBH* of the trapezoids have equal areas.

7. a. Always true; since a median of a triangle always has a midpoint of a side as one of its endpoints, the two triangular parts of the original triangle have equal bases. The altitude from the other endpoint of the median is the same for both the triangular parts. Triangles with equal bases and equal altitudes have the same area.

   b. True for special cases; if △*ABC* is isosceles, with *AB* = *BC*, and you

cut along the altitude from *B* to $\overline{AC}$, then the statement is true, since that altitude is also a median.

   c. True for special cases; this is true only for the nonbase angle of an isosceles triangle, since the angle bisector coincides with the median.

7. d–g. See back of book.

8. Refer to the seven shapes below. Use measurements for parts (a)–(h). Give reasons for your responses.

a. Find two shapes with equal areas.

b. Group the shapes by area.

c. Is the area of shape A greater than, less than, or equal to the area of shape D?

Compare the areas of the following pairs of shapes as you did for shapes A and D.

d. A and C **e.** B and C **f.** B and E **g.** F and G **h.** B and G

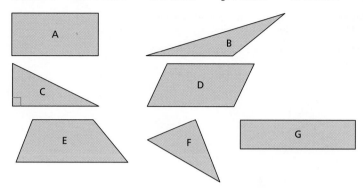

9. Give each value for the right triangle shown.

a. the height from vertex A to base $\overline{BC}$

b. the area of the triangle

c. **Take It Further** the height from vertex C to base $\overline{AB}$

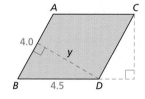

10. **Standardized Test Prep** Parallelogram ABCD and $\triangle XYZ$ have the same area. What is the height of parallelogram ABCD relative to $\overline{AB}$?

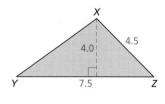

A. $3\frac{1}{3}$ **B.** $3\frac{1}{2}$ **C.** $3\frac{3}{4}$ **D.** $7\frac{1}{2}$

8. a–b. Shapes B, C, F, and G have the same area; shapes B, C, and F are all triangles with the same base and height, while shape G is a rectangle with the same base length as shapes B, C, and F, but half the height. Shapes A, D, and E have the same area. Shapes A and D are parallelograms with the same base and height, and shape E is a trapezoid that has the same height as shapes A and D, and that has the average of its base lengths equal to the base length of shapes A and D.

c. equal to

d. area of A > area of C

e. area of B = area of C

f. area of B < area of E

g. area of F = area of G

h. area of B = area of G

9. a. 4 cm

b. 6 cm²

c. 2.4 cm

10. C

11. $AC \cdot h = AB \cdot BC$

12. The product of the length of a side of a triangle and the length of altitude to that side is always twice the area of the triangle.

13. Since M is the midpoint of $\overline{AB}$, $AM = MB$. The altitude from C to $\overline{AM}$ in $\triangle ACM$ is the same as the altitude from C to $\overline{MB}$ in $\triangle MCB$. It follows that $\triangle ACM$ and $\triangle MCB$ have equal areas. By similar reasoning, $\triangle APM$ and $\triangle MPB$ have equal areas. But area($\triangle ACM$) = area($\triangle APC$) + area($\triangle APM$) and area($\triangle MCB$) = area($\triangle PBC$) + area($\triangle MPB$). Therefore, area($\triangle APC$) = area ($\triangle PBC$).

11. In △ABC, m∠ABC = 90° and h is the altitude to base $\overline{AC}$. Compare the quantities $AC \cdot h$ and $AB \cdot BC$.

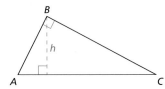

12. Show that for any triangle, the product of the length of a side and the length of the altitude to that side is the same for all three sides.

13. **Take It Further** Segment CM is a median. P is a point on $\overline{CM}$. Show that △APC has the same area as △PBC.

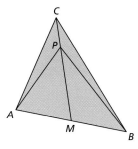

In previous exercises you dissected parallelograms into rectangles without restrictions. Suppose, however, that the rectangle must have a specific base length. The following two exercises address this problem.

14. **Take It Further** Show how to dissect this parallelogram into a rectangle with the same base and height shown. Trace the figures and cut them out to work with, or use geometry software.

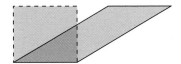

Habits of Mind

Represent the result. You may find it helpful to draw the desired rectangle. Then try to fill it with pieces of the parallelogram.

Answers

14. See back of book.

15. Take It Further The parallelogram at the right is an extreme example of the one in Exercise 14. Trace and copy it. Then figure out how to dissect it into a rectangle with one side congruent to the shorter side of the parallelogram.

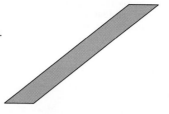

Maintain Your Skills

Exercises 16–18 ask you to think about how the area formulas for triangles, trapezoids, and parallelograms are related. The diagrams below show one way you can dissect a trapezoid into a parallelogram.

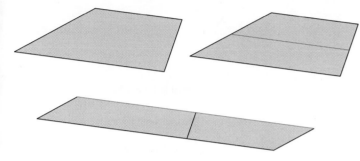

16. a. Describe the dimensions of the parallelogram in terms of the dimensions of the original trapezoid.

b. Describe the area of the parallelogram in terms of the area of the original trapezoid.

c. Derive an area formula for trapezoids from this relationship.

17. a. In your head, imagine redoing Exercise 16 with a trapezoid in which one base is a few centimeters in length, but the other is so small that it can hardly be seen. What does such a situation tell you about the area formula for triangles?

b. What does the area formula for trapezoids suggest if one of the bases is extremely small—practically a single point—compared to the other?

18. What happens to the area formula for trapezoids if both bases are the same size? What kind of figure is a trapezoid with congruent bases?

Go Online
PHSchool.com

For additional practice, go to **Web Code: bea-0308**

Habits of Mind

Represent the Extreme. For Exercise 17a, picture a trapezoid like this one,

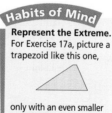

only with an even smaller base on top— "infinitesimally small," a mathematician might say.

EXERCISE 15 You may wish to provide copies of Blackline Master 3.8B for students to use.

Additional Resources

PRINT RESOURCES
• Solution Manual
• Practice Workbook
• Assessment Resources
• Teaching Resources

TECHNOLOGY
• Interactive Textbook
• TeacherExpress CD-ROM
• **Exam**View CD-ROM
• **PHSchool.com**
  – Additional Practice
  – Mid-Chapter and Chapter Tests
  – Video Tutors
  – Vocabulary Puzzles

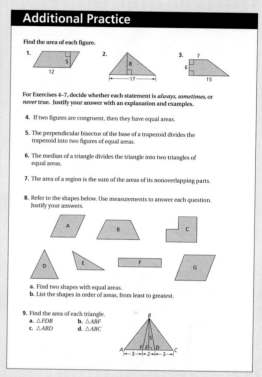

Practice: For Lesson 3.8, assign Excercises 1–9.

15. See back of book.

16. a. Two sides of the parallelogram have a length equal to the sum of the lengths of the bases of the trapezoid. The height of the parallelogram is half the height of the trapezoid.

b. The area of the parallelogram is equal to the area of the trapezoid.

c. $A = \frac{1}{2}h(a + b)$, where A is the area of the trapezoid, h is the height, and a and b are the lengths of the bases.

17. a. If b is the length of the longer base, a the length of the shorter base, and h the height of the trapezoid, then the area formula for a triangle with base b and height h will give a value close to the area of the trapezoid.

b. If the length of one of the bases of the trapezoid goes to zero, the formula for the area is identical to the formula for the area of a triangle.

18. It is same as the area formula for a parallelogram; it would be a parallelogram.

Mathematical Reflections

EXERCISES 6–8: At the start of the investigation, you may have assigned these as Questions 1–3 for students to think and write about.

Mathematical 3B Reflections

In this investigation, you found and proved formulas for calculating areas of parallelograms, triangles, and trapezoids. These questions will help you summarize what you have learned.

1. In kite *ABCD* at the right, *AC* = 3 cm, *DH* = 2 cm, and *BH* = 5 cm. What is the area of *ABCD*?

2. Two triangles have the same area. Does this mean that they are congruent? Explain with an example.

3. In hexagon *ABCDEF*, $\overline{AB}$ and $\overline{DE}$ are congruent and parallel. Also, $\overline{AE} \perp \overline{DE}$. Is hexagon *ABCDEF* scissors-congruent to a rectangle? If you think so, write down the steps that are necessary for dissecting it into a rectangle.

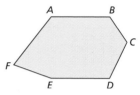

4. You dissect a parallelogram with area 32 into a square. What is the side length of the square?

5. Can two parallelograms with base lengths of 34 and 53 have the same area? If so, describe how.

6. If two figures are scissors-congruent, do they have the same area? Explain.

7. Are all squares with the same area congruent?

8. What is the area formula for a parallelogram? For a triangle? For a trapezoid?

Vocabulary

In this investigation, you learned these terms. Make sure you understand what each one means and how to use it.

- **base**
- **height**

You can assemble the table leaves and the tabletop. The total area remains the same.

Answers

Mathematical Reflections

1. 10.5 cm^2

2. Answers may vary. Sample: A right triangle with legs of lengths 2 and 12 has the same area as, but is not congruent to, a right triangle with legs of lengths 3 and 8.

3. Yes; dissect △*AEF* into a rectangle with base $\overline{AE}$, and dissect △*BCD* into a rectangle with base $\overline{BD}$.

4. $4\sqrt{2}$

5. yes, if the ratio of their heights is $\frac{34}{53}$

6. Yes; changing the positions of the pieces that form the figure does not change the total area.

7. yes

8. $A = bh$, where b and h are the base and height, respectively; $A = \frac{1}{2}bh$, where b and h are the base and height, respectively; $A = \frac{1}{2}h(a + b)$, where h is the height and a and b are the lengths of the bases.

Go Online
PHSchool.com

For a mid-chapter test,
go to Web Code: bea-0352

1. Copy and dissect each figure into a rectangle. Draw diagrams to illustrate the algorithm you use. Justify each step of the algorithm.

a.

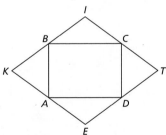

b.

c.

2. Quadrilateral *KITE* is a kite. *A, B, C,* and *D* are midpoints of the sides of *KITE. IE* = 12 and *KT* = 17. Find the perimeter of *ABCD*.

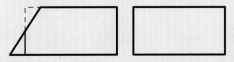

3. The following questions refer to Exercise 1. Justify each answer.

a. Will your dissection in part (a) work for any triangle?

b. Will your dissection in part (b) work for any right triangle?

c. Will your dissection in part (c) work for any trapezoid?

4. Find the area of each figure.

a.

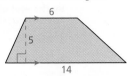

b.

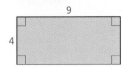

c.

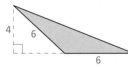

d.

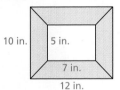

5. Tom is making a picture frame that will hold a 5 in.-by-7 in. picture centered in a 10 in.-by-12 in. frame. He wants to cover each trapezoidal piece of wood with gold leaf before putting the frame together. What is the area of each trapezoid?

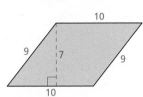

10 in. 5 in.

7 in.

12 in.

Mid-Chapter Test

Assessment Resources

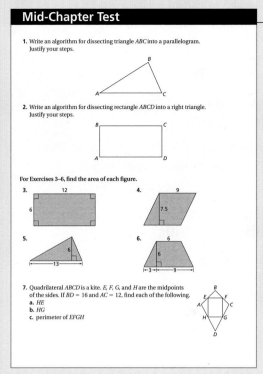

Also available: Form B

Mid-Chapter Test

1. a–b. Answers may vary. Samples are given.

a–b. See back of book.

c. Cut along the segment perpendicular to the base that has one endpoint on the midpoint of the side of the trapezoid that is not perpendicular to the base. Rotate the triangle 180° about the midpoint.

2. 29

3. Check students' work.

4. a. 50

b. 70

c. 36

d. 12

5. Each small trapezoid has an area of 18.75 in.^{2}; each large trapezoid has an area of 23.75 in.^{2}.

Investigation Overview

This investigation presents students with many different proofs of the Pythagorean Theorem. To perform calculations using the Pythagorean Theorem, students will need to have some experience with square roots.

You may wish to assign Questions 1–3 for students to think and write about during the investigation.

Learning Goals

- Build a formal proof of the Pythagorean Theorem.
- Find lengths of sides of right triangles.
- Analyze proofs of the Pythagorean Theorem.

Habits and Skills

- Follow the logical reasoning and fill in missing steps in proofs.
- Identify the critical features in a proof without words.
- See where and how to use the Pythagorean Theorem to find missing lengths in figures.

Investigation 3C

Proof by Dissection

In *Proof by Dissection*, you will study several dissect-and-rearrange proofs of the famous Pythagorean Theorem.

By the end of this investigation, you will be able to answer questions like these:

1. What is a proof without words?

2. What does the Pythagorean Theorem say about triangles?

3. What is a Pythagorean triple?

You will learn how to

- build a formal proof of the Pythagorean Theorem

- find lengths of sides of right triangles

- analyze proofs of the Pythagorean Theorem

You will develop these habits and skills:

- Follow the logical reasoning and fill in missing steps in proofs.

- Identify the critical features in a proof without words.

- See where and how to use the Pythagorean Theorem to find missing lengths in figures.

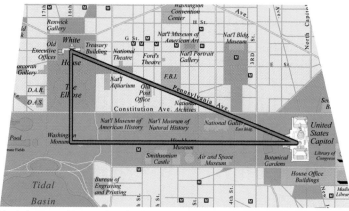

The Pythagorean Theorem relates the distance between the White House and the United States Capitol to the distances between those two buildings and the grounds of the Washington Monument.

Investigation Road Map

LESSON 3.9, *Getting Started*, presents the Pythagorean Theorem and gives students a proof without words to analyze.

LESSON 3.10, *The Pythagorean Theorem*, has students use a dissection argument to prove the Pythagorean Theorem.

LESSON 3.11, *Pick a Proof*, has students choose and explain one of several proofs without words for the Pythagorean Theorem.

Getting Started

Reasoning about dissection and rearrangement has been useful throughout mathematics. Many proofs of the Pythagorean Theorem, a famous and valuable fact about right triangles, use dissection. Euclid's classic text, *Elements*, states the theorem this way:

Theorem 3.2 Pythagorean Theorem

In a right triangle, the square built on the longest side has area equal to the sum of the areas of the squares built on the other two sides.

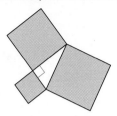

As worded, the theorem is about a relationship involving three squares. That is how Euclid meant it.

> Euclid viewed the Pythagorean Theorem differently than we do today.

Today, most people think of the theorem as stating a relationship involving three numbers, a, b, and c, that represent the side lengths of a right triangle.

If c is the length of the hypotenuse (the longest side), then c^2 is the area of the square on the hypotenuse. The theorem states that the area of that square is the same as the combined area of the other two squares: $c^2 = a^2 + b^2$.

Lesson Overview

GOALS

- Warm up to the ideas of the investigation.
- Use a thoughtful approach to develop mathematical habits of mind.

This lesson presents the Pythagorean Theorem and has students analyze a proof without words.

FOR YOU TO EXPLORE	HOMEWORK
• Core: 1	• Core: 2, 3
• Optional: none	• Optional: 4

Launch

Review the Pythagorean Theorem with your students. They have probably seen this theorem in earlier courses, but you should still have them take the time to read through the material that appears here.

Explore

Assign Problem 1 for students to complete with a partner or in groups. If students study the diagram and do not make much progress, show them the labels and the added segment in the figure below. This should help them determine how to rearrange the pieces to form the new figure.

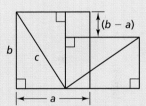

Wrap Up

Have groups present to the class their solutions to Problem 1.

Exercises

HOMEWORK
- Core: 2, 3
- Optional: 4

On Your Own

EXERCISES 2 AND 3 Students discover that the length of a diagonal of a square with side length s is $s\sqrt{2}$.

EXERCISE 3 has students look for a pattern. The pattern is obvious only if students express the lengths of the diagonals of the squares in radical form. If students are not familiar with simplified radicals, suggest that they look for patterns in the squared side lengths.

For You to Explore

1. Many people have written proofs of the Pythagorean Theorem. Below is a famous one-word proof by Bhāskara Acharya (1114–1185), an Indian mathematician. Study this proof and explain each step.

Behold!

Acharya published a book, *Lilavati*, named after his daughter. His focus was algebra, and the book included work with Pythagorean triples. Three numbers a, b, and c form a **Pythagorean triple** if $a^2 + b^2 = c^2$. Keep an eye out for Pythagorean triples throughout this Investigation.

Exercises Practicing Habits of Mind

On Your Own

2. Find the length of the diagonal of a square with sides having each given length.

   a. 1 foot   **b.** 2 feet   **c.** 4 feet

   d. 10 feet   **e.** 100 feet

3. Find a pattern in the lengths of the diagonals of the squares in Exercise 2. Write a simple rule relating a square's diagonal length to its side length.

Maintain Your Skills

4. A baseball diamond is a square 90 ft on a side. How far is second base from home plate?

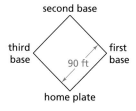

second base

third base   90 ft   first base

home plate

Go Online
Video Tutor
PHSchool.com

Web Code: bee-0775

Answers

For You to Explore

1. See back of book.

Exercises

2. **a.** $\sqrt{2}$ ft
   b. $2\sqrt{2}$ ft
   c. $4\sqrt{2}$ ft
   d. $10\sqrt{2}$ ft
   e. $100\sqrt{2}$ ft

3. If x is the length of a side of a square, then the length of a diagonal is $x\sqrt{2}$.

4. $90\sqrt{2}$ ft

The Pythagorean Theorem

The proof outlined below is probably from China, about 200 B.C. Most likely, the author of the proof developed the theorem statement independently, rather than learning of it from another mathematician.

n-Class Experiment

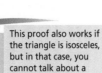

For the proof outline, follow the directions at each step and answer the questions as you work. When you are finished, you will have constructed a proof of the Pythagorean Theorem.

tep 1 Construct an arbitrary (scalene) right triangle. Label the short leg a, the long leg b, and the hypotenuse c.

> This proof also works if the triangle is isosceles, but in that case, you cannot talk about a "short leg" and a "long leg."

tep 2 Construct two squares with sides of length $a + b$.

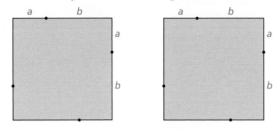

tep 3 Dissect one of the squares as shown below.

- a square with side length b in one corner
- a square with side length a in the opposite corner
- two rectangles cut at their diagonals into two triangles each

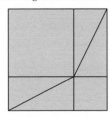

1. Show that each of the four triangles you have just cut is congruent to the original right triangle.

In-Class Experiment

1. The four right triangles are congruent to the original triangle by SAS.

GOALS
- Build a formal proof of the Pythagorean Theorem.
- Find lengths of sides of right triangles.

This lesson presents a proof by dissection of the Pythagorean Theorem.

CHECK YOUR UNDERSTANDING
- Core: 1, 2, 3, 4, 5
- Optional: none

HOMEWORK
- Core: 6, 7, 8, 9, 10, 11
- Optional: 12

MATERIALS
- protractors
- rulers

Launch

Prepare a transparency of the proof that the In-Class Experiment outlines. Have cut-outs of the pieces available so you can move them around on the overhead projector.

Discuss the Pythagorean Theorem and its converse. Students will prove these in Exercises 1 and 2.

Explore

As a class, work through the steps of the proof. Students should follow along with the proof, dissecting and rearranging, as the whole class works through this In-Class Experiment.

Wrap Up

Assign the Check Your Understanding exercises for in-class work.

Assessment Resources

Step 4 Dissect the other square into five parts as shown below.
- four triangles congruent to the original right triangle
- a remaining piece in the center

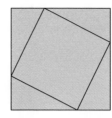

2. Show that the piece in the center is a square with side length c.

Step 5 The two original squares have the same area.

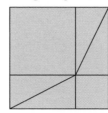 =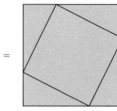

Area of this square   equals   area of this square.

The eight triangles in the two dissections are congruent. So the four from the first square are equal in area to the four from the second square.

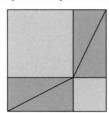 =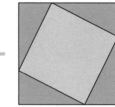

Dark area here   equals   dark area here.

Step 6 Remove the four triangles from each square. What remains in the first square must have the same area as what remains in the second square.

Answers

2. Each side of the piece in the center is the hypotenuse of one of four congruent right triangles with hypotenuses of length c. At each vertex of the quadrilateral, there are three angles. The segments of lengths a and b are parts of a side of the original square and hence are collinear. The acute angles of the right triangle are complementary, so the third angle must have a measure of 90°.

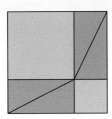

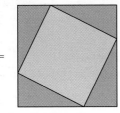

Light area here   equals   light area here.

You have proved the Pythagorean Theorem as Euclid knew it!

The modern algebraic statement

$$a^2 + b^2 = c^2$$

follows from the formula for the area of a square. The areas of the two squares on the left above are a^2 and b^2. The area of the square on the right is c^2. Geometric reasoning tells us that the areas on the left $(a^2 + b^2)$ and on the right (c^2), are equal: $a^2 + b^2 = c^2$.

You can state the Pythagorean Theorem this way: If $\triangle ABC$ is a right triangle, then the sum of the squares on the legs equals the square on the hypotenuse.

You can also use the *converse* of this theorem: If the sum of the squares on two sides of a triangle equals the square on the third side, then the triangle is a right triangle.

You now have the tools you need to prove the converse of the Pythagorean Theorem. You must use what you know about triangle congruence.

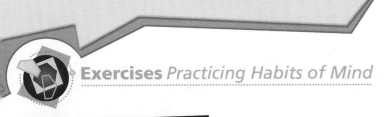

Check Your Understanding

1. An outline for a proof of the converse of the Pythagorean Theorem follows. Fill in the gaps to complete the proof.

   Given $\triangle ABC$, where the lengths of the sides satisfy $a^2 + b^2 = c^2$

   Prove $\triangle ABC$ is a right triangle.

Exercises

1. **a.** Check students' work.
   b. The length of the hypotenuse is c by the Pythagorean Theorem.
   c. by SSS
   d. It is congruent to the right triangle from part (a).

Exercises

HOMEWORK
- Core: 6, 7, 8, 9, 10, 11
- Optional: 12

Check Your Understanding

EXERCISES 1 AND 2 have students write proofs of the converse of the Pythagorean Theorem.

a. Construct a right triangle with legs of lengths a and b.

b. What is the length of the hypotenuse of this right triangle? Explain.

c. Your new triangle and $\triangle ABC$ are congruent. Explain.

d. $\triangle ABC$ must be a right triangle. Explain.

2. Write a formal proof for the following: If a triangle has sides whose lengths satisfy the equation $a^2 + b^2 = c^2$, then the triangle is a right triangle.

3. Verify the Pythagorean Theorem numerically by testing a specific case.

a. Construct a right triangle with one leg 3 inches long and the other leg 4 inches long. What is the area of your triangle?

b. Construct a square with sides of length 7 inches ($a + b = 3 + 4$). What is the area of your square?

c. Dissect the square into five pieces as shown at the right.

  • four right triangles congruent to the original one

  • one square in the middle

Find the area of the square in the middle by subtracting the areas of the four right triangles.

d. Calculate $a^2 + b^2 = 3^2 + 4^2$. Is the sum equal to the area of the middle square in part (c)?

4. How long is one side of the middle square in Exercise 3?

> If you know the area of a square, how can you find the length of a side?

On Your Own

5. Draw a right triangle with legs 5 cm and 12 cm. Draw a square with one side that is the hypotenuse of this triangle.

a. Use the Pythagorean Theorem to find the area of this square.

b. What is the perimeter of this square?

> How long is one side?

6. The diagram shows squares on the sides of a right triangle. It gives the areas of two of the squares.

a. Find the area of the third square.

b. Find the lengths of the three sides of the triangle.

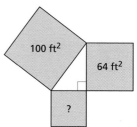

Answers

2. Construct a right triangle with legs of length a and b. By the Pythagorean Theorem, the hypotenuse must have length c, since you know that c is the number satisfying the equation $a^2 + b^2 = c^2$. The original triangle and the triangle you have just constructed are congruent by SSS, and therefore all the angles are congruent as well, by CPCTC.

3. **a.** 6 in.^{2}
   b. 49 in.^{2}
   c. 25 in.^{2}
   d. yes

4. 5 in.

5. **a.** 169 cm^2
   b. 52 cm

6. **a.** 36 ft^2
   b. 6 ft, 8 ft, 10 ft

7. Construct a right triangle with a 17-cm hypotenuse and a leg of length 8 cm. Draw a square on the other leg of the triangle.

   a. What is the area of the square you have drawn?

   b. What is the length of the other leg of the triangle?

Habits of Mind

Visualize. Think of what the triangle must look like. In your "picture," think of what you are given. Then plan how to use what you know to do the construction.

8. You are standing at one corner of a rectangular parking lot. The lot measures 100 feet by 300 feet.

   a. You walk along the sides of the parking lot to the opposite corner. How far do you walk?

   b. You walk diagonally across the parking lot back to your starting point. How far do you walk? How much shorter or longer is this path?

   c. There might be cars in the parking lot. This could block you from walking directly on the diagonal. How might a path along the sides of the whole parking lot differ in length from a zig-zag path through the lot? Explain.

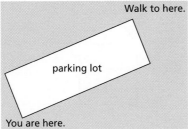

Walk to here.

parking lot

You are here.

9. You have seen this figure before. Suppose $AE = BF = CG = DH = 3$, and $EB = FC = GD = HA = 1$. Find each of the following.

   a. EF

   b. perimeter of $ABCD$

   c. area of $ABCD$

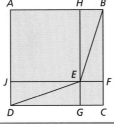

10. Standardized Test Prep Three squares are arranged so that they meet at their vertices to form a right triangle. Which are possible areas of the three squares?

   A. $(3, 4, 5)$ **B.** $(5, 12, 13)$

   C. $(25, 16, 51)$ **D.** $(9, 16, 25)$

Go Online
PHSchool.com
For additional practice, go to Web Code: bea-0310

Maintain Your Skills

11. In this familiar figure, two smaller squares $CGEF$ and $AHEJ$ are inside the large square $ABCD$. Suppose $CF = 1$ and $BF = 3$. Find each of the following.

   a. AB **b.** BE

   c. BJ (not drawn)   **d.** HJ (not drawn)

   e. CE (not drawn)   **f.** area of $AHEJ$

   g. area of $CGEF$ **h.** area of $\triangle BEF$

---

7. a. 225 cm^2
   b. 15 cm

8. a. 400 ft
   b. $\sqrt{100,000} \text{ ft}$, or about 316 ft; about 84 ft less
   c. The difference will be less than 84 ft; it is not possible to know the exact difference without information on the way the cars are parked in the lot. However, the straight distance from corner to corner is least, so 84 ft is the maximum difference. By sticking as close as you can to the

diagonal, you can probably save several feet of walking.

9. a. $\sqrt{10}$
   b. 16
   c. 16

10. D

11. a. 4
   b. $\sqrt{10}$
   c. 5
   d. $3\sqrt{2}$
   e. $\sqrt{2}$
   f. 9
   g. 1
   h. 1.5

On Your Own

EXERCISES 6–8 give students a chance to practice using the Pythagorean Theorem and its converse. In Exercise 8, students may find the construction challenging.

EXERCISES 9–11 are examples of exercises in which students will need to use the Pythagorean Theorem without being instructed to do so.

Additional Resources

PRINT RESOURCES
- Solution Manual
- Practice Workbook
- Assessment Resources
- Teaching Resources

TECHNOLOGY
- Interactive Textbook
- TeacherExpress CD-ROM
- **Exam**View CD-ROM
- **PHSchool.com**
  - Additional Practice
  - Mid-Chapter and Chapter Tests
  - Video Tutors
  - Vocabulary Puzzles

Additional Practice

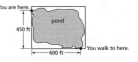

Verify the Pythagorean Theorem numerically by testing a specific case.

1. Construct a right triangle with one leg 7 cm long and the other leg 24 cm long. What is the area of the triangle?

2. Construct a square with sides of length 31 cm. What is the area of the square?

3. Dissect the square in Exercise 2 into five pieces: four right triangles congruent to the triangle in Exercise 1, and one square in the middle. Find the area of the square in the middle by subtracting the areas of the four right triangles.

4. Calculate $a^2 + b^2$, or $7^2 + 24^2$. Is this sum equal to the area of the middle square in Exercise 3?

For Exercises 5–8, draw a right triangle with legs of the given lengths. Then draw a square with one side that is the hypotenuse of the triangle. Find the area and the perimeter of the square.

5. 3 cm, 4 cm   **6.** 6 cm, 8 cm

7. 8 cm, 15 cm   **8.** 9 cm, 12 cm

9. You are standing at one end of a shallow pond. There is a rectangular walking path around the pond.

You are here.
pond
450 ft
600 ft
You walk to here.

   a. You walk along the path to the other end of the pond. How far do you walk?
   b. You decide to wade diagonally across the pond back to your starting point. How much shorter or longer is this method than walking on the path?

A triangle has sides of the given lengths. Decide whether each triangle is a right triangle. Explain.

10. 6, 7, 12   **11.** 9, 40, 41   **12.** 3, 8, 11

Practice: For Lesson 3.10, assign Exercises 1–12.

Lesson Overview

GOALS

- Find lengths of sides of right triangles.
- Analyze proofs of the Pythagorean Theorem.

Although the proofs in this lesson are mathematically elegant and worthwhile for students to see, this section is optional if you are pressed for time. If you do not assign the proofs for in-class work, you may still wish to use the exercises for extra practice.

This lesson has students study and explain three famous proofs without words of the Pythagorean Theorem.

CHECK YOUR UNDERSTANDING
- Core: 1, 2, 3
- Optional: none

MATERIALS
- Blackline Master 3.11

HOMEWORK
- Core: 4, 5, 6, 7, 8, 9, 10, 11, 12, 13
- Optional: 16
- Extension: 14, 15

Launch

Split students up into pairs or small groups.

Explore

Have each pair or group of students choose one proof featured in this lesson to read through, study, and learn. Then have each pair or group present their findings to the class. You can use the presentations as an informal assessment.

Wrap Up

After students present their explanations, assign the Check Your Understanding exercises for in-class work.

3.11 Pick a Proof

The following famous proofs of the Pythagorean Theorem are proofs without words. Choose one of them to study and explain.

The first dissection proof is based on Euclid's proof of the Pythagorean Theorem. It is Proposition 47 in Book 1 of *Elements*.

Euclid's *Elements* is a collection of 13 books.

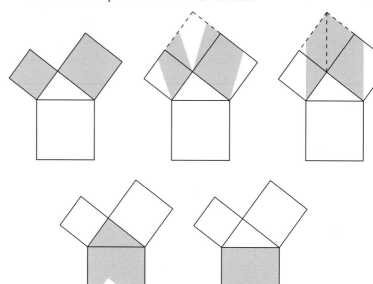

The second proof is by Henry Perigal (1801–1898). Henry Perigal was a stockbroker who lived in London. He discovered this dissection proof of the Pythagorean Theorem around 1830. He liked it so much that he had the diagram printed on his business cards.

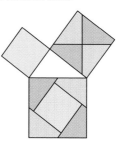

James Garfield (1831–1881) was the 20th President of the United States. Five years before becoming president, he discovered this proof of the Pythagorean Theorem.

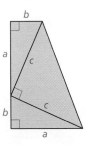

$$\tfrac{1}{2}(a + b)(a + b) = \tfrac{1}{2}(ab) + \tfrac{1}{2}(ab) + \tfrac{1}{2}c^2$$

$$a^2 + 2ab + b^2 = 2ab + c^2$$

$$a^2 + b^2 = c^2$$

Exercises *Practicing Habits of Mind*

Check Your Understanding

Your earlier proofs all showed that things were what they seemed to be. In Exercise 1 on the next page, proof is essential, but in an upside-down kind of way. You *do not* want to believe the result. You want to show that something is *not* what it seems to be.

When something is not what it seems, you usually want to explain why.

Exercises

HOMEWORK
- Core: 4, 5, 6, 7, 8, 9, 10, 11, 12, 13
- Optional: 16
- Extension: 14, 15

Check Your Understanding

EXERCISE 1 has students explain why what seems to be correct on paper is, in fact, not correct. The diagrams in this exercise seem to show that an 8 × 8 square and a 5 × 13 rectangle have equal areas. You can give students copies of Blackline Master 3.11 for this exercise if you wish.

On Your Own

EXERCISES 2 AND 3 are similar to Exercises 2 and 3 from Lesson 3.9, in that students must look for a pattern. Again, the pattern is obvious only if students express the heights of the triangles in radical form.

EXERCISE 5 will be much easier if students have knowledge of radicals.

EXERCISE 6 has students use the Pythagorean Theorem to find a length in a three-dimensional object.

EXERCISE 7 Students use the Pythagorean Theorem to analyze an airplane's trip. They should realize that this will not provide the precise distance because the distances given are on the surface of the earth, which is not a two-dimensional plane.

EXERCISE 8 Students use the Pythagorean Theorem to find the area of a nonright triangle. To get the area of $\triangle ABC$, students can either use the given information to find the areas of the two smaller right triangles and then add those areas, or they can find the length of $\overline{AB}$ by finding the missing side lengths of the two smaller triangles and then multiplying AB by the height of the triangle.

---

1. Carefully copy the square at the right onto a separate sheet of paper. It is eight units on a side. (You may want to use graph paper.) Then cut your copy into four pieces as indicated by the sketch.

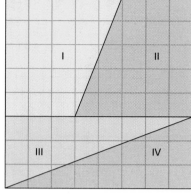

   a. What is the area of an 8×8 square?

   Now rearrange the pieces into the following figure.

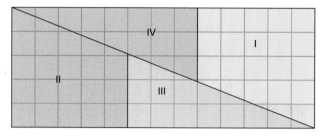

   b. What is the area of a 5-by-13 rectangle?

   c. **What's Wrong Here?** The same four pieces seem to make both a square and a rectangle. Yet, if you find the two areas by using the area formula, the areas are not the same! Explain.

On Your Own

2. Find the height of an equilateral triangle with sides of the given length.

   a. 1 cm   **b.** 2 cm   **c.** 3 cm

   d. 10 cm   **e.** 100 in.

3. Find a pattern in the heights you found in Exercise 2. Write a rule that relates the height of an equilateral triangle to the length of its sides.

4. An equilateral triangle has side length s. Find a formula for its area in terms of s.

Answers

Exercises

1. **a.** 64
   b. 65
   c. Answers may vary. Sample: The measures of the upper left and lower right angles of the 5-by-13 "rectangle" are about 88.8°. This is close enough to a right angle to fool the eye, but the figure is in fact not precisely a rectangle, and so you cannot use the formula for the area of a rectangle.

2. **a.** $\frac{\sqrt{3}}{2}$ cm
   b. $\sqrt{3}$ cm
   c. $\frac{3\sqrt{3}}{2}$ cm
   d. $5\sqrt{3}$ cm
   e. $50\sqrt{3}$ cm

3. If s is the length of the sides of an equilateral triangle, then $\frac{s\sqrt{3}}{2}$ is the length of each altitude of the triangle.

4. $A = \frac{s^2\sqrt{3}}{4}$

5. Find the length of each segment shown in blue. Describe a pattern in the lengths.

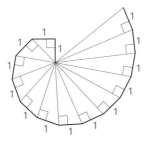

6. The diagram below shows a cube and one of its diagonals. The edges of the cube are 10 inches long. How long is the diagonal?

7. An airplane leaves Los Angeles. It flies 100 miles north. It turns due east and flies 600 miles. Then it turns north again and flies 350 miles. About how far is the airplane from its starting point?

> Why does the Pythagorean Theorem not give the precise distance here?

8. What is the area of the plot of land shown in the diagram? (State any assumptions you make.)

400 ft

200 ft

300 ft

9. Find the area of △ABC.

C

10   17
   8

A   B

Habits of Mind

Be critical.
Do you think the measure of ∠ACB is less than 90°, equal to 90°, or greater than 90°?

A Pythagorean triple is a set of three positive integers (a, b, c), such as $(3, 4, 5)$, that satisfy the equation $a^2 + b^2 = c^2$. If you have a Pythagorean triple (a, b, c), you can build a right triangle with side lengths a, b, and c.

10. Look back through your work in this section. Find two other Pythagorean triples.

In this lesson, the first proof without words of the Pythagorean Theorem shows a right triangle with a square constructed on each side. Would the proof work if the figure constructed on each side of the right triangle was a figure other than a square? For instance, if the figure constructed on each side of the right triangle was a semicircle or some other polygon, would the sum of the areas of the two smaller figures still equal the area of the largest figure? Use geometry software to investigate.

1. Construct a right triangle using dynamic geometry software.
2. On each side of the right triangle, construct a semicircle. Make sure that the diameter of the semicircle is the same as the length of the side of the right triangle.
   Tell students they may have to leave the entire circle in the sketch. Some software programs will not hide only half the circle.
3. Now calculate the areas of the three semicircles. What is their relationship?
4. Investigate what happens when you construct equilateral triangles on all three sides of the right triangle, or rectangles, or nonsquare polygons.
5. Can the Pythagorean Theorem be "unsquared"? Explain what shapes you can construct on the sides of a right triangle with areas that will satisfy the Pythagorean Theorem.
6. For an extra challenge, include an algebraic explanation of your findings.

---

5. $\sqrt{2}$; $\sqrt{3}$; $\sqrt{4}$, or 2; $\sqrt{5}$; $\sqrt{6}$; $\sqrt{7}$; $\sqrt{8}$; $\sqrt{9}$, or 3; $\sqrt{10}$; $\sqrt{11}$; $\sqrt{12}$; $\sqrt{13}$; $\sqrt{14}$; the length of the nth unlabeled segment is $\sqrt{n+1}$.

6. $10\sqrt{3}$

7. about 750 miles

8. 84

9. Assume the figure is a trapezoid with one side perpendicular to the bases. The area is $70{,}000 \text{ ft}^2$.

10. $(5, 12, 13)$, $(8, 15, 17)$

Maintain Your Skills

EXERCISE 16 gives students the identity that generates Pythagorean triples. Let students discover that this is the purpose of the exercise before you discuss it.

Additional Resources

PRINT RESOURCES
- Solution Manual
- Practice Workbook
- Assessment Resources
- Teaching Resources

TECHNOLOGY
- Interactive Textbook
- TeacherExpress CD-ROM
- **Exam**_View_ CD-ROM
- PHSchool.com
  - Additional Practice
  - Mid-Chapter and Chapter Tests
  - Video Tutors
  - Vocabulary Puzzles

Additional Practice

1. Find the length of the hypotenuse of an isosceles right triangle with legs of each given length.
   a. 2 in.   b. 4 in.   c. 5 in.   d. 13 in.   e. s

2. Find a pattern in the hypotenuse lengths you found in Exercise 1. Write a rule that relates the leg lengths of an isosceles right triangle to the length of its hypotenuse.

3. The figure is a rectangular box with the given dimensions. Find *d*, the length of the diagonal.

4. A triangle has side lengths 4, 4√3, and 8.
   a. Numerically show that the triangle is a right triangle.
   b. Would you consider these lengths a Pythagorean triple? Explain.

For Exercises 5 and 6, find the area of each triangle.

5.   6.

7. a. Find a Pythagorean triple not mentioned in Lesson 3.11.
   b. List four triples that would be members of its family.

8. A car drives due north for 4 miles. It turns right and drives due east for 3 miles. Then it turns right again and drives due south for 8 miles.
   a. How far is the car from its starting point?
   b. Describe a situation that might require this route, rather than a direct route from start to finish.

9. The radius of a regular hexagon is the measure from its center to any vertex. The radius is congruent to each side. Find the area of a regular hexagon with side lengths of 10.

Practice: For Lesson 3.11, assign Exercises 1–9.

---

11. The following triples are members of a family of Pythagorean triples. (There are other Pythagorean triples that do not belong to this family.) Check that each triple listed below is a Pythagorean triple. How are these triples enough alike to justify calling them a family?
    - (3, 4, 5)
    - (6, 8, 10)
    - (30, 40, 50)
    - (45, 60, 75)
    - (300, 400, 500)

12. Draw triangles with the following side lengths. What do the triangles have in common?
    a. 6 cm, 8 cm, 10 cm   **b.** 3 in., 4 in., 5 in.   **c.** 15 cm, 20 cm, 25 cm

13. **Standardized Test Prep** Which of the following does NOT belong to the same family of Pythagorean triples?
    A. (21, 28, 35)   **B.** (9, 40, 41)   **C.** (7.5, 10, 12.5)   **D.** (39, 52, 65)

14. **Take It Further** Explain the following picture-proof of the Pythagorean Theorem. It was probably devised by George Biddel Airy (1801–1892), an astronomer. It is more difficult than the ones already shown in this investigation, but the poem to the right of the diagram may help you explain the proof.

    Here I am as you may see,
    $a^2 + b^2 - ab$.
    When two triangles on me stand,
    Square of hypotenuse is planned.
    But if I stand on them instead,
    The squares of both the sides are read.

15. **Take It Further** The Pythagorean Theorem makes a statement about the areas of squares built on the sides of a right triangle. What can you say if the shapes built are not squares? What would you find if the shapes you constructed on the sides of a right triangle were semicircles? Equilateral triangles? Rectangles? Construct various shapes on the sides of a right triangle. Explore the cases for which it is possible to relate the three areas in some way.

Maintain Your Skills

16. Use at least 5 pairs of numbers to verify the following identity.
    $$(x^2 + y^2)^2 = (x^2 - y^2)^2 + (2xy)^2$$

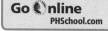
For additional practice, go to Web Code: bea-0311

Answers

11. Each of the triples has the form (3*t*, 4*t*, 5*t*), where *t* is a positive integer.

12. The sizes of the triangles are different, but their shapes are exactly alike.

13. B

14. The lightly shaded piece is the "I" in the poem. When you place the two dark triangles on top of it, you form the square of the hypotenuse of the triangles. When you place the same triangles below it, you form the squares of the legs of the triangles. The two shapes have the same area, since they are made of the same pieces.

15. Answers may vary. Sample: An analog of the Pythagorean Theorem holds for semicircles and equilateral triangles. An analog of the Pythagorean Theorem holds for rectangles only when all three rectangle have sides that are in the same proportion to each other.

16. See back of book.

3C

Mathematical Reflections

In this investigation, you studied several dissect-and-rearrange proofs of the Pythagorean Theorem. You also applied the Pythagorean Theorem. These questions will help you summarize what you have learned.

1. **a.** State the Pythagorean Theorem in terms of side lengths.

   b. State the Pythagorean Theorem in terms of areas.

2. Find the length of a diagonal of a square that has a side length of 4 cm.

3. What is the area of the parallelogram below?

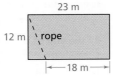

25 | 20
|— 43 —|

4. Find the height of an isosceles triangle with a base that is 120 cm long and congruent sides that are 100 cm long.

5. Suppose you need to divide a pool into an area for adults to swim and an area for children to swim. How much rope would you need to divide the pool as shown?

23 m
12 m \ rope
|— 18 m —|

6. What is a proof without words?

7. What does the Pythagorean Theorem say about triangles?

8. What is a Pythagorean triple?

Vocabulary

In this investigation, you learned this term. Make sure you understand what it means and how to use it.

• **Pythagorean triple**

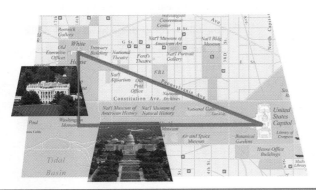

The ground was too marshy at the vertex of the right angle, so builders moved the Washington Monument site a bit to the east.

Mathematical Reflections

EXERCISE 6–8 at the start of the investigation, you may have assigned these as Questions 1–3 for students to think and write about.

Mathematical Reflections

1. **a.** If the legs of a right triangle have lengths a and b, and the hypotenuse has length c, then $a^2 + b^2 = c^2$.

   b. In a right triangle, the area of the square built on the hypotenuse is equal to the sum of the areas of the squares built on the other two sides.

2. $4\sqrt{2}$

3. 1160

4. 80

5. 13 m

6. A proof without words is a diagram that is clear enough and suggestive enough to allow a person to see the relationships that can be the basis of a formal proof.

7. The Pythagorean Theorem states that square of the length of the hypotenuse of a right triangle is equal to the sum of the squares of the other two sides.

8. A Pythagorean triple is a set of three positive integers that satisfy the equation $a^2 + b^2 = c^2$.

Investigation Overview

You may notice that this investigation has less experimentation and proof than the preceding investigations. This investigation presents formulas as they appear on many standardized tests, which students should practice using. Students will explore the material more thoroughly in Chapters 5 and 6.

This investigation explores surface area via the concept of nets, which appeared in Chapter 1. Students use those nets to understand what surface area is, and then to find the surface areas of polyhedrons, as well as curved solids (cones, cylinders, and spheres). Students also learn the difference between lateral surface area and total surface area.

This investigation briefly presents volume formulas, which students will explore in more detail in Chapter 6.

You may wish to assign Questions 1–3 for students to think and write about during the investigation.

Learning Goals

- Find surface area of a solid using a net.
- Interpret and use formulas for lateral and surface areas of prisms, pyramids, cylinders, and cones.
- Interpret and use formulas for volumes of prisms, pyramids, cylinders, and cones.

Habits and Skills

- Visualize a net for a three-dimensional object.
- Understand surface area and volume.
- Identify measurements needed to find surface area and volume for different types of solids.
- Reason by continuity to connect formulas for prisms and pyramids to formulas for cylinders and cones.

Investigation 3D Measuring Solids

In *Measuring Solids*, you will learn some similarities between plane figures and space figures.

In a plane,
- a polygon or a circle forms a boundary between the inside and the outside of the figure
- the perimeter of a figure is the total length of the figure's boundary
- the area of a figure is the measure of the part of the plane enclosed by the boundary

In space,
- the surface of a solid forms a boundary between its inside and outside
- the surface area of a solid is the total area of the solid's boundary
- the volume of a solid is the measure of the part of space enclosed by the boundary

By the end of this investigation, you will be able to answer questions like these:

1. How can you use perimeter and area of two-dimensional shapes to find surface area and volume of three-dimensional solids?

2. What is the relationship between a prism and a cylinder? Between a pyramid and a cone?

3. A cylinder and a cone have the same base. The height of each is equal to the radius of its base. What is the ratio of their lateral surface areas?

You will learn how to
- find surface area of a solid using a net
- interpret and use formulas for lateral and surface areas and for volume

You will develop these habits and skills:
- Visualize a net for a three-dimensional object.
- Understand surface area and volume.
- Reason by continuity to connect formulas.

This diamond mine in Russia suggests a cone. It is about 525 m deep and 1250 m across.

Investigation Road Map

LESSON 3.12, *Getting Started,* introduces surface area of solids.

LESSON 3.13, *Surface Area: Prisms and Pyramids,* introduces formulas for the surface area of prisms and pyramids. Students learn to derive these formulas by finding the sum of the areas of the lateral faces of the polyhedrons.

LESSON 3.14, *Surface Area: Cylinders and Cones,* introduces formulas for the lateral and total surface areas of cylinders and cones by describing the two-dimensional shapes you obtain if you unfold these solids.

LESSON 3.15, *Volumes of Solids,* generalizes the formula $V = Bh$ for the volume of prisms or cylinders from the familiar formula $V = \text{length} \times \text{width} \times \text{height}$ for the volume of a box.

In Chapter 1, you made nets of three-dimensional objects. Now you can use the net of a three-dimensional solid to find the **surface area** of the solid.

Example

Problem Draw a net for this cube. Use the net to find the surface area of the cube.

3 cm
3 cm
3 cm

Solution Think of cutting the cube along some edges and opening the cube to lie flat. Here is a possible net.

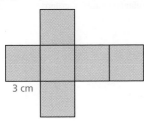

3 cm

The surface area of the cube is the total area of the six squares.

$$\text{Surface Area} = 6 \cdot \text{Area of Square}$$
$$= 6 \cdot 3^2$$
$$= 6 \cdot 9$$
$$= 54$$

The surface area of the cube is 54 cm^2.

Habits of Mind

Visualize. You can cut different edges to make different nets. It is easy to see, however, that all of the nets are scissors-congruent.

Lesson Overview

GOALS

- Warm up to the ideas of the investigation.
- Use a visual approach to develop mathematical habits of mind.
- Find surface area of a solid using a net.

This lesson introduces surface area of solids. Students use nets to help them find the surface areas of various solids.

FOR YOU TO EXPLORE
- Core: 1, 2, 3, 4
- Optional: none

HOMEWORK
- Core: 5, 6, 7, 8
- Optional: 9, 10, 11, 12, 13
- Extension: 14

VOCABULARY
- parallelepiped
- slant height
- surface area
- tetrahedron

Launch

Review the Example, which reminds students of their work with nets in Chapter 1.

Explore

Have students work individually or in pairs on Problems 1–4 in the For You to Explore section. Point out the special features of each solid. You do not need to require students to memorize each solid's characteristics because memorization is not the focus of this lesson. Instead, students should strive to make accurate sketches of the nets of each solid.

Wrap Up

Before assigning homework, allow students some time to discuss their results to Problems 1–4 in the For You to Explore section.

For You To Explore

PROBLEMS 1–4 Students use what they already know about nets to find the surface areas of certain polyhedrons.

For You to Explore

For Problems 1–4, sketch a net of the solid. Use the net to find the surface area of the solid.

1. a right rectangular prism (All six faces are rectangles.)

2. a tetrahedron (All four faces are equilateral triangles.)

3. a right square pyramid (The base is square; the triangular faces are congruent.)

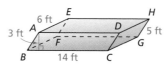

4. a parallelepiped (Here, faces *ABCD* and *EFGH* are parallelograms; the other faces are rectangles.)

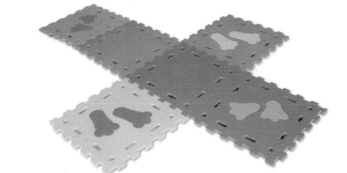

> A parallelepiped is a kind of prism that can be "slanty." Opposite faces are congruent parallelograms.

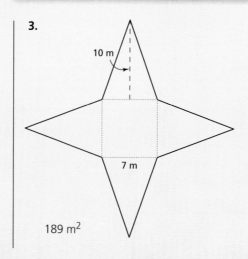

When you assemble the box, the surface area of its faces . . .

Answers

For You to Explore

1–4. Sketches of nets may vary. Samples are given.

1.

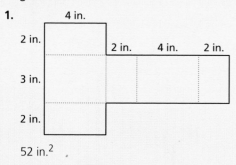

52 in.²

2. See back of book.

3.

189 m²

4.

312 ft²

Exercises *Practicing Habits of Mind*

On Your Own

5. Write About It The three triangles are drawn to scale.

a. Does knowing the area of one triangle help you find the areas of the other two? Explain.

b. Does knowing the perimeter of one triangle help you find the perimeters of the other two? Explain.

6. Write About It The three parallelograms are drawn to scale.

a. Does knowing the area of one parallelogram help you find the areas of the other two?

b. Does knowing the perimeter of one parallelogram help you find the perimeters of the other two? Explain.

7. a. You have a rectangular box that measures 1 in. by 3 in. by 5 in. What is the surface area of the box?

b. Suppose you have another box with length, width, and height that are all twice those of your original box. How does the surface area of the larger box compare to the surface area of the smaller box?

8. a. Write a formula for the surface area of a right rectangular prism (a box) in terms of its length ℓ, width w, and height h.

b. Write a formula for the surface area of a cube in terms of its side length s.

c. Explain how you can use the first formula to find the second.

> Surface area is the sum of the face areas.

. . . remains the same.

Exercises

HOMEWORK
- Core: 5, 6, 7, 8
- Optional: 9, 10, 11, 12, 13
- Extension: 14

On Your Own

EXERCISES 5 AND 6 Students need to understand that the distance between parallel lines is constant.

EXERCISE 8 Draw students' attention to the margin note that is associated with this exercise. It points out that sometimes it is easier to calculate surface area by adding the areas of all faces of an object, rather than by remembering a formula.

Exercises

5. a. Yes; all the areas are equal, since the bases are equal and the heights are equal.

b. No; you can change the perimeter of any of the triangles by moving its top vertex farther to the right (or left) along the top dashed line.

6. a. Yes; all the areas are equal, since the bases are equal and the heights are equal.

b. No; you can change the perimeter of any of the parallelograms by dragging the top side of the parallelogram farther to the right (or left) along the top dashed line.

7. 46 in.^{2}; the surface area of the larger box is 4 times that of the smaller box.

8. a. $SA = 2(\ell w + wh + \ell h)$

b. $SA = 6s^2$

c. For a cube, ℓ, w, and h are all equal to s. Substitute in the formula from part (a). Simplify to get $SA = 6s^2$.

Maintain Your Skills

These exercises give students practice calculating surface area, but they also preview upcoming lessons.

9. Suppose you connect small cubes face to face in the manner suggested here.

a. How many of the original cube faces are hidden from view when you use 4 cubes? 8 cubes? *n* cubes?

b. How many of the original cube faces are visible when you use 4 cubes? 8 cubes? *n* cubes?

c. When you add a new cube at the end, what is the increase in the number of visible faces? In the number of hidden faces?

10. You build each structure shown below from six 1-in. cubes. Find the surface area of each structure by counting the visible faces.

a. **b.** **c.**

Maintain Your Skills

In Exercises 11–13, find the surface area of the indicated solid for the side lengths given.

11. right rectangular prism

   a. 1 cm by 5 cm by 4 cm   **b.** 2 cm by 4 cm by 4 cm

   c. 3 cm by 3 cm by 4 cm   **d.** 1 cm by 5 cm by 6 cm

   e. 2 cm by 4 cm by 6 cm   **f.** 3 cm by 3 cm by 6 cm

Go Online
Video Tutor
PHSchool.com
Web Code: bee-0775

12. right triangular prism

   a. 1 cm by 2 cm by $\sqrt{5}$ cm, height 4 cm

   b. 1 cm by 3 cm by $\sqrt{10}$ cm, height 4 cm

   c. 2 cm by 2 cm by $2\sqrt{2}$ cm, height 4 cm

13. **Take It Further** right square pyramid

   a. 4 cm by 4 cm, height 1 cm

   b. 4 cm by 4 cm, height 2 cm

   c. 4 cm by 4 cm, height 3 cm

Habits of Mind

Visualize. Use this right triangle inside the pyramid to help you find the *slant height* ℓ. (The **slant height** is the height of each triangular face.)

Answers

9. a. 6; 14; $2n - 2$
   b. 18; 34; $4n + 2$
   c. 4 more; 2 more

10. a. 26 in.^{2}
   b. 22 in.^{2}
   c. 24 in.^{2}

11. a. 58 cm^2
   b. 64 cm^2
   c. 66 cm^2
   d. 82 cm^2
   e. 88 cm^2
   f. 90 cm^2

12. a. $(14 + 4\sqrt{5})$ cm^2
   b. $(19 + 4\sqrt{10})$ cm^2
   c. $(20 + 8\sqrt{2})$ cm^2

13. a. $(16 + 8\sqrt{5})$ cm^2
   b. $(16 + 16\sqrt{2})$ cm^2
   c. $(16 + 8\sqrt{13})$ cm^2

13 Surface Area: Prisms and Pyramids

To measure perimeter and area of two-dimensional figures, you first classify them (squares, rectangles, triangles, and so on). Then you sort them according to properties that help you find their measurements. You do the same to measure solids.

or Discussion

Here are some solids.

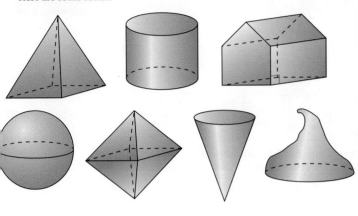

1. How are these solids alike? How are they different?

You may have noticed that some solids have all flat surfaces and all straight edges. If these surfaces are polygons, the solid is a **polyhedron.** Each polygon on the surface of a polyhedron is a **face.**

In Lesson 3.12, you found the surface area of a polyhedron by adding the areas of the polygons in its net. This method works for any polyhedron, but finding the net can be cumbersome. Now you will develop faster methods for two special special types of polyhedrons: prisms and pyramids.

> *Poly-* is from the Greek word for "many." What do you think *hedron* means?

risms

You may have used a glass object, called a prism, to separate light into the entire color spectrum. Here is an example of a right triangular prism.

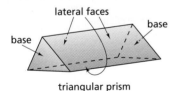

triangular prism

For Discussion

1. Answers may vary. Sample: Each solid has height, width, and depth. The second, fourth, sixth, and seventh solids have cross sections that are circles, while the others do not.

Lesson Overview

GOAL

- Interpret and use formulas for lateral areas and total surface areas of prisms, pyramids, cylinders, and cones.

This lesson introduces two solids, prisms and pyramids.

CHECK YOUR UNDERSTANDING

- Core: 1, 2, 3, 4

MATERIALS

- models of solids

HOMEWORK

- Core: 5, 6, 7, 8a–b, 9, 10
- Optional: 11, 12, 13
- Extension: 8c

VOCABULARY

- apex
- base
- face
- lateral face
- lateral surface area
- oblique (prism, pyramid)
- polyhedron
- prism
- pyramid
- right (prism, pyramid)

Launch

As with much of this investigation, your class time during this lesson will be mostly spent reviewing vocabulary and the different parts and characteristics of various solids.

Use the first For Discussion section to help students group the various solids into categories. One way that you might categorize these solids is into two groups: solids with flat faces and solids with curved faces.

Explore

Review vocabulary and the different parts and characteristics of prisms and pyramids.

PRISMS You may wish to have some models of various prisms to show your class as you discuss the features of this solid.

A triangular prism has two congruent triangular faces, one on each end. The other faces are quadrilaterals. (Are the lateral faces a special kind of quadrilateral? How do you know?) It is classified as a prism because the two triangles are in parallel planes. Each solid pictured below is also a prism. As you can see, the term *prism* identifies a wider range of solids than just those with triangles on the ends.

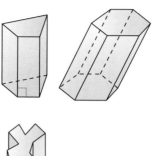

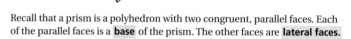

A prism base can have any shape or number of sides. A triskaidecagonal prism has a base with 13 sides. The third prism shown here is a triskaidecagonal prism.

Recall that a prism is a polyhedron with two congruent, parallel faces. Each of the parallel faces is a **base** of the prism. The other faces are **lateral faces.**

In Problem 1 of Lesson 3.12, you saw this right rectangular prism.

2 in.
3 in.
4 in.

The prism is rectangular because the bases are congruent rectangles. It is a **right prism** because its lateral edges are perpendicular to the bases. The bases are also congruent to each other. So all of the lateral faces of any right prism are rectangles.

Which pair of faces would be the bases in a right rectangular prism?

If the lateral edges are not perpendicular to the bases, the prism is called an **oblique prism.** The hexagonal prism shown above is oblique.

For Discussion

2. A lateral face of any prism must be a quadrilateral. How do you know? Is it any special kind of quadrilateral? For each of the four prisms shown above, determine the type of quadrilateral for each lateral face. Explain your answers.

Answers

For Discussion

2. Answers may vary. Sample: When you translate a segment and connect the corresponding endpoints of the original segment and the translated segment, you get four line segments; the lateral faces of any prism are parallelograms; since the first, third, and fourth prisms are all right prisms, they have rectangles as lateral faces. The second prism is oblique, so its faces are parallelograms, though as many as two faces may also be rectangles.

yramids

The pyramid is another special type of polyhedron.

Definitions

A **pyramid** is a polyhedron with one **base** that can be any polygon. The **lateral faces** are triangles that have a common vertex, the **apex** of the pyramid.

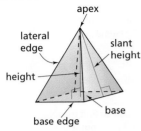

The Pyramid of Khufu in Giza, Egypt

The pyramids at Giza in Egypt are regular pyramids. They have a regular polygon (a square) for the base. These pyramids are also **right pyramids** because the line through the apex and the center of the base is perpendicular to the base.

> In a regular polygon, all sides are the same length. All angles of a regular polygon are congruent.

In an **oblique pyramid,** the line through the apex and the center of the base is not perpendicular to the base. Unless otherwise stated, you can assume in this book that a pyramid is a right regular pyramid.

oblique hexagonal pyramid

For Discussion

3. Show that the lateral faces of a square pyramid are congruent isosceles triangles.

4. Show that the lateral faces of an oblique square pyramid are not congruent triangles and are not all isosceles.

Facts and Notation

Total surface area and lateral surface area are distinct ideas. To find total surface area of a polyhedron, include the area of every face. To find the **lateral surface area,** include the area of every lateral face but not the area of any base.

> Why do we make this distinction? As you will soon see, the surface area formulas can be simplified more easily if you focus on just the lateral surface area.

For Discussion

3. Answers may vary. Sample: The height of the pyramid, the lateral edges, and the diagonals of the base form four triangles that are congruent by SAS. The lateral edges are congruent by CPCTC, so the four faces of the pyramid are all isosceles triangles. Since the base is a square, the four faces are also congruent to one another by SSS.

4. Since the height of an oblique square pyramid does not pass through the center of the base, at least one side of the square base is closer to the height of the pyramid than the side of the base opposite to it. Because of this, the triangles that have bases on these segments have different heights and are therefore not congruent to each other. Likewise, at least two opposite lateral faces have altitudes that do not bisect the base of the triangle. Therefore, the triangles are not isosceles.

PYRAMIDS After reviewing the definition of *pyramid*, point out the labeled parts of the figure. It is important that students understand the difference between the height and the slant height of a pyramid. Another name for the slant height is the altitude of the face. You should also point out that, even though it may not be stated, the pyramids in this investigation are right pyramids.

Wrap Up

Use the Facts and Notation section to point out the important difference between lateral surface area and total surface area. Then assign the Check Your Understanding exercises for in-class work.

Assessment Resources

Lesson Quiz 3.13

For Exercises 1 and 2, find the lateral and total surface areas of each solid.

1. a rectangular prism: base side lengths 2 and 6, height 8

2. a regular triangular pyramid: base side length 10, slant height 12

3. A regular hexagonal pyramid has a height of 12 in. and a base side length 4 in. Find its lateral area.

4. The total surface area of a square prism is 250 m². If a base side length is 5 m, what is the height of the prism?

Exercises

- Core: 5, 6, 7, 8a–b, 9, 10
- Optional: 11, 12, 13
- Extension: 8c

Check Your Understanding

EXERCISE 3 The slant height is a critical measurement when you find the surface area of a pyramid. Part (c) gives only the height of the pyramid, so students must find the slant height.

On Your Own

EXERCISE 5 In parts (b) and (c), students must use the given information and (b) the height and (c) the length of each edge of a square pyramid to find the surface area of the pyramid. Students must first determine the slant height of the pyramid. In each case, there is a right triangle in the pyramid with hypotenuse that is the slant height of the pyramid. These right triangles may be difficult to visualize, though. Encourage students to sketch a picture and label what they know and what information they want to find.

EXERCISE 9 has students derive the formulas for the surface areas of various geometric solids. However, students do not need to memorize these formulas. There are very few problems for which these results would be helpful, and the formulas are not difficult to derive. It is more efficient to derive the formula when you need it, rather than memorize it.

Answers

Exercises

1. **a.** 45 cm^2
   b. 60 cm^2
   c. 75 cm^2
   d. 15n cm^2

2. Exercise 1a: $\left(45 + \frac{25\sqrt{3}}{2}\right)$cm^2

   Exercise 1b: 110 cm^2

3. **a.** 36 cm^2
   b. 48 cm^2
   c. 60 cm^2

4. Exercise 3a: $(36 + 9\sqrt{3})$ cm^2;
   Exercise 3b: 84 cm^2; Exercise 3c: 96 cm^2

Check Your Understanding

1. Each of the following prisms is right and regular. The side length of each base is 5 cm. The height of each prism is 3 cm. Find the lateral surface area of each prism.
   a. a triangular prism
   b. a square prism
   c. a pentagonal prism
   d. an *n*-gonal prism (a base has *n* sides)

2. With your current knowledge and experience, you are able to find the total surface area for some of the polyhedrons in Exercise 1. Figure out which ones. Then find their total surface areas.

3. Each pyramid described below has a base with side length 6 cm. Find the lateral surface area of each prism.
   a. a triangular pyramid with slant height 4 cm
   b. a square pyramid with slant height 4 cm
   c. a square pyramid with height 4 cm

4. With your current knowledge and experience, you are able to find the total surface area for some of the polyhedrons in Exercise 3. Figure out which ones. Then find their total surface areas.

On Your Own

5. The Pyramid of Kukulcán at Chichén Itzá in Mexico (shown here) is a square pyramid. To the nearest foot, its base has side length 180 feet. Its height is 98 feet.
   a. What is the slant height of a square pyramid with base length 180 ft and height 98 ft?
   b. What is the lateral surface area of such a pyramid?
   c. If the pyramid is made from blocks 1 ft by 1 ft by 3 ft, estimate how many blocks are on the outside of the pyramid. Assume that the side of a block facing outward measures 1 ft by 3 ft.

5. **a.** $2\sqrt{4426}$ ft $\approx$ 133 ft
   b. $720\sqrt{4426}$ ft^2 $\approx$ 47900 ft^2
   c. $240\sqrt{4426} \approx 15{,}967$

6. **a.** $SA = b^2 + 2bs$, where SA is surface area, b is the side length of the base, and s is the slant height
   b. $SA = b^2 + b\sqrt{b^2 + 4h^2}$, where SA is surface area, b is the side length of the base, and h is the height
   c. $SA = b^2 + b\sqrt{4c^2 - b^2}$, where SA is surface area, b is the side length of the base, and c is the

   length of an edge connecting the apex to a vertex of the base

7. **a.** $\frac{3}{2}$ ft
   b. 4 cm by 4 cm by 8 cm
   c. $(24 + 3\sqrt{3})$ in.^{2}

8. **a.** 6 m
   b. The base is $4\sqrt{2}$ cm by $4\sqrt{2}$ cm, and the slant height is $8\sqrt{2}$ cm.
   c. $\frac{3\sqrt{67} + 3\sqrt{3}}{2}$ in.^{2}

9. **a.** $SA = \sqrt{3}s^2$
   b. $SA = 6s^2$
   c. $SA = 2\sqrt{3}s^2$
   d. $SA = 5\sqrt{3}s^2$

6. In a square pyramid, find the total surface area if you know the length of a side of the base square and each of the following.

  a. the slant height   **b.** the height

  c. the length of each edge

7. a. The total surface area of a right rectangular prism is 119 square feet. Its base measures 5 feet by 8 feet. What is its height?

  b. Another right rectangular prism has total surface area 160 cm². It has a square base and is twice as tall as it is wide. What are its dimensions?

  c. **Take It Further** A right, regular hexagonal prism has height 4 in. Its base has side length 1 in. What is its total surface area?

8. a. The total surface area of a square pyramid is 84 m². It has a slant height of 4 m. How wide is its base?

  b. Another square pyramid has total surface area 160 cm². It has a slant height equal to twice the side length of its base. What are its dimensions?

  c. **Take It Further** A hexagonal pyramid has height 4 in. Its base has side length 1 in. What is its total surface area?

9. Write a formula for the total surface area of each given solid. Let *s* be the length of an edge.

  a. tetrahedron   **b.** cube

  c. octahedron   **d.** icosahedron

10. **Standardized Test Prep** What is the lateral surface area of a right square pyramid with base edge length 12 cm and height 8 cm?

  A. 192 cm²   **B.** 240 cm²

  C. 346.13 cm²   **D.** 384 cm²

Maintain Your Skills

In Exercises 11–13, assume that each cube is 1 inch on a side.

11. If you connect two cubes face to face, all the polyhedrons you form will be congruent. Sketch the resulting polyhedron. Find its surface area. Is it a prism? A pyramid?

12. If you connect three cubes face to face, you can form two different polyhedrons. Sketch both polyhedrons. Find their total surface areas. Is either a prism? A pyramid?

13. If you connect four cubes face to face, you can form six different polyhedrons. Sketch the polyhedrons. Find their total surface areas. Identify any prisms or pyramids.

Go Online
PHSchool.com

For additional practice, go to **Web Code: bea-0313**

Any other polyhedron you make will be congruent to one of these two.

Additional Resources

PRINT RESOURCES
- Solution Manual
- Practice Workbook
- Assessment Resources
- Teaching Resources

TECHNOLOGY
- Interactive Textbook
- TeacherExpress CD-ROM
- **Exam**View CD-ROM
- **PHSchool.com**
  - Additional Practice
  - Mid-Chapter and Chapter Tests
  - Video Tutors
  - Vocabulary Puzzles

Additional Practice

Find the lateral and total surface areas for each figure.

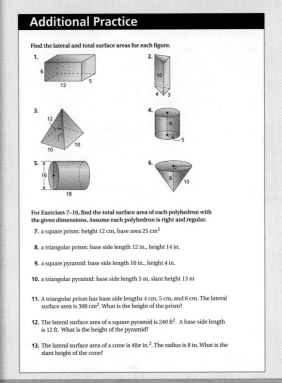

For Exercises 7–10, find the total surface area of each polyhedron with the given dimensions. Assume each polyhedron is right and regular.

7. a square prism: height 12 cm, base area 25 cm²

8. a triangular prism: base side length 12 in., height 14 in.

9. a square pyramid: base side length 10 in., height 4 in.

10. a triangular pyramid: base side length 5 m, slant height 13 m

11. A triangular prism has base side lengths 4 cm, 5 cm, and 6 cm. The lateral surface area is 300 cm². What is the height of the prism?

12. The lateral surface area of a square pyramid is 240 ft². A base side length is 12 ft. What is the height of the pyramid?

13. The lateral surface area of a cone is 48π in². The radius is 8 in. What is the slant height of the cone?

Practice: For Lesson 3.13, assign Exercises 1–12.

10. B

11.

The polyhedron is a prism. Its surface area is 10 in.²

12.

Both polyhedra are prisms, and both have a surface area of 14 in.²

13.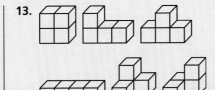

The first figure has surface area 16 in.². All the others have surface area 18 in.². The first four polyhedra are prisms. None are pyramids.

Lesson Overview

GOALS

- Find surface area of a solid using a net.
- Interpret and use formulas for lateral areas and surface areas of prisms, pyramids, cylinders, and cones.

Consider taking two days to complete this lesson. On the first day, review students' work with prisms and pyramids from the previous lesson, and work through the material on cylinders. On the second day, work through the material on cones. See the Daily Planner at the beginning of the chapter for suggested homework assignments.

This lesson has students look at another category of solids: cylinders and cones. Students find the lateral suface area and total surface area of these solids.

CHECK YOUR UNDERSTANDING
- Core: 1, 2, 3
- Optional: none

MATERIALS
- models of solids
- $8\frac{1}{2}$ in.-by-11 in. paper

HOMEWORK
- Core: 4, 5, 6, 7, 8, 9
- Optional: 13, 14, 15
- Extension: 10, 11, 12

VOCABULARY
- apex
- base
- circumference
- cone
- cylinder
- frustum
- lateral surface
- perimeter
- pi, π

Launch

Begin by discussing the differences and similarities between prisms, pyramids, cylinders, and cones.

Explore

CYLINDERS After reviewing the definition of cylinder, discuss the margin note about oblique cylinders. Remind students that the cylinders in this lesson are right cylinders, even if the text does not specifically state this fact. Have your class read the Minds in Action section. Use the first For Discussion section to summarize. Then go over the Developing Habits of Mind section, which points out the similarities between the formulas for lateral surface areas of a cylinder and a prism.

3.14 Surface Area: Cylinders and Cones

You started this investigation by looking at polyhedrons—solids with polygonal faces. Now you will look at some common solids that have rounded edges.

Cylinders

Definitions

> A **cylinder** is a solid with two congruent parallel circles as its **bases**, joined by a curved, smooth **lateral surface.**

A cylinder is like a prism, in that it has two congruent, parallel bases. But those bases are circles. Also, the lateral surface is curved. So a cylinder is not a polyhedron.

How do you find the surface area of a cylinder?

Like prisms or pyramids, cylinders can be either right or oblique, as shown below.

The cylinders in this book will be right cylinders unless stated otherwise.

Minds in Action   episode 8

Derman and Tony are trying to figure out the lateral surface area of a cylinder.

Derman   I only know how to find the lateral surface area of a polyhedron. You add the areas of the faces that aren't bases. But a cylinder isn't a polyhedron. So how am I supposed to start?

Tony   Remember when we started talking about surface area? We started with nets. We talked about unfolding a cube into a net, and looking at the faces? Well, what happens if we unfold a cylinder?

Derman   Unfold? Yeah, I think we did this before.

Tony   Yes, back in Chapter 1. When we made a net for a cylinder, the curved sides made a rectangle.

Derman   Right! You don't unfold the cylinder, you *unroll* it. So it just comes down to finding the area of that unrolled rectangle: length times width.

Tony   But what are the length and the width?

For Discussion

1. What are the length and width of the rectangle that is formed when you unroll the lateral surface of a cylinder?

Developing Habits of Mind

Generalize. When you unroll a cylinder, you see a net like the one on the left. You can unfold a right prism in the same way—keeping all the lateral faces together. For a triangular prism, you get the net on the right.

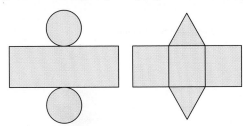

The lateral surfaces look alike—one large rectangle. You should be able to make a general formula that works for both types of solids.

The measure of the right and left sides of each rectangle is the same as the *height* of the solid before you unfolded it. The top and bottom edges of the rectangle went around the base of the solid. For the triangular prism, the length of the rectangle is the perimeter of the triangle. For the cylinder, the length of the rectangle is the circumference of the circle.

With this in mind, you can write one formula for the lateral surface area of both a prism and a cylinder.

lateral surface area (LA) = Ph,

where P is the perimeter (or circumference) of the base, and h is the height of the solid.

Remember...

Even though they are different words, **perimeter** and **circumference** measure the same thing—the length of the border of a two-dimensional shape.

To find the total surface area for a cylinder (or a prism), add the area of the bases to the lateral surface area.

Remember...

The circumference of a circle is $2\pi r$. The area of a circle is πr^2. In both of these formulas, r is the radius of the circle. Pi (π) is the infinite nonrepeating decimal constant that begins 3.14159. . . .

For You to Do

Sketch each solid. Find its lateral surface area. Find its total surface area.

2. a right square prism with base edge length 5 cm and lateral edge length 9 cm

3. a cylinder with base radius 4 in. and height 7 in.

4. A right triangular prism has bases that are isosceles triangles. The base of each triangle is 6 feet. The height of each triangle is 4 feet. A lateral edge of the prism is 20 feet.

For You to Do

Students most likely know the formulas for the area and circumference of a circle, and have worked with π in previous courses. Point out the margin note about these formulas. In Chapter 5, students will formally treat the area and circumference of a circle.

Answers

For Discussion

1. The length and width are the circumference of the base of the cylinder and the height of the cylinder.

For You to Do

2. $LA = 180 \text{ cm}^2$, $SA = 230 \text{ cm}^2$

3. $LA = 56\pi \text{ in.}^2$, $SA = 8\pi \text{ in.}^2$

4. $LA = 320 \text{ ft}^2$, $SA = 344 \text{ ft}^2$

CONES Review the definition of *cone*. Point out the names of the labeled parts in the corresponding figure. Note that the names of the labeled parts are the same as those in a pyramid.

Work through the Example, which shows how to make a net from an "unrolled" cone. The margin note on the following page states the circumference and area formulas for a circle.

The For Discussion and For You to Do sections that follow help summarize the work that the Example presents.

Cones

Definitions

A **cone** is a solid with one **base** that is a circle and a curved, smooth **lateral surface** that comes to a point, the **apex.**

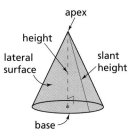

A cone has a curved lateral surface, so it is not a polyhedron. Even so, a cone is like a pyramid because it has a single base, and the lateral surface comes to a point at a vertex opposite the base. The difference is that the base is a circle.

How do you find the surface area of a cone? You can start by studying a net for a cone, just as Tony and Derman did with a cylinder.

Example

Problem Find the lateral surface area of this cone.

Solution First, slice the cone from the apex to the base. Lay out the lateral surface to get a net. The edge of the cone's base becomes the curved edge shown here. (The base of the cone is omitted from this diagram.)

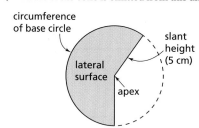

The lateral surface area of the cone is the area of the portion of the circle shown above.

You have

$$\frac{\text{lateral surface area of cone}}{\text{area of circle}} = \frac{\text{edge length of portion of circle}}{\text{circumference of circle}}$$

The edge length of the portion of the circle is the circumference of the base of the cone. Therefore,

$$\frac{\text{lateral suface area of cone}}{(\pi 5^2)} = \frac{\text{circumference of base of cone}}{2\pi(5)} = \frac{2\pi(3)}{2\pi(5)}$$

$$\text{lateral surface area of cone} = \frac{3}{5}\pi(5^2)$$

$$= 15\pi$$

Remember...

For a circle of radius r, the circumference is $2\pi r$. The area is πr^2.

For Discussion

5. A cone has base radius r and slant height ℓ. Find a formula for the lateral surface area.

6. A cone has base circumference C and slant height ℓ. Find a formula for the lateral surface area.

For You to Do

Use either formula you found in Problems 5 and 6. Find the lateral surface area of the cone with the given measurements.

7. base diameter 5 m, slant height 12 m

8. base radius 3 mm, slant height 5 mm

9. base circumference 4π in., slant height 3 in.

Developing Habits of Mind

Make and verify a conjecture. Earlier in this lesson, you used the idea that the perimeter of a polygon and the circumference of a circle measure the same thing. You found that for the lateral surface area of both a prism and a cylinder,

$$LA = Ph$$

where P is the perimeter (or circumference) of the base and h is the height of the solid.

In the For Discussion above, you found a formula for the lateral surface area of a cone based on its circumference and slant height. What conjecture can you make about a possible formula for the lateral surface area of a pyramid based on its base perimeter and slant height?

For Discussion

Note that having students memorize these formulas is not as important as whether they can derive the formulas. Students should be able to find the lateral surface area of the cone by deconstructing it.

Answers

For Discussion

5. $LA = \pi r \ell$
6. $LA = \frac{1}{2}C\ell$

For You to Do

7. 30π m^2
8. 15π mm^2
9. 6π in.^{2}

Wrap Up

Use the second Developing Habits of Mind section and the For Discussion section that follows to help students make the connections between the formulas for the lateral surface areas of right prisms and cylinders and of right pyramids and cones.

Assessment Resources

Lesson Quiz 3.14

For Exercises 1–4, find the lateral and total surface areas of each solid.

1. a cylinder: diameter 14, height 12

2. a cylinder: radius 6, height 10

3. a cone: radius 8, height 15

4. a cone: diameter 8, height 16

5. A cone has radius 15 m and height 20 m. A cylinder has the same height and the same lateral surface area as the cone. What is the radius of the cylinder?

For a triangular pyramid with slant height ℓ and a base with side length s,

$$LA = \tfrac{1}{2} s\ell + \tfrac{1}{2} s\ell + \tfrac{1}{2} s\ell$$
$$= \tfrac{1}{2}(3s)\ell$$
$$= \tfrac{1}{2} P\ell$$

where P is the perimeter of the base.

For Discussion

10. Explain how the formula $LA = \tfrac{1}{2} P\ell$ extends to any kind of pyramid.

In this book, you can assume that a pyramid is a right regular pyramid.

Facts and Notation

Here are the simplified formulas for lateral surface area of special solids. P is the perimeter or circumference of the base, h is the height of the prism or cylinder, and ℓ is the slant height of the pyramid or cone.

Right prisms and cylinders: $LA = Ph$

Right pyramids and cones: $LA = \tfrac{1}{2}P\ell$

Exercises *Practicing Habits of Mind*

Check Your Understanding

1. Right square prism A has a base edge length 2 m. Right square prism B has a base edge length $\sqrt{2}$ m. Cylinder C has base radius 1 m. Each shape has height 4 m.

   a. Find the lateral surface area of each shape.

   b. Which shape has the least total surface area? The greatest total surface area?

   c. Draw three bases for the shapes so that they all have the same center. How are they related? Does this agree with your results for part (b)?

Answers

For Discussion

10. You do not need to know how many sides the base of the pyramid has. All you need to know is the perimeter of the base and the slant height of the pyramid.

Exercises

1. a. 32 m^2; 16$\sqrt{2}$ m^2; 8π m^2

   b. Prism B; Prism A

   c. Cylinder C is inside Prism A. Prism B is inside Cylinder C; yes.

2. a. 4$\sqrt{17}$ m^2

   b. 2$\sqrt{33}$ m^2

   c. $\pi\sqrt{17}$ m^2

3. a. 168π cm^2; 84π cm^2; 96π cm^2

   b. Cone B; Cylinder A

4. a. 168π ft^2; 266π ft^2

   b. 168π ft^2; 456π ft^2

   c. 156π ft^2; 192π ft^2

   d. 156π ft^2; 198.25π ft^2

2. In Exercise 1, replace "prism" with "pyramid." Replace "cylinder" with "cone." Do part (a).

3. Cylinder A has a height of 8 cm. Cone B has a slant height of 8 cm. Cone C has a height of 8 cm. Each shape has a base radius of 6 cm.

   a. Find the total surface area of each shape.

   b. Which shape has the least total surface area? The greatest total surface area?

On Your Own

4. Find the lateral and total surface areas for the solids described.

   a. a right circular cylinder: radius 7 ft, height 12 ft

   b. a right circular cylinder: radius 12 ft, height 7 ft

   c. a right circular cone: diameter 12 cm, slant height 13 cm

   d. a right circular cone: diameter 13 cm, slant height 12 cm

5. You can make two different cylinders by taping together opposite edges of a standard $8\frac{1}{2}$ in.-by-11 in. sheet of paper. (You tape together either the two short edges or the two long edges.) For each cylinder, find the radius, height, lateral surface area, and total surface area (including bases).

6. A cone has base radius 15 cm and height 20 cm. A cylinder has the same height and the same lateral surface area as the cone. What is the radius of the cylinder?

7. A cylinder has base radius 10 cm and height 20 cm. A cone has a base congruent to that of the cylinder and the same lateral surface area as the cylinder. What is the height of the cone?

8. **What's Wrong Here?** Tony and Sasha were making up problems so they could practice finding surface area. They made up one problem that asked for the lateral surface area of a cone with radius 13 cm and slant height 5 cm.

   a. Sasha said, "Hey! Wait a minute! This cone isn't possible!" Draw a picture to show why.

   b. Tony said, "You're right. But I think we *can* have a cone with radius 13 cm and height 5 cm." Find the slant height of this cone. Then find its lateral surface area.

   c. What does this exercise tell you about how the slant height and the radius of a cone are related?

9. **Standardized Test Prep** What is the lateral surface area of an ice cream cone with diameter 3 in. and height 4 in.?

   A. 18.85 in.^{2} B. 37.70 in.^{2}

   C. 40.26 in.^{2} D. 47.12 in.^{2}

---

5. shorter cylinder: $r = \frac{11}{2\pi}$ in.,

   $h = 8.5$ in., $LA = 93.5$ in.^{2},

   $SA = \left(93.5 + \frac{121}{2\pi}\right)$ in.^{2};

   taller cylinder: $r = \frac{17}{4\pi}$ in.,

   $h = 11$ in., $LA = \left(93.5 \text{ in.}^2,\right.$

   $SA = 93.5 + \frac{289}{8\pi}\left.\right)$ in.^{2}

6. 8.625 cm

7. $10\sqrt{15}$ cm

8. a. See back of book.

   b. $\sqrt{194}$ cm; $13\pi\sqrt{194}$ cm^2

   c. In any right cone, the slant height is greater than the radius.

9. D

On Your Own

EXERCISE 4 allows students to get practice computing surface areas of cylinders and cones. Students see how the radius and height (or slant height) affect the lateral surface area and the total surface area of each solid.

EXERCISE 8 has students think more deeply about what appears to be a simple computation. Although it is possible to substitute the values given in this exercise into the formula for the lateral surface area of a cone in order to get the result, that result is meaningless because the cone that the exercise describes does not really exist. This exercise helps students think about the limitations inherent in the definition of a cone. As with the sides of a triangle, not just any measurements are possible.

EXERCISE 10 In Exercise 8, students discovered that a cone with radius 13 cm and slant height 5 cm does not exist. However, a frustum with those same dimensions does exist. Students can think of a frustum as the solid that results when the slant height of a cone is too short to reach the apex of the cone. So instead of having an apex, a frustum has a circular face. Students visualize and generalize to draw conclusions about the dimensions of the given frustum.

EXERCISES 11 AND 12 In these exercises, students begin to consider the limitations on the dimensions of a given frustum. It is a critical mathematical habit of mind to be able to visualize and consider extreme cases. Students who will study calculus will find this skill very handy.

EXERCISE 11 Part (c) has students consider the frustum in which the radii of the top and bottom circular faces are equal. This special case of the frustum is a cylinder.

EXERCISE 12 asks students to consider another special case of the frustum—the cone.

Additional Resources

PRINT RESOURCES
- Solution Manual
- Practice Workbook
- Assessment Resources
- Teaching Resources

TECHNOLOGY
- Interactive Textbook
- TeacherExpress CD-ROM
- **Exam**_View_ CD-ROM
- PHSchool.com
  – Additional Practice
  – Mid-Chapter and Chapter Tests
  – Video Tutors
  – Vocabulary Puzzles

Additional Practice

Find the lateral and total surface areas for each figure.

1.

2.

3.

4.

5.

6.

For Exercises 7–10, find the total surface area of each polyhedron with the given dimensions. Assume each polyhedron is right and regular.

7. a square prism: height 12 cm, base area 25 cm²

8. a triangular prism: base side length 12 in., height 14 in.

9. a square pyramid: base side length 10 in., height 4 in.

10. a triangular pyramid: base side length 5 m, slant height 13 m

11. A triangular prism has base side lengths 4 cm, 5 cm, and 6 cm. The lateral surface area is 300 cm². What is the height of the prism?

12. The lateral surface area of a square pyramid is 240 ft². A base side length is 12 ft. What is the height of the pyramid?

13. The lateral surface area of a cone is 48π in.². The radius is 8 in. What is the slant height of the cone?

Practice: For Lesson 3.14, assign Exercise 13.

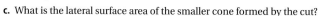

Cut a cone parallel to its base to get two pieces as in the diagram. The top piece is a new, smaller cone. The bottom piece is a **frustum.**

} frustum

10. **Take It Further** A frustum has bottom radius 12 cm, top radius 9 cm, and height 4 cm.

    a. What is the slant height of the frustum?

    b. What was the slant height of the original cone before the cut? (*Hint:* Draw a cross section of the original cone. Think about the slope of a line.)

    c. What is the lateral surface area of the smaller cone formed by the cut?

    d. What is the lateral surface area of the frustum?

    e. What is the total surface area of the frustum?

11. **Take It Further** Many different frustums have a bottom radius of 13 cm and a slant height of 5 cm. The radius of the top of these frustums must fall within a certain range of values.

    a. How small can the radius of the top circle be?

    b. How large can the radius of the top circle be? (Remember that even though the bottom circle has radius 13 cm, that does not necessarily mean that it is the larger circular end of the frustum.)

    c. Think of a frustum with its top circle halfway between the two extremes. There is a special name for this frustum. What is it?

12. **Take It Further** If you had a frustum with one of the circles having radius 0, what else could you call this shape?

Maintain Your Skills

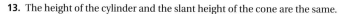

A cylinder and a cone have the same radius. What is the ratio of the lateral surface area of the cylinder to the lateral surface area of the cone for each given condition?

13. The height of the cylinder and the slant height of the cone are the same.

14. The cylinder and cone have the same height.

15. The cylinder and the cone have the same base and the same lateral surface area. What is the ratio of the height of the cylinder to the slant height of the cone?

Go Online
PHSchool.com

For additional practice, go to Web Code: bea-0314

Answers

10. a. 5 cm
    b. 20 cm
    c. 135π cm²
    d. 105π cm²
    e. 330π cm²

11. a. 8 cm
    b. 18 cm
    c. a cylinder

12. a cone

13. $\frac{2}{1}$

14. $\frac{2h}{\sqrt{r^2 + h^2}}$

15. $\frac{1}{2}$

15 Volumes of Solids

Now you will explore the **volumes** of some special solids.

Prisms and Cylinders

The first volume you encountered was probably that of a box (a right rectangular prism). You likely think of volume as the following formula.

$$\text{volume} = \text{length} \times \text{width} \times \text{height}$$

This formula works well for a right rectangular prism. But will it work for other solids?

Volume is measured in cubic units, such as cubic meters (m^3), cubic centimeters (cm^3), cubic feet (ft^3), and cubic inches ($in.^3$). When you measure the volume of a solid, you are trying to determine how many cubes of a particular size would fit inside the solid. The process is similar to how you measure area in Lesson 3.7.

> You sometimes see the abbreviation "cc" for cubic centimeter (cm^3), often for medicine and motorcycles.

Suppose you have a box that is 4 in. long, 3 in. wide, and 2 in. tall.

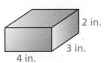

You can draw a number of cubes inside the box, each with a side length of 1 in. Then you can count how many cubes fill the box.

 Each cube measures 1 in. by 1 in. by 1 in.

When you say the volume of the box is 24 cubic inches, you mean that you can fit 24 cubes, each with side length 1 inch, inside the box.

24 cubes fill the box.

Lesson Overview

GOAL

• Interpret and use formulas for volumes of prisms, pyramids, cylinders, and cones.

This lesson has students explore the volumes of special solids: prisms, cylinders, pyramids, and cones.

CHECK YOUR UNDERSTANDING
• Core: 1, 2, 3

MATERIALS
• card stock
• rice or dry sand
• tape
• Blackline Masters 3.15A–B

HOMEWORK
• Core: 4, 5, 6, 7, 8, 9
• Optional: 11, 13, 14, 15, 16
• Extension: 10, 12

VOCABULARY
• volume

Launch

Begin this lesson by asking your students what they already know about volume. Draw their attention to the discussion about cubic units.

Explore

PRISMS AND CYLINDERS Be sure to spend some time discussing the similarities between calculating the area and calculating the volume of a solid. The lesson presents a dissection argument for finding the volume of a prism.

Wrap Up

Draw students' attention to the list of volume formulas at the end of the lesson, but emphasize that they do not need to memorize it. They should remember the more general formulas $V = Bh$ and $V = \frac{1}{3}Bh$.

Assessment Resources

Problem Find the volume of this right triangular prism. The base is a right triangle.

7 ft
4 ft 3 ft

Solution The base of the prism is a right triangle. So you can take a copy of the prism and place it next to the original to make a box. And you know how to find the volume of the box! So all you have to do is find the volume of the box and divide by 2.

The volume of the box is length × width × height.

$$V_B = 3 \times 4 \times 7$$
$$= 84 \, \text{ft}^3$$

The volume of the original triangular prism is half of that.

$$V_P = \frac{84}{2}$$
$$= 42 \, \text{ft}^3$$

For You to Do

Find the volume of each right prism.

1. a right square prism with base side length 4 cm and height 100 cm

2. a right octagonal prism with base area 145 cm^2 and height 2 cm

3. a cube with side length 3 ft

4. a cylinder with base radius 1 in. and height 1 ft

Is it possible that the rules and formulas you learned earlier in this chapter will help you compute volume? Indeed, it is! Just like cutting a polygon and rearranging it leaves area unchanged, so cutting and rearranging a solid leaves volume unchanged. The diagrams show how to cut an oblique prism, rearrange the pieces, and make a right prism with the same volume.

Cut here.   Move over.

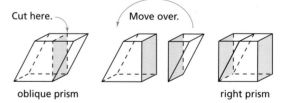

oblique prism   right prism

Answers

For You to Do

1. 1600 cm^3

2. 290 cm^3

3. 27 ft^3

4. π ft^3

When you find volume, you can use the same view of cylinders that helped you find surface area. Visualize a cylinder as a prism with many, many sides.

Here is a general formula for volume of prisms and cylinders.

acts and Notation *Volume of a Prism or Cylinder*

$$V = Bh$$

where B is the area of a base and h is the height.

acts and Notation

There are other units (besides cubic units) used to measure volume. These include fluid ounces, gallons, liters, and milliliters. You can define these units to be equal to specific cubic measurements. For example, a milliliter is the same amount as a cubic centimeter (1 mL = 1 cm^3). A gallon is exactly 231 cubic inches.

yramids and Cones

There is a relationship between the volumes of a pyramid and a prism when the two figures have the same height and base area.

n-Class Experiment

Estimating volume. In this experiment, you compare the volumes of a pyramid and a prism with the same base and height.

You will need rice or dry sand, 1 hollow square prism, and 1 hollow square pyramid. Both must have the same base area and height as well as an open base.

Fill the pyramid completely with the rice or sand. Then pour the contents of the pyramid into the prism. Continue to fill the pyramid and pour into the prism until the prism is full. Keep track of how many times you pour.

5. How many pyramids full of rice does the prism hold? How many times can you fill the pyramid from a full prism? Explain why your results suggest that a formula for the volume of a pyramid is

$$V = \frac{1}{3}Bh$$

In-Class Experiment

5. 3; the volume of the prism is Bh, so the volume of the pyramid is $\frac{1}{3}Bh$.

PYRAMIDS AND CONES You can have pairs or small groups of students perform the In-Class Experiment or you can do it as a demonstration. Blackline Masters 3.15A and 3.15B provide nets for a square prism and a square pyramid. You may want to enlarge the images on these masters before copying them onto cardstock and cutting them out. You will also need rice or dry sand to pour into the pyramid.

You may want your students to make their own nets for the practical experience of determining which measurements will work and deciding how to arrange the faces to make an appropriate net. Students can use geometry software to draw the nets once they determine the measurements of the pyramid and prism.

Here is another way to make sense of the formula for the volume of a pyramid. Take a cube and dissect it along its diagonals. You get 6 identical square pyramids.

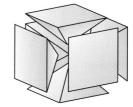

Since the pyramids are identical, they all have a volume that is $\frac{1}{6}$ that of the cube. The height of each pyramid is $h = \frac{1}{2}s$. The area of each base is $B = s^2$.

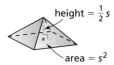

height $= \frac{1}{2}s$

area $= s^2$

The volume of the cube must be s^3, so the volume of each pyramid must be $\frac{1}{6}s^3$.

$$V = \frac{1}{6}s^3$$
$$= \frac{1}{3} \cdot \frac{1}{2} \cdot s \cdot s^2$$
$$= \frac{1}{3} \cdot s^2 \cdot \frac{1}{2}s$$
$$= \frac{1}{3}Bh$$

You can generalize this volume formula by visualizing a cone as a pyramid with a base of many, many sides.

Facts and Notation

In the following formulas, *B* is base area, and *h* is height of the solid.

Volume of prism or cylinder	Volume of pyramid or cone
$V = Bh$	$V = \frac{1}{3}Bh$

By substituting the area formulas for the bases, you have these common volume formulas:

Cube	$V = s^3$
Rectangular prism (box)	$V = \ell wh$
Cylinder	$V = \pi r^2 h$
Square pyramid	$V = \frac{1}{3}s^2 h$
Cone	$V = \frac{1}{3}\pi r^2 h$

Go Online
PHSchool.com

For a real-world example involving surface area and volume, go to
Web Code: bee-9031

Exercises *Practicing Habits of Mind*

Check Your Understanding

1. Find the volume of each solid.

   a. a right triangular prism with a base that is an equilateral triangle of side length 4 inches, and with a height that is 10 inches

   b. a square pyramid with height 3 ft and base side length 2 ft

   c. a cylinder with radius 12 cm and height 13 cm

   d. a cone with radius 12 cm and slant height 13 cm

2. A pyramid and a prism have the same regular hexagonal base and the same volume. The pyramid has a base with side length 4 in. and height 13 in. Find the dimensions of the prism.

3. A cylinder and a cone have the same height and the same volume. The radius of the cylinder is 9 cm. What is the radius of the cone?

On Your Own

4. You have some apple cider in a cylindrical pot that has a radius of 4 in. You pour cider from the pot into a cup that has a radius of $1\frac{1}{2}$ in. until the cider in the cup is 4 in. deep. How much did the level of cider in the pot go down?

5. A square prism and a cylinder have the same volume. The side length of the base of the prism is the same as the radius of the cylinder. The height of the prism is 7 cm. What is the height of the cylinder?

6. A factory has three cylindrical chimneys to release waste gases. Each chimney is 150 feet tall. The base of a chimney has a diameter of 15 feet. A can of paint can cover 100 square feet of surface. How many cans of paint are needed to paint the outsides of all three chimneys?

7. The factory in Exercise 6 needs to install filters inside the chimneys. The filter completely fills the interior of each chimney. The thickness of each chimney wall is $1\frac{1}{2}$ feet. How many cubic feet of filter is needed to fill the chimneys?

8. Sean is making a replica of the Washington Monument for history class. He decides to simplify the structure so that the replica resembles a square prism on the bottom and a square pyramid on the top. Sean's measurements are listed below.

   • The total height of the replica is 24 inches.

   • The height of the pyramid at the top is 4 inches.

   • The length of one side of the square base of the replica is 3 inches.

   What is the volume of Sean's model?

Exercises

HOMEWORK
• Core: 4, 5, 6, 7, 8, 9
• Optional: 11, 13, 14, 15
• Extension: 10, 12

Answers

Exercises

1. a. $40\sqrt{3}$ in.^{3}
   b. 4 ft^3
   c. 1872π cm^3
   d. 240π cm^3

2. The height of the prism is $\frac{13}{3}$ in.

3. $9\sqrt{3}$ cm

4. $\frac{9}{16}$ in.

5. $\frac{7}{\pi}$ cm

6. 213 cans

7. $16{,}200\pi$ ft^3

8. 192 in.^{3}

On Your Own

EXERCISE 12 Students will need to know the definition of *frustum* to complete this exercise. Have them refer to Exercises 10–12 in Lesson 3.14.

Additional Resources

PRINT RESOURCES
- Solution Manual
- Practice Workbook
- Assessment Resources
- Teaching Resources

TECHNOLOGY
- Interactive Textbook
- TeacherExpress CD-ROM
- **Exam**View CD-ROM
- **PHSchool.com**
  - Additional Practice
  - Mid-Chapter and Chapter Tests
  - Video Tutors
  - Vocabulary Puzzles

Additional Practice

For Exercises 1–6, find the volume of each figure.

1.

2. 14, 16

3. 17

4. 24, 10, 22

5. 8 10 8 10, 20, 40, 20

6. 10, 4, 15

7. A regular square pyramid has height 15 m and volume 1815 m³. What is the length of a base side?

8. A cylindrical water tower holds 100,000π cubic feet of water. The diameter of the tower is 100 feet. What is the height of the tower?

9. A cone fits inside a cylinder so that they share a base and have the same height. The radius of the base is 4 in. and the height of the cylinder and cone is 13 in. What is the volume of air between the cone and cylinder?

10. A farmer builds a rectangular storage shed large enough to hold 1000 bales of hay. A bale of hay is 4 ft by 2 ft by 1 ft.
   a. What is total volume of hay in 1000 bales?
   b. The base of the shed is 50 ft by 20 ft. What minimum shed height, floor to ceiling, allows the farmer to store 1000 bales?

11. The diameters of two water pipes of the same length are 6 in. and 8 in. A single pipe of the same length replaces the two pipes. The single pipe has the same volume as the two original pipes combined. What is the diameter of the new pipe?

Practice: For Lesson 3.15, assign Exercises 1–11.

---

9. Standardized Test Prep Chef Jasper's signature dessert is an individual carrot cake in the form of a right circular cone. The diameter of the cone is 3 in. and the height is 4 in. What is the approximate volume of carrot cake in each dessert?

A. 9.425 in.³   **B.** 12 in.³   **C.** 28.27 in.³   **D.** 37.70 in.³

10. Take It Further Margherite wants to make a more accurate replica of the Washington Monument. She determined the measurements as follows.

- The height of her replica is 22 inches.
- The length of one side of the square at the base of her replica is 2 inches.
- The length of one side of the square at the base of the pyramid at the top is $1\frac{3}{8}$ inches.
- The height of the pyramid is 2 inches.

Margherite has one quart of plaster. Does she have enough to make the model?

11. Terry wants to find out how much liquid a paper cup will hold. He measures the cup to be 4 inches high. The diameter of the bottom of the cup is 2 inches. The diameter of the top is 3 inches. How many fluid ounces of liquid can the cup hold?

12. Take It Further A tall cone has radius 5 m and height 9 m. A short cone has radius 9 m and height 5 m.

   a. Find the volume of each cone. Which has a greater volume, the tall cone or the short cone?

   b. Cut another cone off of the tip of the cone that has the greater volume. Your goal is to leave a frustum that has the same volume as the smaller of the two original cones. What must be the height of the cone you cut off?

Remember...

1 gal = 231 in.³
1 gal = 128 fl oz
1 gal = 4 qt

Maintain Your Skills

13. Find the volume and total surface area of a right rectangular prism that measures 1 cm by 2 cm by 4 cm.

14. Two other right rectangular prisms with whole number centimeter measurements have the same volume as the prism in Exercise 13. Find their dimensions and surface areas.

15. A right rectangular prism with whole-number centimeter dimensions has volume 7 cm³. What are its dimensions and total surface area?

16. Is it true that solids with greater volume have greater total surface area? If so, explain why. If not, provide a counterexample.

Go Online
PHSchool.com

For additional practice, go to Web Code: bea-0315

Answers

9. A

10. yes

11. $\frac{19}{3}\pi$ in.³

12. a. The volume of the tall cone is 75π m³. The volume of the short cone is 135π m³. The short cone has a greater volume.

   b. $5\sqrt[3]{\frac{4}{9}}$ m

13. 8 cm³; 28 cm²

14. 1 cm-by-1 cm-by-8 cm, 34 cm²; 2 cm-by-2 cm-by-2 cm, 24 cm²

15. 1 cm-by-1 cm-by-7 cm; 30 cm²

16. No; answers may vary. Sample: A 2 cm-by-2 cm-by-2 cm right regular prism has a volume of 8 cm³ and a surface area of 24 cm². A 1 cm-by-1 cm-by-7 cm right regular prism has a volume of 7 cm³ and a surface area of 30 cm².

3D

In this investigation, you found surface area and total area of solids by visualizing their nets. You also used formulas to calculate volumes. These questions will help you summarize what you have learned.

1. Draw a net for the regular tetrahedron shown at the right.

5 cm

2. What is the total surface area of a cylinder with diameter 108 cm and height 18 cm?

3. Two cones have slant height 8 in. The first has a radius of 4 in. The second cone has a diameter of 12 in. What is the ratio of their lateral surface areas?

4. Stephanie has a goldfish who lives in a tank like the one shown at the right. The cone juts up into the tank to give the fish something to swim around. How much water does Stephanie need to fill the tank? (Disregard the volume of the fish.)

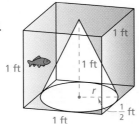

1 ft

1 ft

1 ft

r

$\frac{1}{2}$ ft

1 ft

5. How can you use perimeter and area of two-dimensional shapes to find surface area and volume of three-dimensional solids?

6. What is the relationship between a prism and a cylinder? Between a pyramid and a cone?

7. A cylinder and cone have the same base. The height of each is equal to the radius of its base. What is the ratio of their lateral surface areas?

Vocabulary

In this investigation, you learned these terms. Make sure you understand what each one means and how to use it.

- apex
- base
- circumference
- cone
- cylinder
- face
- frustum
- lateral faces
- lateral surface area
- oblique prism
- perimeter
- polyhedron
- pyramid
- right pyramid
- slant height
- surface area
- volume

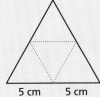

About how many cubic meters of earth have miners dug from this mine?

Mathematical Reflections

1.

5 cm   5 cm

2. 7776π cm^2

3. $\frac{2}{3}$

4. $\left(1 - \frac{\pi}{12}\right)$ ft^3, or about 0.7382 ft^3 (approximately $5\frac{1}{2}$ gal)

5. Answers may vary. Sample: For prisms and cylinders, use the product of the height of the solid and the perimeter of the base to calculate the lateral area. Add the areas of the bases to the product to calculate total surface area.

6. See back of book.

7. $\sqrt{2}$ or $\frac{\sqrt{2}}{2}$

Mathematical Reflections

EXERCISE 5–7: At the start of the investigation, you may have assigned these as Questions 1–3 for students to think and write about.

Surface Area and Volume of a Sphere

The formulas for volume and surface area of a sphere are difficult to justify without quite a bit more mathematics. But you do not have to let that stop you from making sense of the formulas and using them.

Materials

paper, pencil, large orange

Surface Area

It might make sense to compare the surface area of a sphere to another round area we know—the area of a circle. Try this experiment:

- Cut in half an orange that is nearly spherical. Estimate your cut so that it passes through the center of the orange.

- Place a half of the orange cut-side side down on a piece of paper. Trace around it, making several copies of a great circle for your sphere.

- Peel the orange halves. Fit the pieces of peel into the circles you traced. How many circles can you fill?

1. Use the results of your experiment with the orange. Estimate the surface area of a sphere by comparing it to the area of a circle with the same radius. What formula for the surface area of a sphere would you write from your estimate?

Volume

To make sense of the formula for the volume of a sphere, you can compare it to formulas for the volumes of some other solids you know how to measure. If you find a solid that can contain the sphere, you will know that the sphere's volume is less than the solid. Then, if you find another solid that can fit inside the sphere, the sphere's volume must be greater.

2. Find the dimensions of the largest double cone—two cones joined at the base—that can be contained by a sphere of radius r. Then find the volume of the double cone. What can you conclude about the volume of the sphere?

3. Find the dimensions of the smallest cylinder that could contain a sphere of radius r. Then find the volume of that cylinder. What can you conclude about the volume of the sphere?

Although you have not derived the formula for the volume of a sphere, you can see that formula (given below) is at least within the limits you found in Problems 2 and 3.

Here are the formulas for a sphere.

The volume of a sphere is

$$V = \frac{4}{3}\pi r^3$$

The surface area of a sphere is

$$SA = 4\pi r^2$$

4. Find the surface area of a sphere with volume 10 cm³.

Answers

Project

1. $SA = 4\pi r^2$

2. For both cones, the radius of the base and the height are equal to the radius of the sphere; $\frac{2}{3}\pi r^3$; the volume of the sphere is greater than the volume of the double cone.

3. The radius of the cylinder is r and the height of the cylinder is $2r$;

$2\pi r^3$; the volume of the sphere is less than the volume of the cylinder.

4. $4\pi\left(\sqrt[3]{\dfrac{15}{2\pi}}\right)^2$ cm² ≈ 22.45 cm²

Find the volume of a sphere with surface area 10 cm².

A cylindrical steel pipe is 12 feet long. It has an outer diameter of 4 inches and an inner diameter of $3\frac{3}{4}$ inches.

a. What is the volume of the steel that makes up the pipe in cubic inches?

b. What is the volume of the largest sphere that could fit inside the pipe?

c. What is the surface area of that largest sphere?

a. Find the volume and surface area of a sphere with radius 8 in.

b. A cylinder has the same volume and radius as the sphere in part (a). Find its height and surface area.

c. A cone has the same volume and radius as the sphere in part (b). Find its height and surface area.

d. Which of the solids of equal radius has the most surface area for the same amount of volume?

Tennis balls are often sold in cans of three. The tennis balls are stacked inside a cylindrical can that fits tightly around them. Which distance is greater, the height of the can or the circumference of the can?

9. a. Suppose you double the radius of a cone but leave the height unchanged. How will the volume of the new cone compare to that of the original?

b. Suppose you double the radius of a cylinder but leave the height unchanged. How will the volume of the new cylinder compare to that of the original?

c. Suppose you double the radius of a sphere. How will the volume of the new sphere compare to that of the original?

10. A cone for ice cream has diameter 3 in. and height 5 in. The cone is completely filled with ice cream. There is a hemisphere of ice cream balanced on the base of the cone. Its diameter is also 3 in. What is the approximate volume of the ice cream?

11. A certain cold medicine comes in a capsule that is 20 mm long. The capsule shape is a cylinder of diameter 6 mm, with a hemisphere on each end. Each hemisphere also has diameter 6 mm. What is the volume available for the medicine inside the capsule?

Sections of a sphere were the basis for the roof design of the Opera House in Sydney, Australia.

5. $\frac{4}{3}\pi\left(\sqrt{\frac{5}{2\pi}}\right)^3$ cm² ≈ 2.97 cm²

6. a. $\frac{279}{4}\pi$ in.³ ≈ 219.13 in.³

b. $\frac{1125}{128}\pi$ in.³ ≈ 27.61 in.³

c. $\frac{225}{16}\pi$ in.² ≈ 44.18 in.²

7. a. $\frac{2048}{3}\pi$ in.³ ≈ 2144.66 in.³; 256π in.² ≈ 804.25 in.²

b. $\frac{32}{3}$ in. ≈ 10.67 in.; $\frac{896}{3}\pi$ in.² ≈ 938.29 in.²

c. 32 in.; $64\pi(\sqrt{17} + 1)$ in.² ≈ 1030.06 in.²

d. the cone

8. the circumference

9. a. The new volume is 4 times the original volume.

b. The new volume is 4 times the original volume.

c. The new volume is 8 times the original volume.

10. about 19 in.³

11. 162π mm³ ≈ 509 mm³

Go Online
PHSchool.com

For vocabulary review,
go to Web Code: bej-0351

In **Investigation 3A** you learned to

- change one shape into another by making cuts and rearranging the parts

- tell when two shapes are scissors-congruent

- prove the Midline Theorem using cuts and rearrangement

  The following questions will help you check your understanding.

1. Describe an algorithm for dissecting this trapezoid into a rectangle.

2. In △*ABC*, call *M* the midpoint of $\overline{AC}$. Draw ℓ, the parallel line to $\overline{BC}$ through *M*. The intersection of ℓ with $\overline{AB}$ is *F*. Mark point *E* (different from *F*) on ℓ such that *EM* = *MF*, and connect *E* and *C*. Prove the following.

   a. $\overline{EC} \parallel \overline{AB}$

   b. *BCEF* is a parallelogram.

   c. $FM = \frac{1}{2}BC$

In **Investigation 3B** you learned to

- calculate the area of a parallelogram, of a triangle, and of a trapezoid

- prove the formulas for calculating the areas above

- tell the difference between two figures being scissors-congruent and having the same area

  The following questions will help you check your understanding.

3. In trapezoid *ABCD*, $\overline{AB} \parallel \overline{CD}$. What is the area of trapezoid *ABCD*?

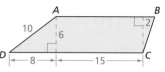

4. What is the area of this pentagon?

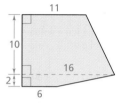

5. If two rectangles have the same area, are they scissors-congruent? Explain.

Answers

Review

1. Answers may vary. Sample: Mark the midpoints *M* and *N* of the nonparallel sides. Draw lines through *M* and *N* perpendicular to the parallel sides. Two triangles will be formed. Rotate each triangle 180° about the midpoint that it has as a vertex.

2. **a.** $\overline{AM} \cong \overline{CM}$ because *M* is the midpoint of $\overline{AC}$. $\overline{FM} \cong \overline{EM}$ by construction. ∠*AMF* ≅ ∠*CME* by the Vertical Angle Theorem. Therefore △*AFM* ≅ △*CEM* by SAS. This means that △*FAM* ≅ △*ECM* by CPCTC, and $\overline{EC} \parallel \overline{AB}$ by AIP.

   b. $\overline{BC} \parallel \overline{FE}$ by construction, and $\overline{EC} \parallel \overline{FB}$ by part (a). Therefore *BCEF* is a parallelogram.

   c. Because △*AFM* ≅ △*CEM*, you know that $\overline{EC} \cong \overline{AF}$. Because *BCEF* is a parallelogram, you know that $\overline{EC} \cong \overline{FB}$. Therefore $\overline{AF} \cong \overline{FB}$, and *F* is the midpoint

In Investigation 3C you learned to

- follow the logical reasoning and fill in missing steps in proofs of the Pythagorean Theorem
- identify the critical features in a proof without words
- see where and how to use the Pythagorean Theorem to find missing lengths in figures

  The following questions will help you check your understanding.

6. Write your favorite proof of the Pythagorean Theorem.

7. How far is the cat from the bird?

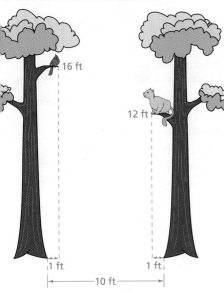

8. Draw two parallel lines *a* and *b* that are 3 in. apart. Choose point *A* on line *a* and point *B* on line *b* such that *AB* = 5 in. Draw line *c* through point *B* and perpendicular to line *b*. Let *C* be the intersection of lines *a* and *c*. How far is *C* from *A*?

In Investigation 3D you learned to

- find the surface area of solids by visualizing their nets
- estimate the volumes of solids
- use formulas for the volumes of certain solids

  The following questions will help you check your understanding.

9. A friend of yours has made a replica of a traditional Sioux tepee, and she needs to know its volume. Suppose the inside of her tepee is a cone of radius 4 m, with slant height 8 m. What is the approximate volume of the tepee?

10. What is the total surface area of the cone shown below?

11. What is the volume of the solid below?

of $\overline{AB}$. By construction, *M* bisects $\overline{AC}$ and $\overline{FM}$ is parallel to $\overline{BC}$, so $\overline{FM}$ is a midline. By the Midline Theorem, $FM = \frac{1}{2}BC$.

3. 120

4. 157

5. yes

6. Check students' work.

7. $4\sqrt{5}$ ft

8. 4 in.

9. 116.1 m³

10. 864π in.²

11. 128π in.³

Chapter Test

Assessment Resources

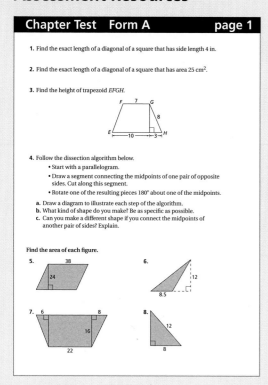

Chapter Test   Form A   **page 1**

1. Find the exact length of a diagonal of a square that has side length 4 in.

2. Find the exact length of a diagonal of a square that has area 25 cm².

3. Find the height of trapezoid *EFGH*.

4. Follow the dissection algorithm below.
   - Start with a parallelogram.
   - Draw a segment connecting the midpoints of one pair of opposite sides. Cut along this segment.
   - Rotate one of the resulting pieces 180° about one of the midpoints.

   a. Draw a diagram to illustrate each step of the algorithm.
   b. What kind of shape do you make? Be as specific as possible.
   c. Can you make a different shape if you connect the midpoints of another pair of sides? Explain.

   Find the area of each figure.

   5.   6.

   7.   8.

Also available: Form B

Go Online
PHSchool.com

For a chapter test, go to
Web Code: **bea-0353**

Multiple Choice

1. Kendra started with △*ABC*. Then she constructed the midpoint of $\overline{AB}$ and labeled it *E*. She used point *E* and △*EBD* to construct trapezoid *AFDC*. How did Kendra construct the trapezoid?

   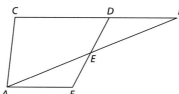

   A. She translated △*EBD* from point *E* to point *A*.

   B. She rotated △*EBD* about point *D*.

   C. She reflected △*EBD* over $\overline{DF}$.

   D. none of the above

2. In the diagram, points *D*, *E*, and *F* are the midpoints of $\overline{AB}$, $\overline{BC}$, and $\overline{AC}$, respectively. Suppose the area of △*ABC* is 8 cm². What is the area of polygon *GDHIEJKFL*? (Assume lines that appear parallel are parallel.)

   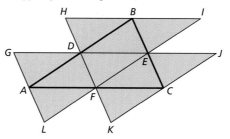

   A. 12 cm²   **B.** 16 cm²

   C. 18 cm²   **D.** 20 cm²

Open Response

3. Cori dissected the triangle into a parallelogram.

   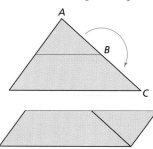

   What does she have to specify about the cut to guarantee that $\overline{AB}$ will match up with $\overline{BC}$?

4. Jamil says he can turn any kite into a rectangle using this algorithm.

   Jamil's Algorithm

   - Start with kite *ABCD*.
   - Find the midpoint of $\overline{AB}$ and call it *X*.
   - Find the midpoint of $\overline{BC}$ and call it *Y*.
   - Draw $\overline{XY}$.
   - Drop a perpendicular from *B* to $\overline{XY}$. Call the point where it hits the segment *Z*.
   - Cut along the two segments you drew.
   - Rotate △*BXZ* 180° around *X*, so that $\overline{BX}$ lines up with $\overline{AX}$.
   - Rotate △*BYZ* 180° around *Y*, so that $\overline{BY}$ lines up with $\overline{CY}$.
   - Now find the midpoint of $\overline{AD}$, and call it *M*.
   - Find the midpoint of $\overline{CD}$, and call it *N*.
   - Draw $\overline{MN}$.
   - Drop a perpendicular from *D* to $\overline{MN}$. Call the point where it hits the segment *O*.
   - Rotate △*MOD* 180° around *M*, so that $\overline{DM}$ lines up with $\overline{AM}$.
   - Rotate △*DON* 180° around *N*, so that $\overline{DN}$ lines up with $\overline{CN}$.
   - Now you have a rectangle!

Answers

Test

1. D

2. D

3. *B* is the midpoint of $\overline{AC}$, and the cut is parallel to the base of the triangle.

4. a. See back of book.

   b. Each pair of segments are congruent segments that are halves of a side of *ABCD*.

   c. The corners are all right angles because the angles are the result of a cut along an altitude, which is by definition perpendicular to the base of the triangle. The short sides are straight because the three angles that make up each of them are the three angles of a triangle, which has an angle sum of 180°. The long sides are straight because the angles that make them up formed straight lines in the original triangle.

   d. Bisect a different set of adjacent sides to start the dissection.

a. Draw pictures to illustrate the steps of the algorithm.

b. Justify why the following pairs of segments are congruent.
- $\overline{BX}$ and $\overline{AX}$
- $\overline{BY}$ and $\overline{CY}$
- $\overline{DM}$ and $\overline{AM}$
- $\overline{DN}$ and $\overline{CN}$

c. Is the final figure really a rectangle? Justify your answer based on the cutting algorithm. (*Hint:* Is it really a quadrilateral? Does it have right angles?)

d. Explain how to use Jamil's algorithm to dissect the kite into a second rectangle.

5. Find the area and perimeter of each figure.

a.

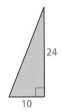

b.

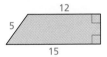

c.

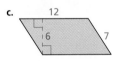

6. Tell whether each triple is a Pythagorean triple. Explain.

a. 1, 2, 3

b. 6, 8, 10

c. 5, 13, 12

d. 1, $\sqrt{3}$, 2

e. 5, 3, 4

f. $\sqrt{3}$, $\sqrt{4}$, $\sqrt{5}$

7. A right square prism has volume 45 ft^3 and height 5 ft. Find each of the following.

a. the side length of a base

b. the total surface area of the prism

c. the volume of a pyramid with the same base and height

8. Find the slant height, total surface area, and volume of this cone.

In Exercises 9 and 10, find the total surface area and volume of the indicated solid for the lengths given.

9. right rectangular prism

a. 4 cm by 5 cm by 6 cm

b. 3.5 cm by 3.5 cm by 3.5 cm

10. cylinder

a. radius 6 cm, height 18 cm

b. radius 18 cm, height 6 cm

11. Write About It Explain the difference between a right prism and an oblique prism.

12. Take It Further Cylinder A is a right cylinder. It has base radius 4 cm and height 6 cm. Cylinder B is an oblique cylinder. It has base radius 6 cm and height 4 cm. Which cylinder can hold more oatmeal?

5. a. $A = 120$; $P = 60$

b. $A = 54$; $P = 36$

c. $A = 78$; $P = 38$

6. a. no; $1^2 + 2^2 \neq 3^2$

b. yes; $6^2 + 8^2 = 10^2$

c. yes; $5^2 + 12^2 = 13^2$

d. No; $\sqrt{3}$ is not an integer.

e. yes; $3^2 + 4^2 = 5^2$

f. No; $\sqrt{3}$ and $\sqrt{5}$ are not integers.

7. a. 3 ft

b. 78 ft^2

c. 15 ft^3

8. slant height $= 13$ cm, $SA = 90\pi$ cm^2, $V = 100$ cm^3

9. a. $SA = 148$ cm^2; $V = 120$ cm^3

b. $SA = 73.5$ cm^2; $V = 42.875$ cm^3

10. a. $SA = 64\pi$ cm^2; $V = \frac{64}{3}\pi$ cm^3

b. $SA = 48\pi$ cm^2; $V = 32\sqrt{3}\pi$ cm^3

11. The angles between the sides and the bases of a right prism are right angles. This is not the case for oblique prisms.

12. Cylinder B

Chapter 4 Similarity

In this chapter, students examine similarity, a relationship that captures the essence of the idea of making scale drawings. Students first look for invariants in drawings that are scaled copies of each other. They then construct their own scaled drawings. This gives them further experience with the relationship of similarity. These activities lead to a mathematical distillation of the notion of similarity. Students use the ideas of proportionality and dilation to prove some critical results.

Chapter Overview

- Investigation 4A, *Scaled Copies,* introduces students to the idea of similarity.
- Investigation 4B, *Curved or Straight? Just Dilate!,* has students learn two techniques—the ratio and parallel methods—to construct dilations.
- Investigation 4C, *The Side-Splitter Theorems,* centers around the proofs and applications of the parallel and the proportional side-splitter theorems.
- Investigation 4D, *Defining Similarity,* formally defines similarity and adapts the tests for triangle congruence to tests for triangle similarity.

For more information on the investigations, see
- Chapter Road Map, pp. 260 and 261
- Investigation Road Maps, pp. 262, 288, 304, 322

PROJECT The Project near the end of the chapter is optional. You can assign the Project at any time during the chapter depending on how often and how long you feel students should work on it.

Pacing Suggestions and Materials

Investigation 4A *Scaled Copies*

DAY	LESSON	HOMEWORK
1	4.1 Getting Started Core: 1, 2, 3, 4, 5, 6 Optional: none	Core: 7, 8, 9 Optional: 10
2	4.2 Scale Factors—Day 1 Core: 1, 2, 3 Optional: none	Core: 9, 10, 11 Optional: none
3	4.2 Scale Factors—Day 2 Core: 4, 5, 6, 7, 8, 14 Optional: none	Core: 12, 13 Optional: 16, 17; Extension: 15, 18
4	4.3 What Is a Well-Scaled Drawing? Core: 1, 2, 3, 7 Optional: none	Core: 4, 5, 6 Optional: 8
5	4.4 Testing for Scale Core: 1, 2, 3, 4, 9 Optional: none	Core: 5, 6, 7, 8 Optional: 10, 11
6	4.5 Checking for Scaled Copies—Day 1 Core: 1, 2 Optional: none	Core: 3, 4 Optional: none
7	4.5 Checking for Scaled Copies—Day 2 Core: 5, 6, 12 Optional: none	Core: 7, 8, 9 Optional: 10, 11, 13

Investigation 4B *Curved or Straight? Just Dilate!*

DAY	LESSON	HOMEWORK
1	4.6 Getting Started Core: 1, 2, 3 Optional: none	Core: 4, 5, 6, 7, 8, 9, 10 Optional: 11, 12, 13
2	4.7 Making Scaled Copies Core: 1, 2, 3, 4, 10 Optional: none	Core: 5, 6, 7, 8, 9 Optional: 12; Extension: 11
3	4.8 Ratio and Parallel Methods—Day 1 Core: 1, 2, 3, 4, 5 Optional: 6	Core: 9, 10 Optional: 17
4	4.8 Ratio and Parallel Methods—Day 2 Core: 7, 8, 15 Optional: none	Core: 11, 12 Optional: 13–17; Extension: 14, 16

Investigation 4C *The Side-Splitter Theorems*

DAY	LESSON	HOMEWORK
1	4.9 Getting Started Core: 1, 2, 3 Optional: none	Core: 4, 5, 6 Optional: 7
2	4.10 Nested Triangles—Day 1 Write up results of experiments.	Core: 1, 2 Optional: none
3	4.10 Nested Triangles—Day 2 Core: 3, 4, 5, 7 Optional: none	Core: 6, 8 Optional: 9, 10
4	4.11 Proving the Side-Splitter Theorems Core: 1, 2, 3, 4 Optional: none	Core: 5, 6, 7 Optional: 10; Extension: 8, 9
5	4.12 The Side-Splitter Theorems (continued) Core: 1, 2, 3, 7 Optional: none	Core: 4, 5, 6 Optional: 11; Extension: 8, 9, 10

NOTES	MATERIALS
	• rulers • Blackline Masters 4.1A–B
Work through the first For Discussion.	• rulers • Blackline Master MC10
Begin with the In-Class Experiment.	• rulers
	• graph paper for homework • rulers • Blackline Master 4.3
	• rulers • scissors
	• rulers • Blackline Master 4.5A
	• protractors • rulers • Blackline Master 4.5B

NOTES	MATERIALS
	• geometry software (optional) • rulers
	• geometry software (optional) • mirrors for Exercises 6–9 • rulers
Work through the first For You to Do.	• rulers • Blackline Master 4.8A
Begin with the Example for the parallel method.	• geometry software • rulers • Blackline Master 4.8B

NOTES	MATERIALS
	• geometry software
Work through In-Class Experiment Parts 1A and 1B	• geometry software • rulers
Begin with In-Class Experiment Part 2.	• geometry software • protractors • rulers
Work through the proof of the first part of the Parallel Side-Splitter Theorem.	• Blackline Masters 4.11A–B
	• scissors

Mathematics Background

SCALED COPIES Students become familiar with the idea of similarity by looking at maps and diagrams drawn to scale. They learn that the scale factor describes how much a map, blueprint, or picture has been reduced or enlarged. Students then practice scaling figures by different factors. They see that when they scale a figure by the factor r, the scaled copy has lengths r times the corresponding lengths of the original figure. Students learn to recognize the characteristics of a well-scaled copy of a figure. They learn to develop tests to decide whether figures are scaled copies of each other. They also develop the idea of proportionality between figures, that is, that corresponding sides of scaled figures are proportional.

THE RATIO METHOD OF DILATION In the Ratio Method of Dilation, to scale a figure by a factor r, students construct points that are r times as far from the center of dilation as the original points. For example, to scale quadrilateral $KLMN$ by the factor r, find K' on $\overrightarrow{DK}$ such that $\frac{DK'}{DK} = r$, L' on $\overrightarrow{DL}$ such that $\frac{DL'}{DL} = r$, M' on $\overrightarrow{DM}$ such that $\frac{DM'}{DM} = r$, and N' on $\overrightarrow{DN}$ such that $\frac{DN'}{DN} = r$.

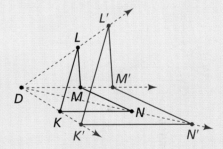

The Proportional Side-Splitter Theorem then guarantees that corresponding sides in the original figure and in the resulting dilation are parallel to each other.

continued on p. 260c

continued from p. 260b

THE PARALLEL METHOD OF DILATION In the Parallel Method of Dilation, students scale a figure by a factor r by constructing one image point that is r times as far from the center of dilation as its corresponding point on the original figure. Then they construct parallels to sides of the figure from that point. They locate other image points at the intersection of those parallels with lines through the center of dilation and points of the original figure. For example, to scale quadrilateral $KLMN$ by the factor r, find K' on $\overrightarrow{DK}$ such that $\frac{DK'}{DK} = r$.

Then construct ℓ parallel to $\overline{KL}$ through K'. The intersection of ℓ and $\overrightarrow{DL}$ is L'. Construct m parallel to $\overline{LM}$ through L'. The intersection of m and $\overrightarrow{DM}$ is M'. Construct n parallel to $\overline{MN}$ through M. The intersection of n and $\overrightarrow{DN}$ is N'.

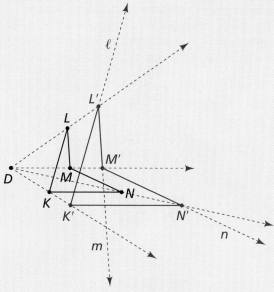

In this method, it is clear immediately that corresponding segments in the original figure and the image are parallel. It is not necessarily clear that all the image points are r times as far from the center of dilation as points on the original figure. The Parallel Side-Splitter Theorem shows that this is true.

Pacing Suggestions and Materials

Investigation 4D *Defining Similarity*

DAY	LESSON	HOMEWORK
1	4.13 Getting Started Core: 1, 2, 3, 4, 5 Optional: none	Core: 6, 7, 8, 9 Optional: 10
2	4.14 Similar Figures Core: 1, 2, 3, 4, 5, 9 Optional: none	Core: 6, 7, 8 Optional: 10
3	4.15 Tests for Similar Triangles—Day 1 In-Class Experiments, For Discussion Problems 5, 6, 7	Core: 3 Optional: none
4	4.15 Tests for Similar Triangles—Day 2 For Discussion Problem 8, For You to Do Problem 9, For Discussion Problem 10	Core: 1, 2, 4, 5 Optional: none
5	4.15 Tests for Similar Triangles—Day 3 Core: 6, 7, 8, 9 Optional: 10, 11	Core: 12, 13 Optional: 15, 16, 17, 18; Extension: 14
6	4.16 Areas of Similar Polygons—Day 1 In-Class Experiment	Read through the dialog, For Discussion Pr
7	4.16 Areas of Similar Polygons—Day 2 Core: 1, 2, 3, 8 Optional: none	Core: 4, 5, 6, 7 Optional: 9, 10, 11, 12

NOTES	MATERIALS
	• protractors • rulers
Work through For Discussion Problem 7 in class.	• protractors • rulers
Begin the second day of this lesson with the SAS Similarity Theorem.	
Begin the third day of this lesson by reviewing as a whole class the Check Your Understanding exercises.	
Work through the In-Class Experiment.	• protractors • rulers
Begin the second day of this lesson with For Discussion Problem 10.	

THE SIDE-SPLITTER THEOREMS Two of the most profound theorems in geometry have to do with proportions:

- The Parallel Side-Splitter Theorem *A line that is parallel to one side of a triangle divides the other two sides proportionally.*

Its converse:

- The Proportional Side-Splitter Theorem *A line that divides two sides of a triangle proportionally is parallel to the third side.*

The proofs chosen for these theorems come directly from Euclid. These proofs use the fact that if two triangles have the same base and equal heights, the triangles have the same area. Students use the side-splitter theorems to show that the two very different methods for constructing dilations they learn in this chapter actually produce equivalent results.

SIMILARITY Students develop their own tests for triangle similarity by adapting tests they already know for triangle congruence. They see the value in making a minimal list of requirements. They also reinforce their work with area by examining the effect of the scale factor on the area of a scaled copy. Students see for themselves that the area of a scaled copy is proportional to the area of the original figure with a ratio equal to the square of the scale factor.

Similarity will continue to be a key relationship that students will use in proofs throughout the course, especially in Chapter 6. There, students apply similarity to many different mathematical contexts, including trigonometry.

Developing Students' Mathematical Habits

This chapter informally introduces students to the idea of dilation—a transformation that maps points away from or toward a fixed center by scaling the distance from that point by a fixed number (the "scale factor"). So, a dilation of factor 2 scales points twice as far away from the center. Key intuitions developed here are:

- Dilations preserve angles.
- Dilations preserve collinearity.
- Dilations multiply distances by the scale factor.

Habits such as looking for invariance and reasoning by continuity (especially if students use geometry software) are central to this chapter.

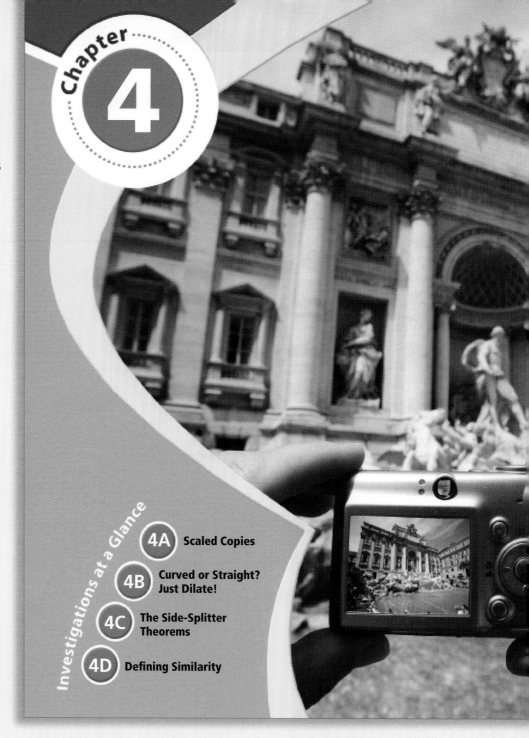

Chapter 4

Investigations at a Glance

4A Scaled Copies

4B Curved or Straight? Just Dilate!

4C The Side-Splitter Theorems

4D Defining Similarity

Chapter Road Map

INVESTIGATION 4A, *Scaled Copies,* introduces students to the idea of similarity through maps and diagrams drawn to scale. Students learn to recognize the attributes of a well-scaled copy of a figure. They develop the idea of proportionality between figures. They also develop tests to decide whether figures are scaled copies of each other.

INVESTIGATION 4B, *Curved or Straight? Just Dilate!,* has students produce scaled copies for themselves through dilation. They learn two techniques to construct dilations—the ratio and parallel methods. Students also realize that if a drawing is a scaled copy of an original drawing, then it must be congruent to some dilation of the original.

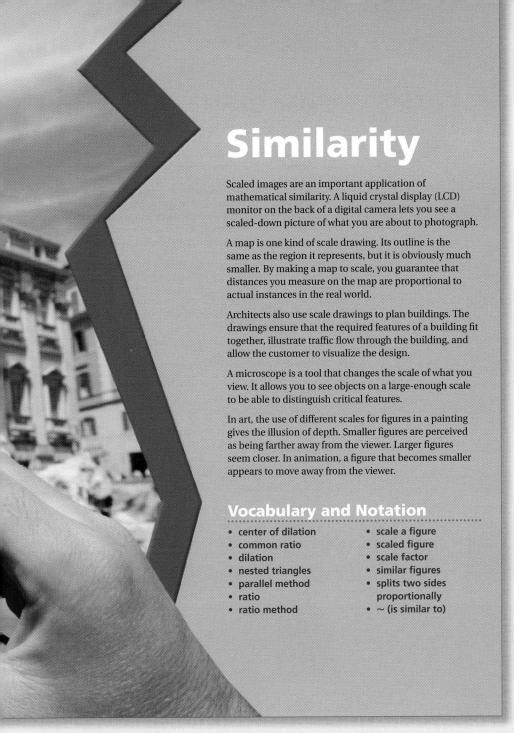

Similarity

Scaled images are an important application of mathematical similarity. A liquid crystal display (LCD) monitor on the back of a digital camera lets you see a scaled-down picture of what you are about to photograph.

A map is one kind of scale drawing. Its outline is the same as the region it represents, but it is obviously much smaller. By making a map to scale, you guarantee that distances you measure on the map are proportional to actual instances in the real world.

Architects also use scale drawings to plan buildings. The drawings ensure that the required features of a building fit together, illustrate traffic flow through the building, and allow the customer to visualize the design.

A microscope is a tool that changes the scale of what you view. It allows you to see objects on a large-enough scale to be able to distinguish critical features.

In art, the use of different scales for figures in a painting gives the illusion of depth. Smaller figures are perceived as being farther away from the viewer. Larger figures seem closer. In animation, a figure that becomes smaller appears to move away from the viewer.

Vocabulary and Notation

- center of dilation
- common ratio
- dilation
- nested triangles
- parallel method
- ratio
- ratio method
- scale a figure
- scaled figure
- scale factor
- similar figures
- splits two sides proportionally
- ~ (is similar to)

Chapter Vocabulary and Notation

The following list gives the key vocabulary and notation used in the chapter. Selected new vocabulary and notation items are shown in boldface on the student page.

- center of dilation, p. 291
- common ratio, p. 310
- dilation, p. 291
- enlargement, p. 274
- nested triangles, p. 307
- parallel method, p. 297
- ratio, p. 279
- ratio method, p. 295
- reduction, p. 274
- scale a figure, p. 267
- scale factor, p. 266
- scaled figure, p. 267
- similar figures, pp. 323, 325
- similar, p. 325
- slider point, p. 300
- splits two sides proportionally, p. 310
- well-scaled copy, p. 274
- ~ (is similar to), p. 326

Chapter Technology

INVESTIGATION 4B *Geometry Software*

- **LESSON 4.6** Find areas and perimeters of a figure and its scaled copy, p. 290.

- **LESSON 4.7** Move and trace points to illustrate the concept of dilation, p. 294.

- **LESSON 4.8** Use the parallel method to dilate; observe the effects of moving a slider point, p. 300. Calculate a scale factor; construct a square that satisfies certain criteria, p. 301.

INVESTIGATION 4C *Geometry Software*

- **LESSON 4.9** Explore by moving points; relate areas of figures, p. 305.

- **LESSON 4.10** Trace the path of a point as you move it, pp. 308–309. Find the ratio of the lengths of the sides of a triangle, p. 309.

CHAPTER PROJECT *Geometry Software*
Construct midpoint quadrilaterals and explore their properties, pp. 344–345.

Support for the use of technology is available in the Technology Handbook. See p. 712.

INVESTIGATION 4C, *The Side-Splitter Theorems,* centers around two critical theorems—the Parallel and the Proportional Side-Splitter Theorems. The investigation guides students through proofs of these theorems. Students see how to apply the theorems in order to identify polygons as scaled copies of each other as well as to prove other geometric results.

INVESTIGATION 4D, *Defining Similarity,* has students use their experience to formally define similarity. They learn the symbol for similarity ($\sim$) and relate it to the symbol for congruence ($\cong$). Students adapt the familiar tests for triangle congruence to develop a set of tests for triangle similarity. They refine their understanding of what requirements are mathematically necessary to guarantee similarity. Students also see the relationship between the ratio of the corresponding sides of two similar figures and the ratio of the areas of the figures.

Investigation Overview

In this investigation, students read maps and blueprints. They use the provided scales to calculate distances and lengths. Students examine enlargements and reductions to formulate their own tests for deciding what makes a well-scaled copy. They then apply this knowledge to pairs of triangles and polygons, again developing methods to recognize scaled copies.

You may wish to assign Questions 1–3 for students to think and write about during the investigation.

Learning Goals

- Understand that a scale factor measures the change in linear dimensions when you scale a picture.
- Approximate the scale factor relating two pictures by measuring.
- Use a given scale factor to interpret a map or blueprint.
- Decide whether two figures are well-scaled copies of each other.

Habits and Skills

- Identify scaled copies of figures.
- Use a scale factor to approximate distances on blueprints and maps.
- Apply a scale factor to make similar figures.

Investigation 4A
Scaled Copies

In *Scaled Copies,* you will learn how you can model a very large or very small figure with a figure that is a manageable size. For example, you could sketch a rough map of your school on paper. You could show some important locations, such as drinking fountains and the cafeteria. You might, however, need the map for something more precise, such as a science project on air quality and ventilation. Then you would want to show more detail, such as the dimensions of rooms and hallways.

You could draw your map *to scale.* Then the dimensions of any room on your map would be proportional to the actual dimensions by the *scale factor* of your map.

By the end of this investigation, you will be able to answer questions like these:

1. Why is it important to know the scale factor when reading a map?

2. What is a well-scaled drawing?

3. How can you decide whether two rectangles are scaled copies of each other?

You will learn how to

- approximate the scale factor relating two pictures by measuring

- use a given scale factor to interpret a map or blueprint

- decide whether two figures are well-scaled copies of each other

You will develop these habits and skills:

- Identify scaled copies of figures.

- Use a scale factor to approximate distances on blueprints and maps.

- Apply a scale factor to make similar figures.

How can a grid help you draw a scaled copy?

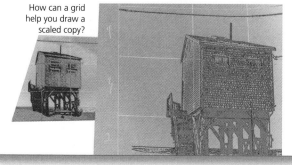

Investigation Road Map

LESSON 4.1, *Getting Started,* presents students with a map with which they practice finding approximate measurements.

LESSON 4.2, *Scale Factors,* introduces the term *scale factor.* Students determine whether two figures are scaled copies and find a scale factor.

LESSON 4.3, *What Is a Well-Scaled Drawing?,* helps students determine which features identify a well-scaled drawing and looks at ratios of corresponding sides.

LESSON 4.4, *Testing for Scale,* uses measurements and calculations to identify scaled copies.

LESSON 4.5, *Checking for Scaled Copies,* introduces visual tests to determine whether figures are scaled copies.

Activating Prior Knowledge
Exploring New Ideas

You can draw a whole city, a state, or an even larger region with a given scale so that it can fit on a piece of paper. In reading a map, it is important to keep the scale in mind.

For You to Explore

Here is a map of Sasha's neighborhood.

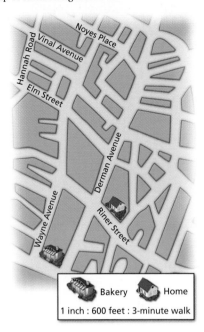

Bakery   Home
1 inch : 600 feet : 3-minute walk

1. The scale shows that 1 inch on the map represents 600 feet of actual distance. It also says that an inch on the map represents about a three-minute walk. What distance does it suggest you can walk in one minute? Is this reasonable?

2. In Sasha's neighborhood, find the actual distance between the following locations. (Travel only on streets.)
   a. the Bakery and the intersection of Wayne Avenue and Noyes Place
   b. Sasha's house and the Bakery

3. Sasha is at the Bakery. She will walk to meet a friend at the intersection of Vinal Avenue and Hannah Road. About how much time will her walk take?

4. Recalculate your answers to Problem 2 using the scale 1 inch : 450 feet.

Answers

For You to Explore

1. 200 ft; yes

2–6. Answers may vary. Samples:

2. a. about 1840 ft
   b. about 1050 ft

3. about 10 min

4. a. about 1380 ft
   b. about 790 ft

Lesson Overview

GOALS

- Explore ideas that are basic to the goals of this investigation.
- Use a given scale factor to interpret a map or blueprint.

This lesson has students work with a map and a blueprint. Students practice using the scale factor to find actual distances.

FOR YOU TO EXPLORE	HOMEWORK
• Core: 1, 2, 3, 4, 5, 6	• Core: 7, 8, 9
• Optional: none	• Optional: 10

MATERIALS
- rulers
- Blackline Masters 4.1A–B

Launch

Discuss any previous experience your students may have had working with maps. You may wish to have a transparency of a map of your neighborhood to review with them.

Explore

Assign Problems 1–6 to individuals or pairs. You may want to use Blackline Masters 4.1A and 4.1B on an overhead so students can explain their answers.

Wrap Up

Review student answers to the For You to Explore problems. Discuss different interpretations of the measurements on the map and blueprint.

For You to Explore

PROBLEMS 1–4 have students answer questions about the map of a fictional neighborhood. These problems provide a good opportunity to review some of the basic properties of ratios and proportions. For instance, if 1 inch on the map represents 600 feet, then how many feet do 5 inches represent? (Answer: 3000 feet) Maps are examples of places where students may have encountered scaling.

PROBLEMS 5 AND 6 are about the blueprint showing the floor plan of the second floor of a house. The answers your students obtain will probably vary since their measurements may not be entirely precise.

An architect's plans for an apartment building, a house, a school, an office, a park, or a sports complex can include many different sketches. Each sketch serves a different purpose. This blueprint drawing shows the floor plan of the second story of a house.

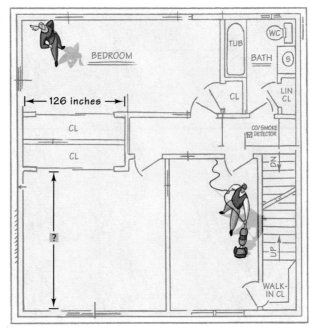

SECOND FLOOR PLAN

5. In this floor plan, someone erased a measurement and replaced it with "?". Calculate the missing value.

6. Find the actual dimensions of the entire second story.

Answers

5. about 168 in.

6. about 358 in. by 364 in.

Exercises *Practicing Habits of Mind*

On Your Own

7. Drivers sometimes estim___ ___ ___ wo points based on
their average d___ ___ ften surprised by
ho___ ___ ___ easons that a trip

___ ___at has a scale
___ the trip from
___ ances in

Zumberge Library
Title: CME project : geometry.
ID: 32260009792229
Due: Tuesday, December 11, 2012

Total items: 1
8/28/2012 2:27 PM

Renew by phone: 616-331-3500
or at gvsu.edu/library

___away!"

___ly a half of a

___cows,
___il is about

9. ___nt to
___w much

a. ___et.)
b. ___ ___Give

c. I___
th___

Main

10. Find the ___ ___ensions.
a. 1 in. by ___
b. 2 in. by ___
c. 3 in. by 9 ___
d. 4 in. by 12 in.
e. n in. by $3n$ in.

Exercises

7. Answers may vary. Samples:
city traffic conditions, condition
of roads and highways, terrain
(mountainous or flat), weather,
daytime vs. nighttime driving

8. a. 45 mi
b. 22.5 mi
c. about 5.6 mi

9. a. about 249.5 in. by 113.9 in.
b. about 28,418.1 in.^{2}
c. about 22 yd^2

10. a. 8 in., 3 in.^{2}
b. 16 in., 12 in.^{2}
c. 24 in., 27 in.^{2}
d. 32 in., 48 in.^{2}
e. $8n$ in., $3n^2$ in.^{2}

Exercises

HOMEWORK
- Core: 7, 8, 9
- Optional: 10

On Your Own

EXERCISE 7 asks about factors that may lengthen
an estimated driving time between two points.
Students' answers will vary depending on their
experiences with driving and traffic.

Go Online
Video Tutor
PHSchool.com
Web Code: bee-0775

Lesson Overview

GOALS

- Understand that a scale factor measures the change in linear dimensions when you scale a picture.
- Approximate the scale factor relating two pictures by measuring.

You will probably want to spend more than one day working on the activities and exercises. See the Daily Planner at the beginning of the chapter for an example of how to split up the lesson and exercises. In this lesson, students develop a more precise definition of scale factor. They learn how to calculate the scale factor by several different methods. Students also find the relationship between the areas and volumes of a figure and its scaled copy.

CHECK YOUR UNDERSTANDING
- Core: 1, 2, 3, 4, 5, 6, 7, 8, 14
- Optional: none

MATERIALS
- rulers
- Blackline Master MC10

HOMEWORK
- Core: 9, 10, 11, 12, 13
- Optional: 16, 17
- Extension: 15, 18

VOCABULARY
- scale a figure
- scale factor
- scaled figure

Launch

Begin by having the whole class discuss the first For Discussion. Students discuss what it means to scale a square by the factor $\frac{1}{2}$. There is more than one way to interpret this statement. Some students may assume that scaling by $\frac{1}{2}$ means that the side lengths of the scaled copy will be half as long as the side lengths of the original square. Some students may think the area of the scaled copy will be half the area of the original square. Both ideas are certainly valid, but the former interpretation is the standard one. Give students Blackline Master MC10. Allow them to work with a copy of the square and try to scale it by the factor $\frac{1}{2}$.

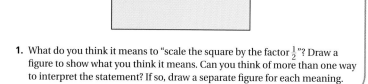

4.2 Scale Factors

Maps and blueprints provide scales that allow you to calculate actual distances and lengths. Depending on the map, 1 inch might represent 1 mile, or 1 inch might represent 100 miles. The **scale factor** is a number that describes how much you reduce or enlarge a map, blueprint, or picture. In this lesson, you will develop a more precise definition of scale factor and learn how to calculate it.

For Discussion

Each side of this square has length 2 inches.

1. What do you think it means to "scale the square by the factor $\frac{1}{2}$"? Draw a figure to show what you think it means. Can you think of more than one way to interpret the statement? If so, draw a separate figure for each meaning.

Minds in Action   episode 9

Tony and Amy have different meanings for scaling the square by the factor $\frac{1}{2}$. See if you agree with either of their explanations.

Tony   To scale by $\frac{1}{2}$, I drew a square that is half the size of the first one. You know, half the area. The area of the original square is 2×2 or 4 square inches. I made a square with an area of 2 square inches. A neat way to do this is to fold all four corners of the square to the center.

Habits of Mind

Visualize. Why does Tony's folding method work? How long are the sides of his new square?

Answers

For Discussion

1. Answers may vary. Samples: to draw a square with sides half as long as those of the given square; to draw a square with half the area of the given square; check students' diagrams.

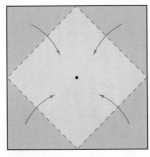

Amy   I think that scaling by half means we are supposed to draw the sides half as long. The first square has sides that are 2 inches long, so the scaled square should have sides that are 1 inch long. I drew a horizontal line and a vertical line on the square to divide the length and width in half. This gives me four squares, each scaled by the factor $\frac{1}{2}$.

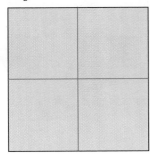

In fact, there is more than one correct way to interpret the phrase *scale by $\frac{1}{2}$*. Words can mean different things to different people. But Amy's meaning is the one that most people use.

Definition

When you **scale a figure** by the factor *r*, you draw a new figure, called a **scaled figure**, that is the same shape as the given figure. In the scaled figure, each length is *r* times the corresponding length of the original figure. The scale factor *r* can be any positive number, including a fraction.

Sometimes a scale factor is not given. You may, however, be able to compare parts of figures to calculate the scale factor.

Explore

After talking about the For Discussion, have the class read through Amy and Tony's dialog. Then give the definition of scale factor.

Use the Example to demonstrate how to calculate a scale factor. Remind students that if they know that the two given figures are scaled copies of each other, then one set of distances is enough to determine the scale factor. In part (b), for example, students could pick two of the tips of the kites (making sure to pick the same tips in both kites), measure the distance between both sets of tips, and then calculate the ratio of the distances. Another way is that students could measure the length of a side of each kite (making sure to pick corresponding sides) and then compute the ratio of the side lengths. Emphasize that all methods should produce the same answer, with slight variations due to measuring inaccuracies.

continued on p. 268

continued from p. 267

Use the In-Class Experiment and the For Discussion that follows to talk about scaling in two dimensions. Students should come to the conclusion that if they scale a 1-inch square by a positive integer r, then r^2 copies of the original square will fit inside the scaled copy. You may want to associate scaling in two dimensions with the exponent 2 in the r^2 copies.

continued on p. 269

Example

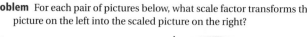

Problem For each pair of pictures below, what scale factor transforms the picture on the left into the scaled picture on the right?

a.

b.

Solutions

a. Measure each side of the first figure. Compare the lengths to the lengths of the sides in the second figure. You will find that each length in the second figure is $\frac{1}{3}$ the length in the first figure. The scale factor is $r = \frac{1}{3}$.

b. Rotate the kite on the right clockwise to match the orientation of the kite on the left. Once you have done this, measure the distances between corresponding points. For example, the distance from L to M is 1.5 cm. The distance from L' to M' is 1.2 cm. This gives a scale factor of $\frac{1.2}{1.5}$, or $\frac{4}{5}$.

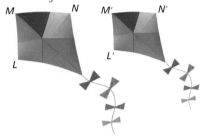

For You to Do

2. For each part of the Example, by what factor should you scale the smaller figure on the right to get the figure on the left?

In-Class Experiment

3. Draw a square with 1-inch sides. Scale the square by the factor 2. How many copies of the 1-inch square fit inside the scaled square?

4. Start with a 1-inch square again. Scale the square by the factor 3. How many copies of the 1-inch square fit inside the scaled square?

Answers

For You to Do

2. 3; $\frac{5}{4}$

In-Class Experiment

3. Check students' diagrams; 4.

4. Check students' diagrams; 9.

For Discussion

5. If you scale a 1-inch square by a positive integer r, how many copies of the 1-inch square fit inside the scaled square?

Minds in Action   episode 10

Derman and Tony have just finished the In-Class Experiment and are trying to apply what they learned to the following problem.

> A cube has edges of length 1 inch. You scale the cube by the factor 2. How long are the sides of the new cube? How many copies of the original cube fit inside the scaled cube?

Tony   Well, if you scale the cube by the factor 2, then the new cube must be twice as big. Two cubes fit inside the scaled cube!

Derman   That sounds right. The original cube has edges that are 1 inch long. The scaled cube must have edges that are 2 inches long.

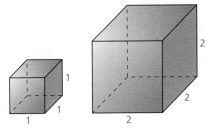

Derman   Wait! Look at the picture, Tony. Your answer can't be right! More than two of the original cubes are going to fit into the big cube.

Tony   Nothing is ever that easy. So, how many 1-inch cubes fit into the scaled cube?

Derman   The volume of the original cube is $1 \times 1 \times 1$, or 1 cubic inch. The volume of the scaled cube is $2 \times 2 \times 2$, or 8 cubic inches. Think of the larger cube as a box. You pack in four small cubes to fill the bottom. Then pack in one more layer of four small cubes to fill the box.

continued from p. 268

Use the dialog between Tony and Derman to lead your class through two students' ideas about scaling in three dimensions. Students should come to the conclusion that if they scale a cube by the factor r, then r^3 copies of the original cube will fit inside the scaled copy. You may want to associate scaling in three dimensions with the exponent 3 in the r^3 copies.

For Discussion

5. r^2 copies

Wrap Up

Use For Discussion Problems 6 and 7 to wrap up your discussion of scale factor. Review how to find a scale factor. Summarize the relationship between scaling in two and three dimensions and finding how many scaled copies will fit in the original figure. Then assign the Check Your Understanding exercises for work in class.

Assessment Resources

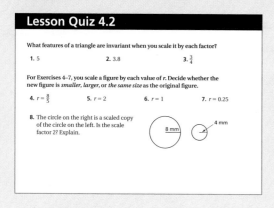
Exercises

HOMEWORK
- Core: 9, 10, 11, 12, 13
- Optional: 16, 17
- Extension: 15, 18

Check Your Understanding

EXERCISE 1 reminds students that not all features of a figure change when you scale it—the square, for instance, maintains its 90° angles.

For Discussion

6. If you scale the original cube by the factor 3, how long are the sides of the new cube? How many copies of the original cube fit inside the scaled cube?

7. If you scale the original cube by a positive integer r, how many copies of the original cube fit inside the scaled cube?

Exercises *Practicing Habits of Mind*

Check Your Understanding

1. What features of a square are invariant when you scale the square by the factor $\frac{1}{2}$?

2. You scale a figure by each given value of r. Will the new figure be smaller, larger, or the same size as the original figure?

  a. $r = \frac{3}{5}$ **b.** $r = 1$

  c. $r = 3$ **d.** $r = 0.77$

3. For each pair of figures, determine whether one figure was scaled by the factor $\frac{1}{2}$ to obtain the other figure. Explain.

  a.   **b.**

  c.

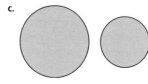

Answers

For Discussion

6. 3 in.; 27 copies

7. r^3 copies

Exercises

1. Answers may vary. Samples: angle measures, congruence of sides, perpendicularity of diagonals

2. **a.** smaller
    b. same size
    c. larger
    d. smaller

4. For each pair of figures, what scale factor transforms the picture on the left into the scaled picture on the right?

a.

b.

5. For each pair of figures in Exercise 4, what scale factor transforms the picture on the right into the scaled picture on the left?

6. Compare the scale factors you found for Exercises 4 and 5. How are they related?

7. This equilateral triangle has 2-inch sides.

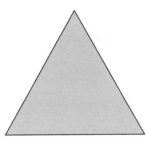

a. Draw a scaled version of the triangle. Use the factor $\frac{1}{2}$. How many of the scaled triangles fit inside the original triangle?

b. Draw a scaled version of the triangle using the factor $\frac{1}{3}$. How many of the scaled triangles fit inside the original triangle?

8. Suppose you scale a 6 in.-by-6 in. square by each factor. How many 1-in. squares will fit inside each scaled square?

a. $\frac{1}{3}$ **b.** 3   **c.** $\frac{2}{3}$

Scale the house at the far left by the factor 1/42. You get a 4-ft wide model.

3. a. No; the rectangles are not the same shape.
b. Yes; the side lengths of the smaller triangle are half the corresponding side lengths of the larger triangle.
c. No; the diameter of the smaller circle is not half the diameter of the larger circle.

4. a. about $\frac{4}{7}$ **b.** 1

5. about $\frac{7}{4}$; 1

6. They are reciprocals.

7. a. 4 copies   **b.** 9 copies

8. a. 4   **b.** 324   **c.** 16

9. Many photocopy machines allow you to scale (reduce or enlarge) a picture. You enter the desired percent and press Copy.

   a. If you enter 80%, by what factor do you scale the picture?

   b. To scale a picture by the factor $\frac{3}{4}$, what percent should you enter?

copier panel for entering a reduction or enlargement percent

10. Label the two scalings as *same* or *different*.

    a. scaling by 2 and scaling by $\frac{1}{2}$

    b. scaling by $\frac{1}{3}$ and scaling by 30%

    c. scaling by $\frac{3}{5}$ and scaling by 0.6

    d. scaling by 1 and scaling by 100%

11. Give a scale factor that changes the quadrilateral *MEOW* as indicated.

    a. shrinks it   b. enlarges it

    c. shrinks it very slightly   d. keeps it the same size

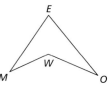

12. A rectangle has width 12 inches and length 24 inches. You scale it using the following factors. In each case, what are the dimensions of the scaled rectangle?

    a. $\frac{1}{3}$ b. $\frac{1}{4}$ c. 0.3   d. 2.5   e. 0.25

13. Examine each pair of figures below.

    - What scale factor can you apply to figure X to get figure Y?
    - What scale factor can you apply to figure Y to get figure X?
    - How are the two scale factors you found related?

a.

X   Y

b.

X   Y

c.

X   Y

Answers

9. a. 0.8, or $\frac{4}{5}$

   b. 75%

10. a. different

   b. different

   c. same

   d. same

11. a. Answers may vary. Sample: $\frac{2}{3}$

   b. Answers may vary. Sample: $\frac{5}{2}$

   c. Answers may vary. Sample: $\frac{15}{16}$

   d. 1

12. a. 4 in. × 8 in.

   b. 3 in. × 6 in.

   c. 3.6 in. × 7.2 in.

   d. 30 in. × 60 in.

   e. 3 in. × 6 in.

13. a. $\frac{1}{3}$; 3; they are reciprocals.

   b. $\frac{1}{5}$; 5; they are reciprocals.

   c. 6; $\frac{1}{6}$; they are reciprocals.

14. Standardized Test Prep Jamal scales a triangle by the factor 4. How many copies of the original triangle can he use to fill the scaled copy?

A. 4   **B.** 8   **C.** 12   **D.** 16

15. Take It Further Suppose you scale a picture by the factor $\frac{1}{2}$. Then you scale your scaled picture by the factor $\frac{1}{4}$. By what overall factor have you scaled the original picture?

Maintain Your Skills

16. Scale each figure below by the factor 4.
- What are the dimensions of the scaled figure?
- How many of the original figures fit into the scaled figure?

a.

6
3

b.
6   6
6

c.

3
3
3

17. Apply the scale factor $\frac{1}{3}$ to each figure in Exercise 16.
- What are the dimensions of the scaled figure?
- How many of the original figure fit into the scaled figure?

18. Take It Further Apply a scale factor n to each figure in Exercise 16.
- What are the dimensions of the scaled figure?
- How many of the original figure fit into the scaled figure?

Go Online
PHSchool.com

For additional practice, go to **Web Code: bea-0402**

14. D

15. by the factor $\frac{1}{8}$

16. a. 24 × 12; 16
   b. all sides 24; 16
   c. 12 × 12 × 12; 64

17. a. 2 × 1; 0
   b. all sides 2; 0
   c. 1 × 1 × 1; 0

18. a. $6n \times 3n$; n^2
   b. all sides $6n$; n^2
   c. $3n \times 3n \times 3n$; n^3

On Your Own

EXERCISE 15 has students apply a scale factor to a figure that they have already scaled.

EXERCISES 16 AND 17 Students see how the area and volume of a scaled copy relate to the area and volume of the original figure.

Additional Resources

PRINTED RESOURCES
- Solution Manual
- Practice Workbook
- Assessment Resources
- Teaching Resources

TECHNOLOGY
- Interactive Textbook
- TeacherExpress CD-ROM
- **Exam**View CD-ROM
- **PHSchool.com**
  - Additional Practice
  - Mid-Chapter and Chapter Tests
  - Video Tutors
  - Vocabulary Puzzles

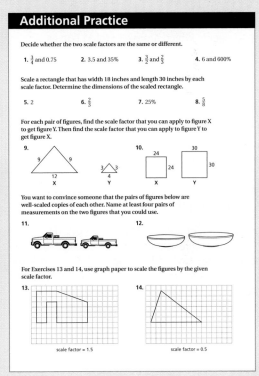

Additional Practice

Decide whether the two scale factors are the same or different.

1. $\frac{3}{4}$ and 0.75   2. 3.5 and 35%   3. $\frac{3}{2}$ and $\frac{2}{3}$ 4. 6 and 600%

Scale a rectangle that has width 18 inches and length 30 inches by each scale factor. Determine the dimensions of the scaled rectangle.

5. 2   6. $\frac{2}{3}$ 7. 25%   8. $\frac{5}{8}$

For each pair of figures, find the scale factor that you can apply to figure X to get figure Y. Then find the scale factor that you can apply to figure Y to get figure X.

9.   10.

You want to convince someone that the pairs of figures below are well-scaled copies of each other. Name at least four pairs of measurements on the two figures that you could use.

11.   12.

For Exercises 13 and 14, use graph paper to scale the figures by the given scale factor.

13.   14.

scale factor = 1.5   scale factor = 0.5

Practice: For Lesson 4.2, assign Exercises 1–10.

Lesson Overview

GOAL
- Decide whether two figures are well-scaled copies of each other.

This lesson has students decide what characteristics make an accurate enlargement or reduction. Students take measurements to decide whether two figures are well-scaled copies of each other.

CHECK YOUR UNDERSTANDING
- Core: 1, 2, 3, 7
- Optional: none

MATERIALS
- graph paper
- rulers
- Blackline Master 4.3

HOMEWORK
- Core: 4, 5, 6
- Optional: 8

VOCABULARY
- enlargement
- reduction
- well-scaled copy

Launch

Have your students look at the pictures of the dog and try to decide which are well-scaled copies.

Explore

With your class, read through the Minds in Action. Use the For Discussion to talk about well-scaled drawings. You may wish to provide students with Blackline Master 4.3.

For Discussion

When you ask your students how they decided which dogs are well-scaled copies of the original picture, they may say, "It just doesn't look right." Try to get your students to be more specific. Emphasize that they should think about finding measures of angles and ratios of corresponding lengths to decide whether two figures are scaled copies of each other.

Wrap Up

Assign the Check Your Understanding exercises for work in class.

4.3 What Is a Well-Scaled Drawing?

The map and blueprint in Lesson 4.1 are both well-scaled drawings. Sometimes, though, a reduction or enlargement is not a good copy of the original. When you look at yourself in a funhouse mirror, you see that your body is scaled in a very unusual way indeed. The mirror might stretch your image so that you appear as skinny as a matchstick. It might shrink your image so that you appear one foot tall!

Here is a picture of a dog.

Here are four other images of the dog.

I.

II.   III.

IV.

Tony and Sasha try to decide which images could be accurate reductions or enlargements of the dog picture.

Tony   If one of these pictures is an accurate copy of the original dog picture, it's got to look exactly like the original, right?

Sasha   Well, we're not necessarily looking for an exact copy of the original. We're just looking for a picture that keeps the same shape, but not necessarily the same size. The original picture may have been enlarged or shrunk down—like on a copy machine.

Tony   The first copy is shorter than the original, but it's not smaller all around. It just looks like someone stepped on it. If we're looking for an accurate smaller copy of the original picture, the copy needs to be smaller all around.

Sasha   I know what you mean. The fourth copy is bigger than the original, but it's not bigger all around. It got bigger, but it's too long.

For Discussion

1. Decide which of the four images are accurate enlargements or reductions of the original dog picture.

2. What characteristics of the dog images helped you make your decisions?

Exercises Practicing Habits of Mind

Check Your Understanding

Exercises 1–3 on the next page will help you make decisions about whether you are looking at a good copy or a bad copy. You will use measurements rather than just judging by eye.

Answers

For Discussion

1. Only (III) is scaled accurately.

2. Answers may vary. Sample: height in relation to length, angles formed by bones in legs

Assessment Resources

Lesson Quiz 4.3

Use the figures for Exercises 1–3.

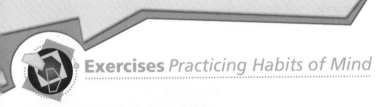

1. AB, CD, EF, and GH are the distances between pairs of points on the pineapples. AB = 5 inches, CD = 10 inches, EF = 4 inches, and GH = 8 inches. How can you use this information to convince someone that the pineapples are well-scaled copies of each other?

2. Points A, B, C, and D show four locations on the doll. What does $\frac{AB}{CD}$ represent?

3. Name at least four different measurements you could take to show that the two letters are well-scaled copies of each other.

Exercises

HOMEWORK
- Core: 4, 5, 6
- Optional: 8

Check Your Understanding

EXERCISES 1–3 are important for you to assign in class because they illustrate how to compute ratios to compare parts of figures.

On Your Own

EXERCISES 4–6 Students will need graph paper to complete these exercises. The exercises provide students with a picture and a scale factor. They require students to draw the new scaled picture on the graph paper.

1. Here are drawings of two baby chicks with points labeled *A* through *H*.

   Here are the distances between some of the points.

   $AB = 4$ cm $CD = 2$ cm $EF = 2.5$ cm $GH = 1.25$ cm

   How can you use these measurements to help convince someone that the two chicks are well-scaled copies of each other? Are there other measurements that could be important to compare?

2. The labels *A*, *B*, *C*, and *D* name four points on this fish. The fish is not drawn to scale.

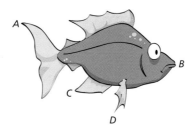

   Jo measures the distance *AB*, as well as the distance *CD*. She calculates that $\frac{AB}{CD} = 2.6$. Michael sees her answer and asks, "But what's your unit? Is the answer 2.6 centimeters, 2.6 inches, 2.6 feet, or something else?"

   How would you respond to Michael's question?

3. Name at least four different pairs of measurements you could take on these two figures to convince someone that the two figures are well-scaled copies of each other.

Answers

Exercises

1. Compare ratios of corresponding distances, such as $\frac{AB}{EF}$ and $\frac{CD}{GH}$.

2. The choice of unit does not affect the ratio.

3. Answers may vary. Sample: the width of the bottom of each letter, the length of the horizontal bar in each letter, the height of each letter, the length of the "legs" of each letter

4.

5.

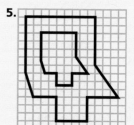

6. Check students' work. The dimensions of the letters in the scaled copy should be twice the dimensions of the original letters.

7. B

On Your Own

For Exercises 4–6, use graph paper to scale the pictures by the given scale factor.

4.

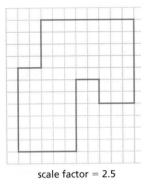

scale factor = 2.5

5.

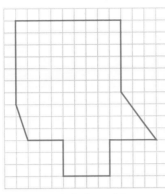

scale factor = 0.5

6.

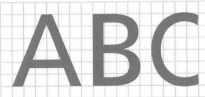

scale factor = 2

7. Standardized Test Prep A rectangle has dimensions 25 cm by 10 cm. It is scaled by the factor $\frac{3}{5}$. What is the perimeter of the scaled rectangle?

A. 35 cm **B.** 42 cm **C.** 70 cm **D.** 90 cm

Maintain Your Skills

8. A rectangle has dimensions 3 cm by 4 cm. You scale it using the following factors. Find the area of each scaled rectangle.

a. 2 **b.** 3 **c.** 0.5
d. $\frac{5}{12}$ **e.** n

Go Online
PHSchool.com

For additional practice, go to Web Code: bea-0403

8. a. 48 cm^2
b. 108 cm^2
c. 3 cm^2
d. $\frac{25}{12}$ cm^2
e. 12n^2 cm^2

Additional Resources

PRINTED RESOURCES
• Solution Manual
• Practice Workbook
• Assessment Resources
• Teaching Resources

TECHNOLOGY
• Interactive Textbook
• TeacherExpress CD-ROM
• **Exam***View* CD-ROM
• **PHSchool.com**
  – Additional Practice
  – Mid-Chapter and Chapter Tests
  – Video Tutors
  – Vocabulary Puzzles

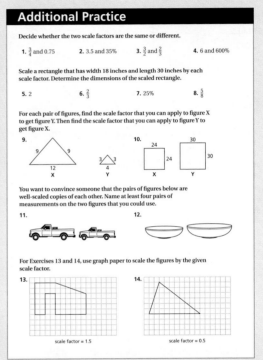

Additional Practice

Decide whether the two scale factors are the same or different.

1. $\frac{3}{4}$ and 0.75   2. 3.5 and 35%   3. $\frac{3}{2}$ and $\frac{2}{3}$ 4. 6 and 600%

Scale a rectangle that has width 18 inches and length 30 inches by each scale factor. Determine the dimensions of the scaled rectangle.

5. 2   6. $\frac{2}{3}$ 7. 25%   8. $\frac{5}{8}$

For each pair of figures, find the scale factor that you can apply to figure X to get figure Y. Then find the scale factor that you can apply to figure Y to get figure X.

You want to convince someone that the pairs of figures below are well-scaled copies of each other. Name at least four pairs of measurements on the two figures that you could use.

For Exercises 13 and 14, use graph paper to scale the figures by the given scale factor.

Practice: For Lesson 4.3, assign Exercises 11–14.

Lesson Overview

GOAL

- Decide whether two figures are well-scaled copies of each other.

This lesson introduces students to the fact that corresponding sides of well-scaled figures are proportional.

CHECK YOUR UNDERSTANDING

- Core: 1, 2, 3, 4, 9
- Optional: none

MATERIALS

- scissors
- rulers

HOMEWORK

- Core: 5, 6, 7, 8
- Optional: 10, 11

VOCABULARY

- ratio

Launch

Read through the text at the beginning of this lesson with your students. Point out that the term *scaled* will now be used to mean a "well-scaled" drawing.

Explore

The text at the beginning of this lesson and the Example introduce students to the fact that corresponding sides of well-scaled figures are proportional.

Have students try the problem in the Example before you provide the answers. It is important that you properly use the terms *corresponding sides* and *proportional,* as they make talking about scaled copies much simpler. In the rectangles provided, the shorter sides of lengths 2 and 3 are corresponding sides, as are the sides of lengths 6 and 9. You can say either that the ratios for these corresponding sides are equal or that the corresponding sides are proportional.

Wrap Up

Summarize some of the different approaches for deciding whether two rectangles are scaled copies:

- Check whether the ratio of the lengths of the rectangles is equal to the ratio of the widths.
- Check whether the length-to-width ratio of one rectangle equals the length-to-width ratio of the other rectangle.

Summarize some of the different approaches for deciding whether two triangles are scaled copies:

- Check that corresponding angles have the same measurements and that corresponding sides are proportional.

4.4 Testing for Scale

In Lesson 4.3, you thought about the characteristics that did or did not make pictures of a dog well-scaled copies of each other. Now you will do the same for pairs of simple geometric figures such as rectangles, triangles, and other polygons.

Here are two rectangles.

To tell whether one rectangle is a scaled copy of the other, you could look for a scale factor that would work. In this case, scale the left rectangle by the factor $\frac{3}{2}$ to get the right rectangle.

Some people use the phrase *corresponding sides*, or "sides that match up," when talking about scaled copies. If you scale one side, you get the corresponding side of the other figure. For the two rectangles above, the 2-unit side and the 3-unit side are corresponding. Also, the 6-unit side and the 9-unit side are corresponding. Corresponding sides of scaled figures are proportional. Corresponding sides in these rectangles are proportional because $\frac{2}{3} = \frac{6}{9}$.

> **Mathematicians** usually use *scaled,* rather than *well-scaled,* to refer to proportional figures. From here on, you will use *scaled* rather than *well-scaled.* Both terms have the same meaning.

> **Remember...**
> You use *corresponding sides* here the same way you used it for congruent figures.

Example

Problem The lengths and widths of seven rectangles A–G are given. Match the rectangles that are scaled copies of each other.

- A: 4 in. by 1 in.
- B: 3 in. by 2 in.
- C: 10 in. by 5 in.
- D: 4 in. by 6 in.
- E: 5 in. by 3 in.
- F: 16 in. by 4 in.
- G: 8 in. by 4 in.

Solutions There are three pairs of scaled copies. Rectangles C and G are scaled copies (since $\frac{10}{8} = \frac{5}{4}$), as are A and F (since $\frac{4}{16} = \frac{1}{4}$).

Rectangles B and D are also scaled copies. Notice, however, that $\frac{3}{4} \neq \frac{2}{6}$. To see that the rectangles have equal ratios, you need to make your ratios in a consistent way. If one ratio is in the form of $\frac{\text{shorter side}}{\text{shorter side}}$, then the other must be $\frac{\text{longer side}}{\text{longer side}}$. Thus, you have $\frac{2}{4} = \frac{3}{6}$.

Exercises *Practicing Habits of Mind*

Check Your Understanding

1. The ratio of length to width for a particular rectangle is 1.5. A scaled copy has width 6. What is the length of the scaled copy?

2. Two rectangles are scaled copies of each other. The ratio of their lengths is 0.6. The smaller rectangle has width 3. What is the width of the larger rectangle?

> A **ratio** is the quotient of two numbers. If only one number is given, the second number is understood to be 1. *A ratio of 1.5 really means "1.5 to 1."*

3. Are the two triangles below scaled copies of each other? Take measurements and do calculations as necessary. Explain what you find.

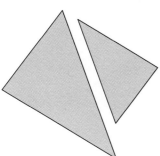

4. Kaori has two triangles that have all corresponding angles congruent. The sides of one triangle are 4, 6, and 8. The sides of the other are 9, 6, and 12. She says that because

$$\frac{4}{9} = 0.44\ldots,$$
$$\frac{6}{6} = 1,$$

and

$$\frac{8}{12} = 0.66\ldots,$$

the triangles are not scaled copies. Do you agree?

Answers

Exercises

1. 9

2. 5

3. These triangles are scaled copies. Explanations may vary. Sample: By measurement, the lengths of the corresponding sides are proportional, and the corresponding angles have equal measures.

4. no

- Check whether each side of one triangle has length *r* times the corresponding side length of the other triangle, for some positive number *r*.
- Compute the ratios of the lengths of corresponding sides to see whether the ratios are all equal.
- Measure corresponding angles to see whether they are congruent.

Then assign the Check Your Understanding exercises for in-class work.

Assessment Resources

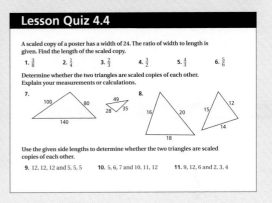

Exercises

HOMEWORK
- Core: 5, 6, 7, 8
- Optional: 10, 11

Check Your Understanding

EXERCISE 1 has students use information about a rectangle to figure out the length of a scaled copy of the rectangle.

EXERCISE 3 has students measure corresponding parts of two triangles to determine whether the triangles are scaled copies of each other.

EXERCISE 4 presents students with one student's work for figuring out whether two triangles are scaled copies of each other. Students must critique the work. It turns out the student has mistakenly compared noncorresponding sides, so her ratios are incorrect.

On Your Own

EXERCISES 5, 7, AND 8 require that students use their knowledge of scale factor and ratios to determine whether two figures are scaled copies of each other. Students will need scissors and rulers for Exercise 8.

Additional Resources

PRINTED RESOURCES
- Solution Manual
- Practice Workbook
- Assessment Resources
- Teaching Resources

TECHNOLOGY
- Interactive Textbook
- TeacherExpress CD-ROM
- **Exam**View CD-ROM
- **PHSchool.com**
  – Additional Practice
  – Mid-Chapter and Chapter Tests
  – Video Tutors
  – Vocabulary Puzzles

Additional Practice

Two rectangles are scaled copies of each other. The ratio of the length of one rectangle to the length of the other is $\frac{4}{5}$. The width of the smaller rectangle is given. Find the width of the larger rectangle.

1. 20   **2.** 12   **3.** 18   **4.** 10   **5.** 6   **6.** 11

The length of a side of a scaled square is given. The scale factor is 1.5. Find the length of a side of the original square.

7. 3   **8.** 15   **9.** 1   **10.** 21   **11.** 78   **12.** 2

Use the side lengths of the two triangles to decide whether the triangles are scaled copies. Explain.

13. Triangle A: 5, 6, 10
Triangle B: 10, 11, 15

14. Triangle C: 8, 12, 7
Triangle D: 21, 24, 36

15. Triangle E: 10, $3\frac{1}{2}$, $7\frac{1}{2}$
Triangle F: 12, 4, 9

Draw a figure inside the original figure that is a scaled copy. (You choose the scale factor.) Explain how to do it.

16.   **17.**

You scale a polygon by each factor. Find (a) the ratio of the lengths of any two corresponding sides of the original polygon to the scaled one, and (b) the ratio of the measures of any two corresponding angles of the original polygon to the scaled one.

18. $\frac{8}{5}$ **19.** 7   **20.** 5.4   **21.** 0.9   **22.** $\frac{3}{5}$ **23.** 1

Use the angle measures to decide whether the two triangles are scaled copies. Explain.

24. Triangle G: 45°, 45°
Triangle H: 45°, 90°

25. Triangle J: 133°, 11°
Triangle K: 35°, 11°

26. Triangle M: 55°, 82°
Triangle N: 43°, 55°

27. Triangle P: 79°, 81°
Triangle Q: 81°, 20°

28. Triangle R: 102°, 53°
Triangle S: 25°, 53°

29. Triangle V: 139°, 5°
Triangle W: 26°, 139°

Practice: For Lesson 4.4, assign Exercises 1–15.

On Your Own

5. Can a 3 foot-by-9 foot rectangle be a scaled copy of a 3 foot-by-1 foot rectangle? Explain.

6. You scale a square by the factor 2.5. The resulting square has a side length of 8 inches. What is the length of a side of the original square?

7. One triangle has side lengths of 21, 15, and 18. Another triangle has side lengths of 12, 14, and 16. Are these triangles scaled copies? How can you tell?

8. Carefully trace the triangles below. Cut out the traced triangles. Decide whether any two of the triangles are scaled copies of each other. Use any of the methods discussed in class.

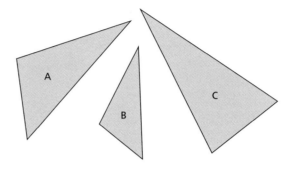

9. Standardized Test Prep Elisha has two triangles. One triangle has side lengths of 3 cm, 5 cm, and 7 cm. The other triangle has side lengths of 40 cm, 24 cm, and 56 cm. Are the two triangles scaled copies of each other? If so, what is the scale factor of the first triangle to the second triangle?

A. No, the two triangles are not scaled copies of each other.

B. yes; $\frac{1}{8}$ **C.** yes; $\frac{40}{3}$ **D.** yes; $\frac{24}{5}$

Maintain Your Skills

10. Suppose $f(x, y) = xy$. Evaluate each of the following.

a. $f(2, 3)$ **b.** $f(4, 6)$ **c.** $f(6, 9)$

d. $f(a, b)$ **e.** $f(2a, 2b)$ **f.** $f(ka, kb)$

11. Write an algebraic equation to define a function that has a rectangle's length and width as input and the area of the rectangle as output.

For additional practice, go to Web Code: bea-0404

Answers

5. Yes; all the angles are right angles, and in each rectangle, the ratio $\dfrac{\text{length of short side}}{\text{length of long side}}$ is $\frac{1}{3}$.

6. 3.2 in.

7. No; the ratios $\frac{15}{12}$, $\frac{18}{14}$, and $\frac{21}{16}$ are not equal.

8. Triangles A and B are scaled copies of each other.

9. B

10. a. 6
    b. 24
    c. 54
    d. ab
    e. $4ab$
    f. k^2ab

11. $f(\ell, w) = \ell w$, where ℓ and w are, respectively, the length and width of the rectangle

Think for a moment about congruent triangles. Recall how you determine whether two triangles are congruent without taking measurements or performing calculations.

One way is to cut out the triangles and lay one on top of the other. If you can arrange the triangles so that they perfectly coincide, then they are congruent.

Perhaps there is also a visual way to test whether two shapes are scaled copies of each other without having to take measurements.

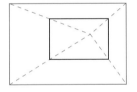 **Minds in Action** episode 12

Hannah and Derman are trying to determine whether the pairs of rectangles in each figure below are scaled copies.

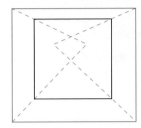

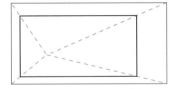

Hannah Why are there dashed lines in these figures? They're just confusing me!

Derman I don't know—let's just try to ignore them for now. How are we going to decide whether the rectangles are scaled copies?

Hannah Well, we've been taking measurements and comparing corresponding sides. Let's do that here.

Derman Do that with the first pair of rectangles. I'm going to try to decide this without measuring.

Moments later . . .

Lesson Overview

GOAL
- Decide whether two figures are well-scaled copies of each other.

This lesson introduces visual methods to test without measuring whether two figures are scaled copies.

CHECK YOUR UNDERSTANDING	**HOMEWORK**
• Core: 1, 2, 5, 6, 12	• Core: 3, 4, 7, 8, 9
• Optional: none	• Optional: 10, 11, 13

MATERIALS
- protractors
- rulers
- Blackline Masters 4.5A–B

Launch

Have students read through the Minds in Action individually or aloud.

Explore

Minds in Action

In the dialog, two students examine three pairs of rectangles that may be scaled copies. The dialog presents two different lines of thinking, one that uses measurement and one that does not. After students read and discuss the dialog, have them answer For Discussion Problem 1.

The For Discussion that follows this dialog asks students to think about the purpose of the dashed lines in each figure. This is *not* explained in the student text—although the dialog presents some conjectures. Students will see these dashed lines again later in this chapter.

It is possible that if your students' measurements are not exact, they will say that *none* of the rectangle pairs are scaled copies of each other. In this case, mention that because of measuring inaccuracies, even well-scaled figures might not have the numbers work out perfectly.

Hannah I measured the sides of the first pair of rectangles in centimeters. I made ratios of the sides for each rectangle. I got $\frac{2.7}{4.3}$ and $\frac{2.7}{3.8}$. The ratios aren't equal, so they're not scaled copies of each other.

Derman I thought the second pair might be scaled copies. I wanted to be sure, so I measured them, too. They are. So I decided to trace them, cut them out, and fool around with them. I wanted to see whether there is another way to show they're scaled copies.

I noticed a couple of things with the second pair of rectangles.

First, I can fit four copies of the small rectangle perfectly inside the big rectangle.

And, I can draw one diagonal in both rectangles. Then, when I slide the small rectangle down to one corner, the diagonals match up perfectly.

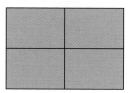 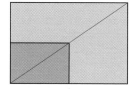

Hannah That's cool. Did your cutting and moving tests work with the third pair of rectangles?

Derman Well, the first test didn't work. I couldn't fit copies of the small rectangle perfectly inside the big one. But I *could* show that the diagonals match up.

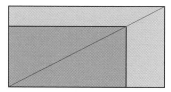

Hannah So, does that mean that the two rectangles in the third pair are scaled copies of each other?

For Discussion

1. What do you think? Are the rectangles in the second pair scaled copies? Are the rectangles in the third pair scaled copies? Can you figure out what the dashed lines in the original figures might be for? Explain.

Answers

For Discussion

1. Check students' responses.

The triangles in each pair below are scaled copies of each other. Trace and cut out the triangles in each pair. Then move the triangles around. Look for some visual clues that suggest good tests for recognizing scaled triangles. For instance, if you place one angle on top of another and find they match, what do you notice about the triangles' corresponding sides?

2.

3.

or Discussion

4. Share your findings with your class. Did placing one angle on top of a matching angle help you decide whether the triangles are scaled copies? What other tests did you use?

In-Class Experiment

Distribute Blackline Master 4.5A to students. This experiment encourages students to find ways to check for scaled triangles without taking any measurements. When students cut out and move the scaled triangles in the first problem, they might overlap the triangles so that they meet at a common vertex *A*, as shown in the figure below.

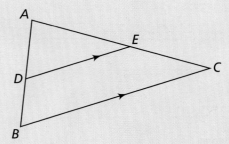

When the triangles are aligned this way, notice that
- a pair of corresponding angles overlaps perfectly at ∠*A*
- $\overline{AD}$ and $\overline{AB}$, as well as $\overline{AE}$ and $\overline{AC}$, line up
- $\overline{DE}$ is parallel to $\overline{BC}$

Wrap Up

Emphasize that there are different visual approaches for deciding whether two rectangles are scaled copies:
- Draw the diagonals of both rectangles. Put the smaller rectangle on top of the larger one, matching up a corner. Then decide whether the diagonals line up.
- Put one rectangle on top of the other. Draw segments connecting corresponding vertices. Then decide whether the segments meet at a single point.

Summarize some of the different visual approaches for deciding whether two triangles are scaled copies:
- Place one triangle on top of the other to see whether they line up.
- Study the two triangles visually. If they are not scaled copies, it is often easy to see this without measuring. (They just do not look the same.)

In-Class Experiment

2. Check students' work.

3. Check students' work.

For Discussion

4. Check students' responses.

Assessment Resources

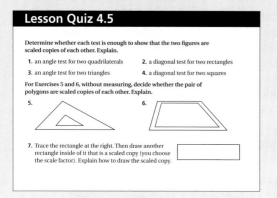
Exercises

HOMEWORK
- Core: 3, 4, 7, 8, 9
- Optional: 10, 11, 13

Check Your Understanding

The Minds in Action, In-Class Experiment, and For Discussions in this lesson may take an entire class period (or longer). You may wish to assign some of these exercises for homework and have students complete the rest of them in class the following day.

EXERCISE 2 presents students with an incorrect method for making a scaled copy of a triangle. Students must test the given method on several triangles. They then explain why it does not work.

In the figure below, $\overline{DE} \parallel \overline{BC}$. Prove that all pairs of corresponding angles for $\triangle ADE$ and $\triangle ABC$ are congruent.

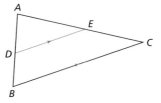

Proof

Because $\overline{DE}$ is parallel to $\overline{BC}$, it follows that $\angle ADE \cong \angle ABC$ and $\angle AED \cong \angle ACB$. Since $\angle A \cong \angle A$, you know that $\triangle ADE$ and $\triangle ABC$ have congruent corresponding angles.

If two triangles have congruent corresponding angles, does that mean that the triangles are scaled copies of each other? It seems like a reasonable conjecture, and it is, in fact, true. You will prove it in the next Investigation.

Exercises *Practicing Habits of Mind*

Check Your Understanding

1. Martin thinks that the angle test for triangles might also be a good way to check whether other polygons (such as rectangles) are scaled copies. If the angles of polygon $ABCD$ are congruent to the corresponding angles of polygon $A'B'C'D'$, are the polygons scaled copies? Explain.

2. Sheena has an idea for making a scaled copy of a triangle.

> Measure the sides of the triangle. Then add the same constant value (such as 1, 2, or 3) to each side length. Draw a triangle with these new side lengths.

Will this new triangle be a scaled copy of the original? Try it.

Answers

Exercises

1. No; explanations may vary. Sample: All rectangles have 4 right angles, but not all rectangles are scaled copies of each other.

2. no

3. a. yes
   b. No; explanations may vary. Sample: In both figures, the polygons have the same angle measures, but only the first pair has corresponding side lengths with equal ratios.

You now have tests for scaled rectangles and triangles. How can you test other polygons?

3. For each figure, decide whether the two polygons are scaled copies. Explain your decision.

a.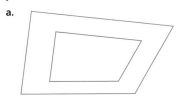

b.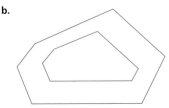

4. Trace trapezoid *ABCD*. Inside the traced trapezoid, draw another trapezoid that is a scaled copy. (You choose the scale factor.) Explain how you made the scaled copy.

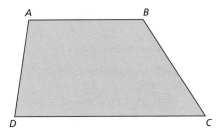

5. You scale a polygon by the factor $\frac{3}{4}$. You then compare the original polygon to the scaled one. Find each ratio.

a. the lengths of any two corresponding sides

b. the measures of any two corresponding angles

6. Is either statement below a valid test for whether two polygons are scaled copies? Explain. If the test is not valid, what additional requirement(s) would make each test work?

- Two polygons are scaled copies if you can show that their corresponding angles all have equal measures.
- Two polygons are scaled copies if you can show that the lengths of their corresponding sides are all in the same ratio.

On Your Own

7. Two angles of one triangle measure 28° and 31°. Another triangle has two angles that measure 117° and 31°. Are the triangles scaled copies? How can you tell?

8. How can you tell whether two squares are scaled copies of each other?

EXERCISE 3 requires students to decide whether polygons that look scaled are, in fact, scaled copies. In part (b), it turns out that, even though corresponding angle measures are equal, the polygons are not scaled copies of each other.

EXERCISE 4 asks students to draw a scaled copy of a trapezoid. They use a scale factor of their choosing. You may wish to provide students with a copy of Blackline Master 4.5B for use with this exercise.

On Your Own

EXERCISE 7 gives students angle information for two triangles and asks whether these triangles are scaled copies. Students must know that the sum of the angle measures in any triangle is 180°. They must assume from their experimenting in this investigation that if two triangles have the same angle measures, they are scaled copies of each other. In this case, the triangles share only one congruent angle pair.

EXERCISE 9 challenges students to draw a quadrilateral that has sides that are twice as long as the corresponding sides of another quadrilateral, but which is *not* a scaled copy of the original. Students must realize that proportional sides are not the only requirement for well-scaled figures. Students can easily see this with a square with side length *s* and a rhombus with side length 2*s*.

---

4. Answers may vary. Sample: Draw the diagonals and mark the point *P* where they intersect. Mark the midpoints of $\overline{PA}$, $\overline{PB}$, $\overline{PC}$, and $\overline{PD}$. Connect the midpoints, in order, to get the scaled trapezoid.

5. a. $\frac{3}{4}$ or $\frac{4}{3}$ **b.** 1

6. No; I. Corresponding sides must have the same ratio.
II. Corresponding angles must be congruent.

7. No. The angle measures for the first triangle are 28°, 31°, and 121°. The angle measures for the second triangle are 31°, 32°, and 117°.

8. All squares are scaled copies of each other.

PRINTED RESOURCES
- Solution Manual
- Practice Workbook
- Assessment Resources
- Teaching Resources

TECHNOLOGY
- Interactive Textbook
- TeacherExpress CD-ROM
- **Exam**View CD-ROM
- **PHSchool.com**
  – Additional Practice
  – Mid-Chapter and Chapter Tests
  – Video Tutors
  – Vocabulary Puzzles

Additional Practice

Two rectangles are scaled copies of each other. The ratio of the length of one rectangle to the length of the other is $\frac{4}{5}$. The width of the smaller rectangle is given. Find the width of the larger rectangle.

1. 20   **2.** 12   **3.** 18   **4.** 10   **5.** 6   **6.** 11

The length of a side of a scaled square is given. The scale factor is 1.5. Find the length of a side of the original square.

7. 3   **8.** 15   **9.** 1   **10.** 21   **11.** 78   **12.** 2

Use the side lengths of the two triangles to decide whether the triangles are scaled copies. Explain.

13. Triangle A: 5, 6, 10
Triangle B: 10, 11, 15

14. Triangle C: 8, 12, 7
Triangle D: 21, 24, 36

15. Triangle E: 10, $3\frac{1}{2}$, $7\frac{1}{2}$
Triangle F: 12, 4, 9

Draw a figure inside the original figure that is a scaled copy. (You choose the scale factor.) Explain how to do it.

16.   **17.**

You scale a polygon by each factor. Find (a) the ratio of the lengths of any two corresponding sides of the original polygon to the scaled one, and (b) the ratio of the measures of any two corresponding angles of the original polygon to the scaled one.

18. $\frac{8}{5}$ **19.** 7   **20.** 5.4   **21.** 0.9   **22.** $\frac{3}{5}$ **23.** 1

Use the angle measures to decide whether the two triangles are scaled copies. Explain.

24. Triangle G: 45°, 45°
Triangle H: 45°, 90°

25. Triangle J: 133°, 11°
Triangle K: 35°, 11°

26. Triangle M: 55°, 82°
Triangle N: 43°, 55°

27. Triangle P: 79°, 81°
Triangle Q: 81°, 20°

28. Triangle R: 102°, 53°
Triangle S: 25°, 53°

29. Triangle V: 139°, 5°
Triangle W: 26°, 139°

Practice: For Lesson 4.5, assign Exercises 16–29.

Answers

9. Check students' work.

10. a. Sample counterexample: a 1-by-2 rectangle and a 1-by-3 rectangle

b. All angles measure 90°, and ratios of corresponding sides are always equal.

c. Sample counterexample: a 1-by-2 rectangle and a 1-by-3 rectangle

d. Sample counterexample: an equilateral triangle and a triangle that is not equilateral

e. Sample counterexample: an equilateral triangle and a nonequilateral isosceles triangle

f. Both triangles have angles 45°, 45°, and 90°. If the legs of the triangles have measures m and n, then the hypotenuses have measures $m\sqrt{2}$ and $n\sqrt{2}$. Hence the ratio of corresponding sides is $\frac{m}{n}$ for all pairs of corresponding sides.

---

9. Draw two quadrilaterals that are not scaled copies but in which the sides of one quadrilateral are twice as long as the corresponding sides of the other quadrilateral.

10. Explain why the figures in each pair below are scaled copies of each other, or give a counterexample to show that they need not be scaled copies.

a. two quadrilaterals

b. two squares

c. two quadrilaterals with equal corresponding angle measures

d. two triangles

e. two isosceles triangles

f. two isosceles right triangles

g. two equilateral triangles

h. two rhombuses

i. two regular polygons with the same number of sides

11. Must any two figures of each type below be scaled copies of each other? Explain why or give a counterexample.

a. rectangles   **b.** parallelograms
c. trapezoids   **d.** isosceles trapezoids
e. regular hexagons   **f.** octagons
g. circles   **h.** cubes
i. spheres   **j.** cylinders
k. boxes   **l.** cones

12. Standardized Test Prep Which two figures are not necessarily scaled copies of each other?

A. two rhombuses   **B.** two squares
C. two circles   **D.** two isosceles right triangles

Maintain Your Skills

13. Scale this circle by the given scale factors.

a. 2   **b.** 2.5
c. 0.5   **d.** 1

Habits of Mind

Simplify. When you must show an example, keep it simple. For Exercise 13a, which length related to a circle is easy to double?

---

g. All angle measures are 60°. In each triangle, the side lengths do not vary, so the ratios of the lengths of corresponding sides do not vary.

h. Sample counterexample: a rhombus with angle measures of 60°, 120°, 60°, and 120°, and a rhombus with angle measures of 50°, 130°, 50°, and 130°

i. Each polygon is equilateral, so the ratio of side lengths does not vary. If the polygons have n sides, then each angle measure is $\frac{(n-2)180°}{n}$.

11. a–l. If no, a sample counterexample is given.

a. no; a 1-by-2 rectangle and a 1-by-3 rectangle

b. no; a 1-by-2 rectangle and a 1-by-3 rectangle

c. no; a trapezoid with bases of lengths 1 and 5 and a trapezoid with bases of lengths 2 and 4

d. No; take an isosceles trapezoid and draw the segment connecting the midpoints of the legs. This segment divides the original isosceles trapezoid into two smaller isosceles trapezoids. No two of the three

In this investigation, you studied scaled copies—accurate reductions or enlargements of given figures. You used scale factors to draw similar figures and to approximate distances on blueprints and maps. You also studied ways to decide whether two shapes were well-scaled copies of each other. These questions will help you summarize what you have learned.

1. Give an approximate scale factor for the following pairs of figures. If you think that the figures are not scaled copies of each other, explain why.

a.

b.

c.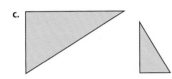

2. Scale the triangle at the right by the factor $\frac{1}{4}$.

3. Check, without measuring, whether the two rectangles below are scaled copies of each other. Explain.

32   24

4. Why is it important to know the scale factor when reading a map?

5. What is a well-scaled drawing?

6. How can you decide whether two rectangles are scaled copies of each other?

Copy a gridded figure frame by frame into a larger grid to get a scaled copy of the original.

Vocabulary

In this investigation, you learned these terms. Make sure you understand what each one means and how to use it.

- ratio
- scale a figure
- scaled figure
- scale factor

---

isosceles trapezoids are scaled copies of each other.

e. yes; special case of Exercise 10 (i)

f. no; an octagon that is regular and one that is not

g. Yes; all radii of a circle are congruent, so the ratios of radii of two circles will always be equal.

h. Yes; all edge lengths of a cube are congruent, so the ratios of edges of two cubes will always be equal.

i. Yes; all radii of a sphere are congruent, so the ratios of radii of two spheres will always be equal.

j. no; any cylinder and one of the cylinders obtained by cutting the original cylinder in half with a plane perpendicular to its axis

k. no; a 1-by-2-by-3 box and a 1-by-2-by-4 box

l. no; any cone and a cone with the same base, but different height

12. A

13. a–d. Check students' work.

Mathematical Reflections

1. a. about $\frac{1}{3}$ or 3

Mathematical Reflections

EXERCISES 4–6 At the start of the investigation, you may have assigned these as Questions 1–3 for students to think and write about.

b. They are not scaled copies of each other. The ratio of height to width is not the same for the two figures.

c. about 2 or $\frac{1}{2}$

2. Diagrams may vary. Sample:

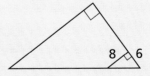

8   6

3. They are scaled copies of each other. Check students' work.

4. Answers may vary. Sample: The scale factor tells how map distances relate to actual distances.

5. a drawing that preserves all ratios and relative positions of the original figure

6. Answers may vary. Sample: Check whether the ratio of their lengths equals the ratio of their widths.

Investigation Overview

This investigation introduces a useful way to scale both polygons and curved figures—the dilation method.

You may wish to assign Questions 1–3 for students to think and write about during the investigation.

Learning Goals

- Describe and use methods for constructing enlargements or reductions of shapes.
- Explain and contrast the ratio method and parallel method for dilation.
- Identify parallel segments and corresponding segments in a drawing and its scaled copy.

Habits and Skills

- Identify a dilation as an enlargement or reduction by looking at the scale factor.
- Dilate figures using the ratio method and the parallel method.
- Describe the effects of the choice for center of dilation on the resulting dilation.

Investigation 4B

Curved or Straight?
Just Dilate!

In *Curved or Straight? Just Dilate!*, you will learn two techniques for making scaled copies. The process of making a scaled copy is called *dilation*. The copy you make may sometimes be larger or smaller than the original figure, depending on the scale factor of the dilation.

By the end of this investigation, you will be able to answer questions like these:

1. What is the mathematical meaning of *dilation*?

2. How do you use the parallel method to scale a polygon?

3. What is the result of applying scale factor 3 to a polygon? The result of applying scale factor $\frac{1}{3}$?

You will learn how to

- describe and use methods for constructing enlargements or reductions of shapes

- explain and contrast the ratio method and parallel method for dilation

- identify parallel segments and corresponding segments in a drawing and its scaled copy

You will develop these habits and skills:

- Identify a dilation as an enlargement or reduction by looking at the scale factor.

- Dilate figures using the ratio method and the parallel method.

- Describe the effects of the choice for center of dilation on the resulting dilation.

Why is it important that Russian nesting dolls be scaled copies of one another?

Investigation Road Map

LESSON 4.6, *Getting Started,* requires students to enlarge three different figures by the factor 2: a square, a star, and a spiral. Students will probably use techniques they learned in the last investigation to enlarge the square and the star, but will need to be creative to enlarge the spiral.

LESSON 4.7, *Making Scaled Copies,* introduces the process of dilation using a center of dilation. Students choose several points on a figure. They use a ruler, the center of dilation, and the given scale factor to find corresponding points on the new figure.

LESSON 4.8, *Ratio and Parallel Methods,* has students learn two methods—the ratio and parallel methods—for dilating simple figures such as polygons.

Getting Started

Activating Prior Knowledge
Exploring New Ideas

You have thought about what a scaled copy is. You have learned to recognize a well-scaled copy. Now you may be wondering how to make scaled copies.

or You to Explore

1. Use only a ruler and pencil. Try to scale figures like these by the factor 2.

a.   **b.**   **c.**

2. Share your drawings with classmates. Decide which drawings are well scaled. Discuss why.

3. Of the scaling processes that seem to work, describe the two that you think work best.

Exercises *Practicing Habits of Mind*

On Your Own

4. Find several meanings of the word *dilation*.

5. Trace this figure onto a sheet of paper. Then use a ruler to scale the traced figure by the given scale factors.

   a. 0.5   **b.** 1

   c. $\frac{3}{2}$ **d.** $\frac{3}{4}$

6. Describe the effect of each scale factor in Exercise 5.

Answers

For You to Explore

1–3. See back of book.

Exercises

4. Answers may vary. Sample: the act of expanding; abnormally enlarging an organ or canal in the body of an animal; a lengthy explanation of a subject

5. **a–d.** Check students' work. Each length in the scaled copy should be

   a. $\frac{1}{2}$ as long   **b.** the same size

   c. $\frac{3}{2}$ as long   **d.** $\frac{3}{4}$ as long

   as the corresponding length of the original hexagon.

6. See Exercise 5 answers.

Lesson Overview

GOAL
• Warm up to the ideas of the investigation.

This lesson introduces the concept of dilation by having students scale figures. Students also explore perimeters and areas of figures and their scaled copies. This lesson sets the stage for future lessons in which students learn specific methods for dilation.

Launch

You may wish to have students work in pairs or small groups.

FOR YOU TO EXPLORE
• Core: 1, 2, 3
• Optional: none

MATERIALS
• geometry software
• rulers

HOMEWORK
• Core: 4, 5, 6, 7, 8, 9, 10
• Optional: 11, 12, 13

Explore

For You to Explore

PROBLEM 1 requires that students choose or invent a way to scale the given figures by the factor 2.

Students can use methods learned previously for the square and the star, but will need to invent a way to scale the spiral in part (c).

Note: For part (c), if students pick a point at or near the center of the original spiral, their scaled copy will overlap the original.

Wrap Up

Before assigning homework, allow students some time to discuss and summarize their findings.

Exercises

HOMEWORK
• Core: 4, 5, 6, 7, 8, 9, 10
• Optional: 11, 12, 13

On Your Own

EXERCISES 5 AND 6 Students had some experience with different scale factors in the previous investigation. These exercises require students to apply scale factors to a regular hexagon and then to describe each result.

EXERCISES 8 AND 10 have students describe the effects of a scale factor on the area and perimeter of a figure. The perimeter of the scaled copy is equal to the perimeter of the original figure multiplied by the scale factor. The area of the scaled copy is equal to the area of the original figure multiplied by the square of the scale factor. Students will explore areas of similar polygons in more depth in Lesson 4.16.

7. Use geometry software. Construct a rectangle. Find its area and perimeter. Then scale your rectangle by each scale factor given below. Record the area and perimeter of the scaled copy.

   a. 2   **b.** 3   **c.** $\frac{1}{2}$ **d.** $\frac{1}{3}$

See the Technology Handbook for ways to scale a figure.

8. For a given rectangle, describe the effects of a scale factor on the area and perimeter. Can you predict the area and perimeter of a scaled copy without first scaling the original rectangle? Without finding the dimensions of the scaled copy?

9. Use geometry software. Construct a triangle. Find its area and perimeter. Scale your triangle by each scale factor given below. Record the area and perimeter of each scaled copy.

   a. 4   **b.** 0.1   **c.** $\frac{3}{5}$ **d.** $\frac{1}{7}$

Go Online
Video Tutor
PHSchool.com

Web Code: bee-0775

10. For a given triangle, describe the effects of a scale factor on the area and perimeter. Can you predict the area and perimeter of a scaled copy without first scaling the original triangle? Without finding the dimensions of the scaled copy?

Maintain Your Skills

11. Use the figure below to find each length.

   a. AZ
   b. BY
   c. CX
   d. DW
   e. EV

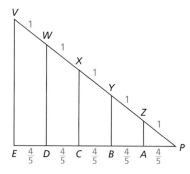

12. $\overline{AZ}$, $\overline{BY}$, $\overline{CX}$, $\overline{DW}$, and $\overline{EV}$ are corresponding sides in triangles AZP, BYP, CXP, DWP, and EVP, respectively. Use your results from Exercise 11. Find each ratio.

   a. $\frac{AZ}{AZ}$ **b.** $\frac{BY}{AZ}$ **c.** $\frac{CX}{AZ}$ **d.** $\frac{DW}{AZ}$ **e.** $\frac{EV}{AZ}$

13. How do the ratios you found in Exercise 12 compare to the ratios of other pairs of corresponding sides in the triangles AZP, BYP, CXP, DWP, and EVP?

Answers

7. The area A and the perimeter P of the original rectangle may vary. The areas and perimeters of the corresponding scaled copies are
   a. area = $4A$, perimeter = $2P$
   b. area = $9A$, perimeter = $3P$
   c. area = $\frac{1}{4}A$, perimeter = $\frac{1}{2}P$
   d. area = $\frac{1}{9}A$, perimeter = $\frac{1}{3}P$

8. The area of the scaled rectangle is equal to the area of the original rectangle multiplied by the square of the scale factor. The perimeter of the scaled rectangle is equal to the perimeter of the original rectangle multiplied by the scale factor. Yes, provided you know the area and perimeter of the original rectangle and the value of the scale factor.

9. The area A and the perimeter P of the original triangle may vary. The areas and perimeters of the corresponding scaled copies are
   a. area = $16A$, perimeter = $4P$
   b. area = $0.01A$, perimeter = $0.1P$
   c. area = $\frac{9}{25}A$, perimeter = $\frac{3}{5}P$
   d. area = $\frac{1}{49}A$, perimeter = $\frac{1}{7}P$

Making Scaled Copies

To scale an image on film, a light source sends beams of light through the film. A screen that is parallel to the film catches the beams. This is a "point-by-point" process.

Here the enlargement is by the factor 2. Point A' is twice as far from the center of dilation as point A. Concisely put, $LA' = 2LA$. Likewise, $LB' = 2LB$.

In mathematics, the procedure of scaling a figure is called **dilation.** In the figure above, the point that corresponds to the light source is the **center of dilation.** The rays coming from it represent the beams of light. The points farther out along the rays (like A' and B') represent the screen images of points on the film (A and B, respectively). To get more image points, draw more rays.

You can think of dilation as a particular way of scaling a figure. If you are asked to "dilate a figure by 2," this means to use dilation to scale it by 2.

Habits of Mind

Communicate context.
You can use *dilation* to refer to the dilation copy when this meaning is clear in context.

Developing Habits of Mind

Make strategic choices. Representing a scaled figure on paper is sometimes easy but can also be challenging. To dilate a line segment, you need to dilate only two points. Which two are they?

To dilate the film image above and get a reasonably good copy, you must dilate many points. The more points you choose to dilate and the more strategically you choose them, the more accurate your dilation.

How many points would you have to dilate to make a good sketch of each of the following?

- a triangle
- a square
- a circle with a given center
- a circle with its center not given

The number needed is not necessarily obvious. For a square, three points are enough. On the other hand, even four points (as suggested in the diagram) might not be enough if the points are not well chosen.

---

10. The area of the scaled triangle is equal to the area of the original triangle multiplied by the square of the scale factor. The perimeter of the scaled triangle is equal to the perimeter of the original triangle multiplied by the scale factor. Yes, provided you know the area and perimeter of the original triangle and the value of the scale factor.

11. a. $\frac{3}{5}$ **b.** $\frac{6}{5}$

   c. $\frac{9}{5}$ **d.** $\frac{12}{5}$

   e. 3

12. a. 1   **b.** 2   **c.** 3
   d. 4   **e.** 5

13. They are the same.

Lesson Overview

GOAL
- Describe and use methods for constructing enlargements or reductions of shapes.

This lesson introduces the process of dilation. Students use a center of dilation and dilate "point by point." They see that the more points they choose, and the more strategically they choose the points, the more accurate their representation of the dilation copy will be.

CHECK YOUR UNDERSTANDING
- Core: 1, 2, 3, 4, 10
- Optional: none

MATERIALS
- geometry software
- mirrors
- rulers

HOMEWORK
- Core: 5, 6, 7, 8, 9
- Optional: 12
- Extension: 11

VOCABULARY
- center of dilation
- dilation

Launch

Ask your class how they dilated the curve in For You to Explore Problem 1c in the Getting Started lesson. Then read through the explanation of dilation on this page of the text. Students will practice this method of dilating a figure in the Check Your Understanding exercises.

Explore

Assign the Check Your Understanding exercises as in-class work. As your students work through these exercises, here are some points to keep in mind:
- Remind students that they can pick the "center of dilation" point to be anywhere they like. Its location only affects where they draw the scaled image. You can stress this idea by asking each student to pick a different center of dilation and then have students compare their work. (See Check Your Understanding Exercise 1b.)
- One key point to make is that a dilated copy always has the same orientation as the original. (See Exercise 2b.)
- Spend some time dilating figures only by the factor 2 so that students get a feel for how the method works. Then ask them to extend the method so that they can dilate by other factors. (See Exercise 3.)

Wrap Up

Before assigning homework, allow students time to discuss and summarize their answers to the Check Your Understanding exercises.

Exercises

HOMEWORK

- Core: 5, 6, 7, 8, 9
- Optional: 12
- Extension: 11

Answers

Exercises

1. a. Check students' work.

b. The location of the center of dilation affects where the scaled copy is located in relation to the original circle.

2. a. Check students' work. Each side of the scaled copy should be twice as long as the corresponding side of the original tilted square.

b. They are the same.

c. no

3. Answers may vary. Sample: To dilate a circle by the factor $\frac{1}{2}$ using point C as the center of dilation, select a point A on the circle. Draw $\overrightarrow{CA}$. Then mark point A' on $\overrightarrow{CA}$ such that $CA' = \frac{1}{2}$ CA. Point A' will be on the scaled copy. Repeat

---

Exercises *Practicing Habits of Mind*

Check Your Understanding

1. Draw a circle on a piece of paper.

   a. Use dilation to scale the circle by the factor 2. Choose enough points on the circle that you can judge whether your dilation really does produce a scaled copy.

   > Pick any center of dilation that you want.

   b. Compare your results with your classmates' work. How does the choice of center of dilation affect the result?

2. **a.** Draw a tilted square on a piece of paper. Dilate it by the factor 2. Dilate at least eight points before drawing the entire dilation image.

   b. How does the orientation of the dilated square compare with that of the original tilted square?

   c. Is orientation affected by your choice for the center of dilation?

a tilted square

3. Explain how to dilate a circle or square by the factor $\frac{1}{2}$. Explain how to dilate it by the factor 3.

4. The ornamental pattern on the left below was dilated by the factor 2. The dilation copy is on the right. Locate the center of dilation.

---

this procedure for several other points of the original circle. Sketch the circle through all the resulting points for the scaled copy. The procedure for dilating the circle by the factor 3 is similar, except this time A' is a point such that $CA' = 3CA$.

To dilate a square, find the points on the dilated square that correspond to the vertices of the original square. Connect these points in order to get the dilated square.

4. Draw the line that passes through the top points of the two figures. Then draw the line that passes through the bottom points of the figures. The point where the two lines intersect is the center of dilation.

5. Choose a favorite picture. It might be like Trig, the horse shown here. Dilate the picture by the factor 2 to make a scaled sketch. You do not need to scale all the details from your picture. A rough outline is fine, but be sure to include at least the important ones.

In Exercises 6–9, you can investigate a dilation that has surprising results. Stand in front of a mirror (perhaps a bathroom mirror at home). Trace your image with a bar of soap. Include important features like your eyes, nose, mouth, and chin.

6. Use a ruler. Measure a few of the distances on your mirror picture. How far apart are your eyes? How wide is your mouth? How far is it from your chin to the top of your head?

7. Compare the distances you've measured on the mirror to the actual measurements of your face. Are they the same?

8. How can the concept of dilation help explain your results?

9. Stand in front of the mirror again. Have a friend trace the image of your face.

s the picture the same as the one you traced? Explain.

Check Your Understanding

EXERCISE 1 has students dilate a circle by the factor 2. Part (b) asks students to compare their results with their classmates'. There should be a variety of centers of dilation.

EXERCISE 3 is the first exercise in which students dilate with a scale factor less than 1. This results in a reduction instead of an enlargement.

EXERCISE 4 It is important to assign this exercise, as it is the first time students have to locate the center of dilation, given the original figure and its enlarged copy.

On Your Own

EXERCISES 6–9 In these exercises, students use a mirror and soap (or grease pencil that can be washed off) to trace their face, and they experiment with dilations. Exercise 9 requires students to have a partner. If you assign these exercises for homework, suggest that a sibling or parent help out.

This mirror activity gives surprising results. When students stand in front of a mirror and trace the image of their face, the mirror image is half the size of their face.

5. Check students' work. The orientation of the two pictures should be the same, but each length in the scaled copy should be twice as long as the corresponding length in the original.

6. Check students' work. Measurements will vary depending on the size of students' faces and on how far away from the mirror students stand.

7. No, the actual measurements on the face are about twice those of the mirror image.

8. The image you see on "the other side" of the mirror appears the same distance behind the mirror that you are in front of the mirror. Imagine drawing lines from your eyes to the image on the other side of the mirror. Think of your eyes as the center of dilation. The mirror is halfway between, so the image on the mirror appears half the size of your actual face.

9. No; the friend is probably to the left or right of where you are and a different distance from the mirror.

Additional Resources

PRINTED RESOURCES
- Solution Manual
- Practice Workbook
- Assessment Resources
- Teaching Resources

TECHNOLOGY
- Interactive Textbook
- TeacherExpress CD-ROM
- **Exam***View* CD-ROM
- PHSchool.com
  - Additional Practice
  - Mid-Chapter and Chapter Tests
  - Video Tutors
  - Vocabulary Puzzles

Additional Practice

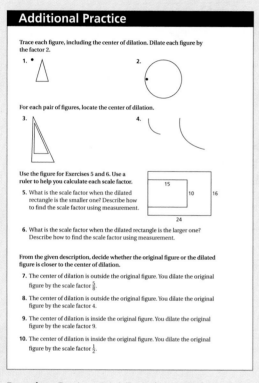

Trace each figure, including the center of dilation. Dilate each figure by the factor 2.

1.

2.

For each pair of figures, locate the center of dilation.

3.

4.

Use the figure for Exercises 5 and 6. Use a ruler to help you calculate each scale factor.

5. What is the scale factor when the dilated rectangle is the smaller one? Describe how to find the scale factor using measurement.

6. What is the scale factor when the dilated rectangle is the larger one? Describe how to find the scale factor using measurement.

From the given description, decide whether the original figure or the dilated figure is closer to the center of dilation.

7. The center of dilation is outside the original figure. You dilate the original figure by the scale factor $\frac{5}{8}$.

8. The center of dilation is outside the original figure. You dilate the original figure by the scale factor 4.

9. The center of dilation is inside the original figure. You dilate the original figure by the scale factor 9.

10. The center of dilation is inside the original figure. You dilate the original figure by the scale factor $\frac{1}{2}$.

Practice: For Lesson 4.7, assign Exercises 1–4.

---

10. **Standardized Test Prep** Suppose you dilate a square by the factor 2. How does the area of the dilated square compare to the area of the original square?

   A. It is the same.   **B.** It is 2 times greater.

   C. It is 4 times greater.   **D.** It is 8 times greater.

11. **Take It Further** Dilating a figure with a pencil and ruler takes plenty of patience. You need to dilate many points to get a good outline of the scaled copy. Geometry software lets you speed up the process.

With geometry software, draw $\overline{AB}$. Construct its midpoint, M. Select points B and M. Use the Trace feature to indicate that you want the software to keep track of the paths of B and M.

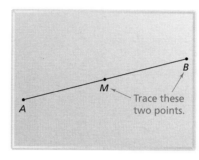

Trace these two points.

  a. Move point B around the screen to draw a picture or perhaps sign your name. Compare point B's path to the path traced by point M. Are they the same? How are they related?

> Point A should stay fixed as you move point B.

  b. Use the software's segment tool. Draw a polygon on your screen. Move point B along the sides of the polygon. Describe the path traced by point M.

  c. As you move point B, trace $\overline{AB}$ as well as points B and M. How does your final picture illustrate the concept of dilation?

> Move point B fairly quickly. If you move it slowly, the screen fills up with traced segments and the picture is hard to see.

Maintain Your Skills

12. Trace this figure. Scale it using the given scale factors. You can choose your own center of dilation.

  a. 2   **b.** 0.5

  c. 1   **d.** 0.1

Go Online
PHSchool.com

For additional practice, go to **Web Code: bea-0407**

Answers

10. C

11. a. No; the path of M is a dilated version of the path of B. The scale factor is $\frac{1}{2}$.

  b. The path of M is a polygon that is a dilated version of the polygon that B traces. The center of dilation is A. The scale factor is $\frac{1}{2}$.

  c. When you trace the entire segment AB, you see the figure that B traces, the scaled copy that M traces, and the segments of the rays you used to make the dilation.

12. a–d. Check students' work. Each length in the scaled copy should be

  a. twice as long **b.** $\frac{1}{2}$ as long

  c. the same size **d.** $\frac{1}{10}$ as long as the corresponding length of the original figure.

Ratio and Parallel Methods

When you use dilation to scale a figure such as a horse's head, you need to dilate a fair number of points before the scaled copy is recognizable. For figures made of line segments, such as polygons, you need to keep track of only a few critical points.

In this lesson, you will learn two shortcuts, the **ratio method** and the **parallel method**. You can use each method with those critical points to make the dilation process much faster.

Habits of Mind

Make strategic choices. For dilating a segment, you choose the endpoints of the segment. Are they strategically good choices? Explain.

Example 1

The Ratio Method

Problem Use point L as the center of dilation. Dilate polygon $ABCDE$ by $\frac{1}{2}$.

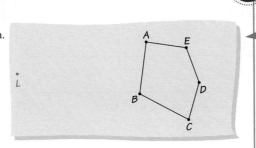

See the Technology Handbook to learn how to use the ratio method with geometry software.

Solution

Step 1 Draw a ray from point L through each vertex of the polygon.

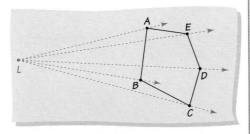

Step 2 Find the midpoint of each of the segments $\overline{LA}$ through $\overline{LE}$.

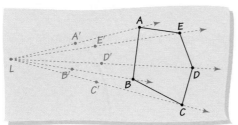

Lesson Overview

GOAL
- Explain and contrast the ratio method and parallel method for dilation.

This lesson formally presents the ratio and parallel methods for dilations. Students also observe the effects of moving the center of dilation.

CHECK YOUR UNDERSTANDING	**HOMEWORK**
• Core: 1, 2, 3, 4, 5, 7, 8, 15	• Core: 9, 10, 11, 12
• Optional: 6	• Optional: 13, 17
	• Extension: 14, 16

MATERIALS
- geometry software
- rulers
- Blackline Masters 4.8A–B (optional)

VOCABULARY
- parallel method
- ratio method
- slider point

Launch

The exercises in Lesson 4.7 are an introduction to the ratio method of dilation that this lesson formally presents. Begin by leading students through Example 1, which demonstrates the ratio method. You may wish to provide students with copies of Blackline Master 4.8A so they can follow along with this example. The Blackline Master may also be helpful as students complete For You to Do Problems 3 and 4.

Explore

Use For Discussion Problems 1 and 2 to summarize the ratio method. Then assign the For You to Do so students can see what happens when they move the center of dilation.

The second method for dilating polygons, the parallel method, requires students to draw segments parallel to the sides of their original polygon. If you do not have geometry software available, ask the students to draw the segments as best they can, judging by eye what looks parallel. If you do have geometry software, the software can automatically construct the parallel lines. You will find a description of the geometry software method in Exercises 13 and 14. Modeling the parallel method with dynamic geometry also has another benefit—students can "slide" their dilated polygon back and forth and watch as it grows and shrinks, always remaining a scaled copy of the original polygon.

Lead students through Example 2, which illustrates the parallel method. You may wish to provide students with copies of Blackline Master 4.8B. Use the For Discussion that follows to summarize.

Wrap Up

Assign the Check Your Understanding exercises for in-class work so students get practice using both the ratio and parallel methods.

If you choose to spend two days on this lesson, on the second day, you may wish to give students an opportunity to try some of the geometry software suggestions explained above.

Step 3 Connect the midpoints to form a new polygon, $A'B'C'D'E'$.

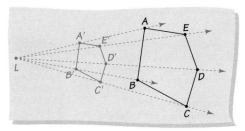

Habits of Mind

Check your results. You can take measurements to check your work. How many measurements would you take to convince yourself that the polygon is a scaled copy of the original? Explain.

For Discussion

1. Is your new polygon a scaled $\left(\text{by } \frac{1}{2}\right)$ copy of the original? How can you tell?

2. There seem to be many pairs of parallel segments in the figure above. Label the parallel segments you see on your own drawing.

For You to Do

3. Draw a triangle. Choose a center of dilation that is inside the triangle. Use the ratio method to scale your triangle by a factor of your choice.

   Does the ratio method work if the center of dilation is inside the polygon?

4. Choose a center of dilation that is on your polygon. Does the ratio method still work?

   Look at each figure you have drawn of a polygon and its dilated companion. The polygons are oriented the same way, and their sides are parallel. This observation suggests another way to dilate.

Answers

For Discussion

1. Yes; the lengths of corresponding sides are proportional, and corresponding angles are congruent.

2. Check students' work.

For You to Do

3. Yes; check students' work.

4. yes

Example 2

The Parallel Method

Problem Use point *E* as the center of dilation. Dilate polygon *ABCD* by 2.

Solution

Step 1 Draw a ray from *E* through each vertex.

Step 2 Along one ray ($\overrightarrow{EA}$ below), find a point that is twice as far from *E* as the vertex *A*. Mark this location *A'*.

Step 3 Start at point *A'*. Draw segments parallel to $\overline{AB}$, $\overline{BC}$, $\overline{CD}$, and finally $\overline{DA}$.

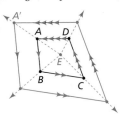

See the Technology Handbook to learn how to use the parallel method with geometry software.

Estimate the parallel segments as best you can.

For Discussion

5. Is your new polygon a scaled (by the factor 2) copy of the original? How can you tell?

6. Label the pairs of parallel segments on your drawing.

For You to Do

7. Draw a triangle. Choose a center of dilation that is on the triangle. Use the parallel method to scale your triangle by a factor of your choice. Does the parallel method work if the center of dilation is on the polygon?

8. Try the parallel method again. This time choose a center of dilation that is outside your polygon. Does the parallel method still work?

For Discussion

5. Yes; the lengths of corresponding sides are proportional, and corresponding angles are congruent.

6. Check students' work.

For You to Do

7. Yes; check students' work.

8. Check students' work; yes.

Exercises

HOMEWORK
- Core: 9, 10, 11, 12
- Optional: 13, 17
- Extension: 14, 16

Check Your Understanding

EXERCISE 3 shows what happens when students pick a center of dilation that coincides with a vertex of the polygon they want to scale.

EXERCISE 4 is worth spending some time on because it illustrates a common mistake that students make when dilating figures.

Exercises Practicing Habits of Mind

Check Your Understanding

As well as making half-size reductions, the ratio method demonstrated in this lesson can dilate a figure by any scale factor you choose.

1. Start with a polygon. Use the ratio method to dilate it by the factor $\frac{1}{3}$.

2. Use the ratio method to enlarge a polygon by the factor 2.

3. Rosie wants to make two scale drawings of $\triangle ABC$. One is to be dilated by the factor 2. The other is to be dilated by the factor 3. She decides to make the triangle vertex A her center of dilation. Draw a picture like the one below. Then finish her construction.

> **Habits of Mind**
>
> **Visualize.** When you have to draw a picture carefully, such as in a construction, it can be very helpful to first sketch what the final picture should look like.

4. **What's Wrong Here?** Steve uses the ratio method to enlarge $\triangle ABC$ below by the factor 2.

He follows this procedure. (See diagram at the top of the next page.)

- He measures the distance DA to be 1. He moves out along $\overrightarrow{DA}$ until he finds a point A' such that $AA' = 2$ (twice as much as DA).

- He measures the distance DB to be 2. He moves out along $\overrightarrow{DB}$ until he finds a point B' such that $BB' = 4$ (twice as much as DB).

- He measures the distance DC to be 1.5. He moves out along $\overrightarrow{DC}$ until he finds a point C' such that $CC' = 3$ (twice as much as DC).

- He draws $\triangle A'B'C'$.

Answers

Exercises

1–2. Check students' work.

3.

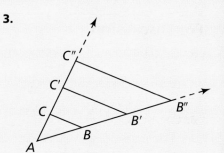

4. 3 times as long; he should have used $DA' = 2$, $DB' = 4$, and $DC' = 3$.

To Steve's surprise, △A'B'C' has sides that are proportional to the sides of △ABC, but they are not twice as long. How many times as long are they? What is the matter here?

5. Oh no! There is a problem at the printing press. The picture below was supposed to show △ABC and its dilated companion, △A'B'C'. But an ink spot spoiled the page. Can you salvage something from this disaster by calculating how much △ABC has been scaled?

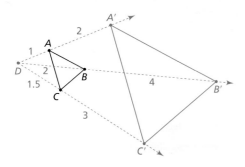

6. Trace the figure below onto a sheet of paper, including the center of dilation, D. Use the ratio method to scale the figure by the given factor.

   a. $\frac{3}{4}$　　　　　　　　　　b. 1.5

7. Draw a polygon. Use the parallel method to reduce the polygon by the factor $\frac{1}{2}$.

8. Draw a polygon. Use the parallel method to enlarge the polygon by the factor 3. Make three enlargements. Locate the centers of dilation inside the polygon, on the polygon, and outside the polygon.

Go Online
PHSchool.com

For a dilation activity,
go to **Web Code: bee-9031**

EXERCISES 7 AND 8 give students a chance to use the parallel method with scale factors other than 2. Exercise 8 encourages students to use different centers of dilation.

5. The scale factor is about 1.4.

6. a–b. Check students' work.

7–8. Check students' work.

On Your Own

EXERCISE 11 asks students to make a scaled copy of a polygon so that one side of the copy contains the corresponding side of the original. Students can do this by making the center of dilation a point on the polygon.

EXERCISES 13, 14, AND 16 give students an opportunity to use geometry software to perform dilations.

9. Draw any polygon. Scale it by 2 using the ratio method. Let the center of dilation be as given.

    a. outside the polygon   b. inside the polygon   c. on the polygon

    d. Explain how the location of the center of dilation affects the scaled copy.

10. Draw a polygon. Make a scaled copy that shares a vertex with the original. Use any scale factor you like (other than 1).

11. Draw a polygon. Make a scaled copy that has one side containing the corresponding side of the original.

> One side of the copy contains the corresponding side of the original. From this, what can you conclude about the dilation?

12. Julia scaled a polygon three times.

    a. The first scaled copy was closer to the center of dilation than the original polygon. What can you say about the scale factor?

    b. The second scaled copy was farther from the center of dilation than the original polygon. What can you say about the scale factor?

    c. The third scaled copy was the same distance from the center of dilation as the original polygon. What can you say about the scale factor? Be careful!

If you use the parallel method with geometry software, you can make a whole series of different-sized scaled polygons. And you don't have to start from scratch each time. The next exercise describes how to do it.

13. Use geometry software. Construct a polygon and a center of dilation. Construct rays from this center through the polygon's vertices. Then place a point anywhere along one of the rays. This will be a "slider point." It will control the amount of dilation.

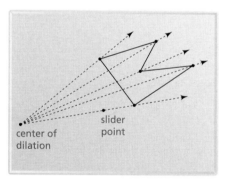

center of dilation   slider point

Answers

9. **a–c.** Check students' work.

    d. Answers may vary. Sample: If the center of dilation *P* is inside the original polygon, then that polygon will be inside the new polygon. If *P* is on the original polygon, then one or two sides of the original will be contained in the sides of the new, and the rest of the original will be inside the new. If *P* is outside the original polygon, then part or all of the new polygon will be outside the original.

10. Check students' work. One of the polygons should have two of its sides contained in the corresponding sides of the other.

11. Check students' work. The scale factor should be greater than 1.

12. **a.** 0 < scale factor < 1

    b. scale factor > 1

    c. scale factor = 1

Use the slider point as the starting point for the dilated image. With the parallel method, complete a dilated copy of the polygon. When your dilated copy is complete, move the slider point back and forth along its ray. Describe what happens.

14. **Take It Further** With your polygon and its scaled copy from Exercise 13, use the software to calculate the scale factor. This scale factor should update itself automatically as you move the slider point. For what location(s) of the slider point is the scale factor as follows?

   a. less than one   **b.** greater than one   **c.** equal to one

15. **Standardized Test Prep** One figure is made of segments. A second figure is made of segments *and* curved parts. Why is the first figure easier to dilate?

   A. You can easily move the center of dilation of the first figure.

   B. You only have to dilate the endpoints of the first figure's segments and then connect those points.

   C. It is easier to place the center of the dilation inside the first figure.

   D. You can draw parallel segments more easily.

16. **Take It Further** Draw △*ABC* with pencil and paper or geometry software. Your challenge is to construct a square with one side lying on $\overline{BC}$ and the other two vertices on sides $\overline{AB}$ and $\overline{AC}$.

Habits of Mind

Visualize. You can shrink the square, keeping three vertices on the triangle. This should suggest an enlargement dilation that will reveal the construction steps.

Maintain Your Skills

17. Use both the ratio method and the parallel method to scale the figure below by the given scale factors.

   a. 2.5
   b. $\frac{1}{2}$
   c. $\frac{5}{2}$
   d. $\frac{1}{4}$

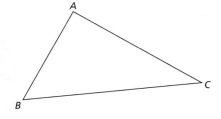

Go Online
PHSchool.com

For additional practice, go to Web Code: bea-0408

Additional Resources

PRINTED RESOURCES
• Solution Manual
• Practice Workbook
• Assessment Resources
• Teaching Resources

TECHNOLOGY
• Interactive Textbook
• TeacherExpress CD-ROM
• **Exam**View CD-ROM
• **PHSchool.com**
   – Additional Practice
   – Mid-Chapter and Chapter Tests
   – Video Tutors
   – Vocabulary Puzzles

Additional Practice

Trace each figure, including the center of dilation. Dilate each figure by the factor 2.

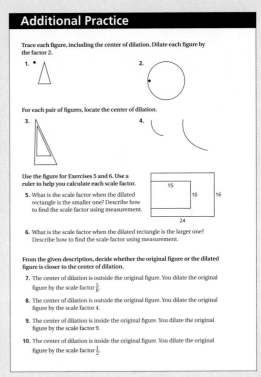

1.

2.

For each pair of figures, locate the center of dilation.

3.

4.

Use the figure for Exercises 5 and 6. Use a ruler to help you calculate each scale factor.

5. What is the scale factor when the dilated rectangle is the smaller one? Describe how to find the scale factor using measurement.

6. What is the scale factor when the dilated rectangle is the larger one? Describe how to find the scale factor using measurement.

From the given description, decide whether the original figure or the dilated figure is closer to the center of dilation.

7. The center of dilation is outside the original figure. You dilate the original figure by the scale factor $\frac{5}{8}$.

8. The center of dilation is outside the original figure. You dilate the original figure by the scale factor 4.

9. The center of dilation is inside the original figure. You dilate the original figure by the scale factor 9.

10. The center of dilation is inside the original figure. You dilate the original figure by the scale factor $\frac{1}{2}$.

Practice: For Lesson 4.8, assign Exercises 7–10.

---

13. The dilated polygon changes size depending on the distance of the slider point from the center of dilation.

14. Call the center of dilation *C*, let *P* be the point on the original polygon, and let *S* be the slider point.
   a. *S* between *C* and *P*
   b. positions of *S* for which *CS>CP*
   c. *S* coinciding with *P*

15. B

16. Answers may vary. Sample: Construct square *BCED* so that the interiors of △*ABC* and *BCED* do not overlap. Draw $\overline{AD}$ and $\overline{AE}$, and call the points where these segments intersect $\overline{BC}$ the points *F* and *G*, respectively. Use the parallel method of dilation, with *A* as the center of dilation, to construct the square that lies inside △*ABC* and has $\overline{FG}$ as a side. This is the desired square.

17. **a–d.** Check students' work.

Mathematical Reflections

EXERCISES 6–8 At the start of the investigation, you may have assigned these as Questions 1–3 for students to think and write about.

4B

Mathematical Reflections

In this investigation, you explored dilations. You applied scale factors to construct enlargements and reductions. You explored choices for the center of dilation. Also, you learned the ratio and parallel methods. These questions will help you summarize what you have learned.

1. You scale a figure by the factor $\frac{3}{5}$. How do the areas of the original figure and the scaled copy compare?

2. Draw $\triangle ABC$ and a point X outside of $\triangle ABC$. Use the ratio method or parallel method. Scale $\triangle ABC$ by $\frac{3}{2}$. Use X as the center of dilation.

3. Trace polygon $ABCD$ and point X. Use the parallel method. Dilate $ABCD$ by the factor $\frac{1}{5}$. Use X as the center of dilation.

4. Explain how to find the center of dilation that maps $\triangle ABC$ to $\triangle DEF$.

5. If you scale the regular tetrahedron at the right by the factor 2, how do the surface areas of the original figure and the scaled copy compare?

6. What is the mathematical meaning of *dilation*?

7. How do you use the parallel method to scale a polygon?

8. What is the result of applying scale factor 3 to a polygon? The result of applying scale factor $\frac{1}{3}$?

Vocabulary

In this investigation, you learned these terms. Make sure you understand what each one means and how to use it.

- center of dilation
- dilation
- parallel method
- ratio method

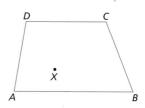

If nesting dolls are dilation images of one another, where is the center of dilation?

Answers

Mathematical Reflections

1. area of scaled copy $= \frac{9}{25}$ (area of original)

2. Check students' work.

3. Check students' work.

4. The center of dilation is the intersection of $\overleftrightarrow{AD}$, $\overleftrightarrow{CF}$, and $\overleftrightarrow{BE}$.

5. surface area of scaled copy $= 4$(surface area of original)

6. Answers may vary. Sample: the process of expanding or shrinking a figure without changing its shape

7. Draw the rays that have the center of dilation C as endpoints and that pass through the vertices of the polygon. Choose a vertex of the polygon and dilate it along the ray that passes through it using the scale factor. Draw lines parallel to consecutive sides of the original polygon, finding the intersections with the corresponding ray. These points will be vertices of the scaled copy.

8. The side lengths will be 3 times those of the original, but the angle measures will not change; the side lengths will be $\frac{1}{3}$ times those of the original, but the angle measures will not change.

4 Mid-Chapter Test

 **Go Online**
PHSchool.com

For a mid-chapter test,
go to Web Code: bea-0452

Multiple Choice

1. You scale a triangle by the factor 3. Then you scale the resulting triangle by the factor 4. What is the ratio of a side length of the original triangle to the corresponding side length of the final triangle?

A. 1 : 12   **B.** 3 : 4   **C.** 4 : 3   **D.** 12 : 1

2. Cube A has a volume of 27 cm³. Cube B is a scaled copy of cube A. You can fit exactly 27 copies of cube A inside cube B. What is the scale factor you can use to transform cube B into cube A?

A. $\frac{1}{9}$ **B.** $\frac{1}{3}$ **C.** 3   **D.** 9

3. You dilate the inner square by the factor 2. The image of the dilation is the outer square. Which point is the center of the dilation?

A. A   **B.** B   **C.** C   **D.** D

Open Response

4. A map gives a scale factor of 1 inch to 5 miles to 10 minutes average driving time.

  a. How far will you travel if your route measures 3.5 inches on the map?

  b. How long will a "3.5-inch trip" take?

  c. What map length represents a 28-mile trip?

5. A square has an area of 80 square inches. Another square has an area of 5 square inches. Can these squares be scaled copies of each other? If so, give a scale factor. If not, explain why not.

6. Copy polygon *WORD* and point *A*. Use any method to dilate *WORD*. Use *A* as the center of dilation and scale factor $\frac{3}{4}$.

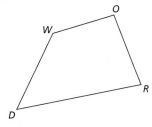

7. You want to scale a polygon by $\frac{1}{3}$. Where would you have to place the center of dilation to have the scaled copy located as follows?

  a. to the left of (possibly overlapping) the original polygon

  b. inside the original polygon

  c. sharing a vertex with the original polygon

8. In the book *Gulliver's Travels*, a grown man from our world visits the land of Lilliput. In Lilliput, the people and things are scaled copies of the people and things in our world. Every length in Lilliput is $\frac{1}{12}$ the corresponding length in our world.

Trace your hand on a piece of paper. Pick a center of dilation. Dilate your tracing to find the size of a Lilliputian student's hand.

9. You scale a cube with 5-inch sides by the factor $\frac{1}{3}$. What is the volume of the scaled cube? How does the volume of the original cube compare to the volume of the scaled tube?

Mid-Chapter Test

1. A

2. B

3. C

4. a. 17.5 mi
  b. 35 min
  c. by a path 5.6 in. long

5. Yes; 16 or $\frac{1}{16}$

6. Check students' work.

7. a. to the left of the original polygon
  b. inside the original polygon
  c. at a vertex of the original polygon

8. Check students' work.

9. $\frac{125}{27}$ in.³; $\frac{\text{volume of original}}{\text{volume of scaled}} = 27$

Investigation Overview

In this investigation, students perform experiments that lead to two important results about triangles: the parallel and proportional side-splitter theorems. Students prove these theorems by exploring a proof attributed to Euclid.

You may wish to assign Questions 1–3 for students to think and write about during the investigation.

Learning Goals

- Investigate proportional relationships in nested triangles.
- Investigate how lines parallel to a side of a triangle cut the other two sides.
- Prove the side-splitter theorems.

Habits and Skills

- Use ratios and proportions.
- Prove conjectures using scaled figures.
- Identify invariants.

Investigation 4C

The Side-Splitter Theorems

In *The Side-Splitter Theorems*, you will dilate a triangle using one of its vertices as the center of dilation. You will examine the result in detail and develop some very useful theorems.

By the end of this investigation, you will be able to answer questions like these:

1. If a point D is on side $\overline{AB}$ of $\triangle ABC$, E is on $\overline{AC}$, and $\overline{DE}$ is parallel to $\overline{BC}$, then what can you say about the relationship between $\triangle ABC$ and $\triangle ADE$?

2. What are the side-splitter theorems?

3. If two triangles have the same height, and you know the ratio of their areas, what is the ratio of the lengths of their bases?

You will learn how to

- investigate proportional relationships in nested triangles
- investigate how lines parallel to a side of a triangle cut the other two sides
- prove the side-splitter theorems

You will develop these habits and skills:

- Use ratios and proportions.
- Prove conjectures using scaled figures.
- Identify invariants.

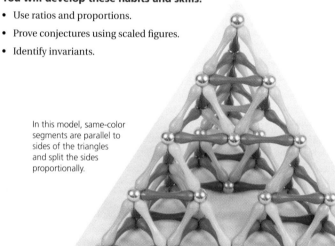

In this model, same-color segments are parallel to sides of the triangles and split the sides proportionally.

Investigation Road Map

LESSON 4.9, *Getting Started,* has students work on some exercises to prepare them for the proofs they have to write in this investigation.

LESSON 4.10, *Nested Triangles,* has students work on an In-Class Experiment that will lead them to the important Parallel and Proportional Side-Splitter Theorems.

LESSON 4.11, *Proving the Side-Splitter Theorems,* provides an outline of the first part of the Parallel Side-Splitter Theorem. The Check Your Understanding exercises ask students to prove the Proportional Side-Splitter Theorem in the same manner.

LESSON 4.12, *The Side-Splitter Theorems (continued),* proves the remainder of the Parallel Side-Splitter Theorem.

Getting Started

In this investigation, you will construct proofs for most parts of the side-splitter theorems. At the core of these proofs is an ingenious area argument devised by Euclid. To prepare for the proofs, you have several questions about area to work on first.

For You to Explore

1. Points A and B of $\triangle ABC$ are fixed on line ℓ. Line m is parallel to line ℓ. Point C, which is not shown, is free to wander anywhere along line m. For what location of point C is the area of $\triangle ABC$ the greatest? Explain.

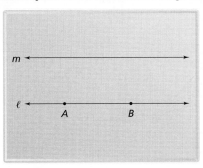

Geometry software makes it easy for you to experiment with different locations of point C.

In Exercises 2 and 3, you prove that if two triangles have the same height, the ratio of their areas is the same as the ratio of their bases.

2. Both $\triangle ABC$ and $\triangle DEF$ have height h. Write an expression for the area of each triangle. Then show that the ratio of their areas is $\frac{AC}{DF}$.

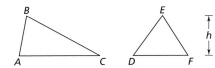

3. The area of $\triangle GEM$ is 3 square inches. The area of $\triangle MEO$ is 2 square inches. What is the value of $\frac{GE}{EO}$? Explain. Also, find the value of $\frac{GE}{GO}$.

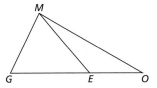

Lesson Overview

GOALS
- Warm up to the ideas of the investigation.
- Use an exploratory approach to develop mathematical habits of mind.

This lesson prepares students for the proofs of the side-splitter theorems. Students work on problems and answer questions about area to build a basis for the proofs.

CHECK YOUR UNDERSTANDING	HOMEWORK
• Core: 1, 2, 3	• Core: 4, 5, 6
• Optional: none	• Optional: 7

MATERIALS
- geometry software

Launch

You may wish to have students work in pairs or small groups.

Explore

Have students begin with the For You to Explore problems. You may need to remind them of the formula for the area of a triangle.

For You to Explore

PROBLEM 1 Given two parallel lines and two points on one of those lines, students experiment with making different triangles. Students choose a point on the second line, draw a triangle, and measure its area. Geometry software makes this activity much more dramatic and elegant. Students can simply place a point on the second line, draw the triangle, and then drag that point back and forth along the line and watch the area change—or in this case, *not* change. Students need to recall that the perpendicular distance between two parallel lines (which, in this figure, is the height of the triangle) is constant.

PROBLEMS 2 AND 3 have students calculate the areas of triangles and the ratios of their areas. In Problem 2, students let the height of all triangles in the figure be h. Students then write expressions for the areas of the triangles.

Answers

For You to Explore

1. Area ($\triangle ABC$) does not change as C moves along line m; the height of $\triangle ABC$ when measured from C to line ℓ is always the same.

2. Area($\triangle ABC$) = $\frac{1}{2}h(AC)$ and Area ($\triangle DEF$) = $\frac{1}{2}h(DF)$, so
$$\frac{\text{Area}(\triangle ABC)}{\text{Area}(\triangle DEF)} = \frac{\frac{1}{2}h(AC)}{\frac{1}{2}h(DF)} = \frac{AC}{DF}.$$

3. $\frac{GE}{EO} = \frac{3}{2}$; all triangles in the figure have the same height h (measured from M), so $\frac{1}{2}h(GE) = 3$ in.^{2} and $\frac{1}{2}h(EO) = 2$ in.^{2}. Use division with these equations to get $\frac{GE}{EO} = \frac{3}{2}$. $\frac{GE}{GO} = \frac{3}{5}$.

Wrap Up

Before assigning homework, allow students some time to discuss and summarize their findings.

Exercises

HOMEWORK
- Core: 4, 5, 6
- Optional: 7

On Your Own

EXERCISE 5 Students need to know the formula for area of a triangle ($A = \frac{1}{2}bh$) to complete this exercise. They will also need to use what they found in Problems 1–3.

On Your Own

4. In this figure, $\dfrac{\text{area} \triangle PQS}{\text{area} \triangle RPS} = \dfrac{1}{2}$. If $SQ = 4$ and $PS = 6$, find the lengths PQ, SR, QR, and PR.

Go Online
Video Tutor
PHSchool.com

Web Code: **bee-0775**

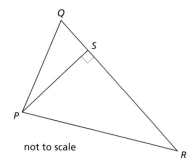

not to scale

5. Quadrilateral *ABCD* is a trapezoid with $\overline{AB} \parallel \overline{DC}$.

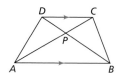

   a. Explain why the area of $\triangle ACB$ is equal to the area of $\triangle ADB$.

   b. Name two other pairs of triangles in the figure that have equal areas. Explain how you know.

6. *GRAM* is a parallelogram. Which of $\triangle GAM$, $\triangle ARM$, $\triangle MRG$, and $\triangle RAG$ has the greatest area? Explain.

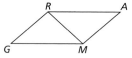

Maintain Your Skills

7. This figure is a scaled copy. Draw an original figure that would result in this copy for each of the following scale factors.

   a. 2   **b.** 3

   c. 0.5   **d.** 0.1

Answers

Exercises

4. $PQ = 2\sqrt{13}$, $SR = 8$, $QR = 12$, $PR = 10$

5. The triangles have a common base and equal heights (measured from *C* and *D*); by similar reasoning, $\triangle ADC$ and $\triangle BCD$ have equal areas.

6. All will have the same area; they have congruent bases ($\overline{RA}$ and $\overline{GM}$) and equal heights (the distance between $\overleftrightarrow{RA}$ and $\overleftrightarrow{GM}$).

7. **a–d.** Check students' work.

Nested Triangles

Here are a polygon (black) and a dilated copy (blue). The copy was made using the parallel method.

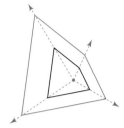

a polygon and its scaled companion

The four pictures below show the same polygons. Each picture highlights a pair of **nested triangles**—one triangle inside another. Notice that each pair of nested triangles contains a side from the original polygon and a parallel side from the scaled polygon.

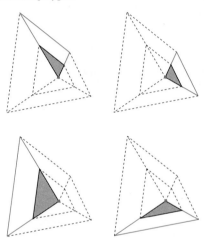

four pairs of nested triangles

In the In-Class Experiment that follows, you should discover some important relationships between parallel lines and the sides of the triangles that they intersect.

Go Online
PHSchool.com

For a famous example of nested triangle, go to Web Code: bee-9031

Lesson Overview

GOALS
- Investigate proportional relationships in nested triangles.
- Investigate how lines parallel to a side of a triangle cut the other two sides.

It will probably take a couple of class periods to complete the In-Class Experiment, to introduce the theorems, and to work on the Check Your Understanding exercises. See the Daily Planner at the beginning of the chapter for suggestions for assigning the exercises.

The ratio and parallel methods both produce scale drawings, but why do they work? This lesson begins to answer that question by noting that each dilation picture consists of *nested triangles*.

CHECK YOUR UNDERSTANDING
- Core: 3, 4, 5, 7
- Optional: none

MATERIALS
- protractors
- rulers
- geometry software

HOMEWORK
- Core: 1, 2, 6, 8
- Optional: 9, 10

VOCABULARY
- common ratio
- nested triangles
- splits two sides proportionally

Launch

Review this picture of nested triangles with your whole class to be sure that students see the outlined triangles in the pictures.

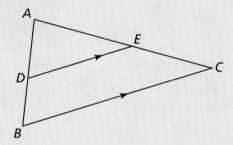

Explore

After you review nested triangles, have students work in pairs or small groups on the In-Class Experiment.

In-Class Experiment

Parts 1A and 1B are designed to be used with geometry software. If you have only one computer in your classroom, a whole-class demonstration would be suitable. If you decide not to use software, students will need to make several drawings and take measurements using a ruler.

In-Class Experiment

Part 1A   Parallel Lines and Midpoints

Draw a picture like the one below. Show two parallel lines and a point. Make the distance between the point and the closer line equal to the distance between the two lines.

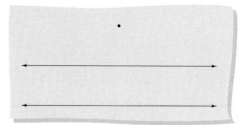

1. Use your picture. Find a quick way to draw ten segments so that each will have its midpoint automatically marked.

2. Find a way to position two parallel lines and a point that gives a quick way to draw ten segments with each segment divided into two smaller segments with lengths in the ratio 1 to 3.

Part 1B   Midpoints and Parallel Lines

Use geometry software. Draw $\overleftrightarrow{XY}$. Construct a point A on $\overleftrightarrow{XY}$ and a point B that is not on $\overleftrightarrow{XY}$. Draw $\overline{AB}$ and construct its midpoint M. Drag point A back and forth along the entire length of $\overleftrightarrow{XY}$ while tracing the path of point M.

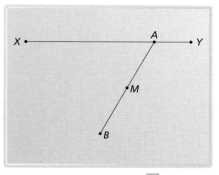

Drag point A along $\overleftrightarrow{XY}$.

3. a. Describe the path traced by M.

   b. How does the path traced by point M compare to $\overleftrightarrow{XY}$?

4. Repeat the construction above. This time, instead of constructing the midpoint of $\overline{AB}$, place the point M somewhere else on $\overline{AB}$. How does the position of M affect the path traced by M?

Answers

In-Class Experiment

1. Call the point P. Call the line closest to P line ℓ and the other line m. If Q is any point on line m, then the point where $\overline{PQ}$ intersects line ℓ is automatically the midpoint of $\overline{PQ}$.

2. Answers may vary. Sample: Draw two parallel lines. Mark a point P between them that is twice as far from one of the lines as it is from the other. If you draw a line through P that intersects the parallel lines at points A and B, then P divides $\overline{AB}$ in the ratio 1 to 3.

3. a. It is the segment whose endpoints are the midpoints of $\overline{BX}$ and $\overline{BY}$.

   b. It is parallel to $\overline{XY}$ and half as long as $\overline{XY}$.

4. The path traced by point M will be a segment $\overline{RS}$, where R is on $\overline{BX}$ and S is on $\overline{BY}$. $\overline{RS} \parallel \overline{XY}$ and the points R, M, and S divide $\overline{BX}$, $\overline{BA}$, and $\overline{BY}$, respectively, in the same ratio.

5. Use geometry software. Draw $\overline{XY}$. Locate a point A on $\overline{XY}$. Then construct three segments, each with A as an endpoint. Construct the midpoints M_1, M_2, and M_3 of the three segments. Move point A back and forth along $\overline{XY}$ while tracing the paths of these midpoints. Describe the paths of the midpoints, including what you know about their locations and lengths.

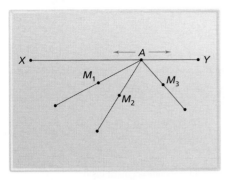

Part 2 Splitting Two Sides of a Triangle

Use geometry software. Draw $\triangle ABC$. Place a point D anywhere on side $\overline{AB}$. Then construct a segment $\overline{DE}$ that is parallel to $\overline{BC}$.

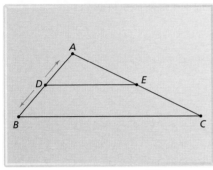

Drag point D along $\overline{AB}$.

$\triangle ADE$ and $\triangle ABC$ are a pair of nested triangles.

6. Use the software to find the ratio $\frac{AD}{AB}$.

7. Find two other length ratios with the same value. Do all three ratios remain equal to each other when you drag point D along $\overline{AB}$?

8. As you drag D along $\overline{AB}$, describe what happens to the figure. Make a conjecture about the effect of $\overline{DE}$ being parallel to $\overline{BC}$.

5. Let $\overline{B_1A}$, $\overline{B_2A}$, and $\overline{B_3A}$ be the segments that have midpoints M_1, M_2, and M_3, respectively. The paths of M_1, M_2, and M_3 are segments parallel to $\overline{XY}$ and half as long as $\overline{XY}$. The endpoints of the paths are the midpoints of segments joining B_1, B_2, and B_3 to X and Y.

6. Check students' work.

7. $\frac{AE}{AC}$ and $\frac{DE}{BC}$; yes

8. check students' work; $\frac{AE}{EC}$

Assessment Resources

Lesson Quiz 4.10

Use the figure for Exercises 1–7. In the figure, $\overline{DE} \parallel \overline{BC}$.

1. When $AD = 10$, $DB = 6$, and $AE = 12$, what is EC?
2. When $AE = 40$, $AC = 72$, and $DE = 50$, what is BC?
3. When $AE = 24$, $BC = 38$, and $DE = 20$, what is EC?
4. When $AD = 8$, $BD = 6$, and $AC = 7$, what is EC?
5. When $BC = 18$, $DB = 12$, and $DE = 10$, what is AD?
6. When $AD = 9$ and $AB = 20$, what is the value of $\frac{DE}{BC}$?
7. When $AD = 27$, $AB = 42$, and $AE = 24$, what is the value of $\frac{BD}{CE}$?

Tony and Sasha are finishing the In-Class Experiment.

Tony   I like dragging points on the computer screen and watching what happens.

Sasha   Me too. Triangle ADE and the ratios all got small when we dragged D close to A.

Tony   And when we dragged D close to B, the two triangles were almost the same, and the ratios were almost 1!

Sasha   The two triangles always had the same shape too. I think that happened because we constructed $\overline{DE}$ parallel to $\overline{BC}$.

Tony   The parallel segment seemed to make everything work nicely.

Sasha   So, can we make a conjecture about what having a parallel segment like $\overline{DE}$ does for the figure?

Tony   Can we say something like "A parallel-to-one-side segment inside a triangle makes two proportional triangles"?

Sasha   Hmm. I get the idea. I think we have to work on the wording.

Sasha and Tony need a definition of what it means for a segment to divide two sides of a triangle proportionally.

Definitions

In $\triangle ABC$ with D on $\overline{AB}$ and E on $\overline{AC}$, $\overline{DE}$ **splits two sides proportionally** ($\overline{AB}$ and $\overline{AC}$) if and only if $\frac{AB}{AD} = \frac{AC}{AE}$.

You call the ratio $\frac{AB}{AD}$ the **common ratio.**

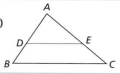

The In-Class Experiment may have suggested statements like the two theorems that follow. You will prove these theorems in the next two lessons.

Theorem 4.1   The Parallel Side-Splitter Theorem

If a segment with endpoints on two sides of a triangle is parallel to the third side of the triangle, then

- the segment splits the sides it intersects proportionally

- the ratio of the length of the side of the triangle to the length of the parallel segment is the common ratio.

$$\frac{AB}{AD} = \frac{AC}{AE} = \frac{BC}{DE}$$

Theorem 4.2   The Proportional Side-Splitter Theorem

If a segment with endpoints on two sides
of a triangle splits those sides proportionally,
then the segment is parallel to the third side.

$$\frac{AB}{AD} = \frac{AC}{AE} \Rightarrow \overline{DE} \parallel \overline{BC}$$

Exercises *Practicing Habits of Mind*

Check Your Understanding

In Exercises 1–5, $\overline{DE} \parallel \overline{BC}$.

1. If $AD = 1$, $AB = 3$, and $AE = 2$, what is AC?

2. If $AE = 4$, $AC = 5$, and $AB = 20$, what is AD?

3. If $AD = 3$, $DB = 2$, and $AE = 12$, what is EC?

4. If $AE = 1$, $AC = 4$, and $DE = 3$, what is BC?

5. If $AD = 2$ and $DB = 6$, what is the value of $\frac{DE}{BC}$?

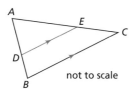

not to scale

On Your Own

6. Understanding Theorems 4.1 and 4.2 by reading
through their words can be difficult. It may help to
replace some of the words with actual segment
names. Rewrite each theorem using the nested
triangles shown here as a reference. Make each
theorem as specific as possible. If a theorem
mentions a segment length or a proportion,
substitute the name of that segment or
proportion in place of the words.

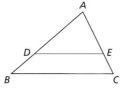

Exercises

Check Your Understanding

EXERCISES 1–5 To complete these exercises, students
need to assume that the Parallel Side-Splitter
Theorem is true.

On Your Own

EXERCISE 6 asks students to rewrite the Parallel and
Proportional Side-Splitter Theorems using actual
segment names in order to understand the
theorems better.

Answers

Exercises

1. 6   **2.** 16   **3.** 8

4. 12   **5.** $\frac{1}{4}$

6. Answers may vary. Sample: For
   the Parallel Side-Splitter Theorem,
   suppose $\triangle ABC$ is any triangle and
   $\overline{DE} \parallel \overline{BC}$, where D is between A
   and B, and E is between A and C.
   Then (1) $\frac{AB}{AD} = \frac{AC}{AE}$, and (2) $\frac{BC}{DE}$
   is equal to $\frac{AB}{AD}$ and $\frac{AC}{AE}$. For the
   Proportional Side-Splitter Theorem,
   suppose $\triangle ABC$ is any triangle, D
   is between A and B, E is between
   A and C, and $\frac{AB}{AD} = \frac{AC}{AE}$. Then
   $\overline{DE} \parallel \overline{BC}$.

EXERCISE 8 has students explain a shortcut for remembering the Parallel Side-Splitter Theorem: "whole is to part as whole is to part," "part is to part as part is to part," or "part is to whole as part is to whole."

Additional Resources

PRINTED RESOURCES
- Solution Manual
- Practice Workbook
- Assessment Resources
- Teaching Resources

TECHNOLOGY
- Interactive Textbook
- TeacherExpress CD-ROM
- **Exam**View CD-ROM
- **PHSchool.com**
  - Additional Practice
  - Mid-Chapter and Chapter Tests
  - Video Tutors
  - Vocabulary Puzzles

Additional Practice

Use the figure for Exercises 1–10. In Exercises 1–9, $\overline{DE} \parallel \overline{BC}$.

1. When $AD = 15$, $DB = 9$, and $AE = 10$, what is EC?
2. When $AE = 18$, $EC = 12$, and $BC = 20$, what is DE?
3. When $AD = 9$, $BC = 24$, and $DE = 8$, what is AB?
4. When $AD = 8$, $AE = 10$, and $AB = 15$, what is AC?
5. When EC is half of AE, and $DE = 2.4$, what is BC?
6. When EC is 1.5 times AE, and $BC = 60$, what is DE?
7. When $DE = 12$, $BC = 15$, and $AC = 24$, what is EC?
8. When $AD = 14$ and $BD = 21$, what is the value of $\frac{DE}{BC}$?
9. When $AD = 15$, $AE = 12$, and $EC = 10$, what is the value of $\frac{BC}{DE}$?
10. Suppose you do not know whether $\overline{DE} \parallel \overline{BC}$, but you do know that $AD = 24$, $AC = 48$, $AE = 18$, and $DB = 40$. Is $\overline{DE} \parallel \overline{BC}$? Explain.

Use the figure for Exercises 11–19. In Exercises 11–18, $\overline{ST} \parallel \overline{UV}$, $\overline{UV} \parallel \overline{QR}$, and $\overline{ST} \parallel \overline{QR}$.

11. When $PS = 9$, $PU = 17$, and $TV = 6$, what is PT?
12. When $PS = k$, $SU = 10$, $TV = 15$, and $UQ = 18$, what is VR?
13. When $PS = 90$, $SU = 18$, and $PT = 110$, what is TV?
14. When $UV = 32$, $PV = 44$, and $PT = 8$, what is ST?
15. When $PS = 6$, $SU = 7$, $UQ = 8$, and $TR = 21$, what is PR?
16. When $PT = 7$ and $TR = 21$, what is the value of $\frac{ST}{QR}$?
17. When $SQ = 50$, $QU = 30$, and $VR = 25$, what is the value of $\frac{TV}{VR}$?
18. Is $\frac{PS}{PT} = \frac{PQ}{PR}$? Explain.
19. Suppose you do not know whether $\overline{ST} \parallel \overline{UV}$, $\overline{UV} \parallel \overline{QR}$, or $\overline{ST} \parallel \overline{QR}$, but you do know that $\frac{TV}{SU} = \frac{VR}{UQ}$. Which segments are parallel?

Practice: For Lesson 4.10, assign Exercises 1–19.

---

7. **Standardized Test Prep** In $\triangle ABC$, suppose $\overleftrightarrow{DE} \parallel \overleftrightarrow{BC}$. Which proportion is NOT correct?

   a. $\frac{AD}{AB} = \frac{AE}{AC}$ **b.** $\frac{AD}{DB} = \frac{AE}{EC}$

   c. $\frac{AD}{DB} = \frac{DE}{BC}$ **d.** $\frac{AD}{AB} = \frac{DE}{BC}$

8. **Write About It** The Parallel Side-Splitter Theorem says that a segment parallel to a side of a triangle with endpoints on the other two sides "splits the other two sides proportionally."

   Tammy Jo has three sayings that help her remember this:

   Whole is to part as whole is to part.

   Part is to part as part is to part.

   Part is to whole as part is to whole.

   What do these sayings mean?

Maintain Your Skills

For Exercises 9 and 10, use the figure at the right. $\overline{DE} \parallel \overline{BC}$.

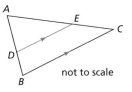

9. Find EC given the following conditions.

   a. $AD = 1$, $DB = 4$, and $AE = 3$
   b. $AD = 1$, $DB = 4$, and $AE = 7$
   c. $AD = 1$, $DB = 7$, and $AE = 4$
   d. $AD = 1$, $DB = 10$, and $AE = 10$
   e. $AD = 1$, $DB = \frac{1}{2}$, and $AE = 3$
   f. $AD = 1$, $DB = x$, and $AE = y$

10. Find EC given the following conditions.

    a. $AE = 1$, $AD = 4$, and $DB = 8$
    b. $AE = 1$, $AD = 8$, and $DB = 4$
    c. $AE = 1$, $AD = 2$, and $DB = 10$
    d. $AE = 1$, $AD = 2$, and $DB = \frac{1}{2}$
    e. $AE = 1$, $AD = \frac{1}{2}$, and $DB = 2$
    f. $AE = 1$, $AD = x$, and $DB = y$

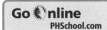

Go Online
PHSchool.com

For additional practice, go to Web Code: bea-0410

Answers

7. C

8. Answers may vary. Sample: For the figure in Exercise 6, "whole is to part as whole is to part" means $\frac{AB}{AD} = \frac{AC}{AE}$, "part is to part as part is to part" means $\frac{AD}{DE} = \frac{AE}{EF}$, and "part is to whole as part is to whole" means $\frac{AD}{AB} = \frac{AE}{AC}$.

9. **a.** 12   **b.** 28   **c.** 28
   d. 100   **e.** $\frac{3}{2}$ **f.** xy

10. **a.** 2   **b.** $\frac{1}{2}$ **c.** 5
    d. $\frac{1}{4}$ **e.** 4   **f.** $\frac{y}{x}$

Proving the Side-Splitter Theorems

Recall what the first part of the Parallel Side-Splitter Theorem says:

> If a segment with endpoints on two sides of a triangle is parallel to the third side of the triangle, then it splits the sides it intersects proportionally.

To prove this theorem, you can show that, in the figure below, if $\overline{VW} \parallel \overline{RT}$, then $\frac{SV}{VR} = \frac{SW}{WT}$.

In the figures below, triangles SVW and RVW have the same height. This means that the ratio of their areas is equal to the ratio of their base lengths, SV and VR.

$$\frac{\text{area}(\triangle SVW)}{\text{area}(\triangle RVW)} = \frac{SV}{VR}$$

> **This fact comes from Lesson 4.9.**

In the figures below, triangles SVW and TVW have the same height. Thus, the ratio of their areas is equal to the ratio of their base lengths, SW and WT.

$$\frac{\text{area}(\triangle SVW)}{\text{area}(\triangle TVW)} = \frac{SW}{WT}$$

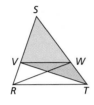

Habits of Mind

Understand the process. A "tidy" proof like this may not necessarily be easy to write. You build it from many notes, sketches, erasures, more sketches, more notes, and plenty of talking to yourself!

You have two fractions with the same numerator,

$$\frac{\text{area}(\triangle SVW)}{\text{area}(\triangle RVW)} \text{ and } \frac{\text{area}(\triangle SVW)}{\text{area}(\triangle TVW)}.$$

The denominators are not the same, but are they equal? Recall Problem 1 from Lesson 4.9 Getting Started. Triangles RVW and TVW share the same base $\overline{VW}$. They have the same height since $\overline{VW}$ is parallel to $\overline{RT}$. So they have the same area.

You can combine all of these results to draw a conclusion about SV, VR, SW, and WT.

$$\frac{SV}{VR} = \frac{\text{area}(\triangle SVW)}{\text{area}(\triangle RVW)} = \frac{\text{area}(\triangle SVW)}{\text{area}(\triangle TVW)} = \frac{SW}{WT}$$

For You to Do

1. Using what has been outlined in this lesson, write a complete proof of the first part of the Parallel Side-Splitter Theorem.

For You to Do

1. Check students' work.

Lesson Overview

GOAL
• Prove the side-splitter theorems.

This lesson provides an outline of the first part of the Parallel Side-Splitter Theorem: If a segment is parallel to one side of a triangle, then it splits the other two sides proportionally.

CHECK YOUR UNDERSTANDING	**HOMEWORK**
• Core: 1, 2, 3, 4	• Core: 5, 6, 7
• Optional: none	• Optional: 10
MATERIALS	• Extension: 8, 9
• Blackline Masters 4.11A and B (optional)	

Launch

It may be helpful if you make transparencies of the pictures and explanations in the student text using Blackline Master 4.11A. Then you can go over this proof outline as a whole class. In order for students to understand Euclid's proof, they need to be comfortable with the result stated in Lesson 4.9 Problem 2: If two triangles have the same height, the ratio of their areas is the same as the ratio of their base lengths.

Explore

Review the outline of the first part of the Parallel Side-Splitter Theorem as a whole class. Once students have worked through these steps they should work on the For You to Do, which asks them to write out the proof of the first part of the theorem.

Wrap Up

Assign the Check Your Understanding exercises for work in class. You may want to help students outline the proof of the Proportional Side-Splitter Theorem in Exercise 1.

In each figure in Exercises 1 and 2, $\overline{AB} \parallel \overline{DE}$. Find as many lengths as you can.

1.

2.

For Exercises 3 and 4, use the given lengths in each figure to decide whether $\overline{AB}$ is parallel to $\overline{DE}$. Explain.

3.

4.

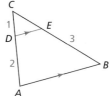

Exercises Practicing Habits of Mind

Check Your Understanding

1. Recall the Proportional Side-Splitter Theorem:

> If a segment with endpoints on two sides of a triangle splits those sides proportionally, then the segment is parallel to the third side.

This time, the proof is up to you. Use the same setup that you used to prove the Parallel Side-Splitter Theorem. Write your proof so that someone else can follow it.

2. In the diagrams below, $\overline{AB}$ is parallel to $\overline{DE}$. Find as many lengths as you can.

a.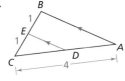

b. (diagram)

c.

The main entrance to the Rock and Roll Hall of Fame is at the base of this glass-and-steel triangle. Can you find horizontal steel ribbing in the triangle that is half the length of the base? Three fourths the length of the base?

Answers

Exercises

1. Reverse some of the steps in the proof of the Parallel Side-Splitter Theorem to show that

$\frac{SV}{VR} = \frac{SW}{WT}$ implies $\frac{\text{Area }(\triangle SVW)}{\text{Area }(\triangle RVW)} =$ $\frac{\text{Area }(\triangle SVW)}{\text{Area }(\triangle TVW)}$ and that this implies Area $(\triangle RVW) = $ Area$(\triangle TVW)$. Since Area$(RVWT)$ is equal to both Area$(\triangle RVW) + $ Area$(\triangle RWT)$ and Area$(\triangle TVW) + $ Area$(\triangle RVT)$, it follows that Area $(\triangle RVT) = $ Area$(\triangle RWT)$. In $\triangle RVT$, draw the altitude $\overline{VM}$ from V to $\overline{RT}$, and in $\triangle RWT$, draw the altitude $\overline{WN}$ from W to $\overline{RT}$. Use the area formula with $\triangle RVT$ and $\triangle RWT$ to get $\frac{1}{2}(RT)(VM) = \frac{1}{2}(RT)(WN)$, from which it follows that $VM = WN$. Conclude that

$MVWN$ is a parallelogram (two sides parallel and congruent) and hence that $\overline{VM} \parallel \overline{RT}$.

2. a. $CD = 2$, $AD = 2$, $BC = 2$
b. $BC = 4.5$, $CD = 1.5$, $AC = 3$
c. $CD = 1$, $CE = 1$, $BC = 2$

3. Use the lengths given in each figure below to decide whether $\overline{AB}$ is parallel to $\overline{DE}$. Explain.

a.

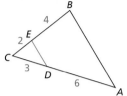

b.

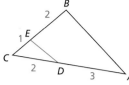

c.

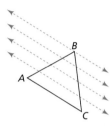

On Your Own

4. Standardized Test Prep In $\triangle STR$, $\overline{VU} \parallel \overline{TS}$. Suppose that $TS = 540$, $VU = 180$, $US = 667$, and $RT = 600$. What is RV?

A. 200 **B.** 240 **C.** 270 **D.** 333

5. The dashed lines in the diagrams are all parallel to $\overline{AC}$ and equally spaced. What can you conclude about how they intersect $\overline{AB}$ and $\overline{BC}$?

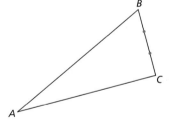

6. Make two copies of this diagram.

Use the fact that the points shown in red trisect $\overline{BC}$ to do the following.

a. Trisect $\overline{AB}$.

b. Trisect $\overline{AC}$.

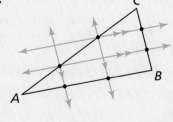

> **Habits of Mind**
>
> **Make connections.**
> How does the definition of *bisect* help you define *trisect*?

Exercises

HOMEWORK
- Core: 5, 6, 7
- Optional: 10
- Extension: 8, 9

Check Your Understanding

EXERCISE 1 asks students to write a proof of the Proportional Side-Splitter Theorem using as a guide the proof of the Parallel Side-Splitter Theorem that they wrote in For You to Do Problem 1.

On Your Own

EXERCISE 5 shows students a triangle that has sides that are "4-sected." The Parallel Side-Splitter Theorem leads students to make conclusions about how the dashed lines intersect the sides of the triangle.

EXERCISE 6 gives students a triangle with one trisected side. Students must use what they know about the Parallel Side-Splitter Theorem to trisect the other sides. You may wish to provide students with copies of Blackline Master 4.11B for this exercise.

---

3. a. no **b.** yes **c.** yes

4. A

5. They cut $\overline{AB}$ and $\overline{BC}$ into four congruent segments.

6. a.

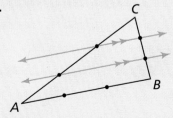

b.

Additional Resources

PRINTED RESOURCES
- Solution Manual
- Practice Workbook
- Assessment Resources
- Teaching Resources

TECHNOLOGY
- Interactive Textbook
- TeacherExpress CD-ROM
- **Exam***View* CD-ROM
- **PHSchool.com**
  - Additional Practice
  - Mid-Chapter and
    Chapter Tests
  - Video Tutors
  - Vocabulary Puzzles

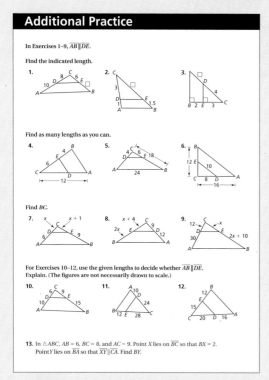

Additional Practice

In Exercises 1–9, $\overline{AB} \parallel \overline{DE}$.

Find the indicated length.

1.   2.   3.

Find as many lengths as you can.

4.   5.   6.

Find BC.

7.   8.   9.

For Exercises 10–12, use the given lengths to decide whether $\overline{AB} \parallel \overline{DE}$. Explain. (The figures are not necessarily drawn to scale.)

10.   11.   12.

13. In $\triangle ABC$, $AB = 6$, $BC = 8$, and $AC = 9$. Point X lies on $\overline{BC}$ so that $BX = 2$. Point Y lies on $\overline{BA}$ so that $\overline{XY} \parallel \overline{CA}$. Find BY.

Practice: For Lesson 4.11, assign Exercises 1–6.

---

7. Both $\overline{AB}$ and $\overline{BC}$ are cut into five equal-length segments by the dashed lines. What can you conclude?

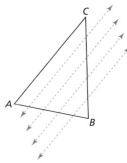

The first part of the Parallel Side-Splitter Theorem tells you that two sides of a triangle are split proportionally. By now, you should suspect that there are several proportions possible, such as $\frac{AB}{AD} = \frac{AC}{AE}$ and $\frac{DB}{AD} = \frac{EC}{AE}$ in the triangle below.

Exercises 8 and 9 show how to prove that these proportions are two different ways of writing the same information.

8. Take It Further First, you can prove a related fact using algebra. Suppose that r, s, t, and u are any four nonzero numbers. If $\frac{r}{s} = \frac{t}{u}$, explain why it is also true that $\frac{r-s}{s} = \frac{t-u}{u}$.

Hint: $\frac{r-s}{s} = \frac{r}{s} - \frac{s}{s}$

9. Take It Further Use Exercise 8 as a guide. Explain how the proportion $\frac{AB}{AD} = \frac{AC}{AE}$ leads directly to $\frac{DB}{AD} = \frac{EC}{AE}$.

Maintain Your Skills

10. Does the given information guarantee that $\overline{BC} \parallel \overline{DE}$?

a. $AB = 1$, $BD = 4$, $AC = 3$, $CE = 12$
b. $AB = 8$, $BD = 4$, $AC = 16$, $CE = 8$
c. $AB = 3$, $BD = 12$, $AC = 4$, $CE = 1$
d. $AB = 7$, $BD = 3$, $AC = 7$, $CE = 8$
e. $AB = 0.5$, $BD = 7$, $AC = 28$, $CE = 2$

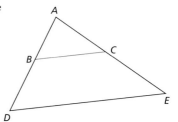

Go Online
PHSchool.com

For additional practice, go to Web Code: bea-0411

Answers

10. (a) and (b)

7. All the dashed lines are parallel to $\overline{AC}$.

8. If $\frac{r}{s} = \frac{t}{u}$, then $\frac{r}{s} - 1 = \frac{t}{u} - 1$. Hence $\frac{r}{s} - \frac{s}{s} = \frac{t}{u} - \frac{u}{u}$, or $\frac{r-s}{s} = \frac{t-u}{u}$.

9. In $\frac{AB}{AD} = \frac{AC}{AE}$, substitute $DB + DA$ for AB, and $EC + AE$ for AC. Subtract 1 from each side of the resulting equation and simplify.

Now you will finish proving the Parallel Side-Splitter Theorem. Recall that the theorem says

If $\overline{VW}$ is parallel to $\overline{RT}$, then $\frac{SR}{SV} = \frac{ST}{SW} = \frac{RT}{VW}$.

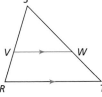

In Lesson 4.11, you proved that $\frac{SV}{VR} = \frac{SW}{WT}$. You can use this to show that $\frac{SR}{SV} = \frac{ST}{SW}$.

$$\frac{SV}{VR} = \frac{SW}{WT}$$

$$\frac{VR}{SV} = \frac{WT}{SW}$$

$$1 + \frac{VR}{SV} = 1 + \frac{WT}{SW}$$

$$\frac{SV}{SV} + \frac{VR}{SV} = \frac{SW}{SW} + \frac{WT}{SW}$$

$$\frac{SV + VR}{SV} = \frac{SW + WT}{SW}$$

$$\frac{SR}{SV} = \frac{ST}{SW}$$

In-Class Experiment

Trace and make paper cutouts of $\triangle SVW$ and $\triangle SRT$. Place them on top of each other. Slide $\triangle SVW$ along $\overline{SR}$ until vertices V and R coincide.

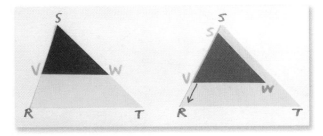

1. Why does $\angle SVW$ fall precisely on top of $\angle SRT$?

2. Draw a picture of how the triangles look after you slide $\triangle SVW$ to $\overline{RT}$.

3. Which two segments are now parallel? Explain.

In-Class Experiment

1. They are corresponding angles formed by 2 parallel lines and a transversal.

2. Check students' work.

3. $\overline{SW}$ and $\overline{ST}$

Lesson Overview

GOALS
• Prove the side-splitter theorems.

In this lesson students use what they have learned to prove the second part of the Parallel Side-Splitter Theorem: The ratio of the length of the parallel side to a given segment is equal to the common ratio.

CHECK YOUR UNDERSTANDING	HOMEWORK
• Core: 1, 2, 3, 7	• Core: 4, 5, 6
• Optional: none	• Optional: 11
MATERIALS	• Extension: 8, 9, 10
• scissors	

Launch

With your class, read the summary of the Parallel Side-Splitter Theorem and the algebra that follows.

Explore

Assign the In-Class Experiment to pairs or groups of students.

For Discussion

PROBLEM 5 Earlier, students learned two scaling methods—the ratio and parallel methods. The side-splitter theorems provide the basis for understanding that the two methods produce the same image.

For example, suppose students use the ratio method to scale a polygon by a scale factor k such as, $k = 2.5$,. They dilate the endpoints of each side by factor k and then connect the images.

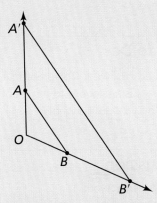

The Parallel Side-Splitter Theorem tells us that $\overline{AB} \parallel \overline{A'B'}$, so that if you apply the parallel method of dilation (with scale factor k) to $\overline{AB}$, the image also is $\overline{A'B'}$.

Similarly, if you scale $\overline{AB}$ by the parallel method with scale factor k to get $\overline{A'B'}$, the Proportional Side-Splitter Theorem guarantees that each point on $\overline{A'B'}$ is k times as far from the corresponding point on $\overline{AB}$.

Wrap Up

Use the For Discussion Problems to help your students understand that whether they use the ratio method or the parallel method to dilate, the result will be the same.

Then assign the Check Your Understanding exercises for work in class.

Assessment Resources

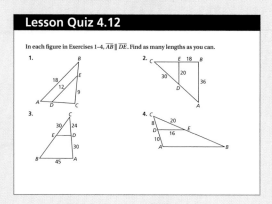
Answers

For You to Do

4. Check students' work. The proof that $\frac{RT}{VW} = \frac{SR}{SV}$ is analogous to the proof (for the original positions) that $\frac{SR}{SV} = \frac{ST}{SW}$.

For Discussion

5. Check students' work.

Exercises

1. $AE = 4$, $EC = 4$, $AD = 3$, $BD = 3$

2. $AD = 1\frac{2}{3}$, $AB = 2\frac{2}{3}$, $EC = 1\frac{1}{3}$, $BC = 2\frac{2}{3}$

3. $AB = 12$, $AD = 4$, $CE = 3$, $BE = 6$

For You to Do

4. Use the setup from the In-Class Experiment to prove the last part of the Parallel Side-Splitter Theorem—namely, that $\frac{RT}{VW}$ equals both $\frac{SR}{SV}$ and $\frac{ST}{SW}$.

For Discussion

5. Show that if $\overline{AB}$ is dilated from O using first the ratio method and then the parallel method, you get the same result.

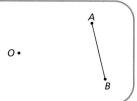

Exercises *Practicing Habits of Mind*

Check Your Understanding

In Exercises 1–3, $\overline{AC} \parallel \overline{DE}$. Copy the diagrams. Find as many lengths as you can.

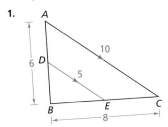

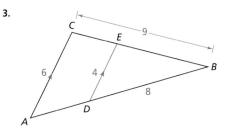

4. a. Answers may vary. Sample: Label the large rectangle *ABCD* and label the small rectangle *AEFG* with *E* on $\overline{AB}$ and *G* on $\overline{AD}$. Use the Parallel Side-Splitter Theorem to show that $\frac{AE}{AB} = \frac{EF}{BC}$. This means that corresponding sides of the rectangles are proportional. All angles of the rectangles are right angles. Therefore, the rectangles are scaled copies of each other.

b. Answers may vary. Sample: Label the rectangle *ABCD*. Use corresponding vertices and label the small rectangle as *LMNP*. Label the point where the dashed segments meet as point *O*. Apply the Parallel Side-Splitter Theorem to △*OBA* and △*OML* to get $\frac{OM}{OB} = \frac{ML}{BA}$. Similarly, in △*OBC* and △*OMN*, show that $\frac{OM}{OB} = \frac{MN}{BC}$. This implies $\frac{ML}{BA} = \frac{MN}{BC}$. Therefore, the rectangles are scaled copies of each other.

4. Use the side-splitter theorems. Explain why the two rectangles in each figure below are scaled copies of each other.

a.

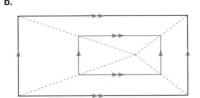

b.

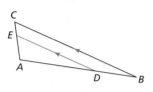

5. In the triangle shown here, $\overline{DE} \parallel \overline{BC}$. Explain why $\triangle ABC$ is a scaled copy of $\triangle ADE$.

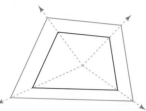

6. You draw the sides of the outer polygon parallel to the sides of the inner polygon as shown at the right. Explain why the polygons are scaled copies.

7. Standardized Test Prep Suppose $\triangle ABC \sim \triangle BED$. Which of the following lists the congruent corresponding angles of these two triangles?

A. $\angle A \cong \angle DBE$, $\angle ABC \cong \angle BDE$, $\angle C \cong \angle DEB$

B. $\angle A \cong \angle DBE$, $\angle ABC \cong \angle BED$, $\angle C \cong \angle BDE$

C. $\angle A \cong \angle DBE$, $\angle ABC \cong \angle BED$, $\angle B \cong \angle BDE$

D. $\angle A \cong \angle DBE$, $\angle ABC \cong \angle BDE$, $\angle C \cong \angle DEB$

How might you extend the idea of nested triangles to nested circles? What proportional relationships do nested circles suggest? Find out in Lesson 5.9.

Exercises

HOMEWORK
- Core: 4, 5, 6
- Optional: 11
- Extension: 8, 9, 10

Check Your Understanding

EXERCISES 1–3 provide students with practice using the results of the Parallel Side-Splitter Theorem.

On Your Own

EXERCISES 4 Students first see figures similar to these in the Minds in Action in Lesson 4.5. At the time, students may not have known why the dashed lines are in the figure. Students may have made this conjecture: If the dashed lines that join the corresponding vertices all meet at a single point, then the rectangles are scaled copies. Now students can prove that this is indeed true.

EXERCISES 8 AND 9 give students a method for constructing a triangle (without taking any measurements) that has the same area as a given polygon.

EXERCISE 10 is a challenging extension to the conclusion to Problem 1 in Lesson 4.9—triangles that share the same base and height have the same area.

5. Since $\overline{DE} \parallel \overline{BC}$, it follows that corresponding angles of the two triangles are congruent. Use the Parallel Side-Splitter Theorem to show that corresponding sides are proportional. Therefore, the triangles are scaled copies of each other.

6. Use the Parallel Side-Splitter Theorem to show that corresponding sides are proportional. The dashed lines divide pairs of corresponding angles into two parts whose measures can be added to show that corresponding angles are congruent. Therefore, the polygons are scaled copies of each other.

7. B

Additional Resources

PRINTED RESOURCES
- Solution Manual
- Practice Workbook
- Assessment Resources
- Teaching Resources

TECHNOLOGY
- Interactive Textbook
- TeacherExpress CD-ROM
- **Exam**View CD-ROM
- PHSchool.com
  - Additional Practice
  - Mid-Chapter and Chapter Tests
  - Video Tutors
  - Vocabulary Puzzles

Additional Practice

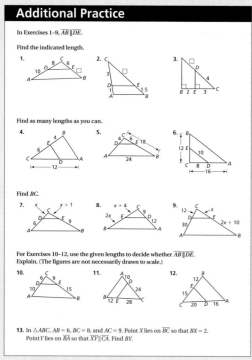

In Exercises 1–9, $\overline{AB} \parallel \overline{DE}$.

Find the indicated length.

1.   2.   3.

Find as many lengths as you can.

4.   5.   6.

Find BC.

7.   8.   9.

For Exercises 10–12, use the given lengths to decide whether $\overline{AB} \parallel \overline{DE}$. Explain. (The figures are not necessarily drawn to scale.)

10.   11.   12.

13. In $\triangle ABC$, $AB = 6$, $BC = 8$, and $AC = 9$. Point X lies on $\overline{BC}$ so that $BX = 2$. Point Y lies on $\overline{BA}$ so that $\overline{XY} \parallel \overline{CA}$. Find BY.

Practice: For Lesson 4.12, assign Exercises 7–13.

Answers

8. $\triangle ADC$ and $\triangle ACE$ have the same area since they have the common base $\overline{AC}$ and congruent altitudes (from D and from E to $\overleftrightarrow{AC}$). So
Area($ABCD$)
= Area($\triangle ABC$) + Area($\triangle ADC$)
= Area($\triangle ABC$) + Area($\triangle ACE$)
= Area($\triangle ABE$).

9. Extend $\overleftrightarrow{CD}$ in both directions. Construct segments from A parallel to $\overline{AD}$ and $\overline{AC}$, intersecting $\overleftrightarrow{CD}$ at F and G respectively. Construct segments $\overline{AF}$ and $\overline{AG}$. $\triangle AGF$ is the desired triangle.

10. Draw $\overline{AC}$, and then construct $\overline{BD}$ parallel to $\overline{AC}$ through B, intersecting the line that C lies on at D. Draw $\overline{AD}$. $\overline{AD}$ is the new border since Area($\triangle AEB$) = Area($\triangle CED$).

---

8. Take It Further Here is a way to construct $\triangle ABE$ to have the same area as quadrilateral $ABCD$, without taking any measurements.

First, draw diagonal $\overline{AC}$. Then draw a line through point D parallel to $\overline{AC}$. Extend $\overline{BC}$ to meet the parallel at point E.

This completes the construction. The area of $\triangle ABE$ is equal to the area of quadrilateral $ABCD$. Explain why.

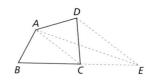

9. Take It Further Extend the method used in Exercise 8. Construct a triangle with area equal to that of pentagon $ABCDE$ shown here.

10. Take It Further $\overline{AB}$ and $\overline{BC}$ represent the border between land owned by Wendy and land owned by Juan. How can you replace these segments with a single segment such that the amount of land owned by each person does not change? Justify your answer.

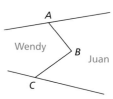

Maintain Your Skills

11. Decide whether $\overline{AB}$ is parallel to $\overline{DE}$. In each case, give a reason for your decision. The triangles are not necessarily drawn to scale.

a.   b.

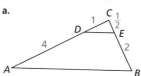   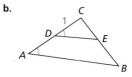

c.   d.

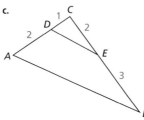   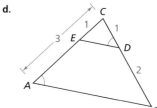

11. a. yes, since $\dfrac{CE}{EB} = \dfrac{CD}{DA}$

b. yes, since $\angle CDE \cong \angle CAB$

c. no, since $\dfrac{CD}{DB} \neq \dfrac{CE}{EA}$

d. yes, $\dfrac{CE}{CA} = \dfrac{CD}{CB}$

Go Online PHSchool.com

For additional practice, go to Web Code: bea-0412

4C

Reflections

In this investigation, you explored parallels and proportions in nested triangles. You proved the side-splitter theorems. These questions will help you summarize what you have learned.

1. In $\triangle ABC$, $\overline{DE} \parallel \overline{AC}$, $DB = \frac{1}{3}AB$, $AB = 6$, $BE = 3$, and $AC = 12$. What are BC, DE, and DB?

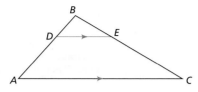

2. $EFGH$ is a quadrilateral. $CH = \frac{1}{3}HE$, $HD = \frac{1}{3}HG$, $AF = \frac{1}{4}EF$, and $BF = \frac{1}{4}FG$. Prove that $\overline{AB} \parallel \overline{CD}$.

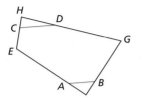

3. Use the side-splitter theorems to prove the Midline Theorem.

4. Suppose you want to scale a segment, $\overline{AB}$, by the factor $\frac{1}{3}$ and use a point O not on $\overline{AB}$ as the center of dilation. Describe each step you would use. Give a reason for each step.

5. In the diagram at the right, $AD = 24$, $ED = 8$, $DC = 21$, and $DF = 7$. $\triangle HBG$ is a scaled copy of $\triangle ABC$ such that its area is $\frac{1}{9}$ the area of $\triangle ABC$. Prove that $EFGH$ is a parallelogram.

6. If a point D is on side $\overline{AB}$ of $\triangle ABC$, E is on $\overline{AC}$, and $\overline{DE}$ is parallel to $\overline{BC}$, then what can you say about the relationship between $\triangle ABC$ and $\triangle ADE$?

7. What are the side-splitter theorems?

8. If two triangles have the same height, and you know the ratio of their areas, what is the ratio of the lengths of their bases?

Vocabulary

In this investigation, you learned these terms. Make sure you understand what each one means and how to use it.

- **common ratio**
- **nested triangles**
- **splits two sides proportionally**

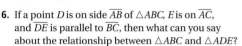

The Midline Theorem is a special case of the side-splitter theorems.

Mathematical Reflections

1. $BC = 9$, $DE = 4$, $DB = 2$

2. In $\triangle EHG$, $\overline{CD} \parallel \overline{EG}$ by the Proportional Side-Splitter Theorem. Likewise, $\overline{AB} \parallel \overline{EG}$ in $\triangle EFG$. Since $\overline{AB}$ and $\overline{CD}$ are both parallel to $\overline{EG}$, they are parallel to each other.

3. Let $\triangle ABC$ have D as the midpoint of $\overline{AB}$ and E as the midpoint of $\overline{AC}$. By the Proportional Side-Splitter Theorem, $\overline{DE} \parallel \overline{BC}$. Since D is a midpoint, $AD = \frac{1}{2}AB$. By the Parallel Side-Splitter Theorem, $DE = \frac{1}{2}BC$.

4. Answers may vary. Sample: Draw $\overline{OA}$ and $\overline{OB}$ to form $\triangle OAB$. Mark points C and D on $\overline{OA}$ and $\overline{OB}$ respectively so that $3 \cdot OC = OA$ and $3 \cdot OD = OB$. $\overline{CD}$ is the desired dilation since $\overline{CD} \parallel \overline{AB}$ by the Proportional Side-Splitter Theorem, and $CD = \frac{1}{3}AB$ by the Parallel Side-Splitter Theorem.

5. Use the side-splitter theorems to show that $\overline{EF}$ and $\overline{HG}$ are both parallel to $\overline{AC}$ and have a length equal to $\frac{1}{3}AC$. It follows that $EFGH$ is a parallelogram,

Mathematical Reflections

EXERCISES 6–8 At the start of the investigation, you may have assigned these as Questions 1–3 for students to think and write about.

since it has a pair of opposite sides that are parallel and congruent.

6. They are scaled copies of each other.

7. The Proportional Side-Splitter Theorem says that if a segment with endpoints on two sides of a triangle splits those sides proportionally, then it is parallel to the third side. The Parallel Side-Splitter Theorem says that if a segment that splits two sides of a triangle is parallel to the third side, then it splits the two sides proportionally.

8. the same as the ratio of the areas

Investigation Overview

This investigation introduces students to two definitions of *similarity*. They learn about the similarity notation, ~, as well as prove triangle similarity theorems. Both Lessons 4.15 and 4.16 are lengthy and may take multiple days to work through. See the Daily Planner for suggestions on how to manage your time.

You may wish to assign Questions 1–3 for students to think and write about during the investigation.

Learning Goals

- Identify corresponding parts of similar triangles.
- Develop and use the AAA, SAS, and SSS tests for similarity in triangles.
- Understand that the ratio between the area of a polygon and the area of a copy of that polygon scaled by the factor r will be r^3.

Habits and Skills

- Visualize similar triangles.
- Look for invariant ratios.
- Make logical inferences to prove similarity.

Defining Similarity

In *Defining Similarity*, you formally define the mathematical term *similar.* You will closely tie its definition to all the work you have done on scaled copies. Your ability to recognize and create scaled copies will be very useful. You will learn the implications of similarity. You will also learn how to test for similarity in triangles and other figures.

By the end of this investigation, you will be able to answer questions like these:

1. What does it mean for two figures to be similar?

2. What are some tests for triangle similarity?

3. If the common ratio of two similar figures is r, what is the ratio of their areas?

You will learn how to

- identify corresponding parts of similar triangles

- develop and use the AAA, SAS, and SSS tests for similarity in triangles

- understand that the ratio between the area of a polygon and the area of a copy of that polygon scaled by the factor r will be r^2

You will develop these habits and skills:

- Visualize similar triangles.

- Look for invariant ratios.

- Make logical inferences to prove similarity.

Each sheet of origami paper is a square. Describe the figures that result if you follow the same origami pattern to fold each sheet.

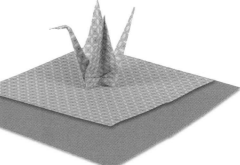

Investigation Road Map

LESSON 4.13, *Getting Started,* revisits the definition of *scaled copies* and introduces the term *similar.* Students expand their dilation definition of similarity to include figures with a different orientation.

LESSON 4.14, *Similar Figures,* provides two definitions of *similar figures* and introduces the symbol for similarity. Students also practice identifying corresponding parts of similar figures.

LESSON 4.15, *Tests for Similar Triangles,* compares similarity tests to the tests for congruent triangles and introduces the AA, SAS, and SSS Similarity Theorems.

LESSON 4.16, *Areas of Similar Polygons,* teaches that areas of similar polygons are proportional to the squares of the corresponding side lengths.

Words such as *enlargements, reductions, scale factors,* and *dilations* are some of the terms you have met again and again in this chapter.

The common theme uniting them is called *similarity*. By enlarging or reducing a picture, you make another picture that is similar to the first. One way to define *similar figures* in geometry is as follows.

• Two figures are similar if one is a scaled copy of the other.

You can also use the word "dilation" to define similar.

• Two figures are similar if one is a dilation of the other.

To test this definition, look at the picture of the head of Trig the horse. Trig is accompanied here by his little sister, Girt. Girt is smaller than Trig but her head shares all of his features.

Remember...

You can use dilation to refer to the dilation image when this meaning is clear in context.

or You to Explore

1. Is Girt a dilated copy of Trig? If so, find the center of dilation.

2. Is the picture of Girt similar to the picture of Trig?

   Here is another family portrait of Trig and Girt, this time in a different pose.

3. Is the picture of Girt still similar to the picture of Trig?

4. Can you still dilate one picture onto the other? Explain.

5. Expand the dilation definition of similar so you can say that even these two pictures are similar.

Answers

For You to Explore

1. Yes; check students' work.

2. yes

3. yes

4. No; the orientations are different.

5. Answers may vary. Sample: Two figures are similar if you can rotate and/or flip one of them so that it can then be dilated to obtain the other.

Lesson Overview

GOAL
• Explore ideas that are basic to the goals of this investigation.

This lesson revisits the ideas of scaled copies and dilation and then introduces students to the term *similar*. Students expand their dilation definition of similarity to include figures with different orientations from each other.

FOR YOU TO EXPLORE	HOMEWORK
• Core: 1, 2, 3, 4, 5	• Core: 6, 7, 8, 9
• Optional: none	• Optional: 10

Launch

With your whole class, review the terms listed in the first sentence of the lesson (*enlargements, reductions, scale factors, dilations*).

Explore

The lesson gives two possible definitions of similarity—one involving scaling and the other dilation. The dilation definition is not quite complete. It says that two figures are similar if one is a dilation of the other. While this is true, it limits similar figures to those that are oriented in the same way. (Recall that dilation does not change the orientation of a figure.) To help students see that this definition does not encompass all similar figures, the For You to Explore shows a horse and its scaled copy pointing in opposite directions. Ask students if they can modify the definition to include this case.

For You to Explore

PROBLEM 2 Using the dilation definition of *similar*, students determine that the two pictures are similar.

PROBLEMS 3–5 give students two pictures that are similar, but not oriented the same way. Students must determine whether the pictures are truly similar by deciding whether they can still dilate one picture onto the other. Students then expand the dilation definition of similarity to work in this situation.

Wrap Up

Before assigning homework, allow students some time to discuss and summarize their findings.

Exercises

HOMEWORK
- Core: 6, 7, 8, 9
- Optional: 10

On Your Own

EXERCISE 6 prepares students for exploration of the similarity tests. It asks students to look at their notes from Investigation 4A and recall how they tested whether two triangles are scaled copies.

EXERCISE 7 gives students two similar triangles and asks them to identify corresponding parts.

On Your Own

6. Look at your notes for Investigation 4A. Write your test for telling whether two figures are scaled copies of each other.

7. These two triangles are scaled copies of each other.

   List the angle measurements that are equal and the side lengths that are proportional.

8. If two polygons are dilations of each other, describe how to find the center of dilation. Is that center unique?

9. Will you always be able to find a center of dilation for two similar polygons? If so, describe how to do it. If not, sketch a counterexample.

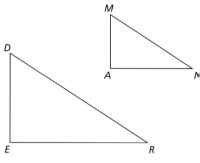

Maintain Your Skills

10. Use a standard rectangular sheet of paper that measures $8\frac{1}{2}$ in. by 11 in. For parts (a)–(d) below, fold the paper in half the given number of times by matching the two shorter sides. When done folding, do the following.

    - Unfold the paper.

    - Count the number of rectangles that are formed.

    - Find the dimensions of each rectangle.

    - Decide whether each rectangle is similar to the shape of the original sheet of paper.

    a. Make one fold.   b. Make two folds.

    c. Make three folds.   d. Make four folds.

    e. Some numbers of folds produce rectangles that are similar to the shape of the original sheet of paper. What do these combinations have in common?

Answers

Exercises

6. Check students' work.

7. $\angle D \cong \angle M$, $\angle E \cong \angle A$, $\angle R \cong \angle N$,
   $\frac{DE}{MA} = \frac{DR}{MN} = \frac{ER}{AN}$, $\frac{DE}{ER} = \frac{MA}{AN}$,
   $\frac{DE}{DR} = \frac{MA}{MN}$, $\frac{DR}{ER} = \frac{MN}{AN}$

8. Draw lines through pairs of corresponding points, and mark their point of intersection; yes.

9. No; the sketch should feature two similar polygons that are reflected as well as dilated.

10. a. two; 8.5 in. by 5.5 in.; no
    b. four; 4.25 in. by 5.5 in.; yes
    c. eight; 2.75 in. by 4.25 in.; no
    d. sixteen; 2.125 in. by 2.75 in.; yes
    e. Answers may vary. Sample: Each combination had the same number of folds along both the length and width of the paper.

Similar Figures

Here are some suggestions for ways to define similar figures using dilation terminology.

efinitions

- Two figures are **similar** if you can rotate and/or flip one of them so that you can dilate it onto the other.

- Two figures are **similar** if one is congruent to a dilation of the other.

or Discussion

In Lesson 4.13, you tried to extend a dilation definition of similarity so that it would work with the second family portrait of Trig and Girt.

1. Do the two definitions above solve any problems you may have had?

2. Are the two definitions above equivalent?

eveloping Habits of Mind

Consider the converse. If two figures are congruent, are they similar? If two figures are similar, are they congruent?

If the two congruent figures below are similar, then you must be able to apply a scale factor to one of them and produce the other.

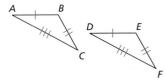

In this case, a scale factor of 1 applied to $\triangle ABC$ will produce $\triangle DEF$. But here are two similar figures that are obviously not congruent.

For Discussion

1. Definition 1 lets you say that the portraits of Trig and Girt are similar.

2. The two definitions are not equivalent.

For You to Do

Make sure the students understand the two different tests for similar triangles—the "Congruent Angles, Proportional Sides test" and the "Congruent to a Dilation test." Then have them work individually or in pairs on For You to Do Problem 5.

Wrap Up

Assign the Check Your Understanding exercises for students to work on in class.

Assessment Resources

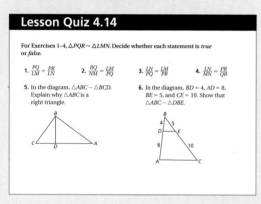

Lesson Quiz 4.14

For Exercises 1–4, $\triangle PQR \sim \triangle LMN$. Decide whether each statement is *true* or *false*.

1. $\frac{PQ}{LM} = \frac{PR}{LN}$ 2. $\frac{RQ}{NM} = \frac{LM}{PQ}$ 3. $\frac{LN}{PQ} = \frac{LM}{PR}$ 4. $\frac{LN}{MN} = \frac{PR}{QR}$

5. In the diagram, $\triangle ABC \sim \triangle BCD$. Explain why $\triangle ABC$ is a right triangle.

6. In the diagram, $BD = 4$, $AD = 8$, $BE = 5$, and $CE = 10$. Show that $\triangle ABC \sim \triangle DBE$.

The symbol for similarity, $\sim$, is the upper part of the symbol $\cong$ for congruence. Thus, you read the statement $ABCD \sim EFGH$ as "$ABCD$ is similar to $EFGH$." It means that the two polygons are scaled copies of each other.

$$ABCD \sim EFGH$$

The similarity symbol, $\sim$, means "has the same shape as," and the congruence symbol, $\cong$, means "has the same shape *and* the same size as."

For congruent triangles, the statement $\triangle ABC \cong \triangle XYZ$ conveys specific information about their corresponding parts. For figures that are similar, the order of their vertex letters also specifies which parts correspond, but the conclusions you draw will be different.

For You to Do

$\triangle ABC \sim \triangle XYZ$ and $ABCDE \sim PQRST$. Copy the figures. Label the vertices of $\triangle XYZ$ and $PQRST$ correctly.

3.

4.

In Investigation 4A, you devised several ways to test whether two triangles are similar. (Only then, you used the phrase *scaled copies*.) One test was probably the following.

> Two triangles are similar (scaled copies) if their corresponding angles are congruent and their corresponding sides are proportional.

For future reference, you can call this the Congruent Angles, Proportional Sides test.

Remember...

When you say $\triangle ABC \cong \triangle XYZ$, you can draw many conclusions about congruence. Which segments are congruent to each other? Which angles are congruent?

Answers

For You to Do

3.

4.

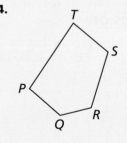

Using the word *dilation*, here is another test for similar triangles.

Two triangles are similar if one is congruent to a dilation of the other.

You can refer to this as the Congruent to a Dilation test.

For You to Do

5. Suppose that $\triangle NEW \sim \triangle OLD$. If $m\angle N = 19°$ and $m\angle L = 67°$, find the measures of the other angles.

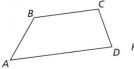

Exercises *Practicing Habits of Mind*

Check Your Understanding

1. Is each given similarity statement true or false? Take measurements to decide. Explain your answer.

a. $ABCD \sim EFGH$

b. $ABCD \sim EFGH$

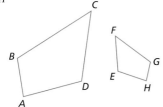

c. $\triangle ABC \sim \triangle DEF$

Exercises

HOMEWORK
• Core: 6, 7, 8
• Optional: 10

Check Your Understanding

EXERCISE 1 Students need a ruler and protractor to measure the sides and angles of the quadrilaterals. They use the measurements to determine whether the corresponding angles are congruent and whether the corresponding angles' sides are proportional.

For You to Do

5. $m\angle E = 67°$, $m\angle W = 94°$, $m\angle O = 19°$, $m\angle D = 94°$

Exercises

1. a. Yes; corresponding angles are congruent, and corresponding sides are proportional.

b. No; corresponding angles are not congruent.

c. No; corresponding angles are not congruent.

EXERCISE 3 The text shows a figure with two similar overlapping triangles. Students must use the given figure to explain why the large triangle is isosceles. You may want to suggest they "pull apart" the figure and draw two similar triangles oriented the same way.

EXERCISE 4 Students must use the Midline Theorem to determine lengths of sides of the given figure and to show that the two given triangles are similar.

EXERCISE 5 uses the figure from Exercise 3. Students must use given lengths and angle measurements to find the missing measurements.

2. Suppose $\triangle ABC \sim \triangle DEF$. Must each statement be true?

a. $\frac{AB}{DE} = \frac{BC}{EF}$

b. $\frac{AC}{BC} = \frac{DF}{EF}$

c. $\frac{BC}{AB} = \frac{DF}{DE}$

d. $AC \cdot DE = AB \cdot DF$

3. In the figure below, $\triangle ABC \sim \triangle BDA$. Explain why $\triangle ACB$ is isosceles.

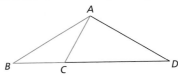

Habits of Mind

Think it through.
Recall some conditions for a triangle to be isosceles.

4. In the figure at the right, F, G, and H are midpoints of the sides of $\triangle ABC$. Show that $\triangle ABC \sim \triangle GHF$.

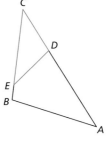

5. Make a large copy of the figure from Exercise 3. On your copy, mark the measurements shown at the right. Then fill in the rest of the angle measures and side lengths.

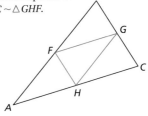

Go Online
Video Tutor
PHSchool.com

Web Code: bee-0775

On Your Own

6. In the figure, $\triangle ABC \sim \triangle CDE$.

Decide whether each statement is correct or incorrect.

a. $\triangle ABC \sim \triangle DEC$ b. $\triangle BCA \sim \triangle DEC$

c. $\triangle BAC \sim \triangle DEC$ d. $\triangle CAB \sim \triangle ECD$

e. $\triangle CBA \sim \triangle ECD$ f. $\triangle CBA \sim \triangle CDE$

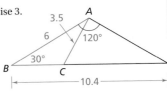

Answers

2. (a), (b), and (d)

3. Since $\triangle ACB \sim \triangle BAD$, $\angle B \cong \angle D$. Therefore $\overline{AB} \cong \overline{AD}$, and $\triangle BAD$ is isosceles. Any triangle similar to an isosceles triangle must itself be isosceles, so $\triangle ACB$ is isosceles.

4. Answers may vary. Sample: By the Midline Theorem, the lengths of the sides of $\triangle GHF$ are half the lengths of the corresponding sides of $\triangle ABC$. Since a midline is parallel to the third side of its triangle, it follows that $AFGH$, $FGCH$, and $FBCH$ are parallelograms. Opposite angles of a parallelogram are congruent, so the corresponding angles of $\triangle GHF$ and $\triangle ABG$ are congruent. Therefore, $\triangle ABC \sim \triangle GHF$.

5. $m\angle BAC = 30°$, $m\angle DAC = 90°$, $m\angle BCA = 110°$, $m\angle ACD = 60°$, $m\angle ADB = 30°$, $BC = 3.5$, $CD = 6.9$, $AD = 6$

6. (b), (c), and (f)

7. $\triangle QRS \sim \triangle VUT$.

Decide whether each statement is correct or incorrect.

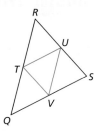

a. $\dfrac{QR}{TU} = \dfrac{SR}{TV}$ **b.** $\dfrac{QR}{SR} = \dfrac{TU}{TV}$

c. $\dfrac{QR}{QS} = \dfrac{UV}{TV}$ **d.** $\dfrac{QT}{QV} = \dfrac{RT}{TU}$

e. $\dfrac{QR}{TV} = \dfrac{SR}{TU}$ **f.** $\dfrac{QS}{VT} = \dfrac{RS}{UT}$

8. $\triangle CAT \sim \triangle DOT$.

Complete each statement.

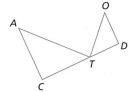

a. $\angle C \cong$ _?_ **b.** $\angle CTA \cong$ _?_

c. $\angle DTO \cong$ _?_ **d.** $\angle A \cong$ _?_

e. $\angle D \cong$ _?_ **f.** $\angle O \cong$ _?_

9. Standardized Test Prep In the figure at the right, $\triangle ABC \sim \triangle BED$. Which length correctly completes the following proportion?

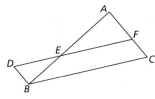

$$\dfrac{AB}{BE} = \dfrac{AC}{\blacksquare}$$

A. BD **B.** ED **C.** BC **D.** EB

Maintain Your Skills

10. $\triangle PLU \sim \triangle ABC$. Find AC and BC for each of the given lengths of AB.

a. $AB = 1$ **b.** $AB = 2$

c. $AB = 3$ **d.** $AB = 4$

e. $AB = x$

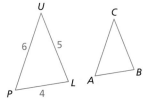

not to scale

Go Online
PHSchool.com

For additional practice, go to **Web Code: bea-0414**

Additional Resources

PRINTED RESOURCES
- Solution Manual
- Practice Workbook
- Assessment Resources
- Teaching Resources

TECHNOLOGY
- Interactive Textbook
- TeacherExpress CD-ROM
- **Exam**View CD-ROM
- **PHSchool.com**
  - Additional Practice
  - Mid-Chapter and Chapter Tests
  - Video Tutors
  - Vocabulary Puzzles

Additional Practice

Use the figure for Exercises 1–14. $\triangle PQS \sim \triangle RPS$. $m\angle Q = 56°$, $m\angle PRS = 87°$, $PQ = 36$, $QS = 60$, and $RP = 30$.
Find each measure.

1. $m\angle PRQ$ **2.** $m\angle QPR$ **3.** $m\angle RPS$ **4.** $m\angle QPS$

5. $m\angle S$ **6.** PS **7.** RS **8.** QR

Decide whether each statement is correct.

9. $\triangle PSQ \sim \triangle RSP$ **10.** $\triangle PRS \sim \triangle QPS$ **11.** $\triangle RPS \sim \triangle SQP$

12. $\triangle SQP \sim \triangle SPR$ **13.** $\triangle QSP \sim \triangle RSP$ **14.** $\triangle SQP \sim \triangle SPR$

In Exercises 15–22, $\triangle FAR \sim \triangle TEH$. Complete each statement.

15. $\dfrac{FR}{TH} = \dfrac{AF}{\square}$ **16.** $\dfrac{EH}{TE} = \dfrac{\square}{FA}$ **17.** $\dfrac{\square}{RA} = \dfrac{HT}{HE}$

18. $\angle A \cong \square$ **19.** $\angle T \cong \square$ **20.** $\angle H \cong \square$

21. $\triangle ARF \sim \square$ **22.** $\triangle ETH \sim \square$

23. The sides of a triangle have lengths 5, 6, and 8. A triangle similar to it has a side of length 10. Write all side lengths of each possible similar triangle.

24. The sides of a triangle have lengths 12, 18, and 18. A triangle similar to it has a side of length 8. Write all side lengths of each possible similar triangle.

25. A triangle has sides of length 5, 7, and 8. A triangle similar to it has a perimeter of 15. What are the lengths of the sides of this triangle?

26. A triangle has sides of length 9, 12, and 15. A triangle similar to it has a perimeter of 40. What are the lengths of the sides of this triangle?

Use the diagram for Exercises 27–29.

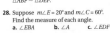

27. Figure $ABCD$ is a parallelogram. Prove that $\triangle ABF \sim \triangle DEF$.

28. Suppose $m\angle E = 20°$ and $m\angle C = 60°$. Find the measure of each angle.
a. $\angle EBA$ **b.** $\angle A$ **c.** $\angle EDF$

29. Is $\triangle ABF \sim \triangle CEB$? Explain.

Practice: For Lesson 4.14, assign Exercises 1–22.

---

7. (c), (d), and (f)

8. a. $\angle D$
  b. $\angle DTO$
  c. $\angle CTA$
  d. $\angle O$
  e. $\angle C$
  f. $\angle A$

9. A

10. a. $AC = \dfrac{3}{2}$, $BC = \dfrac{5}{4}$

  b. $AC = 3$, $BC = \dfrac{5}{2}$

  c. $AC = \dfrac{9}{2}$, $BC = \dfrac{15}{4}$

  d. $AC = 6$, $BC = 5$

  e. $AC = \dfrac{3}{2}x$, $BC = \dfrac{5}{4}x$

Lesson Overview

GOAL
- Develop and use the AAA, SAS, or SSS tests for similarity in triangles.

This lesson may take more than one day to cover because it includes an In-Class Experiment, several proofs to review, and For You to Do activities.

This lesson proves the AA, SAS, and SSS Similarity Theorems. Since these theorems form the basis for many topics that students will encounter in the future, including trigonometry, you should find time to cover them.

CHECK YOUR UNDERSTANDING
- Core: 6, 7, 8, 9
- Optional: 10, 11

HOMEWORK
- Core: 1, 2, 3, 4, 5, 12, 13
- Optional: 15, 16, 17, 18
- Extension: 14

MATERIALS
- protractors
- rulers

Launch

Have students work individually or in pairs to complete the In-Class Experiment.

Explore

After students have developed their own possible triangle similarity theorems in the In-Class Experiment, you can start with the AAA test. The For You to Do sets up the proof of this theorem. Use the For Discussion that follows to help students through the proof. The Developing Habits of Mind explains why you can rewrite this theorem as the AA Similarity Theorem.

The SAS Similarity Theorem and its proof follow the proof of the AA Similarity Theorem. The proof of the SAS Similarity Theorem is similar to the proof of the AA Similarity Theorem. If you wish, you can have students try to prove the SAS Similarity Theorem on their own before reading through the second Developing Habits of Mind.

For Discussion Problem 8 asks whether students can abbreviate the SAS test the way they abbreviate the AAA test to AA. This will get students thinking about what these initials mean as well as how the similarity tests differ from the congruence tests.

The last theorem the lesson presents is the SSS Similarity Theorem. The proof of this theorem is slightly more complicated. It uses the dilation definition of similarity. For You to Do Problem 9 sets up this proof. As a class complete For Discussion Problem 10.

4.15 Tests for Similar Triangles

You know several tests to decide whether triangles are congruent, for example SSS. It would be useful to have comparable tests for similar triangles.

In-Class Experiment

The main tests for congruent triangles are SAS, ASA, AAS, and SSS. Are there similar tests for similar triangles? Below are some possibilities. For each proposed test, draw a pair of triangles that share the attributes listed. Then check to see whether they must be similar. See if you can find a counterexample.

1. Three angles of one triangle are congruent to three angles of the other. Must the two triangles be similar? (AAA similarity)

2. Two triangles have a pair of proportional side lengths and a pair of congruent corresponding angles. Must the two triangles be similar? (SA similarity)

3. Two triangles have two pairs of proportional side lengths and the included angles are congruent. Must the two triangles be similar? (SAS similarity)

4. Two triangles have three pairs of proportional side lengths. Must the two triangles be similar? (SSS similarity)

AAA Similarity

Suppose $\triangle ABC$ and $\triangle PQR$ have congruent corresponding angles. Can you prove that the triangles are similar?

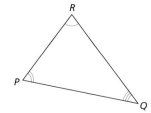

In previous lessons, you checked whether triangles were scaled copies (similar to each other) by placing one triangle inside the other triangle to form a pair of nested triangles.

Answers

In-Class Experiment

1–4. Tests 1, 3, and 4 appear to work. Counterexample for 2:

So try placing △ABC inside △PQR so that congruent angles C and R coincide. The triangles line up because ∠C and ∠R are congruent. The rays that form the angles lie on top of each other.

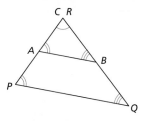

For You to Do

5. Use the figure above to prove that $\overline{AB}$ is parallel to $\overline{PQ}$. Then apply the Parallel Side-Splitter Theorem to write several proportions using the side lengths of the two triangles. Which definition of similarity allows you to conclude that △ABC ∼ △PQR?

Theorem 4.3   AAA Similarity Theorem

If three angles of one triangle are congruent to three angles of another triangle, the triangles are similar.

△**ABC** ∼ △**DEF**

For Discussion

6. Use the information from Problem 5 to prove the AAA Similarity Theorem.

Developing Habits of Mind

Simplify. In a sense, the requirement that the three angles of one triangle be congruent to the three angles of the other triangle is too much.

The AAA test can actually be replaced by an AA test. Once you know the measures of two angles of a triangle, the measure of the third angle is completely determined, since the sum of the measures of the three angles of a triangle is 180°. Thus, you can rewrite the theorem as follows.

If two angles of one triangle are congruent to two angles of another triangle, then the triangles are similar.

> When you write proofs, you may use the AA Similarity Theorem, instead of the AAA Similarity Theorem.

For You To Do

5. $\overline{AB} \parallel \overline{PQ}$ because corresponding angles formed by the transversals $\overleftrightarrow{AP}$ and $\overleftrightarrow{BQ}$ with $\overleftrightarrow{AB}$ and $\overleftrightarrow{PQ}$ are congruent. It follows by the Parallel Side-Splitter Theorem that $\frac{RP}{CA} = \frac{RQ}{CB} = \frac{PQ}{AB}$. One triangle is congruent to a dilation of the other.

For Discussion

6. $\overline{AB} \parallel \overline{PQ}$ because corresponding angles formed by the transversals $\overleftrightarrow{AP}$ and $\overleftrightarrow{BQ}$ with $\overleftrightarrow{AB}$ and $\overleftrightarrow{PQ}$ are congruent. It follows by the Parallel Side-Splitter Theorem that $\frac{RP}{CA} = \frac{RQ}{CB} = \frac{PQ}{AB}$.

Wrap Up

Post the three similarity theorems (and their proofs if you have space) somewhere in your room so students may easily refer to them.

Assign the Check Your Understanding exercises for in-class work.

7. Does it make sense to have an ASA test for triangle similarity? Explain.

SAS Similarity

Is there an SAS similarity test? If such a theorem did exist, you might state it as follows.

Theorem 4.4 **SAS Similarity Theorem**

If two triangles have two pairs of proportional side lengths and the included angles are congruent, the triangles are similar.
$\frac{AC}{AB} = \frac{DF}{DE}$; $\angle A \cong \angle D \Rightarrow \triangle ABC \sim \triangle DEF$

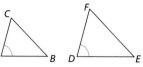

Developing Habits of Mind

Think it through. Suppose you have two triangles, $\triangle ABC$ and $\triangle DEF$, such that the following statements are true:

$$\frac{AC}{DF} = \frac{AB}{DE} \text{ and } \angle A \cong \angle D$$

These are the hypotheses of the SAS test. Now you need to show that the triangles are similar.

The key is to arrange the triangles, one inside the other, so that the congruent angles at A and D line up:

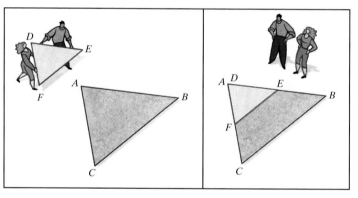

Because of the equal ratios given above, the Proportional Side-Splitter Theorem implies that $\overline{FE}$ is parallel to $\overline{CB}$. So you know that $\angle DFE \cong \angle ACB$ and $\angle DEF \cong \angle ABC$.

Answers

For Discussion

7. no, since the AAA Similarity Theorem can be applied

Moreover, the Parallel Side-Splitter Theorem tells you that

$$\frac{AC}{DF} = \frac{AB}{DE} = \frac{CB}{FE}.$$

Thus, the angles of the two triangles are congruent and corresponding sides are proportional, so

$$\triangle ABC \sim \triangle DEF.$$

This proves the SAS similarity theorem.

For Discussion

8. The AAA condition was too strong. Is SAS too strong as well?

SSS Similarity

Is there an SSS similarity test? If such a theorem did exist, you might state it as follows.

Theorem 4.5 SSS Similarity Theorem

If two triangles have all three pairs of side lengths proportional, the triangles are similar.

$$\frac{AC}{DF} = \frac{AB}{DE} = \frac{CB}{FE} \Rightarrow \triangle ABC \sim \triangle DEF$$

If you try to prove this theorem with the method used in the AAA and SAS proofs, something does not work.

In the AAA and SAS proofs, you had at least one pair of corresponding angles that you knew were congruent. This meant you could fit one triangle inside the other so that the congruent angles aligned perfectly. In the case of SSS, however, you have no congruent angles to use.

Since the Congruent Angles, Proportional Sides method does not seem well suited to prove SSS, try using the Congruent to a Dilation definition of similar triangles instead.

Habits of Mind

Make a choice. When you know equivalent definitions, use the one that best suits your needs.

For Discussion

8. no

1. In $\triangle JKL$, points M and N are on $\overline{JL}$ and $\overline{KL}$, respectively. Given that $\angle J \cong \angle MNL$, prove that $\triangle JKL \sim \triangle NML$.

For Exercises 2 and 3, $\triangle ABC$ is similar to $\triangle PQR$ and has sides that are $\frac{2}{3}$ as long. Find the numerical value of each ratio. Name the triangle similarity theorem that allows you to draw your conclusion.

2. the ratio of any two corresponding sides

3. the ratio of any two corresponding altitudes

4. The quadrilateral $ABCD$ is an isosceles trapezoid with $\overline{AB} \parallel \overline{DC}$. Prove $\triangle ABH \sim \triangle CDH$.

For You to Do

9. Suppose the corresponding side lengths of $\triangle ABC$ and $\triangle PQR$ are proportional.

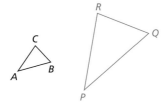

a. Write the proportionality statement for the side lengths of these two triangles.

b. If $\frac{PQ}{AB} = k$, where k is some positive number, complete each of the following statements.

- $\blacksquare = k(AB)$

- $\blacksquare = k(BC)$

- $\blacksquare = k(CA)$

Next, dilate $\triangle ABC$ by k, picking any point as the center of dilation.

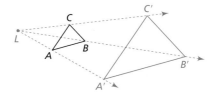

c. How do the sides of the dilated triangle $\triangle A'B'C'$ compare with the sides of $\triangle PQR$? Justify your answer.

d. Is it true that $\triangle A'B'C' \cong \triangle PQR$? Which congruence postulate can you use?

e. Is $\triangle PQR$ congruent to a dilation of $\triangle ABC$? Explain your answer.

For Discussion

10. Using your results from Problem 9, prove the SSS Similarity Theorem.

Answers

For You to Do

9. a. $\frac{PQ}{AB} = \frac{QR}{BC} = \frac{RP}{CA}$

b. PQ; QR; RP

c. The corresponding sides are congruent by the side-splitter theorems.

d. yes; SSS Congruence Assumption

e. yes; $\triangle PQR \cong \triangle A'B'C'$

For Discussion

10. By part (e), $\triangle A'B'C' \cong \triangle PQR$, and since $\triangle ABC \sim \triangle A'B'C'$, $\triangle ABC \sim \triangle PQR$.

Exercises Practicing Habits of Mind

Check Your Understanding

1. △*JKL* has *JK* = 8, *KL* = 12, and *LJ* = 16. Points *M* and *N* are on $\overline{JK}$ and $\overline{KL}$ respectively, with *JM* = 6 and *LN* = 9.

  a. Explain why $\overline{MN} \parallel \overline{JL}$.

  b. Prove △*MKN* ~ △*JKL* in three ways. Use each of the following similarity theorems.

   • AA   • SAS   • SSS

2. △*DEF* is similar to △*ABC* and has sides that are three times as long. Find the ratios of the lengths of the segments listed below. Name the triangle similarity theorem that allows you to draw your conclusion.

  a. two corresponding altitudes

  b. two corresponding angle bisectors that terminate on the opposite side

  c. two corresponding medians

For Exercises 3 and 4, decide whether quadrilaterals *ABCD* and *EFGH* are similar for the given conditions. Prove what you decide either as a theorem or by finding a counterexample.

3. The angles of one are congruent to the corresponding angles of the other.

4. Three corresponding sides are proportional and two corresponding included angles are congruent.

5. In the figure below, $\overline{DG} \parallel \overline{BC}$ and $\overline{EF} \parallel \overline{BA}$. Prove that △*ABC* ~ △*FHG*.

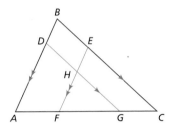

6. Standardized Test Prep Suppose △*ABC* ~ △*FHG*. *AB* = 10 ft, *AC* = 20 ft, *BC* = 25 ft, and $\frac{AB}{FH}$ = 2.5 ft. What is *FG*?

  A. 4 ft   **B.** 8 ft   **C.** 10 ft   **D.** 50 ft

Exercises

HOMEWORK
• Core: 1, 2, 3, 4, 5, 12, 13
• Optional: 15, 16, 17, 18
• Extension: 14

Check Your Understanding

EXERCISE 1 Students need the Proportional Side-Splitter Theorem, the AA Similarity Theorem, the Parallel Side-Splitter Theorem, the SAS Similarity Theorem, and the SSS Similarity Theorem to complete these proofs.

EXERCISE 2 This is a lengthy exercise that involves knowledge of algebra, angle bisectors, medians, altitudes, and the triangle similarity theorems.

EXERCISE 4 requires students to write a proof that SAS is a valid similarity theorem for quadrilaterals. The proof requires understanding of the SAS Similarity Theorem.

EXERCISE 5 This proof uses the parallel postulates as well as the AA Similarity Theorem.

Exercises

1. a. Note that $\frac{KM}{KJ} = \frac{KN}{KL} = \frac{1}{4}$, and then use the Proportional Side-Splitter Theorem.

  b. i. Since $\overline{MN} \parallel \overline{JL}$, ∠*KMN* ≅ ∠*KJL* and ∠*KNM* ≅ ∠*KLJ*. △*MKN* ~ △*JKL* by the AA test.

   ii. From part (a), $\frac{KM}{KJ} = \frac{KN}{KL}$. And since both triangles share a common angle, △*MKN* ~ △*JKL* by the SAS Test.

   iii. By the Parallel Side-Splitter Theorem, $\frac{KM}{KJ} = \frac{KN}{KL} = \frac{MN}{JL}$. By the SSS Theorem, △*MKN* ~ △*JKL*.

2. a. 3; AA Similarity Theorem

  b. 3; AA Similarity Theorem

  c. 3; SAS Similarity Test

3. No; answers may vary. Sample: A square with sides of length 1 is not similar to a rectangle that has length 2 and width 1.

4. In quadrilaterals *ABCD* and *EFGH*, let $\frac{AB}{EF} = \frac{AD}{EH} = \frac{CD}{GH}$, and ∠*BAD* ≅ ∠*FEH* and ∠*ADC* ≅ ∠*EHG*. By the SAS Similarity Theorem, △*ABD* ~ △*EFH* and △*CDA* ~ △*GHE*. Therefore, ∠*CAD* ≅ ∠*GEH*, and $\overline{AC}$ and $\overline{EG}$ are proportional. ∠*BAC* ≅ ∠*FEG* because each is the difference of congruent angles. By the SAS Similarity Theorem, △*ABC* ~ △*EFG* and △*BCD* ~ △*FGH*. Therefore, *BC* and *FG* are proportional to *AB* and *EF*. Corresponding angles in similar triangles are congruent, so ∠*ABC* ≅ ∠*EFG* and ∠*BCD* ≅ ∠*FGH*. All corresponding sides of *ABCD* and *EFGH* are proportional and all corresponding angles are congruent, so the quadrilaterals are similar.

5. For parallel lines cut by a transversal, corresponding angles are congruent, so ∠*HFG* ≅ ∠*A* and ∠*HGF* ≅ ∠*C*. Therefore, △*ABC* ~ △*FHG* by the AA Similarity Test.

6. B

On Your Own

EXERCISES 7 AND 8 require knowledge of the SSS Similarity Theorem. Exercise 7 gives students two similar triangles and four side lengths. Students must find the missing side lengths. In Exercise 8, students use the side lengths of one triangle and the perimeter of a second triangle to find the second triangle's side lengths.

7. The sides of a triangle have lengths 4, 5, and 8. Another triangle similar to it has one side of length 3. What are the lengths of its other two sides? Is more than one answer possible?

8. A triangle has sides of lengths 2, 3, and 4 inches. Another triangle similar to it has a perimeter of 6 inches. What are the side lengths of this triangle?

9. In the figure at the right, $\angle ADE \cong \angle ACB$. Explain why $\triangle ADE \sim \triangle ACB$.

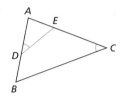

10. In the figure at the right, $AB = 2$ and $BC = 1$. Without making any measurements, find the values of $\frac{AD}{DE}$ and $\frac{AF}{FG}$. Explain how you got your answers.

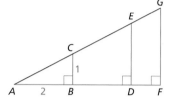

11. Draw a nonisosceles right triangle ABC. Draw the altitude from the right angle to the hypotenuse. The altitude divides $\triangle ABC$ into two smaller right triangles.

   a. There are two pairs of congruent angles (other than the right angles) in your picture. Find and label them.

   b. Make a copy of your triangle. Then cut out the two smaller right triangles. Position them in such a way as to convince yourself that they are similar to each other and to $\triangle ABC$.

   c. Explain why all three of these triangles are similar.

12. In the figure at the right, $AB = 4$, $BC = 5$, $AC = 6$, $DC = 2.5$, and $EC = 3$. Prove that $\triangle ABC \sim \triangle EDC$. Find the length of $\overline{DE}$.

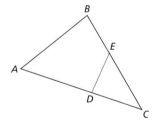

Answers

7. $\frac{15}{4}$ and 6; or $\frac{12}{5}$ and $\frac{24}{5}$; or $\frac{3}{2}$ and $\frac{15}{8}$; yes

8. $\frac{4}{3}$, 2, and $\frac{8}{3}$

9. AA Similarity test (since $\angle A \cong \angle A$ and $\angle ADE \cong \angle C$)

10. 2, 2; the three triangles are similar (AA Similarity), so both ratios are equal to $\frac{AB}{BC}$, or 2.

11. a–b. Check students' work.

   c. AA Similarity Test

12. $\frac{AC}{EC} = \frac{BC}{DC} = 2$, and $\angle C$ is common to the two triangles. Hence $\triangle ABC \sim \triangle EDC$ by the SAS Similarity Theorem; 2.

13. a. $\angle TRA \cong \angle RTS$ and $\angle RAS \cong \angle AST$, since alternate interior angles formed by two parallel lines and a transversal are congruent. Hence $\triangle ROA \sim \triangle TOS$ by the AA Similarity Test.

   b. In similar triangles, ratios of lengths of corresponding sides are equal.

13. Quadrilateral *RATS* is a trapezoid with $\overline{RA} \parallel \overline{ST}$. Diagonals $\overline{RT}$ and $\overline{AS}$ meet at *O*.

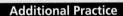

a. Explain why $\triangle ROA \sim \triangle TOS$.

b. From part (a) you can say that $\frac{RO}{TO} = \frac{OA}{OS}$. Explain.

c. Mary Elizabeth knows that $\frac{RO}{TO} = \frac{OA}{OS}$ and $\angle ROS \cong \angle TOA$. She claims that $\triangle ROS \sim \triangle TOA$ by the SAS similarity test. Is this true? Explain.

14. Take It Further Take a square sheet of paper. Fold back one fourth of it. You are left with a rectangle. The challenge is to fold the sheet of paper to form a rectangle that is similar to this one, but has half its area. You may not use a ruler.

> Even though you have folded part of the square, you can still unfold it and work with the entire square.

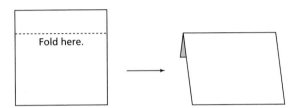

Maintain Your Skills

15. Although similarity for three-dimensional shapes has not been defined here, you can think about what it means to scale a three-dimensional figure. You would make a new figure with sides proportional to the sides of the original figure. For example, scale a rectangular prism 1 cm by 2 cm by 3 cm by the factor 2. You get a new rectangular prism measuring 2 cm by 4 cm by 6 cm.

a. What are the surface area and volume of the original 1 cm-by-2 cm-by-3 cm rectangular prism?

b. What are the surface area and volume of the scaled copy?

In Exercises 16–18, scale a 1 cm-by-2 cm-by-3 cm rectangular prism by the given factor. What are the dimensions, the surface area, and the volume of the scaled copy?

16. scale factor 3

17. scale factor 4

18. scale factor *k*

Go Online
PHSchool.com

For additional practice, go to **Web Code: bea-0415**

EXERCISE 13 has several parts. In part (a) students show that triangles are similar by the AA Test. Part (c) has students disprove the claim that two triangles in the given figure are similar by the SAS Test.

EXERCISE 14 You may want to assign this exercise as a project. It requires students to fold a square piece of paper into a rectangle. Then they fold a similar rectangle that has half the area of the original rectangle.

Additional Resources

PRINTED RESOURCES
- Solution Manual
- Practice Workbook
- Assessment Resources
- Teaching Resources

TECHNOLOGY
- Interactive Textbook
- TeacherExpress CD-ROM
- **Exam***View* CD-ROM
- **PHSchool.com**
  - Additional Practice
  - Mid-Chapter and Chapter Tests
  - Video Tutors
  - Vocabulary Puzzles

Additional Practice

Use the figure for Exercises 1–14. $\triangle PQS \sim \triangle RPS$.
$m\angle Q = 56°$, $m\angle PRS = 87°$, $PQ = 36$, $QS = 60$, and $RP = 30$.
Find each measure.

1. $m\angle PRQ$ **2.** $m\angle QPR$ **3.** $m\angle RPS$ **4.** $m\angle QPS$

5. $m\angle S$ **6.** PS **7.** RS **8.** QR

Decide whether each statement is correct.

9. $\triangle PSQ \sim \triangle RSP$ **10.** $\triangle PRS \sim \triangle QPS$ **11.** $\triangle RPS \sim \triangle SQP$

12. $\triangle SQP \sim \triangle SPR$ **13.** $\triangle QSP \sim \triangle RSP$ **14.** $\triangle SQP \sim \triangle SPR$

In Exercises 15–22, $\triangle FAR \sim \triangle TEH$. Complete each statement.

15. $\frac{FR}{TH} = \frac{AF}{\square}$ **16.** $\frac{EH}{TE} = \frac{\square}{FA}$ **17.** $\frac{\square}{RA} = \frac{HT}{HE}$

18. $\angle A \cong \square$ **19.** $\angle T \cong \square$ **20.** $\angle H \cong \square$

21. $\triangle ARF \sim \square$ **22.** $\triangle ETH \sim \square$

23. The sides of a triangle have lengths 5, 6, and 8. A triangle similar to it has a side of length 10. Write all side lengths of each possible similar triangle.

24. The sides of a triangle have lengths 12, 18, and 18. A triangle similar to it has a side of length 8. Write all side lengths of each possible similar triangle.

25. A triangle has sides of length 5, 7, and 8. A triangle similar to it has a perimeter of 15. What are the lengths of the sides of this triangle?

26. A triangle has sides of length 9, 12, and 15. A triangle similar to it has a perimeter of 40. What are the lengths of the sides of this triangle?

Use the diagram for Exercises 27–29.

27. Figure *ABCD* is a parallelogram. Prove that $\triangle ABF \sim \triangle DEF$.

28. Suppose $m\angle E = 20°$ and $m\angle C = 60°$. Find the measure of each angle.
a. $\angle EBA$ **b.** $\angle A$ **c.** $\angle EDF$

29. Is $\triangle ABF \sim \triangle CEB$? Explain.

Practice: For Lesson 4.15, assign Exercises 23–29.

---

c. No; $\frac{RO}{TO}$ is equal to $\frac{OA}{OS}$, not to $\frac{OS}{OA}$.

14. Fold the corners of the original square into the center to form a new square with half the area. Then fold back a rectangular strip with $\frac{1}{4}$ the area of the smaller square.

15. a. surface area = 22 cm², volume = 6 cm³
b. surface area = 88 cm², volume = 48 cm³

16. 3 cm × 6 cm × 9 cm, surface area = 198 cm², volume = 162 cm³

17. 4 cm × 8 cm × 12 cm, surface area = 352 cm², volume = 384 cm³

18. k cm × $2k$ cm × $3k$ cm, surface area = $22k^2$ cm², volume = $6k^3$ cm³

Lesson Overview

GOAL

- Understand that the ratio between the area of a polygon and the area of a copy of that polygon scaled by the factor r will be r^3.

In this lesson, students discover how scaling affects the areas of rectangles and triangles. Students then generalize these results for polygons.

CHECK YOUR UNDERSTANDING
- Core: 1, 2, 3, 8
- Optional: none

HOMEWORK
- Core: 4, 5, 6, 7
- Optional: 9, 10, 11, 12

MATERIALS
- protractors
- rulers

Launch

Have students begin with the In-Class Experiment. You may wish to have students work in pairs or small groups.

Explore

In-Class Experiment

One of the most effective ways for students to see how a change in scale affects the area of a rectangle or triangle is for them to draw the figure, scale it, and see how many copies of the scaled copy fit inside the original. In this In-Class Experiment, students either draw and scale the figures by hand, or use geometry software to scale the figures.

When students have completed the In-Class Experiment, have them read through the Minds in Action and do For Discussion Problem 10. It asks students to answer the question Derman poses.

4.16 Areas of Similar Polygons

How do the areas of similar polygons compare? Checking simple polygons, such as rectangles, is a good place to start.

In-Class Experiment

Draw a rectangle. Scale it by the factor 2.

1. How do the dimensions of the original rectangle compare with the dimensions of the scaled rectangle?

2. How many copies of the original rectangle fit into the scaled rectangle?

3. How does the area of the scaled rectangle compare to the area of the original rectangle?

Draw a rectangle. Scale it by the factor $\frac{1}{3}$.

4. How do the dimensions of the two rectangles compare?

5. How many copies of the scaled rectangle fit into the original rectangle?

6. How do the areas of the two rectangles compare?

If two triangles are similar and the scale factor is r, you know that the ratio of the lengths of two corresponding sides is r. Show that the following statements are true.

7. The ratio of their perimeters is r.

8. The ratio of the lengths of two corresponding altitudes is also r.

9. The ratio of their areas is r^2.

Minds in Action   episode 14

Hannah and Derman complete the In-Class Experiment.

Hannah: According to the In-Class Experiment, if you scale a triangle by 4, then 16 copies of it should fit inside the scaled copy.

Derman: That sounds like a lot of triangles. Let's try to draw it out.

Answers

In-Class Experiment

1. They are $\frac{1}{2}$ the dimensions of the scaled copy.

2. 4

3. It is 4 times the area of the original.

4. The dimensions of the scaled copy are $\frac{1}{3}$ the dimensions of the original.

5. 9

6. The area of the scaled copy is $\frac{1}{9}$ the area of the original.

7. If the side lengths of the original triangle are a, b, and c, then

$$\frac{\text{Perimeter of copy}}{\text{Perimeter of original}} = \frac{r \cdot a + r \cdot b + r \cdot c}{a + b + c} = \frac{r \cdot (a + b + c)}{a + b + c} = r$$

8. Suppose $\triangle ABC \sim \triangle XYZ$ with $\frac{XY}{AB} = r$. Let $\overline{BP}$ be the altitude drawn from B to $\overleftrightarrow{AC}$, and let $\overline{XQ}$ be the corresponding altitude in $\triangle XYZ$. $\triangle BPC$ and $\triangle YQZ$ are right triangles and are similar by the AA Similarity Test. Hence

Hannah: It's easy! Look, here's a small triangle. And here's a picture showing 16 copies of the small triangle inside the triangle that has been scaled by 4.

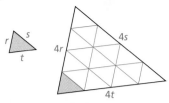

Derman: Okay, that works. But what if you scale a triangle by $2\frac{1}{2}$? Then there should by $6\frac{1}{4}$ copies of the original triangle inside the scaled one. What would that look like?

For Discussion

10. Draw a figure that answers Derman's question. Show that if you scale a triangle by the factor $2\frac{1}{2}$, then you can fit $6\frac{1}{4}$ copies of the original triangle inside the scaled one.

Now that you have calculated the areas of similar rectangles and triangles, take a look at similar polygons with any number of sides.

For You to Do

In the figures below, you scale polygon 1 by the factor r to obtain polygon 2. You divide polygon 1 into four triangles with areas a, b, c, and d.

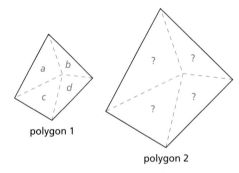

polygon 1

polygon 2

11. What are the areas of the corresponding triangles in polygon 2?

12. What is the total area of polygon 2?

13. What is the total area of polygon 1?

For You to Do

PROBLEMS 11–13 help students work toward discovering Theorem 4.6: If you scale a polygon by some positive number r, then the ratio of the area of the scaled copy to the area of the original polygon is r^2. The area of polygon 1 is $a + b + c + d$. The area of polygon 2 is $ar^2 + br^2 + cr^2 + dr^2$. In order for students to see that the ratio of their areas is r^2, you may need to point out that they can rewrite the area of polygon 2 as $r^2(a + b + c + d)$.

The Developing Habits of Mind provides a proof of Theorem 4.6. Problem 14 asks students to draw the pictures for this proof.

Wrap Up

Assign the Check Your Understanding exercises for work in class.

Assessment Resources

$\dfrac{YQ}{BP} = \dfrac{YZ}{BC} = r$. A similar argument shows that the other corresponding altitudes have the ratio r.

9. Use the altitudes in the answer for Exercise 8. Area($\triangle ABC$) = $\frac{1}{2}(AC)(BP)$ and Area($\triangle XYZ$) = $\frac{1}{2}(r \cdot AC)(r \cdot BP)$. So $\dfrac{\text{Area}(\triangle XYZ)}{\text{Area}(\triangle ABC)} = r^2$.

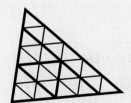

For Discussion

10. Answers may vary. Sample:

For You to Do

11. ar^2, br^2, cr^2, dr^2

12. $ar^2 + br^2 + cr^2 + dr^2$, or $(a + b + c + d)r^2$

13. $a + b + c + d$

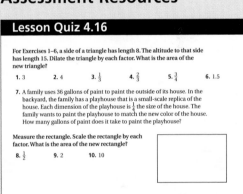

The results of your work lead to the following theorem.

Theorem 4.6

If you scale a polygon by some positive number r, then the ratio of the area of the scaled copy to the area of the original polygon is r^2.

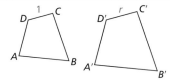

Developing Habits of Mind

Prove a special case. An argument for a special case can suggest how an argument could be made in general. Here's a proof of Theorem 4.6 for a quadrilateral. It suggests how a proof might proceed for any polygon.

Suppose you scale $ABCD$ by r to get $A'B'C'D'$. Pick a point O inside $ABCD$. Connect it to each of the vertices, dividing $ABCD$ into triangles. (There would be four in this case, but in general there would be as many as there are sides.) Let the areas of these triangles be a, b, c, and d. Then

$$\text{area}(ABCD) = a + b + c + d$$

If the image of O is O', then the triangle AOB gets scaled by a factor of r to triangle $A'O'B'$, and so on. So, by the results of Problem 9 of the In-Class Experiment, the area of the triangles in $A'B'C'D'$ are r^2a, r^2b, r^2c, and r^2d. Then

$$\begin{aligned} \text{area}(A'B'C'D') &= r^2a + r^2b + r^2c + r^2d \\ &= r^2(a + b + c + d) \\ &= r^2 \cdot \text{area}(ABCD) \end{aligned}$$

> There are some quadrilaterals for which picking an inside point would not necessarily work. For example:
>
>
>
> A complete proof would have to cover all possible cases, including ones like these.

For You to Do

14. Draw diagrams to go along with the above proof. Label them to help you understand this proof.

Answers

For You to Do

14. Answers may vary. Sample:

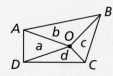

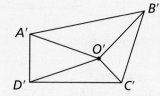

Exercises *Practicing Habits of Mind*

Check Your Understanding

1. One side of a triangle has length 10. The altitude to that side has length 12. If you make a new triangle for which all the sides of the original triangle are tripled, what is the area of the new triangle?

2. Jerry wants to plant two cornfields. One measures 400 ft by 600 ft. The other measures 200 ft by 300 ft. Becky, the owner of the seed-and-grain store, says, "The big field will take eight bags of seed. The small field has sides half as big, so you'll need four more bags for that. Will that be cash or charge?" A few days later, Jerry returns to the store very upset. Explain.

3. **a.** Trace this polygon onto a sheet of paper. Estimate its area in square centimeters.

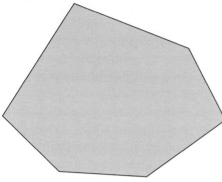

> **Habits of Mind**
>
> **Recall what you know.** Think about figures for which a ruler can help you find area. Can you see such figures in this polygon?

b. If you scale the polygon by the factor 1.5, what will be the area of the scaled copy?

On Your Own

4. The area of one square is 12 times the area of another square. Find the ratio of the lengths of the following.

   a. their sides

   b. their diagonals

5. You scale a rectangle by the factor $\frac{1}{4}$. Compare the area of the scaled rectangle to the area of the original rectangle.

Exercises

HOMEWORK
- Core: 4, 5, 6, 7
- Optional: 9, 10, 11, 12

Check Your Understanding

EXERCISE 3 Students estimate the area of an arbitrary polygon—possibly by triangulating. Then they scale the polygon by the factor 1.5 and predict the area of the new polygon.

On Your Own

EXERCISE 4 To understand this exercise students should be comfortable working with square roots. This exercise gives students a square that has an area that is 12 times the area of another square. Students then have to find the ratio of the lengths of the two squares' sides and of their diagonals.

EXERCISES 5–7 give students practice using Theorem 4.6.

Exercises

1. 540

2. He needed only 2 bags of seed for the small field.

3. **a.** about 31 cm² or 4.8 in.²
   b. about 70 cm² or 11 in.²

4. **a.** $\sqrt{12}$ or $\frac{\sqrt{12}}{12}$

   b. $\sqrt{12}$ or $\frac{\sqrt{12}}{12}$

5. The area of the scaled copy is $\frac{1}{16}$ times the area of the original.

Additional Resources

PRINTED RESOURCES
- Solution Manual
- Practice Workbook
- Assessment Resources
- Teaching Resources

TECHNOLOGY
- Interactive Textbook
- TeacherExpress CD-ROM
- **Exam***View* CD-ROM
- **PHSchool.com**
  - Additional Practice
  - Mid-Chapter and Chapter Tests
  - Video Tutors
  - Vocabulary Puzzles

Additional Practice

1. A side of a triangle has length 9. The altitude to that side has length 16. When you make a new triangle for which you double the lengths of all the sides of the original triangle, what is the area of the new triangle?

In Exercises 2 and 3, the ratio of the areas of two rectangles is $\frac{9}{16}$.

2. If the smaller rectangle has width 27 cm, what is the width of the larger rectangle?

3. If the larger rectangle has width 27 cm, what is the length of the smaller rectangle?

4. Rachel mows a yard 150 ft by 220 ft in 1.5 hours. At that rate, how long does it take her to mow a yard that is 300 ft by 440 ft?

5. A plot of land that is 360 ft by 242 ft can produce 44 bushels of wheat. Robert purchases a plot of land that is 540 ft by 363 ft. How many bushels of wheat can his land produce?

6. A blue square has an area that is 18 times the area of a red square. What is the ratio of the length of a side of the blue square to the length of a side of the red square?

7. The area of a triangle is 72 square inches. The area of a similar triangle is 16 square inches. What is the ratio of the height of the original triangle to the height of the similar triangle?

8. A colt's paddock has an area of 300 square feet. The colt is growing, and his owner wants to scale the paddock dimensions by the factor 3.5. What is the area of the new paddock?

9. You scale a triangle by the factor 20. What is the ratio of the area of the scaled triangle to the area of the original one?

10. A rectangle has an area of 126 square inches. When you scale the lengths of the sides by the factor $\frac{2}{3}$, what is the area of the new rectangle?

11. You increase the width of a rectangle by the factor 4. You decrease the length by the factor 4. What is the ratio of the area of the new rectangle to the area of the original rectangle? Explain.

12. You increase the height of a triangle by the factor 8. The length of the base stays the same. What is the ratio of the area of the new triangle to the area of the original triangle? Explain.

13. You decrease the length of a rectangle by the factor $\frac{5}{8}$. By what factor should you change the width so that the area of the new rectangle is the same as that of the original rectangle? Explain.

14. You increase the lengths of the sides of a cube by the factor 1.5. What is the ratio of the volume of the new cube to that of the original? Explain.

Practice: For Lesson 4.16, assign Exercises 1–14.

---

6. You scale a triangle by the factor 5. Compare the area of the scaled triangle to the area of the original triangle.

7. The area of a polygon is 17 square inches. You scale the polygon by the factor 2. What is the area of the new polygon?

8. **Standardized Test Prep** The area of a regular hexagon with 10-cm sides is 259.8 cm². To the nearest square centimeter, what is the area of a regular hexagon with 5-cm sides?

   A. 130 cm²   **B.** 100 cm²   **C.** 65 cm²   **D.** 52 cm²

Maintain Your Skills

In Exercises 9–12, find the volume of each figure. Then apply the given scale factor and find the volume of the new figure.

9. scale factor = 3

rectangular prism

10. scale factor = 2

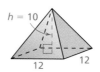

square pyramid

11. scale factor = 5

cylinder

12. scale factor = r

rectangular prism

Go Online
PHSchool.com

For additional practice, go to Web Code: bea-0416

Answers

6. The area of the scaled copy is 25 times the area of the original.

7. 68 in.²

8. C

9. 315; 8505

10. 480; 3840

11. 112π; $14{,}000\pi$

12. 108; $108r^3$

4D

In this investigation, you studied similar figures—figures with congruent corresponding angles and proportional corresponding sides. You used the AA, SAS, and SSS tests to determine whether two triangles are similar. You also used scale factors to find the areas of two similar figures. These questions will help you summarize what you have learned.

1. In the figure at the right, suppose $\overline{CD} \perp \overline{AB}$. How many similar triangles can you find? Prove that all the ones you find are similar. Use the triangle similarity tests.

2. In the figure at the right, $\triangle ABC \sim \triangle EDC$. Prove that $\triangle FDA \sim \triangle FBE$.

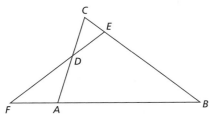

3. In a quadrilateral $EFGH$, $\overline{EF} \parallel \overline{HG}$ and $\overline{EH} \perp \overline{EF}$. $EF = 6$, $FG = 5$, $GH = 10$, and $EH = 3$.

   a. Find the area of $EFGH$.

   b. Scale $EFGH$ by 3. Call the scaled copy $IJKL$, so that $EFGH \sim IJKL$. Find the area of $IJKL$.

   c. What is the ratio of the areas of $EFGH$ and $IJKL$?

4. What does it mean for two figures to be similar?

5. What are some tests for triangle similarity?

6. If the common ratio of two similar figures is r, what is the ratio of their areas?

Vocabulary and Notation

In this investigation, you learned this term and this symbol. Make sure you understand what each one means and how to use it.

- similar figures
- ~ (is similar to)

The two different-sized squares have similar fold patterns. Fold them and you get two origami figures that are similar.

Mathematical Reflections

EXERCISES 4–6 At the start of the investigation, you may have assigned these as Questions 1–3 for students to think and write about.

Mathematical Reflections

1. 3 similar triangles; each of the two small right triangles is congruent to the large right triangle by the AA Similarity test. Hence the small triangles are similar to each other.

2. Since $\triangle ABC \sim \triangle EDC$ it follows that $\angle CAB \cong \angle C \cong \angle CED$ and $\angle CDE \cong \angle B$. Since $\angle FAD$ and $\angle FEB$ are supplements of congruent angles, they are congruent. $\angle CDE$ and $\angle FDA$ are vertical angles, hence congruent, and so $\angle FDA \cong \angle B$. Since

the angles at D and A in $\triangle FDA$ are congruent, respectively, to the angles at B and E in $\triangle FBE$, $\triangle FDA \sim \triangle FBE$ by the AA Similarity Test.

3. **a.** 24   **b.** 216   **c.** $\frac{1}{9}$

4. Answers may vary. Sample: One figure is a scaled copy of the other.

5. Answers may vary. Sample: AA Similarity Test, SAS Similarity Test, SSS Similarity Test

6. r^2

Project

You could assign this project to small groups. Give groups some time to experiment in class. Then you could plan a day for groups to present to the whole class.

Midpoint Quadrilaterals

Use either pencil and straightedge or geometry software. Draw quadrilateral *ABCD*. Construct the midpoint of each side. Label the midpoints of $\overline{AB}$, $\overline{BC}$, $\overline{CD}$, and $\overline{DA}$ as *E*, *F*, *G*, and *H*, respectively.

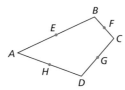

Connect the midpoints to form quadrilateral *EFGH*. Call this the midpoint quadrilateral.

1. Describe the features of your midpoint quadrilateral *EFGH*.

2. Try to classify it as a particular kind of quadrilateral.

   • If you are using geometry software, experiment by moving the vertices and sides of *ABCD*.

   • If you are working on paper, repeat the experiment with a significantly different starting quadrilateral.

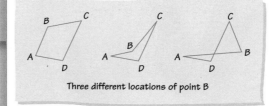

Three different locations of point B

3. Does the midpoint quadrilateral retain its special features?

4. Use the Proportional Side-Splitter Theorem. Prove that each conjecture you have made about a midpoint quadrilateral is correct. Make sure that your proof is valid for each of the three locations of *B* shown in the preceding diagram. It may help to draw the diagonals of each quadrilateral.

Remember, in this book, the term *quadrilateral* does not include self-intersecting quadrilaterals like this one. However, your proof could work for self-intersecting quadrilaterals, as well.

5. Suppose the diagonals of quadrilateral *ABCD* measure 8 inches and 12 inches. What is the perimeter of the midpoint quadrilateral?

Using the Midline Theorem

Juan said that he did not use a side-splitter theorem in his proof for his conjecture about midpoint quadrilaterals. Here is an outline of his proof.

   • In quadrilateral *ABCD*, find the midpoints and connect them in order to make the midpoint quadrilateral.

   • Draw the diagonal $\overline{AC}$. Two opposite sides of the midpoint quadrilateral are parallel to and half as long as $\overline{AC}$ because of the Midline Theorem. To see this, you just have to look at *ABCD* as two triangles that share a base $\overline{AC}$.

6. Write out Juan's proof. Include a statement of his conjecture, any helpful diagram(s), and a conclusion about the midpoint quadrilateral.

Answers

Project

1. Opposite sides are parallel, and the angles are congruent to the angles formed by the intersection of the diagonals of the original quadrilateral.

2. It is a parallelogram.

3. yes

4. Conjectures may vary. Sample: The midpoint quadrilateral is a parallelogram. Opposite sides of the midpoint quadrilateral are parallel to a diagonal and therefore parallel to each other. The midpoint quadrilateral is a parallelogram by definition of parallelogram.

5. 24

6. Since the Midline Theorem is a special case of the side-splitter theorems, this proof is the same

as the proof for Exercise 4, using the Midline Theorem instead of the Proportional Side-Splitter Theorem.

7. Yes. For a rhombus or kite, the midpoint quadrilateral is a rectangle. The diagonals of a rhombus or kite are perpendicular, so the midlines are perpendicular and the midpoint parallelogram has perpendicular sides. For a rectangle or isosceles trapezoid, the midpoint quadrilateral is a rhombus. The diagonals of a rectangle

or isosceles trapezoid are congruent, so the four midlines are congruent. For a square, the midpoint quadrilateral is a rhombus and a rectangle, and therefore a square, by the previous two proofs.

8. Conjectures may vary. Sample: Any point in the plane, except the vertices of the midpoint parallelogram, may be a vertex of *ABCD*. Let *EFGH* be the midpoint quadrilateral. Choose point *A* not equal to *E*, *F*, *G*, or *H*. Point *A* cannot be on both $\overleftrightarrow{EF}$ and $\overleftrightarrow{HG}$, so assume it is not on $\overleftrightarrow{EF}$. Draw $\overline{AE}$.

pecial Quadrilaterals

ecial types of quadrilaterals include

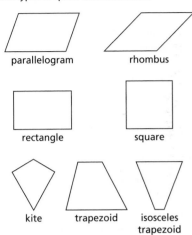

parallelogram   rhombus

rectangle   square

kite   trapezoid   isosceles
trapezoid

Does any special type of quadrilateral have a special midpoint quadrilateral (different from what you found in the preceding exercises)? Prove each conjecture you make.

If quadrilateral *ABCD* has a square (or rhombus or rectangle) as a midpoint quadrilateral, make a conjecture about *ABCD*. Prove your conjecture. How can you support your conjecture using software?

xtending the Idea

Describe a connection between midpoint quadrilaterals and dilations. (*Hint:* A midpoint quadrilateral has, of course, its own midpoint quadrilateral. Think about the sequence of midpoint quadrilaterals for a given figure. One such sequence is shown on the computer screen that follows.)

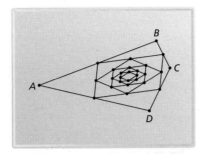

Jessica extended her investigation. She used a diagram like this to make a conjecture. She claimed that she could prove her conjecture using the Proportional Side-Splitter Theorem.

10. a. Describe the points that Jessica connected in her diagram. It may help to redraw the diagram and label some points.

   b. Use the Proportional Side-Splitter Theorem to prove that the inner quadrilateral is a parallelogram.

11. Here is another "inside quadrilateral" that Jessica's diagram suggests. Make a thoughtful conjecture about this quadrilateral. Prove, or at least give some support for, your conjecture.

Proof: The triangles formed by opposite sides of the inside quadrilateral and the outside parallelogram are congruent by SAS, so opposite sides of the inside quadrilateral are also congruent. Therefore the inside quadrilateral is a parallelogram.

Extend $\overline{AE}$ to *B* so that *AE = EB*. Draw $\overline{BF}$. Extend $\overline{BF}$ to *C* so that *BF = CF*. Draw $\overline{CG}$. Extend $\overline{CG}$ to *D* so that *CG = GD*. *ABCD* is the desired quadrilateral. *H'*, the midpoint of $\overline{AD}$, is the same as *H*, because both $\overline{EH}$ and $\overline{EH'}$ are parallel to and the same length as $\overline{FG}$ (by the Midline Theorem).

9. Suppose *EFGH* is a midpoint quadrilateral of *ABCD*. The midpoint quadrilateral of *EFGH*'s midpoint quadrilateral is a dilation of *EFGH* by the factor $\frac{1}{2}$, with a center of dilation

at the common point where each quadrilateral's diagonals intersect.

10. a. Jessica trisected each side of the quadrilateral and connected corresponding points on adjacent sides.

   b. The proof follows exactly the same steps as the proof in the solution to Exercise 4.

11. Conjectures may vary. Sample: If the "outside" quadrilateral is a parallelogram, then the "inside" quadrilateral is also a parallelogram.

Answers

Review

1. Check students' diagrams. Sample:

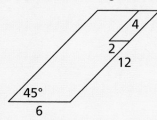

2. No; check students' work.

3. a. Yes; all angles are congruent and corresponding sides are proportional.

b. No; answers may vary. Sample: a square and a trapezoid

c. Yes; answers may vary. Sample: Two spheres always have the same shape, though their sizes may be different.

d. No; answers may vary. Sample: a kite with diagonals of lengths 1 and 2 and a kite with diagonals of lengths 1 and 4

e. No; answers may vary. Sample: a rhombus with sides of length 2 and angles of 60° and 120° and a rhombus with sides of length 2 and angles of 40° and 140°

f. No; answers may vary. Sample: An equilateral triangle is not similar to a right triangle.

g. No; answers may vary. Sample: An isosceles right triangle is not similar to a scalene right triangle.

h. Yes; for any two equilateral triangles, the ratio of corresponding sides is constant and all angles of the triangles have a measure of 60°.

4. Check students' work.

In **Investigation 4A**, you learned to

- apply a scale factor to make similar figures

- decide whether two figures are well-scaled copies of each other

- use a scale factor to approximate distances in blueprints and maps

The following questions will help you check your understanding.

1. Scale this parallelogram by the factor $\frac{1}{3}$.

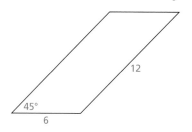

2. Without measuring, check whether the figures below are scaled copies of each other.

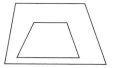

3. Decide whether all members of each collection below must be scaled copies of each other. Explain why they are, or find a counterexample.

a. all regular pentagons

b. all quadrilaterals

c. all spheres

d. all kites

e. all rhombuses

f. all triangles

g. all right triangles

h. all equilateral triangles

In **Investigation 4B**, you learned to

- describe and use the ratio method and the parallel method to make dilations

- identify a dilation as an enlargement or reduction by looking at the scale factor

- describe the effect of the choice for center of dilation on the resulting dilation

The following questions will help you check your understanding.

4. Trace the pentagon and point *T* onto a sheet of paper. Use the ratio method to scale the pentagon by the factor 1.5. Use *T* as the center of dilation.

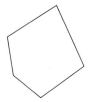

5. Trace *ABCDEF* and point *O* onto a sheet of paper. Use the parallel method to scale the hexagon by the factor $\frac{1}{3}$. Use *O* as the center of dilation.

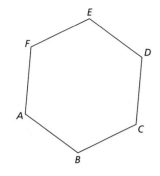

In **Investigation 4C**, you learned to

- decide how lines parallel to a side of a triangle split the other two sides

- understand and prove the side-splitter theorems

- use ratios and proportions.

The following questions will help you check your understanding.

6. In the diagram below, $EB = \frac{1}{3}AB$, $BC = 3BF$, $DA = 2AH$, and $DG = \frac{1}{2}DC$. Prove that *EFGH* is a trapezoid.

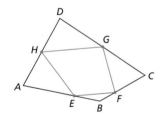

7. $\triangle ABC$ is a right triangle. $AC = 10$, $AD = 4$, $CB = 15$, and $EB = 6$. Prove that $\triangle DEC$ is a scaled copy of $\triangle ABC$.

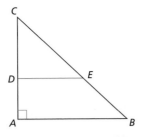

8. Draw a triangle. Label its vertices *A*, *B*, and *C*. Choose point *P* on $\overline{AC}$ such that $\frac{PA}{AC} = \frac{2}{9}$. Then choose point *Q* on $\overline{BC}$ such that $\frac{BQ}{CB} = \frac{6}{27}$. If $AB = 27$, what is *PQ*?

In **Investigation 4D**, you learned to

- identify corresponding parts of similar triangles

- use the AA, SAS, and SSS tests for similarity in triangles

- understand that the ratio between the area of a polygon and the area of a copy of that polygon scaled by the factor *r* must be r^2

The following questions will help you check your understanding.

9. Draw a square and its diagonals. How many similar triangles can you find? Prove that they are similar. Use the triangle similarity tests.

10. You scale an *n*-gon by the factor 7. What is the ratio of the areas of the scaled *n*-gon and the original *n*-gon?

5. Check students' work.

6. Since $\overline{GH}$ splits $\overline{AD}$ and $\overline{CD}$ proportionally, $\overline{GH} \parallel \overline{AC}$. Since $\overline{EF}$ splits $\overline{AB}$ and $\overline{CB}$ proportionally, $\overline{EF} \parallel \overline{AC}$. Therefore $\overline{EF} \parallel \overline{GH}$ and *EFGH* is a trapezoid.

7. Since $\frac{AD}{AC} = \frac{EB}{CB} = \frac{2}{5}$, $\overline{DE} \parallel \overline{AB}$. Therefore $\angle CDE \cong \angle CAB$. $\triangle ABC \sim \triangle DEC$ by the AA test for similarity.

8. 21

9. 8 similar triangles; all 8 of the triangles are isosceles right triangles with angle measures 45°, 45°, and 90°. They are similar by the AA Similarity Test.

10. 49

Test

Assessment Resources

Also available: Form B

Answers

Test

1. C

2. C

3. C

4. A

5.
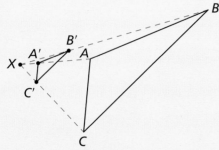

Multiple Choice

1. In this triangle, $\overline{BC} \parallel \overline{DE}$. Also, $AB = DE = 5$, and $BC = 7$. What is DB?

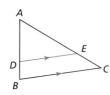

   A. $\frac{7}{25}$ **B.** $\frac{25}{7}$ **C.** 5   **D.** 7

2. In the triangle below, $\overline{DE} \parallel \overline{AB}$. Which of the following is true?

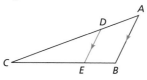

   A. $\frac{AD}{BE} = \frac{CE}{AD}$ **B.** $\frac{AB}{DE} = \frac{BC}{BE}$

   C. $\frac{DE}{AB} = \frac{CE}{BC}$ **D.** $\frac{DE}{CE} = \frac{AC}{BC}$

3. In the figure below, $\angle B \cong \angle E$. Which of the following does NOT allow you to conclude that $\triangle ABC \sim \triangle DEF$?

   A. $\frac{AB}{DE} = \frac{BC}{EF}$ **B.** $\angle C \cong \angle F$

   C. $\frac{AB}{DE} = \frac{AC}{DF}$ **D.** $\angle C \cong \angle D$

4. Why can you say that an AAA test for triangle similarity is "too strong?"

   A. Only two pairs of congruent angles are needed to prove that two triangles are similar.

   B. An AAA test determines whether two triangles are congruent, and congruence is stronger than similarity.

   C. Three angles of one triangle can be congruent to three angles of another triangle, but the triangles need not be congruent.

   D. You only need one pair of congruent angles to prove that two triangles are similar.

Open Response

5. Copy the figure below onto a sheet of paper. Use the ratio method or the parallel method to scale $\triangle ABC$ by $\frac{1}{4}$.

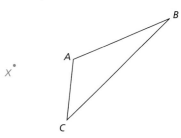

6. Draw a rectangle with sides of 6 cm and 4 cm. This is your original rectangle.

   a. Draw a new rectangle with sides that are 2 cm shorter than the corresponding sides of your original rectangle.

   b. Draw a new rectangle with sides that are $\frac{1}{2}$ as long as the corresponding sides of your original rectangle.

   c. Is either of the rectangles you drew in parts (a) and (b) a scaled copy of the original rectangle? Are they both scaled copies? Explain.

   d. What kind of rectangle must you start with to have the directions in both parts (a) and (b) produce scaled copies of the original rectangle?

---

6. a. Check students' work.
   b. Check students' work.
   c. Yes, the rectangle in part (c) is a scaled copy of the original. No; the lengths of the sides of the rectangle in part (b) are not proportional to those of the original.
   d. a square

7. Given: $SUZI \sim CUHE$. Determine whether each of the following statements is *true* or *false*.

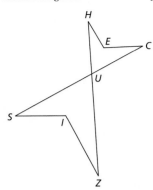

a. $\angle S \cong \angle C$ **b.** $\dfrac{CU}{SU} = \dfrac{ZU}{HU}$

c. $\angle E \cong \angle C$ **d.** $\angle CUH \cong \angle SUZ$

e. $\dfrac{HU}{ZU} = \dfrac{CU}{SU}$ **f.** $\dfrac{CH}{SZ} = \dfrac{CE}{IZ}$

8. Are the triangles in each pair possibly scaled copies of each other or definitely not scaled copies of each other? Explain.

a.

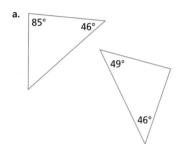

b.

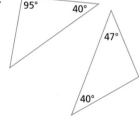

9. Explain how you know that any two squares are similar.

10. Consider the following figure.

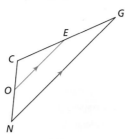

$\overline{OE}$ is parallel to $\overline{NG}$.

a. If $CN = 5$, $CO = 1$, and $CE = 2$, what is CG?

b. If $CG = 7.5$, $CO = 3$, and $CN = 6$, what is CE?

c. If $CE = 3$, and $CG = 12$, what is the value of $\dfrac{CO}{CN}$?

d. If $CO = 1$, and $ON = 4$, what is the value of $\dfrac{OE}{NG}$?

11. Given: $BC = 3 \cdot EC$, and $AC = 3 \cdot CD$

Prove: $\triangle BAC \sim \triangle EDC$

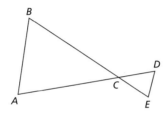

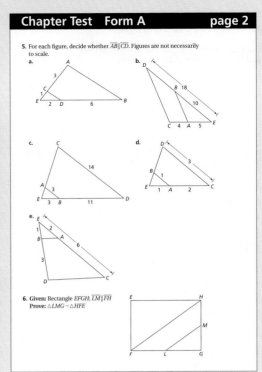
7. a. true
  b. true
  c. false
  d. true
  e. true
  f. false

8. a. Scaled copies; the angles of one triangle are congruent to those of the other.
  b. Not scaled copies; one triangle has angle measures 40°, 45°, 95°, and the other has angle measures 40°, 47°, 93°.

9. Answers may vary. Sample: All angles are right angles and hence the angles of one square are congruent to those of the other. All corresponding sides have the same ratio.

10. a. 10
  b. 3.75
  c. $\dfrac{1}{4}$
  d. $\dfrac{1}{5}$

11. $\dfrac{BC}{AC} = \dfrac{3 \cdot EC}{3 \cdot CD} = \dfrac{EC}{CD}$ and $\angle BCA \cong \angle DCE$ (vertical angles). Hence $\triangle BAC \sim \triangle EDC$ by the SAS Similarity Test.

Cumulative Review

Assessment Resources

1. Start with a parallelogram. Decide whether or not you can dissect it into pieces that can form the following. If you can, write a specific and clear algorithm.

   a. an isosceles triangle

   b. a right triangle

   c. a trapezoid

   d. a rectangle

2. The base of a triangle has a length of 16 inches. How long is the segment that joins the midpoints of the other two sides?

3. Given $\triangle ACE$ with $\overline{BCD}$.

   a. In what ways are $\triangle ACE$ and $\triangle BCD$ the same?

   b. In what ways are $\triangle ACE$ and $\triangle BCD$ different?

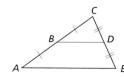

   c. Make a conjecture about the two triangles that are formed by a midsegment.

4. Suppose a kite has diagonals of 12 and 20. Find the perimeter and area of the quadrilateral formed by joining the midpoints of the kite's sides.

5. Which of the following quadrilaterals have the same area? Are any congruent?

   i.   ii.

   iii. 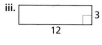 iv.

In 6–8, find the area of the figure.

6.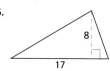

7.

8.

9. Draw a right triangle with legs 6 and 8. Draw a square whose side is the hypotenuse of this triangle.

   a. Find the square's area.

   b. What is the square's perimeter?

   c. Draw a triangle with legs of 15 and 36. Repeat (a) and (b).

10. Can the following side lengths make a right triangle?

   a. 5, 9, 12   **b.** 9, 40, 41   **c.** 10, 11, 21

11. A rectangle has diagonal length 17 m and a base 8 m. Find the rectangle's height.

12. Explain why $\angle A$ must be a right angle.

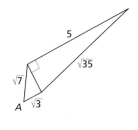

Answers

Cumulative Review

1. a. This is possible with a dissection from B to E and D to F. Flip $\triangle ABE$ and flip $\triangle CDF$ and attach it to DE. If $\overline{DE} \cong \overline{DF}$. An isosceles triangle would be formed.

   b. This is possible if $\overline{BE} \cong \overline{ED}$. Make a cut from B to E and attach $\overline{BE}$ to $\overline{ED}$.

   c. Make a cut from B to E and flip $\triangle ABE$ to form a trapezoid.

   d. Make a cut either from B to E or from to D to F. Flip the triangle and attach to opposite side.

2. 8 in.

3. a. Both triangles share angle B. Also, $\angle A \cong \angle B$, $\angle E \cong \angle D$.

   b. The triangles have sides with different lengths.

   c. The triangles are similar.

4. perimeter: 32 units; area: 60 units^2

5. Figures (a), (c), and (d) have the same area. None of the figures are congruent.

6. 68 units^2

7. 90 units^2

8. 90 units^2

9. Check students' work.

   a. 100 units^2

   b. 40 units

   c. check students' work; area: 1521 units^2; perimeter: 156 units

10. a. no

   b. yes

   c. no

11. 15m

12. $\angle A$ is a right angle because the sides of the triangle show that $(\sqrt{3})^2 + (\sqrt{7})^2 = (\sqrt{58})^2$.

3. The radius of a hexagon is the measure from the center of the hexagon to a vertex. The radius of a regular hexagon and its sides are always congruent. Find the area of the regular hexagon with side lengths of 12 m.

4. Find the lateral and surface areas for each labeled figure.

a.

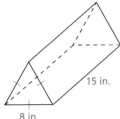

15 in.

8 in.

b.

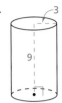

3

9

c.

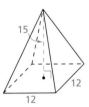

15

12

12

d.

5

13

15. A parallelogram that has a length of 18 inches and a height of 9 inches is scaled using the following scale factors r. What are the parallelogram's new dimensions after being scaled?

a. $r = \frac{5}{3}$　　**b.** $r = 3.5$　　**c.** $r = \frac{4}{9}$

16. Name at least four different measurements you could take on the following pair of figures to convince someone that the two figures are well-scaled copies of each other.

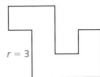

17. Use graph paper to scale the figure by the given scale factor.

$r = 3$

18. Determine whether or not the following can be scaled copies and explain your answer.

a. One triangle has side lengths of 3, 4, and 5. Another triangle has side lengths of 7.5, 10 and 12.

b. One rectangle has dimensions of 4 feet and 11 feet. Another has dimensions of 11 feet and 30 feet.

19. A scaled rhombus now has sides of length 12 cm. If the scale factor was $\frac{2}{3}$, what was the length of the sides of the original rhombus?

20. Decide if the pair of polygons are scaled copies. Explain how you made your decision.

21. A polygon is scaled by a factor of 150%. The original polygon is then compared to the scaled one. Find the ratio of any two corresponding sides and any two corresponding angles of the polygons.

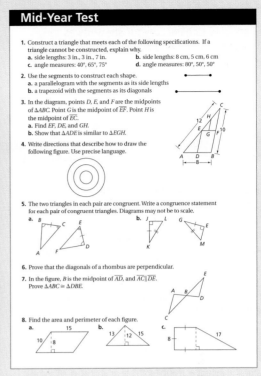
13. $216\sqrt{3}$ m^2

14. a. 360 in.^{2}; ≈387.7 in.^{2}
　b. 54π units^2; 72π units^2
　c. ≈387.7 units^2; ≈531.7 units^2
　d. 65π units^2; 90π units^2

15. a. 30 inches, 15 inches
　b. 63 inches, 31.5 inches
　c. 8 inches, 4 inches

16. Answers may vary.

17. Check students' work.

18. a. No; the sides are not proportional.
　b. No; the sides are not proportional.

19. 18 cm

20. Answers may vary.

21. The ratio of corresponding sides will be 2:3. The ratio of corresponding angles will be 1:1.

Chapter 5
Circles

Circles are very familiar to your students as they have worked with them since elementary school. In this course, students have already encountered circles, cylinders, cones, and spheres, but only in an introductory way. Students had to accept without proof the formulas they used to find area, circumference, volume, and surface area.

In this chapter, students will dig deeper and develop a better understanding of the circle. However, some proofs will still be beyond students' current level of skill because you cannot compose circles from straight lines. You cannot decompose circles into a finite number of triangles. Measuring perimeter and area of circles (and volume and surface area for three-dimensional shapes such as cylinders, cones, and spheres) will require new ways of thinking. If you do not know how to measure the length of a curve or the area bounded by a curve, you will have to approximate those curves with line segments. This chapter introduces students to limits. Students get better approximations for perimeter and area by working with shorter and shorter line segments. They will develop a deeper understanding of what length and area are and what it means to measure them. The chapter also exposes students to a subspecialty in Geometry: proofs involving circles, lines and angles intersecting circles, and polygons inscribed in or circumscribed about circles. Students also see how area relates to probability.

Chapter Overview

- **INVESTIGATION 5A,** *Area and Circumference,* explores techniques to approximate the area and perimeter of closed curves and develops formulas to calculate area.

- **INVESTIGATION 5B,** *Circles and 3.141592...,* introduces π and develops formulas to calculate the area and circumference of a circle in terms of π.

- **INVESTIGATION 5C,** *Classical Results About Circles,* introduces arcs, chords, central angles, secants, and tangents of circles.

- **INVESTIGATION 5D,** *Geometric Probability,* unearths the relationship between the probability of an event and the area of a region.

For more information on the investigations, see
- Chapter Road Map, p. 352
- Investigation Road Maps, pp. 354, 374, 388, 420

CHAPTER PROJECT The Chapter project near the end of the chapter is optional. You can assign the Project at any time during the chapter depending on how often and how long you feel students should work on it.

Pacing Suggestions and Materials

Investigation 5A *Area and Circumference*

DAY	LESSON	HOMEWORK
1	5.1 *Getting Started* Core: 1, 2, 3 Optional: none	Core: 4, 5 Optional: 6, 7, 8
2	5.2 *Area and Perimeter—Day 1* Core: 1, 4 Optional: 2, 3	Core: 11, 15 Optional: 16, 17, 18; Extension: 12
3	5.2 *Area and Perimeter—Day 2* Core: 5, 6, 7, 8, 9, 10 Optional: none	Core: 13, 14 Optional: 19, 20
4	5.3 *Connecting Area Circumference—Day 1* Core: 1, 2 Optional: none	Have students read through For Discussion Problem 7 and come to class prepared to talk about their ideas.
5	5.3 *Connecting Area Circumference—Day 2* Core: 3, 4 Optional: none	Core: 5, 7, 8 Optional: 6, 11; Extension: 9, 10

Investigation 5B *Circles and 3.14159265...*

DAY	LESSON	HOMEWORK
1	5.4 *Getting Started* Core: 1, 2, 3 Optional: none	Core: 4, 5 Optional: 6
2	5.5 *An Area Formula for Circles* Core: 1, 2 Optional: 3	Core: 4, 6, 8 Optional: 5, 7, 10; Extension: 9
3	5.6 *Circumference* Core: 1, 2, 3, 4 Optional: none	Core: 5, 6, 8 Optional: 7, 10; Extension: 9, 11

Investigation 5C *Classical Results About Circles*

DAY	LESSON	HOMEWORK
1	5.7 *Getting Started* Core: 1, 2, 3, 4, 5 Optional: none	Core: 6, 7 Optional: 8, 9, 10
2	5.8 *Arcs and Central Angles—Day 1* Core: 1 Optional: none	Assign For You to Do Problem 3. Students can sketch a proof to discuss at beginning of the next class.
3	5.8 *Arcs and Central Angles—Day 2* Core: 3, 4 Optional: 2	Core: 5, 7, 8, 9 Optional: 6, 11, 12, 13, 14, 15, 16; Exten
4	5.9 *Chords and Inscribed Angles—Day 1* Core: 1, 2 Optional: none	Core: 6, 7, 9 Optional: none

NOTES	MATERIALS
	• graph paper • rulers • Blackline Masters 5.1 A-B
	• compasses • graph paper • large paper • map of the U.S. • Blackline Masters MC 6-9
Begin by discussing Archimedes' method for estimating perimeter. Pay particular attention to Exercise 9.	• compasses • graph paper • rulers • Blackline Masters 5.2 A-B
Work through For You to Do Problems 5 and 6.	• compasses • graph paper • rulers • Blackline Master 5.3A
Begin with For Discussion Problem 7.	• compasses • graph paper • rulers • Blackline Masters 5.3B

NOTES	MATERIALS
	• compasses • geometry software • graphing calculators • rulers • Blackline Masters 5.4, MC 6-9
In this lesson, it is useful to have reviewed Exercise 1.	• compasses • graphing calculators • protractors • rulers
	• graphing calculators • protractors

NOTES	MATERIALS
Students will use these dynamic circle constructions to understand the concept of *invariant*.	• compasses • geometry software • rulers
Work through In-Class Experiment Problem 2.	• compasses • geometry software • rulers • tracing paper
Begin with For You to Do Problem 3.	• compasses • rulers • tracing paper
Work through For Discussion Problem 3 on the first day of this lesson.	• compasses • protractors • rulers

Mathematics Background

DEFINING π There are several definitions of π that a geometry course could use. You will often see it defined as the ratio of the circumference of a circle to its diameter. This course uses the definition that π is the area of a circle of radius 1. You can usefully combine this definition with several other facts your students already know.

For example, your students will conclude that all circles are similar, and therefore are scaled copies of each other. They also know that the ratio of the area of a scaled copy to the area of the original is equal to the square of the scale factor. To get a circle of radius r, you scale a circle of radius 1 by the factor r. The area of the scaled copy is r^2 times the area of the circle of radius 1. Since the circle of radius 1 has area π, the circle of radius r has area πr^2. Using this definition for π makes the area formula automatic.

FINDING NONPOLYGONAL AREAS When finding the area of a shape bounded by a curve, students assume that the shape has a well-defined area. Your students will approximate areas of blob shapes by placing them on a grid of squares. Students use the grid to either underestimate or overestimate the area of the blob. Students see that using a finer mesh with smaller squares creates a better estimate of the area. They also see that they can get an estimate of the blob's area as close to its actual area as they like, as long as they use a fine enough mesh.
In future courses, a set of axioms such as these will define area:

• Congruent shapes have the same area.

• If shape B completely contains shape A, then the area of shape A is less than or equal to the area of shape B.

• When you combine two shapes, the area of the combined shape is equal to the sum of the areas of the two original shapes, minus the area of their intersection.

• The area of a rectangle is equal to the product of its length and width.

Students will find formulas for the areas of polygons by drawing conclusions from these axioms. Then they will extend these ideas of area to accommodate a curved shape. The definition for the area of a curved shape turns out to be the limit of the inside and outside grid approximations as the area of each grid square approaches 0. This definition is consistent with all the axioms of area that students use to find areas of polygons, so it is a valid extension.

PROBABILITY AS MEASURE It might seem counterintuitive to include an investigation about probability in this chapter, but probability is a measure just as area is a measure. It follows a set of axioms that are equivalent to those for area. Through the Monte Carlo Method, students can see the relationship between area and probability. In the Monte Carlo Method for computing probability, you think about dropping tiny objects (such as poppy seeds or droplets of paint) onto a surface that you mark with different regions. The probability of your tiny object hitting a particular region on the surface is proportional to the ratio of the area of that region to the area of the entire surface.

Another nice connection between this investigation and the rest of the chapter is that Monte Carlo techniques give students a way to produce a numerical approximation for π.

Pacing Suggestions and Materials

Investigation 5C *Classical Results About Circles*   *continued*

DAY	LESSON	HOMEWORK
5	5.9 *Chords and Inscribed Angles—Day 2* Core: 5 Optional: 3, 4	Core: 10, 12, 14, 15 Optional: 8, 11, 13, 16
6	5.10 *Secants and Tangents* Core: 1, 2, 3 Optional: 4, 5	Core: 6, 7, 8, 9 Optional: 11, 13, 14; Extension: 10, 12
7	5.11 *Power of a Point* Core: 1, 2, 3 Optional: none	Core: 4, 5, 6, 8 Optional: 7, 11, 12, 13, 14; Extension: 9

Investigation 5D *Geometric Probability*

DAY	LESSON	HOMEWORK
1	5.12 *Getting Started* Core: 1, 2, 3, 4, 5 Optional: 6, 7	Core: 8, 9 Optional: 10, 11, 12
2	5.13 *Probability as a Ratio of Areas* Core: 1 Optional: 2, 3	Core: 4, 5, 7, 8 Optional: 6, 10; Extension: 9
3	5.14 *Sets of Measure 0* Core: 1, 2, 3 Optional: none	Core: 4, 6, 7 Optional: 5, 9; Extension: 8

NOTES	MATERIALS
Begin with the definition of *inscribed angle* and In-Class Experiment Problems 4 and 5.	• compasses • geometry software • rulers
	• compasses • geometry software • rulers
	• compasses • geometry software • rulers

NOTES	MATERIALS
	• compasses • large paper or thin cardboard • spinners • tape • Blackline Masters 5.12 A-C
• Have students come up with their own example of a set of measure zero.	

Developing Students' Mathematical Habits

In this chapter, students use reasoning by continuity when they approximate lengths and areas of curves and consider limits. They will visualize curves approximated by chains of congruent line segments and areas approximated by squares in a grid. Reasoning by continuity will help students picture the results of using smaller line segments or grid squares to develop better approximations. As they use smaller grid squares, the inner and outer approximations of the area must approach each other. Students can then justify the assertion that a curved shape does have a well-defined area, and this area must be equal to the limit of the inner and outer sums. Finally, students will search for invariants and use deductive reasoning to write proofs when they look at the chords, arcs, secants, and tangents of circles.

Chapter 5

Investigations at a Glance

5A Area and Circumference

5 Circles and 3.14159265358979...

5C Classical Results About Circles

5D Geometric Probability

Chapter Road Map

INVESTIGATION 5A, *Area and Circumference,* introduces the grid method to estimate areas of blobs (i.e., irregular shapes with rounded edges). You place the blob on a grid and count the squares inside the blob and the squares inside or touching the blob. Students use this method to approximate the area of a circle with radius one inch. After presenting a method for estimating the perimeter of blobs, the investigation ends with a lesson that introduces the formula $A = \frac{1}{2}Cr$.

INVESTIGATION 5B, *Circles and 3.141592...,* derives the area and circumference formulas for circles and gives a historical introduction to π. Lesson 5.5 uses the area of a circle with radius one to find the area of any circle. Students prove Theorem 5.4 that says the area of a circle with radius r is kr^2, where k is the area of a circle with radius one. Students do not immediately label the area of a unit circle π.

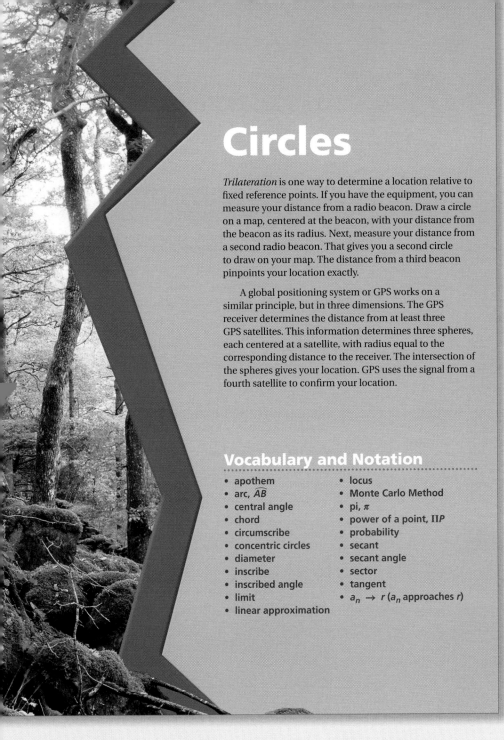

Circles

Trilateration is one way to determine a location relative to fixed reference points. If you have the equipment, you can measure your distance from a radio beacon. Draw a circle on a map, centered at the beacon, with your distance from the beacon as its radius. Next, measure your distance from a second radio beacon. That gives you a second circle to draw on your map. The distance from a third beacon pinpoints your location exactly.

A global positioning system or GPS works on a similar principle, but in three dimensions. The GPS receiver determines the distance from at least three GPS satellites. This information determines three spheres, each centered at a satellite, with radius equal to the corresponding distance to the receiver. The intersection of the spheres gives your location. GPS uses the signal from a fourth satellite to confirm your location.

Vocabulary and Notation

- apothem
- arc, $\widehat{AB}$
- central angle
- chord
- circumscribe
- concentric circles
- diameter
- inscribe
- inscribed angle
- limit
- linear approximation

- locus
- Monte Carlo Method
- pi, π
- power of a point, ΠP
- probability
- secant
- secant angle
- sector
- tangent
- $a_n \rightarrow r$ (a_n approaches r)

INVESTIGATION 5C, *Classical Results About Circles,* presents the definitions of *arc, chord, central angle,* and *circumscribed angle.* The lesson explores the classical theorems (and proofs) that relate these terms to each other.

INVESTIGATION 5D, *Geometric Probability,* explores geometric probability and the Monte Carlo Method. In the final lesson, students have the opportunity to discuss whether a probability of 0 implies that a certain event is impossible.

Chapter Vocabulary and Notation

The following list gives key vocabulary and notation used in the chapter. Selected new vocabulary and notation items are shown in boldface on the student page.

- adjacent chords, p. 403
- apothem, p. 367
- arc AB, ($\widehat{AB}$), p. 392
- central angle, p. 392
- chord, p. 392
- circumscribe, p. 361
- concentric circles, p. 404
- degree measure, p. 394
- diameter, p. 392
- discrete case, p. 425
- inscribe, p. 361
- inscribed angle, p. 401
- limit, p. 359
- linear approximation, p. 361

- locus, p. 390
- major arc, p. 394
- minor arc, p. 394
- measure zero set, p. 429
- Monte Carlo Method, p. 425
- pi (π) p. 377
- power of a point (ΠP), p. 418
- probability, pp. 413, 424
- secant, p. 406
- secant angle, p. 407
- sector, p. 379
- similar, p. 375
- tangent, p. 406
- $a_n \rightarrow r$ (a_n approaches r), p. 369

Chapter Technology

Support for the use of technology is available in the Technology Handbook. See p. 712.

Investigation 5A *Geometry Software*

- **LESSON 5.2** Inscribe and circumscribe squares, p. 363.

Investigation 5B *Geometry Software*

- **LESSON 5.4** Compare the number of sides of a polygon with the ratio of its perimeter to the length of its apothem, p. 375.

Investigation 5B *Calculator*

- **LESSON 5.6** Determine whether $\frac{ns_n}{2}$ approaches π, p. 384.

Investigation 5C *Geometry Software*

- **LESSON 5.7** Move and trace points along a specified path between two points, p. 389.

- **LESSON 5.8** Trace circles and arcs to explore central angles, p. 393.

Investigation 5D *Geometry Software*

- **LESSON 5.10** Move and trace points and lines to explore tangents and secants, p. 406.

- **LESSON 5.10** Move and trace points to explore inscribed angles, p. 412.

- **LESSON 5.11** Move and trace points and lines to explore the power of a point, p. 413.

- **LESSON 5.11** Move and trace points and lines to explore constant area rectangles, p. 415.

CHAPTER PROJECT Move and trace points to explore intersecting circles, p. 434.

Investigation Overview

This investigation describes techniques to approximate the area and perimeter of closed curves, and therefore of circles, using inner and outer sums. Lesson 5.3 introduces the formula for the area of regular polygons (half the perimeter times the apothem) and its analogous formula for the area of a circle (half the circumference times the radius).

You may wish to assign Questions 1–3 for students to think and write about during the investigation.

Learning Goals

- Approximate areas of closed curves with inner and outer sums.
- Approximate perimeters of closed curves with linear approximation.
- Establish that the area of some regular polygons is half the perimeter times the apothem.
- Approximate areas and perimeters of circles with inscribed and circumscribed regular polygons.

Habits and Skills

- Visualize the effect of a finer mesh on area approximation or smaller segments on perimeter approximation.
- Determine the effect of scaling on the area of a figure.
- Relate areas and perimeters of regular polygons with increasing numbers of sides to the area and circumference of a circle.

Investigation 5A
Area and Circumference

In *Area and Circumference*, you will learn ways to find the areas of figures that have curved edges. The methods you learned for finding area in Chapter 3 work only for polygons and circles. Now you will use those methods to help you find areas of figures with other types of curved edges, such as figures formed by spilled paint.

By the end of this investigation, you will be able to answer questions like these:

1. How can you calculate the area of a blob?
2. What is the circumference of a circle?
3. What formula relates the area of a circle to its circumference?

You will learn how to

- approximate areas of closed curves with inner and outer sums
- approximate perimeters of closed curves with linear approximation
- establish that the area of some regular polygons is $\frac{1}{2}$ the perimeter times the apothem
- approximate areas and perimeters of circles with inscribed and circumscribed regular polygons

You will develop these habits and skills:

- Visualize the effect of a finer mesh on area approximation or smaller segments on perimeter approximation.
- Determine the effect of scaling on the area of a figure.
- Relate areas and perimeters of regular polygons with increasing numbers of sides to the area and circumference of a circle.

How would you measure the size of an oil spill?

Investigation Road Map

LESSON 5.1, *Getting Started,* introduces the technique for approximating the area of a blob with a grid via inner and outer sums.

LESSON 5.2, *Area and Perimeter,* teaches students to refine their approximation by using grids with a finer mesh. It also describes the linear approximation method used to determine perimeters of blobs.

LESSON 5.3, *Connecting Area Circumference,* begins with an exploration of the apothem and perimeter of a regular polygon. The lesson then develops the formula that relates the area of a circle to its radius and circumference.

Getting Started

Triangles and other polygons are convenient geometric shapes to study, but many objects in our world are not composed of line segments. Circles, egg shapes, and curves of all types are as common as polygons. How can you find the area of a shape that has curves?

or You to Explore

One way to find the area of a polygon is to divide it into triangles and then find the area of each triangle. What can you do for a figure that is not a polygon? For example, how can you estimate the area of this blob? Can you find it exactly?

For shapes such as this, the best you can do is estimate the area.

1. List several ways that you can estimate the area of an irregular shape such as the blob above.

2. List several ways that you can estimate the perimeter of an irregular shape such as the blob above.

3. Try each of your methods with the blob or some other shape.

Lesson Overview

GOALS

- Warm up to the ideas of the investigation.

- Approximate areas of closed curves with inner and outer sums.

This lesson introduces a technique to approximate the area of figures referred to as *blobs*. Lessons 5.1 and 5.2 will serve as groundwork for many ideas that students will encounter in calculus. It is intended to be an informal, intuitive introduction to concepts such as sequences and limits.

FOR YOU TO EXPLORE	HOMEWORK
• Core: 1, 2, 3	• Core: 4, 5
• Optional: none	• Optional: 6, 7, 8

MATERIALS
- graph paper
- rulers
- Blackline Masters 5.1 A-B

Launch

Begin this lesson by assigning Problems 1, 2, and 3 to individuals or to small groups. You may wish to provide students with a ruler and graph paper for these problems. The blob is reproduced in Blackline Master 5.1A. Blackline Masters MC 6–9 are $\frac{1}{16}$, $\frac{1}{8}$, $\frac{1}{4}$, and $\frac{1}{2}$ inch grids, which your students can use throughout this Investigation.

Explore

Listen to some student answers to the For You to Explore problems and introduce the technique of finding upper and lower bounds.

Wrap Up

Make sure students understand the concept of upper and lower bounds. It should be clear that an upper bound of a number is a higher value that cannot become less than the number itself. Similarly, a lower bound of a number is a lower value that cannot become greater than the number itself.

Answers

For You to Explore

1. Answers may vary. Sample:
   Method 1. Copy the blob on a sheet of graph paper. Count the squares that lie entirely inside the blob. Estimate fractional parts for squares that are partially inside the blob. Find the total of the whole squares and parts. (Use a single grid square as the unit of area.) *Method 2.* Time

yourself in seconds as you shade in a figure whose area you know. Do the shading at a steady rate. Then time yourself as you work at the same rate to shade in the blob. Use a proportion to estimate the area of the blob.

2. See back of book.

3. Check students' work.

Exercises

HOMEWORK
- Core: 4, 5
- Optional: 6, 7, 8

On Your Own

EXERCISES 4 AND 5 introduce the concept of inner and outer sums, which students will develop in the following lesson.

Exercises *Practicing Habits of Mind*

On Your Own

One mathematical habit for estimating a value is to find upper and lower bounds for the value. Then you squeeze those bounds together. Follow the steps in Exercises 4 and 5 to find bounds for the area of the blob.

4. Begin by placing the blob on a piece of graph paper that has $\frac{1}{2}$ in.-by-$\frac{1}{2}$ in. squares.

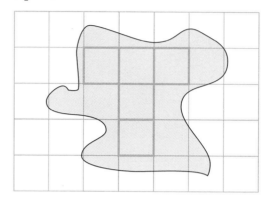

   a. Count the number of squares that are completely inside the figure.

   b. Add the areas of those inner squares to find an area that is definitely less than the area of the blob.

5. Now count all the squares that are either inside the blob or touching it.

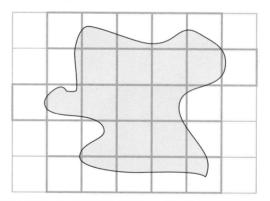

Answers

Exercises

4. **a.** There are 5 squares inside the figure.
   b. Each square has an area of $\frac{1}{4}$ square inch. The area covered by the squares is $\frac{5}{4}$ square inches, which is definitely less than the area of the blob.

5. **a.** There are 27 squares contained by or touching the figure.
   b. Each square has an area of $\frac{1}{4}$ square inch. The area covered by the squares is $\frac{27}{4}$ square inches, which is definitely greater than the area of the blob.

a. How many of these squares are there?

b. Add the areas of these squares to find an area that is definitely greater than the area of the blob.

Maintain Your Skills

6. Trace this square and scale it by a factor of $\frac{1}{2}$.

What is the area of the initial square? What is the area of the scaled square?

7. Trace this octagon and scale it by a factor of 2.

What is the approximate area of the initial octagon? What is the approximate area of the scaled octagon?

8. Trace this parallelogram and scale it by a factor of $\frac{1}{3}$.

What is the approximate area of the initial parallelogram? What is the approximate area of the scaled parallelogram?

> In order to scale these polygons, you should measure their sides. To calculate their areas, either use a formula or think of a way to estimate each area.

Go Online
Video Tutor
PHSchool.com

Web Code: **bee-0775**

6. Check students' diagrams. Answers may vary. Sample: 4 cm²; 1 cm²

7. Check students' diagrams. Answers may vary. Sample: about 4.8 cm²; about 19.3 cm²

8. Check students' diagrams. Answers may vary. Sample: about 2.31 cm²; about 0.26 cm²

- Approximate areas of closed curves with inner and outer sums.
- Approximate perimeters of closed curves with linear approximation.

It may take two class periods to work through all of the content in this lesson. Refer to the Daily Planner at the beginning of the chapter for one way to split the lesson into two days.

This lesson serves as groundwork for concepts students will encounter if they study calculus. When students reach calculus, they do not always get the chance to take measurements and try out this grid method for approximating area. By giving them the chance to do so now, you will help them build their understanding so that they will be ready for a more formal approach in calculus.

This lesson also contains an informal introduction to perimeter. The basic question is: *How can you estimate the perimeter of a curve and then improve your estimate?* Students should be able to suggest the approach presented here, which is to estimate the perimeter with a series of straight lines. This lesson is also a good place to teach students some simple constructions of regular polygons. In the Wrap Up section there are steps for drawing an equilateral triangle, a square, a regular pentagon, and a regular hexagon.

CHECK YOUR
UNDERSTANDING
- Core: 1, 4, 5, 6, 7, 8, 9, 10
- Optional: 2, 3

MATERIALS
- compasses
- graph paper
- large paper
- map of the U.S.
- rulers
- Blackline Masters 5.2 A-B, MC 6-9

HOMEWORK
- Core: 11, 13, 14, 15
- Optional: 16, 17, 18, 19, 20
- Extension: 12

VOCABULARY
- circumscribe
- inscribe
- limit
- linear approximation

Launch

Start this lesson by recalling Exercises 4 and 5 from the previous lesson and have students read or act out the Minds in Action.

5.2 Area and Perimeter

Now you can refine your approach to find the area of an irregular shape, such as the area of the blob in Lesson 5.1.

Minds in Action   episode 15

Tony and Sasha are discussing the method for finding the area of the blob in Exercises 4 and 5.

Tony   There's a pretty wide range between the inner and outer areas we found for the blob in these two exercises.

Sasha   Well, the grid that the blob is on is made of really big squares. I bet if we put the blob on a grid with smaller squares, there will be less of a range. By doing that, more of the blob will be covered by whole squares.

Tony   Let's try this grid. Each square is $\frac{1}{4}$ in. by $\frac{1}{4}$ in. So each square has an area of $\frac{1}{16}$ square inch.

> Mathematicians say that you are making a "finer mesh."

Sasha   I'll take it from here. There are 32 squares completely inside the blob. So that's $32 \times \frac{1}{16}$ square inch, or $\frac{32}{16}$ square inches. There are 47 border squares. So that's $(32 + 47) \times \frac{1}{16}$ square inch, or $\frac{79}{16}$ square inches.

Tony   Hmm, the area of the blob must be somewhere in between those two numbers.

Sasha   That's really not very accurate. We'd better make a finer mesh!

In this picture, the squares on the graph paper are $\frac{1}{8}$ in. by $\frac{1}{8}$ in.

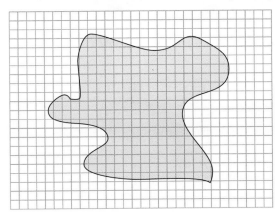

1. **a.** What is the area of each small square?

   b. Calculate the inner sum and the outer sum to place the area of the blob between two numbers.

   c. Are these numbers closer to each other than the numbers Sasha found?

2. Give an argument to support the claim that as the number of squares per inch gets larger (that is, as the mesh of the graph paper gets finer), the difference between the outer sum and the inner sum gets smaller.

You now have the basic idea behind how the area of a closed curve (like the blob) is defined. In summary:

- You cover the region with graph paper and compute the inner and outer sums. You make the mesh finer and repeat the process.

- This produces a sequence of inner and outer sums. The difference between these inner and outer sums can be made as small as you want by making the mesh even finer.

- This means the inner and outer sums get closer and closer to a single number. This is the **limit** of the whole process.

- This single number is the area of the region.

You already know a way to compare the areas of two polygons when one is a scaled copy of the other. If a polygon is scaled by some positive number r, then the ratio of the area of the scaled copy to the original is r^2. Is this true for blobs, too?

Answers

For You to Do

1. **a.** Each small square has area $\frac{1}{64}$ in.^{2}.

   b. Answers may vary. Sample:
   $176\left(\frac{1}{64}\right) = \frac{176}{64}$, or $2\frac{3}{4}$;
   $(176 + 82)\left(\frac{1}{64}\right) = \frac{258}{64}$, or $4\frac{1}{32}$

   c. Results may vary. Sample is given based on sample answer for part (b): Sasha's numbers

yield $\frac{79}{16} - \frac{32}{16} = \frac{47}{16}$, or $2\frac{15}{16}$;
$\frac{258}{64} - \frac{176}{64} = \frac{82}{64}$, or $1\frac{9}{32}$;
yes.

2. Answers may vary. Sample: As the number of squares per inch increases, the difference between the outer sum and the inner sum decreases because the number of squares inside the figure increases by the square of the number of squares along the edge of the figure.

Imagine that a blob and a grid of squares are drawn onto a big rubber sheet.

The area of these 228 squares gives a reasonably good estimate of the blob's area.

Now imagine that the rubber sheet is stretched uniformly in all directions by a factor of 2. This causes the blob and the squares to be scaled by 2 as well.

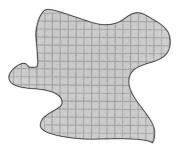

Estimate the area of the blob, now that the squares have been stretched by a factor of 2.

3. By what factor did the area of each square increase?

4. What is a good estimate for the blob's area in terms of the number of squares?

5. If the area of one square before was S, what is it now? What is the area of the 228 stretched squares?

For You to Do

6. What would have happened if you had stretched the rubber sheet uniformly in all directions by a factor of r? Answer the questions from the In-Class Experiment for a rubber sheet stretched by a factor of r.

Answers

In-Class Experiment

3. The area of each square increased by a factor of 2^2, or 4.

4. In terms of the number of squares, the area stayed the same, 288 squares.

5. $4S$; $4(288) = 912$

For You to Do

6. The area of each square would increase by a factor of r^2; in terms of the number of squares, the area would remain the same, 288 squares; $r^2 \cdot S$; $288r^2$.

Archimedes used a **linear approximation** method for estimating the length of a curved path that is easy to apply. Just approximate the curve with line segments and add the lengths of the segments.

Archimedes was born around 287 B.C. in Syracuse, Sicily, which was a Greek city-state.

For You to Do

7. Approximate the perimeter of the blob above using this linear approximation technique.

For Discussion

8. How can you improve your estimate?

Perimeters of Circles

Of all curves, perhaps the most recognizable is the circle. The name given to the perimeter of a circle is one you already know—the circumference. Circumference is reserved for circles and the round cross sections of three-dimensional shapes such as spheres and cylinders.

The perimeter of a circle can be found through the following process.

- Inscribe a regular polygon in the circle. Circumscribe a regular polygon with the same number of sides around the circle.

- Calculate the perimeter of each polygon.

- Make another pair of inscribed and circumscribed polygons with double the number of sides. Then calculate the perimeters of the new polygons.

- Continue this process. The inner and outer perimeters will approach a common value. That number is the circle's circumference.

To **inscribe** a polygon in a circle means to draw it so that all of its vertices are on the circle. To **circumscribe** a polygon around a circle means to draw it so that all of its sides are touching the circle.

7. Answers may vary. Sample: $8\frac{3}{8}$ in.

For Discussion

8. Answers may vary. Sample: You can improve your estimate by using shorter line segments.

Explore

For Discussion

Use shorter segments to get a better estimate. You will get a better approximation of the curve, and therefore, a better estimate of its perimeter. You can improve the estimate as much as you want by using even shorter segments.

PERIMETERS OF CIRCLES extends the perimeter estimation technique to circles and introduces the important idea of circumscribing polygons about and inscribing polygons inside a circle. Familiarize students with the terms *circumscribe* and *inscribe*. Explain that

- each vertex of an inscribed polygon is on the circle

- each side of a circumscribed polygon touches the circle in a single point

Consider introducing the term *tangent*, which Lesson 5.10 defines.

Wrap Up

Assign the Check Your Understanding exercises for work in class. Blackline Master 5.2A provides pictures of 4-, 8-, and 16-sided polygons inscribed in and circumscribed about a circle. If you use the Blackline Masters, students only have to take measurements. You also can use geometry software to draw the figures and measure the sides of the regular polygons.

EQUILATERAL TRIANGLE

1. Draw one side of the triangle. Label it $\overline{AB}$.

2. Draw a circle with center A and radius AB. Draw a second circle with center B and radius AB.

3. Select one of the two intersections of the circles. This is the third vertex of the equilateral triangle.

SQUARE

1. Draw one side of the square. Label it $\overline{AB}$.

2. Draw a line perpendicular to $\overline{AB}$ through A. Draw a line perpendicular to $\overline{AB}$ through B.

3. Draw a circle with center A and radius AB. Choose one of its intersections with the perpendicular line through A.

4. Through this chosen intersection draw a line parallel to $\overline{AB}$.

REGULAR PENTAGON

1. Draw a circle with center O and two perpendicular diameters $\overline{AX}$ and $\overline{TY}$.

2. Choose radius $\overline{OY}$ and find its midpoint M.

3. Connect M and A.

4. Bisect $\angle AMT$.

5. Let K be the intersection of $\overline{AO}$ and the angle bisector from Step 4.

6. Draw the line through K that is parallel to $\overline{TY}$. Label the intersections of the line and circle B and E. Points B, E, and A are all vertices of the pentagon.

7. Draw a circle with center E and radius AE and a circle with center B and radius AB. The intersections of these circles and the circle with center O are the 4th and 5th vertices.

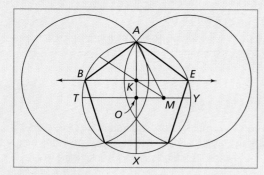

REGULAR HEXAGON

1. Draw a circle with center O.

2. Draw diameter $\overline{AD}$. Points A and D are opposite vertices of the hexagon.

3. Draw a circle with center A and radius AO.

4. Draw a circle with center D and radius DO.

5. The two intersections of the circles with centers A and O and the two intersections of circles with centers D and O form the other four vertices of the hexagon.

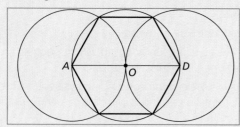

Exercises *Practicing Habits of Mind*

Check Your Understanding

1. Draw a circle of radius one inch and approximate its area using each of the following mesh sizes. Describe any patterns that show up in your estimates.

 a. $\frac{1}{2}$ in. **b.** $\frac{1}{4}$ in. **c.** $\frac{1}{8}$ in. **d.** $\frac{1}{16}$ in.

2. a. Explain in words a method you have used to approximate the area of an irregular shape.

 b. Using what you learned in Chapter 3, find the area of a right triangle with sides 3 in., 4 in., and 5 in.

 c. Suppose you did not know the area formula for a triangle. Go through the inner and outer sums process for a 3-4-5 triangle to approximate its area. See how close you can get to the actual area.

3. The two crescent moons are scaled copies of each other. What is the ratio of their areas?

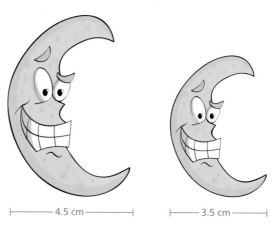

├───── 4.5 cm ─────┤   ├───── 3.5 cm ─────┤

4. How do the areas of the two circles compare?

 a. A circle of radius 2 is scaled to a circle of radius 6.

 b. A circle of radius 2 is scaled to a circle of radius 1.

> **Habits of Mind**
>
> **Strategize.** Sometimes a shape has symmetry that allows you to make counting easier with shortcuts. Use shortcuts wherever possible.

Answers

Exercises

1. The following answers assume that two grid lines pass through the center of the circle.

 a. Inner area = 1 in.²; outer area = 4 in.²; area of circle is between these measures.

 b. Inner area = 2 in.²; outer area = 3.75 in.²; area of circle is between these measures.

 c. Inner area = 2.56 in.²; outer area = 3.5 in.²; area of circle is between these measures.

 d. Inner area = 2.86 in.²; outer area = 3.34 in.²; area of circle is between these measures.

2. a. Answers may vary. Sample: Place a grid of squares over the shape. To get a low estimate, count grid squares that lie entirely inside the shape and multiply by the area of a grid square. To get a high estimate, count grid squares that lie inside or partially

In Exercises 5–10, you will practice the process of drawing inscribed and circumscribed polygons for a circle. If you are not able to make the drawings yourself, just copy and complete the table in Exercise 8 by taking measurements directly from the drawings provided.

5. Draw a circle. Inscribe a square in the circle and circumscribe a square around the circle. Calculate the perimeters of the two squares and thus place the circumference of the circle between two numbers.

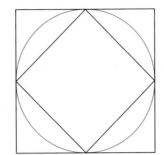

> **Remember...**
>
> *Draw* means to use either pencil-and-paper drawing tools or geometry software.

6. Using a circle of the same size, inscribe a regular octagon in the circle and circumscribe a regular octagon around the circle. Calculate the perimeter of the two octagons and thus place the circumference of the circle between two numbers.

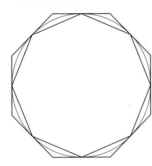

7. Carry this process one step further with inscribed and circumscribed 16-gons.

Go Online
PHSchool.com

For more information about inscribed and circumscribed polygons, go to **Web Code: bee-9031**

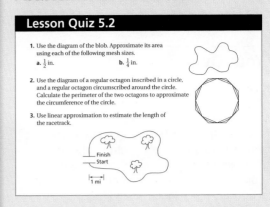
Exercises

HOMEWORK
- Core: 11, 13, 14, 15
- Optional: 16, 17, 18, 19, 20
- Extension: 12

Check Your Understanding

EXERCISE 1 begins to develop the area formula for circles. It asks students to draw a circle with a 1-inch radius and estimate its area. Once students know the area of a circle with radius 1 inch, they will be able to figure out the area of any circle. Use Blackline Masters MC 6–9.

EXERCISES 5–7 Blackline Master 5.2A depicts the figures so that students do not have to draw them.

---

inside the shape and multiply by the area of a grid square. In most cases, the smaller the grid squares, the better the estimates will be.

b. 6 in.^{2}

c. Answers may vary. Sample: inner area = 5.25 in.^{2}, outer area = 6.75 in.^{2} (You obtain these values by using a grid of $\frac{1}{4}$ in.-by-$\frac{1}{4}$ in. squares, with the perpendicular sides of the triangle lying along grid lines.)

3. ratio of area of smaller to area of larger = $\left(\frac{3.5}{4.5}\right)^2$, or about 0.605

4. a. The area of the larger circle is 9 times the area of the smaller circle.

b. The area of the smaller circle is $\frac{1}{4}$ the area of the larger circle.

5–7. Check students' work.

EXERCISE 9 Notice that if the circle is a unit circle, the perimeter will be an approximation of 2π. You might point this out and refer to it in Investigation 5B.

On Your Own

EXERCISE 11 You might wish to give your students Blackline Masters MC 8–9. In this exercise, the scaling of the blob and of the squares does not happen simultaneously. So the squares you count for the inner and outer sums might not be exactly the same. However, when you place the original or scaled blob on grid paper, the inner and outer sums should not vary much (and less and less as the mesh gets finer).

Maintain Your Skills

EXERCISES 13 Blackline Master 5.2B is of the Exercise 13 blob.

EXERCISES 16–20 Exercises 16–19 ask the same questions about a cube that you scale by a different factor each time. If you choose to assign these exercises you should assign at least one among 16, 17, 18, and both 19 and 20.

8. Copy the table. Use the data from Exercises 5–7 to fill it in.

Number of Sides	Outer Perimeter	Inner Perimeter	Difference
4	■	■	■
8	■	■	■
16	■	■	■

9. Give an approximation for the perimeter of your circle.

10. Explain why the difference between the outer and inner perimeters gets smaller as the number of sides gets bigger.

On Your Own

11. **a.** Draw a blob.
    - Estimate its area using a mesh of $\frac{1}{2}$ in.
    - Estimate the same blob's area using a mesh of $\frac{1}{4}$ in.

    b. Now draw the blob again, scaled by a factor of 2. Estimate the new blob's area three times. Use a mesh of $\frac{1}{2}$ in., $\frac{1}{4}$ in., and 1 in.

    c. Which estimates in part (a) and part (b) are approximately the same?

    d. Explain the following claim. You have a good estimate for a blob's area in terms of a number of squares on graph paper. That same number of squares is a good estimate if the graph paper and the blob get stretched by a factor of r.

12. **Take It Further** Imagine that a blob and a grid of squares are drawn onto a big rubber sheet. The area of these 228 squares gives a good estimate of the blob's area.

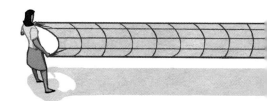

Answers

8. Tables may vary depending on art used. Sample:

Number of Sides	Outer Perimeter	Inner Perimeter	Difference
4	20.4 cm	14.4 cm	6 cm
8	16.8 cm	15.2 cm	1.6 cm
16	16 cm	15.5 cm	0.5 cm

9. Answers may vary. Sample: 15.75 cm

10. As the number of sides of the inscribed and circumscribed polygons increases, the polygons get to be more like the circle.

11. **a.** Check students' work.
    b. Check students' work.
    c. Answers may vary. Sample: The number of $\frac{1}{2}$-inch squares inside the original blob is approximately the same as the number of 1-inch squares inside the dilated blob.
    d. If the blob and the grid are both dilated by a factor of k, then the number of grid squares for the inner and outer areas will not change.

Imagine that the rubber sheet is stretched in just one direction. Now all of the squares have one side length doubled and one unchanged.

a. What shape do the squares become?

b. What is the area of the new shapes compared to the area of the squares?

c. What happens to the area of the blob?

d. Is the blob a scaled copy of the original? If your answer is yes, what is the scale factor? If your answer is no, explain why not.

Sasha has a way to make the linear approximation technique easier. She uses what she calls a regular approximation for a curve. She picks some length, say $\frac{1}{4}$ in., and marks it off around the curve until she gets too close to the starting point to mark another segment. Then she just multiplies the number of segments by $\frac{1}{4}$ and adds on the last little gap.

13. Use Sasha's regular approximation method to estimate the length of the curve below.

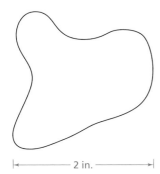

|← —————— 2 in. —————— →|

14. Many people use Sasha's regular approximation to estimate distance on road maps.

a. Explain how this works.

b. Use a road map and regular approximation to estimate the distance between your hometown and a city many states away.

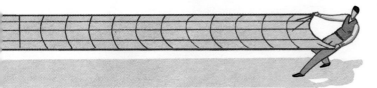

Additional Resources

PRINTED RESOURCES
- Texas Instruments Activities Workbook
- Cabrilog Activities
- Teaching Resources
- Practice Workbook
- Assessment Resources

TECHNOLOGY
- TeacherExpress CD-ROM
- **Exam** *View* CD-ROM
- **PHSchool.com**
  - Homework Help
  - Video Tutors
  - Multiple Choice
  - Crosswords

Additional Practice

1. Draw a circle of radius 2 inches. Approximate its area using each of the following mesh sizes.

   a. $\frac{1}{2}$ in.   **b.** $\frac{1}{4}$ in.   **c.** $\frac{1}{8}$ in.   **d.** $\frac{1}{16}$ in.

2. How do the areas of the two circles compare?
   a. A circle of radius 4 is scaled to a circle of radius 8.
   b. A circle of radius 4 is scaled to a circle of radius 1.

3. **a.** Draw a circle. Inscribe an equilateral triangle in the circle and circumscribe an equilateral triangle around the circle. Calculate the perimeters of both triangles.
   b. Using the same circle, inscribe a regular hexagon in the circle and circumscribe a regular hexagon around the circle. Calculate the perimeters of both hexagons.
   c. Using the same circle, inscribe a dodecagon (12-gon) in the circle and circumscribe a dodecagon around the circle. Calculate the perimeters of both dodecagons.
   d. Use the data from parts (a)–(c) to give an approximation for the perimeter of your circle.

4. **a.** Draw a blob. Estimate its area using a mesh of $\frac{1}{2}$ in. Estimate the same blob's area using a mesh of $\frac{1}{4}$ in.
   b. Draw the original blob scaled by a factor of 3. Estimate the new blob's area using a mesh of $\frac{1}{2}$ in. and $\frac{1}{4}$ in.
   c. A blob and its grid of squares is scaled. Explain the relationship of the areas of both shapes.

5. Use linear approximation to estimate the following distances.
   a. the perimeter of a lake
   b. the length of a cross-country running course

Practice: For Lesson 5.2, assign Exercises 1–5.

12. a. *s*-by-2*s* rectangles, where *s* is the length of a square of the original grid
   b. twice the area of a square of the original grid
   c. It doubles.
   d. No; in a scaled copy, all the lengths change by the same factor.

13. The curve is approximately $7\frac{1}{8}$ inches long.

14. a. Answers may vary. Sample: The linear approximation technique uses the principle that the length of a path can be approximated by finding the length of a path made up only of segments that is close to the actual path.
   b. Check students' work.

15. Standardized Test Prep The circle has a square circumscribed around it. It has another square inscribed inside it. Which value best describes the ratio of the perimeter of the circumscribed square to the perimeter of the inscribed square?

A. $\sqrt{2}$ **B.** 2   **C.** $2\sqrt{2}$ **D.** 4

Maintain Your Skills

For Exercises 16–19, answer parts (a), (b), and (c).

a. What is the new side length of the cube?

b. What was the area of a face on the original cube? What is the new area of a face?

c. What was the volume of the original cube? What is the new volume?

16. A cube with side length 1 cm is scaled by a factor of 2.

17. A cube with side length 1 cm is scaled by a factor of 3.

18. A cube with side length 1 cm is scaled by a factor of $\frac{1}{2}$.

19. A cube with side length 1 cm is scaled by a factor of r.

20. You learned how to approximate the area of 2-dimensional blobs with squares. In a similar way, you can approximate the volume of 3-dimensional blobs with cubes. Write a rule that tells how the volume of such a blob changes when it is scaled by a factor of r.

For additional practice, go to **Web Code: bea-0502**

How can volume help you guess the number of pennies that would fill the jar?

Answers

15. A

16. a. 2 cm
    b. 1 cm^2; 4 cm^2
    c. 1 cm^3; 8 cm^3

17. a. 3 cm
    b. 1 cm^2; 9 cm^2
    c. 1 cm^3; 27 cm^3

18. a. $\frac{1}{2}$ cm
    b. 1 cm^2; $\frac{1}{4}$ cm^2
    c. 1 cm^3; $\frac{1}{8}$ cm^3

19. a. r cm
    b. 1 cm^2; r^2 cm^2
    c. 1 cm^3; r^3 cm^3

20. If you scale a 3-dimensional blob by a factor of r, then the volume of the new blob is r^3 times the volume of the original blob.

5.3 Connecting Area, Circumference

In Lesson 5.2, you approximated the circumference of a circle with inscribed and circumscribed polygons. Now the idea is to find a formula that connects the area of a circle to its circumference. First you must learn about the *apothem* of a regular polygon.

Definition

The **apothem** a of a regular polygon is a perpendicular segment from the center point of the polygon to one of its sides.

For Discussion

1. Find the area of a regular hexagon of side 12 in.

> A regular hexagon's side is the same length as the radius of its circumscribed circle. Can you explain why?

In-Class Experiment

In this experiment, you will find a formula for the areas of regular polygons.

2. Look at the regular pentagon and divide it into five congruent triangles meeting at the center. What role does the apothem a of the pentagon play for each of these triangles?

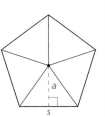

3. If s is the length of each side of the pentagon, what is the area of each congruent triangle? What is the area of the whole pentagon?

4. What would change if the regular polygon had four sides, six sides, or n sides? Can you find the polygon's perimeter somewhere in the formula for its area?

For Discussion

1. $216\sqrt{3}$ in.^{2}

In-Class Experiment

2. For each of the isosceles triangles, the apothem is the length of the altitude to the base.

3. $\frac{1}{2}sa$; $\frac{5}{2}sa$

4. The expressions for the area A of a regular 4-gon, 6-gon, and n-gon will be $\frac{4}{2}sa$ (that is, $2sa$), $\frac{6}{2}sa$ (that is, $3sa$), and $\frac{n}{2}sa$, respectively. In $A = \frac{n}{2}sa$, the product ns is the perimeter of the regular n-gon.

Lesson Overview

GOALS

- Establish that the area of some regular polygons is the perimeter times the apothem.

- Approximate areas and perimeters of circles with inscribed and circumscribed regular polygons.

It may take two class periods to work through this lesson. Refer to the Daily Planner at the beginning of the chapter for one way to split the lesson into two days.

This lesson defines *apothem* and introduces the area formula for regular polygons $\left(A = \frac{1}{2}Pa \right)$. The lesson uses the relationship between a polygon's apothem, perimeter, and area to derive a relationship between a circle's radius, circumference, and area. Since you can estimate the area of a circle by inscribing a polygon in it, you should be able to use the polygon area formula to estimate the area of a circle. The approximation will get better and better as the number of polygon sides increases. The resulting formula $\left(A = \frac{1}{2}Cr \right)$ appears as a theorem.

If you have not taught students to draw the regular polygons described in the Lesson 5.2 Teacher Edition notes, here is another place to do so. It is important for students to learn that the side of a regular hexagon inscribed in a circle is the same length as the circle's radius, but that this does not hold for any other regular polygon.

CHECK YOUR UNDERSTANDING	**HOMEWORK**
• Core: 1, 2, 3, 4	• Core: 5, 7, 8
• Optional: none	• Optional: 6, 11
	• Extension: 9, 10
MATERIALS	**VOCABULARY**
• compasses	• apothem
• graph paper	• $a_n - r$, a_n approaches r
• rulers	
• Blackline Master 5.3A-B	

Launch

Start this lesson by reading the definition of the apothem of a regular polygon and assign the first For Discussion.

Explore

For Discussion

PROBLEM 1 To find the area of any regular polygon, draw segments from the polygon's center to each vertex. This will divide the polygon into n congruent triangles, where n is the number of polygon sides. Any apothem you draw will be an altitude of one of the triangles. Since the triangles are congruent, the altitudes (apothems) will all be congruent.

For Discussion

PROBLEM 7 Use Blackline Master 5.3A for the measurements of the first three polygons. Since these are inscribed polygons, the length of the apothem will always be less than the length of the radius. With each polygon, the sides get closer to the circle so the apothem gets a little longer. Since the shortest distance between two points is a straight line, the arc of the circle must be longer than the side of the polygon. There will be *n* arcs making up the circumference of the circle and *n* sides making up the perimeter of the polygon, so the circumference is always greater than the perimeter.

Since the vertices of the polygon are on the circle and its sides are inside the circle, the polygon lies completely inside the circle and hence has smaller area.

You also can tell that the area must increase at each stage because you can figure out the area for each polygon from its perimeter and apothem by $A = \frac{1}{2}Pa$. You know from earlier questions that both the perimeter and apothem increase at each stage, so the area must increase as well.

The result of the In-Class Experiment is important enough to record as a theorem.

Theorem 5.1

The area *A* of a regular polygon is equal to half of the product of its perimeter *P* and its apothem *a*.

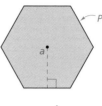

$$A = \frac{1}{2}Pa$$

For You to Do

5. What is the area of a regular hexagon with side length 8?

6. Use the area formula $A = \frac{1}{2}Pa$ to calculate the area of a square with side length 12. Check your result by calculating the area of the square another way.

For Discussion

7. Below are three regular polygons, each inscribed in a circle with radius *r*. The number of sides in each polygon increases from 4 to 8 to 16. Imagine that these pictures continue for a sequence of regular polygons with more and more sides inscribed in this same circle.

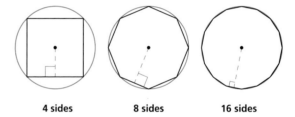

| 4 sides | 8 sides | 16 sides |

Think about how the length of each polygon's apothem changes as you draw polygons with more and more sides. Compare each polygon's perimeter and area with the circumference and area of the circle each is inscribed in.

Habits of Mind

Detect the key characteristics. As the number of sides in each polygon increases, it becomes very difficult to distinguish the polygon from the circle and an apothem from a radius.

Answers

For You to Do

5. $96\sqrt{3}$

6. 144; 144 (using $A = s^2$)

For Discussion

7. Answers may vary. Sample: As the number of sides increases, the perimeter of the polygon approaches but is still less than the circumference of the circle; as the number of sides increases, the area of the polygon approaches but is still less than the area of the circle.

Tony and Sasha look at Theorem 5.1.

Sasha Tony, do you think we could find a similar formula relating the area of a circle to its perimeter?

Tony Well, I know that circumference is a circle's perimeter. How does the apothem a for different shapes compare to the radius r?

Sasha The apothem is the distance from the center of a regular polygon to any of its sides. A circle is like a regular polygon with an infinite number of sides. The equivalent of the apothem in a circle has to be the radius.

Tony Ah . . . now I get it! So the formula for the area of a circle should be something like one half the circumference times the radius.

Sasha I think we can basically prove that by approximating circles with polygons. We could inscribe a sequence of regular polygons in a circle and study their areas. Let's try . . .

Facts and Notation

To make this more precise, use the following notation.

- Let A, C, and r be the area, circumference, and radius of the circle.

- Number the polygons in the sequence 1, 2, 3, ...

- Let the areas of the polygons be A_1, A_2, A_3, . . . ; let their perimeters be P_1, P_2, P_3, . . . ; and let their apothems be a_1, a_2, a_3, ...

Instead of saying that the length of the apothem approaches the radius as n gets larger and larger, write $a_n \rightarrow r$. Using this shorthand notation, rewrite the assumptions as follows.

1. $a_n \rightarrow r$ 2. $P_n \rightarrow C$ 3. $A_n \rightarrow A$

> This arrow notation means something quite precise in calculus. It means that you can make the difference between the length of the apothem and the radius as small as you want by making the number of polygon sides big enough.

Here is the formula for the area of the nth regular polygon in the sequence.

$$A_n = \tfrac{1}{2} P_n a_n$$

Now, because of the three assumptions, as n gets larger and larger, you can rewrite the formula.

$$\tfrac{1}{2} P_n a_n \rightarrow \tfrac{1}{2} Cr$$

You can conclude the following.

$$A_n \rightarrow A$$

Wrap Up

Assign the Check Your Understanding exercises for work in class.

Assessment Resources

Exercises

HOMEWORK
- Core: 5, 7, 8
- Optional: 6, 11
- Extension: 9, 10

You can think of it this way.

$$A_n = \tfrac{1}{2} P_n\, a_n$$
$$\downarrow \quad \downarrow \downarrow \quad \downarrow \quad \downarrow$$
$$A = \tfrac{1}{2} C \quad r$$

This argument leads to the following theorem.

Theorem 5.2

The area of a circle is one half its circumference times its radius.

$$A = \tfrac{1}{2} Cr$$

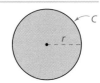

To make this proof completely rigorous, you would need to fill in several gaps about limits and be more precise about the definitions of area and circumference. For now, an intuitive understanding is sufficient.

For a precise proof of this theorem, you will have to wait until you study calculus.

For You to Do

8. A flying disc has area 154 in.^{2} and diameter 14 in. Find its circumference.

Exercises Practicing Habits of Mind

Check Your Understanding

1. A circular garden has a radius of 1 meter and a circumference of about 6.25 meters. What is the area of the garden?

2. A square with side 2 cm is inscribed in a circle.

   a. Find the radius of this circle.

   b. What is the area of the circle if its circumference is 8.9 cm?

Answers

For You to Do

8. about 44 in.

Exercises

1. about 3.125 m^2

2. a. $\sqrt{2}$ cm

   b. about 6.29 cm^2

3. Why is a regular hexagon's side the same length as the radius of its circumscribed circle? Explain your answer with a proof.

4. A regular hexagon is inscribed in a circle of radius 1 in.

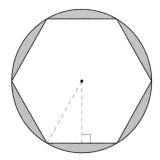

If the area of the shaded region is 0.54 square inch, what is the circumference of the circle?

On Your Own

5. Find the area of each figure.

    a. A stop sign has sides that are 6 inches long and an apothem that is 7.2 inches.

    b. In the figure, an equilateral triangle is inscribed in a circle of radius 2 cm. The center of the circle that circumscribes a triangle is the triangle's circumcenter. The circumcenter of a triangle divides each of the triangle's medians into two segments. One is twice as long as the other. This should give you enough information to find the side length of the equilateral triangle using the shaded triangle in the figure.

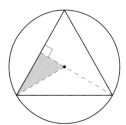

---

3. Answers may vary. Sample: Suppose *ABCDEF* is a regular hexagon and that point *O* is the center of the circumscribed circle. The sum of the angle measures of *ABCDEF* is 4 · 180°, or 720°. If you draw the radii from *O* to the vertices of *ABCDEF*, you divide the hexagon into six congruent isosceles triangles (congruent by SSS, isosceles because radii of the same circle are congruent). It follows that the angles of each triangle all have a measure of 60°. Therefore, the triangles are equilateral, and hence the radii are congruent to the sides of the hexagon.

4. about 6.28 in.

5. a. about 172.8 in.²

    b. $3\sqrt{3}$ cm²

On Your Own

EXERCISE 10 Exercises 10 and 11 in Lesson 5.6 use this formula again. Students will find it easier to do both exercises if they have had the opportunity to solve this exercise.

Maintain Your Skills

EXERCISE 11 is about regular polygons, in particular a triangle and a hexagon. The exercise is made up of five parts that lead the student to the proof of the following statement: If a regular hexagon and an equilateral triangle are inscribed in the same circle, then the hexagon's apothem is half the length of the triangle's side. You do not have to assign all the parts, but if you choose one part, assign all the preceding parts. Use Blackline Master 5.3B so that students do not have to trace the figure.

Additional Resources

PRINTED RESOURCES
- Texas Instruments Activities Workbook
- Cabrilog Activities
- Teaching Resources
- Practice Workbook
- Assessment Resources

TECHNOLOGY
- TeacherExpress CD-ROM
- **Exam** *View* CD-ROM
- **PHSchool.com**
  - Homework Help
  - Video Tutors
  - Multiple Choice
  - Crosswords

Additional Practice

1. Find the area of the following figures.

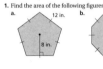

a. 12 in. b. c. 7 in. 8 in.

8 in. 9 in. 3 in.

2. A town is planning a circular walkway that will be 2 meters wide. The walkway will have an inner radius of 5 meters with a circumference of about 31.4 meters. Find the area of the walkway.

3. A regular hexagon is inscribed in a circle of radius 4 inches.
   a. Find the area of the hexagon.
   b. Find the area that lies between the hexagon and circle.

4. A square with side length 10 cm is inscribed in a circle.
   a. Find the radius of the circle.
   b. Find the area of the circle if its circumference is 69.7 cm.

5. Find the area of an equilateral triangle inscribed in a circle with a radius of 5 in.

6. Find the area of a regular octagon with a perimeter of 96 m and an apothem of 5 m.

7. The circle in the figure has a radius of 3 in. Find the area of the shaded region.

8. A bicycle's tires have a radius of 13 inches. How far does the bike travel when the tires rotate exactly 3 times?

Practice: For Lesson 5.3, assign Exercises 1–8.

---

6. Can you use the formula $A = \frac{1}{2}Pa$ for irregular polygons? Explain.

7. A wheel of a toy car has an area of 5 cm² and a radius of 1.26 cm. There is a mark on the point of the wheel that touches the floor. You start pushing the car forward and the marked point does not touch the floor any more. What is the shortest distance you have to push the car for the mark to touch the floor again?

8. **Standardized Test Prep** Beth wants to find the area she can enclose with 264 mm of string. She makes a circle so that the ends of the string touch. The circle has a radius of 42 mm. What is its area?

   A. 1764 mm²   **B.** 3353 mm²   **C.** 5544 mm²   **D.** 11,088 mm²

9. **Take It Further** The Moriarity sisters have to move the shed in their backyard. They jack up the shed and slip two pipes under it, each with a circumference of 8 inches. The sisters get the pipes to roll three revolutions. How far do the sisters move the shed?

10. **Take It Further** A regular polygon with *n* sides and side length *s* is inscribed in a circle of radius 1. Show that a regular polygon with 2*n* sides inscribed in the same circle has side length $\sqrt{2 - \sqrt{4 - s^2}}$.

Maintain Your Skills

11. *J* is the midpoint of side $\overline{NM}$ of an equilateral triangle inscribed in a circle. A regular hexagon is also inscribed in the circle. $\overline{OH}$ is an apothem of the triangle, and $\overline{OK}$ is an apothem of the hexagon.

    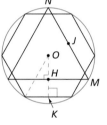

    a. Trace the figure onto a sheet of paper. Draw the radius $\overline{NO}$ and the segment $\overline{OJ}$.

    b. Find the degree measure for each of the following angles.
    - ∠BKO
    - ∠KOB
    - ∠OBK
    - ∠JON
    - ∠ONJ
    - ∠NJO

    c. Now consider △BKO and △OJN. Prove that they are congruent.

    d. Now show that $\overline{OK}$ and $\overline{NJ}$ are congruent.

    e. Compare the hexagon's apothem with the triangle's side. Explain your conclusion.

Go Online
PHSchool.com

For additional practice, go to **Web Code: bea-0503**

Answers

6. No; answers may vary. Sample: In the formula $A = \frac{1}{2}Pa$, the letter *a* represents the apothem of the polygon you are working with. The definition of *apothem* assumes the polygon has a center point and that the distance from the center point to a side is the same for all sides. This is equivalent to requiring that the polygon be a regular polygon.

7. about 7.9 cm

8. C

9. 12 ft

10. See back of book.

11. See back of book.

In this investigation, you explored ways to find the perimeters and areas of shapes with curved edges. These questions will help you summarize what you have learned.

Mathematical Reflections

1. Describe a technique you learned in this investigation for approximating the perimeter of a curve. Use the method you described to approximate the perimeter of the curve at the right.

2. Bill spilled paint and left the blob at the right. Describe how you would use the grid method to estimate the area of Bill's mess.

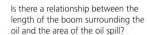

3. What is the area of a regular octagon with apothem 15 in. and side length 11.7 in.?

4. What is the area of a regular hexagon with side length 3 cm?

5. What is the approximate area of a circular pool with an approximate circumference of 12.6 ft and radius 2 ft?

6. How can you calculate the area of a blob?

7. What is the circumference of a circle?

8. What formula relates the area of a circle to its circumference?

Is there a relationship between the length of the boom surrounding the oil and the area of the oil spill?

Vocabulary and Notation

In this investigation, you saw these terms and this symbol for the first time. Make sure you understand what each one means and how to use it.

- **apothem**
- **circumscribe**
- **inscribe**
- **linear approximation**
- **limit**
- $a_n \to r$ (a_n approaches r)

Mathematical Reflections

1. See back of book.

2. See back of book.

3. about 744 in.^{2}

4. $\frac{27\sqrt{3}}{2}$ cm^2

5. about 12.6 ft^2

6. See the answer for Exercise 2. You can start with grid squares of any size you please. For the low and high estimates, count squares and multiply by the area of a single square. To refine the low and high

estimates, use a grid with smaller squares.

7. the distance around the circle

8. $A = \frac{1}{2}Cr$, where A is the area of the circle, C is the circumference, and r is the radius.

Investigation Overview

In this investigation, students develop the circumference and area formulas for circles and develop a substantial understanding of π. To derive the area formula for a circle, students need to know the area of a circle with radius one inch (Exercise 1 of Lesson 5.2). Now is a good time to review this exercise.

The investigation incrementally builds to the area formula of a circle, making the following key points.

- If you scale a circle by r, then the ratio of the area of the scaled copy to the original is r^2. This results in a general formula for the area of a circle. If the area of a circle with radius 1 is k, then the area of a circle with radius r is kr^2.

- The value of k is approximately 3.14 and is known as π.

- Students derive a general formula for the circumference of a circle by substituting the formula for the area of a circle into $A = \frac{1}{2}Cr$.

You may wish to assign Questions 1–3 for students to think and write about during the investigation.

Learning Goals

- Use the definition of π as the area of the unit circle.
- Develop and use the formula $A = \pi r^2$.
- Develop and use the formula $C = 2\pi r$.

Habits and Skills

- Realize that any decimal or fractional representation of π is only an approximation.
- Apply the area formula for circles to find areas of composite shapes.
- Relate and use different definitions of π.

Investigation 5B
Circles and 3.14159265358979 . . .

In *Circles and 3.14159265358979 . . .*, you will examine the circle formulas that you have known for years. In Investigation 5A, you connected perimeter and area for inscribed and circumscribed polygons to circumference and area for circles. Now you can expand these concepts and develop a deeper understanding of circles and the role of π.

By the end of this investigation, you will be able to answer questions like these:

1. What is π?

2. How can you express the area and the circumference of a circle in terms of π?

3. What is the exact area of the shaded portion of the circle with center O?

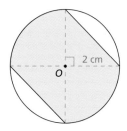

You will learn how to

- use the definition of π as the area of the unit circle
- develop and use the formula $A = \pi r^2$
- develop and use the formula $C = 2\pi r$

You will develop these habits and skills:

- Realize that any decimal or fractional representation of π is only an approximation.
- Apply the area formula for circles to find areas of composite shapes.
- Relate and use different definitions of π.

What questions could you ask about these crop circles?

Investigation Road Map

LESSON 5.4, *Getting Started,* asks students to scale one circle so it becomes congruent to a second circle. This previews Theorem 5.3, which students will see in lesson 5.5.

LESSON 5.5, *An Area Formula for Circles,* develops π as the numerical value of the area of a unit circle. The lesson then presents the formula $A = \pi r^2$.

LESSON 5.6, *Circumference,* presents the formula $C = 2\pi r$. The Historical Perspective gives some notable facts about π.

Getting Started

You have already learned quite a bit about circles in this chapter. It is time to pull together some ideas.

r You to Explore

All circles are similar. This means that all circles have the same shape, but not necessarily the same size.

1. Two circles have radii 12 cm and 30 cm. Can one of them be scaled to give a congruent copy of the other? Explain.

2. Two circles have radii r and R. Can one of them be scaled to give a congruent copy of the other? Explain.

3. a. Use a ruler and compass or geometry software to copy and complete this table. All the polygons are regular.

Number of Sides	Perimeter Apothem
4	■
6	■
8	■
16	■

b. Continue the table for larger numbers of sides.

c. Do the ratios seem to approach any particular number?

Habits of Mind

Visualize. Why do you think all circles are similar?

Exercises *Practicing Habits of Mind*

On Your Own

4. This figure is made up of a quarter circle with radius 1 cm and two equilateral triangles. If the circumference of the whole circle is 6.28 cm, what is the perimeter of the whole shape?

Answers

For You to Explore

1. Yes, either circle can be scaled to get a copy congruent to the other. If you scale the smaller circle by a factor of $\frac{5}{2}$, the scaled copy will have radius 30 cm. If you scale the larger circle by a factor of $\frac{2}{5}$, the scaled copy will have radius 12 cm.

2. Yes, either circle can be scaled to get a copy congruent to the other. If you scale the circle of radius r by a factor of $\frac{R}{r}$, you get a circle of radius R. If you scale the circle of radius R by a factor of $\frac{r}{R}$, you get a circle of radius r.

3–4. See back of book.

Lesson Overview

GOAL

• Warm up to the ideas of the investigation.

This lesson pulls together the core ideas about scaling circles and working with regular polygons that students will see throughout the investigation.

FOR YOU TO EXPLORE	HOMEWORK
• Core: 1, 2, 3 • Optional: none	• Core: 4, 5 • Optional: 6

MATERIALS	VOCABULARY
• compasses • geometry software • graphing calculators • rulers • Blackline Masters 5.4, MC 6–9	• similar

Launch

Start with a discussion of the term *similar*. Point out two objects in the classroom that are similar such as an orange and a globe. Assign all the For You to Explore problems.

Explore

This lesson contains only three For You to Explore problems. If you have been using the Blackline Masters, here is a good place to teach your students to draw regular polygons (especially the triangle, square, and hexagon) with geometry software or a ruler and compass.

Wrap Up

If there is extra time, have your students start the On Your Own exercises.

Exercises

HOMEWORK
- Core: 4, 5
- Optional: 6

Maintain Your Skills

EXERCISE 6 leads students to see that the ratio of the circumference over the diameter of a circle is constant. They can use the grid method introduced in Investigation 5A to estimate the areas of the circles. Blackline Master 5.4 is of the four circles and table. The grids are available in Blackline Masters MC 6–9. Then students can indirectly estimate the circumference using the formula $C = \frac{2A}{r}$. Some students might prefer to estimate the circumferences first and then use a formula for the areas. When students recognize that the ratios $\frac{A}{r^2}$ and $\frac{C}{2r}$ are approximately the same, they are prepared for Lessons 5.5 and 5.6.

On Your Own

5. A circle's area is 25.1 square centimeters. A square is inscribed in the circle. Its apothem is 2 cm. What is the total area of the shaded regions shown in the figure?

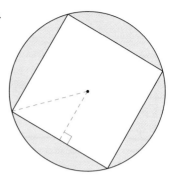

Maintain Your Skills

6. Look at the circles below.

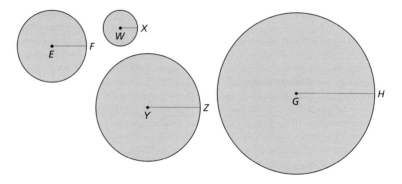

a. Estimate the area A of each circle using any method.

b. Use a ruler to measure each circle's radius r. Then copy and complete the following table.

Circle With Radius	A	$\frac{A}{r^2}$	C	$2r$	$\frac{C}{2r}$
$\overline{EF}$	■	■	■	■	■
$\overline{WX}$	■	■	■	■	■
$\overline{YZ}$	■	■	■	■	■
$\overline{GH}$	■	■	■	■	■

> **Habits of Mind**
>
> **Look for relationships.**
> You might want to look at your answer to Problem 3 in this lesson and see if there are any similarities.

c. Compare the data in the columns of the table and look for invariants.

Answers

5. about 5.57 cm

6. a. See the table in part (b).
   b. Answers may vary. Sample:

Circle With Radius	A	$\frac{A}{r^2}$	C	$2r$	$\frac{C}{2r}$
$\overline{EF}$	1.1 cm²	3.1	3.8 cm	1.2 cm	3.2
$\overline{WX}$	9.1 cm²	3.1	10.6 cm	3.4 cm	3.1
$\overline{YZ}$	4.5 cm²	3.1	7.5 cm	2.4 cm	3.1
$\overline{GH}$	24.5 cm²	3.1	17.5 cm	5.6 cm	3.1

   c. Answers may vary. Sample: The ratios $\frac{A}{r^2}$ and $\frac{C}{2r}$ are invariant.

An Area Formula for Circles

How does the area of a circle change when the circle is scaled? Since you know you can approximate a circle's area with a sequence of regular *n*-gons, you can scale all of the polygons by *s* to approximate the area of the scaled circle. The polygons' areas would all change by a factor of s^2, so it seems plausible that the circle's area would, too.

Below is a theorem that summarizes this.

Theorem 5.3

If a circle is scaled by a positive number *s*, then its area is scaled by s^2.

For You to Do

In Exercise 1 in Lesson 5.2, you approximated the area of a circle with radius one inch to be a bit more than three square inches. Use that result and the theorem above to find a good approximation for the area of a circle with each radius.

1. 2 inches

2. 5 inches

3. 6 inches

4. $\sqrt{3}$ inches

5. $7\frac{1}{2}$ inches

Theorem 5.4

If the area of a circle with radius 1 is *k*, then the area of a circle with radius *r* is kr^2.

This theorem says that you can find the area of any circle once you know the area of a circle with radius 1. As you have calculated, the value of that area is a bit more than 3. Rather than call it *k*, most people call it *pi* and represent it with the Greek letter π.

Definition

Pi (π) is the numerical value of the area of a circle with radius 1.

For You to Do

1–5. Answers may vary. Samples are given.

1. 12.4 in.^{2}

2. 77.5 in.^{2}

3. 111.6 in.^{2}

4. 9.3 in.^{2}

5. 174.4 in.^{2}

Lesson Overview

GOALS

- Use the definition of π as the area of the unit circle.
- Develop and use the formula $A = \pi r^2$.

Students will derive the formula for the area of a circle. The lesson builds up to the area formula in increments. The lesson also presents the definition of π and a short description of its irrational nature.

CHECK YOUR UNDERSTANDING	HOMEWORK
• Core: 1, 2	• Core: 4, 6, 8
• Optional: 3	• Optional: 5, 7, 10
	• Extension: 9
MATERIALS	**VOCABULARY**
• compasses	• pi
• graphing calculators	• sector
• protractors	
• rulers	

Launch

Start this lesson by discussing Theorem 5.3. Here are some of the key points of the lesson:

- The area of a circle with radius one inch is approximately 3.1 square inches.
- When you scale a curved figure (in particular, a circle) by the factor *r*, its area changes by r^2.
- A circle with a radius of 5 inches has an area of approximately $3.1(5)^2$ square inches.

Explore

THEOREM 5.4 In general, you can obtain any circle with radius *r* by scaling the 1-inch radius circle by *r*. This multiplies the area by the factor r^2, so you would estimate that the circle with radius *r* has an area of approximately $3r^2$.

Notice that this text does not immediately label the area of a unit circle π. Instead, it stresses the idea that π is a constant.

It is also important to note that the text defines π as the numerical value of the area of a circle with radius 1, because π is a pure number. (It has no unit.)

For Discussion

Tony is certainly correct that a circle of radius 1 foot does not have the same area as a circle of radius 1 inch. What is true, however, is that the circle of radius 1 foot will have an area of π square *feet*, and the circle of radius 1 inch will have an area of π square *inches*.

Wrap Up

When the definition of π is clear to your students, assign the Check Your Understanding exercises.

Assessment Resources

Lesson Quiz 5.5

1. Find the *exact* area of a circle with the given dimensions.
   a. a radius of 12 m
   b. a diameter of 6 in.

2. The angle of a sector in a circle is 90°. Find the *exact* area of the sector given the following conditions.
   a. The circle has an area of 20π in.^{2}.
   b. The circle has a diameter of 6 cm.

3. Find the area of each shaded region.
   a.
   b.

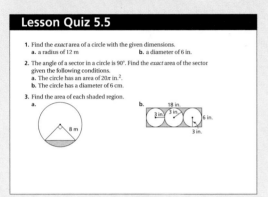

Exercises

HOMEWORK
- Core: 4, 6, 8
- Optional: 5, 7, 10
- Extension: 9

Therefore, thanks to Theorem 5.4, there is a formula you can use for calculating the area of a circle when you know only its radius.

Theorem 5.5

The area of a circle of radius *r* is π times the radius squared.

$$A = \pi r^2$$

If you ask a person to tell you the value of π, you might hear 3.14 or $\frac{22}{7}$. While these are indeed approximations of π, neither is equal to π. In fact, π cannot be represented as a ratio of two whole numbers because π is not a rational number. Since π is irrational, its decimal representation is infinite and nonrepeating.

> π is usually defined as the ratio of the circumference of a circle to its diameter.

Often, people leave the result of calculations about circles in terms of π. That way, anyone who wants a numerical approximation of the result can use whichever approximation for π he or she prefers.

For Discussion

6. Tony is puzzled. He asks himself, "What do they mean π is the area of a circle of radius 1? One what? If you have a circle of radius 1 foot, it can't have the same area as a circle whose radius is 1 inch. This is all nonsense." Suggest an answer to Tony's question.

Exercises *Practicing Habits of Mind*

Check Your Understanding

1. Find the area of a circle with the given dimension.
   a. a radius of 10 in.
   b. a radius of 5 cm
   c. a diameter of 3 ft
   d. the circle obtained by scaling a circle of radius 2 in. by a factor of 5

Answers

For Discussion

6. The definition says that π is the *numerical value* of the area of a circle whose radius is 1. That means the number of square units. A foot is a larger unit of length than an inch, and a square foot is a larger unit of area than a square inch.

Exercises

1. a. 100π in.^{2}
   b. 25π cm^2
   c. $\frac{9}{4}\pi$ ft^2
   d. 100π in.^{2}

2. The angle of the wedge in the circle is 45°. The radius of the circle is 1.

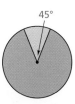

45°

This wedge is really called a **sector** of the circle, which is a region bound by two radii and the circle.

  a. What fraction of the circle's area is the wedge?

  b. What is the exact area of the circle?

  c. What is the exact area of the wedge?

  d. Use two common approximations for π to find the area of the wedge.

Go Online
Video Tutor
PHSchool.com

Web Code: bee-0775

3. Find the area of each shaded region.

a.

10

b.

12

On Your Own

4. Find the area of each shaded region.

a.

60°   5

b.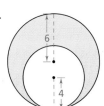

6

4

5. An equilateral triangle with sides of length 6.9 cm is inscribed in a circle.

  a. Find the length of the apothem and draw a sketch.

  b. Find the area of the circle.

  c. Shade the part of the circle that is outside the triangle. Find that area.

---

2. a. $\frac{1}{8}$

  b. π

  c. $\frac{\pi}{8}$

  d. Answers may vary. Sample: $\frac{11}{28}$ (using $\pi \approx \frac{22}{7}$), 0.3925 (using $\pi \approx 3.14$)

3. a. 25π

  b. $144\pi - 72$

4. a. $\frac{25\pi}{6}$

  b. 20π

5. a. Answers may vary. Sample:

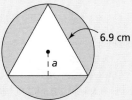

6.9 cm

a

length of apothem
= $1.05\sqrt{3}$ cm²

  b. $A = \pi(2.1\sqrt{3})^2 = 13.23\pi$ cm².

  c. See part (a) for sample sketch; $A = 13.23\pi - 10.8675\sqrt{3}$ cm².

On Your Own

EXERCISE 9 Students see multiple definitions of π and prove that these definitions are equivalent.

Maintain Your Skills

EXERCISE 10 If you do not want to assign all parts of this exercise, assign two or three consecutive sectors and part (g). The idea is that each shaded region (sector) is a fraction of the total area of the circle. Students should see that the ratio of the angles that describe the sector and the whole circle (360°) is the same as the ratio of the areas of the sector and the whole circle.

Additional Resources

PRINTED RESOURCES
- Texas Instruments Activities Workbook
- Cabrilog Activities
- Teaching Resources
- Practice Workbook
- Assessment Resources

TECHNOLOGY
- TeacherExpress CD-ROM
- **Exam***View* CD-ROM
- **PHSchool.com**
  - Homework Help
  - Video Tutors
  - Multiple Choice
  - Crosswords

Additional Practice

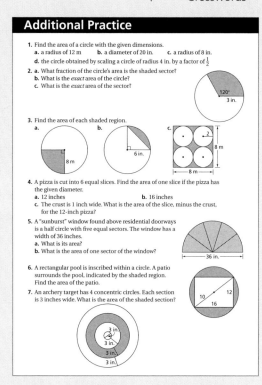

1. Find the area of a circle with the given dimensions.
   a. a radius of 12 m   b. a diameter of 20 in.   c. a radius of 8 in.
   d. the circle obtained by scaling a circle of radius 4 in. by a factor of $\frac{1}{2}$

2. a. What fraction of the circle's area is the shaded sector?
   b. What is the *exact* area of the circle?
   c. What is the *exact* area of the sector?

3. Find the area of each shaded region.
   a.   b.   c.

4. A pizza is cut into 6 equal slices. Find the area of one slice if the pizza has the given diameter.
   a. 12 inches   b. 16 inches
   c. The crust is 1 inch wide. What is the area of the slice, minus the crust, for the 12-inch pizza?

5. A "sunburst" window found above residential doorways is a half circle with five equal sectors. The window has a width of 36 inches.
   a. What is its area?
   b. What is the area of one sector of the window?

6. A rectangular pool is inscribed within a circle. A patio surrounds the pool, indicated by the shaded region. Find the area of the patio.

7. An archery target has 4 concentric circles. Each section is 3 inches wide. What is the area of the shaded section?

Practice: For Lesson 5.5, assign Exercises 1–7.

---

6. Suppose the side length of each square is 6 cm. Find the area of each shaded region and each white region.

a.
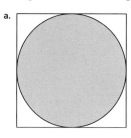

b.
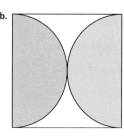

c. Compare your answers for parts (a) and (b) above. What do you notice? Explain.

7. The square at the right is inscribed in a circle. The square's apothem is 2 cm. What is the total area of the shaded region?

8. **Standardized Test Prep** For Zach's birthday, his grandmother makes an extra large cheesecake. She usually uses a pan that has a 7-inch diameter. This time she uses a pan with a 14-inch diameter. She usually serves wedges that are $\frac{1}{12}$ of the cake. This time Zach asks for a wedge with an angle twice the usual size. How many times greater than normal is the area of Zach's birthday serving?

   A. 2 times   **B.** 4 times   **C.** 6 times   **D.** 8 times

9. **Take It Further** In this lesson, π is defined as the area of the unit circle. In a note, another definition given is $\pi = \frac{C}{d}$. Other definitions of π could be as follows.

   a. $\pi = \frac{A}{r^2}$ **b.** $\pi = \frac{C}{2r}$

   c. π is the number you can approximate better and better by calculating the ratio $\frac{P}{2a}$ for regular polygons with perimeter P and apothem a that have more and more sides.

   d. π is half the circumference of the unit circle.

   e. π is the circumference of the circle with a unit diameter.

   Choose at least two of these definitions of π and prove that they are equivalent to one of the two definitions given in this lesson.

Answers

6. **a.** shaded: 9π cm²;
      white: $(36 - 9\pi)$ cm²
   b. shaded: 9π cm²;
      white: $(36 - 9\pi)$ cm²
   c. The areas of the shaded regions are the same, and so are the areas of the white regions; if you cut the figure in part (a) vertically through the center and translate the part on the left 6 cm to the right, you get the figure in part (b), provided you ignore the segment down the middle.

7. $(8\pi - 16)$ cm²

8. D

9. See back of book.

0. The following figures are unit circles with a shaded sector. Find the area of each sector.

a.

b.

c.

d.

e.

f.

g. When the angle grows by 10°, how does the area of the sector change?

Go Online
PHSchool.com

For additional practice,
go to **Web Code: bea-0505**

Historical Perspective
Representations of π

The number π has intrigued people for centuries. The number π is not the ratio of two integers, but there are many ways to represent it. Here are a few. The numbers given in parentheses represent the years in which the equations were discovered.

(1579, Wallis) $\quad \dfrac{\pi}{2} = \dfrac{2 \cdot 2}{1 \cdot 3} \cdot \dfrac{4 \cdot 4}{3 \cdot 5} \cdot \dfrac{6 \cdot 6}{5 \cdot 7} \cdots$

(1593, Vieta) $\quad \dfrac{2}{\pi} = \sqrt{\dfrac{1}{2}} \cdot \sqrt{\dfrac{1}{2} + \dfrac{1}{2}\sqrt{\dfrac{1}{2}}} \cdot \sqrt{\dfrac{1}{2} + \dfrac{1}{2}\sqrt{\dfrac{1}{2} + \dfrac{1}{2}\sqrt{\dfrac{1}{2}}}} \cdots$

(1671, Euler) $\quad \dfrac{\pi^2}{6} = 1 + \dfrac{1}{4} + \dfrac{1}{9} + \dfrac{1}{16} + \dfrac{1}{25} + \cdots$

(1914, Ramanujan)

$\dfrac{1}{\pi} = \dfrac{5}{2^4} + \dfrac{47}{2^{13}} + \dfrac{3^3 \cdot 89}{2^{25}} + \dfrac{5^3 \cdot 131}{2^{34}} + \cdots + \binom{2n}{n}^3 \dfrac{42n + 5}{2^{12n+4}} + \cdots$

The notation $\binom{n}{k}$ stands for the kth entry in the nth row of Pascal's Triangle. For example, $\binom{4}{3} = \dfrac{4!}{(4-3)! \cdot 3!} = \dfrac{4 \cdot 3 \cdot 2 \cdot 1}{1 \cdot 3 \cdot 2 \cdot 1} = 4.$

10. a. $\dfrac{\pi}{36}$

   b. $\dfrac{\pi}{18}$

   c. $\dfrac{\pi}{12}$

   d. $\dfrac{\pi}{9}$

   e. $\dfrac{5\pi}{36}$

   f. $\dfrac{\pi}{6}$

   g. It increases by $\dfrac{\pi}{36}$.

Lesson Overview

GOAL

- Develop and use the formula $C = 2\pi r$.

This lesson guides students through a derivation of the formula for circumference of a circle with radius r (Theorem 5.6).

CHECK YOUR UNDERSTANDING
- Core: 1, 2, 3, 4
- Optional: none

HOMEWORK
- Core: 5, 6, 8
- Optional: 7, 10
- Extension: 9, 11

MATERIALS
- graphing calculators
- protractors

Launch

Start this lesson by reviewing the two formulas for the area of a circle that students have learned in previous lessons, $A = \frac{1}{2}Cr$ and $A = \pi r^2$.

Explore

Students should work individually on For Discussion Problem 1. Discuss answers as a class and lead students into Theorem 5.6. Then have them work individually or in small groups on For You to Do Problems 2 and 3.

Wrap Up

Assign the Check Your Understanding exercises for in-class work.

5.6 Circumference

You can use Theorem 5.2 to express the circumference of a circle in terms of its radius. Suppose a circle has radius r, circumference C, and area A. You know the following two formulas, so you just need to do some algebra.

$$A = \frac{1}{2}Cr \qquad A = \pi r^2$$

For Discussion

1. Combine the two equations above and write a formula for C (the circumference) in terms of r (the radius).

Your answer is very important and you should remember it as a theorem.

Theorem 5.6

The circumference of a circle of radius r is 2π times the radius.

$$C = 2\pi r$$

For You to Do

2. The circumference of a circle is approximately how many times its radius?

   A. five   **B.** six   **C.** seven

3. The circumference of a circle is approximately how many times its diameter?

   A. three   **B.** four   **C.** five

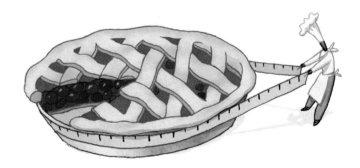

Answers

For Discussion

1. $C = 2\pi r$

For You to Do

2. B

3. A

Exercises *Practicing Habits of Mind*

Check Your Understanding

For Exercises 1–3, you are given a circle of radius 2 cm. Draw a sector of the given size. The sector determines two arcs on the circle. How long is each arc in centimeters?

> An *arc* is the set of points on a circle that lie on the round edge of a sector.

1. 60°

2. 30°

3. 45°

4. True or false: The ratio of a circle's circumference to its diameter is the same for all circles. Explain your answer.

On Your Own

5. The table gives one piece of information about four different circles. Copy the table and find the missing parts for each circle.

Radius	Diameter	Area	Circumference
3	▦	▦	▦
▦	3	▦	▦
▦	▦	3	▦
▦	▦	▦	3

6. A canister contains three tennis balls each with a diameter of 2.5 in. Which distance do you think is greater, the height of the canister or the circumference of the canister? Guess the answer and then do the calculations to see if your guess is correct.

> **Habits of Mind**
> **Experiment.** Find a tennis ball canister and check this out!

7. Good'n Yummy Spaghetti Company makes canned spaghetti. The cans measure 5 in. high and 3 in. in diameter. What size piece of paper does the company need to make a label for the outside of its can?

8. **Standardized Test Prep** The rotating globe Eartha in Yarmouth, Maine is 12.535 meters in diameter. Imagine there is a satellite orbiting one meter above Eartha's equator. How much longer than Eartha's circumference would the path of this satellite be?

A. 1 meter

B. 3.142 meters

C. 6.283 meters

D. one half of 12.535 meters

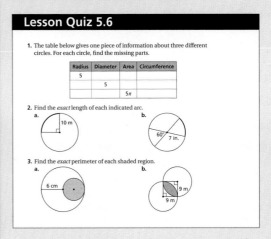
Exercises

HOMEWORK
- Core: 5, 6, 8
- Optional: 7, 10
- Extension: 9, 11

Check Your Understanding

EXERCISES 1–3 ask for the length in centimeters of six arcs. Central angles (which are given as the degree measure of a sector) intercept the arcs. At this point students will see arcs only as "the round edge of a sector," as mentioned in the margin note.

EXERCISE 4 You could ask students to prove that $\frac{A}{r^2} = \frac{C}{2r}$ for all circles. Students already empirically verified this fact in Exercise 6 of Lesson 5.4.

Exercises

1. small arc: $\frac{2\pi}{3}$ cm; large arc: $\frac{10\pi}{3}$ cm

2. small arc: $\frac{\pi}{3}$ cm; large arc: $\frac{11\pi}{3}$ cm

3. small arc: $\frac{\pi}{2}$ cm; large arc: $\frac{7\pi}{2}$ cm

4. true; the formula $C = \pi d$ implies $\frac{C}{d} = \pi$.

5.

Radius	Diameter	Area	Circumference
3	6	9	6
$\frac{3}{2}$	3	$\frac{9\pi}{4}$	3
$\frac{\sqrt{3}}{\sqrt{\pi}}$	$\frac{2\sqrt{3}}{\sqrt{\pi}}$	3	$2\sqrt{3\pi}$
$\frac{3}{2\pi}$	$\frac{3}{\pi}$	$\frac{9}{4\pi}$	3

6. circumference of canister ($C = 2\pi r$, $h = 6r$, and $2\pi > 6$)

7. rectangle 5 in. tall and 3π in. wide

8. C

Maintain Your Skills

EXERCISE 10 is easier if students solved Exercise 10 of Lesson 5.3.

Additional Resources

PRINTED RESOURCES
- Texas Instruments Activities Workbook
- Cabrilog Activities
- Teaching Resources
- Practice Workbook
- Assessment Resources

TECHNOLOGY
- TeacherExpress CD-ROM
- **Exam**View CD-ROM
- **PHSchool.com**
  - Homework Help
  - Video Tutors
  - Multiple Choice
  - Crosswords

Additional Practice

1. Given a circle with the following dimensions, find its circumference.
   a. a radius of 5 m   **b.** a diameter of 12 in.   **c.** an area of 49π cm^2

2. Compare the circumferences of two circles, one with a radius of 1 inch and the other with a radius of 2 inches. Is the ratio of the diameter to the circumference the same for both circles?

3. Use a circle of radius 4 cm.
   a. Draw a sector of 90°. Find the length of each arc the sector has formed.
   b. Draw a sector of 120°. Find the length of each arc the sector has formed.

4. The table at the right gives one piece of information about four different circles. For each circle, find the missing parts.

Radius	Diameter	Area	Circumference
8			
	8		
		8	
			8

5. The circumference of a circle is 144π m.
   a. Find the radius of the circle.   **b.** Find the arc length of a 60° sector.

6. Find the length of the arc shown on each circle.
   a.   **b.**   **c.**

7. Find the perimeter of the shaded region. The outer square has a side of 16 cm.

8. In one revolution, how much farther does a point 12 in. from the center of a tire travel than a point 4 in. from the center?

Practice: For Lesson 5.6, assign Exercises 1–8.

---

9. **Take It Further** A speedometer company makes electronic speedometers for bicycles. The device consists of a small magnet on a spoke and a sensor on the fork of the same wheel. The magnet sends a signal every time the wheel makes one revolution. When you install one on your bike, you need to know how far the wheel travels in one revolution. The instructions say to use the rollout method: Put a chalk mark on the tire where it touches the ground (and mark the ground, too). Then roll the bike until the mark comes back to the ground and measure the distance between the chalk marks. What is an easier way to find the distance for one revolution? Try both methods with a bike.

Maintain Your Skills

10. The Bernoulli sisters claim to have a way to calculate π. They calculate two sequences of numbers, n and s_n, and then find $\frac{ns_n}{2}$.

n	s_n	$\frac{ns_n}{2}$
6	1	3
12	0.51763809	3.105828541
24	▨	▨
48	▨	▨

Each n is twice the one above it. Each s_n is computed from the previous one with the following steps.

a. Square the previous s_n.   **b.** Subtract the result from 4.

c. Take the square root of the result from part (b).

d. Subtract the result from part (c) from 2.

e. Take the square root of the result from part (d).

You can represent steps (a)–(e) with this formula.

$$s_n = \sqrt{2 - \sqrt{4 - \left(\frac{s_n}{2}\right)^2}}$$

Copy the Bernoulli table. Use a calculator to complete it. See whether $\frac{ns_n}{2}$ gets close to π as n increases. The formula below is from Exercise 10 in Lesson 5.3. How is it related to the formula for s_n above?

$$\sqrt{2 - \sqrt{4 - s^2}}$$

Answers

9. Calculate $2\pi r$, where r is the distance from the center of the wheel to the outside edge of the tire.

10.

n	s_n	$\frac{ns_n}{2}$
6	1	3
12	0.51763809	3.10582854
24	0.26105238	3.13262861
48	0.13080626	3.13935020

The expression $\sqrt{2 - \sqrt{4 - s^2}}$ was used to calculate the length of a side of a $2n$-gon inscribed in a circle of radius 1, where s is the length of a side of an n-gon inscribed in the circle.

11. Take It Further Explain why the steps described in the previous exercise work. Why does $\frac{ns_n}{2}$ get closer to π as n increases?

Go Online
PHSchool.com

For additional practice, go to **Web Code: bea-0506**

Historical Perspective
Pieces of π

The number π has intrigued people for centuries. Below are a few interesting facts and an experiment you can try.

Marc Umile set an American record in 2007 by listing 12,887 digits of pi from memory.

- Around 2000 B.C., the Egyptians knew π to nearly 2 decimal places and used the number $3\frac{13}{81}$.

- Around 200 B.C., Archimedes found π to be between $3\frac{10}{71}$ and $3\frac{1}{7}$ (about 3.14). To obtain these values, Archimedes calculated the perimeters of polygons with $6 \cdot 2^n$ sides inscribed and circumscribed about a circle of diameter 1. This is known as the method of exhaustion.

- In the 1500s, Ludolph van Ceulen calculated π to 35 decimal places and had the result carved on his tombstone. To this day, Germans still refer to π as *die Ludolphsche Zahl* (the Ludolphine number).

- In 1991, David and Gregory Chudnovsky calculated π to more than 2,260,821,336 decimal places. To perform the calculation, the brothers built a supercomputer assembled from mail-order parts and placed it in what used to be the living room of Gregory's apartment.

- Ten decimal places of π would be enough to calculate the circumference of Earth to within a fraction of an inch if Earth were a smooth sphere.

- Do an experiment, either with a computer or by polling people in the halls of your school or at lunch. Get many pairs of whole numbers, chosen at random. If you can, get 1000 such pairs. Count the number of pairs that have no common factor (such as (5, 8) or (9, 16)). Then take this number and divide it by the total number of pairs. Your answer should be close to $\frac{6}{\pi^2} \approx 0.6079$.

11. The ratio $\frac{ns_n}{2}$ gets closer to π as n increases, because ns_n approaches the circumference of a circle with a radius of 1.

Historical Perspective
The Historical Perspective can lead to student projects.

Mathematical Reflections

EXERCISES 6–8 At the start of the Investigation, you may have assigned these as Questions 1–3 for students to think and write about.

5B

Mathematical Reflections

In this investigation, you explored relationships between π and measurements of circles. These questions will help you summarize what you have learned.

1. Why is it possible to calculate the circumference of a circle when you know only the length of its radius? Explain in detail.

2. What is the perimeter of a circle with diameter 2.5 in.?

3. What is the area of the shape at the right, composed of a square and a semicircle of radius 4 cm?

4. Find the radius of a circle with area 8π.

5. What is the area of the blue sector?

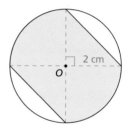

45°
9 cm

6. What is π?

7. How can you express the area and the circumference of a circle in terms of π?

8. What is the exact area of the shaded portion of the circle with center O?

2 cm
O

Vocabulary and Notation

In this investigation, you saw these terms and this symbol for the first time. Make sure you understand what each one means and how to use it.

- pi, π
- sector

The technology behind crop circles is the compass.

Mathematical Reflections

1. You can use the formula $C = 2\pi r$.

2. 2.5π in.

3. $(8\pi + 64)$ cm^2

4. $2\sqrt{2}$

5. $\dfrac{81\pi}{8}$ cm^2

6. Answers may vary. Sample: the numerical value of the area of a circle with a radius of 1

7. $A = \pi r^2$ and $C = 2\pi r$, where r is the radius of the circle.

8. $(2\pi + 4)$ cm^2

Mid-Chapter Test

Go Online PHSchool.com — For a mid-chapter test, go to Web Code: bea-0552

1. The area of a blob drawn on a sheet of rubber is 34 in.² What is the area of the blob when the sheet is stretched or shrunk uniformly by the following factors?

   a. 2 **b.** 6 **c.** $\frac{1}{3}$ **d.** $\frac{1}{4}$

2. What is the formula for the area of a regular polygon in terms of its perimeter and apothem? What is the formula for the area of a circle in terms of its circumference and radius? Explain the analogies between the two formulas.

3. Find the area of each figure described below.

   a. a regular pentagon with side 4.52 in. and apothem 3.11 in.

   b. an equilateral triangle with apothem 2 cm

   c. a regular hexagon with apothem $\sqrt{5}$ in.

4. Calculate the areas of the following figures. The figures are made of polygons and circle sectors.

   a.

   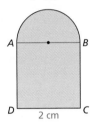

   ABCD is a square and $\widehat{AB}$ is a semicircle.

   b.

   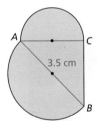

   Triangle *ABC* has angles of 45°, 45° and 90°. $\widehat{AC}$ and $\widehat{AB}$ are semicircles.

5. The wheel of a bicycle has a diameter of 2 ft. If you mark with chalk the point of the wheel that touches the ground, how many times does the mark touch the ground while the bicycle travels 27 ft?

6. Find the area and the perimeter of a regular hexagon with apothem 1 in.

7. Find the area of a regular hexagon with apothem equal to 4 cm.

8. Tony rolled his bicycle along a straight line that was 7 feet long. How long would the radius of his wheels have to be for each point on the wheel to touch the ground exactly once in that distance?

9. Suppose the area of the regular hexagon below is $6\sqrt{3}$. Find the area of the shaded region.

   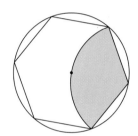

Mid-Chapter Test

Assessment Resources

Mid-Chapter Test

1. Julia makes Star 1 with 10 inches of string so that the ends touch. She makes a larger star, Star 2, that is mathematically similar to Star 1 using 20 cm of string.

   Star 1 Star 2

   If the area of Star 1 is S_1, what is the area of Star 2 in terms of S_1?

2. **a.** Can the apothem of a regular polygon be longer than a segment that connects the center of the polygon to one of its vertices? Explain.
   b. Can a segment that connects the center of a regular polygon to one of its vertices have the same length as the polygon's side? If so, give an example. If not, explain.
   c. Give an example of a regular polygon with an apothem that is half the length of its side.

3. **a.** What is the area of a regular hexagon with side length 4 cm?
   b. What is the perimeter of a regular hexagon that has an area of $\frac{3\sqrt{3}}{2}$ square inches?

4. A hardware washer has a diameter of 5 cm. The hole has a circumference of 2π cm. What is the area of the washer, represented by the shaded region at the right?

5. A train's wheels have a 15-inch radius. The wheels need to be inspected every 10,000 miles. How many rotations does one wheel make between inspections if the train travels *exactly* 10,000 miles? (*Hint:* There are 63,360 inches in a mile.)

6. A soccer ball is made of 32 pieces of leather sewn together. Twenty pieces are regular hexagons with a side length of 2 inches, and twelve pieces are regular pentagons with an apothem of 1.376 inches. How much leather do you need to produce one soccer ball?

7. A particular baseball field is a quarter circle with a radius of 290 feet. The baseball diamond is a square with a side length of 90 feet, and bases at its vertices. What is the area of the shaded section of the field?

Also available: Form B

Mid-Chapter Test

1. **a.** 136 in.²
   b. 1224 in.²
   c. $\frac{34}{9}$ in.²
   d. $\frac{17}{8}$ in.²

2. $A = \frac{1}{2}Pa$; $A = \frac{1}{2}Cr$; *P* is the distance around a regular *n*-gon, and *a* is the distance from the center of the *n*-gon to the *n*-gon. *C* is the distance around the circle, and *r* is the distance from the center of the circle to the circle.

3. **a.** 35.143 in.²
   b. $12\sqrt{3}$ cm²
   c. $6\sqrt{3}$ in.²

4. **a.** $\left(4 + \frac{\pi}{2}\right)$ cm²
   b. $\left(\frac{77}{16}\pi + \frac{49}{16}\right)$ cm²

5. 4 times

6. area = $2\sqrt{3}$ in.², perimeter = $4\sqrt{3}$ in.

7. $32\sqrt{3}$ cm²

8. $\frac{7}{2\pi}$ ft (about 1.11 ft)

9. $\frac{4\pi}{3}$

Investigation Overview

This investigation contains classical results about circles. Lesson 5.7, Getting Started, defines *locus* and students start thinking of a circle as a set of points, all of which are a given distance from a given point. The following lessons explore properties of circles. Students learn definitions and explore how specific lines and angles of interest relate to each other.

You may wish to assign Questions 1–3 for students to think and write about during the investigation.

Learning Goals

- Recognize the relationship between inscribed angles and their corresponding central angles.
- Prove and use general theorems on chords and inscribed angles.
- Identify properties of tangents.
- Apply the theory of proportion to chords, secants, and tangents of circles.

Habits and Skills

- See a circle as the set of points with a given distance from one point.
- See "traced paths" as sets of points with a common property.
- Compare chords and arcs of a circle.
- Make logical inferences to prove results about similar triangles with sides that are secants or tangents with respect to a circle.

Investigation 5C
Classical Results About Circles

In *Classical Results About Circles*, you will study lines passing through circles and the angles formed by these lines. Studying their many relationships will improve your inductive reasoning, proof-writing skills, and understanding of circles.

By the end of this investigation, you will be able to answer questions like these:

1. What are arcs and chords in circles?

2. How much smaller is the measure of an inscribed angle than the measure of its corresponding central angle?

3. What is the power of a point? What are the maximum and minimum values of the power of a point in a circle with radius *r*?

You will learn how to

- recognize the relationship between inscribed angles and their corresponding central angles

- prove and use general theorems on chords and inscribed angles

- identify properties of tangents

- apply the theory of proportion to chords, secants, and tangents of circles

You will develop these habits and skills:

- See a circle as the set of points with a given distance from one point.

- See "traced paths" as sets of points with a common property.

- Compare chords and arcs of a circle.

- Make logical inferences to prove results about similar triangles with sides that are secants or tangents with respect to a circle.

In a windmill pitch, the hand sweeps out a circle relative to the pitcher's shoulder.

Investigation Road Map

LESSON 5.7, *Getting Started,* introduces *loci.* Students recognize a circle as the set of points a given distance from one point and an ellipse as the set of points with a total distance from two given points that is constant.

LESSON 5.8, *Arcs and Central Angles,* gives definitions and some properties of a *central angle,* an *arc,* and a *chord.* Students will use geometry software.

LESSON 5.9, *Chords and Inscribed Angles,* gives more theorems about chords and inscribed angles.

LESSON 5.10, *Secants and Tangents,* introduces secant and tangent lines to a circle, along with some of their properties.

LESSON 5.11, *Power of a Point,* gives the definition of *power of a point* with respect to a circle, and students discover some of its properties.

Getting Started

Activating Prior Knowledge
Exploring New Ideas

To understand relationships between circles and lines, it is helpful to see figures in motion. It is good practice to try visualizing such motion in your mind's eye. It is also helpful to see the motion on a computer screen.

For You to Explore

1. Draw a circle and a line. Depending on where you draw your line, you will notice a different number of intersection points. List all the possibilities.

2. Draw two circles. How many intersections can two circles have? List all the possibilities.

3. Use the figure to answer the following questions.

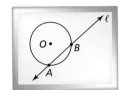

   a. If you move ℓ around and leave A fixed, what happens to $\overline{AB}$? Under which conditions does $\overline{AB}$ disappear?

   b. In what position does $\overline{AB}$ have the greatest possible length? What does this length represent?

   c. Draw a segment that you could measure to find the distance of $\overline{AB}$ from the center of the circle. When is this distance at a maximum? When is it at a minimum?

4. The circles with centers A and B are congruent. For which points P on either of the two circles does $PA = PB$? Explain.

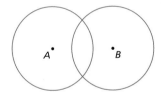

Answers

For You to Explore

1. Check students' drawings; 0, 1, or 2 intersection points.

2. Check students' drawings; 0, 1, or 2 intersection points.

3. a. $\overline{AB}$ gets shorter or longer (but never longer than the diameter of the circle). There is no segment when ℓ intersects the circle only at A.

   b. when ℓ passes through O; $2AO$, or the diameter of the circle

   c. If there actually is a segment $\overline{AB}$, there is no maximum distance actually attained, though the distance *approaches* a maximum equal to the radius of the circle; the minimum distance is 0, and it occurs when ℓ passes through the center of the circle.

4. See back of book.

Lesson Overview

GOALS

- Warm up to the ideas of the investigation.
- Use a hands-on approach to develop mathematical habits of mind.

This lesson starts students thinking about the relationships between circles and lines. Make sure students are familiar with circle vocabulary. They should know and understand that a circle is the locus of the points whose distance from one point (the center) is given (the length of the radius). Students also practice using symmetric reasoning in this lesson.

FOR YOU TO EXPLORE
- Core: 1, 2, 3, 4, 5
- Optional: none

MATERIALS
- compasses
- geometry software
- rulers

HOMEWORK
- Core: 6, 7
- Optional: 8, 9, 10

VOCABULARY
- locus

Launch

Have students work on For You to Explore problems in pairs or small groups.

Explore

For You to Explore

PROBLEM 3 requires students to visualize movement. If your students have difficulty with this, have them use geometry software to construct the original figure and manipulate it. Students will get a feel for some properties of tangents to a circle. Do not expect them to come up with proofs, but only experimental results.

Wrap Up

Before assigning homework, allow students some time to discuss and summarize their findings.

Exercises

HOMEWORK
- Core: 6, 7
- Optional: 8, 9, 10

On Your Own

EXERCISE 6 This is an exercise on loci: the path of P is the set of points with a given property (locus). It is important that you assign this exercise because it previews concepts in Lesson 5.11 on power of a point. You should have students pay particular attention to the definition of locus (in the side note) and ask them to find the defining property in all six parts of this exercise.

Maintain Your Skills

EXERCISES 9 AND 10 require students to remember that the diagonals of a kite are perpendicular. They must also look for similar triangles and remember that the ratio of their corresponding sides is constant.

5. The two circles below have radii r_A and r_B respectively.

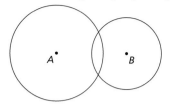

a. For which points P on either of the two circles is the sum of the distances from the two centers equal to the sum of the lengths of the two radii $(PA + PB = r_A + r_B)$?

b. Are there any other points P (not on either circle) for which $PA + PB = r_A + r_B$? Describe the locus of points.

> A **locus** is a set of points that all have a given property. For example, the locus of points r units from a given point P is the circle with center P and radius r.

Exercises *Practicing Habits of Mind*

On Your Own

6. On paper or with geometry software, draw two points, A and B, that never move. Make the distance between them less than 6 units. Imagine a point P that can move along various paths described in terms of these points. Draw and describe what the path of P looks like in each case.

a. P moves along a path so that PA always equals PB. What is the shape of the path?

b. This time the path of P keeps $PA = 5$.

c. P moves along a path where $PA + PB = 6$.

d. $m\angle APB = 90°$, no matter where P is along this path.

e. $m\angle APB = 60°$, no matter where P is along this path.

f. $m\angle APB = 30°$, no matter where P is along this path.

Answers

5. a. the intersection points of the two circles

 b. Yes; the locus is an oval-shaped curve. The points A and B are inside the oval, and the oval is symmetric with respect to $\overleftrightarrow{AB}$ and the perpendicular bisector of $\overline{AB}$.

6. a. Check students' drawings. The path is the perpendicular bisector of $\overline{AB}$.

 b. Check students' drawings. The path is the circle with center A and radius 5.

 c. Check students' drawings. The path is an oval, with A and B in its interior. (See the answer for Ex. 5b.)

 d. Check students' drawings. all points on the circle with diameter $\overline{AB}$, except for the points A and B

6. e–f. See back of book.

7. Draw a circle with a diameter having endpoints A and B. Now choose a point P on the circle that is not A or B and answer the following questions.

a. What kind of triangle is $\triangle APB$?

b. On which side of $\triangle APB$ does the center of the circle lie, and what is its position on that side?

c. Where would a point Q be if $m\angle AQB < 90°$? Where would Q be if $m\angle AQB > 90°$?

8. How could you draw a circle if you were given tacks, a length of string, and a pencil? Explain why your method works.

Maintain Your Skills

Use this construction for Exercises 9 and 10. A triangle inscribed in a semicircle has one side that is a diameter of the semicircle. All three of its vertices lie on the circle. Assume that the following statement is true: Any triangle inscribed in a semicircle is a right triangle. Draw a semicircle and inscribe a triangle in it. Then reflect your drawing about the diameter of the semicircle. Now you have a circle with a quadrilateral inscribed in it, as shown in this figure.

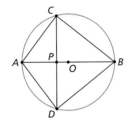

Habits of Mind

Look for relationships.
Look for similar triangles in the semicircle that contains $\triangle ABC$. How many can you find? How can you compare the lengths of their sides?

9. Suppose $AP = 3\,\text{cm}$ and $PB = 5\,\text{cm}$. Find CD.

10. Use the construction above. Suppose $AP = a$ and $PB = b$. Find $CP = c$ as a function of a and b.

Circles are a compulsory element in the ribbon component of rhythmic gymnastics. What length ribbon would you use?

7. a. right triangle
b. $\overline{AB}$ (the hypotenuse), midpoint
c. outside the circle (but not on $\overleftrightarrow{AB}$); inside the circle

8. Tie the string to a tack and to a pencil. Fix the tack to a piece of paper and pull the pencil to make the string tight. Keep the string tight and move the pencil around the tack, drawing as you go. The string keeps the distance between the tack and the pencil constant, so the pencil draws a circle centered at the tack with radius equal to the

length of the string between the tack and the pencil.

9. $2\sqrt{15}$

10. $CP = \sqrt{ab}$

Lesson Overview

GOAL

• Prove and use general theorems on chords.

You may want to spend two days on this lesson. It contains a large amount of new vocabulary and a lengthy In-Class Experiment. This lesson introduces central angles, arcs, and chords. Students learn these definitions and how these parts of a circle relate to each other. The experiment provides a chance for students to see that arcs are congruent if and only if the central angles that intercept them are congruent, which otherwise is subtle. The proof of Theorem 5.7 descends from this result.

CHECK YOUR UNDERSTANDING

• Core: 1, 3, 4
• Optional: 2

MATERIALS

• compasses
• geometry software
• rulers
• tracing paper

HOMEWORK

• Core: 5, 7, 8, 9
• Optional: 6, 11, 12, 13, 14, 15, 16
• Extension: 10

VOCABULARY

• arc
• central angle
• chord
• degree measure
• diameter
• major arc
• minor arc

Launch

Start this lesson by giving the definitions of *central angle, arc,* and *chord.* These are the concepts students will be working with during the lesson.

Here are some definitions you need.

Definitions

A **central angle** for a circle is an angle that has its vertex at the center of the circle.

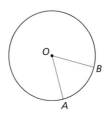

The set of points on a circle that lie in the interior of a particular central angle is called the **arc** intercepted by the angle. If the central angle is ∠AOB, then you refer to the arc as "the arc *AB* intercepted by angle *AOB*."

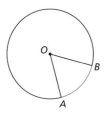

A **chord** is a segment that connects two points on a circle. Any chord through the center of the circle is a **diameter**.

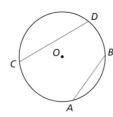
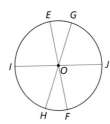

Looking at the definition of diameter, *Tony wonders about chords.*

Tony   I once heard that the diameter is the longest chord you can draw for a given circle. Did you know that, Sasha?

Sasha   As a matter of fact, I did! I think I can prove it. Let's see.

Tony   Well, make life simple and start with the first circle at the bottom of the last page. You already have a chord, *CD*.

Sasha   Right! All we have to do is look for triangles, and I love triangles! Connect *C*, *D*, and *O*. Now I remember that in a triangle the sum of two sides is always greater than the third one. So $CD < CO + OD$.

Tony   You're brilliant! I know what to do now. I just noticed that *CO* and *OD* are two radii, so their sum is equal to the diameter. So we've proven that any chord *CD* is shorter than a diameter.

For Discussion

1. How does Sasha and Tony's discussion prove that the diameter is the longest chord of a circle?

In-Class Experiment

2. Use geometry software or tracing paper.

   a. Draw a black circle with center *O*. Choose points *A* and *B* on the circle.

   b. Choose two more points *C* and *D* such that $\overset{\frown}{AB} = \overset{\frown}{CD}$. You can do this by tracing your circle in blue on tracing paper and marking *A* and *B* on it. Then choose *C* on the black circle and pin the centers together with the blue circle on top. Rotate the blue circle until *A* is on top of *C*. Now mark the point on the black circle that corresponds to the position of *B*. This is point *D*.

   You have two arcs $\overset{\frown}{AB}$ and $\overset{\frown}{CD}$. Compare $\angle AOB$ and $\angle COD$.

For You to Do

3. Use a technique similar to the one above to prove the following statement.

   If two central angles are congruent, then their intercepted arcs are congruent.

> **Remember...**
> This is the inverse of what you proved in the In-Class Experiment above.

Explore

Students can act out or simply read the dialog between Tony and Sasha. Use the For Discussion that follows to complete the proof that a diameter is the longest chord in a circle. Then start the In-Class Experiment. Assign the Check Your Understanding exercises as in-class work.

In-Class Experiment

PROBLEMS 2 AND 3 You can express the result of this experiment as follows:

If two arcs are congruent, then the central angles that intercept them are congruent.

This experiment uses what Euclid called a "rigid movement," which is, in this case, a rotation. To prove the congruence of two central angles in the same circle that intercept congruent arcs, first you must construct the congruent arcs. This is done by superimposing a third arc, drawn on a circle congruent to the first, and "copying" it to a new position on the first circle. This way it is clear that the sides of the central angles of the first circle must both coincide with those of the central angle intercepting the third arc (i.e., they are both congruent to the third central angle). Therefore, thanks to the transitive property of congruence, the two central angles are congruent.

Answers

For Discussion

1. Answers may vary. Sample: $d = 2r = CO + DO$; since the sum $CO + DO$ is greater than any chord on the circle, *d* is greater than any chord on the circle.

In-Class Experiment

2. **a–b.** Check students' work.
   $\angle AOB \equiv \angle COD$

For You to Do

3. Answers may vary. Sample. Draw a circle and two congruent angles. Use tracing paper to trace the arc intercepted by one of the central angles. Rotate the tracing paper to see that the arc you just traced matches up with the arc intercepted by the other central angle.

Wrap Up

Before assigning homework, review the proof of Theorem 5.7.

Assessment Resources

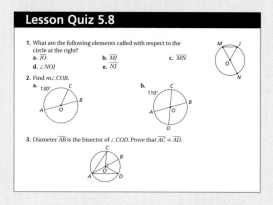

Lesson Quiz 5.8

1. What are the following elements called with respect to the circle at the right?
   a. $\overline{JO}$ b. $\overline{MJ}$ c. $\overline{MN}$
   d. $\angle NOJ$ e. $\overline{NI}$

2. Find $m\angle COB$.
   a. 130°   b. 110°

3. Diameter $\overline{AB}$ is the bisector of $\angle COD$. Prove that $\overline{AC} \cong \overline{AD}$.

For Discussion

4. Tony is a bit confused by the definition of arc. He thinks, "How can a single arc be intercepted by a central angle? I see two arcs intercepted by $\angle AOB$ because the circle is divided into a big part and a little part. Which part is the intercepted arc?" How could you answer Tony's questions?

The confusion arises from the uncertainty about the central angle. If it is not specified, the interior of $\angle AOB$ refers to the convex region enclosed by the angle. A good way to avoid confusion is to define a **major arc** and a **minor arc** for each central angle. The major arc is the larger part of the circle, and the minor arc is the smaller part of the circle. In this book, you may assume that an arc is a minor arc unless stated otherwise.

Arcs, as well as angles, can be measured in degrees. The **degree measure** of an arc is the measure of the central angle that intercepts it. If the degree measure of a minor arc is x, then the degree measure of the corresponding major arc is $360° - x$.

The corresponding chord of a minor arc is the segment with ends that are the intersections of the central angle with the circle. Now you can prove a theorem on minor arcs and chords.

Remember...

The degree measure of an arc divided by 360 tells you how much of the circle is used by the arc.

Theorem 5.7

Two chords are congruent if and only if their corresponding arcs are congruent.

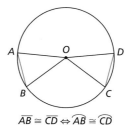

$$\overline{AB} \cong \overline{CD} \Leftrightarrow \overset{\frown}{AB} \cong \overset{\frown}{CD}$$

Proof If you start with two congruent chords, then $\triangle COD$ and $\triangle AOB$ are congruent by SSS. Therefore, all of their corresponding elements are congruent. In particular $\angle AOB \cong \angle COD$. So the corresponding arcs are congruent.

If you start with two congruent arcs $\overset{\frown}{AB}$ and $\overset{\frown}{CD}$, the two central angles that intercept them on the circle are congruent (as you saw in the In-Class Experiment on the previous page). Therefore, $\triangle AOB$ and $\triangle COD$ are congruent by SAS, because $\overline{AO}$, $\overline{OD}$, $\overline{OB}$, and $\overline{OC}$ are all radii of the same circle. All their corresponding elements are congruent, so sides $\overline{AB}$ and $\overline{CD}$ are congruent.

Answers

For Discussion

4. Answers may vary. Sample: If the central angle is not 180°, you could define the intercepted arc to be the smaller of the two arcs. Alternatively, you could specify explicity whether you mean the larger arc or the smaller one.

Exercises Practicing Habits of Mind

Check Your Understanding

1. What parts of the circle are the following elements?

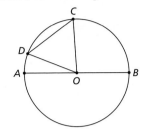

   a. $\overline{AB}$

   b. $\overline{OB}$

   c. $\overline{OD}$

   d. $\overline{CD}$

   e. $\angle COD$

   f. $\angle AOC$

   g. $\overset{\frown}{CD}$

   h. $\overset{\frown}{AB}$

2. In a circle with center O and radius 1 inch, $\overset{\frown}{MN}$ is an arc that measures 60°. What are $m\angle MON$, MN, and OH, where H is the base of the height through O of $\triangle MON$?

3. Look at this picture, where $m\overset{\frown}{AB} = 60°$, $m\overset{\frown}{CD} = 30°$, and $m\angle AOC = 45°$.

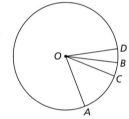

   Find the measures of the following elements. (The arcs are all minor arcs.)

   a. $\angle AOB$

   b. $\angle COD$

   c. $\overset{\frown}{AC}$

   d. $\overset{\frown}{CB}$

   e. $\angle COB$

   f. $\angle BOD$

   g. $\overset{\frown}{AD}$

4. Is it true that if point C is on minor arc $\overset{\frown}{AB}$ of a circle with center O, then $m\overset{\frown}{AC} + m\overset{\frown}{CB} = m\overset{\frown}{AB}$? Explain.

> This is known as the Arc Addition Postulate.

Exercises

1. a. chord, diameter
   b. radius   c. radius
   d. chord   e. central angle
   f. central angle   g. minor arc
   h. semicircle

2. $m\angle MON = 60°$, $MN = 1$ in., $OH = \dfrac{\sqrt{3}}{2}$ in.

3. a. 60°   b. 30°   c. 45°   d. 15°
   e. 15°   f. 15°   g. 75°

4. Yes. Explanations may vary. Sample: Given circle O with minor arc and points as described. Assume $m\overset{\frown}{AC} = x$ and $m\overset{\frown}{CB} = y$. Then $m\angle AOC = x$ and $m\angle COB = y$. Therefore $m\angle AOC + m\angle COB = x + y$. And since $\angle AOC$ and $\angle COB$ are adjacent, we know that $m\angle AOC + m\angle COB = m\angle AOB = x + y$. And since the arc associated with $\angle AOB$ is $\overset{\frown}{AB}$, we know that $m\overset{\frown}{AB} = m\angle AOB = x + y = m\overset{\frown}{AC} + m\overset{\frown}{CB}$.

Exercises

HOMEWORK
- Core: 5, 7, 8, 9
- Optional: 6, 11, 12, 13, 14, 15, 16
- Extension: 10

On Your Own

EXERCISE 7 Students need to remember the definition of distance from a point to a line. It is important to review the definition even if you decide not to assign this exercise because they will use it in Lesson 5.9.

EXERCISE 11 guides students in looking for useful congruent or similar triangles. With practice, they should be able to find such triangles on their own. If your students feel comfortable by this point, you can assign this exercise in the following form:

"Look at the figure. Knowing that $\overset{\frown}{AB} \cong \overset{\frown}{CD}$, prove that $\overset{\frown}{AD} \parallel \overset{\frown}{BC}$."

On Your Own

5. $\overline{OZ}$ is the bisector of $\angle QOR$. Prove that $\overline{QP}$ is congruent to $\overline{PR}$.

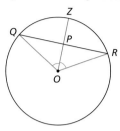

Go Online
Video Tutor
PHSchool.com

Web Code: bee-0775

6. Draw a circle and two congruent chords $\overline{FH}$ and $\overline{JI}$ that intersect at point E (not the center O).

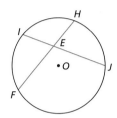

   Prove that $\angle OFH$, $\angle FHO$, $\angle OJI$, and $\angle JIO$ are congruent.

7. Prove that chords of equal lengths are equally distant from the center of the circle.

> How do you measure the distance from a chord to the center?

8. Construct two congruent circles. Draw two noncongruent chords—one in each circle. Which chord is closer to the center of its circle? Explain.

Answers

5. $\overline{OQ} \cong \overline{OR}$, since radii of the same circle are congruent. Hence $\triangle OQR$ is isosceles. But the bisector of the vertex angle of an isosceles triangle is a median. Thus P is the midpoint of $\overline{QR}$, and so $\overline{QP} \cong \overline{PR}$.

6. The angles in question are base angles of congruent isosceles triangles $\triangle FOH$ and $\triangle IOJ$. Since the base angles of an isosceles triangle are congruent, it follows that all four of the angles are congruent.

7. If the chords of equal length are diameters, then both pass through the center of the circle and are therefore at a distance of 0 from the center. If $\overline{AB}$ and $\overline{CD}$ are chords of circle O, have the same length, and do not pass through O, then $\triangle OAB$ and $\triangle OCD$ are congruent isosceles triangles (SSS). Corresponding altitudes of congruent triangles are congruent (AAS), so the altitudes from O are congruent. Therefore, $\overline{AB}$ and $\overline{CD}$ are equally distant from O.

8. the longer chord

9. Standardized Test Prep In the diagram, O is the center of the circle and $\overline{AB} \cong \overline{CD}$. Which statement is NOT necessarily true?

A. $\triangle ABO \cong \triangle DCO$

B. $\triangle ABO$ is isosceles.

C. $\overset{\frown}{AC} \cong \overset{\frown}{DB}$

D. $\triangle DCO$ is equilateral.

10. Take It Further Two lines r and r' cut a circle in four points as shown. If $\overset{\frown}{AB} \cong \overset{\frown}{CD}$, prove that $\angle APO$ and $\angle OPD$ are congruent.

> Lines that cut a circle in two points are called *secants*.

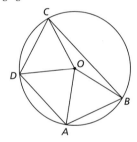

11. Look at the following figure.

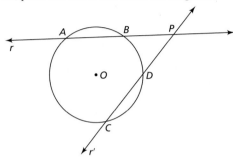

a. Knowing only that $\overset{\frown}{AB} \cong \overset{\frown}{CD}$, give a reason for each of the following statements.

- $\angle AOB \cong \angle COD$
- $\triangle AOB \cong \triangle COD$
- $\overline{AB} \cong \overline{CD}$

b. Now draw the heights through O for the two triangles, $\triangle AOD$ and $\triangle BOC$. Prove that these heights lie on the same line and therefore $\overline{AD} \parallel \overline{BC}$.

---

9. D

10. Let H be the point on $\overline{AB}$ such that $\overline{OH} \perp \overline{AB}$. Let K be the point on $\overline{CD}$ such that $\overline{OK} \perp \overline{CD}$. Congruent minor arcs have congruent chords, so $\overline{AB} \cong \overline{CD}$. It follows from the result in Ex. 7 that $\overline{OH} \cong \overline{OK}$. If you draw $\overline{OP}$, then $\triangle OHP \cong \triangle OKP$ (these are right triangles with the same hypotenuse and a pair of congruent legs). By CPCTC, $\angle HPO \cong \angle KPO$; that is, $\angle APO \cong \angle OPD$.

11. a. $\angle AOB \cong \angle COD$ and $\overline{AB} \cong \overline{CD}$ since, in the same circle, congruent minor arcs have congruent central angles and congruent chords. $\triangle AOB \cong \triangle COD$ by SAS.

11. b. See back of book.

Maintain Your Skills

EXERCISES 12–16 are numerical and preview
Theorem 5.10, which students will prove in Lesson 5.9.

Maintain Your Skills

12. $\overline{BA}$ is the perpendicular bisector of $\overline{DC}$. Assume that the center of the circle O is on $\overleftrightarrow{BA}$, as it appears to be in the figure. Then, given $BA = 5$ in. and $BE = 2$ in., find DC. Justify your answer.

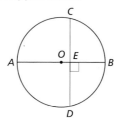

13. $\overline{CD}$ is the perpendicular bisector of $\overline{AB}$. Assume that $\overline{CD}$ is also a diameter of the circle, as it appears to be in the figure. Then, given $CK = 1.5$ cm and $OK = 2$ cm, find DC, AO, and AK. Justify your answers.

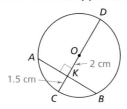

14. $\overline{AB}$ is the diameter perpendicular to $\overline{DC}$. Assume that $\overline{BA}$ bisects $\overline{DC}$. Then, given $BA = 12$ in. and $BE = 3$ in., find DC. Justify your answer.

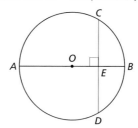

Answers

12. $2\sqrt{6}$ in.

13. $DC = 2CO = 2(3.5)$ cm $= 7$ cm;
    $AO = CO = 3.5$ cm;
    $AK = \sqrt{3.5^2 - 2^2}$ cm
    $$= \sqrt{\frac{33}{4}} \text{ cm} = \frac{\sqrt{33}}{2} \text{ cm}$$

14. $\overline{AB}$ is a diameter, so the radius of
    the circle is $\frac{1}{2}(12)$, or 6 in. Hence
    $OE = 6$ in. $- 3$ in. $= 3$ in., and

$CE = \sqrt{OC^2 - OE^2}$ in. $=$
$\sqrt{36 - 9}$ in. $= 3\sqrt{3}$ in.
Since $\overline{AB}$ bisects $\overline{CD}$,
$CD = 2(3\sqrt{3})$ in. $= 6\sqrt{3}$ in.

15. $\overline{DC}$ is the diameter perpendicular to $\overline{AB}$. Assume $\overline{DC}$ bisects $\overline{AB}$. Suppose $AK = 1.2$ cm and $KO = 3$ cm. Find DC and AB. Justify your answer.

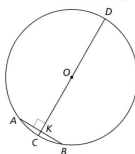

16. Diameter $\overline{JL}$ bisects $\overline{NK}$. Assume that $\overline{JL}$ is also perpendicular to $\overline{NK}$. Suppose $NA = 14$ cm and $OJ = 16$ cm. Find OA. Justify your answer.

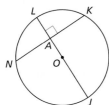

Go Online
PHSchool.com

For additional practice, go to **Web Code: bea-0508**

As the moon rises, the horizon forms a chord that gets longer and then shorter. When is the chord the longest?

Additional Resources

PRINTED RESOURCES
- Texas instruments Activities Workbook
- Cabrilog Activities
- Teaching Resources
- Practice Workbook
- Assessment Resources

TECHNOLOGY
- TeacherExpress CD-ROM
- **Exam**View CD-ROM
- **PHSchool.com**
  - Homework Help
  - Video Tutors
  - Multiple Choice
  - Crosswords

Additional Practice

1. What are the following elements called with respect to the circle?
  a. $\overline{MO}$ **b.** $\overline{MQ}$ **c.** $\overline{MN}$ **d.** $\angle MON$ **e.** $\overline{PQ}$

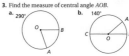

2. Draw a circle of radius 2 cm.
  a. Draw a central angle, $m\angle AOC = 60°$.
  b. Draw $\triangle AOC$. Find its height.

3. Find the measure of central angle AOB.
  a. 290°   **b.** 140°   **c.**

4. Given: Circle A
  Prove: $\overline{BC} \parallel \overline{DE}$

5. Find $m\angle ABC$.
  a.   **b.** 60°   **c.** 120° 140°

6. Find the values of the variables x, y, and z in the diagram.

7. An equilateral triangle JLK is inscribed in a circle. If M and N are midpoints of the arcs $\overarc{LK}$ and $\overarc{KJ}$, what type of quadrilateral is $JNML$?

8. Use the diagram of a regular pentagon inscribed in a circle.
  a. What is the relationship between $m\angle 1$ and $m\angle 2$? Justify your answer.
  b. Find $m\angle 1$ and $m\angle 2$.

9. If two chords of a circle are parallel, prove that the two arcs between the chords are congruent.

Practice: For Lesson 5.8, assign Exercises 1–4.

15. $AO = \sqrt{1.2^2 + 3^2} = \dfrac{3\sqrt{29}}{5}$ cm,

so $DC = \dfrac{6\sqrt{29}}{5}$ cm. $\overline{DC}$ is the perpendicular bisector of $\overline{AB}$, so $AB = 2(1.2)$ cm $= 2.4$ cm.

16. $ON = OJ = 16$ cm, so
$OA = \sqrt{ON^2 - NA^2}$
$= \sqrt{16^2 - 14^2}$ cm $= 2\sqrt{15}$ cm.

Lesson Overview

GOALS

- Recognize the relationship between inscribed angles and their corresponding central angles.
- Prove and use general theorems on chords and inscribed angles.

Spend two days teaching this lesson as it contains a large amount of new information. This lesson teaches theorems that relate a line through the center of a circle and a chord. This starts students thinking about angles whose vertices are inside the circle. They learn the definition of *inscribed angle* and summarize properties of inscribed angles relating to arcs. They also apply properties of inscribed angles to a triangle inscribed in a semicircle.

CHECK YOUR UNDERSTANDING
- Core: 1, 2, 5
- Optional: 3, 4

HOMEWORK
- Core: 6, 7, 9, 10, 12, 14, 15
- Optional: 8, 11, 13, 16

MATERIALS
- compasses
- geometry software
- protractors
- rulers

VOCABULARY
- adjacent chords
- concentric circles
- inscribed angle

Launch

Introduce inscribed angles by drawing diagrams and comparing and contrasting them with central angles.

5.9 Chords and Inscribed Angles

In Lesson 5.8, you studied angles that have a vertex at the center of a circle. In this lesson, angles of interest have their vertices elsewhere inside the circle, or on the circle itself.

In-Class Experiment

1. Draw a circle and a chord, $\overline{AB}$, that is not a diameter. Use a straightedge to draw various lines that are perpendicular to $\overline{AB}$. How many of these perpendicular lines can you draw through the center of the circle?

2. Using the figure from Problem 1, find a proof for the following statement. There is one and only one line perpendicular to $\overline{AB}$ through the center of the circle.

Now you can prove a theorem about chords and lines through the center of a circle. Learn the technique and use it to solve the problems in the For You to Do that follows.

Theorem 5.8

A line through the center of a circle bisects a chord if it is perpendicular to the chord.

> The result of this theorem was assumed in Exercises 14 and 15 of Lesson 5.8.

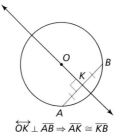

$$\overleftrightarrow{OK} \perp \overline{AB} \Rightarrow \overline{AK} \cong \overline{KB}$$

Proof Consider the line that contains $\overline{OK}$ through the center O of the circle above. Suppose it is perpendicular to $\overline{AB}$. You have to prove that it also bisects $\overline{AB}$. $\triangle AOB$ is isosceles because $AO = r = OB$, where r is the length of the radius of the circle. In any isosceles triangle, the height with respect to the base is also the bisector of the angle and the perpendicular bisector of the side it cuts. Therefore $\overline{AK}$ and $\overline{KB}$ are congruent, which is what you wanted to prove.

Answers

In-Class Experiment

1. Answers may vary. Sample: Exactly one line is perpendicular to $\overline{AB}$ and passes through the center O of the circle.

2. Answers may vary. Sample: The perpendicular bisector of $\overline{AB}$ is the set of all points that are equidistant from A and B. The point O is included in this set since

$\overline{OA}$ and $\overline{OB}$ are radii of the circle. Also, there is one and only one perpendicular to $\overleftrightarrow{AB}$ through the point O.

3. Prove the following theorems. Refer to the figure from Theorem 5.8.

Theorem 5.9

If a line through the center of a circle bisects a chord, then it is perpendicular to the chord.

> The result of this theorem was assumed in Exercise 16 of Lesson 5.8.

Theorem 5.10

The center of a circle lies on the line perpendicular to a chord if and only if the line bisects the chord.

> The result of this theorem was assumed in Exercises 12 and 13 of Lesson 5.8.

Definition

An **inscribed angle** is an angle that has its vertex on the circle and has sides that are chords of the circle. You say that $\angle ABC$ intercepts $\overarc{AC}$ and that it is inscribed in $\overarc{ABC}$.

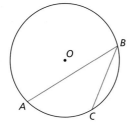

In-Class Experiment

4. Draw a circle and a central angle, $\angle AOC$. How many inscribed angles can you draw that intercept $\overarc{AC}$? Draw a few of these inscribed angles.

5. Measure $\angle AOC$ and then measure all the inscribed angles you drew. Can you find a relationship between them?

Theorem 5.11

The measure of an inscribed angle is equal to half of its intercepted arc.

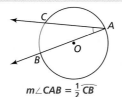

$$m\angle CAB = \tfrac{1}{2}\,\overarc{CB}$$

Explore

For Discussion

THEOREMS 5.9 AND 5.10 Have students draw diagrams to illustrate the theorems. Make sure they have covered all possible cases of chords.

For Discussion

3. See back of book.

In-Class Experiment

4. Check students' diagrams. There are infinitely many inscribed angles that intercept $\overarc{AC}$.

5. All the inscribed angles that intercept the same arc as the central angle have half the measure of the central angle.

PROBLEM 6 Make sure students understand that
△OCB is isosceles (because two of its sides are radii
of the same circle), so its external ∠AOB is twice
∠OCB The measure of ∠AOB is the measure of
∠ACB's intercepted arc.

Wrap Up

Before assigning homework, make sure students
understand the differences in various types of
inscribed angles. Review the definitions.

Assessment Resources

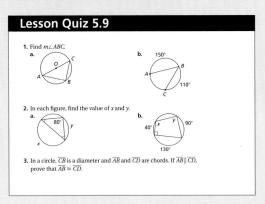

Lesson Quiz 5.9

1. Find $m\angle ABC$.
   a.
   b.   150°
        110°

2. In each figure, find the value of x and y.
   a.   80°
   b.   40° x y 90°
        130°

3. In a circle, $\overline{CB}$ is a diameter and $\overline{AB}$ and $\overline{CD}$ are chords. If $\overline{AB} \parallel \overline{CD}$,
   prove that $\overline{AB} \cong \overline{CD}$.

For Discussion

6. Prove Theorem 5.11 for ∠AOB and ∠ACB.

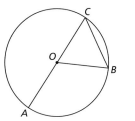

Theorem 5.11 has two important corollaries.

Corollary 5.11.1

Inscribed angles are congruent if and only if they intercept the same arc
or congruent arcs.

Corollary 5.11.2

Any triangle inscribed in a semicircle is a right triangle.

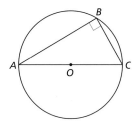

For You to Do

7. In a circle, two parallel chords contain opposite endpoints of a diameter.
   Prove that the chords are congruent.

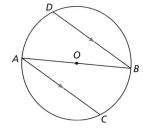

Habits of Mind

Prove. Can you use the
Arc Addition Postulate
to prove Theorem 5.11
in general? See Lesson
5.8 Exercise 4 for a
reminder.

Remember...

One side of a triangle
inscribed in a semicircle is
a diameter of the circle.
So ∠ABC intercepts an
arc of 180° and therefore
measures 90°.

Answers

For Discussion

6. ∠AOB is an exterior
   angle of △BOC, so
   $m\angle AOB = m\angle C + m\angle B$. But
   $m\angle B = m\angle C$, since △BOC is
   isosceles with ∠B and ∠C as base
   angles. Hence $m\angle AOB = 2m\angle C$.
   Thus $m\angle C = \frac{1}{2} m\angle AOB = \frac{1}{2} m\widehat{AB}$.

For You to Do

7. Draw $\overline{AD}$ and $\overline{BC}$. It follows
   from Corollary 5.2 that, in △ADB
   and △ACB, ∠D and ∠C are
   right angles. So $\overline{AD}$ and $\overline{BC}$ are
   perpendicular to parallel lines and
   hence are parallel. It is given that
   $\overline{AC}$ and $\overline{DB}$ are parallel. Hence
   ADBC is a parallelogram, which
   implies that $\overline{AC} \cong \overline{DB}$.

Exercises *Practicing Habits of Mind*

Check Your Understanding

1. What is the measure of any angle inscribed in a semicircle?

2. Choose a point *A* inside a circle. Describe the shortest chord that you can draw through *A*. Justify your answer.

3. Draw a circle and two congruent chords and letter the endpoints *A*, *B*, *C*, and *D* as you go counterclockwise around the circle. Connect *A* with *C* and *B* with *D*. Prove that $\overline{AC}$ and $\overline{BD}$ are congruent.

4. Prove that in a circle two adjacent chords that form equal angles with a radius are congruent.

> Adjacent chords share an endpoint.

5. In the figure, $m\widehat{ABC} = 46°$ and $\widehat{AB} \cong \widehat{BC}$. Find the measures of the inscribed angles.

   a. $\angle CFB$

   b. $\angle CFA$

   c. $\angle CEA$

   d. $\angle FAC$

   e. $\angle FCA$

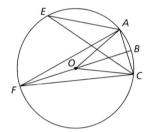

On Your Own

6. The midpoints of two chords of a circle are the same distance from the center *O*. Prove that these chords are congruent.

7. Draw a circle with a 3-cm radius. Consider a chord that is 2 cm long and draw at least ten other chords 2 cm long on the circle. What is the locus of the midpoints of these chords?

> **Remember...**
>
> A locus is a set of points with a given property. In this case, the points are all midpoints of equal-length segments.

Exercises

1. 90°

2. See back of book.

3. See back of book.

4. See back of book.

5. a. 11.5° b. 23° c. 23°

   d. 78.5° e. 78.5°

6. Suppose chord $\overline{AB}$ has midpoint *M*, chord $\overline{CD}$ has midpoint *N*, and *M* and *N* are the same distance from *O*. If the chords are both at a distance of 0 from the center *O*, then they are diameters and hence are congruent. If the distance from the center is greater than 0, then the segments from *O* to the midpoints of the chords are perpendicular to the chords (Theorem 5.9). The Pythagorean Theorem shows that the parts of $\overline{AB}$ are the same length as the parts of $\overline{CD}$. So $\overline{AB} \cong \overline{CD}$.

7. a circle with the same center as the original circle and lying inside that circle

Exercises

HOMEWORK
- Core: 6, 7, 9, 10, 12, 14, 15
- Optional: 8, 11, 13, 16

On Your Own

EXERCISE 7 Point out the margin note about the word *locus*. You may want to have a brief discussion about this if it is a new vocabulary word for your students.

5.9 Chords and Inscribed Angles **403**

8. $\overline{AB}$ is a diameter of a circle. $AB = 2$ in. Draw this circle and diameter and then select a point C on the circle such that $m\angle BAC = 30°$. In how many ways can you choose C? Shade the part of the circle that lies in the interior of $\angle BAC$. What is its area?

9. The line through the center of the circle below is the bisector of $\angle AOB$. Prove that $\overline{AE}$ is congruent to $\overline{BF}$.

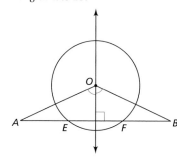

10. If $m\angle CAD = 20°$ and $DP = PB$ in the figure at the right, what is the measure of each of the following angles?

   a. $\angle DPA$, $\angle DPC$, $\angle CPB$, $\angle BPA$ **b.** $\angle ADB$

   c. $\angle AOB$ **d.** $\angle ACB$

   e. $\angle COB$

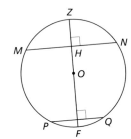

11. Two concentric circles are cut by line ℓ. (Two circles are **concentric circles** if their centers coincide.) Prove that $\overline{AC}$ is congruent to $\overline{DB}$.

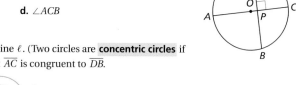

12. In the figure at the right, $FZ = 10$ cm, $PQ = 5$ cm, and the distance from the center of the circle O to $\overline{MN}$ is 2.5 cm. $\overline{FZ}$ is perpendicular to $\overline{MN}$, which is parallel to $\overline{PQ}$. Answer the following questions.

   a. Why is $\overline{FZ}$ the perpendicular bisector of $\overline{PQ}$ and $\overline{MN}$?

   b. What is the radius of the circle?

   c. How long is $\overline{MN}$?

   d. How far is $\overline{PQ}$ from O?

   e. What is $m\angle NOQ$?

Answers

8. 2 ways; $\dfrac{\sqrt{3}}{4} + \dfrac{\pi}{6}$, or $\dfrac{3\sqrt{3} + 2\pi}{12}$

9. Since $\overline{OM} \perp \overline{EF}$, $\overline{OM}$ bisects $\overline{EF}$ (it is the altitude to the base of isosceles $\triangle EOF$). So $EM = MF$. Both angles at M are right angles and hence are congruent. The two small angles at O are congruent, since the diameter bisects $\angle AOB$. $\overline{OM}$ is a common side of $\triangle AOM$ and $\triangle BOM$. So $\triangle AOM \cong \triangle BOM$ by AAS. By CPCTC, it follows that $AM = BM$. Hence $AM - EM = BM - MF$, that is, $AE = BF$. Therefore, $\overline{AE} \cong \overline{BF}$.

10. **a.** 90°, 90°, 90°, 90°

   b. 70°   **c.** 140° **d.** 70°   **e.** 40°

11. See back of book.

12. See back of book.

13. Given $m\widehat{AB} = 30°$ and $m\widehat{CD} = 60°$, find $m\angle APB$.

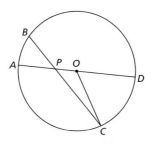

14. The diagram shows a pair of nested circles. One circle is inside the other, and the two circles have point A in common.

  a. Why are the circles similar?

  b. Let the ratio of corresponding lengths be the common ratio for the two circles. In terms of the radii r and R, what is the common ratio?

  c. Any chord $\overline{AB}$ of the larger circle determines a chord $\overline{AC}$ of the smaller circle. Explain why the ratio of AB to AC equals the common ratio.

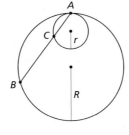

15. Standardized Test Prep What is $m\angle EFH$ if $m\angle EOF = 30°$ and $m\angle FGH = 40°$?

  A. 80°

  B. 110°

  C. 125°

  D. not enough information to answer

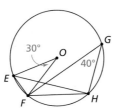

Maintain Your Skills

16. Draw a unit circle and a radius $\overline{OA}$. Label the midpoint of the radius M_1.

  a. Draw a chord with midpoint M_1. How many can you draw? Explain.

  b. Label one of the chords you drew $\overline{C_1D_1}$. How long is it?

  c. Label the midpoint of $\overline{M_1A}$ M_2. Draw a chord $\overline{C_2D_2}$ with midpoint M_2. How long is $\overline{C_2D_2}$?

  d. Label the midpoint of $\overline{M_2A}$ M_3. Draw a chord $\overline{C_3D_3}$ with midpoint M_3. How long is $\overline{C_3D_3}$?

  e. As you continue this process, what happens to $\overline{OM_n}$? To $\overline{C_nD_n}$?

  f. Draw a series of lines ℓ_n through C_n and D_n. What happens to the lines ℓ_n as the value of n increases?

Go Online
PHSchool.com

For additional practice, go to **Web Code: bea-0509**

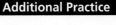
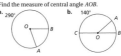

---

13. 45°

14. a. The circles are similar because all circles are similar.

  b. $\dfrac{r}{R}$ or $\dfrac{R}{r}$

  c. Answers may vary. Sample: Suppose the chord $\overline{AB}$ is a diameter of the larger circle. Then the chord $\overline{AC}$ is a diameter of the smaller circle. Then the ratio of $\dfrac{AC}{AB} = \dfrac{d}{D}$, where d is the diameter of the smaller circle and D is the diameter of the larger circle. Since $\dfrac{d}{D} = \dfrac{2r}{2R}$, or $\dfrac{r}{R}$, $\dfrac{AC}{AB} = \dfrac{r}{R}$.

15. B

16. a. One; if a line passes through the center of a circle and bisects a chord that is not a diameter, then the line is perpendicular to the chord.

  b. $\sqrt{3}$ **c.** $\dfrac{\sqrt{7}}{2}$ **d.** $\dfrac{\sqrt{15}}{4}$

  e. The segments $\overline{OM_n}$ are approaching $\overline{OA}$; the segments $\overline{C_nD_n}$ are shorter and shorter.

  f. The lines $\overleftrightarrow{C_nD_n}$ are parallel to the line perpendicular to $\overline{OA}$ at A and are getting closer and closer to that line.

Lesson Overview

GOALS

- Identify properties of tangents.
- Apply the theory of proportion to chords, secants, and tangents of circles.

If you are short on time, you can omit teaching Theorems 5.13 and 5.14. Consider the lesson complete after defining a secant angle. Otherwise, in this lesson, students become familiar with secants and tangents and learn some of their properties. Students learn why a tangent is perpendicular to the radius drawn to the point of contact. They also learn to calculate the measure of secant angles based on the measures of the arcs they intercept.

CHECK YOUR UNDERSTANDING	HOMEWORK
• Core: 1, 2, 3	• Core: 6, 7, 8, 9
• Optional: 4, 5	• Optional: 11, 13, 14
	• Extension: 10, 12

MATERIALS	VOCABULARY
• compasses	• secant
• geometry software	• tangent
• rulers	• secant angle

Launch

Introduce the lesson by asking your class how many ways a circle and a line can intersect. This leads naturally into the In-Class Experiment at the beginning of the lesson.

Explore

Discuss your students' results from the In-Class Experiment. Then have students work through the For You to Do problems.

5.10 Secants and Tangents

Just as chords have special relationships with circles, so do lines that contain the chords.

In-Class Experiment

Use geometry software or a compass and straightedge for the following experiment.

1. Draw a circle of radius 1 and a diameter $\overline{AB}$.

2. Select a point C on the circle and draw $\triangle ABC$. What kind of triangle is it?

3. Move C along the circle. What kind of triangle do you have when C is on the diameter perpendicular to $\overline{AB}$?

4. Is it always true that $m\angle ACB = 90°$? Explain. What is the measure of $\angle ACB$ if C is very close to A or B?

5. If ℓ is the line that coincides with $\overline{CA}$, what happens to ℓ as you move C around? How many intersections does ℓ have with the circle in every position, including when C and A coincide?

6. What is the maximum distance you can find from ℓ to the center of the circle?

In general, if a line has two intersections with a circle it is called a **secant**. When a line has only one intersection point with a circle, it is said to be a **tangent** of the circle or tangent to the circle at the point of contact.

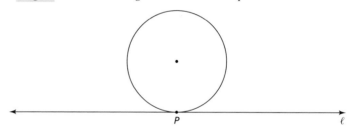

Line ℓ is tangent to the circle at P.

Now you can prove a theorem about your answers to questions 4, 5, and 6 of the In-Class Experiment.

Answers

In-Class Experiment

1. Check students' work.

2. right triangle

3. isosceles right triangle

4. Yes; $\angle ACB$ intercepts a semicircle (an arc of measure 180°); 90°.

5. Line ℓ intersects the circle in two points, except when C is at A. There is no line ℓ when C is at A, since ℓ was defined to be $\overleftrightarrow{CA}$, and

you need two points to determine a line. However, as C approaches A, the position of ℓ approaches the position of the line perpendicular to $\overline{AB}$ at A.

6. The maximum distance is 1 in the sense that 1 is the value the distances approach as the position of ℓ approaches the position of the line perpendicular to $\overline{AB}$ at A.

Theorem 5.12

If a line intersects a circle in one point (that is, the line is tangent to the circle), it is perpendicular to the radius drawn to the point of contact.

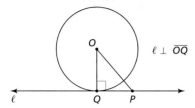

$\ell \perp \overline{OQ}$

Proof Suppose ℓ is tangent to the circle with center O at point Q. Then $\overline{OQ}$ is a radius and $OQ = r$. If you choose a point P on ℓ, other than Q, $OP > r$, because P is outside the circle. So the shortest way to get from O to ℓ is along $\overline{OQ}$. The shortest way to get from O to ℓ is measured along the perpendicular to ℓ, so $\overline{OQ}$ is perpendicular to ℓ.

For You to Do

7. Draw a circle and a point outside of it. Think of all the tangent lines to the circle through that point. How many are there?

8. Draw two circles that intersect. How many lines are tangent to both circles?

9. Draw two circles that do not intersect. How many lines are tangent to both circles?

Definition

A **secant angle** is an angle with sides that are two secants of a circle. A secant angle's vertex can be inside or outside the circle.

Remember...

What do you call a secant angle with its vertex on the circle?

Minds in Action   episode 18

Tony and Sasha were told to find $m\angle APD$ (and therefore $m\angle APC$). They know that $m\widehat{AD} = 122°$ and $m\widehat{BC} = 140°$.

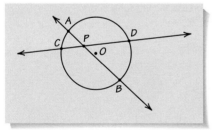

For You to Do

7. two

8. two if the circles intersect in two points, one if the circles intersect in a single point

9. four

Tony   I don't know how to relate the measures of the minor arcs to the angle we are looking for. What can we do?

Sasha   Well, we have to work from the information we have. The measures of the arcs give us the measures of their corresponding central angles and therefore the measures of all the inscribed angles that intercept them.

Tony   Let's try to use triangles. I know how much you like to work with them. You find triangles everywhere!

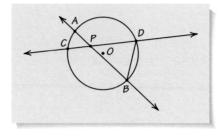

Sasha   Good idea! I see $\triangle PBD$, for example. From the theorem on the external angle of a triangle, we know that
$m\angle APD = m\angle PDB + m\angle PBD.$

Tony   I know that

$$m\widehat{AD} = m\angle AOD = 2m\angle ABD = 2m\angle PBD$$

Sasha   Right! And the same is true for $\angle CDB$, so

$$m\widehat{CB} = m\angle COB = 2m\angle CDB = 2m\angle PDB$$

Tony   So $m\widehat{AD} + m\widehat{CB} = 2m\angle PBD + 2m\angle PDB = 2m\angle APD.$

Sasha   Therefore, $m\angle APD = \frac{1}{2}(m\widehat{AD} + m\widehat{CB}).$

That's pretty neat, isn't it?

You can express the theorem Tony and Sasha found this way.

Theorem 5.13

A secant angle with a vertex inside a circle is equal in measure to half of the sum of the arcs intercepted by it. If you use the lettering in the figure from Minds in Action, the result is below.

$$m\angle APD = \frac{1}{2}(m\widehat{AD} + m\widehat{CB})$$

For You to Do

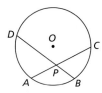

10. If $m\widehat{AB} = 69°$ and $m\widehat{DC} = 163°$, what is $m\angle APB$?

Habits of Mind

Develop your understanding. The difference has to be positive because it is a measure. So it is the measure of the greater of the two intercepted arcs minus the measure of the smaller of the two. You can also say it is the absolute value of the difference of the measures of the arcs.

Theorem 5.14

A secant angle with a vertex outside a circle is equal in measure to half of the difference of the measures of the arcs intercepted by it. If you use the lettering in the figure below, the result is as follows.

$$m\angle APD = \tfrac{1}{2}(m\widehat{AD} - m\widehat{CB})$$

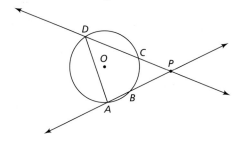

For Discussion

11. Use the figure above to prove Theorem 5.14.

For You to Do

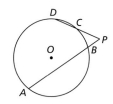

12. If $m\widehat{AD} = 133°$ and $m\widehat{BC} = 48°$, what is $m\angle APD$?

Answers

For You to Do

10. 116°

For Discussion

11. See back of book.

For You to Do

12. 42.5°

Wrap Up

Before assigning homework, allow students time to discuss and summarize their answers to the Check Your Understanding exercises.

Assessment Resources

Exercises

HOMEWORK
- Core: 6, 7, 8, 9
- Optional: 11, 13, 14
- Extension: 10, 12

Exercises *Practicing Habits of Mind*

Check Your Understanding

1. $\overline{PA}$ and $\overline{PB}$ are the tangents to a circle through P. Prove that $\overline{PA} \cong \overline{PB}$.

$\overline{PA}$ and $\overline{PB}$ are called *tangent segments.*

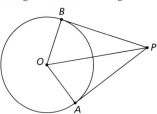

2. $\overline{PA}$ and $\overline{PB}$ are the tangents to a circle through P.

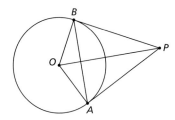

   Prove that $\overline{PO}$ is the perpendicular bisector of $\overline{AB}$.

3. Construct a circle, an external point, and the tangents from the external point to the circle. Describe the steps you take and why your construction works.

4. In the figure, $m\widehat{CB} = 45°$, $m\widehat{AD} = 69°$, $m\angle DCE = 13°$, and $m\angle CPF = 68°$. Find the measures of the following angle and arcs.
   a. $\angle CQB$ b. $\widehat{ED}$ c. $\widehat{FB}$

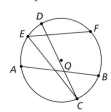

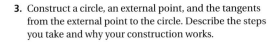

Answers

Exercises

1. The radius drawn to the point where a tangent line touches a circle is perpendicular to the tangent line, so $\triangle OPB$ and $\triangle OPA$ are right triangles. The triangles have a common hypotenuse and the legs $\overline{OB}$ and $\overline{OA}$ are congruent. It follows by the Pythagorean Theorem that $PA = PB$ and hence that $\overline{PA} \cong \overline{PB}$.

2. $\overline{OB}$ and $\overline{OA}$ are radii, so $OB = OA$. From Exercise 1, $PA = PB$. Since P and O are equidistant from A and B, $\overline{PO}$ is the perpendicular bisector of $\overline{AB}$.

3. See back of book.

4. a. 57°   b. 26°   c. 65°

5. In this figure, $m\angle COE = 69°$ and $m\angle EOF = 97°$.

a. What is $m\widehat{FB}$?

b. What is $m\angle CAD$?

c. Suppose you do not know that a tangent is perpendicular to the radius through its point of tangency. Use the formula from Theorem 5.13 or Theorem 5.14 to prove that $\overline{DC}$ is perpendicular to $\overline{AC}$.

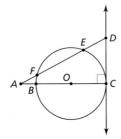

On Your Own

6. In the circle with center O, $OP = 1$ in., $m\angle POQ = 30°$, and $\overline{PQ}$ is tangent to the circle. Find OQ and PQ. Then calculate OQ and PQ for $m\angle POQ = 45°$ and for $m\angle POQ = 60°$.

7. Draw two parallel lines and inscribe a circle between them. What can you say about the segment that connects the intersections of the circle with the parallel lines? Explain.

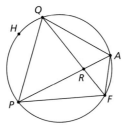

8. **Standardized Test Prep** Given $m\angle AQF = 22°$ and $m\widehat{QHP} = 110°$, what is $m\angle QRP$?

A. 67°

B. 77°

C. 82°

D. 88°

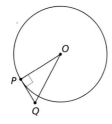

9. Draw a circle and two different-length adjacent chords $\overline{AB}$ and $\overline{AC}$. Mark the midpoints P and Q of the minor arcs $\widehat{AB}$ and $\widehat{AC}$ and connect them. M and N are the points in which this segment intersects $\overline{AB}$ and $\overline{AC}$. Prove that $\overline{AM} \cong \overline{AN}$.

On Your Own

5. See back of book.

6. If $m\angle POQ = 30°$, then

$OQ = \frac{2\sqrt{3}}{3}$ in. and $PQ = \frac{\sqrt{3}}{3}$ in.; If $\angle POQ = 45°$, then $OQ = \sqrt{2}$ in. and $PQ = 1$ in.; If $m\angle POQ = 60°$, then $OQ = 2$ in. and $PQ = \sqrt{3}$ in.

7. The segment connecting the points of tangency is a diameter of the circle. Suppose ℓ and k are parallel and tangent to the circle with center O at points A and B, respectively. $\overleftrightarrow{OA}$ is perpendicular to ℓ, and $\overleftrightarrow{OB}$ is perpendicular to k. But since $\ell \parallel k$, $\overleftrightarrow{OA} \perp k$. Since there is only one line through O perpendicular to k, $\overleftrightarrow{OA}$ and $\overleftrightarrow{OB}$ must be the same line.

8. B

9. See back of book.

Maintain Your Skills

EXERCISE 13 is a guided exercise to help students' comprehension of tangent angles.

Additional Resources

PRINTED RESOURCES
- Texas instruments Activities Workbook
- Cabrilog Activities
- Teaching Resources
- Practice Workbook
- Assessment Resources

TECHNOLOGY
- TeacherExpress CD-ROM
- **Exam**_View_ CD-ROM
- **PHSchool.com**
  - Homework Help
  - Video Tutors
  - Multiple Choice
  - Crosswords

Additional Practice

1. Draw a circle with radius 1 inch.
  a. Place a point A outside the circle. Construct two tangents to the circle, marking the points of tangency as C and D.
  b. Place a point B inside the circle. Construct two secants through point B to points C and D.

2. a. Draw a circle with perpendicular radii $\overline{AO}$ and $\overline{BO}$. Draw tangents to the circle at A and B.
  b. If the tangents meet at point C, what kind of figure is $OACB$? Write a proof to justify your answer.

3. Find the values of x and y.

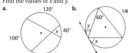
   a.   **b.**   **c.**

4. $\overline{OC}$ is the perpendicular bisector of tangent $\overline{AB}$. Prove that $\widehat{DC} \cong \widehat{EC}$.

5. In the figure, Circle A and Circle B share a common tangent $\overline{CD}$. Prove that $\triangle ACE \sim \triangle BDE$.

6. The power of a point P with respect to a circle is 128. A chord $\overline{JK}$ contains P such that $PK = 16$ in. Find JK.

7. The power of a point P with respect to a circle is 108. Two chords $\overline{LM}$ and $\overline{NQ}$ contain P such that $LP = 12$ and $NQ = 31$. Find PM, NP, and QP.

8. Find the value of x and state the power of point P with respect to each circle. Figures are not to scale.

   a.   **b.**

Practice: For Lesson 5.10, assign Exercises 1–5.

---

10. Take It Further Draw a circle and inscribe a right triangle so that $m\angle ABC = 90°$. Through the center of the circle O, draw a line ℓ parallel to $\overline{AB}$. Draw a line through C that intersects ℓ at P so that $\angle CPO \cong \angle ACB$. In how many ways can you choose P on ℓ? In how many points does the line through C and P intersect the circle?

11. In this figure, the two circles are concentric and $\overline{PA}$, $\overline{PB}$, $\overline{PC}$, and $\overline{PD}$ are tangent to the circle their endpoints lie on.

  a. Prove $\angle APC \cong \angle DPB$.

  b. Prove the quadrilateral $ABDC$ is an isosceles trapezoid.

12. Take It Further Follow these steps to draw a figure.

  a. Draw a circle and call it γ.

  b. Draw a diameter $\overline{AB}$ of γ.

  c. Choose a point D on $\overline{AB}$ and a point C on γ.

  d. Draw the line through A and C. Label it m. Draw the line through C and B. Label it n.

  e. Draw the line through D that is perpendicular to $\overline{AB}$. Label it p. Use E to name the intersection of p and n. Use F to name the intersection of p and m.

  f. Draw the tangent to γ through C. Use M to name its intersection with p.

  If you have drawn the figure correctly, M should be the midpoint of $\overline{EF}$. Prove it.

Maintain Your Skills

13. Use geometry software or a compass and straightedge for the following exercise. Draw a circle and choose two fixed points A and C on it. Now choose a third point B on the circle and move it gradually toward A.

  a. What is the measure of $\angle ABC$ as you move B along the circle?

  b. Draw the line ℓ that contains $\overrightarrow{BA}$ and move B until it coincides with A. What does ℓ become? Explain.

  c. When B coincides with A, what arc does the angle that ℓ forms with $\overline{AC}$ intercept?

  d. Think about the angle that ℓ forms with $\overline{AC}$ when B coincides with A. Can you prove it is congruent to $\angle ABC$ that is formed when B does not coincide with A? Explain.

14. Can Theorem 5.11 be considered a special case of Theorem 5.13 or of Theorem 5.14?

Go Online
PHSchool.com

For additional practice, go to **Web Code: bea-0510**

Answers

10. You can find two positions for the desired point that will work. One is where the tangent line at C intersects ℓ. In that case, $\overleftrightarrow{CP}$ intersects the circle only in the point C. If you reflect P across $\overline{BC}$, you get a point P' that is on ℓ, and for that point you will also have $\angle CP'O \cong \angle ACB$. This time $\overleftrightarrow{CP'}$ intersects the circle in two points.

11. See back of book.

12. See back of book.

13. See back of book.

14. Answers may vary. Sample: In an informal way, Theorem 5.11 deals with limiting cases of both Theorem 5.13 and Theorem 5.14. For the situations in Theorems 5.13 and 5.14, if the point of intersection of the secants is very close to the circle, one of the intercepted arcs will have a measure very close to 0°, and the angle measure will be very close to half the measure of the other arc.

Every point in the plane of a circle has a number associated with it. That number is called the power of the point.

n-Class Experiment

he Power of a Point

1. Draw a circle and pick a point *P* anywhere inside it. Then draw a chord of the circle that passes through *P*. Point *P* divides the chord into two segments $\overline{PA}$ and $\overline{PB}$.

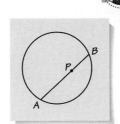

  a. Measure the lengths of these segments and calculate the product $(PA) \cdot (PB)$.

  b. Draw another chord through *P* and calculate the same product of the lengths of its two segments. Record your observations and repeat the process for several more chords.

The product is called the *power of point P with respect to the circle*. You write $\Pi(P)$.

2. The circle below has two chords $\overline{AB}$ and $\overline{CD}$ that intersect at point *P*.

  a. What can you predict about the lengths *PA, PB, PC,* and *PD*?

  b. Copy the figure and add segments $\overline{AC}$ and $\overline{BD}$ to the illustration. The first step in proving your conjecture from part (a) is to show that $\triangle APC \sim \triangle DPB$. Explain why these two triangles must be similar.

  c. Use the fact that $\triangle APC \sim \triangle DPB$ to write a proportion that includes *PA, PB, PC,* and *PD*. Rearrange the proportion to prove your conjecture from part (a).

  d. How does this result prove that the product of the chord lengths is the same for any chord through *P*?

If you see $\Pi(P) = \ldots$ in reference to a circle and a point *P*, you say "the power of *P* with respect to the circle is . . . ."

Hint: $\angle ACD$ and $\angle ABD$ intercept the same arc.

One of the pleasures of mathematics comes from finding an unexpected connection between two topics that seem to have nothing in common. For example, you can use your findings about the power of a point to answer the following question.

Is there a way to construct a rectangle with geometry software so that when you drag a vertex the perimeter changes but the area remains the same?

In-Class Experiment

1. a. Check students' work.
  b. All the products should be equal to the product from part (a).

2. a. $PA \cdot PB = PC \cdot PD$
  b. $\angle C \cong \angle B$ because they are inscribed angles that intercept the same arc. Likewise, $\angle A \cong \angle D$. $\angle APC \cong \angle DPB$ (vertical angles). So $\triangle APC \cong \triangle DPB$ (AA Similarity).

  c. $\dfrac{PA}{PD} = \dfrac{PC}{PB}$ since $\triangle APC \cong \triangle DPB$. The cross products must be equal, so $PA \cdot PB = PC \cdot PD$.

  d. The reasoning in parts (b) and (c) applies to any new chord you might draw through point *P*.

Lesson Overview

GOALS

- Prove and use general theorems on chords and inscribed angles.
- Apply the theory of proportion to chords, secants, and tangents of circles.

This lesson introduces the power of a point with respect to a circle. Students discover three properties of the power of a point.

1. The power of a point outside a circle can be expressed as the square of the length of any tangent segment from the point to the circle.
2. The power of a point on the circle is zero.
3. The locus of points with equal power with respect to two intersecting circles is the line through their common chord.

Students apply findings about the power of a point to other areas of geometry.

CHECK YOUR UNDERSTANDING	HOMEWORK
• Core: 1, 2, 3 • Optional: none	• Core: 4, 5, 6, 8 • Optional: 7, 11, 12, 13, 14 • Extension: 9, 10
MATERIALS	**VOCABULARY**
• compasses • geometry software • rulers	• power of a point, ΠP

Launch

You may wish to have students work in pairs or small groups.

Explore

In-Class Experiment

Make sure students understand the meaning of *power of a point*.

If you could build such a rectangle, you could call it a *constant-area rectangle*.

Derman and Tony are discussing the possible dimensions of different rectangles with an area of 24 square feet.

Derman   Tony, I found two rectangles that have an area of 24 square feet—a 24 ft-by-1 ft and an 12 ft-by-2 ft.

Tony   I think there are more than two rectangles that have an area of 24 square feet! How about a 8 ft-by-3 ft rectangle, or a 6 ft-by-4 ft rectangle?

Derman   Okay, in that case, how about a $\frac{1}{2}$ ft-by-48 ft rectangle?

Tony   Wow, Derman, I wonder how many more 24 square foot rectangles there are.

For Discussion

3. If ℓ represents the lengths of the rectangles in the above dialog and w represents their widths, what is the relationship between ℓ and w?

4. How many rectangles are there with an area of 24 square feet?

Answers

For Discussion

3. $\ell w = 36$

4. infinitely many

Using what you found out about the power of a point, you can construct constant-area rectangles. To begin, the computer screen shows a rectangle on one side and the power-of-a-point construction on the other. The length *PA* and the width *PB* of the rectangle are linked to the corresponding chord segments and are equal to them. So when the chord segment lengths change, the rectangle's dimensions will, too.

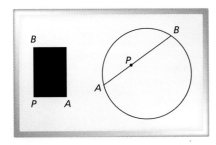

As you move point *A* around the circle, the chord $\overline{AB}$ spins, always passing through the stationary point *P*.

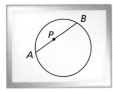 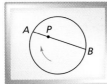 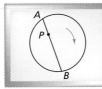

or You to Do

Use geometry software to build a construction like the one described above. Your construction might include an animation button that allows point *A* to travel automatically around the circle.

5. As chord $\overline{AB}$ spins, describe what happens to the rectangle.

6. The purpose of this geometry construction is to create a rectangle of constant area. Explain why you think this construction does or does not satisfy this goal.

7. Does your construction show all possible rectangles that share the same area? Explain.

For You to Do

To begin the construction, draw a circle along with a point *P* in its interior. Place a point *A* on the circle and construct the ray through *A* and *P*. Let *B* be the second point of intersection of this ray with the circle. Construct segments $\overline{PA}$ and $\overline{PB}$ and then hide the ray. This guarantees that as you move *A* around the circle, the chord will change but will always pass through *P*.

For You to Do

5. The length and width of the rectangle will vary, but the area will stay the same.

6. $\prod(P)$ is constant; $\prod(O) = r^2$

7. No; let $\overline{CD}$ be the diameter that passes through *P*. Neither dimension of a rectangle obtainable with the construction described can be less than the smaller of the lengths *PC* and *PD*.

However, you can have a rectangle of area $PA \cdot PB$ that has width *k*, no matter how small a positive number *k* may be.

Wrap Up

Before assigning homework, review the meaning of *power of a point* and give students time to discuss their solutions to the Check Your Understanding exercises.

Assessment Resources

Exercises

HOMEWORK
- Core: 4, 5, 6, 8
- Optional: 7, 11, 12, 13, 14
- Extension: 9, 10

Exercises *Practicing Habits of Mind*

Check Your Understanding

1. Suppose that you decide to build a collection of equal-area rectangles out of pencils. Each rectangle is to have an area of 6 square inches, and no two rectangles can have the same dimensions. You can measure the pencils and then cut them at appropriate places, but that becomes tedious.

   How can the setup below help you make your rectangles?

a few pencils

power of point $P = 6$

> The actual circle and pencils would be larger.

2. The power of point P with respect to a circle is 112. A chord $\overline{ST}$ contains P. If $PT = 32$ in., how long is $\overline{ST}$?

3. Draw a circle with center O, radius r, and a diameter $\overline{AE}$. Find and label the midpoint of $\overline{OE}$ B, the midpoint of $\overline{BE}$ C, and the midpoint of $\overline{CE}$ D. Find $\Pi(B)$, $\Pi(C)$, $\Pi(D)$, and $\Pi(O)$. How would you define $\Pi(E)$?

On Your Own

4. **Write About It** Suppose you want to make a constant-area triangle instead of a rectangle. Describe at least one way to alter the methods in this lesson to make a triangle instead. Include pictures.

Answers

Exercises

1. See back of book.

2. 35.5 in.

3. $\Pi(P) = \frac{3}{4}r^2$; $\Pi(C) = \frac{7}{16}r^2$; $\Pi(D) = \frac{15}{64}r^2$; define $\Pi(E)$ to be 0.

4. Answers may vary. Sample: To construct triangles that have a constant area A, construct a circle

and a point P inside the circle such that $\Pi(P) = 2A$ (see the answer for Exercise 1). Draw a chord through P. Use segments congruent to the two parts of the chord as the legs of a right triangle. Check students' diagrams.

5. Parts a–d give an outline for a proof of your power-of-a-point conjecture. Justify each step and then write the proof.

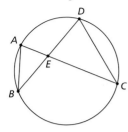

a. $\angle ABE \cong \angle DCE$

b. $\angle AEB \cong \angle DEC$

c. $\triangle ABE \sim \triangle DCE$

d. $\dfrac{AE}{DE} = \dfrac{BE}{CE}$

Hint: Look for inscribed angles.

e. Write the complete proof showing that $(AE)(CE) = (BE)(DE)$.

6. The power of a point P with respect to a circle is 126. Draw two chords $\overline{AB}$ and $\overline{CD}$ through P, such that $AP = 21$ cm and $CD = 25$ cm. Find $PB, CP,$ and DP.

7. Two chords $\overline{AB}$ and $\overline{CD}$ through a point P inside a circle measure 7 cm and 13 cm respectively. If $AP = 3$ cm, find $PB, CP,$ and PD.

8. Standardized Test Prep In the figure, $CD = 7$ cm, $CP = 3$ cm, and $PG = 5$ cm. What is FP?

A. 2.0 cm

B. 2.4 cm

C. 2.5 cm

D. 4.2 cm

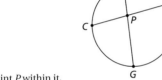

9. Take It Further Draw a circle, a point P within it, and calculate the power of P.

a. Are there other locations for P within the same circle that have the same power? Find a few and explain your reasoning.

b. Find the locations of all points within your circle that have the same power as P. What does this collection of points look like?

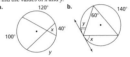

---

5. See back of book.

6. $PB = 6$ cm, $CP = 7$ cm, $DP = 18$ cm (or $CP = 18$ cm, $DP = 7$ cm)

7. $PB = 4$ cm, $CP = 12$ cm, $PD = 1$ cm (or $CP = 1$ cm, $PD = 12$ cm)

8. B

9. a. Yes, infinitely many (assuming P is not the center of the circle); reflect $\overline{AB}$ and P across any diameter of the circle. The images of $\overline{PA}$ and $\overline{PB}$ will have the same lengths as $\overline{PA}$ and $\overline{PB}$.

  b. If the point P that you originally picked is not the center O of the circle, then the set of points with the same power will be the circle with center O and radius OP. If you picked P to be the center O, then the set contains only the point O.

10. Take It Further If *P* is a point outside the circle, as in the figure below left, you can still prove that the product (*PA*)(*PB*) is invariant. Copy the figure below right and connect *B* to *C* and *A* to *D*.

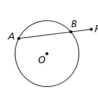 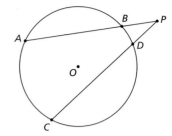

a. Prove that △*PAD* ~ △*PCB*.

b. Write proportions for the sides of the triangles and deduce that (*PA*)(*PB*) is invariant.

You can, therefore, generalize the definition of Π(*P*) this way.

Definition

The **power of a point** *P* with respect to a circle is the product (*PA*)(*PB*), where *A* and *B* are the points of intersection of a line through *P* and the circle.

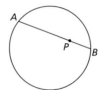

Habits of Mind

Explore. What is the power of *P* if *P* lies *on* the circle?

Maintain Your Skills

For Exercises 11–14, draw a circle and a chord $\overline{AB}$ through a point *P* inside the circle.

11. For Π(*P*) = 6 and *PA* = 3 cm, find *PB* and *AB*.

12. For Π(*P*) = 9 and *AB* = 10 in., find *PA* and *PB*.

13. For Π(*P*) = 28 and *AB* = 16 cm, find *PA* and *PB*.

14. For Π(*P*) = *k* and *AB* = *a* cm, find *PA* and *PB* as functions of *k* and *a*.

Go Online
PHSchool.com

For additional practice, go to **Web Code: bea-0511**

Answers

10. a. ∠*A* ≅ ∠*C* because the angles are inscribed angles that intercept the same arc. ∠*P* is common to △*PAD* and △*PCB*. Therefore △*PAD*~△*PCB* (by AA Similarity).

b. Since △*PAD*~△*PCB*, $\frac{PA}{PC} = \frac{PD}{PB}$. The cross products must be equal, so *PA* · *PB* = *PC* · *PD*.

11. *PB* = 2 cm, *AB* = 6 cm

12. *PA* = 1 in., *PB* = 9 in. (or *PA* = 9 in., *PB* = 1 in.)

13. *PA* = 14 cm, *PB* = 2 cm (or *PA* = 2 cm, *PB* = 14 cm)

14. $PA = \dfrac{a + \sqrt{a^2 - 4k}}{2}$ cm,

$PB = \dfrac{a - \sqrt{a^2 - 4k}}{2}$ cm

$\left(\text{or } PA = \dfrac{a - \sqrt{a^2 - 4k}}{2}, \right.$

$\left. PB = \dfrac{a + \sqrt{a^2 - 4k}}{2} \right)$

Mathematical Reflections

In this investigation, you examined chords, secants, and tangents of circles and proved many relationships involving these figures. These questions will help you summarize what you have learned.

1. In the circle at the right with center O, M is the midpoint of $\overline{AB}$. Prove that $\triangle AOM$ is a right triangle.

2. Draw any right triangle ABC and let $m\angle ABC = 90°$. Why is the median from B to the midpoint of $\overline{AC}$ always half of $\overline{AC}$?

3. In the figure at the right below, $m\angle ABC = 31°$ and O is the center of the circle. What is the measure of each angle?

   a. $\angle AOC$

   b. $\angle AEC$

   c. $\angle CDA$

4. Draw a circle with center O and radius 35 mm, choose a point P on the circle, and draw the line ℓ through P tangent to the circle. What is the distance from O to ℓ?

5. What are arcs and chords in circles?

6. How much smaller is the measure of an inscribed angle than the measure of its corresponding central angle?

7. What is the power of a point? What are the maximum and minimum values of the power of a point in a circle with radius r?

Vocabulary and Notation

In this investigation, you saw these terms and symbols for the first time. Make sure you understand what each one means and how to use it.

- arc, $\overset{\frown}{AB}$
- central angle
- chord
- concentric circles
- degree measure
- diameter
- inscribed angle
- locus
- major arc
- minor arc
- power of a point, ΠP
- secant
- secant angle
- tangent

The ball flies off on a tangent.

Mathematical Reflections

1. $\overline{OM}$ is contained in a line through the center that bisects the chord. By Theorem 5.9, $\overline{OM} \perp \overline{AB}$. So $\triangle AOM$ is a right triangle.

2. If you circumscribe a circle around $\triangle ABC$, $\angle B$ will intercept a semicircle, since $m\angle B = 90° = \frac{1}{2}$ (measure of intercepted arc). Therefore, $\overline{AC}$ is a diameter, and the midpoint M of $\overline{AC}$ is the center

of the circle. Hence $\overline{MA}$, $\overline{MB}$, and $\overline{MC}$ are radii. Therefore $MB = \frac{1}{2}AC$.

3. a. 62°   b. 149°   c. 31°

4. 35 mm

5. See back of book.

6. See back of book.

7. See back of book.

Mathematical Reflections

EXERCISES 5–7 At the start of the Investigation, you may have assigned these as Questions 1–3 for students to think and write about.

Investigation Overview

Investigation 5D applies probability concepts to geometric situations. The investigation begins with students experimenting with a spinner. This gets students thinking about probability and area. Students then use probabilities to solve geometric problems, including problems about area, ratios, and proportions. Students also learn about sets of measure zero and begin to think about different properties of measure.

You may wish to assign Questions 1–3 for students to think and write about during the investigation.

Learning Goals

- Compute the probability that a tiny rain drop will hit a certain area of a board.
- Use the Monte Carlo Method to approximate areas.
- Recognize sets of measure zero.

Habits and Skills

- Relate ratios of areas to probability.
- Use probability experiments to approximate π.
- Work to understand an abstract definition of a mathematical object.

Geometric Probability

In *Geometric Probability*, you may be surprised to see concepts from probability applied to geometric situations. Most people have thought about probability in contexts such as rolling number cubes, flipping coins, drawing playing cards, or other random events. How does probability relate to geometry? As you will see, you can use certain types of random events to approximate areas of figures. Through these experiments, you will experience a new way to think about measurement.

By the end of this investigation, you will be able to answer questions like these:

1. What is the probability that a tiny rain drop will hit a certain region on a board?

2. How can you estimate areas with the Monte Carlo Method?

3. What is the probability of a spinner landing on a line?

You will learn how to

- compute the probability that a tiny rain drop will hit a certain area of a board

- use the Monte Carlo Method to approximate areas

- recognize sets of measure zero

You will develop these habits and skills:

- Relate ratios of areas to probability.

- Use probability experiments to approximate π.

- Work to understand an abstract definition of a mathematical object.

The larger the web, the smaller the probability that a bug can fly through without getting caught.

Investigation Road Map

LESSON 5.12, *Getting Started*, contains an In-Class Experiment to help students see the relationship between probability and area. Student will also think about ratios of areas.

LESSON 5.13, *Probability as a Ratio of Areas*, introduces the Monte Carlo Method in which the relationship of direct proportionality becomes explicit.

LESSON 5.14, *Sets of Measure 0*, uncovers the difference between a very small probability and a probability of zero. It also summarizes the properties of measure with which students are familiar.

In some games you spin a pointer. You proceed with the game based on the outcome of the spin.

n-Class Experiment

For this experiment, you will need a spinner provided by your teacher.

1. Label the sections on your spinner A, B, C, D, E, and F. Spin the spinner 50 times and keep track of which letter the pointer lands on each time. Compare your results with other students' results.

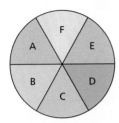

2. Change the names of the slices so that your spinner looks like this:

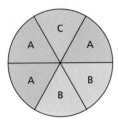

Spin the spinner 50 times. Keep track of which letter the pointer lands on each time. Compare your results with other students' results. Do you get the same results as in Problem 2? Explain.

3. Draw another circle with the same radius as your spinner. Cut it out and tape it to the spinner. Now divide your spinner so that $\frac{1}{4}$ of it is the A region, $\frac{5}{8}$ of it is the B region, and $\frac{1}{8}$ of it is the C region. Did all of your classmates divide the spinner in the same way? Does it matter? Spin the spinner 50 times and mark what letter the pointer lands on. What is the greatest number of times the pointer lands on a zone? Why do you think this region has the greatest number?

Answers

In-Class Experiment

1–3. Check students' work.

Lesson Overview

GOALS

- Warm up to the ideas of the investigation.
- Use a hands-on approach to develop mathematical habits of mind.

The In-Class Experiment helps students understand that the greater the area on the board, the greater the probability that the needle will land on that area. The For You to Explore problems also convey this idea through the image of tiny drops falling randomly on different areas of boards.

MATERIALS	FOR YOU TO EXPLORE
• compasses	• Core: 1, 2, 3, 4, 5
• large paper or thin cardboard	• Optional: 6, 7
• spinner	**HOMEWORK**
• tape	• Core: 8, 9
• Balckline Masters 5.12 A–C	• Optional: 10, 11, 12

Launch

You will need a spinner for each student (or pair of students). If you do not have pre-made spinners available, you can make spinners using Blackline Masters 5.12 A–B. Glue copies of the spinner to cardboard circles. Use a paper clip as the spinner by holding a pen point down through the paper clip and flicking the paper clip around with a finger to make it spin.

Explore

If students recall theoretical probability from earlier courses, review the difference between theoretical and experimental probability before students do the In-Class Experiment. Make sure they understand that they will be finding experimental probability and their results may not match the theoretical probability of each result.

Wrap Up

Before assigning homework, allow students time to complete the For You to Explore problems. Encourage them to compare their results with each other.

Exercises

HOMEWORK
- Core: 8, 9
- Optional: 10, 11, 12

On Your Own

EXERCISES 8–11 Students should understand that the probability of a drop landing on a certain area is proportional to the ratio of the region's area to the board's area. It may help students to think of the percents as $\frac{1}{2}$, $\frac{1}{4}$, $\frac{3}{4}$, and $\frac{1}{3}$ of the board.

For You to Explore

For the following problems, imagine poppy seeds falling on the figures. For each figure, predict whether the seeds will land more frequently on the blue part or on the white part. Explain your reasoning. You may wish to measure the figures with a ruler.

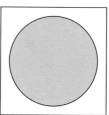

Imagine that the seeds fall with equal probability anywhere on the figure.

4. 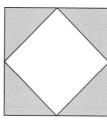 **5.**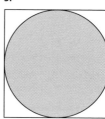

6. 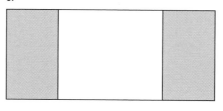 **7.**

![Exercises Practicing Habits of Mind]

On Your Own

For the following exercises, imagine poppy seeds falling anywhere on a board with equal probability.

8. Shade the board with two different colors so that there is a 50% probability that a poppy seed will fall on each color.

Answers

For You to Explore

4. About as frequently in the white region as in the shaded region; the areas of the regions are equal.

5. More frequently in the shaded region; the area of the shaded region is greater than that of the white region.

6. About as frequently in the white region as in the shaded region; the areas of the regions are equal.

7. More frequently in the white region; the area of the white region is greater than that of the shaded region.

8. Check students' work. The areas for the two colors should be approximately equal.

9. Shade the board with two different colors so that there is a 25% probability that a poppy seed will fall on one of the colors.

10. Shade the board with two different colors so that there is a 75% probability that a poppy seed will fall on one of the colors.

11. Shade the board with two different colors so that there is a 33% probability that a poppy seed will fall on one of the colors.

Maintain Your Skills

12.

Go Online
Video Tutor
PHSchool.com

Web Code: bee-0775

Ms. Belanger's class made a board that measures 8 feet by 6 feet and divided it into eight color regions. The class threw a table-tennis ball dipped in yellow paint 100 times. The ball had equal probabilities of hitting any of the eight regions. The center of each hit was marked with a black dot. The figure shows the black dots as they appeared on the full-sized board. Count the black dots in each region. Copy and complete the table.

Color	h = number of hits (out of 100)	A = area of the region	$\dfrac{h}{100}$	$\dfrac{A}{48}$
R	■	■	■	■
G	■	■	■	■
B	■	■	■	■

Are the last two columns similar? What do you think would have happened if the class had thrown the table-tennis ball 200 times or 1000 times?

---

9. Check students' work. The area for one color should be about 3 times the area for the other.

10. Check students' work. The area for one color should be about 3 times the area for the other.

11. Check students' work. The area for one color should be about 2 times the area for the other.

12. Tables will vary. Theoretically, in each row, the last two numbers should be approximately equal. The difference of the last two numbers should approach 0 as the number of trials increases.

Maintain Your Skills

EXERCISE 12 Blackline Master 5.12C depicts the table so that students do not have to copy it.

Lesson Overview

GOALS

- Compute the probability that a tiny drop will hit a certain area of a board.
- Use the Monte Carlo Method to approximate areas.

This lesson makes explicit the fact that the probability of a drop landing on a certain region is the ratio between the area of the region and that of the whole board. Then the Monte Carlo Method is introduced as a new way of estimating areas.

CHECK YOUR UNDERSTANDING
- Core: 1
- Optional: 2, 3

HOMEWORK
- Core: 4, 5, 7, 8
- Optional: 6, 10
- Extension: 9

VOCABULARY
- discrete case
- probability
- Monte Carlo Method

Launch

Review students' work on Exercises 8–11 from Lesson 5.12.

Explore

Have students read aloud or act out the Minds in Action dialog. Students may benefit from performing the Monte Carlo simulation to verify that it works.

5.13 Probability as a Ratio of Areas

The sizes of shapes affect geometric probability.

For Discussion

1. If a tiny drop of ink randomly hit the figure, would the drop be more likely to land on the blue region or the white region?

2. If the probability of the drop landing on the blue region is P, would you reduce or enlarge the blue region to make the probability $\frac{P}{2}$? To make the probability $\frac{P}{4}$?

3. What is the relationship between P and the blue region?

Facts and Notation

The **probability** P that a tiny drop will land on a region of area s on a board of area b is equal to the ratio of the areas of the shaded region and of the whole board. ($b \neq 0$)

$$P = \frac{s}{b}$$

Habits of Mind

Develop your understanding. Can P ever be greater than 1? Explain.

For You to Do

A circular board has radius r. There is a shaded concentric circle on the board. What would the radius of this shaded circle have to be in order for the probability of a tiny drop landing on it to be the following?

4. $\frac{1}{4}$ 5. $\frac{1}{3}$ 6. $\frac{1}{2}$

Minds in Action   episode 20

Sasha and Tony were asked to estimate the area of a blob inside a circular board with a radius of 2 in., without using the grid method.

Tony The probability that a tiny drop will land on a certain region of a board is equal to the ratio of the areas of the shaded region and of the whole board. The area of the board is $2^2\pi$ in.^{2} = 4π in.^{2}.

Sasha I think you're going in the right direction, but if we want to use the formula $P = \frac{s}{b}$, we need to know the probability a tiny drop will land in the blob. How can we get that?

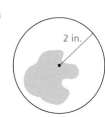

2 in.

Answers

For Discussion

1. blue region

2. reduce; reduce

3. $P = \dfrac{\text{area of shaded region}}{\text{area of square}}$

For You to Do

4. $\dfrac{r}{2}$

5. $\dfrac{r\sqrt{3}}{3}$

6. $\dfrac{r\sqrt{2}}{2}$

Tony	Well, I remember the In-Class Experiment at the beginning of this investigation. We related the number of times the pointer landed on a certain slice of the spinner to the area of that region of the spinner. Do you think we could do something like that?
Sasha	That's a good idea, Tony! Let's think. We could find the ratio between the number of times a drop lands on the blob and the number of times a drop hits the board anywhere. How could we relate this to the probability P, which is the likelihood a drop will hit the blob rather than some other point on the board?
Tony	I'd say the greater your ratio is, the greater the probability P will be. And we can assume them to be directly proportional, because if the ratio is twice as big, then it's twice as likely that a drop hits the blob. If the ratio is three times as big then P has to triple, too, and so on.
Sasha	Good thinking! So if we could do a drop experiment, we could come up with the ratio that is directly proportional to P. And P is directly proportional to the area of the blob divided by the area of the board.

It is hard to randomly generate tiny ink drops, so Sasha and Tony simulate this using the following method.

Step 1 Cut out the board with the blob.

Step 2 Sprinkle 200 poppy seeds randomly on the board.

Step 3 Count the poppy seeds that landed on the blob.

Step 4 Calculate the ratio of poppy seeds on the blob to the total number of poppy seeds you sprinkled (200).

Sasha's guess that the ratio is directly proportional to P is correct, and in discrete cases the coefficient of proportionality is 1. Therefore, since the number of poppy seeds is relatively large, you can use the ratio R in place of P to estimate the area A of the blob by calculating the following.

$$A \approx R(4\pi)$$

Monte Carlo Method

The method Tony and Sasha just used is called the **Monte Carlo Method.** In general, the Monte Carlo Method is a statistical simulation method that utilizes sequences of random numbers to perform a simulation. It is used in many fields, from the simulation of physical phenomena such as radiation transport in Earth's atmosphere to the simulation of a game.

Because the method can simulate games of chance, it is named after a small European city that is a center for gambling.

A discrete case is a case that deals with finite numbers, such as the number of poppy seeds. In the case of the poppy-seed experiment, the definition of probability is the number of seeds on the blob divided by the total number of seeds on the board.

Go Online
PHSchool.com

For more information about the Monte Carlo Method, go to **Web Code: bee-9031**

Wrap-Up

Before assigning homework, encourage students to redo Sasha and Tony's Monte Carlo simulation using random numbers.

Assessment Resources

Exercises

HOMEWORK
- Core: 4, 5, 7, 8
- Optional: 6, 10
- Extension: 9

Developing Habits of Mind

Find another way. You might be wondering what generating random numbers has to do with Sasha and Tony's poppy-seed experiment. Random numbers can be used to solve probability problems.

Here is a way that a random number generator could simulate the poppy-seed experiment. Think of a board divided into thousands of regions, each the size of a poppy seed. A computer could randomly generate a sequence of numbers from 0 to the total number of regions. Each number would correspond to a tiny region on the board. The generated numbers would correspond to the event of a poppy seed landing inside or outside the shaded region.

You will learn more about probability in Algebra 2.

To get a better estimate for P, you must make sure the number of times you repeat the event is relatively high.

For You to Do

7. Tony and Sasha repeat the poppy-seed experiment three times on a second blob drawn on a board with 2-in. radius. The first time they use 100 poppy seeds, the second time 200 poppy seeds, and the third time 400 poppy seeds. They calculate the ratios $P_1 = 0.716$, $P_2 = 0.768$, and $P_3 = 0.752$. What is the best estimate for the blob's area? Explain.

Exercises *Practicing Habits of Mind*

Check Your Understanding

What is the probability a tiny drop of ink will land on the blue regions of the following square boards? The side length of the square is 3 inches.

1.   **2.**   **3.**

Answers

For You to Do

7. Answers may vary. Sample: about 9.45 in.^{2}; the estimates tend to improve as the number of trials increases.

Exercises

1. $\frac{\pi}{4}$

2. $\frac{3\pi}{16}$

3. $\frac{3\pi}{64}$

4. A circle is inscribed in a square.

Use the Monte Carlo Method to estimate the value of π.

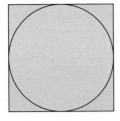

5. Think of a checkerboard made of squares of alternating colors, each with an area of 4 square inches. If you drop a penny (its diameter is $\frac{3}{4}$ in.) on the board, what is the probability it will touch two colors?

6. How could you change the side length of the squares on the checkerboard from Exercise 5 in order for the probability of the penny landing on two colors to be $\frac{1}{2}$, $\frac{1}{3}$, or $\frac{1}{4}$?

7. Two circles are painted on a board. The probability of a drop landing inside only one of the two circles is 0.4. The probability of it landing outside both circles is 0.5. How can this be? What is the probability of the drop landing in the intersection of the two circles? How big is this area if the board's area is 5 square feet?

8. **Standardized Test Prep** Ms. Pryce challenged her students to divide a square into three regions with equal areas. Linette did it by drawing a circle of radius 2 cm inside the square and a smaller concentric circle inside the first circle. What is the radius of the smaller circle?

A. 1 **B.** $\sqrt{2}$ **C.** 2 **D.** 2π

9. **Take It Further** A circle and a square are painted on a board. The probability of a drop landing on the circle is 0.4. The probability of a drop landing on the square is 0.7. Suppose the area of the whole board is 5 square feet and the probability of a drop landing on neither the square nor the circle is 0.3. What is the area of the intersection of the square and the circle? What are the areas of the square and the circle?

Go Online
PHSchool.com

For additional practice, go to **Web Code: bea-0513**

10. Find a toothpick and measure it. Call its length ℓ. On a sheet of paper, draw many parallel lines with a distance of ℓ between them. Drop the toothpick on the sheet of paper many times and mark how many times it landed touching a line. This is known as Buffon's Experiment.

a. Give an estimate for the probability P that the toothpick falls on a line.

b. The exact theoretical value for P is $\frac{2}{\pi}$. Is your estimate close?

c. Design an experiment using the Monte Carlo Method and Buffon's Experiment for estimating π.

You will be able to exactly calculate the value of P after you learn some calculus.

---

4. Check students' work. The theoretical probability is $\frac{\pi}{4}$, or about 0.785.

5. $\frac{2247}{4096} \approx 0.5486$

6. The probability of the penny landing on two colors is $\frac{\frac{39}{16}}{4} = \frac{39}{64} > \frac{1}{2}$.

7. Assuming the area of overlap of the circles is $\frac{1}{10}$ the area of the board; 0.1; 0.5 ft^2

8. B

9. The circle lies entirely inside the square, so their intersection is 2 ft^2; area of square = 3.5 ft^2, area of circle = 2 ft^2.

10. **a.** Answers may vary. Sample: 0.64
b. Answers may vary. Sample: yes
c. Check students' work.

On Your Own

EXERCISE 4 has students use the Monte Carlo Method to estimate the value of π. They will come up with a value (k) for the ratio of the area of the circle over that of the square. (They do not need to know the length of the radius, but just that it is half the side of the square.)

EXERCISE 7 is an example of a property of probability and measure that Lesson 5.14 lists: the *measure* of a set of nonseparate elements is less than the sum of the measures of the individual elements.

Maintain Your Skills

EXERCISE 10 is a version of Buffon's experiment and yet another way of using the Monte Carlo Method for estimating the value of π.

Additional Resources

PRINTED RESOURCES
- Texas instruments Activities Workbook
- Cabrilog Activities
- Teaching Resources
- Practice Workbook
- Assessment Resources

TECHNOLOGY
- TeacherExpress CD-ROM
- **Exam***View* CD-ROM
- PHSchool.com
  - Homework Help
  - Video Tutors
  - Multiple Choice
  - Crosswords

Additional Practice

1. What is the probability that a dart will land in the shaded areas of the following dartboards?

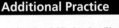

2. The image shows a lid of a child's shape sorter toy. A tiny drop of water falls toward the lid. What is the probability of the drop going through each given hole.
a. the circular hole
b. the square hole
c. the triangular hole

3. A checkerboard is made of 100 squares that each have a side of 30 mm. If you drop each of the following coins on the board, what is the probability that the coin will not touch any edges of any square?
a. a dime with radius 9 mm **b.** a nickel with radius 12 mm
c. a quarter with radius 15 mm

4. A spinner has with 12 equal sectors. Six of the sectors are white, and the others are each painted a different color: red, orange, yellow, green, blue, and purple. Find the probability of the wheel landing on the following sectors.
a. any color except white **b.** red
c. green, blue, or purple

5. A high school homecoming committee decides to have a parachutist land on the emblem of the football field during the game's half time show.
a. What is the probability that the parachutist will land on target?
b. What is the probability that the parachutist will land in one of the two shaded end zones?

Practice: For Lesson 5.13, assign Exercises 1–5.

GOALS

- Compute the probability that a tiny drop will hit a certain area of a board.
- Recognize sets of measure zero.

In this lesson, Tony and Sasha argue whether it is possible for the pointer of a spinner to land on a line that divides two slices. They discuss what the probability of this event might be. Students think about the difference between a measure (such as area or the probability of an event) that is very small and a measure that is zero. It may be a new concept for students to think of probability as a measure. The lesson concludes by listing the properties of measure that students have been working with so far.

CHECK YOUR UNDERSTANDING	HOMEWORK
• Core: 1, 2, 3	• Core: 4, 6, 7
• Optional: none	• Optional: 5, 9
	• Extension: 8

Launch

Have spinners and other models of probability as a ratio of areas available for students during the lesson.

Explore

Have students act out the dialog between Tony and Sasha. Students can then choose a point of view and argue why it is correct. Both are correct for different reasons, which the text clarifies later.

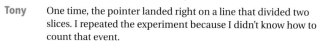

5.14 Sets of Measure 0

It is possible for a region to be very large in one way and very small in another. For example, a line is infinitely long but it has area 0.

Minds in Action   episode 21

Tony has been thinking about a strange event that happened while he was working on the In-Class Experiment at the start of the investigation.

Tony   One time, the pointer landed right on a line that divided two slices. I repeated the experiment because I didn't know how to count that event.

Sasha   Maybe if you had looked harder you would have seen that the pointer was a tiny bit more on one side of the line. I don't think it could really land exactly on a line, because the width of a line is zero. So the probability of the pointer landing on it is zero.

Tony   No, I'm sure it landed right on the line! That event can happen!

For Discussion

1. Who is right? Do you agree with Tony or Sasha? Choose a point of view and argue why it is correct.

In real life, no line or point really has a zero area. Any line you draw is actually a very thin rectangle, and any point is a circle with a very small radius. So in real life, the probability of a pointer landing on a line or a tiny drop of ink landing on a point is very small but not zero.

> How thin the rectangle is and how small the circle's radius is depend on how fine a pen you use for drawing lines and points.

Developing Habits of Mind

Explore real-world constraints. A segment with zero area exists only in an idealized mathematical world. It is often helpful to picture this world when you are conducting an experiment in the real world.

If you imagine a spinner divided into a number of regions, you are pretending that the border between two regions has no width, and therefore no area. You are also pretending that the pointer has no width. The calculated theoretical probability P of the pointer landing on the border is 0. It is important to note that it is not impossible for a pointer with no width to

Answers

For Discussion

1. Check students' work.

land on a border with no width. However, it is so unlikely in this idealized world that the probability it will occur is zero.

In the real world, you can repeat the experiment many times with an actual spinner. The pointer will land on the border with a probability greater than 0 because of real-life constraints. The pointer and border have real width even if it is quite small.

The probability that a dart lands on a border in this game is nearly 0. Why?

For You to Do

2. If you throw a ball at a circular board, can you hit the center? Think of a way to tell exactly where the ball hits the board. What is the probability of hitting the center? What are the real-life limitations?

Measure

You could try to calculate the probability of hitting the exact center of the board in the For You to Do above. Suppose you draw a small circle around the center of the board and calculate the probability of hitting it. If this little circle has a radius of $r_1 = 1$ in. and the board has a radius of 2 feet, the probability is $\frac{1}{576}$, which is small. If the little circle has a radius of $r_2 = \frac{1}{2}$ in., the probability of hitting it is $\frac{1}{2304}$, which is even smaller. Continue this process for r_3, r_4, and r_5, where each radius is half the previous radius. What does the probability of hitting the little circle approach? What happens when that circle becomes a point (a circle of radius zero)?

You are used to measuring a segment by finding its length or measuring a figure on a plane by calculating its area. Probability is another kind of measure. Here is a list of properties of measures with which you have been working.

- The measure of something is always greater than or equal to zero.
- The measure of a set of separate elements is the sum of the measures of the individual elements.
- The measure of a set of nonseparate elements is less than or equal to the sum of the measures of the single elements.
- The measure of the intersection of many elements, each contained in the previous one, is the measure of the smallest one.
- When probability is the measure, the probability of an event can never be greater than 1.

For You to Do

2. Check students' work.

Wrap Up

Before assigning homework, make sure students understand the concept of measure 0.

Assessment Resources

Exercises

HOMEWORK

- Core: 4, 6, 7
- Optional: 5, 9
- Extension: 8

Check Your Understanding

EXERCISE 1 provides another example of sets of measure 0.

EXERCISES 2 AND 3 cover the properties of measure listed at the end of the lesson.

Check Your Understanding

1. If each of the squiggly lines shown on the board is an idealized line with no width, what is the probability of a tiny drop (so small that it has no area) landing on a line? Explain.

2. The side of this square is 6 cm and the radius of each circle is 2 cm. Choose a circle and find the probability of a tiny drop landing inside that circle. Is the probability of the drop landing inside either of the two circles twice the number you just found? If the probability that the drop does not land inside any circle is $\frac{1}{2}$, what is the probability of the drop landing inside both circles? What properties of a measure did you use to solve this exercise?

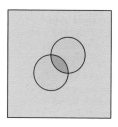

3. The board below is a square with side length 5 cm, and each region is also a square with a side length half the length of the previous one. What is the probability of a tiny drop landing in each of the regions R_1, R_2, R_3, and R_4? Find the probability of a tiny drop landing in each of the regions R_5, R_6, R_7, ... R_n. The last region is a point. What is the probability of a tiny drop landing on it? Of which property of measure is this exercise an example? Explain.

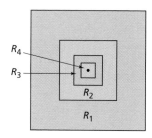

Answers

Exercises

1. 0; answers may vary. Sample: The squiggly lines have no area.

2. $\frac{\pi}{9}$; no; $\frac{4\pi - 9}{18}$; the measure of a set of nonseparate elements is less than or equal to the sum of the measures of the separate elements. The probability of an event can never be greater than 1.

3. $P_1 = 1$, $P_2 = \frac{1}{4}$, $P_3 = \frac{1}{16}$, $P_4 = \frac{1}{64}$, $P_5 = \frac{1}{128}$, $P_6 = \frac{1}{512}$, $P_7 = \frac{1}{2048}$, ..., $P_n = \frac{P_{n-1}}{4}$ (for $n \geq 2$); the measure of the intersection of many elements, each contained in the previous one, is the measure of the smallest one.

On Your Own

4. Look at the figure below. The board's side length is 4 inches.

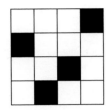

a. What is the probability of a tiny drop landing on a white square?

b. What is the probability of a tiny drop landing on a black square?

c. Of which property of measure is this exercise an example? Explain.

5. An isosceles trapezoid's dimensions are as labeled.

It is cut by three parallel lines separated from each other and from the bases of the trapezoid by a distance of 1 cm. What is the probability of a tiny drop landing in each of the regions *A*, *B*, *C*, and *D* of the trapezoid? Choose two regions. What is the probability of the drop landing in one of the two regions you chose? Are there other ways of getting the same answer?

6. All four of the regions of this board are squares of side length ℓ. What is the probability that a randomly dropped coin with radius *r* would touch all four? What is the probability a tiny drop would land touching all four regions? Explain.

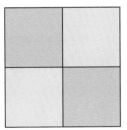

Additional Practice

1. What is the probability of a tiny drop (so small that it has no area) landing on a squiggly line on this board if each of the lines shown is an idealized line with no width? Why?

2. What is the probability of a tiny drop landing in each of the square regions: S_1, S_2, S_3, and S_4? The board is a square with side length 10 cm. Each interior region has its vertices at the midpoint of the sides of the previous larger region.

3. A spinner in a child's game has a needle with negligible width and perfect lines separating each region. What is the probability that a child will have to re-spin because he is unable to determine in which region the spinner lands?

4. At a carnival, Jeff throws darts at this dartboard. Find the probability that Jeff will score the following points with one dart.
  a. 50 points   **b.** 10 points   **c.** 30 points

5. At a school's fundraiser, a dunk tank has a circular target with a 16-in. diameter. If a baseball is randomly thrown at the target, it must hit the exact center of the target to activate the release of the person into the tank.
  a. In this situation, does the center of the target have some measure or is it an idealized center?
  b. What is the probability of the ball hitting the center of the target if the "center" for release is 2 inches in diameter?

6. a. What is the probability that a coin of radius 8 mm will land touching all five shaded regions?
  b. If the lines between the regions are idealized lines and the coin is replaced by a tiny drop, does this change the probability in part (a)? Why?

7. Use the diagram of the equilateral triangles. Each interior triangle has a side length half the length of the larger triangle. The midpoint of the base of each triangle is point *P*. What is the probability of a tiny drop landing in the following regions?
  a. *A*   **b.** *B*   **c.** *C*

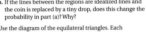
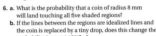

Practice: For Lesson 5.14, assign Exercises 1–7.

---

4. a. $\frac{3}{4}$

b. $\frac{1}{4}$

c. The measure of a set of separate elements is the sum of the measures of the separate elements; there are only two kinds of small squares, white and black.

5. Choices of regions may vary; explanations may vary; check students' work. Area of trapezoid = $\frac{(10 + 3) \cdot 4}{2}$ cm² = 26 cm²; use proportional reasoning to find the lengths of each of the three interior rules (8.25 cm, 6.5 cm, and 4.75 cm) before calculating probabilities.

6. $\frac{\pi r^2}{4\ell^2}$; 0, because the drop can be imagined as a circle of radius $r = 0$.

7. Standardized Test Prep Mario wants to estimate how many times a quarter would land completely inside a square on his chessboard (without touching any other square) in 1000 trials. Assume that in each trial the coin lands randomly on the chessboard. A side of a square on the chessboard is 38.1 mm. The diameter of a quarter is 24.26 mm. Which of the following is the best estimate?

A. 104   **B.** 111   **C.** 132   **D.** 405

8. Take It Further An interesting problem consists of randomly placing a rectangle on a chessboard with its sides parallel to the sides of the chessboard. The rectangle is large enough that it cannot fit in a single square, so it must touch more than one color. The area of the rectangle can be expressed as the sum of the areas of each of the colors it covers. Draw various rectangles, cut them out, and place them on a chessboard. What conditions have to be present for the rectangle to cover an equal area of each color? What is the probability that the rectangle will cover equal amounts of each color?

If you do not have a chess board, you can divide a square piece of paper into an 8-by-8 grid.

For additional practice, go to **Web Code: bea-0514**

Maintain Your Skills

9. Imagine dropping a coin of radius r on a checked board with squares of side length ℓ. What is the probability of the coin landing in each of the following ways?

a. on only one color

b. on two different squares

c. on three different squares

d. on four different squares

e. on two different colors

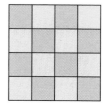

Answers

7. C

8. A side of the rectangle is twice as long as a square of the chessboard, and the point of intersection of the diagonals of the rectangle lies on a line of the chessboard grid; 1.

9. a. $\dfrac{(\ell - 2r)^2}{\ell^2}$

b. $\dfrac{4(\ell - 2r)r}{\ell^2}$

c. $\dfrac{4\left(r^2 - \frac{\pi r^2}{4}\right)}{\ell^2} = r^2 \cdot \dfrac{4 - \pi}{\ell^2}$

d. $\dfrac{\frac{\pi r^2}{4} \cdot 4}{\ell^2} = \dfrac{\pi r^2}{\ell^2}$

e. $1 - \dfrac{(\ell - 2r)^2}{\ell^2} = \dfrac{\pi r^2}{\ell^2}$

5D Mathematical Reflections

In this investigation, you used areas of regions to find geometric probabilities. You also used geometric probabilities to estimate areas of geometric figures. These questions will help you summarize what you have learned.

1. Find the probability of a tiny drop landing on the blue region of the board.

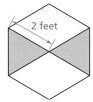

2 feet

2. When sprinkling 500 poppy seeds randomly on a black and white tablecloth, about 310 land on white regions. Approximately what fraction of the tablecloth is black?

3. What is the probability of a tiny drop landing on the blue region of the board?

5 in. | 5 in.

5 in.

4. What is the probability of a tiny drop landing on the blue region on the board?

120°

120°

45 cm

The larger the bug, the smaller the probability that it can fly through the web without getting caught.

5. Describe a set of measure zero and give an example.

6. What is the probability that a tiny rain drop will hit a certain region on a board?

7. How can you estimate areas with the Monte Carlo Method?

8. What is the probability of a spinner landing on a line?

Vocabulary

In this investigation, you saw these terms for the first time. Make sure you understand what each one means and how to use it.

• **Monte Carlo Method**
• **probability**

Mathematical Reflections

EXERCISES 6–8 At the start of the Investigation, you may have assigned these as Questions 1–3 for students to think and write about.

Mathematical Reflections

1. $\frac{1}{3}$

2. about $\frac{19}{50}$

3. $\frac{2}{4 + \pi}$

4. $\frac{1}{3}$

5. Answers may vary. Check students' work.

6. the area of the region divided by the area of the board.

7. Answers may vary. Sample: Randomly sprinkle a number of objects that are small (but large enough to be counted) on the board. Divide the number of objects in the region whose area you want to estimate by the number of objects on the whole board.

8. For an idealized spinner, the theoretical probability is 0.

Project

This project is perfect for a geometry software lab experience. Students construct two intersecting circles and a segment. The radii lengths add up to the length of the segment. Students move given points and visualize the paths drawn by the two circles' intersections. This provides students the opportunity to:

- See a circle as the locus of the points whose distance from one point (the center) is given.
- Use symmetric reasoning.
- Get practice with invariants in a very visual manner.

Project: Using Mathematical Habits

Another Interesting Curve

Use geometry software to construct two intersecting circles in the following way.

- Construct $\overline{AB}$.
- Place point C near the middle of $\overline{AB}$.
- Construct $\overline{AC}$ and $\overline{CB}$.

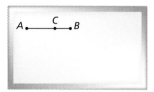

Both $\overline{AC}$ and $\overline{CB}$ have been constructed as segments on top of $\overline{AB}$.

Place points D and E so that their distance from each other is less than AB.

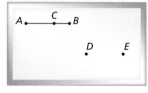

$DE < AB$

- With D as center and AC as radius, construct a circle.
- With E as center and BC as radius, construct a second circle.
- Find the intersections of these two circles.
- Label your entire construction as illustrated below.

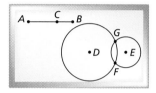

Now work through these exercises to understand what is happening.

1. As you move C back and forth on $\overline{AB}$, notice that the circles do not always intersect. Use the triangle inequality theorem to explain why the circles sometimes intersect and sometimes do not intersect.

2. **Trace** the intersections of these two circles and then experiment with the diagram by dragging A, B, C, D, and E. Patterns that you see as you move these points are kinds of invariants.

3. **Trace** the intersection points (F and G in the picture above). Describe what you see when you move A.

Answers

Project

1. The Triangle Inequality implies that positive numbers x, y, and z cannot be the lengths of the sides of a triangle unless each number is between the sum of the other two numbers and the absolute value of the difference of the other two numbers. This means, for the present situation, that the circles will touch in exactly one point provided DE is equal to $|AC - BC|$ and will intersect in two points if $DE > |AC - BC|$. The circles will not intersect at all if $DE < |AC - BC|$.

2. Check students' work.

3–4. If C is not the midpoint of $\overline{AB}$, F and G both seem to trace a semicircle. The semicircles are on opposite sides of the line through F and G. If C is the midpoint of $\overline{AB}$, then F and G trace rays on the perpendicular bisector of $\overline{DE}$.

4. What shapes do the points trace out as *A* moves?

5. Does the pattern you see as you drag *A* depend on where *C* was initially along $\overline{AB}$? (For example, does it matter if *C* starts out near *A*, far from *A*, or close to the middle of $\overline{AB}$?) What is the invariant?

6. Make a reasoned argument for or against this statement. "Whatever pattern (invariant) I see when I move *A*, I should see exactly the same one when I move *B*."

7. Leave *A* and *B* fixed and move *C* along $\overline{AB}$. What pattern do you find in the intersection points of the circles?

8. Now move *D* or *E* around while leaving everything else fixed. Describe what happens.

9. An ellipse is all the points that are the same total distance from two points. When *C* is moved, you get an ellipse. Explain.

10. Handy objects to have on hand when drawing a circle include tacks, a length of string, and a pencil.

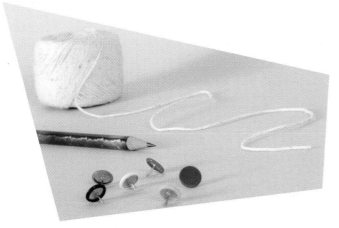

How could you use these same objects to build an ellipse maker? Build one and draw several ellipses of varying sizes.

5. Answers may vary. Sample: You seem to get a pair of semicircles. The size of the semicircles seems to depend on the ratio $\frac{AC}{BC}$ before you started dragging *A*.

6. The statement seems to be true. The ratio $\frac{AC}{BC}$ does not change as you drag *A* or as you drag *B*.

7. The points *F* and *G* trace two halves of an oval.

8. You can get two intersecting circles.

9. $AC + CB = AB$

10. See back of book.

Review

Go Online
PHSchool.com

For vocabulary review,
go to Web Code: bej-055

In **Investigation 5A** you learned to

- approximate the area and perimeter of blobs
- find the area of regular polygons
- solve problems using the relationship between a regular hexagon's side and the radius of the circle it is inscribed in
- find the area of a circle given its circumference

The following questions will help you check your understanding.

1. Estimate the perimeter of the blob and describe your technique.

2. Will the formula $A = \frac{1}{2}Pa$ work on the following pentagon with perimeter 45 units? If it will, find the area of the pentagon; otherwise, explain why it will not work.

In **Investigation 5B** you learned to

- calculate the area of a circle, given its radius
- find the perimeter of a circle, given its radius

The following questions will help you check your understanding.

3. If you scale a circle by 6, how does the radius of the scaled circle compare to the radius of the original circle? How does the area of the scaled circle compare to the area of the original circle?

4. What is the perimeter of a circle of radius 216 cm? What is its area?

In **Investigation 5C** you learned to

- prove and apply theorems about arcs, chords, and inscribed angles of a circle
- prove and apply theorems about secants and tangents of a circle
- look for invariants in circles
- define the power of a point with respect to a circle

The following questions will help you check your understanding.

5. The circle has center P, and $\overline{CB}$ and $\overline{CA}$ are tangent to the circle. Prove that $\overline{PC} \perp \overline{AB}$.

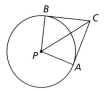

Answers

Review

1. About 11 cm; techniques may vary. Sample: Mark several points around the boundary of the blob and connect them in order to form a polygon. Measure each side of the polygon and add to find the perimeter of the polygon. Use the perimeter of the polygon as an estimate for the perimeter of the blob.

2. No; the formula applies only to polygons that have apothems.

3. 6 times the radius of the original circle; 36 times the area of the original circle

4. 432π cm; 46,656 cm²

5. See back of book.

6. If $m\widehat{AB} = 62°$ and $m\widehat{DC} = 170°$, what is $m\angle APB$?

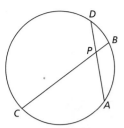

7. What is $\Pi(P)$ in the figure below?

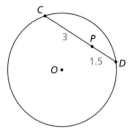

8. Without using a ruler, explain why the measures of the segments in this picture must be incorrect.

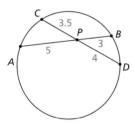

Investigation 5D you learned to

- calculate the probability of a tiny drop landing on a given area of a board
- find the probability of a spinner landing on a line
- use the Monte Carlo Method
- recognize sets of measure zero

The following questions will help you check your understanding.

9. At a fair, Sam wants to win the goldfish game. To play, you toss a table-tennis ball at a table covered with spherical goldfish bowls that have circular openings on top. The diagram below shows a top view. If your ball lands in the water, you win the fish in that bowl; otherwise you have wasted your money.

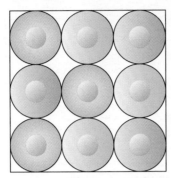

There are 9 adjacent bowls and the diameter of the tops are $\frac{1}{3}$ the diameter of the bowl. The table-tennis ball can fall anywhere on the square table on which the bowls are set. What is the probability that Sam will take home a goldfish if he tosses the ball randomly (but on the table)?

10. Sarah's grandmother is turning 100, so Sarah baked her a birthday cake and covered it completely with red and purple frosting. She placed the 100 candles randomly and 65 of them are on the red frosting. Compare the amount of red frosting to the amount of purple frosting that Sarah used.

11. Can a spinner land on the line separating two of its regions? Explain.

---

6. 116°

7. 4.5

8. Answers may vary. Sample: The information about lengths is inconsistent with the result proved in Ex. 5 of Lesson 5.11. $PA \cdot PB$ should be equal to $PC \cdot PD$, since the figure is clearly drawn to make it appear that $\overline{AB}$ and $\overline{CD}$ are segments that intersect at P.

9. See back of book.

10. $\dfrac{\text{area of red}}{\text{area of purple}} \approx \dfrac{65}{35}$, or $\dfrac{13}{7}$

11. Answers may vary. Sample: Yes, though it is very unlikely.

Chapter Test

Assessment Resources

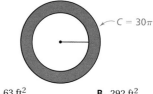
Multiple Choice

1. Which pink region has an area of π square inches?

A.   B.

C.   D.

2. If $m\angle ZPY = 83°$ and $m\widehat{ZY} = 112°$, what is $m\widehat{WX}$?

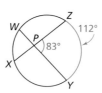

   A. 29°   B. 54°   C. 56°   D. 165°

3. The two circles are concentric. The radius of the smaller circle is $\frac{2}{3}$ the radius of the larger circle. If the larger circle has a circumference of 30π feet, what is the approximate area of the shaded region?

   A. 63 ft²   B. 292 ft²
   C. 314 ft²   D. 471 ft²

Open Response

4. Describe a technique you learned in this chapter for approximating the area of a blob. Use the method you describe to approximate the area of this blob.

Answers

Chapter Test

1. A
2. B
3. B
4. Answers may vary. Sample: Trace the outline of the blob on a piece of grid paper that has fairly small squares. Count the squares that lie entirely inside the blob. Multiply the count by the area of an individual grid square to get a low estimate of the blob's area. Count the squares that lie inside or partially inside the blob. Multiply this second count by the area of an individual grid square to get a high estimate of the blob's area; about 4.7 in.²

5. Find the areas of the following blue circle sectors.

b.

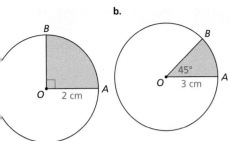

d.

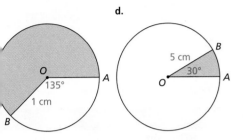

6. Give a definition for the diameter of a circle and prove that a diameter is the longest of all chords of a circle.

7. In the following circle with center O, $\overline{OH}$ is perpendicular to the chord $\overline{AB}$. Find the length of $\overline{AB}$ if the radius of the circle is 5 and $OH = 3$. Justify each step of your answer.

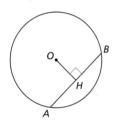

8. In the figure, $m\widehat{ABC} = 52°$. Find the measures of these inscribed angles.

a. $\angle ADC$ b. $\angle AOC$

c. $\angle CEA$ d. $\angle ACF$

e. $\angle AFC$ f. $\angle OCF$

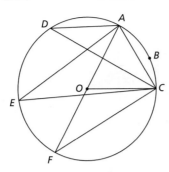

9. What is the power of P in the following figure?

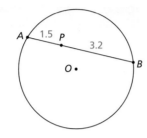

10. What is the probability of a tiny drop landing on the blue region of this board? $ABCD$ is a square inscribed in the circle with center O and radius 2.5 cm.

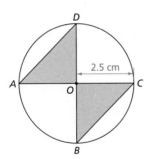

5. a. π cm^2

   b. $\frac{9}{8}\pi$ cm^2

   c. $\frac{5}{8}\pi$ cm^2

   d. $\frac{25}{12}\pi$ cm^2

6. See back of book.

7. By the Pythagorean Theorem,
$AH = HB = \sqrt{5^2 - 3^2} = 4$. So
$AB = AH + HB = 8$.

8. a. $26°$

   b. $52°$

   c. $26°$

   d. $90°$

   e. $26°$

   f. $26°$

9. 4.8

10. $\frac{1}{\pi}$

Chapter 6
Using Similarity

This chapter introduces your students to some of the many faces of similarity. Although the topics presented at first may seem unconnected, all of them have the concept of similarity at their roots. Students will explore the concepts of constructible numbers, trigonometric ratios, and justifications of volume formulas.

Chapter Overview

- **INVESTIGATION 6A,** *Some Uses of Similarity,* explores some classic geometry proofs.
- **INVESTIGATION 6B,** *Exploring Right Triangles,* introduces right-triangle trigonometry.
- **INVESTIGATION 6C,** *Volume Formulas,* has students justify volume formulas by visualizing two-dimensional cross sections of three-dimensional objects.

For more information on the investigations, see
- Chapter Road Map, p. 440
- Investigation Road Maps, pp. 442, 464, 498

PROJECT The Project near the end of the chapter is optional. You can assign the Project at any time during the chapter depending on how often and how long you feel students should work on it.

Pacing Suggestions and Materials

Investigation 6A *Some Uses of Similarity*

DAY	LESSON	HOMEWORK
1	6.1 Getting Started Core: 1, 2, 3 Optional: 4	Core: 6, 11 Optional: 5, 7, 8, 9, 10, 12;
2	6.2 An Inequality of Means Core: 1, 2, 3 Optional: 4	Core: 5, 8, 9 Optional: 6, 7, 10
3	6.3 Similarity in Ancient Greece Core: 2, 4 Optional: 1, 3	Core: 5, 6, 7, 8 Optional: 9, 10, 11, 13; Extension: 12
4	6.4 Concurrence of Medians Core: 1, 2 Optional: 3	Core: 4, 7, 8 Optional: 5, 6, 9; Extension: 10

Investigation 6B *Exploring Right Triangles*

DAY	LESSON	HOMEWORK
1	6.5 Getting Started Core: 1, 2, 4 Optional: 3	Core: 5, 7, 9 Optional: 6, 8, 10, 11, 12, 13
2	6.6 Some Special Triangles Core: 2, 3 Optional: 1, 4	Core: 5, 6, 9, 10, 11 Optional: 7, 8, 12, 13, 14
3	6.7 Some Special Ratios Core: 2, 5 Optional: 1, 3, 4	Core: 6, 7, 9, 11, 15, 16 Optional: 8, 10, 12, 13, 14, 17, 18, 21, 22 Extension: 19, 20
4	6.8 Finding Triangle Areas Core: 1, 4 Optional: 2, 3, 5	Core: 6, 9, 10, 12, 14, 16 Optional: 7, 8, 11, 13, 15, 17, 18, 19, 21; Extension: 20
5	6.9 Extend the Pythagorean Theorem Core: 1, 3 Optional: 2, 4	Core: 5, 7, 9, 10 Optional: 6, 8, 11, 12, 13, 14, 15, 16, 17,

NOTES	MATERIALS
	• rulers and/or yardsticks
	• compasses • rulers
	• compasses • rulers • Blackline Master 6.3
	• geometry software • Blackline Masters 6.4A–B

NOTES	MATERIALS
	• graph paper • materials to build model ramps • protractors • rulers
Have students note vocabulary words in their notebooks.	• calculators • geometry software or protractors, rulers, and compasses • Blackline Master 6.7
	• calculators
	• calculators • compasses • geometry software • markers or colored pencils • protractors • rulers • Blackline Master 6.9

Mathematics Background

CONSTRUCTIBLE NUMBERS If you begin with a unit segment and use only an idealized compass and straightedge, you can construct many different lengths through dilations and other simple constructions involving parallel lines and similar triangles. The diagrams below show the sum, difference, product, and quotient of two lengths a and b.

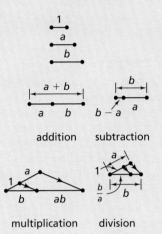

In this chapter, your students will learn a method that allows them to construct a segment with length equal to the square root of any given length. This new operation considerably expands the set of lengths that they can construct. However, you still cannot construct some numbers as lengths. One such number is the cube root of 2, or $\sqrt[3]{2}$. In a similar way, some angles are constructible and some are not.

Carl Friedrich Gauss (1777–1855) proved that the angle that measures $\frac{360°}{17}$ is constructible, and that, therefore, it is possible to construct a regular heptadecagon (17-sided polygon) using a compass and straightedge. It is said that he was so excited about this discovery that he wanted to have a regular heptadecagon carved on his tombstone. The stonemason reportedly refused because the construction would be very difficult, and the final result would just look like a circle.

continued on p. 440c

continued from p. 440b

TRIGONOMETRIC FUNCTIONS This course introduces the trigonometric ratios sine, cosine, and tangent. It defines the sine, cosine, or tangent of an acute angle of a right triangle as the lengths of certain sides of the right triangle. For example, the sine of 30° is equal to the ratio of the side opposite the 30° angle to the hypotenuse of any right triangle that includes a 30° angle. The fact that there is only one such ratio is a consequence of the fact that all right triangles that contain a 30° angle are similar by AA similarity. Students will use the trigonometric ratios to determine missing side lengths and angle measures in triangles.

In Algebra 2, students study trigonometric functions. Students will see the relationship between the trigonometric functions and the coordinates of points on the unit circle. In this context, the cosine of 30° is equal to the x-coordinate of the intersection in the first quadrant of the unit circle and a line through the origin at a 30° angle (measured counter-clockwise) to the x-axis.

Then, in Precalculus, students will expand the notion of trigonometric functions even further, so that they become functions that accept real number inputs and return real number outputs.

DAILY PLANNER

Pacing Suggestions and Materials

Investigation 6C *Volume Formulas*

DAY	LESSON	HOMEWORK
1	6.10 Getting Started Core: 1, 2 Optional: 3, 4	Core: 5, 6, 10 Optional: 7, 8, 9, 11, 12, 13, 14
2	6.11 Cavalieri's Principle Core: 2 Optional: 1, 3	Core: 4, 6, 8, 11 Optional: 5, 7, 9, 10, 12, 13
3	6.12 Proving Volume Formulas Core: 2, 3 Optional: 1, 4, 5	Core: 6, 9, 10, 11 Optional: 7, 8, 12, 13
4	6.13 Volume of a Sphere Core: 1 Optional: 2, 3	Core: 4, 5, 9, 10 Optional: 6, 7, 8, 11, 12

NOTES	MATERIALS
	• cardboard • markers • rulers • scissors • string • tape
	• Blackline Master 6.13

JUSTIFYING VOLUME FORMULAS In Chapter 4, students used some basic volume formulas. Now that they have a broader foundation of mathematical techniques, they can justify these formulas more thoroughly. The technique students use is Cavalieri's Principle.

This involves visualizing a three-dimensional solid as a stack of thin cross sections cut by parallel planes. If two such solids have equal heights and the areas of both of their cross sections are equal at any height, then Cavalieri's Principle says that the volumes of the two solids are equal. This allows students to use volume formulas they know—such as the formula for the volume of a rectangular prism—to justify volume formulas for other kinds of solids.

Of course, to be completely rigorous, the proofs of these volume formulas involve calculus, because you have to consider infinitely many infinitely thin cross sections. However, this technique is an excellent preparation for finding the area under a curve in calculus by approximating the area with a set of thin rectangles of varying height, as well as by finding the volume of various solids of revolution.

Developing Students' Mathematical Habits

Key mathematical habits of mind in this chapter include visualization and extension. Students visualize similar polygons to recreate classical geometric proofs. Students also visualize the right triangles that are contained by, or that contain, general triangles. The trigonometry that this chapter introduces is restricted to right-triangle trigonometry, so students need to see the right triangles in any figure to which they wish to apply trigonometry.

This chapter also challenges students to extend their understanding of the ratio method of dilation to three dimensions, allowing the center of dilation to move outside the plane containing the polygon to be dilated. This allows students to see that when you intersect a pyramid or cone intersected with a plane parallel to its base, the resulting cross section is similar to the base. They can even see that the scale factor of the dilation is equal to the ratio of the distance from the apex to the cutting plane and the height of the pyramid or cone.

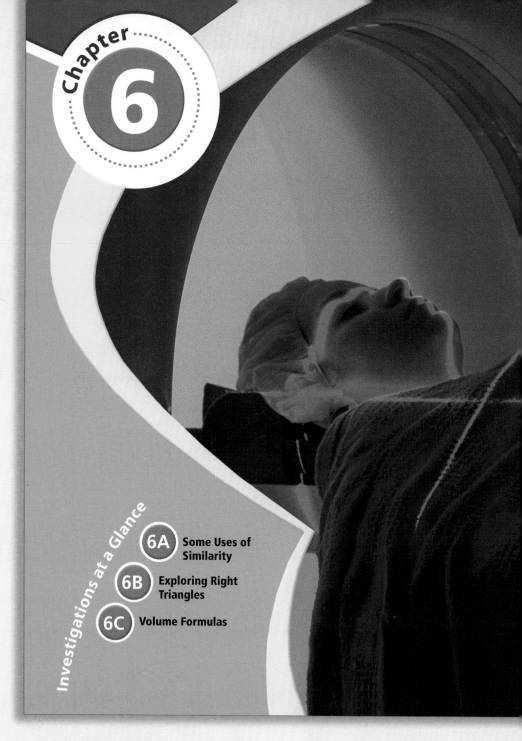

Chapter 6

Investigations at a Glance

6A Some Uses of Similarity

6B Exploring Right Triangles

6C Volume Formulas

Chapter Road Map

INVESTIGATION 6A, *Some Uses of Similarity,* has students study some classical geometry proofs using similarity, including new proofs of the Pythagorean Theorem and concurrence of medians, as well as the Arithmetic-Geometric Mean Inequality.

INVESTIGATION 6B, *Exploring Right Triangles,* introduces students to right triangle trigonometry. The focus is on the definition of trigonometric functions as ratios of side lengths in triangles and using these functions and their inverses to determine unknown side lengths and angle measures in triangles.

INVESTIGATION 6C, *Volume Formulas,* has students further justify the volume formulas they were given in Chapter 4 using Cavalieri's Principle. This principle asks them to visualize three-dimensional solids as a stack of two-dimensional cross sections.

Using Similarity

One application of *trigonometry* (a topic introduced in this chapter) is in *tomographic reconstruction*. This is the process by which three-dimensional images are created in diagnostic medical tests such as CT scans.

In a CT scan, an X-ray machine moves around above the patient as a sensor moves around below. The area to be scanned is between them. The X-ray emission is absorbed in differing amounts by materials of differing density within the patient's body. The intensity of the X-rays coming through the patient is recorded from moment to moment as the scanner moves around. The X-ray sensor data are converted into density readings through a complicated formula involving trigonometric functions and some operations of calculus.

These readings are used to create a two-dimensional scan of a horizontal "slice" of the patient. Many horizontal slices, or cross sections, are "stacked" to create a three-dimensional image. You can picture a three-dimensional object as a stack of two-dimensional cross sections. You can think of this as a CT scan of a geometric solid!

Vocabulary and Notation

arithmetic mean	• sin θ
geometric mean	• cos θ
projection	• tan θ
trigonometry	• sin^{-1} x
sine ratio	• cos^{-1} x
cosine ratio	• tan^{-1} x
tangent ratio	

Chapter Vocabulary and Notation

The following list gives key vocabulary and notation used in the chapter. Selected new vocabulary and notation items are shown in boldface on the student page.

- arithmetic mean, p. 448
- cosine ratio, p. 475
- geometric mean, p. 447
- projection, p. 454
- tetrahedron, p. 517
- sine ratio, p. 475
- tangent ratio, p. 475

- trigonometry, p. 474
- cos θ, p. 475
- cos^{-1} x, p. 476
- sin θ, p. 475
- sin^{-1} x, p. 476
- tan θ, p. 475
- tan^{-1} x, p. 483

Chapter Technology

Support for the use of technology is available in the Technology Handbook. See p. 712.

INVESTIGATION 6A *Geometry Software*

- **LESSON 6.2** Construct rectangles with equal areas, p. 450.
- **LESSON 6.4** Find invariants for triangle medians, p. 458.

INVESTIGATION 6B *Geometry Software*

- **LESSON 6.6** Construct triangles with given measurements, p. 473.
- **LESSON 6.7** Investigate ratios of triangle side lengths, p. 474.
- **LESSON 6.9** Construct a diagram for the proof of the Law of Cosines, p. 490.

INVESTIGATION 6B *Calculator*

- **LESSON 6.7** Evaluate trigonometric ratios, pp. 475, 478, 479, 480. Evaluate inverse trigonometric ratios, p. 476.

Investigation Overview

In this investigation, students discover some applications of similarity. In particular, students see how they can use similarity to indirectly measure heights and distances and to solve other geometric problems. Students will explore some theorems that use similarity.

You may wish to assign Questions 1–3 for students to think and write about during the investigation.

Learning Goals

- State and use the Arithmetic-Geometric Mean Inequality.
- Use similar triangles to find unknown lengths.
- Prove theorems using similarity.

Habits and Skills

- Find invariants in triangles.
- Visualize similar triangles to solve problems.
- Choose and draw strategic circles, segments, and points to solve problems.

Investigation 6A

Some Uses of Similarity

In *Some Uses of Similarity*, you will explore applications of similarity, including its use in some classical Greek proofs. Similarity and proportionality are important ideas in mathematics. They allow you to calculate and prove many things.

By the end of this investigation, you will be able to answer questions like these:

1. What is the Arithmetic-Geometric Mean Inequality?

2. Why does the altitude to the hypotenuse of a right triangle form three similar triangles?

3. In $\triangle ABC$, suppose that $AH = 12$ cm and $BA = 15$ cm. What is HC?

You will learn how to

- state and use the Arithmetic-Geometric Mean Inequality
- use similar triangles to find unknown lengths
- prove theorems using similarity

You will develop these habits and skills:

- Find invariants in triangles.
- Visualize similar triangles to solve problems.
- Choose and draw strategic circles, segments, and points to solve problems.

Drawing details square by square can help you capture a similar image.

Investigation Road Map

LESSON 6.1, *Getting Started,* introduces some interesting applications of similarity, such as how to indirectly find the height of an object.

LESSON 6.2, *An Inequality of Means,* uses the power of a point with respect to a circle introduced in Chapter 5 to prove the Arithmetic-Geometric Mean Inequality.

LESSON 6.3, *Similarity in Ancient Greece,* shows students theorems about similarity in right triangles that the ancient Greeks proved.

LESSON 6.4, *Concurrence of Medians,* contains a proof that uses similarity of the concurrence of the medians of a triangle.

Activating Prior Knowledge
Exploring New Ideas

You can use similar triangles to measure inaccessible distances by comparing them to distances between objects close at hand. You have likely seen (or even used) this technique before.

For You to Explore

1. Choose an object and measure the length of the shadow the object casts in sunlight. Also measure the shadow cast by a yardstick (or some other object of known height) standing straight up on the ground at the same time of day.

   Use the fact that the sun's rays are approximately parallel to set a proportion using similar triangles. Find the height of your object.

2. From their boat off the coast of Maine, two sailors can see the faraway top of Mount Washington, towering 6600 feet above sea level. One of the two sailors holds her left arm straight out in front of her in a "thumbs up" gesture to get an idea of their distance from the base of the mountain.

   She positions herself so that she can see how much of her thumb covers the mountain. She covers the mountain completely—the whole 6600 feet behind her thumb!

   Her companion measures the distance from her eye to the place on her thumb that lines up with the edge of the shore. Then they measure the length of the thumb that covers Mount Washington. Using similar triangles, they calculate their distance to the base of the mountain.

   Here is a rough sketch of the situation.

   a. What assumption is built into the sketch?

   b. Name a pair of similar triangles in the sketch.

   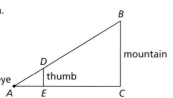

   c. The length of your thumb covering the mountain is 1 inch. The distance from your eye to the bottom of your thumb is 14 inches. Calculate your distance from the mountain.

   d. Measure the length of your thumb. Also measure the distance from the base of your thumb to your eye when your arm is fully extended. If you know the height of an object that is covered by your thumb, you can then determine your distance from that object. Pick an object you know the height of. Use the sailors' technique to figure out how far away it is. Check your results by measuring the actual distance.

> **Remember...**
> You already know that the height of the mountain is 6600 feet.

> **Habits of Mind**
> **Estimate.** You can estimate what your thumb covers. If your thumb covers about one third of a 60-meter building, then about 20 meters are covered.

Lesson Overview

GOALS
- Warm up to the ideas of the investigation.
- Use similar triangles to find unknown lengths.

Over the ages, people have developed clever methods to answer the questions "How far away is that?" and "How tall is that?" This lesson focuses on ways that similarity can answer distance and height questions such as these.

FOR YOU TO EXPLORE
- Core: 1, 2, 3
- Optional: 4

MATERIALS
- rulers and/or yardsticks

HOMEWORK
- Core: 6, 11
- Optional: 5, 7, 8, 9, 10, 12

Launch

Begin this lesson by reminding your students of their previous experiences with similarity. (Refer to Chapter 4.)

Explore

Assign the For You to Explore problems.

Wrap Up

End this lesson by assigning some exercises from the On Your Own section.

Answers

For You to Explore

1. The objects chosen may vary. If the object of known height is a yardstick, a proportion you could use is $\dfrac{\text{height of object}}{\text{height of yardstick}}$
$= \dfrac{\text{length of object's shadow}}{\text{length of yardstick's shadow}}$.

2. **a.** $\overline{DE} \parallel \overline{BC}$
   b. $\triangle ABC$ and $\triangle ADE$
   c. 92,400 ft, or 17.5 mi
   d. Check students' work.

Exercises

HOMEWORK
- Core: 6, 11
- Optional: 5, 7, 8, 9, 10, 12

3. You look out a window and see a person standing far away. The person's image fills just part of the window. If you could trace the image on the window, you could measure the height of the image. You could also find the height of the image if you knew the following.

- the person's height
- your distance from the window
- your distance from the person

Here is a sketch of that situation. Carefully describe how you could use similar triangles to determine how tall the image on the window would be.

4. A tree's shadow is 20 feet long, and a yardstick's shadow is 17 inches long.

a. Draw a diagram that shows the tree, the yardstick, the sun's rays, and the shadows.

b. Find a pair of similar triangles and explain why they are similar.

c. How tall is the tree?

Exercises *Practicing Habits of Mind*

On Your Own

5. On a sunny day, Melanie and Nancy noticed that their shadows were different lengths. Nancy measured Melanie's shadow and found that it was 96 inches long. Melanie found that Nancy's was 102 inches long.

a. Who do you think is taller, Nancy or Melanie? Explain.

b. If Melanie is 5 feet 4 inches tall, how tall is Nancy?

c. If Nancy is 5 feet 4 inches tall, about how tall is Melanie?

Habits of Mind

Represent the situation. Drawing a picture might help you answer these questions.

Answers

3. Answers may vary. Sample: The height of the person is the height of the image, times the distance of the person from you, divided by the distance from you to the image.

4. a. See back of book.
  b. $\triangle ABC \sim \triangle DEF$ by the AA Similarity Test.
  c. about 42.35 ft

5. a. Nancy; her shadow is longer.
  b. 68 in.
  c. about 60.24 in.

6. Use the shadow method to find the height of some tall object for which you can obtain the actual height. Record the details of your measurements and prepare a presentation for your class. By how much did the result of your calculations differ from the actual height? What might cause these differences?

7. Apply your theory from Problem 3. You see a person 5 feet tall standing outside your window about 30 feet away from you. You are about 2 feet from the window. About how tall will the image be?

8. A light-year is a unit of distance—the distance that light travels in 1 year. The star nearest to us (other than our own sun) is about 4 light-years away. Light travels at 186,000 miles per second. How far does light travel in one year? How far away is the nearest star?

9. A planet is the same distance away as the star in Exercise 8 and has the same diameter as Earth. How large will the planet's image appear on a window that is 2 feet away from you?

10. About how much must that image be magnified to be as big as the letter o on this page? Use $\frac{1}{20}$ inch for the width of the letter o.

11. A child $3\frac{1}{2}$ feet tall is standing next to a very tall basketball player. The child's sister notices that the player's shadow is about twice as long as the child's. She quickly estimates the player's height. What value does she get?

Go Online
Video Tutor
PHSchool.com

Web Code: bee-0775

Remember...
The diameter of Earth is approximately 7900 miles.

Maintain Your Skills

12. Find all the similar triangles in each diagram. Explain your answers.

   a. $\triangle ABC$ is isosceles.

   b. $\triangle ACB$ is equilateral.

   c. $\angle ACB$ is a right angle.

   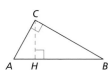

   d.

   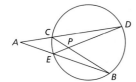

EXERCISE 9 In the 1990s, there were reports of discoveries of planets that are not part of our solar system. Astronomers had reason to believe that such planets existed, but for the first time, it became possible to find the planets. The newspapers gave accounts of the clever techniques that astronomers used to find these planets, despite the fact that the astronomers had not seen the planets themselves. Why the planets are so difficult to see is something you can explain using the concept of similarity.

6. Check students' work.

7. about 4 in.

8. about 5.87×10^{12} mi; about 2.35×10^{13} mi

9. about 8.08×10^{-9} in.

10. about 6.19 million times

11. about 7 ft

12. a. If D, E, and F are the midpoints of the sides of $\triangle ABC$, then by Theorem 2.11, it follows that all the small triangles are congruent and hence similar. Use the angle congruence relationships that

you can get by using CPCTC to conclude that all of the small triangles are similar to $\triangle ABC$.

12. b–d. See back of book.

Lesson Overview

In this lesson, students discover the Arithmetic-Geometric Mean Inequality by using the power of a point with respect to a circle, which was introduced in Chapter 5. Before starting this lesson, you might want to review this concept with students.

Launch

Begin this lesson by having your students work through the For Discussion problem.

The figure below shows a complete rectangle on the left and only the length of another rectangle on the right.

For Discussion

1. How can you construct the missing width of a rectangle with length c, so that both rectangles have the same area? Look at the following pictures and think about how they might be useful to solve your problem.

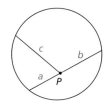
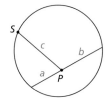
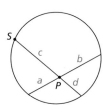

You can construct these equal-area rectangles based on the circle and point P given in the For Discussion section. How are the two rectangles at the ends related? *Hint:* The rectangle at the right is square.

Answers

For Discussion

1. Check students' work.

Tony wants to take the For Discussion idea further.

Tony   It's cool how we can use the power-of-a-point construction to construct the missing width of the rectangle, so that both rectangles have the same area. But I was thinking that it would be even cooler to use the construction to find a square with the same area as this rectangle.

Tony points to a rectangle like the one below.

Tony   But I'm stuck.

Sasha   Well, it's an interesting idea. Let me think about it.

After a while Sasha draws the following diagrams, in which $\overline{AB}$ is a diameter.

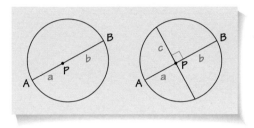

Tony   So you're saying that c is the length of the side of the square we're looking for? How do you know?

For You to Do

2. Explain why Sasha's construction method works.

3. Write a formula that relates a, b, and c. What is the algebraic relationship between a, b, and c?

Definition

The **geometric mean** of a and b is c if $c^2 = ab$. Equivalently, $c = \sqrt{ab}$.

For You to Do

2. The diameter $\overline{AB}$ bisects the other chord through P. Therefore, by Exercise 5 of Lesson 5.11, $a \cdot b = c \cdot c$. So c is the side length of a square with area equal to ab.

3. Since $c > 0$, $a \cdot b = c \cdot c$ implies that $c = \sqrt{ab}$.

Explore

Minds in Action

You may wish to assign roles students and have them act out the dialog. Then have students do Sasha's construction.

Wrap Up

End this lesson by assigning some Check Your Understanding exercises.

Assessment Resources

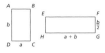

Explore Relationships. The **arithmetic mean,** or average, of two numbers a and b is $\frac{a+b}{2}$.

So the arithmetic mean of 10 and 40 is $\frac{10+40}{2} = 25$. The mean 25 is midway between 10 and 40. Examine the following pairs of equations to see how the arithmetic mean 25 relates to the two numbers 10 and 40.

$$25 - 10 = 15 \qquad\qquad 10 + 15 = 25$$
$$40 - 25 = 15 \qquad\qquad 25 + 15 = 40$$

The geometric mean of two numbers defines a different kind of midway point. The geometric mean is "midway with respect to multiplication." To get from 10 to 40, you can multiply by 2 ($10 \times 2 = 20$) and then by 2 again ($20 \times 2 = 40$). Thus 20, the midway point in your journey, is the geometric mean of 10 and 40. Another way to say that 20 is midway with respect to multiplication between 10 and 40 is to write the proportion $\frac{10}{20} = \frac{20}{40}$.

$$10 \xrightarrow{+\ 15} 25 \xrightarrow{+\ 15} 40 \qquad 10 \xrightarrow{\times\ 2} 20 \xrightarrow{\times\ 2} 40$$
$$\text{arithmetic mean} \qquad\qquad \text{geometric mean}$$

The Arithmetic-Geometric Inequality

Look at the figure below.

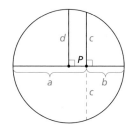

The following relationships hold. If you calculate the power of point P, you get

$$c^2 = a \cdot b$$
$$c = \sqrt{ab}$$

Since d is a radius of the circle, it is half the diameter $a + b$.

$$d = \frac{a+b}{2}$$

You can see from your work that $d \geq c$.

Therefore, you get the Arithmetic-Geometric Inequality.

$$\text{arithmetic mean} \geq \text{geometric mean}$$
$$\frac{a+b}{2} \geq \sqrt{ab}$$

> Can you explain why these relationships are true?

Exercises *Practicing Habits of Mind*

Check Your Understanding

1. Compute the geometric mean and the arithmetic mean of the following pairs of numbers.

    a. 2 and 8

    b. 3 and 12

    c. 4 and 6

    d. 5 and 5

2. If you add two extra segments to the geometric mean, as shown below, three right triangles are formed in the semicircle. Explain.

    Usually, just the right triangles are shown and not the circle that is used to construct them. In the next exercise, the circles were erased after the right triangles were constructed.

3. Find all of the unknown segment lengths in these two figures.

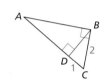

4. Construct a segment with length that is the geometric mean of a 1-inch segment and a 3-inch segment.

Exercises

HOMEWORK
- Core: 5, 8, 9
- Optional: 6, 7, 10

Answers

Exercises

1. **a.** 5; 4   **b.** 7.5; 6

    c. 5; $2\sqrt{6}$ **d.** 5; 5

2. The largest angle with a vertex on the top semicircle intercepts the bottom semicircle and hence has measure $\frac{1}{2} \cdot 180°$, or 90°.

3. first figure: $AC = 5$, $BD = \sqrt{6}$, $AB = \sqrt{10}$, $BC = \sqrt{15}$; second figure: $AC = 4$, $AD = 3$, $AB = 2\sqrt{3}$, $BD = \sqrt{3}$

4. Check students' work.

On Your Own

EXERCISE 7 If you assign this exercise, you should also assign Exercise 6.

EXERCISE 8 previews the Isoperimetric Problem, which students will explore in Chapter 8. An example of an isoperimetric problem is to find the quadrilateral with a given perimeter that encloses the greatest area.

5. **Standardized Test Prep** Three of the following pairs of numbers have the same geometric mean. Which pair has a geometric mean that is different?

   A. 2 and 72   **B.** 3 and 48

   C. 4 and 36   **D.** 6 and 30

6. The illustration below shows four frames from a geometric mean construction as point D moves to the left and point A remains stationary.

   1 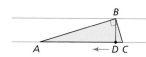   **2**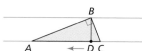

   3 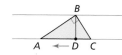   **4**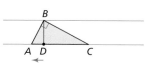

   Make a sketch like this using geometry software.

   a. The product of two lengths remains the same throughout each of these four frames. Which lengths are they?

   b. Use this setup to build a rectangle of constant area sketch.

   c. Does your construction show *all* possible rectangles that share the same area? Explain.

7. **Write About It** Your constant-area-rectangle sketches show rectangles that range from narrow and tall to wide and short. Which of the two constructions—the power of a point or the geometric mean—seems to generate a larger range of constant-area rectangles? Explain.

8. Here is a diagram of a square and a rectangle.

   $\frac{a+b}{2}$ a, b

   a. Which has the greater perimeter?   **b.** Which has the greater area?

   > Try it with numbers.

Answers

5. D

6. **a.** *AD* and *DC*

   b–c. Check students' work.

7. The constructions can give the same ranges of lengths and widths for the constant-area rectangles. In the construction at the beginning of the lesson, c can have any positive number as its value.

8. **a.** The perimeters are equal.
   b. the square

9. Begin with an $a \times b$ rectangle. Explain how to construct a rectangle with length c that has the same area as the $a \times b$ rectangle.

a. Can you use the same circle as in the Minds in Action to complete this construction? Explain.

b. What difficulties do you encounter?

c. Explain how to redraw the circle so that the construction works.

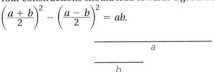

Maintain Your Skills

10. The segments below have lengths a and b. For each value in parts (a)—(d), construct either a segment with that length or a rectangle with that area. Your constructions should lead towards a geometric proof that

$$\left(\frac{a+b}{2}\right)^2 - \left(\frac{a-b}{2}\right)^2 = ab.$$

_____ a

_____ b

All of the constructions can be done with just an unmarked straightedge, a compass, and some lined notebook paper. Resist the urge to measure with a ruler—you will not need to!

a. $a + b$ and $\left(\dfrac{a+b}{2}\right)^2$

b. $a - b$ and $\left(\dfrac{a-b}{2}\right)^2$

c. $\left(\dfrac{a+b}{2}\right)^2 - \left(\dfrac{a-b}{2}\right)^2$

d. ab

e. Use algebra to prove $\left(\dfrac{a+b}{2}\right)^2 - \left(\dfrac{a-b}{2}\right)^2 = ab$. Use the equation to prove the Arithmetic-Geometric Mean Inequality.

Go Online
PHSchool.com

For additional practice, go to **Web Code: bea-0602**

> In which cases will you construct a segment? In which cases will you construct a rectangle?

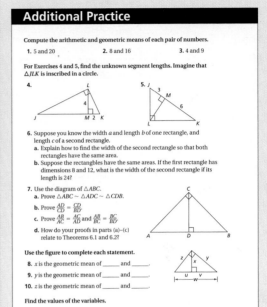

Practice: For Lesson 6.2, assign Exercises 1–6.

---

9. a. No; c is too small. There is no way for the end point of c to stretch from P to the edge of the circle.

b. The small size of the segment of length c makes the construction difficult.

c. The circle would need to be larger than the circle in Minds in Action so that the chord $a + b$ would be far from the center of the circle such that a very small c would stretch between P and the edge of the circle.

10. a–d. Check students' work.

e. $\left(\dfrac{a+b}{2}\right)^2 - \left(\dfrac{a-b}{2}\right)^2 =$
$\dfrac{a^2 + 2ab + b^2}{4} - \dfrac{a^2 - 2ab + b^2}{4}$

$= \dfrac{4ab}{4} = ab$. So $\dfrac{a+b}{2}$

$= \sqrt{ab + \left(\dfrac{a-b}{2}\right)^2} \geq \sqrt{ab}$.

Lesson Overview

GOAL

- Prove theorems using similarity.

This lesson contains a proof of the Pythagorean Theorem that uses similarity. Students discover two additional theorems about similarity in right triangles. These theorems are attributed to the ancient Greeks.

CHECK YOUR UNDERSTANDING
- Core: 2, 4
- Optional: 1, 3

MATERIALS
- rulers
- compasses
- Blackline Master 6.3

HOMEWORK
- Core: 5, 6, 7, 8
- Optional: 9, 10, 11, 13
- Extension: 12

VOCABULARY
- projection

Launch

Begin this lesson by reading the introductory paragraph and assigning For You to Do Problems 1–3.

Explore

Example

Spend time going over the example with students. You may want to review the proofs of the Pythagorean Theorem from Chapter 2 and ask students to compare the different methods of proof.

As you have seen in these lessons and in Chapter 4, similarity is very useful and has a wide variety of applications. In this lesson you will use similarity to prove the Pythagorean Theorem and other theorems of ancient Greece.

For You to Do

In $\triangle ABC$, $\angle ACB$ is a right angle.

1. Why are $\triangle CAH$, $\triangle ABC$, and $\triangle CHB$ right triangles?

2. Why are the two sums $m\angle ACH + m\angle HCB$ and $m\angle ABC + m\angle HCB$ both equal to 90°?

3. Why are the three triangles, $\triangle CAH$, $\triangle ABC$, and $\triangle CHB$, similar?

Example

Problem $\triangle ABC$ is a right triangle with $m\angle ACB = 90°$. Prove the Pythagorean Theorem using similar triangles.

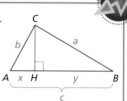

Solution You need to prove that $c^2 = a^2 + b^2$. Consider $\triangle CAH$, $\triangle ABC$, and $\triangle CHB$. They are all right triangles.

Also, $m\angle ACH + m\angle HCB = 90°$ and $m\angle ABC + m\angle HCB = 90°$, so $m\angle ACH \cong \angle ABC$.

By the AAA Similarity Theorem, the three triangles are similar. Therefore, the ratios of corresponding sides are the same.

$$\frac{b}{c} = \frac{x}{b} \text{ and } \frac{a}{c} = \frac{y}{a}$$

So $b^2 = cx$ and $a^2 = cy$. Add these two equations and remember that $x + y = c$.

$$b^2 + a^2 = cx + cy$$
$$= c(x + y)$$
$$= c^2$$

Answers

For You to Do

1. It is given that $\angle ACB$ is a right angle and $\overline{CH} \perp \overline{AB}$.

2. $\angle ACH$ and $\angle HCB$ are the two parts of $\angle ACB$, and $\angle ABC$ and $\angle HCB$ are the acute angles of right $\triangle HCB$.

3. AAA

There are many other proofs of the Pythagorean Theorem. You saw some of the proofs by dissection in Chapter 2. Now you get to see another proof that goes back to Euclid.

In this figure, *ACRS*, *BCPQ*, and *ABNM* are squares constructed on the sides of right triangle *ABC*.

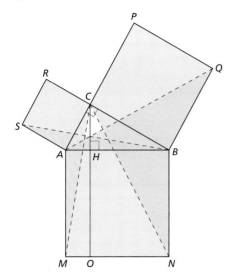

$\triangle ACM$ and $\triangle ASB$ are congruent and $\triangle ABQ$ and $\triangle CBN$ are congruent. Also, remember that the area of a triangle is equal to half the area of a parallelogram with a congruent base and height. So, the area of $\triangle ACM$ is equal to half the area of *AMOH*. The area of $\triangle ASB$ is equal to half the area of *ACRS*.

$$A_{ACRS} = 2A_{ASB} = 2A_{CAM} = A_{AMOH}$$

Why are these two pairs of triangles congruent?

What are the common bases and heights of *ACRS* and *ASB*? Of *AMOH* and *CAM*?

For You to Do

4. Finish proving the Pythagorean Theorem using the method above. Prove that $A_{CBQP} = A_{HONB}$ and that therefore $A_{ABNM} = A_{ACRS} + A_{CBQP}$.

<hr/>

For You to Do

4. Use reasoning similar to that used in the first part of the proof. $\triangle ABQ \cong \triangle NBC$ implies that $2A_{ABQ} = 2A_{NBC}$. But $A_{HONB} = 2A_{NBC}$ and $A_{PQBC} = 2A_{ABQ}$. By the transitive property of equality, $A_{HONB} = A_{PQBC}$. It was proved in the text that $A_{SACR} = A_{AMOH}$. Since $A_{ABNM} = A_{AMOH} + A_{HONB}$, the theorem is proved.

Wrap Up

End this lesson by assigning some Check Your Understanding exercises.

Assessment Resources

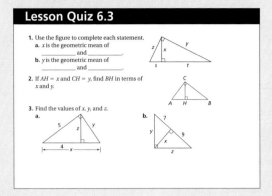

Derman and Sasha are thinking about the following question.

If a triangle has side lengths a, b, and c, such that $c^2 = a^2 + b^2$, is the triangle a right triangle?

Derman   It has to be a right triangle with legs of lengths a and b and hypotenuse c, because if it weren't, then the Pythagorean Theorem wouldn't be true.

Sasha   What do you mean?

> **Habits of Mind**
>
> **Explore.** a, b, c are not zero . . . what would happen if one of them was zero?

For Discussion

5. What do you think Derman means? Pretend that you are Derman. Explain to Sasha why you think that a triangle with sides a, b, and c, such that $c^2 = a^2 + b^2$, must be a right triangle.

There are many more theorems that you can prove using similarity.

Theorem 6.1

In a right triangle, either leg is the geometric mean of its projection on the hypotenuse and the whole hypotenuse.

$$CA^2 = AH \cdot AB$$

$$CB^2 = HB \cdot AB$$

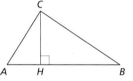

> The **projection** of $\overline{AB}$ onto $\overline{CD}$ is $\overline{EF}$.
>
>

Theorem 6.2

In a right triangle, the altitude relative to the hypotenuse is the geometric mean of the two segments of the hypotenuse.

$$CH^2 = AH \cdot HB$$

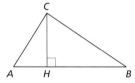

Answers

For Discussion

5. A right triangle with legs of lengths a and b has a hypotenuse of length $\sqrt{a^2 + b^2}$. If $c^2 = a^2 + b^2$, this means the hypotenuse has length c. By SSS, a triangle with side lengths a, b, and c is congruent to the right triangle just described and hence is itself a right triangle.

Exercises *Practicing Habits of Mind*

Check Your Understanding

1. Prove Theorem 6.2.

2. In $\triangle ABC$, $\frac{AH}{CH} = \frac{CH}{HB}$. Prove that $\triangle ABC$ is a right triangle.

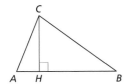

3. Copy the figure onto a separate sheet of paper. Then draw a diameter of the circle below, so that A or B lies on the diameter.

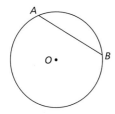

Prove that AB^2 is equal to the product of the diameter and the chord's projection on the diameter.

4. If $AH = r$ and $HB = s$ in the right triangle below, what is CH?

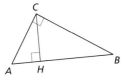

Exercises

Check Your Understanding

EXERCISE 3 You can give students a copy of Blackline Master 6.3 to do this exercise instead of having them copy the diagram.

Exercises

1. Let $\triangle ABC$ be a right triangle with right angle at C. Let $\overline{CH}$ be the altitude from C to $\overline{AB}$. The AA Similarity test shows that $\triangle AHC \sim \triangle CHB$. So $\frac{AH}{CH} = \frac{CH}{BH}$.
It follows that $CH^2 = AH \cdot BH$ and hence that $CH = \sqrt{AH \cdot BH}$.

2. From the given proportion and the fact that the two angles with vertex H are right angles, it follows that $\triangle AHC \sim \triangle CHB$ (you can rotate $\triangle AHC$ so that it can be dilated onto the other triangle). This implies that $\angle A \cong \angle HCB$ and $\angle B \cong \angle ACH$. Since $\angle A$ and $\angle ACH$ are complementary angles, the two small angles with vertex C are complementary. Thus $\angle ACB$ is a right angle. Because $\angle ACB$ is a right angle, $\triangle ABC$ is a right triangle.

3. See back of book.

4. $\sqrt{rs}$

On Your Own

EXERCISE 8 Your students will see a similar configuration in Exercise 19 of Lesson 6.7 when they must find the exact value of the cosine of 72°. The length relationships students discover in this exercise are the foundation of the solution to the later exercise.

On Your Own

5. In the right triangle below, $AH = r$ and $AB = c$. Using similarity, find AC and CB.

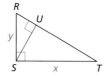

6. **Standardized Test Prep** $\overline{RT}$ is the hypotenuse of $\triangle RST$. $RU = 2$ and $UT = 6$. What are the values of x and y?

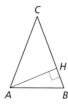

A. $x = 52$, $y = 12$ B. $x = 4\sqrt{3}$, $y = 4$

C. $x = 7$, $y = 15$ D. $x = 40$, $y = 24$

7. Draw a right triangle. Draw a semicircle on each side of the right triangle, such that each side of the right triangle is a diameter of a semicircle. Prove that the area of the semicircle on the hypotenuse is equal to the sum of the areas of the semicircles on the legs of the triangle.

8. The triangle below is isosceles. Prove that $\frac{AC}{AB} = \frac{AB}{2HB}$.

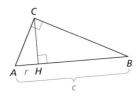

Answers

5. $AC = \sqrt{rc}$, $CB = \sqrt{(c - r)c}$

6. B

7. Let a and b be the lengths of the legs of a right triangle with hypotenuse of length c. The sum of the areas of the semicircles on the legs is $\frac{1}{2}\left(\frac{a}{2}\right)^2 \pi + \frac{1}{2}\left(\frac{b}{2}\right)^2 \pi$. Simplify to get $\frac{1}{8}\pi(a^2 + b^2)$, or $\frac{1}{8}\pi c^2$. But the area of the semicircle on the hypotenuse is $\frac{1}{2}\left(\frac{c}{2}\right)^2 \pi$, or $\frac{1}{8}\pi c^2$.

8. Draw the altitude $\overline{CP}$ from C to $\overline{AB}$. $\triangle ACP \sim \triangle BCP \sim \triangle BAH$, since all three triangles are right triangles with an acute angle congruent to $\angle B$. Use corresponding sides of the first and third triangles to get $\frac{AC}{AP} = \frac{BA}{BH}$. But $AP = \frac{1}{2}AB$, so $\frac{AC}{\frac{1}{2}AB} = \frac{BA}{BH}$. Multiply each side of the last equation by $\frac{1}{2}$ to get $\frac{AC}{AB} = \frac{BA}{2BH}$, or $\frac{AC}{AB} = \frac{AB}{2HB}$.

Use △POD for Exercises 9 and 10.

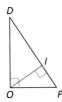

9. $PI = 4$ and $DI = 9$. What is OI?

10. $PI = 7.2$ and $DI = 12.8$. What is PO?

11. In a right triangle ABC with hypotenuse $\overline{BC}$, the altitude from vertex A reaches side $\overline{BC}$ at H. $BH = 3.6$ and the length of the hypotenuse is 10. What are the lengths of the legs of △ABC?

12. Take It Further The mathematicians of ancient Greece proved Theorem 6.1 using a technique like the one in Euclid's proof of the Pythagorean Theorem. At the right is a diagram of the proof. Think about the diagram and write a proof.

Remember...

H is also called the projection of vertex A onto the hypotenuse $\overline{BC}$.

Go Online
PHSchool.com

For additional practice, go to **Web Code: bea-0603**

Maintain Your Skills

13. a. The height from the hypotenuse of a right triangle is 6 cm. A projection of a leg onto the hypotenuse is 4 cm. What is the length of the hypotenuse of the triangle?

b. The two projections of the legs of a right triangle onto its hypotenuse are 5 in. and 45 in. What is the area of the right triangle?

c. In a right triangle the hypotenuse measures 24 cm. The projection of a leg onto the hypotenuse measures 6 cm. What is the triangle's perimeter?

Additional Practice

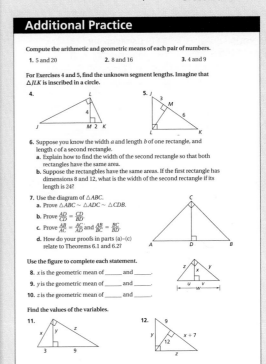

Compute the arithmetic and geometric means of each pair of numbers.

1. 5 and 20   **2.** 8 and 16   **3.** 4 and 9

For Exercises 4 and 5, find the unknown segment lengths. Imagine that △JLK is inscribed in a circle.

4.   **5.**

6. Suppose you know the width a and length b of one rectangle, and length c of a second rectangle.
  a. Explain how to find the width of the second rectangle so that both rectangles have the same area.
  b. Suppose the rectangbles have the same areas. If the first rectangle has dimensions 8 and 12, what is the width of the second rectangle if its length is 24?

7. Use the diagram of △ABC.
  a. Prove △$ABC \sim$ △$ADC \sim$ △CDB.
  b. Prove $\frac{AD}{CD} = \frac{CD}{BD}$.
  c. Prove $\frac{AB}{AC} = \frac{AC}{AD}$ and $\frac{AB}{BC} = \frac{BC}{BD}$.
  d. How do your proofs in parts (a)–(c) relate to Theorems 6.1 and 6.2?

Use the figure to complete each statement.

8. x is the geometric mean of _____ and _____.

9. y is the geometric mean of _____ and _____.

10. z is the geometric mean of _____ and _____.

Find the values of the variables.

11.   **12.**

Practice: For Lesson 6.3, assign Exercises 7–12.

Lesson Overview

GOAL

- Prove theorems using similarity.

This lesson is about the concurrence of the medians in a triangle. The lesson provides a proof that uses similarity to show that the point of intersection of two medians divides each median into two segments, one of which is twice the length of the other.

CHECK YOUR UNDERSTANDING
- Core: 1, 2
- Optional: 3

HOMEWORK
- Core: 4, 7, 8
- Optional: 5, 6, 9
- Extension: 10

MATERIALS
- geometry software
- Blackline Masters 6.4A and 6.4B

Launch

Begin this lesson by assigning the In-Class Experiment.

Explore

In-Class Experiment

If you do not have access to geometry software, you can still assign this experiment. Have students draw several different triangles and construct two medians of each. You can also give students copies of Blackline Master 6.4A and have them construct the medians. The students can investigate any invariants they find and then construct the third median for each triangle. Have students determine whether the invariants they found also hold for the new medians.

Wrap Up

End this lesson by assigning some Check Your Understanding exercises.

6.4   Concurrence of Medians

A median of a triangle is a segment with endpoints that are a vertex of the triangle and the midpoint of the opposite side. Every triangle has three medians.

In-Class Experiment

1. Using geometry software, draw △ABC. Construct the medians from A and B.

2. Drag the vertices of your triangle and describe all the invariants that you can find.

3. Construct the median from C.

4. Drag the vertices of your triangle again. Do the invariants you found in part 2 still hold for the new median?

During the experiment, you made some conjectures about invariants that may have included the following.

Conjecture 6.1

1. **Any two medians of a triangle intersect in a point that divides them into two segments. The length of one of these segments is twice the length of the other.**

2. **The three medians are concurrent at a point G, as shown below.**

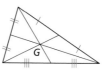

> G is the *centroid* of the triangle.

Answers

In-Class Experiment

1. Check students' work.

2. Answers may vary. Sample: Let K be the point where the medians $\overline{AP}$ and $\overline{BQ}$ intersect. $\frac{KP}{AK}$ and $\frac{KQ}{BK}$ are always $\frac{1}{2}$. The area of △AKB is always $\frac{1}{3}$ the area of △ABC.

3. Check students' work.

4. yes

Tony and Sasha are trying to prove both parts of Conjecture 6.1.

Explore. Think about why this lesson is in an investigation on similarity.

Sasha   I have an idea. In △*ABC*, *M* and *N* are the midpoints of the sides $\overline{AC}$ and $\overline{CB}$. The medians $\overline{AN}$ and $\overline{BM}$ intersect at *G*. *P* and *Q* are the midpoints of $\overline{AG}$ and $\overline{GB}$.

Look at triangles *PQG* and *NMG*.

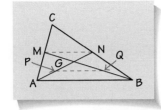

Tony   I wouldn't be surprised if those were congruent triangles.

Sasha   They are, and here's why. Apply the Midline Theorem to △*ABC*. You get $\overline{MN} \parallel \overline{AB}$ and $MN = \frac{1}{2}AB$. Apply the Midline Theorem to △*ABG*. You get $\overline{PQ} \parallel \overline{AB}$ and $PQ = \frac{1}{2}AB$. So $\overline{MN} \parallel \overline{PQ}$ and $MN = PQ$. This means that $\angle QPN \cong \angle PNM$ and $\angle PQG \cong \angle QMN$. Finally, △*PQG* ≅ △*NMG* by ASA. Neat, huh?

Tony   That means we've proven the first conjecture. After all, $\overline{GM} \cong \overline{GQ} \cong \overline{QB}$. That tells us that *G* divides $\overline{BM}$ into two pieces, one of which is twice as long as the other.

Sasha   Right, and $\overline{GN} \cong \overline{GP} \cong \overline{PA}$, so *G* also divides $\overline{AN}$ the same way.

Tony   Wait! There wasn't anything special about *G*. The result must be the same for any two medians. The point of intersection must divide the medians into two segments with one segment twice the length of the other. That means if the third median $\overline{CK}$ intersects $\overline{BM}$ in point *G'*, *G'* has to have the same property. So $CG' = 2G'K$ and $BG' = 2G'M$.

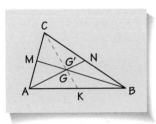

Sasha   But you already know that *G* is the point that divides $\overline{BM}$ into two segments and that one segment is twice the length of the other.

Tony   Right! So *G* = *G'* and therefore, *G* lies on $\overline{CK}$, too.

You proved the Midline Theorem in Chapter 3.

Exercises

HOMEWORK
- Core: 4, 7, 8
- Optional: 5, 6, 9
- Extension: 10

For You to Do

5. Explain why knowing that $\triangle PQG \cong \triangle NMG$ is enough to conclude that $AG = 2GN$ and $BG = 2GM$.

Exercises *Practicing Habits of Mind*

Check Your Understanding

1. **Write About It** Use Sasha's triangle. In your own words, prove Conjecture 6.1, namely that $AG = 2GN$ and $BG = 2GM$.

2. Think about how Sasha proved that $AG = 2GN$ and $BG = 2GM$ in her figure. Can you think of another way of proving the same thing that does not use the congruence of $\triangle PQG$ and $\triangle NMG$? Explain.

Hint: Think about parallelograms.

3. Do you know other special three-segment sets that are concurrent in triangles? List each set of three segments lines you know. Draw a diagram for each set.

On Your Own

4. **Standardized Test Prep** Orhan is calculating the area of $\triangle ABC$. He measures and finds $AC = 9$ cm, $BC = 12$ cm, and $BH = 8$ cm. Find CF.

   A. 7.2 cm   **B.** 8.0 cm   **C.** 9.0 cm   **D.** 36 cm

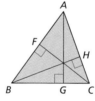

Answers

For You to Do

5. By CPCTC, $\overline{MG} \cong \overline{QG}$. But $\overline{QG} \cong \overline{QB}$, since Q is the midpoint of $\overline{BG}$. So $BG = 2GM$. By similar reasoning, $AG = 2GN$.

Exercises

1. Check students' work.

2. $\overline{PQ}$ and $\overline{MN}$ are both parallel to $\overline{AB}$ and hence are parallel to each other. Sasha's reasoning shows that $MN = PQ$. So $PQNM$ is a parallelogram. The diagonals of a parallelogram bisect each other. The desired result follows at once.

3. Check students' diagrams. For every triangle, the angle bisectors are concurrent, the lines that contains the altitudes are concurrent, and the perpendicular bisectors of the sides of the triangle are concurrent.

5. For this exercise, you need a piece of cardboard or thick paper and a piece of string knotted at one end.

   • Cut a triangle from the cardboard or paper.

   • Construct the medians of the triangle. Mark the point of concurrence.

   • Poke a tiny hole through the centroid you found. Thread the string through the hole.

   • Hold the end of the string. Let the triangle hang down on the knot.

   • Describe the triangle's position when it stabilizes.

6. Copy the figure below onto a separate sheet of paper. Then choose a point P on the median $\overline{CM}$ of $\triangle ABC$.

   a. Draw the heights from P for $\triangle APM$ and $\triangle BPM$.

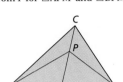

   b. Complete the following statements and justify your answers.

   $$A_{\triangle APC} = A_{\triangle ACM} - A_{\triangle \ ?}$$

   $$A_{\triangle BPC} = A_{\triangle \ ?} - A_{\triangle \ ?}$$

   c. Prove that if P is not on the median $\overline{CM}$, then $A_{\triangle APC} \neq A_{\triangle BPC}$.

   d. Now describe the median $\overline{CM}$ as the set of points with a given property.

7. Use $\triangle ABC$ from Exercise 6. Consider the medians of a triangle as the set of points P with the following property: $A_{\triangle APC} = A_{\triangle BPC}$, (in the case of median $\overline{CM}$). Use an argument similar to Tony's to prove that the three medians of a triangle are concurrent.

8. In this exercise, you will prove that the three altitudes of a triangle are concurrent.

   a. Draw $\triangle ABC$ and its three altitudes.

   b. Through vertex A draw the perpendicular to the altitude through A. Repeat this for the other two vertices.

   c. Mark the three points of intersection of the lines you drew in part (b) and label them D, E, and F.

   d. What are the altitudes of $\triangle ABC$ with respect to $\triangle DEF$?

   e. Explain why the three altitudes of $\triangle ABC$ are concurrent.

> You also can try to balance the triangle on your finger. Where is the balance point?

> **Remember...**
> A *locus* is a set of points with a given property.

On Your Own

EXERCISE 6 You can give students copies of Blackline Master 6.4B and have them pick a point P on the median, $\overline{CM}$.

4. A

5. If the triangle is large enough and the medians are drawn accurately, then the triangle should be parallel to the ground.

6. **a–d.** See back of book.

7. Suppose that in $\triangle ABC$, the medians from C and A intersect at point P. From Exercise 6b, we know that $A_{\triangle APC} = A_{\triangle BPC}$ and $A_{\triangle APC} = A_{\triangle APB}$. Therefore $A_{\triangle BPC} = A_{\triangle APB}$, which implies, by Exercise 6d, that P is on the median from point B. Since P is on all three medians, the medians are concurrent.

8. **a–c.** Check students' work.

   d. The lines containing the altitudes of $\triangle ABC$ are the perpendicular bisectors of the sides of $\triangle DEF$.

   e. The perpendicular bisectors of the sides of $\triangle DEF$ are concurrent.

Maintain Your Skills

EXERCISE 9 Encourage students to solve this exercise in different ways and then compare their answers. Help them understand what happens in the limit cases, when the sum of the lengths of two sides is equal to the length of the third side. Make sure your students use the idea of reasoning by continuity.

Additional Resources

PRINTED RESOURCES
- Texas Instruments Activities Workbook
- Cabrilog Activities
- Teaching Resources
- Practice Workbook
- Assessment Resources

TECHNOLOGY
- TeacherExpress CD-ROM
- *ExamView* CD-ROM
- PHSchool.com
  - Homework Help
  - Video Tutors
  - Multiple Choice
  - Crosswords

Additional Practice

For each given type of triangle, draw the three medians. Then mark the point of concurrence.

1. acute   **2.** obtuse   **3.** right

For each given type of triangle, draw the three altitudes. Mark the point of concurrence.

4. acute   **5.** obtuse   **6.** right

For each given type of triangle, draw the three angle bisectors. Then mark the point of concurrence.

7. acute   **8.** obtuse   **9.** right

For Exercises 10–12, use △ABC where $\overline{AE}$, $\overline{CD}$, and $\overline{BF}$ are medians.

10. If $FB = 12$, find FG.

11. If $GC = 10$, find DC.

12. If $GE = x$, find AE.

13. What type of triangle has three medians that are also the altitudes and the angle bisectors? Justify your answer with a diagram.

14. Prove that the medians drawn to the legs of an isosceles triangle are congruent.

15. Given: Right △JLK; $\overline{AB}$ is the perpendicular bisector of $\overline{LK}$. Prove: $\overline{LA}$ is a median.

16. Draw right scalene △ABC with right ∠C. Then draw median $\overline{CD}$ from ∠C to $\overline{AB}$.
   a. Which segments appear to be congruent to median $\overline{CD}$?
   b. Draw midline $\overline{DE}$. Are there any congruent triangles in your drawing? Prove your answer.
   c. Are there any similar triangles in your drawing? Prove your answer.

Practice: For Lesson 6.4, assign Exercises 1–16.

Maintain Your Skills

9. You can use the following formula to find the area A of a triangle if you know the lengths, a, b, and c, of its sides.

$$A = \sqrt{\left(\frac{a+b+c}{2}\right)\left(\frac{b+c-a}{2}\right)\left(\frac{a-b+c}{2}\right)\left(\frac{a+b-c}{2}\right)}$$

The formula above is called *Heron's formula*. Use Heron's formula to find the areas of the triangles below.

a. a triangle with sides 6 in., 12 in., and 13 in.

b. △ABC

c. an equilateral triangle with sides 3 cm

d. an isosceles triangle with base 43 cm and perimeter 89 cm

e. a triangle with sides 6 cm, 8 cm, and 10 cm

f. a triangle with sides 4, 6, and 10

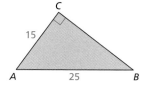

Does Heron's formula make sense? Find the areas of the triangles above in a different way and check the answers you found with Heron's formula.

10. Take It Further Brahmagupta's formula is similar to Heron's formula from Exercise 9. Suppose a quadrilateral with side lengths a, b, c, and d is inscribed in a circle. Brahmagupta's formula finds the area A of the quadrilateral.

Cyclic quadrilaterals are quadrilaterals inscribed in a circle.

$$A = \sqrt{\left(\frac{a+b+c-d}{2}\right)\left(\frac{a+b-c+d}{2}\right)\left(\frac{a-b+c+d}{2}\right)\left(\frac{-a+b+c+d}{2}\right)}$$

a. Use Brahmagupta's formula to find the area of the cyclic quadrilateral at the right.

b. Write About It Compare Heron's formula with Brahmagupta's formula. If $d = 0$, what does Brahmagupta's formula become?

c. Is Brahmagupta's formula a generalization of Heron's formula? Explain.

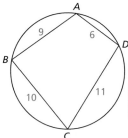

Go Online
PHSchool.com
For additional practice, go to **Web Code: bea-0604**

Answers

Maintain Your Skills

9. a. $\dfrac{\sqrt{20,615}}{4}$ in^2.

   b. 150

   c. $\dfrac{9}{4}\sqrt{3}$ cm^2

   d. $\dfrac{43}{4}\sqrt{267}$ cm^2

   e. 24 cm^2

   f. There is no such triangle.

10. a. $12\sqrt{42}$

   b. Heron's formula

   c. Yes; Brahmagupta's formula becomes Heron's formula when $d = 0$. Note that since every triangle can be inscribed in a circle, every triangle can be thought of as a degenerate cyclic quadrilateral with a side of length 0.

Mathematical Reflections

6A

In this investigation, you learned how to apply properties of similarity, prove theorems using similarity, and draw strategic circles, segments, and points to solve problems. These questions will help you summarize what you have learned.

1. Sophie and Erin are measuring things for a school project. They accidentally drop their yardstick down a hole, where it lies flat along the bottom.

   Erin holds a 12-in. ruler out over the hole at ground level. Sophie looks straight down into the hole and notices that, from her perspective, the ruler *exactly* covers the yardstick.

   If Sophie's eyes are 5 feet above the ruler, how deep is the hole?

2. Find the arithmetic and geometric mean for the numbers 6 and 24. Explain how each of the means is halfway between the two numbers.

3. If the altitude to the hypotenuse of a right triangle is also a median, what can you conclude about the original right triangle? Explain.

4. Prove that if $\triangle ABC \sim \triangle AHB$, then $\triangle AHB \sim \triangle BHC$.

5. Describe how to locate the centroid of a triangle without constructing more than one of its medians.

6. What is the Arithmetic-Geometric Mean Inequality?

7. Why does the altitude to the hypotenuse of a right triangle form three similar triangles?

8. In $\triangle ABC$, suppose that $AH = 12$ cm and $BA = 15$ cm. What is HC?

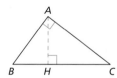

Vocabulary

In this investigation, you saw these terms for the first time. Make sure you understand what each one means and how to use it.

- **arithmetic mean**
- **geometric mean**
- **projection**

Use 1-inch grid paper to capture an image similar to this prince.

Mathematical Reflections

EXERCISES 6–8 At the start of the investigation, you may have assigned these as Questions 1–3 for students to think and write about.

Mathematical Reflections

1. 15 ft deep

2. The arithmetic mean is 15. This number is 9 more than 6 and 9 less than 24. The geometric mean is 12. This number is 2 times 6 and $\frac{1}{2}$ of 24.

3. It is an isosceles right triangle.

4. If $\triangle ABC \sim \triangle AHB$, then $\angle ABC$ is a right angle, since it corresponds to the right angle $\angle AHB$ in $\triangle AHB$. Each of the right triangles

$\triangle AHB$ and $\triangle BHC$ has one of its acute angles in common with $\triangle ABC$, so by the AA Similarity Test, $\triangle AHB \sim \triangle BHC$.

5. Construct one median. The centroid is along the median, two thirds of the way from the vertex to the opposite side.

6. If a and b are positive real numbers, then $\frac{a + b}{2} \geq \sqrt{ab}$.

7. See back of book.

8. 16

Investigation Overview

This investigation introduces students to the sine, cosine, and tangent of acute angles of a right triangle, which are defined as the ratios of certain side lengths of a right triangle. So, in this course, when students consider the sine, cosine, or tangent of an angle, the angle measure must be between 0° and 90°.

Later, in Algebra 2, students will expand their understanding of trigonometry by extending the trigonometric ratios to trigonometric functions. Students will relate these functions to the unit circle and to arc lengths in radians. Then students will be able to find the sine, cosine, or tangent of any angle, not just angles that can occur in right triangles. In this course, however, the text restricts the use of sine, cosine, and tangent to right triangles.

The goal of the investigation is for students to use the information that completely determines a triangle—ASA, SSS, SAS, and so on—to find missing angle measures or missing side lengths. The pursuit of this single goal exposes students to several basic trigonometric identities and to the Law of Cosines. Students also see the Law of Sines and the SAS area formula, but the text does not describe these concepts explicitly because of the limited exposure in this course that students receive to the trigonometric ratios.

You may wish to assign Questions 1–3 for students to think and write about during the investigation.

Learning Goals

- Use the sine, cosine, and tangent ratios and their inverses to find missing side lengths and angle measures in triangles.
- Find the area of any triangle given the lengths of two sides and the measure of their included angle.
- Find the length of the third side of a triangle given the lengths of two sides and the measure of their included angle.

Habits and Skills

- Find invariants in classes of right triangles.
- Visualize right triangles in different problem situations.
- Choose appropriate strategies to find missing angle measures and side lengths.

Investigation 6B

Exploring Right Triangles

In *Exploring Right Triangles*, you will learn a great deal about all triangles, and even all polygons. You already know that every *n*-sided polygon can be subdivided into $n - 2$ or fewer triangles by connecting nonadjacent vertices.

In this investigation, you will see how to use ratios of side lengths in right triangles to determine side lengths and angle measures in triangles and in other figures.

By the end of this investigation, you will be able to answer questions like these:

1. How can you use half of a square or half of an equilateral triangle to evaluate trigonometric functions for angles measuring 30°, 45°, and 60°?

2. Find the sine, cosine, and tangent of α and β in terms of the sides of $\triangle ABC$.

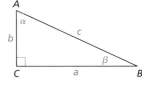

How far out and how high up can the ladder reach?

3. What is the area of $\triangle LMN$? What is the approximate length of $\overline{MN}$?

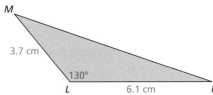

You will learn how to

- use the sine, cosine, and tangent ratios and their inverses to find missing side lengths and angle measures in triangles
- find the area of any triangle given the lengths of two sides and the measure of their included angle
- find the length of the third side of a triangle given the lengths of two sides and the measure of their included angle

You will develop these habits and skills:

- Find invariants in classes of right triangles.
- Visualize right triangles in different problem situations.
- Choose appropriate strategies to find missing angle measures and side lengths.

Investigation Road Map

LESSON 6.5, *Getting Started,* allows students to experience and experiment *steepness.*

LESSON 6.6, *Some Special Triangles,* introduces students to special right triangles for which they can identify the angle measurements given only the side lengths.

LESSON 6.7, *Some Special Ratios,* introduces sine, cosine, and tangent as special ratios in right triangles.

LESSON 6.8, *Finding Triangle Areas,* has students use trigonometry to determine areas and missing measurements of triangles.

LESSON 6.9, *Extend the Pythagorean Theorem,* introduces the Law of Cosines as an extension of the Pythagorean Theorem.

Getting Started

Activating Prior Knowledge
Exploring New Ideas

You have already investigated the Pythagorean Theorem, which explains how the lengths of the sides of right triangles are related to each other. But how can you use information about the lengths of the sides of a right triangle to tell you about the measures of its angles?

In the following In-Class Experiment, you will study a right triangle that is the side view of a ramp. You will vary the lengths of the sides of the triangle. You will develop some conjectures about how different side lengths relate to the ramp's angle of inclination.

n-Class Experiment

You can specify a ramp by giving any two of the measurements indicated in the figure below.

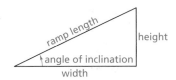

Habits of Mind

Visualize. Why are only two of these measurements enough? What else do you know about the ramp?

1. Decide which ramp is the steepest.

   Use any method you like, such as constructing physical scale models, making graphical models, or using calculations. Be prepared to explain why your method is valid as well as why your choice is the steepest ramp.

   A. width 9.2 feet, height 3.3 feet

   B. ramp length 10.2 m, height 3.8 m

   C. height 3.1 feet, width 8.5 feet

   D. width 9 m, ramp length 10.8 m

   E. ramp length 3 yards, angle of inclination 30°

   F. height 3 feet, width 7 feet

Lesson Overview

GOALS

- Warm up to the ideas of the investigation.

- Use a hands-on approach to develop mathematical habits of mind.

In this lesson, students experiment with the concept of steepness. They will try to find methods to evaluate steepness quantitatively.

FOR YOU TO EXPLORE	HOMEWORK
• Core: 1, 2, 4	• Core: 5, 7, 9
• Optional: 3	• Optional: 6, 8, 10, 11, 12, 13

MATERIALS
- graph paper
- materials to build model ramps
- protractors
- rulers

Launch

Begin this lesson by reading the introductory paragraph and assigning the In-Class Experiment.

Answers

In-Class Experiment

1. D

Explore

Have students work on the For You to Explore problems during class. The goal is for students to experience some of the important concepts that they will learn later in this investigation.

Wrap Up

End this lesson by assigning some On Your Own exercises as homework.

For You to Explore

2. Two ladders are leaned against a wall so that they make the same angle with the ground.

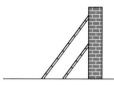

   The 10-foot ladder reaches 8 feet up the wall. How much farther up the wall does the 18-foot ladder reach?

3. Workers accidentally drop a metal pipe that is 10-feet long. It falls into a cylindrical hole with a radius of 4 feet and a grate across the top. The pipe comes to rest leaning across the bottom of the hole. The workers are able to just reach the upper end of the pipe through the grate with a magnet at the end of a rope that is 7-feet long. About how deep is the hole?

4. **Write About It** Describe how to compare the steepness of two ramps given the following measurements for each ramp.
   * ramp length and width
   * ramp length and height
   * width and height

As you raise the truck bed, which measures change?

Answers

For You To Explore

2. 6.4 ft

3. 13 ft

4. Answers may vary. Sample: Find the width and height for each ramp. (Use the Pythagorean Theorem to find an unknown width or height.)

Divide the height of each ramp by its width. If the quotients are equal, the ramps have the same steepness. Otherwise, the steeper ramp is the one for which the quotient is greater.

On Your Own

5. The width and height of four ramps are given. Which ramp is the steepest? Explain.

   A. width 10 feet, height 6 feet

   B. width 5 miles, height 3 miles

   C. width 15 inches, height 9 inches

   D. width 50 cm, height 30 cm

6. **What's Wrong Here?** Derman says that Exercise 5 proves that units are completely irrelevant when you compare the steepness of ramps. Explain how units *can* have an effect when you compare the steepness of two ramps.

7. Hannah's method for comparing the steepness of ramps is to construct a triangle that is similar to the triangle formed by the ramp, but with a width of 1. Then she compares the heights of the similar triangles in order to choose the steepest ramp. Try Hannah's method to determine which of the following ramps is the steepest.

   A. ramp length 18 cm, height 6 cm

   B. ramp length 43 inches, width 41 inches

   C. width 50.9 mm, height 18.5 mm

8. Ramp A has an angle of inclination of 30°. Ramp B has width 8.9 feet and height 5.3 feet. Which ramp is steeper? How did you decide?

9. When you are standing at point *A*, you have to tilt your head up 27° to see the very top of a tree. You are 40 feet from the tree. Approximately how tall is the tree?

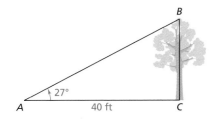

This picture is not exactly right. To simplify the problem, something was ignored. What is it?

On Your Own

EXERCISE 6 If you assign this exercise, also assign Exercise 5. It might be difficult for students to imagine getting information about a ramp if the units for its height and width are not the same. You might want to give an example, such as one inch high to one foot wide as a maximum grade allowed for wheelchair ramps.

EXERCISE 7 To compare the steepness of ramps, students can choose to scale any of the length measurements to 1. They can choose the width (as in this exercise), the height (as in Exercise 13), or the ramp length. Point out to students that the length they choose to scale affects how they should view the result. When the width remains constant, greater heights are steeper. When the height remains constant, greater widths are less steep.

EXERCISE 11 is a comparison of students' results from Exercises 9 and 10.

Exercises

5. All the ramps are equally steep.

6. For each individual ramp, the width and height must be expressed in the same units. Otherwise, the results can be misleading.

7. Ramp C with width 50.9 mm and height 18.5 mm is steepest.

8. Ramp B is steeper; the triangle for a ramp with an angle of inclination of 30° is a 30°-60°-90° triangle (half of an equilateral triangle), so its height-to-width ratio is $\frac{1}{\sqrt{3}}$,

   or about 0.577. The height-to-width ratio for ramp B is $\frac{5.3}{5.9}$, or about 0.596. The greater ratio corresponds to the steeper ramp.

9. about 20.4 ft

10. When you are in a boat at point *A*, you have to tilt your head up 27° to see the very top of the Statue of Liberty. The statue (including its base) is 300 feet tall. Approximately how far are you from the bottom of the base?

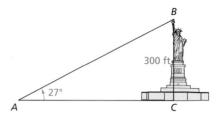

11. Refer to Exercises 9 and 10 to answer the following questions.

    a. List some things that these two problems have in common.

    b. Explain why the value of $\frac{BC}{AC}$ is the same for both triangles.

    c. Measure one of the triangles and calculate this constant value. Did you use this relationship in your solutions to Exercises 9 and 10?

12. You have likely conjectured that there is a relationship between the height-to-width ratio of a ramp and its angle of inclination. The larger the height-to-width ratio, the larger the angle. Estimate the height-to-width ratio for each angle of inclination.

    a. 30°   **b.** 37°   **c.** 45°   **d.** 60°

Maintain Your Skills

13. In the following series of ramps, the height is always 1 foot, but the width of the ramp gets progressively wider.

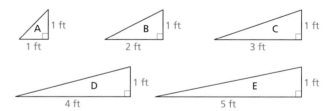

Compute or measure the following quantities for each ramp. Describe how the quantity changes from Ramp A to Ramp E.

    a. ramp length   **b.** angle of inclination

    c. ratio of height to width   **d.** ratio of height to ramp length

Go Online
Video Tutor
PHSchool.com

Web Code: bee-0775

Answers

10. about 589 ft

11. a. Answers may vary. Sample: Both involve right triangles. There is an angle of inclination of 27° in both situations.

    b. The right triangles are similar, since each has an acute angle of 27°.

    c. The height-to-width ratio is about 0.51; yes.

12. a–d. Answers may vary. Samples are given.

    a. 0.58   **b.** 0.75

    c. 1   **d.** 1.73

13. a. A: $\sqrt{2}$ ft; B: $\sqrt{5}$ ft; C: $\sqrt{10}$ ft; D: $\sqrt{17}$ ft; E: $\sqrt{26}$ ft; the lengths increase as the widths increase.

    b. Angle measures are rounded to the nearest degree. A: 45°; B: 27°; C: 18°; D: 14°; E: 11°; the angles get smaller as the widths increase.

13. c–d. See back of book.

468 Chapter 6 Using Similarity

Some Special Triangles

Every triangle has three side lengths and three angle measures. In Chapter 2, you saw that you do not have to know all six measurements to prove that two triangles are congruent. In fact, you only need to know three of the measurements—all three side lengths (SSS), two sides and the included angle (SAS), or two angles and one side length (ASA and AAS). There must be some way to figure out what the other three measurements are from the ones you know.

Minds in Action   episode 25

Tony and Sasha are talking about situations in which they could use three triangle facts to determine the others.

Tony   If you just know three sides of a triangle, how could you ever figure out what the angles are without constructing it?

Sasha   Well, I don't know how to do it for *every* triangle. I bet I can give you three facts that you could use to solve for the other three.

Here's one I *know* you know. What if △ABC has three sides that all measure 6.17 cm? What are its angle measures?

Tony   Okay. That one I get. So I agree that there are some special cases that are possible to do. How about a side-angle-side set?

Sasha   How about △DEF with DE = 4 in., EF = 4 in., and m∠E = 90°?

Tony   With two sides of a right triangle, I can always figure out the third side, but how can I figure out the other two angles? Oh, yeah, it's an isosceles right triangle.

Now I've got an angle-side-angle set for you, Sasha: △GHI where m∠G = 30°, m∠H = 60°, and GH = 6 mm.

Sasha   That one's tricky, but at least it must be a right triangle. I'll draw a sketch.

Hey! This is just half of an equilateral triangle!

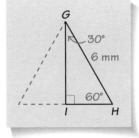

Lesson Overview

GOAL

- Find the length of the third side of a triangle given the lengths of two sides and the measure of their included angle.

This lesson allows students to revisit the relationships between the angle measures and side lengths of some special right triangles.

CHECK YOUR UNDERSTANDING	**HOMEWORK**
• Core: 2, 3	• Core: 5, 6, 9, 10, 11
• Optional: 1, 4	• Optional: 7, 8, 12, 13, 14

Launch

Begin this lesson by having students read and analyze the Minds in Action dialog.

Explore

Example

Spend time as needed going over the completed example. You might want to have students find the side lengths of the triangle for specific values of *a*.

For You to Do

Answer these questions about the several triangles that were mentioned in the Minds in Action.

1. What are the measures of the angles of △*ABC*? Explain.

2. What are the missing measures of △*DEF*? Explain.

3. What are the missing measures of △*GHI*? Explain.

4. Create a new problem in which you specify only three measurements for a triangle. Make sure the other three measurements can be determined from the given information. Exchange problems with a classmate.

In the Minds in Action, Tony and Sasha discussed an isosceles right triangle and a triangle that is half of an equilateral triangle. You already know many properties of these two triangles. Now it is time to learn how the angle measures and the three side lengths in each are related.

> A 30-60-90 triangle is a right triangle that is half of an equilateral triangle.

Example

Problem An altitude of an equilateral triangle cuts it into two right triangles. If the side length of the original triangle is *a*, find all the side lengths and angle measures for one such right triangle.

Solution Here is a diagram of the situation.

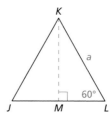

The measure of ∠*KLM* = 60°, because ∠*KLM* is one of the angles of the original equilateral triangle. You also know that *m*∠*LMK* = 90°, because $\overline{KM}$ is an altitude of the equilateral triangle. *m*∠*MKL* = 30°, so the sum of the three angle measures is 180°.

Answers

For You to Do

1. All are 60°; △*ABC* is an equilateral triangle.

2. *DF* = 4√2 in., *m*∠*D* = *m*∠*F* = 45°; △*GHI* is a 45-45-90 triangle. Both legs are congruent and the length of the hypotenuse is √2 times the length of a leg.

3. *HI* = 3 mm and *GI* = 3√3 mm. △*GHI* is a 30-60-90 triangle. The length of the hypotenuse is twice the length of the shorter leg. The length of the longer leg is √3 times the length of the shorter leg.

4. Check students' work.

$KL = a$, because $\overline{KL}$ is one of the sides of the original equilateral triangle. $LM = \frac{a}{2}$, because the altitude of an isosceles triangle bisects the base. You can find KM by using the Pythagorean Theorem.

$$KM^2 + LM^2 = KL^2$$

$$KM^2 + \left(\frac{a}{2}\right)^2 = a^2$$

$$KM^2 = \frac{3a^2}{4}$$

$$KM = \frac{\sqrt{3}a}{2}$$

Here is the triangle with all of its angle measures and side lengths marked. Learn to look for and recognize triangles with these angles, or with side lengths that are proportional to those in this triangle.

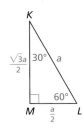

For You to Do

A diagonal of a square cuts it into two congruent right triangles.

5. If the side length of the square is a, find all the side lengths and angle measures for one such right triangle.

A right triangle that is half of a square is an isosceles right triangle. You can also call it a 45-45-90 triangle. Learn to look for and recognize triangles with these angles, or with side lengths that are proportional to those of an isosceles right triangle.

Wrap Up

End this lesson by assigning some Check Your Understanding exercises.

Assessment Resources

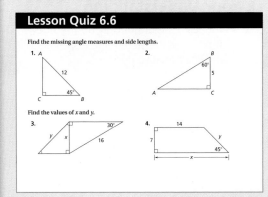

Lesson Quiz 6.6

Find the missing angle measures and side lengths.

Find the values of x and y.

For You to Do

5. The legs have length a, the hypotenuse has length $a\sqrt{2}$, and each acute angle has a measure of 45°.

Exercises

HOMEWORK
- Core: 5, 6, 9, 10, 11
- Optional: 7, 8, 12, 13, 14

Check Your Understanding

EXERCISE 4 emphasizes that not only do the side lengths and angle measures determine a special right triangle, but also their relative positions.

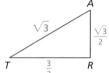

Exercises *Practicing Habits of Mind*

Check Your Understanding

1. When you are trying to recognize the special right triangles discussed in this lesson, it will be useful to remember the converse of the Pythagorean Theorem. If the three side lengths a, b, and c are such that $a^2 + b^2 = c^2$, then the triangle they form must be a right triangle. Prove this.

For Exercises 2 and 3, find the missing angle measures and side length of each triangle. Explain your answers.

2.

3.

4. Suppose you know that two sides of a triangle measure 1 in. and 2 in. One of the angles of this triangle measures 60°. Is this triangle a 30-60-90 triangle? Sketch any possible triangles that meet these requirements.

On Your Own

For Exercises 5–8, find any missing angle measures or side lengths. Explain your answers.

5.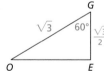

6.

7.

8.

Answers

Exercises

1. A right triangle with legs of lengths a and b has a hypotenuse of length $\sqrt{a^2 + b^2}$. If $c^2 = a^2 + b^2$, this means the hypotenuse has length c. By SSS, a triangle with side lengths a, b, and c is congruent to the right triangle just described and hence is itself a right triangle.

2. $DO = \sqrt{2}$ by the Pythagorean Theorem; $m\angle D = 45°$ because $\triangle DGO$ is isosceles.

3. See back of book.

4. See back of book.

5. $m\angle T = 90°$, $AT = 17$, $AC = 17\sqrt{2}$; $\triangle CTA$ is a 45-45-90 triangle.

6. See back of book.

7. See back of book.

8. $m\angle S = 60°$, $SI = \dfrac{4\sqrt{3}}{3}$, $SC = \dfrac{8\sqrt{3}}{3}$; $\triangle SIC$ is a 30-60-90 triangle.

9. Standardized Test Prep The Garden Club is building a flower garden for Lincoln High School. The design is a square with diagonal walkways. The length of each walkway is 49.5 ft. Find the area of the garden.

A. $1225\,\text{ft}^2$ **B.** $1980\,\text{ft}^2$ **C.** $2450\,\text{ft}^2$ **D.** $4900\,\text{ft}^2$

10. What's Wrong Here? Derman and Sasha made up triangle problems so they could practice with the special right triangles from this lesson.

Derman wrote this problem:

In $\triangle DER$, $DE = 2$ cm, $DR = 1$ cm, and $m\angle EDR = 30°$. Find the missing side lengths and angle measures.

Sasha said, "I don't think we can solve that one yet." Derman said, "Oh come on, it's easy. Here's a picture."

Explain what is wrong with Derman's solution. Use paper and pencil or geometry software to construct the triangle with Derman's given information.

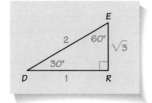

11. A right triangle with a 30° angle has one side that is 1 inch long. Show all possible triangles. Find and label the lengths of the other two sides in each case.

12. A right triangle with a 45° angle has one side that is 1 inch long. Show all possible triangles. Find and label the lengths of the other two sides in each case.

13. Given $AB = 4\sqrt{3}$ cm, find AE.

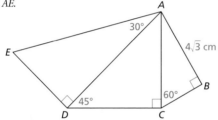

Maintain Your Skills

14. $\triangle ABC$ is a right triangle with $m\angle B = 90°$. Find $\frac{AB}{AC}$, $\frac{BC}{AC}$, and $\frac{AB}{BC}$ for each measure of $\angle C$ below.

a. $m\angle C = 30°$ **b.** $m\angle C = 45°$ **c.** $m\angle C = 60°$

Go Online
PHSchool.com

For additional practice, go to **Web Code: bea-0606**

9. A

10. Derman's figure does not have the side lengths that are correct for a 30°-60°-90° triangle. In a 30°-60°-90° triangle, the side opposite the 30° angle must have half the length of the hypotenuse.

11. See back of book.

12. See back of book.

13. $\dfrac{16\sqrt{6}}{3}$

14. a. $\dfrac{1}{2}$, $\dfrac{\sqrt{2}}{2}$, $\dfrac{\sqrt{3}}{2}$

b. $\dfrac{\sqrt{3}}{2}$, $\dfrac{\sqrt{2}}{2}$, $\dfrac{1}{2}$

c. $\dfrac{\sqrt{3}}{3}$, 1, $\sqrt{3}$

On Your Own

EXERCISES 10–12 are independent, but they all emphasize the importance of the relative positions of the side lengths and angle measures in special right triangles. By looking at several configurations of the same type of triangle, students will become better able to recognize the special right triangles in different contexts.

Maintain Your Skills

EXERCISE 14 previews the trigonometric functions that Lesson 6.7 will introduce.

Additional Resources

PRINTED RESOURCES
- Texas Instruments Activities Workbook
- Cabrilog Activities
- Teaching Resources
- Practice Workbook
- Assessment Resources

TECHNOLOGY
- TeacherExpress CD-ROM
- **Exam***View* CD-ROM
- **PHSchool.com**
  - Homework Help
  - Video Tutors
  - Multiple Choice
  - Crosswords

Additional Practice

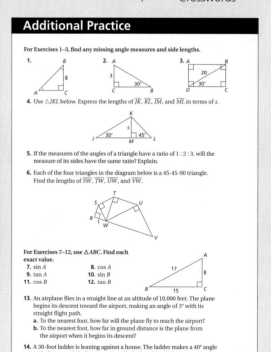

For Exercises 1–3, find any missing angle measures and side lengths.

4. Use $\triangle JKL$ below. Express the lengths of $\overline{JK}$, $\overline{KL}$, $\overline{JM}$, and $\overline{ML}$ in terms of s.

5. If the measures of the angles of a triangle have a ratio of $1:2:3$, will the measure of its sides have the same ratio? Explain.

6. Each of the four triangles in the diagram below is a 45-45-90 triangle. Find the lengths of $\overline{SW}$, $\overline{TW}$, $\overline{UW}$, and $\overline{VW}$.

For Exercises 7–12, use $\triangle ABC$. Find each exact value.

7. sin A   **8.** cos A
9. tan A   **10.** sin B
11. cos B   **12.** tan B

13. An airplane flies in a straight line at an altitude of 10,000 feet. The plane begins its descent toward the airport, making an angle of 3° with its straight flight path.
  a. To the nearest foot, how far will the plane fly to reach the airport?
  b. To the nearest foot, how far in ground distance is the plane from the airport when it begins its descent?

14. A 30-foot ladder is leaning against a house. The ladder makes a 40° angle with the ground. To the nearest tenth of a foot, how high up the side of the house is the top of the ladder?

Practice: For Lesson 6.6, assign Exercises 1–6.

Lesson Overview

GOAL

- Use the sine, cosine, and tangent functions and their inverses to find missing side lengths and angle measures in triangles.

This lesson leads students to a formal definition of sine, cosine, and tangent through a generalization of the special ratios they worked with in the previous lesson.

CHECK YOUR UNDERSTANDING
- Core: 2, 5
- Optional: 1, 3, 4

MATERIALS
- calculators
- geometry software or protractors, rulers, and compasses
- Blackline Master 6.7

HOMEWORK
- Core: 6, 7, 9, 11, 15, 16
- Optional: 8, 10, 12, 13, 14, 17, 18, 21, 22, 23
- Extension: 19, 20

VOCABULARY
- cosine ratio
- sine ratio
- tangent ratio
- trigonometry
- $\cos \theta$
- $\cos^{-1} x$
- $\sin \theta$
- $\sin^{-1} x$
- $\tan \theta$

Launch

Begin this lesson by reading the introductory paragraphs and assigning the In-Class Experiment.

Explore

In-Class Experiment

An easy way to construct a right triangle is to first draw a segment and then draw a circle that has the segment as its diameter. Remind students that any triangle inscribed in a semicircle is a right triangle. The hypotenuse of the right triangle is the diameter of the circle.

If you do not have access to geometry software, you can still assign this experiment. Have students draw several right triangles and use a protractor to measure the angles. You can give students copies of Blackline Master 6.7 to help them draw right triangles.

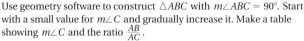

6.7 Some Special Ratios

If you have enough information to determine a triangle completely, then there ought to be a way to figure out all of the missing measurements. Right now, you can figure out the missing measurements for two special triangles: a 30-60-90 triangle and a 45-45-90 triangle.

For example, suppose you know that the hypotenuse of a 30-60-90 triangle is 4 feet long. From this information, you can conclude that the side opposite the 30° angle is 2 feet long. This is because you know that the ratio of the side opposite the 30° angle to the hypotenuse of a 30-60-90 triangle is always $\frac{1}{2}$.

The ratios of the side lengths of other right triangles are also constant ratios. For instance, suppose a nonright angle in one right triangle is congruent to a nonright angle in another right triangle. The two right triangles must be similar by the AA similarity test. So the ratio of two side lengths of the first right triangle must be equal to the ratio of the corresponding two side lengths of the other right triangle.

In the following In-Class Experiment, you will find the ratio of the side opposite a nonright angle to the hypotenuse in different right triangles.

> *To determine a triangle completely* means that you know enough measurements to guarantee that any other triangle with those measurements must be congruent to your triangle.

In-Class Experiment

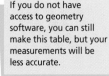

Use geometry software to construct $\triangle ABC$ with $m\angle ABC = 90°$. Start with a small value for $m\angle C$ and gradually increase it. Make a table showing $m\angle C$ and the ratio $\frac{AB}{AC}$.

1. As $m\angle C$ increases, what happens to the value of $\frac{AB}{AC}$?

2. What is the value of $\frac{AB}{AC}$ when $m\angle C = 30°$? When $m\angle C = 45°$? When $m\angle C = 60°$?

3. What value does the ratio $\frac{AB}{AC}$ approach as $m\angle C$ approaches 0°? As $m\angle C$ approaches 90°?

4. If $\frac{AB}{AC} \approx 0.34$, what is an approximate measure for $\angle C$?

Discuss your results with your classmates.

> If you do not have access to geometry software, you can still make this table, but your measurements will be less accurate.

The problems you have been solving in this investigation are all examples of **trigonometry,** the study of triangles, in action. For easy reference, names are given to some of the constant ratios found in right triangles. In right triangle ABC, the names of these ratios are given and defined on the following page.

Answers

In-Class Experiment

1. The value of the ratio increases and gets close to 1.

2. $\frac{1}{2}$; $\frac{\sqrt{2}}{2}$; $\frac{\sqrt{3}}{2}$

3. 0; 1

4. 20°

Trigonometric Ratios

The **sine** of $\angle A$ is defined as $\frac{BC}{AB}$, the ratio of the side opposite $\angle A$ to the hypotenuse.

Sine is often abbreviated as sin, so sin A is the same as sine A.

The **cosine** of $\angle A$ is defined as $\frac{AC}{AB}$, the ratio of the side adjacent to $\angle A$ to the hypotenuse.

Cosine is often abbreviated as cos, so cos A is the same as cosine A.

The **tangent** of $\angle A$ is defined as $\frac{BC}{AC}$, the ratio of the side opposite $\angle A$ to the side adjacent to $\angle A$.

Tangent is often abbreviated as tan, so tan A is the same as tangent A.

In this course, you define the sine, cosine, and tangent ratios of an acute angle of a right triangle as the ratios of the side lengths of the right triangle. So, you define these the trigonometric ratios for angles with measures that are greater than 0° and less than 90°.

In advanced algebra, you will extend the domain of the trigonometric functions and be able to evaluate them for angles that cannot occur in right triangles.

Facts and Notation

When you find the trigonometric ratio of an acute angle of a right triangle, you can identify the acute angle in three ways.

- by degree measure: sin 27°

- by vertex: sin A

- by Greek letter: sin θ

The notation you choose will depend on the figure you are considering. If more than one angle has the same vertex, you have to use a three-letter angle name, such as sin $\angle BAC$. The alternative is to name the interior of each angle with a Greek letter, such as θ.

You can find the values of sine, cosine, and tangent for any angle using the trigonometric functions on your calculator. For example, if you enter "tan 27°" into a calculator, it gives the value 0.51, to the nearest hundredth. Different calculators may evaluate trigonometric functions differently. Determine the keystrokes needed on your calculator to evaluate tan 27°.

Note that your calculator can give you the values of these functions to many decimal places of accuracy. However, even when your calculator shows a full display of digits, it may still be expressing an approximation of the actual value.

Wrap Up

End this lesson by assigning some Check Your Understanding exercises.

Assessment Resources

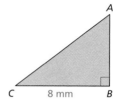

Problem In $\triangle ABC$, $m\angle B = 90°$ and $BC = 8$. The area of $\triangle ABC$ is 24 cm². Find the rest of the side lengths and angle measures of the triangle. Indicate whether your measurements are *exact* or *approximate* in each case.

Solution The height of the triangle relative to $\overline{BC}$ is AB.

To find AB, use the area formula for a triangle.

$$A_{\triangle ABC} = \frac{1}{2}(BC)(AB)$$

$$24 = \frac{1}{2}(8)(AB)$$

$$AB = 6$$

$\overline{AB}$ is exactly 6 cm is long.

Since $\triangle ABC$ is a right triangle, use the Pythagorean Theorem to find AC.

$$8^2 + 6^2 = (AC)^2$$

This gives $AC = 10$ cm, so $\overline{AC}$ is exactly 10 cm long.

To find the angle measures, use the inverse of a trigonometric function on your calculator. The notation $\sin^{-1}(0.6)$ is used for the *inverse* of the sine function. It means, "Find the angle with a sine of 0.6."

$$\sin C = \frac{6}{10}, \text{ so } m\angle C = \sin^{-1}(0.6)$$

$$m\angle C \approx 36.87°$$

Similarly,

$$\cos A = \frac{6}{10}, \text{ so } m\angle A = \cos^{-1}(0.6)$$

$$m\angle A \approx 53.13°$$

For You to Do

5. In $\triangle MIN$, $m\angle M = 25°$, $m\angle N = 90°$, and $MI = 5$ inches. Find the rest of the side lengths and angle measures of the triangle. Indicate whether your measurements are *exact* or *approximate* in each case.

Answers

For You to Do

5. $m\angle I = 65°$, $IN \approx 2.11$ in., $MN \approx 4.53$ in.

Exercises *Practicing Habits of Mind*

In the exercises for this lesson, be sure to indicate whether your solutions are *exact* or *approximate*. Find exact answers when possible.

Check Your Understanding

1. Rewrite these statements using the language of trigonometry:

   a. In right triangle *ABC* with $m\angle A = 40°$, the ratio of the side opposite $\angle A$ to the hypotenuse is 0.64.

   b. In right triangle *DEF* with $m\angle E = 70°$, the ratio of the side adjacent to $\angle E$ to the hypotenuse is 0.94.

   c. In right triangle *GHI* with $m\angle H = 55°$, the ratio of the side opposite $\angle H$ to the side adjacent is 0.82.

   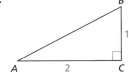

   The ratios in parts (a)–(c) are accurate to two decimal places.

   In Exercises 2 and 3,

   a. Find sin *A*, cos *A*, and tan *A* for each triangle.

   b. Find sin *B*, cos *B*, and tan *B* for each triangle.

   c. Which of your answers from parts (a) and (b) are the same? Explain.

2.

3.

4. Find sin *B* and cos *B* for isosceles triangle *ABC* at the right.

5. An airplane takes off and flies 10,000 feet in a straight line, making a 25° angle with the ground. How high above the ground does the airplane rise?

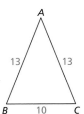

Exercises

HOMEWORK
- Core: 6, 7, 9, 11, 15, 16
- Optional: 8, 10, 12, 13, 14, 17, 18, 21, 22, 23
- Extension: 19, 20

Check Your Understanding

EXERCISE 4 asks students to find trigonometric ratios in a nonright triangle. Since this course only defines the trigonometric ratios in relation to right triangles, students will have to find a right triangle to consider. If they get stuck, suggest that they draw an altitude.

Exercises

1. a. $\sin 40° = 0.64$
   b. $\cos 70° = 0.34$
   c. $\tan 55° = 1.43$

2. a. $\sin A = \frac{4}{5}$, $\cos A = \frac{3}{5}$, $\tan A = \frac{4}{3}$

   b. $\sin B = \frac{3}{5}$, $\cos B = \frac{4}{5}$, $\tan B = \frac{3}{4}$

   c. $\sin A = \cos B$, and $\cos A = \sin B$; leg adjacent and leg opposite switch roles when you switch from $\angle A$ to $\angle B$.

3. a–c. See back of book.

4. $\sin B = \frac{12}{13}$, $\cos B = \frac{5}{13}$

5. about 4226 ft

On Your Own

EXERCISE 12 asks students to interpret their numerical results from Exercise 11, so assign Exercises 11 and 12 together.

On Your Own

6. In $\triangle TUB$, $m\angle T = 90°$, $m\angle U = 70°$, and $TU = 8$ cm. Find the rest of the side lengths and angle measures.

7. Standardized Test Prep Find $\sin \theta$, $\cos \theta$, and $\tan \theta$.

  A. $\sin \theta = \frac{1}{4}$, $\cos \theta = \frac{3}{4}$, $\tan \theta = 3$

  B. $\sin \theta = \frac{3}{\sqrt{10}}$, $\cos \theta = \frac{1}{\sqrt{10}}$, $\tan \theta = 3$

  C. $\sin \theta = 1$, $\cos \theta = 3$, $\tan \theta = \sqrt{10}$

  D. $\sin \theta = \frac{1}{\sqrt{10}}$, $\cos \theta = \frac{3}{\sqrt{10}}$, $\tan \theta = \frac{1}{3}$

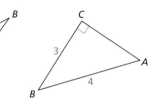

8. Triangle RST is a right triangle with right angle at S. If $\tan R = \frac{2}{3}$, find $\sin R$ and $\cos R$.

9. Triangle JKL is a right triangle with right angle at K. $\overline{JK}$ is three times the length of $\overline{KL}$. Find the sine, cosine, and tangent of $\angle J$ and of $\angle L$.

> Drawing a sketch will help.

10. For each right triangle below, find the exact values for the sine, cosine, and tangent of $\angle A$ and $\angle B$.

11. Use your calculator to evaluate the following expressions. Round your answers to the nearest hundredth.

  a. $\sin 33°$ **b.** $\cos 33°$ **c.** $\tan 33°$ **d.** $\frac{\sin 33°}{\cos 33°}$

  e. $\sin 57°$ **f.** $\cos 57°$ **g.** $\tan 57°$ **h.** $\frac{\sin 57°}{\cos 57°}$

12. In Exercise 11, there are several expressions that have the same value. Identify those expressions. In each case, explain why the two expressions are equal.

Refer to $\triangle ABC$ for Exercises 13–16.

13. Find $\sin \theta$, $\cos \theta$, and $\tan \theta$.

14. How is $\tan \theta$ related to $\sin \theta$ and $\cos \theta$? Write an equation that represents this relationship.

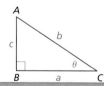

Answers

6. $m\angle B = 20°$, $UB \approx 23.39$ cm, $BT \approx 21.98$ cm

7. D

8. $\sin R = \frac{2\sqrt{13}}{13}$, $\cos R = \frac{3\sqrt{13}}{13}$

9. $\sin J = \frac{\sqrt{10}}{10}$, $\cos J = \frac{3\sqrt{10}}{10}$, $\tan J = \frac{1}{3}$, $\sin L = \frac{3\sqrt{10}}{10}$, $\cos L = \frac{\sqrt{10}}{10}$, $\tan L = 3$

10. See back of book.

11. a. ≈ 0.54 **b.** ≈ 0.84

    c. ≈ 0.65 **d.** ≈ 0.65

    e. ≈ 0.84 **f.** ≈ 0.54

    g. ≈ 1.54 **h.** ≈ 1.54

12. See back of book.

13. $\sin \theta = \frac{c}{b}$, $\cos \theta = \frac{a}{b}$, $\tan \theta = \frac{c}{a}$

14. $\tan \theta = \frac{\sin \theta}{\cos \theta}$

15. Sophia says the following equations are true for all values of θ.

$$\sin \theta = \cos 90° - \theta \qquad \cos \theta = \sin 90° - \theta$$

Is she right? Explain.

16. Joe says the following equation is true for all values of θ.

$$(\sin \theta)^2 + (\cos \theta)^2 = 1$$

Is he right? Try it out for a few numerical values of θ and then in a general triangle with sides a, b, and c.

> You will often see $(\sin \theta)^2$ written as $\sin^2(\theta)$. This is a common notation used to show a trigonometric function raised to a power.

17. To the nearest tenth, the value of $\tan 57°$ is 1.5. To the nearest thousandth, it is 1.540. Solve for the length of $\overline{BC}$ in $\triangle ABC$ using each of these values. By how much do your two answers differ?

18. The piece of paper below originally showed a complete right triangle, $\triangle ABC$, with right angle at C. The paper was ripped, though, so that all you can see now is $\angle A$.

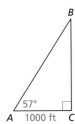

Find as many of these values as you can using a calculator. Some values might not be possible to find.

a. $\dfrac{BC}{AC}$ **b.** $AC + BC$ **c.** $\dfrac{BC}{AB}$ **d.** $AB \times AC$

e. $\dfrac{AC}{AB}$ **f.** $AB - BC$ **g.** $\dfrac{AC}{BC}$

---

15. Yes; use the diagram from Exercise 14. $\cos(90° - \theta) =$ $\cos A = \dfrac{c}{b} = \sin \theta$, and $\sin(90° - \theta) = \sin A =$ $\dfrac{a}{b} = \cos \theta$

16. Yes; use the diagram from Exercise 14. $(\sin \theta)^2 + (\cos \theta)^2 = \left(\dfrac{c}{b}\right)^2 +$ $\left(\dfrac{a}{b}\right)^2 = \dfrac{c^2 + a^2}{b^2} = \dfrac{b^2}{b^2} = 1$

17. With $\tan 57° \approx 1.5$ you get $BC \approx 1500$ ft; with $\tan 57° \approx 1.540$ you get

$BC \approx 1540$ ft. The difference between the two approximate values for BC is 40 ft.

18. a. $\tan 40° \approx 0.84$
　b. not possible
　c. $\sin 40° \approx 0.64$
　d. not possible
　e. $\cos 40° \approx 0.77$
　f. not possible
　g. $\tan 50° \approx 1.19$

EXERCISE 20 Students who do this exercise should first complete Exercise 19.

Additional Resources

PRINTED RESOURCES
- Texas Instruments Activities Workbook
- Cabrilog Activities
- Teaching Resources
- Practice Workbook
- Assessment Resources

TECHNOLOGY
- TeacherExpress CD-ROM
- **Exam**_View_ CD-ROM
- **PHSchool.com**
  - Homework Help
  - Video Tutors
  - Multiple Choice
  - Crosswords

Additional Practice

For Exercises 1–3, find any missing angle measures and side lengths.

1.

2.

3.

4. Use △JKL below. Express the lengths of $\overline{JK}$, $\overline{KL}$, $\overline{JM}$, and $\overline{ML}$ in terms of s.

5. If the measures of the angles of a triangle have a ratio of 1 : 2 : 3, will the measure of its sides have the same ratio? Explain.

6. Each of the four triangles in the diagram below is a 45-45-90 triangle. Find the lengths of $\overline{SW}$, $\overline{TW}$, $\overline{UW}$, and $\overline{VW}$.

For Exercises 7–12, use △ABC. Find each exact value.

7. sin A   8. cos A
9. tan A   10. sin B
11. cos B   12. tan B

13. An airplane flies in a straight line at an altitude of 10,000 feet. The plane begins its descent toward the airport, making an angle of 3° with its straight flight path.
   a. To the nearest foot, how far will the plane fly to reach the airport?
   b. To the nearest foot, how far in ground distance is the plane from the airport when it begins its descent?

14. A 30-foot ladder is leaning against a house. The ladder makes a 40° angle with the ground. To the nearest tenth of a foot, how high up the side of the house is the top of the ladder?

Practice: For Lesson 6.7, assign Exercises 7–14.

---

19. **Take It Further** Follow the steps in parts (a)–(f) below to find the exact value of cos 72°.

The isosceles triangle ABC at the left has base angles measuring 72°. AB = 1 and AC = 1.

The same triangle is at the right with $\overline{BD}$ bisecting ∠B. BD = x.

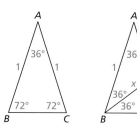

a. Find the lengths of $\overline{BC}$, $\overline{AD}$, and $\overline{DC}$ in terms of x.

b. Explain why △ABC ~ △BCD.

c. Write a proportion involving AB, BC, and CD.

d. Use your proportion from part (c) and the Quadratic Formula to solve for x.

e. Divide △ABC into two right triangles by drawing its altitude from A.

f. Use either of these right triangles and the value of x to find cos 72°.

Now find cos 72° on a calculator. Compare the value the calculator gives to the exact value you found.

20. **Take It Further** Find cos 36° by dividing △ABD in Exercise 19 into two right triangles. As in Exercise 19, compare this exact value to the value a calculator gives for cos 36°.

Maintain Your Skills

For each triangle, find the missing side lengths and angle measures.

21.

22.

23.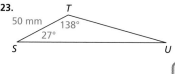

Go Online
PHSchool.com

For additional practice, go to **Web Code: bea-0607**

Answers

19. a. $BC = x$, $AD = x$, $DC = 1 - x$
    b. AA Similarity Test
    c. $\frac{AB}{BC} = \frac{BC}{CD}$, or $\frac{1}{x} = \frac{x}{1 - x}$
    d. $x = \frac{\sqrt{5} - 1}{2}$
    e. Check students' work.
    f. $\frac{\sqrt{5} - 1}{4}$

20. $\frac{1 + \sqrt{5}}{4}$

21. $m\angle N = 63°$, $MO \approx 44.55$ mm, $NO \approx 22.70$ mm

22. $m\angle R = 15°$, $PR \approx 84.72$ mm, $QR \approx 87.71$ mm

23. $m\angle U = 15°$, $SU \approx 129.27$ mm, $TU \approx 87.70$ mm

The trigonometric functions sine, cosine, and tangent have proven very valuable in determining missing side lengths and angle measures in right triangles. In this lesson, you will use trigonometric functions to determine areas and other measurements in nonright triangles.

Go Online
PHSchool.com

For more information about the history of trigonometry, go to
Web Code: bee-9031

Minds in Action   episode 26

Derman has made a discovery!

Derman I can find the area of any triangle if you tell me two sides and the included angle!

Tony Any triangle? Really? Okay, in $\triangle ABC$, $AB = 6$ cm, $AC = 8$ cm, and $m\angle B = 20°$.

Derman Here's my sketch.

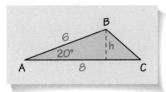

So $\frac{h}{6} = \sin 20°$ and $h = 6 \sin 20°$, which is about 2 cm. That means the area of $\triangle ABC$ is about $\frac{1}{2}(2)(8)$, or about 8 cm^2.

Tony Nice! Does it work if the angle is obtuse? After all, we've only defined the sine function for acute angles.

Derman I'm not sure. Let's try one.

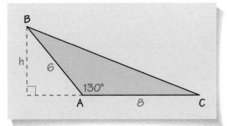

Lesson Overview

GOALS

• Use the sine, cosine, and tangent ratios and their inverses to find missing side lengths and angle measures in triangles.

• Find the area of any triangle given the lengths of two sides and the measure of their included angle.

In this lesson, students learn to use the trigonometric ratios to determine a height or a missing side length of a triangle. The dialog on this page and the worked-out example on page 483 help students understand how to do this.

CHECK YOUR UNDERSTANDING
• Core: 1, 4
• Optional: 2, 3, 5

MATERIALS
• calculators
• Blackline Master 6.8

HOMEWORK
• Core: 6, 9, 10, 12, 14, 16
• Optional: 7, 8, 11, 13, 15, 17, 18, 19, 21
• Extension: 20

VOCABULARY
• $\tan^{-1} x$

Launch

Begin this lesson by having students read and analyze the Minds in Action dialog.

Tony   I see how to do it. You just use the little right triangle that has the height as one of its legs.

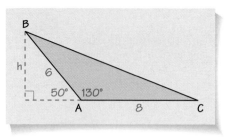

And we've got it. The area is approximately 36.8 cm².

Check Tony's calculations.

For You to Do

Find the area of each triangle.

1.

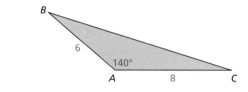

2.

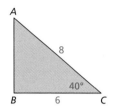

3.

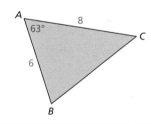

Answers

For You to Do

1. $24 \cdot \sin(40°) \approx 15.43$

2. $24 \cdot \sin(40°) \approx 15.43$

3. $24 \cdot \sin(63°) \approx 21.38$

In this lesson, you have already seen that you can determine the area of any triangle given two sides and their included angle. There should be a way to find approximations for the other two angle measures, and the missing side length, as well. The following example shows one way to do this.

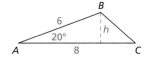

Problem Find the missing side length and angle measures in $\triangle ABC$.

Solution Derman has already found that the height of this triangle is approximately 2 cm. You can use the same technique to find the length marked x, and then y.

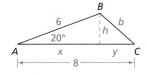

$$\frac{x}{6} = \cos 20° \qquad y = 8 - x$$

$$x = 6 \cos 20° \qquad y \approx 8 - 5.6$$

$$\approx 5.6 \text{ cm} \qquad \approx 2.4 \text{ cm}$$

Since $\tan C = \frac{h}{y}$, you can find $m\angle C$ and $m\angle B$.

$$\tan C = \frac{h}{y} \qquad\qquad m\angle B = 180° - m\angle A - m\angle C$$

$$m\angle C = \tan^{-1}\left(\frac{2}{2.4}\right) \qquad\qquad \approx 180° - 20° - 39.8°$$

$$\approx 39.8° \qquad\qquad \approx 120.2°$$

All that is left to find is b. One way to find it is to see that $\frac{h}{b} = \sin C$.

$$b = \frac{h}{\sin C}$$

$$\approx \frac{2}{0.64}$$

$$\approx 3.1 \text{ cm}$$

Example

Spend time as needed going over this completed example. Make sure students understand the problem. As necessary, help them use their calculators to confirm the solution.

Wrap Up

End this lesson by assigning some Check Your Understanding exercises.

Assessment Resources

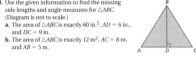
Exercises

For You to Do

4. Find the missing side length and angle measures.

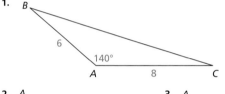

Exercises Practicing Habits of Mind

Check Your Understanding

In Exercises 1–3, find all the missing side lengths and angle measures of each triangle.

1.

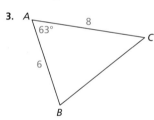

2.

3.

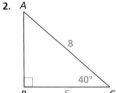

Answers

For You to Do

4. $BC \approx 12.72$; $m\angle B \approx 28.81°$; $m\angle C \approx 21.19°$

Exercises

1. $BC \approx 13.17$; $m\angle B \approx 22.98°$; $m\angle C \approx 17.02°$

2. $AB \approx 5.14$; $m\angle A \approx 48.57°$; $m\angle B \approx 91.43°$

3. $BC \approx 7.51$; $m\angle B \approx 71.62°$; $m\angle C \approx 45.38°$

4. a. Find the area of the triangle in terms of a, b, and θ.

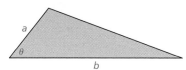

Remember...

θ (the Greek letter *theta*) is a variable that is often used to represent angle measures.

b. Use the area formula from part (a) to show that if you scale the triangle by the factor r, then you scale its area by r^2.

5. Find the area of parallelogram *ABCD*.

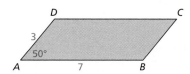

On Your Own

6. The altitude of $\triangle ABC$ from B intersects $\overline{AC}$ at D.

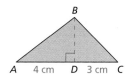

The area of $\triangle ABC$ is exactly 10.5 cm². $AD = 4$ cm and $DC = 3$ cm. Find the missing side lengths and angle measures.

Hint: Find the right triangles.

7. $\triangle DEW$ is isosceles. $DE = 65.3$ mm, $EW = 65.3$ mm, and $DW = 100$ mm. Find angle measures and area of $\triangle DEW$.

8. In $\triangle RAT$, $m\angle A = 80°$, $RA = 1.74$ in., and $AT = 5$ in. Find TR, the other angle measures, and the area of the triangle.

9. The area of $\triangle ABC$ is 30 in.², $AC = 10$ in., and $m\angle C = 45°$. Find the rest of the side lengths and angle measures.

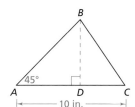

---

4. a. $A = \frac{1}{2}ab\sin\theta$

b. If you scale the given triangle by a factor of r, the lengths of the sides that form the given angle are ar and br. The angle of measure θ still has measure θ. The area of the scaled copy is $\frac{1}{2}(ar)(br)\sin\theta$, or $\left(\frac{1}{2}ab\sin\theta\right) \cdot r^2$.

5. Area(*ABCD*) $\approx$ 16.09

6. $AB = 5$ cm; $BC = 3\sqrt{2}$ cm; $m\angle A \approx 36.87°$; $m\angle C = 45°$

7. $m\angle D = m\angle W \approx 40.03°$; $m\angle E \approx 99.94°$; area($\triangle DEW$) $\approx$ 2100 mm²

8. $TR \approx 5.00$ in.; $m\angle R \approx 79.96°$; $m\angle T \approx 20.04°$; area($\triangle RAT$) ≈ 4.28 in.²

9. $AB \approx 8.49$ in., $BC \approx 7.21$ in.; $m\angle B \approx 78.69°$; $m\angle C \approx 56.31°$

On Your Own

EXERCISE 11 Give students copies of Blackline Master 6.8 and encourage them to divide the octagon into triangles.

10. **Standardized Test Prep** You are given that $AB = 4$, $BC = 5$, $AC = 7$, and the area of $\triangle ABC$ is 9.798. Which value is closest to $m\angle A$?

 A. 39.68 **B.** 44.48 **C.** 68.48 **D.** 708

11. Find the area of a regular octagon that has a side length of 4 inches. You might also consider this picture that shows the octagon sitting in a square. If you can find the area of the square and the four triangles, how will this help?

 Hint: Divide the octagon into triangles and find the area of each one.

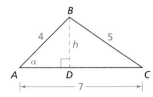

 In Exercises 12–15, find the missing side length and angle measures of each triangle.

12.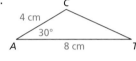

13.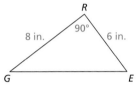

14.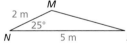

15.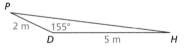

Answers

15. $PH \approx 6.86$ m; $m\angle H \approx 17.93°$; $m\angle P \approx 7.07°$

10. D

11. $(32 + 32\sqrt{2})$ in.^{2}, or about 77.25 in.^{2}; find the area of the square and then subtract the total area of the four triangles.

12. $CT \approx 4.96$ cm; $m\angle C \approx 126.21°$; $m\angle T \approx 23.79°$

13. $EG = 10$ in.; $m\angle E \approx 53.13°$; $m\angle G \approx 36.87°$

14. $MS \approx 3.30$ m; $m\angle M \approx 140.15°$; $m\angle S \approx 14.85°$

The Example earlier in this lesson demonstrated a technique you could use to find all the missing measurements for a triangle given the lengths of two sides and the measure of their included angle.

In Exercises 16–18, you will work through a technique that allows you to find all the missing measurements of a triangle given the measures of two angles and the length of their included side.

16. Explain why each equation is valid for $\triangle ABC$.

a. $h = c \sin 25°$ **b.** $h = a \sin 35°$

c. $c = \dfrac{a \sin 35°}{\sin 25°}$ **d.** $x = c \cos 25°$

e. $y = a \cos 35°$ **f.** $a \cos 35° + c \cos 25° = 9$

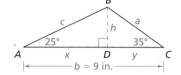

17. Find approximations for a and c in $\triangle ABC$ from Exercise 16.

18. Use the value you found for a and the given values for AC and $m\angle C$ to find c using the method from the Example. Did you get the same value for c as you did in Exercise 17?

19. Find the missing side lengths and angle measure of $\triangle REX$.

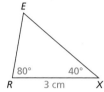

20. **Take It Further** Find the value of α in the triangle below.

Maintain Your Skills

21. There are many triangles with two sides measuring 4 in. and 6 in. Among those triangles, which one has the maximum area? To investigate this question, use $\triangle ABC$ with $AB = 4$ in. and $BC = 6$ in. Using the different values for $m\angle B$ below, calculate the area. Which value of $m\angle B$ gives the largest area for the triangle?

a. $m\angle B = 10°$ **b.** $m\angle B = 30°$ **c.** $m\angle B = 50°$ **d.** $m\angle B = 70°$

e. $m\angle B = 90°$ **f.** $m\angle B = 110°$ **g.** $m\angle B = 130°$

Go Online
PHSchool.com

For additional practice,
go to **Web Code: bea-0608**

---

16. a. definition of sin 25° (using $\triangle ABX$) and basic moves
   b. definition of sin 35° (using $\triangle BCX$) and basic moves
   c. From parts (a) and (b), $c(\sin 25°) = a(\sin 35°)$. Solve for c.
   d. definition of cos 25° (using $\triangle ABX$) and basic moves
   e. definition of cos 35° (using $\triangle BCX$) and basic moves
   f. $AC = x + y$ together with the equations in parts (d) and (e)

17. $a \approx 4.39$ in., $c \approx 5.96$ in.

18. yes

19. $RE \approx 2.23$ cm; $EX \approx 3.41$ cm; $m\angle E = 60°$

20. $\alpha \approx 55.77°$

21. a. about 2.08 in.^{2}
   b. 6 in.^{2}
   c. about 9.19 in.^{2}
   d. about 11.28 in.^{2}
   e. 12 in.^{2}
   f. about 11.28 in.^{2}
   g. about 9.19 in.^{2}
   $m\angle B = 90°$ gives the greatest area.

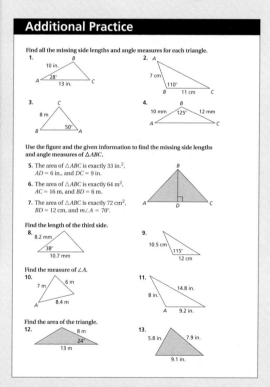

Lesson Overview

In this lesson, students generalize the Pythagorean Theorem into the Law of Cosines, which works for nonright triangles, as well as for right triangles. The Law of Cosines, along with the inverses of the trigonometric ratios, allows students to find the angle measures of a triangle given only its side lengths.

CHECK YOUR UNDERSTANDING
- Core: 1, 3
- Optional: 2, 4

HOMEWORK
- Core: 5, 7, 9, 10
- Optional: 6, 8, 11, 12, 13, 14, 15, 16, 17, 18, 19

MATERIALS
- calculators
- compasses
- geometry software
- markers or colored pencils
- protractors
- rulers
- Blackline Master 6.9

Launch

Begin this lesson by assigning For Discussion Problems 1–3. You may want to divide your students into groups to complete this activity.

You have determined missing side lengths and angle measures in triangles for which you have enough information to determine the triangle completely. Use the For Discussion questions below to reflect on what you have learned.

For Discussion

In your group, discuss one of the following questions. Be prepared to present your results to the class.

1. You have two angle measures and one side length of a triangle. Can you find the missing angle measure and the other two side lengths? If so, explain how.

2. You have two side lengths of a triangle and the measure of their included angle. Can you find the missing angle measures and the other side length? If so, explain how.

3. You have three side lengths of a triangle. Can you find its angle measures? If so, explain how.

If your group discussed Problem 3, you may have felt that it must be possible to use inverse trigonometric functions to find the angle measures of a triangle if you know its side lengths. But you may have had trouble describing a technique. Here is an example that shows you how to do it.

Example

Problem Given $\triangle ABC$ with side lengths a, b, and c, find an equation that relates these side lengths to the measure of angle $m\angle C$.

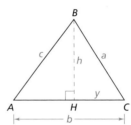

Answers

For Discussion

1. Yes; answers may vary. Sample: find the missing angle by adding the two angle measures and subtracting from 180°. You cannot find the other two side lengths.

2. Yes: answers may vary. Use the sine of the given angle to find the area of the triangle. If you know the area and a given side a, you can find the height h. Use the cosine of the given angle to find the measure of a segment b of the known side. Subtract this number from the known side length $(a - b)$ to find the missing segment of the known side length c. Then, find the tangent of the angle opposite the known angle by using h and c. This provides the measure of another angle. Subtract the sum of the known angles from 180° to find the measure of the third angle.

3. Yes; answers may vary. Sample: Use the inverse trigonometric functions to find the angle measures.

Solution $\triangle BCH$ is a right triangle, so you can use the Pythagorean Theorem.

$$a^2 = y^2 + h^2$$

Similarly, $\triangle ABH$ is a right triangle.

$$c^2 = (b - y)^2 + h^2$$

This leads to the following equation.

$$c^2 = b^2 - 2by + y^2 + h^2$$

Remember that $a^2 = y^2 + h^2$. This means that you can write the following.

$$c^2 = b^2 - 2by + a^2$$

You know that $y = a \cos C$, so with a little rearrangement you get the following.

$$c^2 = a^2 + b^2 - 2ab \cos C$$

You can use a similar process to relate the same three side lengths of $\triangle ABC$ to either of its other angles. Here are the resulting equations.

$$a^2 = b^2 + c^2 - 2bc \cos A$$

$$b^2 = a^2 + c^2 - 2ac \cos B$$

The equations above, called the Law of Cosines, relate the side lengths of a triangle to the measure of one angle of the triangle.

- the third side length of a triangle when you know two side lengths and the measure of the included angle

- the measure of an angle of a triangle when you know the three side lengths

In the second application, you solve for the cosine of the angle. Then you use the inverse of the cosine function to find the angle measure.

> In advanced algebra, you will learn the meaning of cosine for *any* angle. For now, when you use the Law of Cosines with a triangle, you must use the Law of Cosines equation that refers to an angle that you know is acute.

For You to Do

4. Find AC for $\triangle ABC$.

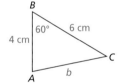

5. Find $m\angle A$ for $\triangle ABC$.

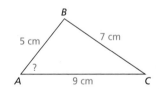

For You to Do

4. about 5.29 cm

5. about 50.70°

Explore

Developing Habits of Mind

Have students work through the proof of the Law of Cosines. Students can construct the diagram for the proof using geometry software or hand construction tools. If students use hand construction tools, you can give them copies of Blackline Master 6.9 to help them start their constructions.

Understand the Process. An efficient way to present an argument is to give its major steps. If the major steps convince others, then you can move on. If not, you can fill in selected details. This saves you from having to provide the details that are already common knowledge.

Watch how this works in the following colorful proof of the Law of Cosines.

Proof of the Law of Cosines, $c^2 = a^2 + b^2 - 2ab\cos C$

The diagram shows $\triangle ABC$ with squares on each side of the triangle. You divide each square into two rectangles by drawing perpendiculars from A, B, and C. You also need dashed $\overline{CQ}$ and $\overline{BV}$.

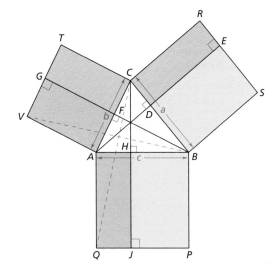

Habits of Mind

Explore the possibilities. If you have access to geometry software, construct the figure. Drag a vertex of $\triangle ABC$ and see what happens to the colored rectangles. When do the blue and green ones disappear?

Complete the steps below to draw the diagram used in this proof. This will help you understand the proof. Use labels to match those shown below.

- Copy $\triangle ABC$ onto a separate sheet of paper.
- Draw squares on each side of $\triangle ABC$.
- Draw perpendiculars from A, B, and C. (Extend the perpendiculars across the squares.)
- Draw dashed segments from C to Q and V to B.

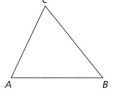

Convince yourself that if each step below is true, then the Law of Cosines is true.

Step 1 The purple rectangles have equal areas.

Step 2 The yellow rectangles have equal areas.

Step 3 The green rectangles have equal areas. The area of each rectangle is $ab\cos C$.

Step 4 This equation refers to the area of each figure:

$$\square ABPQ = \square ACTV + \square BCRS - 2 \text{ green rectangles}$$

Step 5 $c^2 = a^2 + b^2 - 2ab\cos C$

The details below may help you convince yourself that each step above is correct.

Step 1 area $\square AHJQ = 2 \cdot$ area $\triangle AQC$

area $\square AFGV = 2 \cdot$ area $\triangle ABV$

area $\triangle AQC$ = area $\triangle ABV$

area $\square AHJQ =$ area $\square AFGV$

Step 2 You will provide the details for Step 2 in the For You to Do section below.

Step 3 area $\square FCTG = b \cdot CF$ area $\square DCRE = a \cdot CD$

$\cos C = \dfrac{CF}{a}$ (in $\triangle CFB$) $\cos C = \dfrac{CD}{b}$ (in $\triangle CDA$)

$CF = a\cos C$ $\cos C = b\cos C$

So, area $\square FCTG = ab\cos C$.   So, area $\square DCRE = ab\cos C$.

Step 4 In terms of colors, Step 4 says the following.
(purple + yellow) = (purple + green) + (yellow + green) − 2 greens

Step 5 This step follows from the original Step 4 by substituting the equivalent expressions for areas into Step 4.

You may want to fill in even more details.

Step 1 $\square AHJQ$ and $\triangle AQC$ have the same base and height, so area $\square AHJQ = 2 \cdot$ area $\triangle AQC$.
Area $\triangle AQC = \triangle ABV$ because $\triangle AQC \cong \triangle ABV$ by SAS.
$\square AFGV$ and $\triangle ABV$ have the same base and height, so area $\square AFGV = 2 \cdot$ area $\triangle ABV$.

If you need to clarify even more details of the proof, work with a classmate.

For You to Do

6. Fill in the details for Step 2.

Wrap Up

End this lesson by assigning some Check Your Understanding exercises.

Assessment Resources

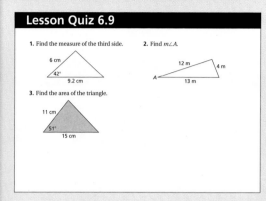
Answers

For You to Do

6. Draw $\overline{AE}$ and $\overline{CQ}$. By SAS, $\triangle ABE \cong \triangle QBC$. But $\triangle ABE$ has half the area of the yellow region that has $\overline{PE}$ as a side, and $\triangle QBC$ has half the area of the yellow region that has $\overline{ZQ}$ as a side. Therefore, the yellow regions have the same area.

Exercises

HOMEWORK
- Core: 5, 7, 9, 10
- Optional: 6, 8, 11, 12, 13, 14, 15, 16, 17, 18, 19

Exercises *Practicing Habits of Mind*

Check Your Understanding

1. Find *AC*.

2. Find *BC*.

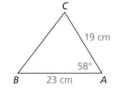

3. Find $m\angle B$.

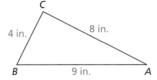

4. Find $m\angle A$.

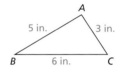

On Your Own

5. Find the missing side length, angle measures, and area of △*CAT*.

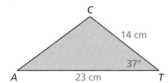

Answers

Exercises

1. about 1.49 m²

2. about 20.66 cm

3. about 62.72°

4. about 93.82°

5. $m\angle A \approx 35.48°$; $m\angle C \approx 107.52°$; $AC \approx 14.51$ cm; area(△*CAT*) ≈ 98.89 cm²

6. Find the missing angle measures and area of △*DOG*.

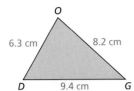

7. Standardized Test Prep A community group is building a fenced-in triangular space for a dog park. They know that two sides of the park will be 35 m and 25 m. Because of a nearby pond, the angle between these two sides will have to measure 40°. What will be the perimeter of the dog park?

A. 23 m   **B.** 60 m

C. 83 m   **D.** 110 m

8. A regular pentagon is inscribed in a circle of radius 1. What is the length of one of its sides?

9. Write About It Explain how the Law of Cosines is an extension of the Pythagorean Theorem.

10. Write About It Explain how you would approach the problem of finding all of the missing angle measures and the area of a triangle for which you know the three side lengths.

11. Write About It You know the lengths of two sides of a triangle and the measure of their included acute angle. Explain how you would find the length of the third side, the measures of the other two angles, and the area of the triangle. How would your work be different if the angle measure you knew was obtuse?

---

6. $m\angle D \approx 59.11°$; $m\angle G \approx 41.25°$;
$m\angle O \approx 79.65°$;
area(△*DOG*) $\approx 25.41\,\text{cm}^2$

7. C

8. about 1.18

9. Answers may vary. Sample: The Pythagorean Theorem tells you how the squares of the lengths of two sides of a triangle are related to the square of the length of the third side if the included angle for the first two sides is a right angle. The Law of Cosines tells you what

the relationship is if the included angle is an acute angle.

10. See back of book.

11. See back of book.

On Your Own

EXERCISES 12 AND 13 give students a preview of the Law of Sines.

12. Find the missing angle measures of △*ABC*. Then compute the ratios below.

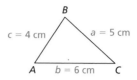

    a. $\frac{\sin A}{a}$ **b.** $\frac{\sin B}{b}$ **c.** $\frac{\sin C}{c}$

13. Find the missing side lengths and angle measure of △*ABC*. Then compute the ratios below.

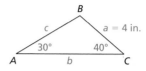

    a. $\frac{\sin A}{a}$ **b.** $\frac{\sin B}{b}$ **c.** $\frac{\sin C}{c}$

14. Find the missing side length and angle measures of △*ABC*. Then compute the ratios below.

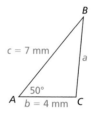

    a. $\frac{\sin A}{a}$ **b.** $\frac{\sin B}{b}$ **c.** $\frac{\sin C}{c}$

Answers

12. a. about 0.165
    b. about 0.165
    c. about 0.165

13. a. about 0.125
    b. about 0.125
    c. about 0.125

14. a. about 0.142
    b. about 0.142
    c. about 0.142

For Exercises 15–18, prove that the area of the figure on the hypotenuse is equal to the sum of the areas of the figures on the legs of the right triangle.

15.

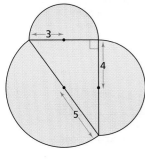

16.

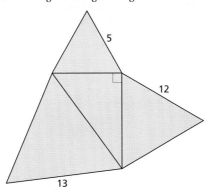

17.

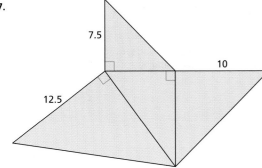

18.

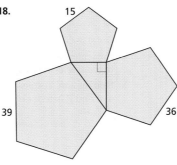

19. Use your results from Exercises 15–18 to prove the Pythagorean Theorem for all sets of similar figures.

Go Online
PHSchool.com

For additional practice, go to **Web Code: bea-0609**

Additional Resources

PRINTED RESOURCES
- Texas Instruments Activities Workbook
- Cabrilog Activities
- Teaching Resources
- Practice Workbook
- Assessment Resources

TECHNOLOGY
- TeacherExpress CD-ROM
- **Exam***View* CD-ROM
- **PHSchool.com**
  - Homework Help
  - Video Turors
  - Multiple Choice
  - Crosswords

Additional Practice

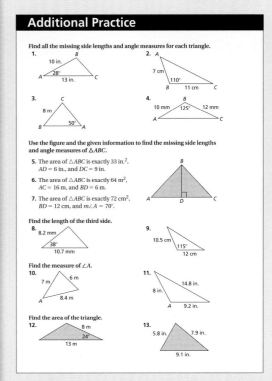

Practice: For Lesson 6.9, assign Exercises 8–13.

---

15. area of the circle on the hypotenuse $= 25\pi$

area of the circle on short leg $= 9\pi$

area of circle on long leg $= 16\pi$

$9\pi + 16\pi = 25\pi$.

16. area of triangle on the hypotenuse $= 42.25\sqrt{3}$

area of triangle on short leg $A = 6.25\sqrt{3}$

area of triangle on long leg $B = 36\sqrt{3}$

$6.25\sqrt{3} + 36\sqrt{3} = 42.25\sqrt{3}$

17. area of triangle on the hypotenuse $= 78.125$

area of triangle on short leg $A = 28.125$

area of triangle on long leg $B = 50$ $28.125 + 50 = 78.125$

18. See back of book.

19. The area of the figures of the legs of all the right triangles equals the area of the figure on the hypotenuse. Therefore, $a^2 + b^2 = c^2$ for all similar figures.

Mathematical Reflections

EXERCISES 4–6 At the start of the investigation, you may have assigned these as Questions 1–3 for students to think and write about.

Mathematical Reflections 6B

In this investigation, you learned how to use trigonometric functions. You found areas, angle measures, and side lengths of triangles. You used right triangles to solve problems. These questions will help you summarize what you have learned.

1. A wheelchair access ramp must slope at a 10° angle.

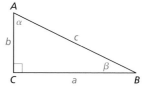

   a. If the ramp meets the ground 25 feet from the base of the building, how long is the ramp?

   b. Construction workers are building a ramp up to a door that is 2 feet off the ground. Find the length of the ramp.

2. $\triangle JKL$ is a right triangle with right angle at K. If $\overline{JK}$ is three times the length of $\overline{KL}$, find the sine, cosine, and tangent of $\angle J$ and $\angle L$.

3. Given $\triangle ABC$ with $AB = 4$, $BC = 3$, and $AC = 6$, find the measure of angle C.

4. How can you use half of a square or half of an equilateral triangle to evaluate trigonometric functions for angles measuring 30°, 45°, and 60°?

5. Find the sine, cosine, and tangent of α and β in terms of the sides of $\triangle ABC$.

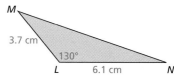

6. What is the area of $\triangle LMN$? What is the approximate length of $\overline{MN}$?

Vocabulary and Notation

In this investigation, you saw these terms and symbols for the first time. Make sure you understand what each one means and how to use it.

- trigonometry
- sine ratio
- cosine ratio
- tangent ratio
- $\sin\theta$
- $\cos\theta$
- $\tan\theta$
- $\sin^{-1} x$
- $\cos^{-1} x$
- $\tan^{-1} x$

The ladder can reach out $\ell\cos\theta$ and up a height of $t + \ell\sin\theta$. ℓ can extend as θ increases.

Mathematical Reflections

1. a. about 25.39 ft
   b. about 11.52 ft

2. $\sin J = \dfrac{\sqrt{10}}{10}$, $\cos J = \dfrac{3\sqrt{10}}{10}$

   $\tan J = \dfrac{1}{3}$, $\sin L = \dfrac{3\sqrt{10}}{10}$,

   $\cos L = \dfrac{\sqrt{10}}{10}$ $\tan L = 3$

3. about 36.34°

4. See back of book.

5. $\sin\alpha = \dfrac{a}{c}$, $\cos\alpha = \dfrac{b}{c}$,

   $\tan\alpha = \dfrac{a}{b}$, $\sin\beta = \dfrac{b}{c}$,

   $\cos\beta = \dfrac{a}{c}$, $\tan\beta = \dfrac{b}{a}$

6. 8.64 cm^2; 8.94 cm

Mid-Chapter Test

Multiple Choice

1. In $\triangle ABC$, $AH = 12$ cm and $HB = 3$ cm. Find CB.

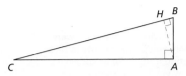

A. 12.4   **B.** 36   **C.** 51   **D.** 153

2. A right triangle with a 45° angle has a hypotenuse of 16. Find the measure of the third angle and the lengths of its legs.

A. 90°, $8\sqrt{2}$, 16   **B.** 45°, $8\sqrt{2}$, $8\sqrt{2}$

C. 45°, 16, 22.6   **D.** 135°, $8\sqrt{2}$, $8\sqrt{2}$

Open Response

3. Find the arithmetic mean and the geometric mean of 4 and 16. Use a numerical computation and then a geometric construction.

4. Construct a rectangle with the same area as $ABCD$ that has $\overline{EF}$ as a side.

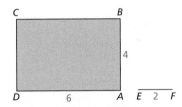

5. Determine whether each statement is true or false. Explain your reasoning.

a. A triangle has three altitudes.

b. The altitudes of a triangle are concurrent.

c. The point in which two altitudes of a triangle intersect divides each altitude into segments with ratio 1 : 2.

d. In an equilateral triangle, the altitudes are concurrent.

e. In an equilateral triangle, the point in which two altitudes intersect divides each altitude into segments with ratio 1 : 2.

6. Find the missing side lengths and angle measures of $\triangle ABC$.

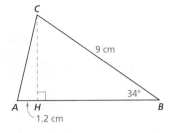

7. The area of the triangle below is 78 cm². $AD = 8$ cm and $m\angle BAD = 60°$. Find the rest of the side lengths and angle measures.

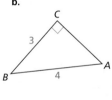

8. For each right triangle below, find the exact values for sine, cosine, and tangent of $\angle A$ and $\angle B$.

a.

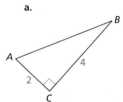

b.

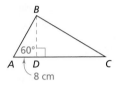

9. Find the missing angle and side lengths for $\triangle MNO$.

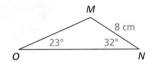

Go Online PHSchool.com

For a mid-chapter test, go to Web Code: bea-0652

Mid-Chapter Test

Assessment Resources

Mid-Chapter Test

1. Find the arithmetic and the geometric means of 7 and 12. Use a numerical calculation and then a geometric construction.

2. Here is a rectangle and one side of a second rectangle. Use the power of a point construction to construct a rectangle with the same area as $ABCD$ that has $\overline{EF}$ as a side.

3. In the triangle below, suppose that $AB = 14$ mm and $HB = 7$ mm. Find CB. (Diagram is not to scale.)

4. Decide whether each statement is true. If the statement is false, explain why.

a. Concurrence of medians means that the three medians of a triangle lie on the same line.

b. The three medians of a triangle intersect in a point.

c. The point at which two medians intersect divides each median in half.

d. In an isosceles triangle, one median is also an altitude.

5. A right triangle with a 30° angle has hypotenuse length 14 m. Find the measure of the third angle and the lengths of the legs.

6. Find the missing side lengths and angle measures of the triangle below.

7. The area of $\triangle ABC$ is 62 in.², $BD = 10$ in., and $m\angle ABD = 30°$. Find the rest of the side lengths and angle measures.

Mid-Chapter Test

1. C   **2.** B   **3.** 10; 8.

4. Check students' work.

5. a. True; a triangle has three vertices, therefore it has three altitudes.

b. True; see Exercise 8 of Lesson 6.4.

c. False; two altitudes of a right triangle intersect at a vertex of the triangle.

6. $AB \approx 8.66$ cm; $AC \approx 5.17$ cm; $m\angle A \approx 76.59°$; $m\angle ACB \approx 69.41°$

7. $AB = 16$ cm; $BC \approx 14.23$ cm; $AC \approx 11.25$ cm; $m\angle ABC \approx 43.23°$; $m\angle C \approx 76.77°$

8. a. $\sin A = \dfrac{2}{\sqrt{5}}$; $\cos A = \dfrac{1}{\sqrt{5}}$; $\tan A = 2$; $\sin B = \dfrac{1}{\sqrt{5}}$; $\cos B = \dfrac{2}{\sqrt{5}}$; $\tan B = \dfrac{1}{2}$

b. $\sin A = \dfrac{3}{4}$; $\cos A = \dfrac{\sqrt{7}}{4}$; $\tan A = \dfrac{3}{\sqrt{7}}$; $\sin B = \dfrac{\sqrt{7}}{4}$; $\cos B = \dfrac{3}{4}$; $\tan B = \dfrac{\sqrt{7}}{3}$

9. See back of book.

Investigation Overview

In this investigation, students will develop new justifications for some of the volume formulas they used in Chapter 4. Students will learn to visualize a solid as a stack of extremely thin cross sections cut by a series of parallel planes. This technique previews ideas essential to calculus, in which students will visualize the area under a curve as a series of extremely thin rectangles or the volume of a solid of revolution as a stack of extremely thin rings.

Cavalieri's Principle allows students to use the formula for the volume of a rectangular prism to prove volume formulas for any prism or cylinder. Students will also use the volume of a square pyramid to prove the volume formulas for a general pyramid or cone. They can do this after they see the relationship between the volumes of a cube and a square pyramid with equal heights and with congruent square bases. Students will also prove the volume formula for a sphere by relating the volume of a sphere to the volume of a cylinder with a double cone removed from it.

You may wish to assign Questions 1–3 for students to think and write about during the investigation.

Learning Goals

- Find the areas of cross sections formed when planes intersect with solids under certain conditions.
- Understand and use Cavalieri's Principle.
- Prove basic volume formulas using Cavalieri's Principle.

Habits and Skills

- Visualize cross sections of solids.
- Use similar triangles to find measurements of cross sections.
- Choose appropriate solids to compare using Cavalieri's Principle.

Investigation 6C

Volume Formulas

In *Volume Formulas*, you will learn a new technique for finding the volume of a solid. In Investigation 3D, you found the volumes and surface areas of some three-dimensional solids.

For many of the solids, you worked with formulas that were given to you. In this investigation, you will learn how to find the volume of a solid by comparing it to a solid of known volume. This technique will allow you to prove some of the formulas you were told about in Chapter 3, including the volume formula for spheres.

By the end of this investigation, you will be able to answer questions like these:

1. A hexagonal pyramid of height h is cut by a plane parallel to its base at height r above the base. How is the shape of the resulting cross section related to the shape of the base of the pyramid? How are their areas related?

2. Explain Cavalieri's Principle.

3. A spherical melon has radius 3 inches. You cut a slice 2 inches from its center. What is the volume of the piece you cut from the melon?

You will learn how to

- find the areas of cross sections formed when planes intersect with solids under certain conditions
- understand and use Cavalieri's Principle
- prove basic volume formulas using Cavalieri's Principle

You will develop these habits and skills:

- Visualize cross sections of solids.
- Use similar triangles to find measurements of cross sections.
- Choose appropriate solids to compare using Cavalieri's Principle.

The two stacks have identical bases and the same height. How do the numbers of napkins in the stacks compare?

Investigation Road Map

LESSON 6.10, *Getting Started,* asks students to reason and visualize dilations in three dimensions using the ratio method from Chapter 4. This lesson introduces ideas that students will use throughout the investigation.

LESSON 6.11, *Cavalieri's Principle,* introduces Cavalieri's Principle for finding the volumes of solids under certain conditions.

LESSON 6.12, *Proving Volume Formulas,* asks students to prove the volume formulas for prisms and cylinders from the volume formula for a rectangular prism and to prove the volume formulas for pyramids and cones from the volume formula for a square pyramid.

LESSON 6.13, *Volume of a Sphere,* has students use Cavalieri's Principle to prove that the volume of a sphere is $\frac{4}{3}\pi$ times its radius cubed by comparing a sphere to the solid formed from a cylinder with a double cone removed from it.

Activating Prior Knowledge
Exploring New Ideas

In Chapter 1, you did some preliminary work in visualizing the cross sections of different three-dimensional objects cut by planes. Now you can describe these cross sections more thoroughly. The Ratio and Parallel methods for dilation that you learned in Chapter 4 also work in three dimensions. Work in groups of at least three to complete the following experiment.

In-Class Experiment

You will need: cardboard, scissors, string, markers, tape, paper, and a ruler.

Step 1 Cut a triangle out of a piece of cardboard.

Step 2 Now punch three small holes near the vertices of your cardboard triangle.

Step 3 Pass the end of a piece of string through each hole.

Step 4 Have one student hold the cardboard triangle so that it is in a plane parallel to the plane of the desk.

Step 5 Have another student gather the three pieces of string together above the triangle.

Step 6 Have the third student stretch the other ends of the strings out and tape them to a piece of paper on the desk. Mark the three points where the strings touch the desk, and connect them to form a new triangle.

Step 7 Mark the strings where they touch the apex A, the cardboard triangle B, and the paper triangle C. Find the ratios $\frac{AB}{AC}$ for each string. How do they compare?

Step 8 Now compare the cardboard triangle to the triangle drawn on the paper.

As you discuss your results with the whole class, relate the experience to dilation by the Ratio Method.

• Where is the center of dilation in this experiment?

• Why were the strings cut proportionally by the cardboard triangle?

• What is the relationship between the cardboard triangle and the paper triangle?

This is a very important job. You must hold the triangle in a plane parallel to the plane of the desk at all times.

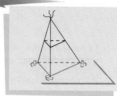

Answers

In-Class Experiment

1-6. Check students' work.

7. The ratios should be about the same.

8. The center of the dilation is at apex A; the strings were cut proportionally because they have the same ratio; the triangles are similar.

Lesson Overview

GOALS

• Warm up to the ideas of the investigation.

• Use a hands-on approach to develop mathematical habits of mind.

• Find the areas of cross sections formed when planes intersect with solids under certain conditions.

This lesson helps students become familiar, once again, with three-dimensional solids. It also allows students to preview ideas that they will be using throughout the investigation. In particular, it introduces the idea of using the ratio method for dilation in three dimensions.

FOR YOU TO EXPLORE
• Core: 1, 2
• Optional: 3, 4

MATERIALS
• cardboard
• markers
• rulers
• scissors
• string
• tape

HOMEWORK
• Core: 5, 6, 10
• Optional: 7, 8, 9, 11, 12, 13, 14

Launch

Begin this lesson by assigning students to work on the In-Class Experiment in groups.

Explore

In-Class Experiment

This experiment helps students gain a concrete visualization of dilation in three dimensions. In three dimensions, dilation works the same as it does in two dimensions. The ratios $\frac{AB}{AC}$ are equal for each string, and the cardboard triangle on the paper is simply a dilation of the cardboard triangle each student made.

Students can prove this by looking at each side of the pyramid that results from uniting the strings. Have students consider one face of the pyramid. It is a triangle cut by a segment (the side of the cardboard triangle) parallel to its base. Therefore, by the Parallel Side-Splitter Theorem, the ratios $\frac{AB}{AC}$ must be the same for each string.

Wrap Up

End this lesson by having students do the For You to Explore problems on the following page.

In the In-Class Experiment, you showed that the Ratio Method works in three dimensions. So when you cut a pyramid with a plane parallel to the base of the pyramid, the resulting cross section will be a polygon similar to the base of the pyramid.

For You to Explore

1. A right square pyramid has a base with side length 6 in. and height 9 in. A plane cuts the pyramid 3 inches above and parallel to the base.

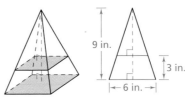

Describe the shape of the intersection of the pyramid with the cross-sectional plane. Calculate the area of the cross section.

2. The pyramid from Exercise 1 is cut by a plane that is parallel to its base and h inches above its base. Describe the resulting cross section. Calculate the area of the cross section in terms of h.

3. The square pyramid below has a base with side length 8 cm and height 5 cm.

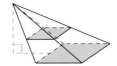

A plane parallel to the plane of its base cuts the pyramid 3 cm below its apex. Describe the resulting cross section. Calculate its area.

4. This cone has height 6 inches and a base with radius 2 inches.

You plan to cut the cone parallel to its base so that the area of the resulting cross section will be 2 square inches. At what height from the base should you cut the cone?

Answers

For You to Explore

1. a square 4 in. on each side; 16 in.^{2}

2. a square $\left(6 - \frac{2}{3}h\right)$ in. on each side; $\left(6 - \frac{2}{3}h\right)^2$ in.^{2}

3. a square 4.8 cm on each side; 23.04 cm^2

4. $6 - \frac{3\sqrt{2}\pi}{\pi}$ in.

Exercises *Practicing Habits of Mind*

On Your Own

5. A line parallel to $\overline{BC}$ intersects $\triangle ABC$ in $\overline{DE}$ as shown.

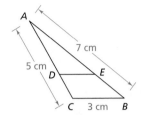

a. Find *DE* if the distance from *D* to $\overleftrightarrow{BC}$ is 1 cm.

b. What is the distance from *D* to $\overleftrightarrow{BC}$ when *DE* is 2 cm?

6. This triangular pyramid has a base with area 4 cm² and height 2 cm.

a. The pyramid is cut by a plane parallel to its base and 1 cm above it. Find the area of the cross section.

b. You want to make a parallel cross section of the pyramid with area 3 cm². How high above the base of the pyramid must you cut?

> **Go Online**
> **Video Tutor**
> PHSchool.com
>
> **Web Code: bee-0775**

7. A line intersects a circle of radius 6 cm.

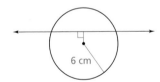

a. If the line is 2 cm from the center of the circle, what is the length of the chord?

b. If the chord has length 10.4 cm, how far is the line from the center?

Exercises

5. a. about 2.31 cm
   b. about 1.44 cm

6. a. 1cm²
   b. $2 - \sqrt{3}$ in.

7. a. $8\sqrt{2}$ cm
   b. $\frac{4\sqrt{14}}{5}$ cm

On Your Own

EXERCISES 10–14 preview Cavalieri's Principle, which students will learn in Lesson 6.11. In these exercises, students find and compare cross sections of two solids at different heights. To use Cavalieri's Principle, students will compare cross sections of two solids at every height.

EXERCISE 10 Encourage your students to find the exact answer to this exercise, as well as a decimal approximation. Remind students that when a square and a circle have equal areas, π must be involved. In this case, $\sqrt{\pi}$ is a factor of the area of the square base of the prism.

8. A plane intersects a sphere of radius 12 cm.

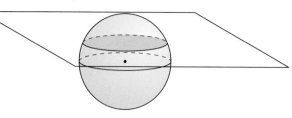

a. If the plane is 3 cm from the center of the sphere, what is the area of the cross section?

b. If the cross section has area 4π cm^2, how far is the plane from the center?

9. In the figure below, $\overline{VH}$ is the altitude of the pyramid $VABC$. $\overline{VH'}$ is an altitude of the smaller pyramid $VA'B'C'$. Determine the scale factor of $\triangle ABC$ and $\triangle A'B'C'$ in terms of VH and VH'.

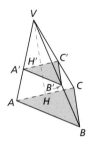

10. The rectangular prism and cone below both have height 8 in.

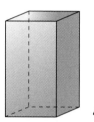

The prism has a square base. The radius of the base of the cone is 4 in. The cross section of the prism has the same area as the cross section of the cone at a height of 3 in. from their bases. What is the side length of the square base of the prism?

Answers

8. a. 135π cm^2

  b. $2\sqrt{35}$ cm

9. $\dfrac{VH'}{VH}$

10. $\dfrac{5}{2}\sqrt{\pi}$ in.

11. You drop a bowling ball with diameter 9.4 inches into a square hole with side length 6 inches. How far into the hole does the bowling ball get stuck?

For each pair of solids in Exercises 12–14, find the height from the bottom at which both solids have the same cross-sectional area.

12. The cylinder has radius 2 in. The cone has radius 4 in. They both have height 5 in.

13. The cylinder has radius 3 in. and height 8 in. The sphere has radius 4 in.

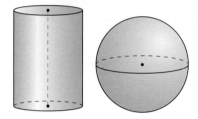

14. The cone has radius 5 in. and height 6 in. The sphere has radius 3 in.

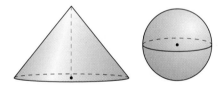

11. $(4.7 - \sqrt{13.09})$ in.

12. 2.5 in.

13. $(4 - \sqrt{7})$ in. or $(4 + \sqrt{7})$ in.

14. $\frac{150}{61}$ in.

Lesson Overview

GOALS

- Find the areas of cross sections formed when planes intersect with solids under certain conditions.
- Understand and use Cavalieri's Principle.

This lesson introduces Cavalieri's principle. Students can use this principle to show that if all planes parallel to a given plane slice two solids into two-dimensional shapes with equal areas, then the two solids have equal volumes.

CHECK YOUR UNDERSTANDING
- Core: 2
- Optional: 1, 3

HOMEWORK
- Core: 4, 6, 8, 11
- Optional: 5, 7, 9, 10, 12, 13

Launch

Begin this lesson by having students discuss their thoughts on the positions of the deck of cards at the beginning of the lesson. Assign the For Discussion problem.

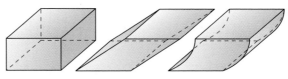

6.11 Cavalieri's Principle

Below are three diagrams of the same deck of cards in three different positions.

deck of cards position 1   deck of cards position 2   deck of cards position 3

For Discussion

1. Compare the volumes of the deck of cards in positions 2 and 3 with the volume of the deck of cards in position 1. Does your result make sense? Explain and discuss your ideas with the class.

Minds in Action   episode 27

Sasha, Tony, and Derman are thinking about the deck of cards in the pictures above.

Tony   I think the volume of the deck in the first position is greatest.

Derman I think the volume is the same in all three positions. After all it's the *same* deck of cards!

Tony   But the deck in position 1 *looks* bigger.

Sasha Well, you know that looks can be deceiving. Think of the deck of cards as a building. Every "floor" of the building has the same area. Each floor is a single card and all the cards in the deck are the same size. Since there are always the same number of cards, or floors, it would make sense that the three volumes are the same.

In the 1600s, an Italian mathematician named Bonaventura Francesco Cavalieri formalized Sasha's idea.

> This is why his name is the one attached to the principle.

Theorem 6.3   Cavalieri's Principle

Two solids of the same height are cut by a plane so that the resulting cross sections have the same area. If the solids also have cross-sectional areas equal to each other when cut by any plane parallel to the first, then they have the same volume.

Answers

For Discussion

1. The volumes of all three stacks are the same. The number of cards has not changed, even though their positions are different in different stacks.

Let's see how Cavalieri's Principle can be used to find the volume of the deck of cards in positions 2 and 3. The bottom card of the deck, in each position, lies in the same plane—the plane of the table. The plane in the figure below is parallel to this bottom plane.

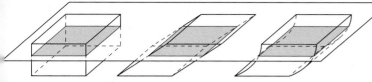

You can see that the intersection of this plane with each solid is a rectangle of equal area—the area of a single card. This means that each cross section has equal area. This is also true for *every* plane parallel to the bottom plane, all the way up to the plane that passes through the top card of each deck.

Example

Problem Show that all pyramids that have the same height and the same base area must have the same volume.

Solution Start with two pyramids with height h and bases with area A. The two bases can be any polygonal shape. Position the pyramids so that their bases both lie in the same plane. Then find any other plane parallel to the plane of the bases that intersects the two pyramids.

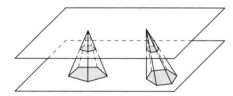

Call the distance of this cutting plane from the apexes of the pyramids b. Think of the apex of each pyramid as a center of dilation in the ratio method. You can conclude that the cross sections created by the cutting plane are similar to the bases of their corresponding pyramids.

You also know the scale factor of the dilation must be $\frac{b}{h}$. Since the area of each base is A, the areas of these cross sections must both be $A\left(\frac{b}{h}\right)^2$.

Both cross sections must have the same area for any height b. So you can conclude that these two pyramids must have the same volume.

Remember...

The area of a dilation is equal to the square of the scale factor multiplied by the area of the original figure.

Explore

For You to Do

Your students may think that they need to use the converse of Cavalieri's Principle for this problem. In Exercise 4, however, they will show that the converse is false. However, both shapes in this problem have the same height (3 inches). Their cross sections are parallel to their bases at any distance d from their apexes. Also, their cross sections are similar to the bases and are scaled by the factor $\frac{d}{h}$. Thus, it is possible to conclude that these two solids have the same cross-sectional areas for every plane parallel to their bases. This is similar to working with two solids that have constant cross-sectional areas (prisms or cylinders). Because the cross-sectional areas vary in the same way, a limited form of the converse of Cavalieri's Principle does apply. Thus, since you know that these two solids have the same volume, you can conclude that their bases must have equal areas.

Wrap Up

End this lesson by assigning some Check Your Understanding exercises.

Assessment Resources

Exercises

HOMEWORK
- Core: 4, 6, 8, 11
- Optional: 5, 7, 9, 10, 12, 13

For You to Do

2. A triangular pyramid and a square pyramid have equal volume and the same height, 3 in. The base of the triangular pyramid has side lengths 3 in., 4 in., and 5 in. Find the side length of the base of the square pyramid.

Exercises *Practicing Habits of Mind*

Check Your Understanding

1. The two shaded circles in the figure below have the same area. Do the two solids have the same volume? Explain.

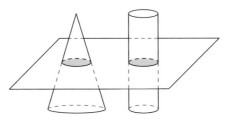

2. You can deform a right prism by pushing it sideways as shown below, to form a new solid. Do the two solids have the same volume? Explain.

 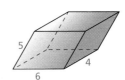

Answers

For You to Do

2. $\sqrt{6}$ in.

Exercises

1. There is not enough information given to tell how the volumes compare.

2. No; the bases of the solids are congruent rectangles and hence have the same area. The right prism has a greater height than the other solid, so it has the greater volume.

3. Here are two rectangular prisms.

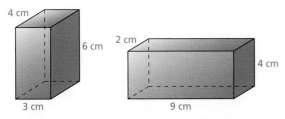

a. Calculate the volume of each prism.

b. Can you use Cavalieri's Principle to conclude that the two prisms have the same volume?

On Your Own

4. The converse of Cavalieri's Principle is not necessarily true.

You have two solids that have equal volumes. Suppose there is a plane that intersects those two solids in equal-area cross sections. This does *not* guarantee that every plane parallel to the first plane will also intersect the solids in equal-area cross sections.

Show an example that demonstrates this. Give enough measurements to define each of the solids. Locate a plane that produces equal-area cross sections and a parallel plane that produces unequal-area cross sections.

5. Write About It What happens to the assertion in Exercise 4 if you are comparing two prisms of equal height? Are there any other shapes that could be included in this exception? Explain.

6. A cylinder has height 6 inches and radius 3 inches. A prism with a square base has the same volume and height. What is the side length of the base of the prism?

Check Your Understanding

EXERCISE 3 Point out to students that in order to use Cavalieri's Principle effectively, it is not only important to choose carefully the solids you compare, but also to orient them correctly. Students can orient these two solids in such a way so they have the same height. If students do that, then Cavalieri's Principle is helpful.

On Your Own

EXERCISE 5 Although the converse of Cavalieri's Principle is not true in general, it does work for certain classes of solids. In this exercise, students consider one of those cases—solids with a constant cross section. If you restrict your consideration to prisms and cylinders, you can conclude that two such solids with equal volumes and heights have equal cross-sectional area. Similarly, as in Exercise 3 in Lesson 6.12, if you restrict consideration to only pyramids and cones with equal volumes and heights, you can conclude that their bases have equal areas.

3. a. 72 cm^3, 72 cm^3

   b. Yes. Position the first figure so that the 4-cm edges of the two figures are parallel.

4. Answers may vary. Sample: Use a sphere with a radius of 1 and a cylinder with height of $\frac{4}{3}$. Both solids have a volume of $\frac{4\pi}{3}$. A plane that contains a diameter of the sphere has the same cross section as a plane parallel to the base of the cylinder. There are no other cross sections that have equal areas.

5. If two prisms have the same height and their bases have equal areas, then their volumes are equal. Within each prism, a cross section determined by a plane parallel to a base is a polygon congruent to the base. So in this situation, the converse of Cavalieri's Principle holds. The same is true for cylinders.

6. $3\sqrt{\pi}$ in.

7. A cylinder and a prism with a square base have the same volume V and height h. The cylinder has radius r. What is the side length of the square base of the prism?

8. **Standardized Test Prep** A right cylinder is cut in half vertically to form a semi-cylinder. It has the same height h as a right cylinder with radius r. What is the diameter of the semi-cylinder?

A. $2r$ **B.** $r\sqrt{2}$ **C.** $2r\sqrt{2}$ **D.** $4r$

Exercises 9 and 10 ask you to think about Cavalieri's Principle in two dimensions.

You can divide the two quadrilaterals in the figure into an equal number of congruent rectangles with height that can be as small as you want. Because the corresponding rectangles in each quadrilateral are always congruent no matter how small they get, the two quadrilaterals must have the same area.

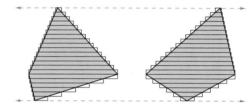

In two dimensions, Cavalieri's Principle can be stated as follows.

Suppose you have two 2-dimensional figures. Draw a line that intersects both figures. In each figure, that intersection will be a segment. If both segments have equal length, and if every line parallel to your original line also intersects both figures in segments of equal length, then the two figures must have equal area.

9. Use Cavalieri's Principle to show that any two triangles that have the same base and height must also have the same area.

10. Two polygons have the same area. Line ℓ intersects them both in segments of equal length. Does this guarantee that every line parallel to ℓ intersects both polygons in segments of equal length? If so, explain your reasoning. If not, give a counterexample.

Habits of Mind

Reason. Reason by continuity, making the heights smaller and smaller. What happens as the height of the rectangles approaches zero?

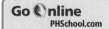

Go Online
PHSchool.com

For a demonstration of Cavalieri's Principle, go to Web Code: bee-9031

Answers

7. $r\sqrt{\pi}$ 8. C

9. Suppose ℓ and m are parallel lines and that $\triangle ABC$ has vertex A on line ℓ and $\overline{BC}$ on line m. A line j that is parallel to ℓ and m and that lies between ℓ and m will intersect $\overline{AB}$ in a point D and $\overline{AC}$ in a point E such that $\triangle ADE \cong \triangle ABC$. If the distance from ℓ to m is h and the distance from ℓ to j is d, then $\frac{d}{h} = \frac{DE}{BC}$. It follows that if $\triangle MNO$ has vertex M on ℓ and $\overline{NO}$ on m, j will intersect $\overline{MN}$ and $\overline{MO}$ in points P and Q, respectively, such that $\frac{d}{h} = \frac{PQ}{NO}$. If $BC = NO$, then $DE = PQ$. It follows by the two-dimensional version of Cavalieri's Principle that $\triangle ABC$ and $\triangle MNO$ have equal areas.

10. No; answers may vary. Sample: A right triangle with legs of length 1 and 2 has the same area as a square with side length 1, but there can only be one pair of cross sections of each figure that have the same area.

1. A hollow square prism with height 1 foot, as pictured below, has the same volume as a solid square prism with the same height and a base with a 2-inch side length.

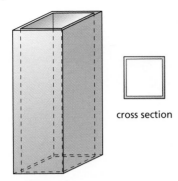

cross section

The thickness of the sides of the hollow square prism is $\frac{1}{4}$ inch. What is the side length of the outside square?

2. A hollow cylindrical pipe with height 1 foot has the same volume as a solid square prism with the same height and a base with a 2-inch side length.

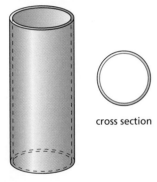

cross section

The thickness of the wall of the cylindrical pipe is $\frac{1}{4}$ inch. What is the radius of the outside circle?

11. $\frac{17}{4}$ in.

12. $\frac{64 + \pi}{8\pi}$ in.

Additional Resources

PRINTED RESOURCES
- Texas Instruments Activities Workbook
- Cabrilog Activities
- Teaching Resources
- Practice Workbook
- Assessment Resources

TECHNOLOGY
- TeacherExpress CD-ROM
- **Exam**_View_ CD-ROM
- **PHSchool.com**
  - Homework Help
  - Video Tutors
  - Multiple Choice
  - Crosswords

Additional Practice

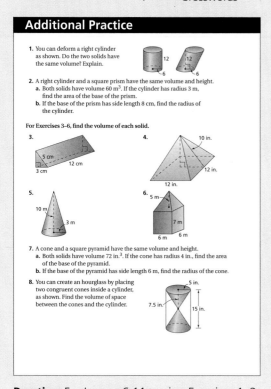

1. You can deform a right cylinder as shown. Do the two solids have the same volume? Explain.

2. A right cylinder and a square prism have the same volume and height.
   a. Both solids have volume 60 m³. If the cylinder has radius 3 m, find the area of the base of the prism.
   b. If the base of the prism has side length 8 cm, find the radius of the cylinder.

For Exercises 3–6, find the volume of each solid.

3.

4.

5.

6.

7. A cone and a square pyramid have the same volume and height.
   a. Both solids have volume 72 in.³. If the cone has radius 4 in., find the area of the base of the pyramid.
   b. If the base of the pyramid has side length 6 m, find the radius of the cone.

8. You can create an hourglass by placing two congruent cones inside a cylinder, as shown. Find the volume of space between the cones and the cylinder.

Practice: For Lesson 6.11, assign Exercises 1–2.

Maintain Your Skills

13. Compare the volumes of each pair of solids. In each case, explain why their volumes are the same or different.

a.
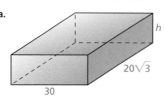
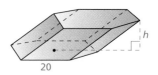

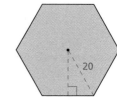

view of top base of prism

b.
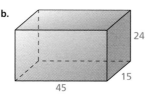
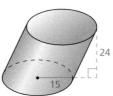

c.

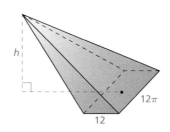

Go Online
PHSchool.com

For additional practice, go to **Web Code: bea-0612**

Answers

13. **a.** Same; the heights are the same, and the bases have an area of $600\sqrt{3}$.

    b. Different; the heights are the same, but the prism has a base area of 675, while the cylinder has a base area of 225π.

    c. Equal; the heights are the same, and the bases have an area of 144π.

.12 Proving Volume Formulas

Cavalieri's Principle is very useful when it comes to proving volume formulas. In this lesson, you will prove formulas for a general prism, a cylinder, a pyramid, and a cone. You will start with the formula for the volume of a right rectangular prism and use Cavalieri's Principle.

Remember...

Do you remember how to find the volume of a right rectangular prism with dimensions a, b, and c?

For You to Do

The picture below represents two prisms: the prism on the left is a right rectangular prism, and the prism on the right has a triangular base and is not right. Both prisms have the same height.

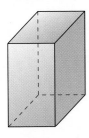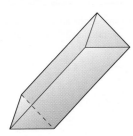

The area of the base of the rectangular prism is 24 cm². The area of the base of the triangular prism is also 24 cm². The heights of the two prisms are both 7 cm.

1. Determine the volume of the triangular prism, if possible. If you cannot, explain why.

You can generalize your solution for the problem above in the For You to Do with the following theorem.

Theorem 6.4

The volume of a prism is equal to the product of the area of its base and its height.

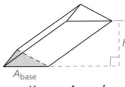

$$V_{prism} = A_{base} \cdot h$$

Lesson Overview

GOALS

- Understand and use Cavalieri's Principle.
- Prove basic formulas using Cavalieri's Principle.

In this lesson, students use Cavalieri's Principle to prove the volume formulas of prisms, cylinders, pyramids, and cones.

CHECK YOUR UNDERSTANDING
- Core: 2, 3
- Optional: 1, 4, 5

HOMEWORK
- Core: 6, 9, 10, 11
- Optional: 7, 8, 12, 13

Launch

Begin this lesson by assigning For You to Do Problem 1.

For You to Do

1. 168 cm³

Explore

Minds in Action

You may wish to assign roles for the dialog and have students present the conversation to the class. This is more effective if you assign the roles one day prior to the presentation. Encourage the students to get into their parts by using their own words instead of memorizing lines.

Suppose the base of the triangular prism in the For You to Do is a circle. You can generalize Theorem 6.4 as follows.

Theorem 6.5

The volume of a cylinder is equal to the product of the area of its base and its height.

$V_{\text{cylinder}} = A_{\text{base}} \cdot h$

For Discussion

The area of the base of the cylinder is the same as the area of the base of the rectangular right prism. The height of the cylinder is the same as the height of the rectangular prism.

2. Explain how to apply Cavalieri's Principle to the two solids.

3. What can you prove about their volumes?

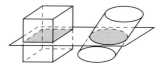

Minds in Action   episode 28

Tony, Sasha, and Derman are trying to use Cavalieri's Principle to find the formula for the volume of the pyramid below.

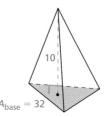

10

$A_{\text{base}} = 32$

Sasha   Let's think of some kind of pyramid we already know how to find the volume of.

Answers

For Discussion

2. The planes that contain the bases of the rectangular prism and the cylinder are parallel. Each plane between these two planes and parallel to them results in a pair of cross sections of equal area. By Cavalieri's Principle, the volumes of the two solids are equal.

3. They are the same.

Tony I know! Look at this. A cube contains exactly three congruent square pyramids.

apex

base on   base on   base at
the bottom   the right   the back

Sasha Great, that's really cool! So we know that the volume of a square pyramid with height equal to the side length of its base is $\frac{1}{3}$ the volume of the cube it's contained in.

Now what if we had a square pyramid with height different from its base?

Derman Oh, that's easy. If the cube's height is scaled by some factor, say, 3, then its volume is three times larger. So the volume of the pyramid must also be three times larger, too, because it was scaled in the same way.

Tony OK, so now if we construct a square pyramid with the same height as our pyramid with base area 32, we can use Cavalieri's Principle.

Each pair of cross sections is similar to the base. For any cutting plane, the scale factor for both cross sections is the same. That means each pair of cross sections will have the same area.

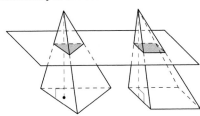

Remember...

Remember the In-Class Experiment in Lesson 6.10? The intersection of a plane parallel to the base of a pyramid with the pyramid is a polygon similar to the base of the pyramid.

Sasha Right! So the volume of our pyramid is $\frac{64 \cdot 10}{3}$.

For You to Do

4. Use Cavalieri's Principle to help you find the volume of a triangular pyramid by comparing it to a square pyramid. Could you find the volume of any pyramid in this way?

Theorem 6.6 summarizes your work.

Theorem 6.6

The volume of a pyramid is equal to a third of the product of the area of its base and its height.

$$V_{\text{pyramid}} = \frac{A_{\text{base}} \cdot h}{3}$$

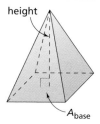

Example

Problem Find a square pyramid that has the same height and volume as a cone of radius r and height h. What is the volume of the square pyramid?

Solution To show that the pyramid and the cone have the same volume, consider the cross sections of the pyramid and the cone that are formed by a set of parallel planes. The corresponding cross sections must have equal areas. It makes the most sense to consider the cross sections that are formed by planes that are parallel to the base of each figure.

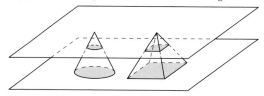

In particular, the area of the square base of the pyramid must be equal to the area of the circular base of the cone. The area of the cone's base is πr^2. For the square to have this area, its side length must be $\sqrt{\pi r^2}$, or $r\sqrt{\pi}$. To be certain that the areas of the corresponding cross sections of the pyramid and cone are the same, remember the ratio method. Suppose a plane intersects the pyramid and the cone at some distance d from the plane that contains the apexes of the pyramid and cone. This plane forms two corresponding cross sections. You can think of these cross sections as the bases of a dilated pyramid and cone. The scale factor is $\frac{d}{h}$. The areas of the dilated bases, or cross sections, will both be equal to $\left(\frac{d}{h}\right)^2$ times the areas of the bases of the original pyramid and cone.

Answers

For You to Do

4. Cavalieri's Principle shows that the volume of a triangular pyramid is equal to the volume of a square pyramid with a base that has the same area as the base of the triangular pyramid and a height equal to the height of the triangular pyramid; yes.

Since the pyramid and the cone have the same height and the same cross-sectional area for any plane that is parallel to their bases, the pyramid and the cone have the same volume. The volume of the square pyramid is $\frac{1}{3}(r\sqrt{\pi})^2 \cdot h$, or $\frac{1}{3}(\pi r^2)(h)$.

Theorem 6.7 is a result of the example above.

Theorem 6.7

The volume of a cone is equal to one third of the product of the area of its base (a circle) and its height.

$$V_{cone} = \frac{A_{base} \cdot h}{3}$$

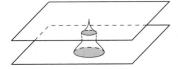

For Discussion

5. Explain why you cannot use the techniques from this lesson to find a volume formula for a figure like the one below.

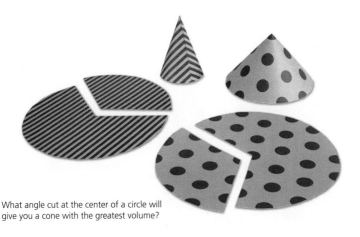

What angle cut at the center of a circle will give you a cone with the greatest volume?

For Discussion

5. It is not true that for all d with $0 < d < h$, the area of a cross section for a plane between and parallel to the given planes is $\left(\frac{d}{h}\right)^2$ times the area of the base.

Wrap Up

End this lesson by assigning some Check Your Understanding exercises.

Assessment Resources

Lesson Quiz 6.12

For Exercises 1–3, find the volume of each solid.

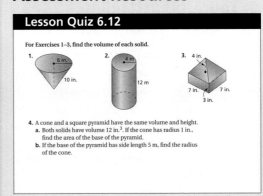

1. 6 in., 10 in.
2. 4 m, 12 m
3. 4 in., 7 in., 7 in., 3 in.

4. A cone and a square pyramid have the same volume and height.
   a. Both solids have volume 12 in.³. If the cone has radius 1 in., find the area of the base of the pyramid.
   b. If the base of the pyramid has side length 5 m, find the radius of the cone.

Exercises

HOMEWORK
- Core: 6, 9, 10, 11
- Optional: 7, 8, 12, 13

Check Your Understanding

EXERCISE 3 has students consider the converse of Cavalieri's Principle for a restricted set of solids—pyramids and cones. For these solids, the cross section is always similar to the base of the solid and scaled by the factor $\frac{d}{h}$, where d is the distance from the apex of the solid to the cross section and h is the height of the solid. This allows you to conclude that pyramids and cones with equal volumes and heights have bases of equal areas. This is similar to the situation in Exercise 5 of Lesson 6.11.

Exercises Practicing Habits of Mind

Check Your Understanding

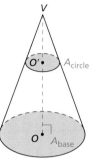

1. Use the cone at the right. A plane containing O' and parallel to the base of the cone intersects the cone in a circle. Prove the following.

$$\frac{A_{\text{circle}}}{A_{\text{base}}} = \frac{(VO')^2}{VO^2}$$

2. Use Cavalieri's Principle to find the volume of the pyramid below.

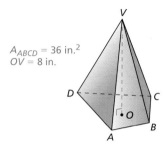

$A_{ABCD} = 36 \text{ in.}^2$
$OV = 8 \text{ in.}$

3. **a.** Find the volume of a triangular pyramid of height 5 cm with a right triangle base with legs that measure 4 cm and 6 cm.

   b. Find the radius of the cone that has the same volume and height as the triangular pyramid.

4. A triangular pyramid and a cone are standing on the same plane. They have equal base areas and the same height h. The cone has base radius r.

   a. What are the dimensions of the base of the pyramid?

   b. A plane parallel to the bases intersects the two solids. What can you say about the resulting cross sections?

5. Use Cavalieri's Principle to conclude that the volume of the cone and the volume of the pyramid from Exercise 4 are the same.

On Your Own

6. The base of a cone has radius 2 ft. The height of the cone is 6 ft. What is the volume of the cone?

Answers

Exercises

1. If r is the radius of the cross section between V and O, and R is the radius of the base, then $\frac{r}{R} = \frac{VO'}{VO}$.

   Thus $\frac{A_{\text{circle}}}{A_{\text{base}}} = \frac{\pi r^2}{\pi R^2} = \frac{r^2}{R^2}$

   $= \left(\frac{r}{R}\right)^2 = \left(\frac{VO'}{VO}\right)^2.$

2. 96 in.^{3}

3. **a.** 20 cm^3

   b. $\frac{2\sqrt{3\pi}}{\pi}$ cm

4. **a.** The triangular pyramid has height h and base area πr^2. There are infinitely many such pyramids.

   b. Every pair of cross sections determined by a plane parallel to the bases of the cone and pyramid have the same area.

5. See back of book.

6. 8π ft^3

7. A prism has a square base of side 4 cm. Its lateral faces are two rectangles and two parallelograms like the ones below. Determine the volume of the prism.

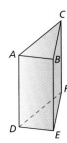

6 cm

6 cm

4 cm

45°

4 cm

8. The area of one face of a regular tetrahedron is $16\sqrt{3}$ cm². What is its volume?

9. Another way to see that the volume of a pyramid is one third the volume of the prism with the same base and height is to look at a triangular prism.

A **tetrahedron** is a pyramid that has congruent equilateral triangles for all faces.

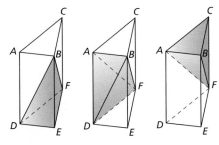

You can cut a triangular prism into three triangular pyramids. In the dissection of the cube in the lesson, the three pyramids were congruent. Here they are not, but you can show that they do have the same volume.

a. Consider the green and blue pyramids. The height of each pyramid is the length of a perpendicular from *C* to plane *ABED*. If the bases are congruent, then they have the same volume. Show that $\triangle BDE \cong \triangle DBA$.

7. $48\sqrt{2}$ cm³

8. $\dfrac{128\sqrt{2}}{3}$ cm³

9. a. $\triangle BDE \cong \triangle DBA$ because a diagonal of a parallelogram divides it into two congruent triangles.

On Your Own

EXERCISE 9 If you plan to have students complete the Chapter 6 Project: Demonstrating a Volume Relationship, you should have them complete this exercise first. It will help them understand the relationships between the three pyramids of equal volumes that comprise the triangular prism.

Additional Resources

PRINTED RESOURCES
- Texas Instruments Activities Workbook
- Cabrilog Activities
- Teaching Resources
- Practice Workbook
- Assessment Resources

TECHNOLOGY
- TeacherExpress CD-ROM
- **Exam**View CD-ROM
- **PHSchool.com**
  - Homework Help
  - Video Tutors
  - Multiple Choice
  - Crosswords

Additional Practice

1. You can deform a right cylinder as shown. Do the two solids have the same volume? Explain.

2. A right cylinder and a square prism have the same volume and height.
   a. Both solids have volume 60 m³. If the cylinder has radius 3 m, find the area of the base of the prism.
   b. If the base of the prism has side length 8 cm, find the radius of the cylinder.

For Exercises 3–6, find the volume of each solid.

3. 5 cm, 3 cm, 12 cm

4. 10 in., 12 in., 12 in.

5. 10 m, 3 m

6. 5 m, 7 m, 6 m, 6 m

7. A cone and a square pyramid have the same volume and height.
   a. Both solids have volume 72 in.³. If the cone has radius 4 in., find the area of the base of the pyramid.
   b. If the base of the pyramid has side length 6 m, find the radius of the cone.

8. You can create an hourglass by placing two congruent cones inside a cylinder, as shown. Find the volume of space between the cones and the cylinder. 5 in., 7.5 in., 15 in.

Practice: For Lesson 6.12, assign Exercises 3–8.

---

b. Consider the green and purple pyramids. The green pyramid has base $\triangle DEF$ and height BE. What base and height for the purple pyramid would show that these two pyramids must have the same volume?

c. Complete the argument to show that the volume of a pyramid is one-third the area of the prism with the same base and height.

10. What is the volume of the solid below?

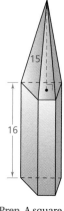

15, 16, 7, 4, 3

The base is a trapezoid.

11. **Standardized Test Prep** A square pyramid has height 10 cm and a base area of 36 cm². A second square pyramid has the same height but the side lengths of its base are double those of the side lengths of the first pyramid. What is the ratio of the volume of the second pyramid to the volume of the first pyramid?

  A. 2 : 1   **B.** 4 : 1   **C.** 6 : 1   **D.** 8 : 1

Go Online
PHSchool.com

For additional practice, go to **Web Code: bea-0612**

Maintain Your Skills

12. Find the volume of a pyramid with height 12 inches and each base described below. Approximate if necessary.
   a. an equilateral triangle with apothem 1 in.
   b. a square with apothem 1 in.
   c. a regular pentagon with apothem 1 in.
   d. a regular hexagon with apothem 1 in.
   e. a regular octagon with apothem 1 in.

13. Find the volume of a cone with height 12 in. and radius 1 in.

Remember...

The apothem a of a regular polygon is a perpendicular segment from the center point of the polygon to one of its sides.

Answers

9. b. *CF* (which equals *BE*)

   c. The green, blue, and purple pyramids have the same volume, so each has a volume that is $\frac{1}{3}$ the volume of the prism.

10. 420

11. B

12. a. $12\sqrt{3}$ in.³
    b. 16 in.³
    c. $5(\sqrt{5}-1)\sqrt{10-2\sqrt{5}}$ in.³ ≈ 14.5309 in.³
    d. $8\sqrt{3}$ in.
    e. $\approx \dfrac{32\sqrt{2-\sqrt{2}}}{\sqrt{2+\sqrt{2}}}$ in.³ ≈ 13.2548 in.³

13. 4π in.³

You can use Cavalieri's Principle to show that two different solids have the same volume. If you know how to find the volume of one of the solids, you can use that result as the volume of the other. You can even develop new volume formulas for new classes of solids. However, the tricky part of using Cavalieri's Principle is that you have to know which two solids to compare.

For Discussion

To find a solid to compare to a sphere of radius r using Cavalieri's Principle, it might be a good idea to use one of the round solids with a volume formula that you already know. The cross sections of a sphere are small circles at first. Then the circles get larger and larger as you approach the center of the sphere. The circles then gradually decrease in size as you move away from the center of the sphere.

1. Would a double cone work?

If so, describe the dimensions of the double cone as completely as possible. If not, describe the problems you encounter.

In fact, this is not a simple problem to solve. The Greek mathematician Archimedes was finally able to prove the volume formula for a sphere. It is said that he was so thrilled that he wanted his solution to the problem to be engraved on his tombstone.

You and your classmates may not have been able to think of a choice of what solid to compare to the sphere. But you can still demonstrate the comparison.

Lesson Overview

GOALS

- Understand and use Cavalieri's Principle.
- Prove basic formulas using Cavalieri's Principle.

In this lesson, students use Cavalieri's Principle to prove the volume formula for a sphere.

CHECK YOUR UNDERSTANDING
- Core: 1
- Optional: 2, 3

MATERIALS
- Blackline Master 6.13

HOMEWORK
- Core: 4, 5, 9, 10
- Optional: 6, 7, 8, 11, 12

Launch

Begin this lesson by reading the introductory paragraph and assigning the For Discussion problem. You may want to divide your students into groups to complete this activity.

For Discussion

1. Answers may vary. Sample: The cross sections of a sphere and a double cone can occur in at most four places. The cross sections are otherwise not equal.

Explore

Minds in Action

You may wish to assign roles to students and have them present the dialog in class. Have them draw the appropriate diagrams as they read through the dialog.

Sasha and Tony are comparing the cross sections of a sphere and a cylinder with a double cone removed from it. The sphere has radius r, and the cross section of the sphere is at a distance h from the center of the sphere. The cylinder with the double cone removed from it has radius r and height 2r.

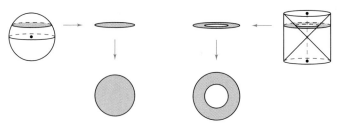

Sasha The cross sections of the cylinder-minus-cones solid will be rings. The outside radius of the ring will always be the same, but the inside radius will get smaller and then larger as you move downward from the top.

Tony We can say that the areas of three cross sections are the same right away. At the very top and bottom, the ring has zero area. At those same two heights, the plane that intersects the sphere will intersect it in a point, so that intersection will have zero area, too.

Sasha Yes, and halfway up the cylinder, the radius of each cone is zero. The intersection with the plane is just a circle of radius r. That's exactly the same area and shape as the intersection of that plane with the sphere.

Tony But now we have to prove it works for all the planes parallel to the base of the cylinder-minus-cones solid.

Sasha I'm guessing similar triangles are going to help us.

We know $\triangle ABD$ is an isosceles right triangle, because the cones each have base radius r and height r. Since $\triangle ECD \sim \triangle ABD$, then it's an isosceles right triangle, too! So we know the inner radius and the outer radius. So we can find the area of the ring.

Tony So now we have to find the area of the intersection of the plane at height h with the sphere. I'm going to label the sphere with everything I know.

If the area of the cross section of the sphere is the same as the ring, we've done it!

How does Sasha know that the two triangles are similar?

For You to Do

Use the figures and dimensions from the Minds in Action. Finish Tony and Sasha's work.

You may want to use the ratio method.

2. Find the area of the intersection of the plane and the cylinder-minus-cones solid using Sasha's similar triangles.

3. Find the area of the cross section of the sphere using Tony's sketch.

4. How can you be sure that these two solids have the same volume? Explain.

5. What is the volume of the cylinder-minus-cones solid?

Your work so far is proof of the following formula.

Theorem 6.8

The volume of a sphere with radius r is $\frac{4}{3}\pi r^3$.

You also can confirm the formula for the surface area of a sphere now that you are sure about its volume. Think of the sphere as being made of some large number n of tiny congruent square pyramids that are all joined so that the apex of each pyramid is at the center of the sphere.

Each pyramid has height r and a square base that is on the sphere. Call the area of each square base b. The areas of all n bases, or nb, is the surface area of the sphere.

Each pyramid has volume $\frac{1}{3}br$. If you add the volumes of the n pyramids, you get the total volume of the sphere, so

$$V_{\text{sphere}} = n\left(\frac{1}{3}br\right)$$

Set the two volume formulas equal to each other.

$$n\left(\frac{1}{3}br\right) = \frac{4}{3}\pi r^3$$

If you solve this equation for nb, you get the formula for the surface area of the sphere.

Theorem 6.9

The surface area of a sphere with radius r is $4\pi r^2$..

Wrap Up

End this lesson by assigning some Check Your Understanding exercises.

Assessment Resources

Lesson Quiz 6.13

1. A sphere has radius r. A plane slices the sphere at a distance h from the center of the sphere.
  a. Draw a diagram to represent the situation.
  b. Find the exact area of the circular cross section if $h = 5$ inches and $r = 13$ inches.
  c. Find the exact area of the circular cross section if $h = 7$ inches and $r = 25$ inches.

2. Use the figure of the sphere with the given dimensions. The area of the shaded region is 25π in.^{2}.
  a. Find h.
  b. If you slice through the sphere at the shaded region, what is the volume of the slice and of the remaining sphere?

Answers

For You to Do

2. $\pi(r^2 - h^2)$

3. $\pi(r^2 - h^2)$

4. Cavalieri's Principle implies that the volumes are equal.

5. $\frac{4}{3}\pi r^3$

Exercises

HOMEWORK
- Core: 4, 5, 9, 10
- Optional: 6, 7, 8, 11, 12

Exercises *Practicing Habits of Mind*

Check Your Understanding

1. Can two parallel planes intersect a sphere and result in cross sections with equal areas? If so, in how many ways can this happen?

   Can two nonparallel planes intersect a sphere and create cross sections with equal areas? If so, in how many ways can this happen? Explain.

2. The figure shows a cylinder with a cone cut out of it.

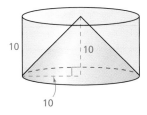

   Find the volume of the cylinder-minus-cone solid. Now, use Cavalieri's Principle to compare that solid to a part of a sphere. What is the radius of the sphere the piece comes from? What is the volume of the piece of the sphere?

   > What fraction of a sphere should you use?

3. You have a piece of cloth with area 45 cm². You can cut the cloth and arrange the pieces any way you like. What is the volume of the greatest sphere you can cover with it?

On Your Own

4. A sphere has radius 15 cm. If the shaded circle has area 25π cm², what is h?

   > Try using Cavalieri's Principle for this.

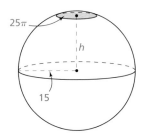

Answers

Exercises

1. Yes; infinitely many ways; yes; infinitely many ways; if the sphere has radius r, then any two planes that are d units from the center of the sphere, where $0 < d < r$, will create two cross sections of equal area.

2. $\frac{2000\pi}{3}$; 10; $\frac{2000\pi}{3}$

3. $\frac{45\sqrt{5\pi}}{2\pi}$ cm³

4. $10\sqrt{2}$ cm

522 **Chapter 6** Using Similarity

5. **Standardized Test Prep** Sasha peels an orange. The peel is 0.5 cm thick and each slice of orange is 5 cm long. What was the volume of the unpeeled orange?

   A. 65.4 cm³   **B.** 113.1 cm³   **C.** 523.5 cm³   **D.** 904.8 cm³

In Exercises 6–9, you will investigate the problem of drilling a cylindrical hole through the center of a sphere. You begin with a wooden sphere with a radius of 5 mm. You plan to drill a cylindrical hole of radius 3 mm through its center to make it into a bead.

The original sphere and the finished bead are shown below.

Notice that the bead is shorter than the original sphere. By drilling the cylinder, you have not precisely cut out a cylinder of wood. Instead you have cut out a sort of cylinder with a rounded top and bottom. In effect, a cap has been cut off of both the top and bottom of the sphere in addition to the cylindrical hole.

6. What is the height of the finished bead?

7. Find the volume of the finished bead. You will want to use the volume of the original wooden sphere, the volume of the cylindrical hole, and the volumes of the rounded caps that were cut off.

8. **a.** What is the radius of the sphere that has the same volume as the finished bead?

   b. Use Cavalieri's Principle to show that the bead and this same-volume sphere actually have the same area at every cross section for planes perpendicular to the bead's cylindrical hole.

   > This is not a coincidence.

9. Find the volume of a bead formed by drilling a cylindrical hole of radius 2 mm through a sphere of radius 6 mm.

---

5. A

6. 8 mm

7. $\frac{256\pi}{3}$ mm³

8. a. 4 mm

   b. A cross section of the bead has area $\pi((\sqrt{5^2 - h^2})^2 - 3^2) = \pi(5^2 - h^2 - 3^2) = \pi(16 - h^2)$, where h is the vertical height from the center of the bead. A cross section of the sphere has area $\pi((\sqrt{4^2 - h^2})^2) = \pi(4^2 - h^2) = \pi(16 - h^2)$.

9. $\frac{512\pi\sqrt{2}}{3}$ mm³

10. You have a perfectly spherical onion with a diameter of 13 cm. You cut off a slice $\frac{1}{2}$ cm thick as shown below.

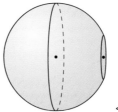

a. The slice created a circular cross section of the onion. What is the radius of that cross section?

b. You want to use Cavalieri's Principle to find the volume of your slice. As in the lesson, you will use the idea of subtracting a cone from a cylinder. What are the dimensions and the volume of the cylinder you should use?

c. You will need to subtract the volume of the frustum of a cone from that of your cylinder because you're not finding the volume of an entire sphere—just a piece. The frustum has two radii—a large radius on top and a smaller radius on the bottom. What are its radii and height?

d. What is the volume of the frustum?

e. What is the volume of your onion slice?

Remember...

Just think of a frustum as the difference of two cones. You start with a large cone and remove its tip parallel to the base of the cone.

Answers

10. a. 2.5 cm

b. radius 6.5 cm, height 0.5 cm,
$V = \frac{169}{8}\pi$ cm^3

c. radii 6.5 cm and 6 cm, height 0.5 cm

d. $\frac{469}{24}\pi$ cm^3

e. $\frac{19}{12}\pi$ cm^3

11. The volume of the hemisphere is 9216 in³.

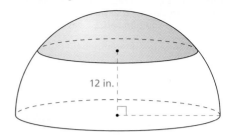

Remember...

A *hemisphere* is half of a sphere.

The vertical segment is 12 inches long. What is the volume of the shaded region?

Maintain Your Skills

12. Each figure below is rotated around line ℓ to make a solid. Find the surface area and volume of each solid.

a.

5 in.

3 in.

ℓ

b.

2 cm

5 cm

ℓ

c.

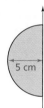

5 cm

ℓ

Habits of Mind

Visualize. If you have trouble visualizing this, tape a cutout of the shape to a pencil, and spin the pencil between your hands. This should help you see what the solid will look like.

d.

5 cm

2 cm

ℓ

e.

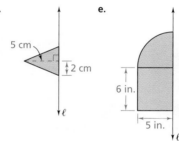

6 in.

5 in.

ℓ

Go Online
PHSchool.com

For additional practice, go to **Web Code: bea-0613**

11. about 902.3

12. a. 80π in.²; 75π in.³

  b. $25\pi + 5\pi\sqrt{29}$ cm²; $\frac{50\pi}{3}$ cm³

  c. 100π cm²; $\frac{500\pi}{3}$ cm³

  d. $10\pi\sqrt{29}$ cm²; $\frac{100\pi}{3}$ cm³

  e. 135π in.²; $\frac{700\pi}{3}$ in.³

On Your Own

EXERCISE 11 You should assign this exercise with Exercise 10, which explicitly leads students through the process of finding the volume of a spherical cap.

Maintain Your Skills

EXERCISE 12 previews an idea that students will see in calculus—solids of revolution. In a solid of revolution, an area is swept around an axis. You can visualize the solid as a series of identical thin sections radiating from a central line, similar to a layer cake cut into slices. If students have trouble visualizing the solids of revolution, you may want to provide them copies of Blackline Master 6.13. Have students tape cutouts of the shapes to a pencil or straw and rotate the pencil.

Additional Resources

PRINTED RESOURCES
- Texas Instruments Activities Workbook
- Cabrilog Activities
- Teaching Resources
- Practice Workbook
- Assessment Resources

TECHNOLOGY
- TeacherExpress CD-ROM
- **Exam**View CD-ROM
- **PHSchool.com**
  - Homework Help
  - Video Tutors
  - Multiple Choice
  - Crosswords

Additional Practice

1. A sphere has radius r. A plane slices the sphere at a distance h from the center of the sphere.
  a. Draw a diagram to represent the situation.
  b. Find the exact area of the circular cross section if $h = 3$ inches and $r = 5$ inches.
  c. Find the exact area of the circular cross section if $h = 8$ inches and $r = 17$ inches.

2. Suppose you double the radius of a sphere. Describe the effect this has on the volume of the sphere.

3. Compare the volumes of a sphere with radius of 3 cm and a hemisphere with radius of 6 cm.

4. A hollow plastic ball has outer radius 8 mm and inner radius 6 mm, as shown. Find the volume of the plastic needed to make the ball.

5. Use the figure of the sphere with given dimensions. The area of the shaded region is 225π in.².
  a. Find h.
  b. If you slice through the sphere at the shaded region, what is the volume of the slice and of the remaining sphere?

6. A farm silo consists of a cylinder with a hemisphere on top. Find the volume of a silo if the radius is 5 meters and the height of the cylinder portion is 20 meters.

7. The container shown below holds three tennis balls. Find the exact volume of space between the tennis balls and the container if the balls fit snugly.

2 in. — 12 in. —

Find the volume of the shaded region.
8.

6 cm

10 cm

9.

20 m²

Practice: For Lesson 6.13, assign Exercises 1–9.

Mathematical Reflections

EXERCISES 4–6 At the start of the investgation, you may have assigned these as Questions 1–3 for students to think and write about.

6C

Mathematical Reflections

In this investigation, you learned how to find areas of cross sections of solids, apply Cavalieri's Principle, and prove basic volume formulas using Cavalieri's Principle. These questions will help you summarize what you have learned.

1. A sphere with radius 5 cm is cut by a plane 3 cm from the top. Find the area of the resulting cross section.

2. An architect created a plan for a four-story building with a central courtyard.

   The building measures 96 feet on each side. The courtyard measures 40 feet on a side. His clients asked him to work out an alternative design with the same volume but without the courtyard. Find the side length of such a building if it is designed as a four-story square prism.

   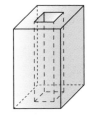

3. **a.** Kirima lives in a hemispherical dome with radius 12 feet. How many square feet should her air conditioner be rated for?

   Kirima discovers that the air conditioner ratings are really based on the cubic footage of air to be cooled, and that the square footage listed is assumed to be in a rectangular room with an 8 foot ceiling.

   b. If she decides to buy an air conditioner based on this discovery, how many square feet should her air conditioner be rated for?

4. A hexagonal pyramid of height h is cut by a plane parallel to its base at height r above the base. How is the shape of the resulting cross section related to the shape of the base of the pyramid? How are their areas related?

5. Explain Cavalieri's Principle.

6. A spherical melon has radius 3 inches. You cut a slice 2 inches from its center. What is the volume of the piece you cut from the melon?

Horizontal cross sections are congruent at every level. The two stacks have equal volumes.

Mathematical Reflections

1. 21π cm^2

2. $8\sqrt{119}$ ft

3. **a.** 144π ft^2

   b. 144π ft^2

4. The cross section is similar to the base; the area of the cross section is $\left(\dfrac{h-r}{h}\right)^2$ times the area of the base.

5. Two solids of the same height are cut by a plane so that the resulting cross sections have the same area. If the solids also have cross-sectional areas equal to each other when cut by any plane parallel to the first, then they have the same volume.

6. $\dfrac{8\pi}{3}$ in.^{3}

Project Using Mathematical Habits

Demonstrating a Volume Relationship

In Investigation 6C, you saw two different ways to explain why the volume of a pyramid is always one third the volume of the prism with the same base and height. One way, shown in episode 28 of Minds in Action, was to decompose a cube into three congruent square pyramids.

The other method, described in Lesson 6.12, showed how to decompose a triangular prism into three triangular pyramids. These pyramids were not necessarily congruent, but they all had equal volumes.

1. Make models of a cube and its corresponding congruent square pyramids to demonstrate the 3 to 1 volume ratio concretely. You should make two sets of nets. You can use your new experience in trigonometry to help you make the nets for the cube and the pyramids.

2. Keep one set of nets flat and unfolded. You can use that set to verify congruence of faces. Cut out, fold, and tape the other set of nets. You can use the three-dimensional models to verify congruence of heights. Confirm that you can fit the three pyramids together to make the cube.

3. Decide on the measurements of the triangular prism that you will decompose into three triangular pyramids of equal volume. Make its net. Again, trigonometry will help you construct this net.

4. Make nets for the three pyramids that the triangular prism can be decomposed into. Use the nets and the three-dimensional models of the solids as before to confirm that the pyramids have equal volumes and that they can fit together to make a copy of the prism.

5. If you are looking for a challenge, choose a nonright triangular prism like this.

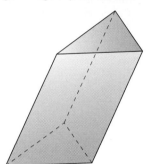

Project

Students' solutions to these problems will vary based on the dimensions of the cube or prism that they choose to dissect. Students should provide the side lengths and angle measures of their nets.

Encourage students to shade with the same color congruent faces of their pyramids. Then students can arrange two pyramids so that the pyramids rest on congruent faces and can demonstrate that their heights are equal by balancing a ruler on the apexes of the pyramids. This shows that their heights relative to these bases are congruent. Students should also be able to construct a cube or prism so that one face opens like the flap of a box. Then, when students fit their three pyramids together, they can place them inside the prism to show that the total volume of the three pyramids is equal to that of the original prism.

Project

1–5. Check students' work.

Go **O**nline
PHSchool.com

For vocabulary review,
go to **Web Code: bej-0651**

In **Investigation 6A** you learned how to

- state and use the Arithmetic-Geometric Mean Inequality
- use similar triangles to find unknown lengths
- use similarity to prove theorems

The following questions will help you check your understanding.

1. Find the arithmetic mean and geometric mean of 4 and 7 in two ways.

   a. Use a numerical calculation.

   b. Use a geometric construction.

2. In the triangle below, $m\angle ACB = 90°$, $AC = 15$, and $AH = 9$. Find the following side lengths.

   a. AB

   b. BC

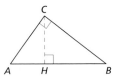

3. How can you use similarity to prove that the medians of a triangle are concurrent?

In **Investigation 6B** you learned how to

- use the sine, cosine, and tangent functions and their inverses to find missing sides and angles in triangles
- find the area of any triangle given two sides and the included angle
- find the length of the third side of a triangle given two sides and the included angle

The following questions will help you check your understanding.

4. A triangle has sides of length 52 meters and 16 meters. If the angle between these two sides is 38°, what is the triangle's area?

5. Find the missing side lengths and angles of the triangle below.

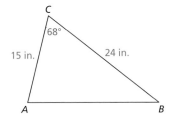

6. Find the perimeter of the triangle below.

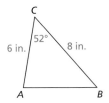

7. The lengths of two sides of a triangle are 11 m and 6 m. The measure of their included angle is 57°. What is the area of the triangle?

Chapter Review

1. a. $\frac{11}{2}$; $2\sqrt{7}$; check students' work.

   b. $\frac{11}{2}$; $2\sqrt{7}$; check students' work.

2. a. $AB = 25$

   b. $BC = 20$

3. Answers may vary. Sample: By Conjecture 6.1, any two medians of a triangle intersect in a point that divides them into two segments. The length of one of these segments is twice the length of the other. Show that the sides of the triangles formed by the medians are in proportion.

4. about 256.12 m^2

5. $AB \approx 23.05$ in.; $m\angle A \approx 74.89°$; $m\angle B \approx 37.11°$

6. about 20.40 in.

7. about 27.67 m^2

In **Investigation 6C** you learned how to

- find the areas of cross sections created when planes intersect solids
- understand and use Cavalieri's Principle
- prove basic volume formulas using Cavalieri's Principle

The following questions will help you check your understanding.

8. Can you use Cavalieri's Principle to determine the volume of the solid below? The solid is made from a deck of cards with volume 90 cm³.

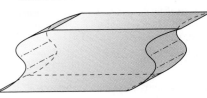

9. You have a piece of cloth with area 64 cm². You can cut and rearrange the cloth however you would like. What is the volume of the greatest cube that you can cover with the cloth?

10. Find the combined volume of the two right pyramids below.

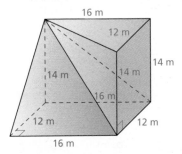

11. Explain how you can use Cavalieri's Principle to prove the volume formula for a sphere of radius r.

---

8. yes

9. $\dfrac{128\sqrt{6}}{9}$ cm³

10. 1792 m³

11. Answers may vary. Sample: Compare the cross sections of a sphere and a cylinder with a double cone removed from it.

Chapter Test

Assessment Resources

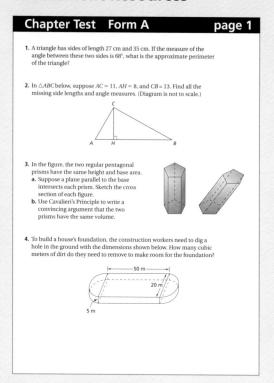
Also available: Form B.

Multiple Choice

1. A triangle has sides of length 45 feet and 57 feet. If the angle between these two sides is 47°, what is the triangle's area?

   A. 682 ft^2 **B.** 938.2 ft^2

   C. 1876.5 ft^2 **D.** 2115 ft^2

2. How many cubic feet of water do you need to fill a cylindrical tank that is 10 feet tall and has a diameter of 3.2 feet?

   A. 32 ft^3 **B.** 80.4 ft^3

   C. 100.5 ft^3 **D.** 320 ft^3

3. The cone has radius 8 inches and height 12 inches. You place the peg in a cylindrical hole of radius 3 inches. How deep into the hole is the apex of the pyramid?

   A. 1 in.   **B.** 3 in.
   C. 4.5 in.   **D.** 5.5 in.

Open Response

4. State Cavalieri's Principle and show an example of when you can use it.

5. Calculate the arithmetic and geometric mean of the following pairs of numbers.

   a. 3, 16   **b.** 45, 56   **c.** 21, 7

6. Find the volume of the prism below.

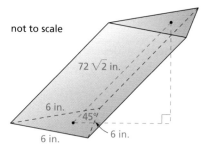

not to scale

72 √2 in.

6 in.   45°

6 in.   6 in.

7. A swimming pool is 50 feet long and 23 feet wide. The pool is 2 feet deep at one end and 12 feet at the opposite end. The pool's bottom is a plane surface.

   a. How many cubic feet of water would you need to fill the pool?

   b. You will fill the pool with a standard water pump, which generates a flow of about 300 GPH (gallons per hour). There are approximately 0.134 cubic feet in a gallon. How long will it take you to fill the pool?

8. The area of the base of the cone below is 40 cm^2 and its height is 15 cm. The heights of the two solids are the same and the areas of the shaded regions are the same.

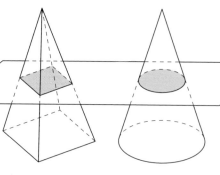

Can you use Cavalieri's Principle to determine the volume of the pyramid? Explain.

Answers

Chapter Test

1. B   **2.** B   **3.** C

4. Cavalieri's Principle: Two solids of the same height are cut by a plane so that the resulting cross sections have the same area. If the solids also have cross-sectional areas equal to each other when cut by any plane parallel to the first, then they have the same volume.

Answers may vary. Sample: You can use Cavalieri's Principle to show that all pyramids that have the same height and the same base area must have the same volume.

5. a. 9.5; 4√3
    b. 50.5; 6√70
    c. 14; 7√3

6. 648 √3 in.^{3}

7. a. 8050 ft^3
    b. about 200.25 h

8. See back of book.

9. For each of the right triangles below, find the exact values for sine, cosine, and tangent of $\angle A$ and $\angle B$.

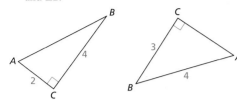

10. Find the missing angle and side lengths for $\triangle MNO$.

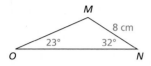

11. You are given a rectangle with the dimensions shown, as well as the length of another rectangle.

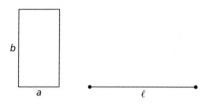

Explain how to find the width of the second rectangle such that both rectangles have the same area.

12. Find the following measures for the cone.

a. volume

b. lateral area

c. surface area

13. What is the volume of the shaded region?

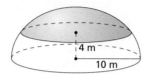

14. You have two beads, one shaped like a rectangular prism and one shaped like a cylinder.

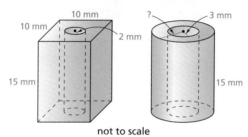

not to scale

The rectangular prism has height 15 mm and a square base with 10-mm side lengths. The hole drilled through the rectangular prism has radius 2 mm. The cylindrical bead has the same height as the rectangular bead, but the hole drilled through it has radius 3 mm. Find the outer radius of the cylindrical bead such that the two beads have equal volume.

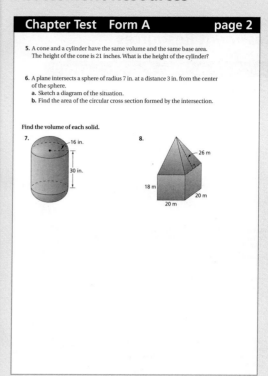
9. a. $\sin A = \dfrac{2\sqrt{5}}{5}$; $\cos A = \dfrac{\sqrt{5}}{5}$;
$\tan A = 2$; $\sin B = \dfrac{\sqrt{5}}{5}$
$\cos B = \dfrac{2\sqrt{5}}{5}$; $\tan B = \dfrac{1}{2}$

b. $\sin A = \dfrac{3}{4}$; $\cos A = \dfrac{\sqrt{7}}{4}$;
$\tan A = \dfrac{3\sqrt{7}}{7}$; $\sin B = \dfrac{\sqrt{7}}{4}$;
$\cos B = \dfrac{3}{4}$; $\tan B = \dfrac{\sqrt{7}}{3}$

10. $m\angle A = 135°$; $OM \approx 10.85$ cm; $ON \approx 16.77$ cm

11. See back of book.

12. a. 56.55   **b.** 12.82   **c.** 76.44

13. 288π m³

14. $\dfrac{\sqrt{100 + 5\pi}}{\pi}$ mm

Cumulative Review

Assessment Resources

1. Draw a circle of radius 2 inches. Approximate its area using the following mesh sizes.
a. $\frac{1}{2}$ in.   **b.** $\frac{1}{4}$ in.
c. $\frac{1}{8}$ in.   **d.** $\frac{1}{16}$ in.

2. Use the linear approximation technique to find the perimeter of the lake below.

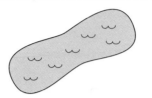
3 mi

3. Find the area of each regular polygon.

a.
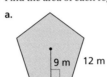
9 m   12 m

b.
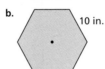
10 in.

c.

3 in.

4. Find the total area of the shaded region in each figure below.

a.   **b.**

4   3

5. Find the area of each circle described below.
a. radius 18 m
b. diameter 13 in.
c. circumference is 19π cm
d. a circle of radius 9 in. scaled by the factor $\frac{2}{3}$

6. Find the exact length of each arc shown in red.

a.   **b.**
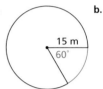
15 m 60°   45° 6 cm

7. Find the circumference of the circle with the following dimensions.
a. radius of 8 m
b. diameter of 22 in.
c. area of 81π cm^2

8. Find m∠1.

a.   **b.**
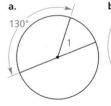   
130° 1   1 225°

9. Find the values of x and y.

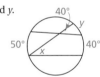
40° y 50° x 40°

10. The power of a point with respect to a circle is 64. Chord $\overline{JK}$ goes through the point such that $PK = 16$ in. What is JK?

Answers

Cumulative Review

1. See back of book.

2. about 24 mi

3. a. 270 m^2 **b.** $150\sqrt{3}$ in.^{2}
c. $27\sqrt{3}$ in.^{2}

4. a. $16(\pi - 2)$ **b.** $\dfrac{18 + 9\pi}{4}$

5. a. 324π m^2 **b.** 42.25π in.^{2}
c. 90.25 cm^2 **d.** 36π in.^{2}

6. a. 5π m   **b.** $\dfrac{9}{2}\pi$ cm

7. a. 16π cm **b.** 22π in. **c.** 18π cm

8. a. 50°   **b.** 135°

9. $x = 35°$
$y = 30°$

10. 4 in.

11. A dart is thrown randomly at the dartboard. What is the probability that it lands in the gold region?

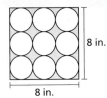

8 in.

8 in.

12. Find the value of each variable.

a.

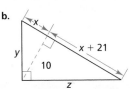

5   7

b.

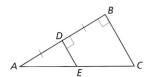

x

x + 21

y

10

z

13. Draw each of the following.

  a. a right triangle and its three perpendicular bisectors

  b. an obtuse triangle and its three altitudes

  c. an acute triangle and its three angle bisectors

14. Given: In $\triangle ABC$, $\overline{DE}$ is the perpendicular bisector of $\overline{AB}$.

Prove: $\overline{BE}$ is a median.

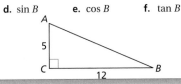

B

D

A   E   C

15. Use the triangle to find the following.

  a. $\sin A$ **b.** $\cos A$ **c.** $\tan A$

  d. $\sin B$ **e.** $\cos B$ **f.** $\tan B$

A

5

C   12   B

16. A redwood that is 100 feet tall casts a shadow that is 179 feet long. What is the measure of the angle of elevation?

17. a. Find all missing angle measures and side lengths.

  b. Find the area of the triangle.

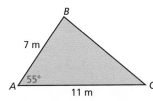

B

7 m

55°

A   11 m   C

18. A plane intersects a sphere h inches from its center. The sphere has radius r.

  a. Draw a sphere that represents the situation.

  b. Find the exact area of the circle formed by this cross section if $h = 6$ and $r = 10$.

19. A triangle with side lengths of 5, 9, and 11 inches is scaled by the factor 3.5.

  a. Find the side lengths of the scaled triangle.

  b. By what scale factor has the area of the original triangle been changed?

20. Construct an equilateral triangle and a square that have equal areas.

21. Given: Circle A and Circle B with common tangent $\overline{CD}$

Prove: $\triangle ACE \sim \triangle BDE$

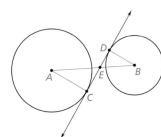

D

A   E   B

C

---

11. $\dfrac{4 - \pi}{4}$

12. a. $x = 2\sqrt{15}$; $y = \sqrt{35}$; $z = 2\sqrt{21}$

  b. $x = 4$; $y = 2\sqrt{29}$; $z = 5\sqrt{29}$

13. See back of book.

14. See back of book.

15. a. $\dfrac{12}{13}$ **b.** $\dfrac{5}{13}$ **c.** $\dfrac{12}{5}$ **d.** $\dfrac{5}{13}$

  e. $\dfrac{12}{13}$ **f.** $\dfrac{5}{12}$

16. about 29.19°

17. a. $BC = 9$ m; $\angle B = 90°$; $\angle C = 35°$

  b. about 31.53

18. See back of book.

19. a. 17.5, 31.5, 38.5

  b. 12.5

20. Check students' work.

21. See back of book.

Chapter 7
Coordinates and Vectors

In this chapter, students learn several ways to connect geometry and algebra. One of the most important connections is a theme that runs through the entire *CME Project* curriculum—the Cartesian coordinate system.

Chapter Overview

- **INVESTIGATION 7A,** *Transformations,* develops the idea that translations and rotations are compositions of reflections.
- **INVESTIGATION 7B,** *Geometry in the Coordinate Plane,* proves the distance and midpoint formulas in the coordinate plane and extends them to three dimensions.
- **INVESTIGATION 7C,** *Connections to Algebra,* identifies vectors with points in the coordinate plane. Students learn how to represent a line with a vector equation.

For more information on the investigations, see

- Chapter Road Map, p. 534
- Investigation Road Maps, pp. 536, 562, 594

CHAPTER PROJECT The Chapter Project near the end of the chapter is optional. You can assign the project at any time during the chapter depending on how often and how long you feel students should work on it.

Pacing Suggestions and Materials

Investigation 7A *Transformations*

DAY	LESSON	HOMEWORK
1	7.1 Getting Started Core: 1, 2, 3, 5 Optional: 4	Core: 6, 7, 8 Optional: 9, 10, 11, 12
2	7.2 Reflections Core: 1, 2 Optional: 3, 4	Core: 5, 6, 7, 10, 11, 12 Optional: 8, 9, 13, 14, 15, 16, 17
3	7.3 Translations Core: 1, 2 Optional: 3	Core: 4, 5, 7, 8, 10 Optional: 9, 11, 12, 13; Extension: 6
4	7.4 Rotations Core: 1, 2, 3 Optional: none	Core: 4, 5, 6, 8 Optional: 9; Extension: 7

Investigation 7B *Geometry in the Coordinate Plane*

DAY	LESSON	HOMEWORK
1	7.5 Getting Started Core: 1, 2, 3, 4 Optional: none	Core: 5, 7, 8 Optional: 6, 11; Extension: 9, 10
2	7.6 Midpoint and Distance Formulas—Day 1 Core: 3a, 4 Optional: none	Core: 6, 7 Optional: none
3	7.6 Midpoint and Distance Formulas—Day 2 Core: 1, 3b Optional: 2, 5, 8, 9	Core: 10, 12, 13, 14, 17, 19 Optional: 11, 15, 16, 18, 20, 21, 22, 23, 24
4	7.7 Parallel Lines and Collinear Points Core: 1, 2 Optional: 3, 4	Core: 6, 7, 9, 10 Optional: 5, 8, 11; Extension: 12
5	7.8 Perpendicular Lines Core: 1, 3 Optional: 2, 4	Core: 5, 6, 7, 9 Optional: 8, 10, 11, 12, 13
6	7.9 Coordinates in Three Dimensions Core: 1, 2 Optional: 3, 4, 5, 6	Core: 7, 8, 9, 10, 11, 13 Optional: 12, 14, 15, 16, 18, 19, 20, 21, 22; Extension: 17

NOTES	MATERIALS
Have students note vocabulary words in their notebooks.	• rulers • Blackline Masters MC11 and MC12
	• rulers, geometry software • Blackline Masters 7.2A and 7.2B
	• geometry software • strightedges
	• geometry software • protractors • rulers

NOTES	MATERIALS
Assign Exercises 5 and 6 if you want to test students' knowledge of the midpoint formula.	• straightedges • graph paper • Blackline Masters MC13 and 7.5
If your students are not familiar with these formulas, you might teach this lesson in 2 days. End day 1 after the For You to Do section on page 568.	• straightedges • graph paper • Blackline Master 7.6
Begin with an introduction of one way to find the midpoint of a segment.	• straightedges • graph paper
	• straightedges • graph paper
	• straightedges • graph paper
This lesson is optional.	• straightedges • Blackline Master 7.9

Mathematics Background

TRANSFORMATIONS You may wonder why students begin their work with transformations by studying reflections. Translations would likely be simpler for students to understand and visualize. But if you compose two translations—in other words, if you translate an original object, and then translate the image—the result is always another translation. With translations alone, you cannot generate any of the other transformations that preserve congruence.

However, if you compose two reflections, the combined result is either a rotation (if the two reflection lines you use intersect) or a translation (if the two lines are parallel). This means that the operation of reflection is a generator for this collection of congruence-preserving transformations. (There is a fourth such transformation that this book does not cover—the *glide reflection*.)

VECTOR METHODS This chapter provides students with an informal introduction to vectors. Students begin by thinking of a vector as an arrow with length and direction. (Mathematicians think about a vector differently—usually as an equivalence class or a translation.) Through their work with transformations, students will see the connection between vectors and translations, and the utility of using a vector to describe a translation. As they explore the idea of equivalent vectors being two arrows with the same length and orientation, they will also expand their informal notion of vector to include this idea of an equivalence class.

Continued on page 534c

Continued from page 534b

FORMAL CONNECTIONS TO ALGEBRA In this course, students have been using theorems and synthetic observations to draw geometric conclusions.

Euclid's geometry is synthetic because it makes no use of algebra, coordinates, or the techniques of calculus. In the nineteenth century, many new disciplines opened up in geometry including projective geometry and other non-Euclidean geometries. Each new discipline had its own set of axioms, and the field of geometry seemed to be splitting into separate subfields.

In 1872, Felix Klein proposed a new and influential research program that would unify all the efforts in synthetic geometry through group theory. This research program, known as the Erlangen Program, suggested that you could solve geometric problems by using group theory to organize geometry knowledge. You could relate the different kinds of geometry to each other just as you could relate subgroups of a symmetry group to each other.

DAILY PLANNER DAILY PLANNER DAILY PI

Pacing Suggestions and Materials

Investigation 7C *Connections to Algebra*

DAY	LESSON	HOMEWORK
1	7.10 Getting Started Core: 1, 2, 4, 6 Optional: 3, 5	Core: 7, 10, 11, 12 Optional: 8, 9, 13, 14, 15, 16, 17
2	7.11 Introduction to Vectors—Day 1 Core: 1, 2 Optional: none	Core: 11, Read the Developing Habits of Mind on page 603 Optional: none
3	7.11 Introduction to Vectors—Day 2 Core: 3, 4, 5, 6 Optional: none	Core: 7, 12, 14, 15, 16 Optional: 8, 9, 10, 13, 17, 18, 19
4	7.12 The Vector Equation of a Line Core: 1, 2, 3 Optional: 4	Core: 5, 8, 10, 11, 12 Optional: 6, 7, 9, 13, 14, 15, 16
5	7.13 Using the Vector Equation of a Line Core: 1, 2 Optional: 3, 4	Core: 5, 6, 8, 9 Optional: 7, 10, 11, 12, 13, 14

NOTES	MATERIALS
Have students note vocabulary words in their notebooks.	• graph paper • straightedges • Blackline Master 7.10
Work through the proof of Theorem 7.7 on day 1 of this lesson.	• graph paper • straightedges
Begin day 2 of this lesson with the Developing Habits of Mind section on page 603.	• graph paper • straightedges • Blackline Master 7.11
This is the first of two lessons on the vector-equation of a line. If you do not have time to complete both, choose this one.	• graph paper • straightedges
If you decide to assign Exercises 3 or 4, assign each after the core Check Your Understanding exercises.	• straightedges

Developing Students' Mathematical Habits

This chapter includes these key mathematical habits of mind:

• **ALGEBRAIC THINKING** Students choose variables and recognize functions to model different situations.

• **ABSTRACTION** Students use specific numerical examples to develop generally applicable cases.

Through Cartesian coordinates, students have the opportunity to translate the theorems they have been studying in geometry into specific algebraic calculations. By looking at geometry through the lens of algebra, students develop insights in both fields.

• After intensely studying the Pythagorean Theorem, students may suddenly find the formula for calculating the distance between two points obvious and simple rather than a complicated formula to memorize.

• Some students who were adept in Algebra 1 but have struggled with the deductive reasoning necessary to construct proofs may find new ways to experiment and develop insight about the theorems they have studied this year.

• By looking at congruence-preserving transformations (reflections, rotations, and translations), students can develop a deeper understanding of congruence. Using algebraic operations on points to produce these effects connects algebra and geometry further.

• Finally, by using vectors to provide new proofs of geometric results, students see another major connection.

Chapter 7

Investigations at a Glance

7A Transformations

7B Geometry in the Coordinate Plane

7C Connections to Algebra

Chapter Road Map

INVESTIGATION 7A, *Transformations,* has students use paper folding and constructions to explore reflections and composition of reflections. Students also generate translations and rotations.

INVESTIGATION 7B, *Geometry in the Coordinate Plane,* is an introduction to the coordinate plane in two and three dimensions. Students study the midpoint and distance formulas, prove whether three points are collinear, and identify parallel and perpendicular lines.

INVESTIGATION 7C, *Connections to Algebra,* has students use points on the coordinate plane as algebraic objects to which they can add and by which they can multiply any real number. Students learn about vectors and use them to find a new form for an equation of a line.

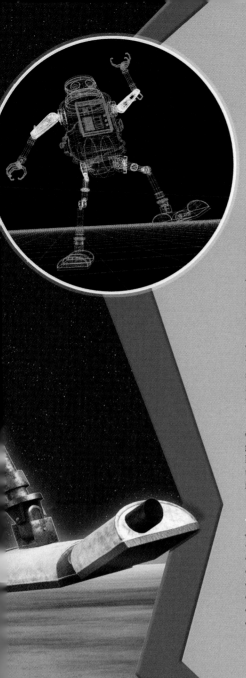

Coordinates and Vectors

Mathematics is at the core of computer graphics technology. Any drawing on a computer depends on analytic geometry, which assigns coordinates to every location in the plane (or in three-dimensional space). Analytic geometry also allows mathematical operations on those coordinates. Computers store drawings as a series of coordinates, along with functions that define relationships and connections between them.

You can draw curves on a computer with a vector pen. This tool allows you to select points and assign a vector to each point. The direction of the vector indicates the slope that the curve will have at that point. The size (or magnitude) of the vector indicates the degree to which that slope will affect surrounding points on the curve.

Computer animation depends heavily on the use of transformations. Transformations are functions on geometric objects. They produce images that are in new locations or orientations—reflections, rotations, and translations. You animate a figure by making a sequence of images under a set of transformations and dilations.

Vocabulary and Notation

- composition
- equivalent vectors
- fixed point
- image
- line of reflection
- ordered triple
- preimage
- reflection
- rotation
- transformation
- translation
- vector ($\overline{AB}$)
- z-axis
- $x \to y$ (x maps to y)

Chapter Vocabulary and Notation

The following list gives the key vocabulary and notation used in the chapter. Selected new vocabulary and notation items are shown in boldface on the student page.

- angle of rotation, p. 556
- center of rotation, p. 556
- collinear, p. 574
- composition, p. 547
- concentric circles, p. 556
- direction, p. 600
- equivalent vectors, p. 600
- F' (F prime), p. 541
- F'' (F double prime), p. 541
- fixed point, p. 540
- head, p. 600
- Head-Minus-Tail Test, p. 602
- image, p. 537
- line of reflection, p. 539
- line of symmetry, p. 544
- maps to, p. 548
- ordered triple, p. 584
- orientation, pp. 535, 602
- preimage, p. 537
- reflection, p. 541
- rotation, p. 556
- slope, p. 572
- subscript, p. 566
- tail, p. 600
- transformation, p. 537
- translation, p. 547
- vector equation of a line, p. 609
- vector ($\overrightarrow{AB}$), p. 600
- x-axis, p. 538
- $x \mapsto y$ (x maps to y), p. 548
- (x_n, y_n), p. 566
- y-axis, p. 538
- z-axis, p. 584
- z-coordinate, p. 584

Chapter Technology

Support for the use of technology is available in the Technology Handbook, See p. 712.

INVESTIGATION 7A *Geometry Software*

- **LESSON 7.2** Reflect a figure over a line, p. 541.
- **LESSON 7.4** Reflect points over intersecting lines, p. 556; find the image of a line segment after a rotation, p. 558.

Investigation Overview

This investigation begins with an In-Class Experiment that uses paper folding to explore reflections in the plane. In the second lesson, students investigate reflections further, learning more about their properties and about compositions of reflections. Students generate translations and rotations through compositions of reflections. In Lessons 7.3 and 7.4, students investigate the properties of translations and rotations. Throughout this investigation, students work both on plain paper and in the coordinate plane.

You may wish to assign Questions 1–3 for students to think and write about during the investigation.

Learning Goals

- Model reflections using paper-folding techniques.
- Model compositions of reflections and classify the resulting transformation as a reflection, rotation, translation, or combination of transformations.
- Model rotations and translations in the plane, with and without coordinates.
- Understand properties of reflection, translation, and rotation in the plane.
- Identify fixed points for a given transformation or composition of transformations.

Habits and Skills

- Use geometric properties of transformations in the coordinate plane.
- Recognize rules that map points onto other points and classify rules as particular transformations.
- Apply transformations to figures and to graphs of functions in the coordinate plane.

Investigation 7A

Transformations

In *Transformations*, you will explore reflections using paper folding or mirrors as well as the coordinate plane. You will also perform multiple reflections to make transformations called translations and rotations.

By the end of this investigation, you will be able to answer questions like these:

1. When you reflect an object over a line, what properties of the object are present in its image?

2. What happens when you compose two reflections? Three reflections? Four reflections?

3. $\triangle ABC$ has vertices $A(2, -1)$, $B(-2, -3)$, and $C(2, -3)$. When you reflect $\triangle ABC$ over the x-axis, what are the coordinates of its image $\triangle A'B'C'$?

You will learn how to

- model reflections using paper-folding techniques

- model compositions of reflections and classify the resulting transformation as a reflection, rotation, translation, or combination of transformations

- model rotations and translations in the plane, with and without coordinates

- understand properties of reflection, translation, and rotation in the plane

- identify fixed points for a given transformation or composition of transformations

You will develop these habits and skills:

- Use geometric properties of transformations in the coordinate plane.

- Recognize rules that map points onto other points and classify rules as particular transformations.

- Apply transformations to figures and to graphs of functions in the coordinate plane.

If a figure reflects onto a line, then the line is symmetry.

Investigation Road Map

LESSON 7.1, *Getting Started,* introduces reflections informally with an In-Class Experiment on paper folding.

LESSON 7.2, *Reflections,* explores the properties of reflections, including the effect that a reflection has on orientation, and which points remain fixed under reflection. Students composs two or more reflections and identify the final images as either translations or rotations of the original figure.

LESSON 7.3, *Translations,* introduces a translation as the transformation produced by composing an even number of reflections over parallel lines. Students see translations as a "slide" in the plane. They examine the properties of translations, both with and without coordinates.

LESSON 7.4, *Rotations,* introduces rotations as the composition of two reflections over intersecting lines. Students see rotations as a "turn" in the plane. They examine the properties of rotations, with and without coordinates.

There are different types of **transformations** in a plane. A reflection suggests a mirror. But you can also experiment with reflections by folding paper.

In-Class Experiment

On a piece of plain paper, draw a capital letter F an inch or two high. Here is how to find the **image** of your letter F (the **preimage**) after reflection over a fold line.

- Fold the paper to cover the letter. The crease, or fold line, can be anywhere you like, but it should not intersect the letter.

- Trace the letter onto the back of the paper.

- Unfold the paper. Trace your tracing onto the front of the paper. Also, draw along the crease to show the fold line better.

This new picture is the image of your original picture after reflection over your fold line. Place a mirror along the fold line and look into the mirror from the side with the preimage. You will see this image in the mirror.

- Label the image with an uppercase letter different from F. Label the fold line with the corresponding lowercase letter.

- Choose some other lines of reflection and repeat this process using your original preimage F. You can have one or two fold lines intersect F.

- Visualize the process to avoid lines that will reflect the preimage off your paper and predict where the image will be on the paper. Check each prediction.

For You to Explore

1. On a plain piece of paper, use a ruler to draw a line segment $\overline{AB}$. Fold the paper by matching point A to point B. Call the fold line ℓ. Call the point where ℓ and $\overline{AB}$ intersect point X.

   a. Which segment has greater length, $\overline{AX}$ or $\overline{BX}$? Explain.

   b. Choose a point C on ℓ but not on $\overline{AB}$. What is the measure of $\angle AXC$?

   c. Describe $\triangle ABC$. Does it have any special characteristics?

   d. Describe the relationship between ℓ and $\overline{AB}$.

Answers

For You To Explore

1. **a.** neither; When you fold the paper along ℓ, $\overline{AX}$ and $\overline{BX}$ coincide.

   b. 90°; When you fold along l, $\angle AXC$ and $\angle BXC$ coincide. Thus, when you unfold, the angles are congruent adjacent angles with the noncongruent sides contained in opposite rays $\overrightarrow{XA}$ and $\overrightarrow{XB}$.

   c. $\triangle ABC$ is isosceles.

   d. ℓ is the perpendicular bisector of $\overline{AB}$.

Lesson Overview

GOALS

- Warm up to the ideas of the investigation.

- Model reflections using paper-folding techniques.

This lesson introduces transformations through paper folding. Students discover important properties of paper folding and of reflections through the In-Class Experiment.

FOR YOU TO EXPLORE
- Core: 1, 2, 3, 5
- Optional: 4

HOMEWORK
- Core: 6, 7, 8
- Optional: 9, 10, 11, 12

MATERIALS
- rulers
- Blackline Masters MC11 and MC12

VOCABULARY
- image
- line of reflection
- preimage
- transformation
- x-axis
- y-axis

Launch

Begin this lesson by assigning the In-Class Experiment.

Explore

In-Class Experiment

Students should notice the following.

- Any reflection image is congruent to its preimage because, when you fold the paper along the line of reflection, the two shapes coincide.

- When you reflect the letter F, its image is backwards. It is not possible to slide or turn the image to make it coincide with the preimage. You would have to pick it up and flip it over.

- When the line of reflection (the fold line) is close to the figure, then so is its image after reflection over that line. When the line is farther away, the image is also farther from the preimage.

- If students choose a line of reflection that intersects the figure F, each point of intersection reflects onto itself. In fact, any point on the line of reflection m reflects onto itself by a reflection over m. Students can reason by continuity to "prove" this. Think of a point getting closer and closer to the line of reflection along a path perpendicular to the line. Think also of the corresponding reflection images. They too get closer and closer to the same point on the line of reflection. Eventually, the point and its image become the same point on the line of reflection.

Wrap Up

Assign the For You to Explore problems. Students may find Blackline Masters MC11 and MC12 helpful. These provide a line segment and a coordinate grid with which they can fold, draw on, and experiment.

Exercises

HOMEWORK
- Core: 6, 7, 8
- Optional: 9, 10, 11, 12

---

2. Look at a reflection you did in the In-Class Experiment. Mark several points on the preimage F. From each point, draw a segment to the corresponding point on the image. How do all these segments seem to relate to one another? How do they relate to the fold line?

3. Mark coordinate axes on a sheet of graph paper. Graph the rectangle $ABCD$ with vertices $A(-3, 4)$, $B(-1, 4)$, $C(-1, 1)$, and $D(-3, 1)$.

   Use rectangle $ABCD$ as a preimage. Find the coordinates of its image after reflection over each of the following lines.

   a. the x-axis (Label the image $EFGH$.)

   b. the y-axis (Label the image $IJKL$.)

   c. the line with equation $x = -1$ (Label the image $MNOP$.)

   You can fold your paper to find image points or to check the correspondence. Also, redraw rectangle $ABCD$ on new sections of graph paper as needed.

4. Look at rectangle $ABCD$ and its images from Exercise 3. For each rectangle listed below, describe the path from vertex to vertex, in alphabetical order, as either clockwise or counterclockwise looking at the front of the paper.

   a. $ABCD$　　　b. $EFGH$　　　c. $IJKL$　　　d. $MNOP$

   e. Do all the paths for the images go in the same direction? Does the path for the preimage go in the same direction?

5. Graph the points $U(-3, -4)$, $V(5, 0)$, and $W(2, 5)$. Find and graph their respective images U', V', and W' from reflection over the line $y = 2$. Then find the following distances.

   a. U to U'　　　b. U to the line $y = 2$　　　c. V to V'

   d. V to the line $y = 2$　　e. W to W'　　　f. W to the line $y = 2$

In this reflection, dotted lines are drawn between pairs of corresponding points.

Habits of Mind

Be systematic. In your answers to Exercise 3, list the points in order as they correspond to the points A, B, C, and D in the preimage.

Exercises *Practicing Habits of Mind*

On Your Own

6. When you reflect a figure using the paper-folding method of the In-Class Experiment, is the image congruent to the original figure (the preimage)? Explain.

Answers

2. The segments are parallel; Each of the segments has the fold line as its perpendicular bisector.

3. a. $E(-3, -4)$, $F(-1, -4)$, $G(-1, -1)$, $H(-3, -1)$
   b. $I(3, 4)$, $J(1, 4)$, $K(1, 1)$, $L(3, 1)$
   c. $M(1, 4)$, $N(-1, 4)$, $O(-1, 1)$, $P(1, 1)$

4. a. clockwise
   b. counterclockwise
   c. counterclockwise
   d. counterclockwise

   e. All paths for the images go counterclockwise; the path for the preimage is clockwise.

5. a. 12　　b. 6　　c. 4　　d. 2
   e. 6　　f. 3

Exercises

6. Yes; when you fold the paper along the line of reflection, the preimage and image coincide.

7. a. $\overline{PQ}$: 1, $\overline{QR}$: $-\frac{1}{2}$, $\overline{RS}$: 1, $\overline{SP}$: $-\frac{1}{2}$;

7. a. Graph quadrilateral *PQRS* with *P*(1, 0), *Q*(5, 4), *R*(9, 2), and *S*(5, −2). Find the slope of each side of *PQRS*. Show that *PQRS* is a parallelogram.

b. Graph the image *P′Q′R′S′* of *PQRS* after reflection over the line $y = -2$.

c. Is *P′Q′R′S′* also a parallelogram? Explain.

d. Are the sides of the image *P′Q′R′S′* parallel to the corresponding sides in the preimage *PQRS*? Explain.

8. a. Graph any quadrilateral and label it *ABCD*.

b. Suppose you walk around your quadrilateral from *A* to *B* to *C* to *D* and then back to *A*. Will a person watching from above see your path as clockwise or counterclockwise?

c. Reflect your quadrilateral over the line $x = -2$. Label the image *EFGH* so that *EFGH* ≅ *ABCD*.

d. Suppose you walk around this new quadrilateral from *E* to *F* to *G* to *H* and then back to *E*. Will a person watching from above see your path as clockwise or counterclockwise?

e. Was the direction (clockwise or counterclockwise) the same for your preimage and for its image after reflection?

9. Plot $\overline{AB}$ on a coordinate plane, with endpoints *A*(2, 5) and *B*(4, 2). Reflect $\overline{AB}$ over the *x*-axis. Write the coordinates of *A′* and *B′*, the images of *A* and *B*.

10. Graph the line $2x + y = 6$. Write an equation for its image after a reflection over the *y*-axis.

Maintain Your Skills

11. On a plain piece of paper, use a ruler to draw scalene △*ABC*. Use the paper-folding method of the In-Class Experiment. Reflect △*ABC* over different lines of reflection. Describe where you fold the paper so that △*ABC* and its image have the following in common.

a. no points   **b.** one point

c. two points   **d.** one side

12. On a plain piece of paper, draw isosceles △*DEF* with $\overline{DE} \cong \overline{DF}$. Fold the paper to find the **line of reflection** for which △*DEF* and its image have all their points in common. Describe the position of this line of reflection.

On Your Own

EXERCISES 11 AND 12 give students additional practice producing reflected images and visualizing the results of a reflection over a specific line.

the slopes of opposite sides of *PQRS* are equal. Hence *PQRS* has its opposite sides parallel. Therefore, *PQRS* is a parallelogram.

b. Check students' diagrams. The vertices of the image are *P′*(1, −4), (5, −8), *R′*(9, −6), *S′*(5, −2).

c. Yes; Answers may vary. Sample: $\overline{P'S'}$ and $\overline{Q'R'}$ are opposite sides, and both have slope $\frac{1}{2}$. $\overline{P'Q'}$ and $\overline{R'S'}$ are opposite sides, and both have slope −1.

Therefore, both pairs of opposite sides are parallel, which means *P′Q′R′S′* is a parallelogram.

d. no

8. See back of book.

9. *A*(2, −5), *B*(4, −2)

10. $-2x + y = 6$

11. See back of book.

12. If $\overline{DE}$ and $\overline{DF}$ are the only sides that are congruent, then the only fold line that will work is the perpendicular bisector of $\overline{EF}$. If all three sides of △*DEF* are congruent, then each line that is a perpendicular bisector of a side will do.

Lesson Overview

GOALS

- Model the composition of reflections over intersecting lines and classify the resulting transformation as a rotation.

- Understand properties of reflection in the plane.

- Identify fixed points for a given reflection or composition of reflections.

This lesson treats reflections and their properties in more detail. Students also compose reflections.

CHECK YOUR UNDERSTANDING
- Core: 1, 2
- Optional: 3, 4

MATERIALS
- geometry software
- rulers
- Blackline Master 7.2A and 7.2B

HOMEWORK
- Core: 5, 6, 7, 10, 11, 12
- Optional: 8, 9, 13, 14, 15, 16, 17

VOCABULARY
- fixed point
- F' (F prime)
- F'' (F double prime)
- line of symmetry
- reflection

Launch

Assign the For Discussion section. You may wish to have students work briefly in pairs or groups before discussing these questions as a class.

Explore

For Discussion

Some of the results from Lesson 7.1 will be useful for Problems 1–3.

In the Getting Started lesson, you worked with reflections in the plane. You saw how you can map all the points of the plane to the points of the plane by reflecting over a line. You learned to find the images of points by folding paper, or by using the "mirror-image" technique.

Does every point map onto a point different from itself? For some reflections the points do, but for some they do not. Look at the following figure.

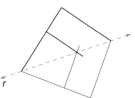

Definition

A point that is its own image after a transformation is a **fixed point**.

For Discussion

1. In the figure above, can you see points that are mapped onto themselves by reflection over r?

2. Draw a geometric object (such as a line, a triangle, or a circle) so that its image after the reflection over r is itself. Are all of its points fixed?

3. Describe all the fixed points for the reflection over line r.

You have seen what happens when you reflect a point over one line. What happens when you reflect a point over one line and then reflect the image of that point over a second line?

A figure that reflects onto itself over a line has line symmetry.

Answers

For Discussion

1. For the figure in the diagram, there are three fixed points, namely, the three points where the figure intersects r.

2. Answers may vary. Sample: A figure whose image coincides with the preimage has fixed points for reflection over r if and only if the figure intersects r. The fixed points are the points that belong to the intersection.

3. the points of intersection of the figure and line r

Use geometry software or paper and pencil.

4. Draw two parallel lines *r* and *s*. Also, draw a letter F like the one on the right.

5. Reflect F over *r*. Refer to this image of F as F'.

6. Reflect F' over *s*. Refer to this image of F' as F".

7. Are there any points in the plane that remained fixed through both reflections?

8. Compare F and F". Is there a single transformation (not necessarily a reflection) that maps F onto F"? Explain.

9. Draw a different line for *s*. Make *s* intersect *r*. Construct F" as before.

10. Are there any points in the plane that remained fixed after reflection over *r* and *s* for your new choice for *s*?

11. Compare F and F". Is there a single transformation that maps F onto F"? Explain.

Read F" as
"F double prime."

For Discussion

Compare results for the In-Class Experiment with other students' in your class. Discuss possible reasons for the differences and similarities you see.

12. What single transformation mapped F onto F"? Did this transformation map F onto F" in both cases?

13. Did anyone have a different kind of single transformation?

14. When *r* and *s* intersected, what were the fixed points after reflection over *r* and then *s*? What were the fixed points when they were parallel?

15. What happens if *r* and *s* are the same line?

In Lesson 7.1, you folded paper and traced to produce a reflected image. You found that the fold line (which is the line of reflection) has a special property. It is the perpendicular bisector of every segment joining a point in the preimage to the corresponding point in the image.

You can use this special property to define *reflection*.

Definition

Suppose *P* is a point and ℓ is a line not containing *P*. A **reflection** over ℓ maps the point to *P'* such that ℓ is the perpendicular bisector of $\overline{PP'}$. If ℓ contains *P*, *P* is its own reflection image.

For Discussion

PROBLEM 15 If *r* and *s* are the same line, every point in the plane is fixed after both reflections. Although any point not on *r* is mapped to a new point after the first reflection over *r*, the new point is mapped back to the original point in the second reflection over *r*. This is an interesting result, because it shows that the inverse operation of a reflection over a line *r* is that same reflection over the line *r*.

Wrap Up

Assign Check Your Understanding Exercises 1 and 2 for work in class.

Assessment Resources

Lesson Quiz 7.2

1. a. Reflect $\overline{AB}$ with endpoints $A(2, 5)$ and $B(0, 4)$ over the line with equation $y = 5$. Write the coordinates of the image.
   b. Reflect the image of $\overline{AB}$ over the line with equation $y = 2$. Write the coordinates of this new image.
   c. Describe a single transformation that maps $\overline{AB}$ onto the final image.

Decide whether each graph has any lines of symmetry. Explain.

2. $y = \sqrt[3]{x}$

3. $y = -x^2 - 4x - 2$

In-Class Experiment

4. Check students' work.

5. Check students' work.

6. Check students' work.

7. No

8. Yes, a translation.

9. Check students' work.

10. One

11. Yes, a rotation.

For Discussion

12–15. Check students' work. Students should see that successive reflections over two parallel lines will be equivalent to a translation. Only a "null" translation (that is, a translation for which each point moves a distance of 0 units) will leave a point of a figure fixed. This is what happens in the "degenerate" case referred to in Problem 4.

Exercises

HOMEWORK
- Core: 5, 6, 7, 10, 11, 12
- Optional: 8, 9, 13, 14, 15, 16, 17

Exercises *Practicing Habits of Mind*

Check Your Understanding

1. Decide whether each statement is *always true*, *sometimes true*, or *always false* for reflection over a line. If a statement is always true or always false, prove it. If a statement is sometimes true and sometimes false, give an example of each case.

   a. A segment in a preimage must be the same length as the corresponding segment in the image.

   b. An angle in a preimage must have the same measure as the corresponding angle in the image.

   c. Collinear points in a preimage must have collinear image points.

   d. The slope of a segment in an image must be the same as the slope of the corresponding segment in the preimage.

   e. Segments in an image that correspond to segments that are parallel in the preimage must be parallel to each other.

   f. Segments in an image that correspond to segments that are perpendicular in the preimage must also be perpendicular.

2. a. Reflect $\overline{AB}$ with endpoints $A(2, 5)$ and $B(4, 2)$ over the line with equation $x = 4$. Write the coordinates of the image.

   b. Now reflect the image of $\overline{AB}$ over the line with equation $x = 8$. Write the coordinates of this new image.

   c. Describe a single transformation that maps $\overline{AB}$ onto the final image.

3. In the diagram below, P' is the image of P over ℓ. The points O and R are on ℓ. Prove $\angle POR \cong \angle P'OR$.

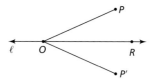

4. Prove that if a segment is parallel to a line of reflection, the image of the segment after reflection is also parallel to the line of reflection.

Answers

Exercises

1. See back of book.

2. a. $A' = (6, 5)$, $B' = (4, 2)$

   b. $A = (10, 5)$, $B = (12, 2)$

   c. a translation 8 units to the right (that is, in the positive direction, parallel to the x-axis)

3. Draw PP' Label point S where PP' and ℓ intersect. Since P' is the reflection of P over ℓ, ℓ is the perpendicular bisector of PP'. $\overline{PS} \cong \overline{P'S}$ by definition of bisector. $\overline{OS} \cong \overline{OS}$ by the reflexive property. $\triangle OSP$ and $\triangle OSP'$ are right triangles. $\triangle OSP \cong \triangle OSP'$ by LL. $\angle POR \cong \angle P'OR$ by CPCTC.

4. Suppose $\overline{AB} \| \ell$, and let $\overline{A'B'}$ be the image of $\overline{AB}$ for reflection over ℓ. Then ℓ is the perpendicular bisector of $\overline{AA'}$ and $\overline{BB'}$. If M is the midpoint of $\overline{AA'}$ and N is the midpoint of $\overline{BB'}$, then $ABNM$ and $A'B'NM$ are rectangles. It follows that $\overline{A'B'} \| \overline{MN}$ and hence that $\overline{A'B'} \| \ell$.

5. Complete parts (a) and (b) to show that the definition of reflection in the lesson describes a unique reflection image.

   a. Given a line ℓ and a point P not on ℓ, how many lines are there through P that are perpendicular to ℓ? Explain how you know.

   b. Given a line ℓ, a point P, and another line m through P and perpendicular to ℓ, explain how you can find a point P' on m such that ℓ is the perpendicular bisector of $\overline{PP'}$. Is there only one such point?

6. Use the definition of reflection to prove that a segment and its reflection image are congruent. In other words:

   Show that if ℓ is the perpendicular bisector of both $\overline{AA'}$ and $\overline{BB'}$, then $\overline{AB} \cong \overline{A'B'}$.

7. a. Reflect $\overline{AB}$ with endpoints $A(1, 2)$ and $B(3, 3)$ over the line $y = \frac{1}{2}$. Write the coordinates of the endpoints of the image.

   b. Now reflect the image of $\overline{AB}$ over the line $y = -1$. Write the coordinates of the endpoints of this new image.

   c. Describe a single transformation that maps $\overline{AB}$ onto the final image.

8. Reflect $\overline{AB}$ with endpoints $A(1, 2)$ and $B(3, 3)$ over the line $x = 4$. Now reflect the image over the line $y = -1$. Write the coordinates of the image of $\overline{AB}$ after these two reflections. Describe a single transformation that maps $\overline{AB}$ onto the final image.

9. Graph the line $x + 3y = 6$. Write an equation for its image after a reflection over the x-axis.

Check Your Understanding

EXERCISES 5 AND 6 ask students to consider a new definition of reflection: *The image of any point P after reflection over a line ℓ is a point P' such that ℓ is the perpendicular bisector of $\overline{PP'}$.* Students confirm several results using this new definition.

5. **a.** One; theorem 2.5 states that if a point P is not on line ℓ, exactly one line through P exists that is perpendicular to ℓ.

   b. Answers may vary. Sample: Let M be the point where m intersects ℓ. Draw the circle with center M that passes through P. Let P' be the second point where m intersects the circle; yes, there is only one such point.

6. See back of book.

7. **a.** $A(1, -1)$, $B(3, -2)$

   b. $A(1, -1)$, $B(3, 0)$

   c. a translation down 3 units

8. $A(7, 2)$, $B(5, 3)$, $A(7, -4)$, $B(5, -5)$; a rotation of 180° around the point with coordinates $(4, -1)$

9. $x - 3y = 6$

EXERCISES 11–14 Provide students with Blackline Master 7.2A. They may find it helpful to draw on and fold the graphs as they decide whether the graphs contain lines of symmetry.

10. **Standardized Test Prep** Reflect point $R(2, -3)$ over the line $y = x$. What are the coordinates of the reflection image of point R?

  A. $(-2, -3)$ **B.** $(-2, 3)$ **C.** $(-3, 2)$ **D.** $(2, 3)$

In Exercises 11–14, you are given an equation and its graph. Decide whether each graph has any lines of symmetry. Prove your conjecture.

> **Remember...**
> If a figure maps onto itself after reflection over a line, then that line is a line of symmetry for the figure.

11. $y = |x|$

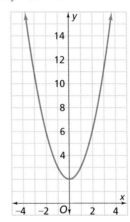

12. $y = x^2$

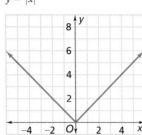

13. $y = x^2 + 2$

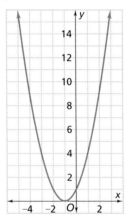

14. $y = x^2 + 2x + 1$

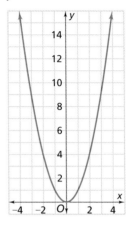

Answers

10. B

11. Yes, the y-axis; Since $|-x| = |x|$, the points with coordinates $(x, |x|)$ and $(-x, |x|)$ are on the graph of $y = |x|$ for every real number x. For $x \neq 0$, these are the endpoints of a horizontal segment of length $2|x|$ whose midpoint is on the y-axis at $(0, |x|)$. For $x = 0$, both $(x, |x|)$ and $(-x, |x|)$ correspond to $(0, 0)$.

12. Yes, the y-axis; the point at $(0, 0)$ is on the graph and on the y-axis. All other points of the graph are above the x-axis. For each $b > 0$, the line with equation $y = b$ intersects the graph of $y = x^2$ at $(-\sqrt{b}, b)$ and $(\sqrt{b}, b)$. These correspond to the endpoints of a segment whose midpoint is $(0, b)$.

13. Yes, the y-axis; all points of the graph lie on or above the line with equation $y = 2$. The line with equation $y = 2$ intersects the graph of $y = x^2 + 2$ at the single point $(0, 2)$. If $b > 2$, then the graphs of

15. Trace the diagram below onto a sheet of plain paper. Use the letter F in this picture as a preimage.

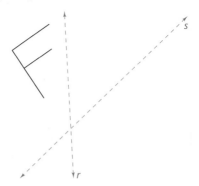

a. Reflect F over line *r*. Label this image *r*(F). Then reflect *r*(F) over line *s*. Label this image *s*(*r*(F)). Compare F and *s*(*r*(F)). Is there a single transformation that maps F onto *s*(*r*(F)) without using reflection?

b. Using the same diagram, draw two more lines. Call them *t* and *w*. Reflect *s*(*r*(F)) over *t* to obtain *t*(*s*(*r*(F))). Compare *F* and *t*(*s*(*r*(F))). Is there a single transformation that maps F onto *t*(*s*(*r*(F))) without using reflection?

c. Is there a single transformation that would map *r*(F) onto *t*(*s*(*r*(F))) without using reflection?

d. Compare F and *w*(*t*(*s*(*r*(F)))). Is there a single transformation that maps F onto *w*(*t*(*s*(*r*(F)))) without using reflection?

e. Find a pattern for your answers to parts (a)–(d).

Is this photograph upside down?

$y = b$ and $y = x^2 + 2$ intersect at the points with coordinates $(-\sqrt{b-2}, b)$ and $(\sqrt{b-2}, b)$. These are the endpoints of a horizontal segment whose midpoint has coordinates (0, b).

14. Yes, the line with equation $x = -1$; all points of the graph lie on or above the *x*-axis. The only point of the graph that is on the *x*-axis is the point with coordinates $(-1, 0)$, which is on the line with equation $x = -1$. If $b > 0$, then the graphs of $y = b$ and $y = x^2 + 2x + 1$

intersect at the points with coordinates $(-1 + \sqrt{b}, b)$ and $(-1 - \sqrt{b}, b)$. These are the endpoints of a horizontal segment whose midpoint has coordinates $(-1, b)$.

15. a. yes　**b.** no　**c.** yes　**d.** yes
e. Answers may vary. Sample: If a figure is reflected over a line, the image over a second line, and so on, and if the number of reflections performed is even, then the final image can be obtained from the original figure by using a single rotation or a single translation.

Additional Resources

Additional Practice

1. a. Reflect $\overline{AB}$ with endpoints $A(4, 5)$ and $B(0, 3)$ over the line with equation $y = -1$. Write the coordinates of the image.
  b. Reflect the image of $\overline{AB}$ over the line with equation $y = 2$. Write the coordinates of this new image.
  c. Describe a single transformation that maps $\overline{AB}$ onto the final image.

2. a. Reflect $\overline{AB}$ with endpoints $A(4, 5)$ and $B(0, 3)$ over the line with equation $x = 3$. Write the coordinates of the image.
  b. Reflect the image of $\overline{AB}$ over the line with equation $x = -1$. Write the coordinates of this new image.
  c. Describe a single transformation that maps $\overline{AB}$ onto the final image.

For Exercises 3–6, decide whether each graph has any lines of symmetry. Prove your conjecture.

3. $y = x^3$

4. $y = \pm\sqrt{x - 2}$

5. $y = \frac{1}{x}$

6. $y = |x + 3|$

7. Suppose that you have point S and its reflection image S'. Describe how you can find the line of reflection.

8. Graph the line $x + 2y = 6$. Write an equation for its image after a reflection over the x-axis.

Practice: For Lesson 7.2, assign Exercises 1–8.

---

16. Think of the circle O and its chord AB as a single figure. Find all lines of symmetry for the figure. Write the equation of each line of symmetry.

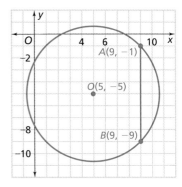

Maintain Your Skills

17. For the letters of the alphabet below, list those that appear to have each of the following.

ABCDEFGHI
JKLMNOPQR
STUVWXYZ

a. a vertical line of symmetry

b. a horizontal line of symmetry

c. both vertical and horizontal lines of symmetry

d. lines of symmetry that are neither horizontal nor vertical

e. rotational symmetry (other than full-turn rotational symmetry)

Having rotational symmetry means that, when you turn the paper, at some angle or angles the letter looks exactly as it did at the start.

Answers

16. $y = -5$

17. a. A, H, I, M, O, T, U, V, W, X, Y
  b. B, C, D, E, H, I, K, O, X
  c. H, I, O, X
  d. none
  e. H, I, N, O, S, X, Z

In the In-Class Experiment of Lesson 7.2, you reflected the letter F over two parallel lines. Here are some conclusions you may have reached.

- The final image was congruent to the original F.
- You could obtain the final image from the original F by a single transformation—a "slide" with no spins or turns.
- No points on the plane were fixed.

This type of transformation is a **translation**. Any translation is a **composition** of two reflections, but you usually do not think of it that way.

For Discussion

1. How can you describe the transformation that maps *ABCD* onto *A'B'C'D'*?

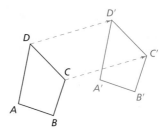

How are the arrows related? Explain.

> In Exercise 6, you will prove that the composition of two reflections over parallel lines produces a translation.

> Try drawing more arrows to corresponding points. Some people call these arrows *vectors*.

Translations enhance the photograph of a flower.

Answers

For Discussion

1. Answers may vary. Sample: The transformation moves all points of *ABCD* in the direction from *D* to *D'* and the same distance as from *D* to *D'*. For all points other than *D*, the arrow from the original point on *ABCD* to the corresponding point on *A'B'C'D'* will be parallel to the arrow from *D* to *D'* and the same length as that arrow.

Lesson Overview

GOALS

- Model the composition of reflections over parallel lines and classify the resulting transformation as a translation.
- Model translations in the plane, with and without coordinates.
- Understand properties of reflection and translation in the plane.

This lesson examines translations as the transformation you obtain by reflecting an object successively over two parallel lines. The lesson starts by analyzing some of your students' results from the In-Class Experiment of Lesson 7.2. The lesson goes on to describe translations in terms of operations on coordinates and to explore the properties of translations.

CHECK YOUR UNDERSTANDING
- Core: 1, 2
- Optional: 3

MATERIALS
- geometry software

HOMEWORK
- Core: 4, 5, 7, 8, 10
- Optional: 9, 11, 12, 13
- Extension: 6

VOCABULARY
- composition
- maps to
- translation
- $x \mapsto y$ (*x* maps to *y*)

Launch

Start this lesson by summarizing the results of the In-Class Experiment of Lesson 7.2. Introduce the concept of translation and assign the For Discussion section.

Explore

For Discussion

The transformation that maps *ABCD* onto *A'B'C'D'* appears to be a translation because you can verify the properties described at the beginning of the lesson. Students might notice that the "arrows" connecting corresponding points appear to be parallel, congruent, and have the same orientation. One way to prove these conjectures is to plot the quadrilateral and its image after the translation on the coordinate plane, as in the Developing Habits of Mind section on the following page.

Write a description. The coordinate plane gives you an algebraic way to describe a translation. The diagram shows a translation of a quadrilateral.

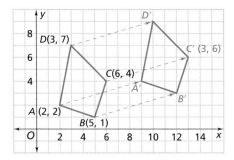

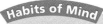
What are the coordinates of A', B', and D'?

Here, you "add" $(7, 2)$ to each point of the preimage to get the image.

In general, a translation on the coordinate plane is a transformation that adds one value to every x-coordinate of the preimage and another (possibly the same) value to every y-coordinate of the preimage. In symbols,

$$(x, y) \mapsto (x + a, y + b)$$

where a and b are any real numbers. This notation describes a mapping. You say, "The translation (a, b) maps (x, y) to $(x + a, y + b)$."

Habits of Mind

Check your work. Verify your conjectures from Problem 1. Use numbers and the coordinate plane.

The relationships you described in Problem 1 are still true, but now you give such descriptions using numbers.

For You to Do

Graph a scalene right triangle. Find its image after applying each rule.

2. $(x, y) \mapsto (x + 8, y + 5)$

3. $(a, b) \mapsto (a - 8, b + 5)$

4. $(a, b) \mapsto (-a, b)$

5. $(x, y) \mapsto (x + 1, y + 2)$

6. $(x, y) \mapsto (x, -y)$

Which rules are translations? What are the other rules?

Answers

For You to Do

2. Answers may vary. Sample: The image can be obtained by moving the preimage right 8 units, then up 5 units.

3. Answers may vary. Sample: The image can be obtained by moving the preimage left 8 units, then up 5 units.

4. Answers may vary. Sample: The image can be obtained by reflecting the preimage over the y-axis.

5. Answers may vary. Sample: The image can be obtained by moving the preimage right 1 unit, then up 2 units.

6. Answers may vary. Sample: The image can be obtained by reflecting the preimage over the x-axis.

Tony and Sasha want to translate the parabola $y = \frac{1}{2}x^2 + 1$ by $(2, -1)$. They also want to write an equation for the image of the parabola after the translation.

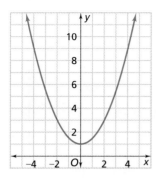

Tony This should be easy. I mean, we know that every point (x, y) maps to $(x + 2, y - 1)$. We can just plug those new expressions in for x and y. That should move everything 2 units to the right and 1 unit down.

Sasha That sounds like it could work.

Tony and Sasha graph $(y - 1) = \frac{1}{2}(x + 2)^2 + 1$.

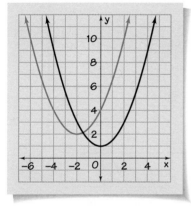

Tony Hey, that's out of order! The image parabola was translated in exactly the wrong direction! Where did we mess up?

Sasha Hmmm . . . wait a minute. The old equation was $y = \frac{1}{2}x^2 + 1$, right?

Tony Yes, so what?

Minds in Action

EPISODE 30 Students usually feel very comfortable expressing a translation such as $(2, -1)$ as a mapping $(x, y) \mapsto (x + 2, y - 1)$, but then are completely baffled by the effect of the same translation on an equation.

This dialog is an example of that confusion. Tony and Sasha know where the image of the parabola is supposed be, and so they realize that substituting $x + 2$ for x and $y - 1$ for y moves the parabola in the wrong direction. For many of your students, this will be the only reason they need to "swap the signs" when doing a translation. They will want to remember this as a rule without understanding the reasons behind it.

However, it is very important to understand why that first intuition does not produce the expected result. It is because the equation for the original parabola is written in terms of the original x and y—before the translation. When you replace x in that equation, you must replace it with something that is equal to the original x. Similarly, when you replace y, you must replace it with something equal to the original y. Tony and Sasha decide to use different variables to describe x and y before and after the translation, and this may help your students.

Wrap Up

Assign Check Your Understanding Exercises 1 and 2 for in class work.

Assessment Resources

Lesson Quiz 7.3

1. The diagram shows the transformation $ABCD \to A'B'C'D'$.
   a. How do you know that the transformation is a translation?
   b. Describe the translation.
   c. Describe the change in the vertex coordinates.

2. Apply the rule $(x, y) \mapsto (x + 4, y - 3)$ to $\triangle ABC$ with vertices $A(0, 0)$, $B(2, 3)$, and $C(5, 0)$. Connect the three image points. Describe how the image relates to $\triangle ABC$.

3. Use rectangle $ABCD$ with vertices $A(-1, 2)$, $B(-3, 4)$, $C(0, 7)$, and $D(2, 5)$.
   a. Reflect $ABCD$ over $y = 3$ and label the vertices $A'B'C'D'$.
   b. Reflect $A'B'C'D'$ over $y = -1$ and label the new vertices $A''B''C''D''$.
   c. Find the coordinates of the vertices of $A'B'C'D'$ and of $A''B''C''D''$.
   d. Is there a single mapping that sends $ABCD$ onto $A''B''C''D''$? If so, describe it.

Sasha   That was written with the old x and the old y. We know that

$$y_{old} = \tfrac{1}{2}(x_{old})^2 + 1$$

But now we're talking about a different x and y.

$$x_{new} = x_{old} + 2$$
$$y_{new} = y_{old} - 1$$

Look, the only equation we have is in terms of x_{old} and y_{old}. We have to substitute something with x_{new} and y_{new} that are equal to x_{old} and y_{old}.

Tony   Oh, I get it! Since

$$x_{old} = x_{new} - 2$$
$$y_{old} = y_{new} + 1$$

we have to plug in $x - 2$ for x and $y + 1$ for y.

Sasha   Cross your fingers. Let's try it.

Tony and Sasha graph $(y + 1) = \tfrac{1}{2}(x - 2)^2 + 1$.

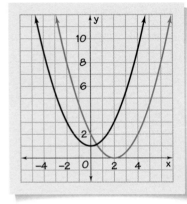

Tony   Go, Sasha!

For You to Do

Translate the parabola with equation $y = \tfrac{1}{2}x^2 + 1$ by each translation below. Write an equation for the parabola's image after each translation.

7. $(0, -2)$

8. $(3, 0)$

9. $(1, 5)$

Answers

For You to Do

7. $y = \tfrac{1}{2}x^2 - 1$

8. $y = \tfrac{1}{2}(x - 3)^2 + 1$

9. $y = \tfrac{1}{2}(x - 1)^2 + 6$

Exercises *Practicing Habits of Mind*

Check Your Understanding

1. The diagram shows the transformation $AKLJ \rightarrow A'K'L'J'$.

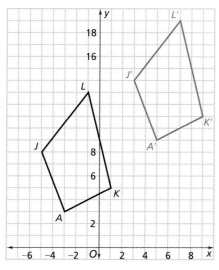

  a. How do you know that the transformation is a translation?

  b. Describe the translation.

  c. Describe what you have to do to the coordinates of the vertices of $AKLJ$ to get the coordinates of the vertices of $A'K'L'J'$.

2. Apply the rule $(x, y) \mapsto (x + 10, y + 6)$ to the vertices of a triangle. Then connect the three image points. What figure do you get? How is it related to your original triangle?

3. Find an equation of the image of line s with equation $2x + y = 3$ after the translation $(6, 7)$.

Go Online
PHSchool.com

For real-world examples of translations, go to
Web Code: bee-9031

Exercises

HOMEWORK
- Core: 4, 5, 7, 8, 10
- Optional: 9, 11, 12, 13
- Extension: 6

Exercises

1. a. Answers may vary. Sample: You can slide the original figure straight from the original to the new position and all vertices will match.

   b. Answers may vary. Sample: It is the translation accomplished by sliding $AKLJ$ to the right 8 units and up 6 units.

   c. $(x, y) \mapsto (x + 8, y + 6)$

2. A triangle; the image is congruent to the original and is obtained by translating the original to the right 10 units and up 6 units.

3. $2x + y = 22$

4. Graph $\overline{AB}$ with endpoints $A(1, 2)$ and $B(2, 5)$.

   a. Reflect $\overline{AB}$ over the line $x = 3$. Call its image $\overline{A'B'}$.

   b. Reflect $\overline{A'B'}$ over the line $x = 6$. Call its image $\overline{A''B''}$.

   c. Find the coordinates of A', B', A'', and B''.

   d. Is there a single mapping that sends $\overline{AB}$ onto $\overline{A''B''}$? If so, describe it. If not, explain why not.

5. Use coordinate methods to show that quadrilateral $AA''B''B$ in Exercise 4 is a parallelogram.

6. **Take It Further** Reflect two points A and B over a line r. Reflect their images over a line s parallel to r, producing the final image points A'' and B''. Prove that the points A, B, B'', and A'' are the vertices of a parallelogram. (Exercise 4 is a specific case of this process.) Assume that $\overline{AB}$ is not parallel to r and s.

Show also that the composition of the reflections over parallel lines r and s is a translation.

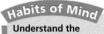

Habits of Mind

Understand the problem. Why are you asked to assume that $\overline{AB}$ is not parallel to lines r and s? Can you prove the result if $\overline{AB}$ is parallel to lines r and s? Try it.

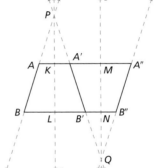

The points P and Q in the diagram might be useful.

Answers

4. See back of book.

5. Answers may vary. Sample: $\overline{AA''}$ and $\overline{BB''}$ have slope 0 and hence are parallel. Also $AA'' = BB'' = 6$. Since $AA''B''B$ has a pair of opposite sides that are parallel and congruent, it is a parallelogram.

6. Check students' work.

7. See back of book.

8. Answers may vary. Sample: The points with coordinates $(-2, 0)$,

$(0, 2)$, and $(2, 0)$; each of the points with these coordinates is 2 units from the origin, and each is on the graph since the coordinates satisfy the equation. This means that the origin is the center of the circle.

   a. $x^2 + (y + 1)^2 = 4$

   b. $x^2 + (y - 1)^2 = 4$

   c. $(x - 6)^2 + y^2 = 4$

   d. $(x - 3)^2 + (y - 4)^2 = 4$

9. Answers may vary. Sample: The points with coordinates $(-3, 0)$, $(-1, 2)$, and $(1, 0)$; the points have coordinates that satisfy the

7. Here is a graph of the parabola with equation $y = -x^2 + 2x$.

  a. Substitute $x + 3$ for x in the equation of the parabola. Graph the result. Describe this result as a translation of the original parabola.

  b. Predict what graph will result if you substitute $x - 2$ for x in the equation. Check by doing the substitution and graphing. Is your prediction correct?

  c. Substitute $y - 2$ for y in the equation of the parabola. Graph the result. Describe this result as a translation of the original parabola.

  d. Predict what graph will result if you substitute $y + 3$ for y in the equation. Check by doing the substitution and graphing the new equation. Is your prediction correct?

8. Look at the circle with equation $x^2 + y^2 = 4$.

Find at least three points on the circle. Prove algebraically that the center of this circle is at the origin. Translate the circle by each translation below. Write an equation for the image of the circle after each translation.

  a. $(0, -1)$ **b.** $(0, 1)$ **c.** $(6, 0)$ **d.** $(3, 4)$

9. Look at the circle with equation $x^2 + y^2 + 2x = 3$.

Find at least three points on the circle. Prove algebraically that its center is at $(-1, 0)$. Translate the circle by each translation below. Write an equation for the image of the circle after each translation.

  a. $(0, -2)$ **b.** $(0, 2)$ **c.** $(3, 0)$ **d.** $(1, 4)$

On Your Own

EXERCISE 7 reinforces students' work on translating equations. Each part of the exercise gives students a particular expression to substitute for x or for y in the equation of the original parabola. They graph the result and describe its location in relation to the original parabola. Students see again that, although the mapping $(x, y) \mapsto (x + 3, y)$ maps any point x to a point 3 units to the right of x, substituting $x + 3$ for x in the equation of the original parabola maps the original parabola to another parabola 3 units to the left.

equation, so the points are on the graph. Each of the points is 2 units from the point with coordinates $(-1, 0)$. Therefore, $(-1, 0)$ is the center of the circle.

  a. $(x + 1)^2 + (y + 2)^2 = 4$
  b. $(x + 1)^2 + (y - 2)^2 = 4$
  c. $(x - 2)^2 + y^2 = 4$
  d. $x^2 + (y - 4)^2 = 4$

Maintain Your Skills

EXERCISES 11–13 reinforce the process of translating a graph with a given equation. Students practice writing equations of circles with different centers. Then they use algebra to show that the translation that should map each circle back to a circle centered at the origin actually does what they think it will. These problems also may encourage students to prefer $(x - a)^2 + (y - b)^2 = r^2$ as the form for the equation of a circle because the calculations with this form are simpler.

Additional Resources

PRINTED RESOURCES
- Texas Instruments Activities Workbook
- Cabrilog Activities
- Teaching Resources
- Practice Workbook
- Assessment Resources

TECHNOLOGY
- TeacherExpress CD-ROM
- **Exam***View* CD-ROM
- **PHSchool.com**
  - Homework Help
  - Video Tutors
  - Multiple Choice
  - Crosswords

Additional Practice

1. a. Apply the rule $(x, y) \mapsto (x - 4, y + 3)$ to parallelogram *ABCD* with vertices *A*(0, 0), *B*(2, 3), *C*(7, 3), and *D*(5, 0). Draw *ABCD* and its image *A'B'C'D'*. Label all vertices.
  b. Describe how *A'B'C'D'* relates to *ABCD*.

2. Use △*ABC* with vertices *A*(2, 3), *B*(5, 4), and *C*(3, 0).
  a. Reflect △*ABC* over the line *x* = 2 and label the vertices *A'B'C'*.
  b. Reflect △*A'B'C'* over the line *x* = −3 and label the new vertices *A"B"C"*.
  c. Find the coordinates of vertices *A'B'C'* and *A"B"C"*.
  d. Is there a single mapping that sends △*ABC* onto △*A"B"C"*? If so, describe it.

3. Use the circle with equation $x^2 + y^2 = 9$.
  a. Substitute *x* + 4 for *x* in the equation. Graph the result. Predict the result if you substitute *x* − 4.
  b. Substitute *y* + 5 for *y* in the equation. Graph the result. Predict the result if you substitute *y* − 5.
  c. Apply the rule $(x, y) \mapsto (x - 4, y - 5)$ to the points on the circle. Describe how your predictions differ from the mapping notation.

For Exercises 4–6, use geometry software or a pencil and paper. Copy each figure. Then find the image of the figure using the given counterclockwise rotation about point *P*.

4. 30°   **5.** 45°   **6.** 120°

7. a. Use △*ABC*. Draw the final image of △*ABC* reflected over lines ℓ and *m*.
  b. Fill in the blank: The composition of the reflections over intersecting lines is equivalent to a _____.
  c. Find the angle of rotation and mark the center of rotation.

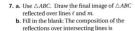

Practice: For Lesson 7.3, assign Exercises 1–3.

---

10. Standardized Test Prep The transformation $(x, y) \rightarrow (x, 2a - y)$ defines a reflection over the line with equation $y = a$. For the point $F(5, 3)$, F' is its reflection image over the line with equation $y = c$. F'' is the reflection image of F' over the line with equation $y = d$. Which of the following best describes the transformation of F' to F''?

A. a reflection defined by $(x, y) \rightarrow (5, 2(c + d) - 3)$

B. a reflection defined by $(x, y) \rightarrow (5, 2(d - c) - 3)$

C. a translation defined by $(x, y) \rightarrow (5, 2(c + d) + 3)$

D. a translation defined by $(x, y) \rightarrow (5, 2(d - c) + 3)$

Maintain Your Skills

11. This is an equation of the circle with radius 5 centered at the origin.

$$x^2 + y^2 = 25$$

Find an equation for the circle with radius 5 centered at each point.

a. $(4, 3)$

b. $(-2, 6)$

c. $(5, -1)$

12. What translation maps the graph of the equation you found in each part of Exercise 11 to an image centered at the origin? How does each translation transform the coordinates of a point (x, y)?

13. Show that the translations you described in Exercise 12 transform the respective equations you found in Exercise 11 into the equation $x^2 + y^2 = 25$.

For additional practice, go to **Web Code: bea-0703**

Answers

10. A

11. a. $(x - 4)^2 + (y - 3)^2 = 25$
  b. $(x + 2)^2 + (y - 6)^2 = 25$
  c. $(x - 5)^2 + (y + 1)^2 = 25$

12. a. the translation that moves the circle left 4 units and down 3 units; $(x, y) \mapsto (x - 4, y - 3)$
  b. the translation that moves the circle right 2 units and down 6 units; $(x, y) \mapsto (x + 2, y - 6)$
  c. the translation that moves the circle left 5 units and up 1 unit; $(x, y) \mapsto (x - 5, y + 1)$

13. a. $(x + 4 - 4)^2 + (y + 3 - 3)^2 = 25$ can be simplified to $x^2 + y^2 = 25$.
  b. $(x - 2 + 2)^2 + (y + 6 - 6)^2 = 25$ can be simplified to $x^2 + y^2 = 25$.
  c. $(x + 5 - 5)^2 + (y - 1 + 1)^2 = 25$ can be simplified to $x^2 + y^2 = 25$.

7.4 Rotations

In the In-Class Experiment in Lesson 7.2, you saw what happened when you reflected the letter F over two lines that are not parallel.

Minds in Action   episode 31

Derman is looking at his work from a recent In-Class Experiment.

Derman Hey Sasha, I've been thinking about the experiment we did in class for Lesson 7.2. I understand how you get a translation when you compose two reflections over parallel lines. But I have trouble understanding what happens when the lines aren't parallel.

Sasha Well, try to think how the final image was different from the original letter F you drew.

Derman Hmmm . . .

The original F and its final image were congruent.

I could have moved the final image and made it match up with the original F without flipping it.

But I couldn't have just translated it, because the transformation was different.

Sasha Right! The transformation involved some kind of a turn.

Derman Yes, and I also thought of another mysterious thing. You know how in a reflection, the line of reflection is fixed? Well, the first line is fixed for the first reflection. The second line is fixed for the second reflection. But the point of intersection is the only point fixed for both reflections! Doesn't that make it special?

Sasha I think there *is* something special about that point, but I don't think it's mysterious!

You can investigate this intersection point in the In-Class Experiment on the next page.

Consecutive faces are reflections. Alternating faces are identical. Why?

Lesson Overview

GOALS

- Model the composition of reflections and classify the resulting transformation as a reflection, rotation, translation, or combination of transformations.
- Model rotations in the plane, with and without coordinates.
- Understand properties of reflection and rotation in the plane.
- Identify fixed points for a given transformation or composition of transformations.

This lesson examines rotations as the transformation you obtain by reflecting an object successively over two intersecting lines. The lesson starts by analyzing some of your students' results from the In-Class Experiment in Lesson 7.2 and goes on to explore the properties of rotations.

CHECK YOUR UNDERSTANDING	HOMEWORK
• Core: 1, 2, 3	• Core: 4, 5, 6, 8
	• Optional: 9
MATERIALS	• Extension: 7
• geometry software	
• protractors	**VOCABULARY**
• rulers	• angle of rotation
	• center of rotation
	• concentric circles
	• rotation

Launch

Start this lesson by reminding students of the results of a composition of reflections over two intersecting lines. Students did this in the In-Class Experiment of Lesson 7.2. Introduce the concept of rotation. Have students read Minds in Action episode 31 and do the In-Class Experiment that follows.

Explore

In-Class Experiment

In each case, the angles, $\angle APA''$, $\angle BPB''$, ... should measure about 70°. This measurement will be more exact if students are able to use geometry software rather than paper and pencil construction with protractor measurements. But it should be clear that each point rotates through congruent angles and that the angle of rotation measures about twice the measure of $\angle RPS$, the angle formed by the intersecting lines. When students do the reflections in the opposite order, point still rotates through an angle with the same measure as before, but in the opposite direction. If one pair of reflections produces a clockwise rotation, a part of reflections in the opposite order produce a counterclockwise rotation, and vice versa.

Wrap Up

Assign Problem 6 in the For You to Do section. Give students some time to work on this proof in pairs or in small groups. Then you can review this proof with the whole class.

Assessment Resources

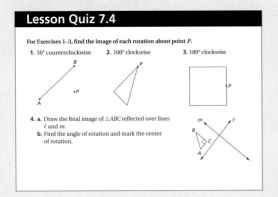

In-Class Experiment

You will need geometry software, or paper, a ruler, a pencil, and a protractor.

Draw two lines, r and s, that intersect in P so that if you choose two points R and S on r and s respectively, $m\angle RPS = 35°$. Choose at least 5 points A, B, C, D, E... in the plane.

1. Reflect your points once over r and then reflect their images over s. Use the following notation. Call A' the image of point A after the reflection over r. Call A'' the image of A' after the reflection over s. Use the same notation for the other points B, B', B'', and so on.

2. Compare $\angle APA''$, $\angle BPB''$, $\angle CPC''$, and so on. If you are using a protractor, your measurements may be inaccurate.

3. Compare $\angle RPS$ with the angles above.

4. What happens if you perform the reflections in the opposite order, that is, first over s and then over r?

> You may choose some points on r or s, but make sure you choose some that are not on the lines, too.

The In-Class Experiment suggests another way to obtain the image of a point after reflections over two intersecting lines. This other transformation is a **rotation.**

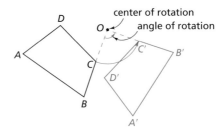

In the figure above, O is the center of rotation. Arcs connecting corresponding points in the preimage and the image lie on concentric circles. If P is a point in the preimage and P' is the image of P, all angles of the form $\angle POP'$ are congruent. For example, in the figure above, $\angle DOD' \cong \angle AOA'$.

> **Remember...**
> Concentric circles have the same center. In this case, the center is O.

Answers

In-Class Experiment

1. Check students' diagrams.

2. These angles seem to be congruent and to have measure 70°.

3. The measure of $\angle RPS$ seems to be half the measure of the angles from Problem 2.

4. The final images of the original points seem to have been obtained by turning the original points around P in the opposite direction from before, but the angle of the turn seems to have the same measure as before.

For Discussion

5. In the figure, $A'B'C'D'$ is the image of $ABCD$ after a rotation.

How can you find the center of rotation and the angle of rotation? Form a conjecture and prove it.

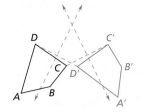

> What lines have been drawn in to help you?

Theorem 7.1

The composition of two reflections over intersecting lines produces a rotation. Its center is the intersection of the lines. The measure of the angle of rotation is equal to twice the measure of the angle formed by the two lines.

Proof Begin with two lines ℓ and m, intersecting at O. Reflect a point P over line ℓ and call the image P'. Then reflect P' over m and call its image P''. Mark Q at the intersection of ℓ and $\overline{PP'}$ and R at the intersection of m and $\overline{P'P''}$. You want to show that a rotation about O through an angle twice the measure of the angle formed by ℓ and m will map P onto P''. You can break this proof down into two parts.

Part 1 Show that $m\angle POP''$ is twice the measure of the angle formed by lines ℓ and m. In other words, $m\angle POP'' = 2m\angle QOR$.

Part 2 Show that the rotation about O through $\angle POP''$ maps P to P''. In other words, P'' is the same distance from O as is P.

> Why does proving Parts 1 and 2 prove that if you rotate P about O through an angle of $2m\angle ROQ$, you get P''?

For a proof of Part 1, you can use triangle congruencies you have already shown.

Since $\triangle PQO \cong \triangle P'QO$, the two angles with measures α in the diagram are congruent. Since $\triangle P'RO \cong \triangle P''RO$, the two angles with measure β are congruent. The angle of rotation, $\angle POP''$, has measure $2\alpha + 2\beta$ or $2(\alpha + \beta)$. The angle formed by lines ℓ and m, $\angle QOR$, has measure $\alpha + \beta$. So the angle of rotation is twice the measure of the angle formed by the intersecting lines of reflection.

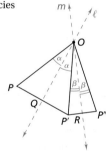

For You to Do

6. Prove Part 2 in the proof of Theorem 7.1.

For Discussion

5. Answers may vary. Sample: Draw the perpendicular bisectors of $\overline{AA'}$, $\overline{BB'}$, $\overline{CC'}$, and $\overline{DD'}$ and mark the point where they intersect. Each point and its image must be the same distance from the center of rotation. Therefore, the center of rotation is the point of intersection of the segments that join preimage to image.

For You to Do

6. Let P be a point in the plane, and let P' be the image of P when P is reflected over ℓ. Either P is on ℓ or it is not. If P is on ℓ, then $P' = P$, so obviously $OP' = OP$. If P is not on ℓ, then ℓ is the perpendicular bisector of $\overline{PP'}$. Since every point on the perpendicular bisector is equidistant from the endpoints of the segment, $OP' = OP$. Similar reasoning shows that if P'' is the image of P' for reflection over m, then $OP'' = OP'$. Hence $OP'' = OP$.

Exercises

HOMEWORK
- Core: 4, 5, 6, 8
- Optional: 9
- Extension: 7

Check Your Understanding

EXERCISE 2 (and Exercise 4 in the On Your Own section) gives students an angle of rotation without a direction (clockwise or counterclockwise). What assumption do students make about the direction of the rotation? Are students aware that they make an assumption? Do students make different choices of direction? Discuss this with your class.

Exercises *Practicing Habits of Mind*

Check Your Understanding

1. In the diagram, reflect quadrilateral *ABCD* over the *y*-axis to obtain *A'B'C'D'*. Reflect *A'B'C'D'* over the *x*-axis to obtain *A"B"C"D"*.

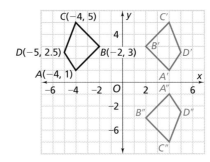

   a. Find the coordinates of the vertices of *A'B'C'D'*.

   b. Find the coordinates of the vertices of *A"B"C"D"*.

   c. You can find a single rotation that maps *ABCD* onto *A"B"C"D"*. What tells you that such a rotation is possible?

   d. Describe the rotation.

   e. Compare the coordinates of the vertices of *ABCD* and of *A"B"C"D"*. What do you find?

2. Use geometry software or a pencil and paper. Draw $\overline{AB}$ and a point *O* not on $\overline{AB}$. Find the image of $\overline{AB}$ after a rotation of 30° about *O*.

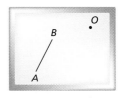

   Do you need to know anything else about the rotation?

3. Think about the rotation that is the composition of reflections over *r* and *s* respectively.

   Find the rotation image of $\overline{AB}$. Which point is the center of rotation? What is the angle of rotation? Could you have known either without finding the image of $\overline{AB}$?

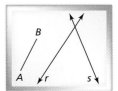

   Habits of Mind

   Experiment. What can you conclude if *O* is on $\overline{AB}$?

Answers

Exercises

1. **a.** *A'*(4, 1), *B'*(2, 3), *C'*(4, 5), *D'*(5, 2.5)

   b. *A"*(4, −1), *B"*(2, −3), *C"*(4, −5), *D"*(5, −2.5)

   c. Theorem 7.1 states that the composition of two reflections about intersecting lines produces a rotation. Its center is the intersection of the lines. The angle of rotation is equal to twice the measure of the angle formed by two lines.

   d. a rotation of 180° around the origin

   e. If (*x*, *y*) are the coordinates of a point of *ABCD*, then the corresponding point of *A"B"C"D"* has coordinates (−*x*, −*y*).

2. See back of book.

3. See back of book.

4. See back of book.

5. Check students' work.

4. Draw $\triangle ABC$ and a point O. Find the image of $\triangle ABC$ after a rotation of 65° about O.

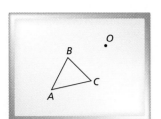

> Try this with your compass and protractor for this exercise.

5. Draw a quadrilateral and a point P. Find the image of the quadrilateral after a counterclockwise rotation with center P.

6. Explain why the vertex C of an isosceles triangle with $\overline{AB}$ as its base is a possible center of a rotation that maps A onto B. What is the angle of rotation?

7. Take It Further Here $\triangle A'B'C'$ is the image of $\triangle ABC$ after a rotation about center O. (B' is off the screen.)

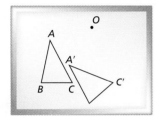

Find two lines over which a composition of reflections maps $\triangle ABC$ onto $\triangle A'B'C'$.

> What angle will these two lines form?

6. $CA = CB$, so A and B are on the circle with center C and radius CA; the measure of the angle of rotation is the same as $m\angle ACB$.

7. Answers may vary. Sample: Draw $\overleftrightarrow{OA}$ and $\overleftrightarrow{OA'}$. Construct the line k that bisects $\angle AOA'$. If you reflect $\triangle ABC$ over $\overleftrightarrow{OA}$ and then reflect the image over k, you get $\triangle A'B'C'$.

Additional Practice

1. **a.** Apply the rule $(x, y) \mapsto (x - 4, y + 3)$ to parallelogram $ABCD$ with vertices $A(0, 0)$, $B(2, 3)$, $C(7, 3)$, and $D(5, 0)$. Draw $ABCD$ and its image $A'B'C'D'$. Label all vertices.
   b. Describe how $A'B'C'D'$ relates to $ABCD$.

2. Use $\triangle ABC$ with vertices $A(2, 3)$, $B(5, 4)$, and $C(3, 0)$.
   a. Reflect $\triangle ABC$ over the line $x = 2$ and label the vertices $A'B'C'$.
   b. Reflect $\triangle A'B'C'$ over the line $x = -3$ and label the new vertices $A''B''C''$.
   c. Find the coordinates of vertices $A'B'C'$ and $A''B''C''$.
   d. Is there a single mapping that sends $\triangle ABC$ onto $\triangle A''B''C''$? If so, describe it.

3. Use the circle with equation $x^2 + y^2 = 9$.
   a. Substitute $x + 4$ for x in the equation. Graph the result. Predict the result if you substitute $x - 4$.
   b. Substitute $y + 5$ for y in the equation. Graph the result. Predict the result if you substitute $y - 5$.
   c. Apply the rule $(x, y) \mapsto (x - 4, y - 5)$ to the points on the circle. Describe how your predictions differ from the mapping notation.

For Exercises 4–6, use geometry software or a pencil and paper. Copy each figure. Then find the image of the figure using the given counterclockwise rotation about point P.

4. 30°   5. 45°   6. 120°

7. **a.** Use $\triangle ABC$. Draw the final image of $\triangle ABC$ reflected over lines ℓ and m.
   b. Fill in the blank: The composition of the reflections over intersecting lines is equivalent to a _____.
   c. Find the angle of rotation and mark the center of rotation.

Practice: For Lesson 7.4, assign Exercises 4–7.

8. **Standardized Test Prep** Rotate the letter W about a point P. Which of the following statements may NOT be true?
   A. The image letter is congruent to the original letter.
   B. The upper left point of the original W and the upper left point (as viewed here) of the image W are the same distance from the point of rotation.
   C. The two angles at the bottom of the original W are congruent to the two angles (as viewed here) at the bottom of the image W.
   D. The image of W looks like M.

Maintain Your Skills

9. You can obtain this figure by beginning with one of the F figures and repeatedly reflecting it over one and then over the other of the two lines.

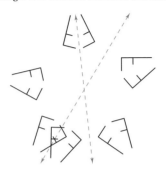

   a. Which F might have been the first? How many could have been the first?
   b. How might this figure continue?
   c. Do you see any other repeated transformations?
   d. Describe the patterns you see.

Answers

8. B

9. **a.** Any of the twelve Fs could have been first.
   b. No new Fs, either forward or backward, will occur.
   c. There are several repeated rotations.
   d. Answers may vary. Sample: The overall figure has both reflection symmetry and rotational symmetry.

7A

Reflections

In this investigation, you learned how to reflect figures over a line, rotate figures in the plane, and apply transformations to figures and graphs of functions in the coordinate plane. These questions will help you summarize what you have learned.

1. Reflect $\overline{AB}$, with endpoints $A(-6,-2)$ and $B(1, 5)$, over the line with equation $x = 3$. Write the coordinates of the image.

2. This parabola is a graph of the equation $y = 2x^2 + 3$.

   Translate the parabola by $(1, 2)$. Write an equation for the translated parabola.

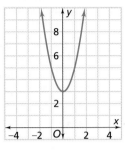

3. Find the coordinates of the endpoints $O(0, 0)$ and $P(3, 2)$ of $\overline{OP}$ after two reflections, the first over the line $y = 1$ and the second over the line $y = 5$. What transformation is the composition of these two reflections? Write a rule in the form $(x, y) \mapsto (\blacksquare, \blacksquare)$ to summarize this transformation.

4. Can you obtain a rotation by composing two other transformations? Explain with an example.

5. When you reflect an object over a line, what properties of the object are present in its image?

6. What happens when you compose two reflections? Three reflections? Four reflections?

7. $\triangle ABC$ has vertices $A(2, -1)$, $B(-2, -3)$, and $C(2, -3)$. When you reflect $\triangle ABC$ over the x-axis, what are the coordinates of its image $\triangle A'B'C'$?

Vocabulary and Notation

In this investigation, you learned these terms and symbols. Make sure you understand what each one means and how to use it.

- angle of rotation
- center of rotation
- composition
- fixed point
- image
- line of reflection
- preimage

- reflection
- rotation
- transformation
- translation
- F′ (F prime)
- F″ (F double prime)
- $x \mapsto y$ (x maps to y)

Mathematical Reflections

EXERCISES 5–7: At the start of the Investigation, you may have assigned these as Questions 1–3 for students to think and write about.

Mathematical Reflections

1. the segment with endpoints $A'(12, -2)$ and $B'(5, 5)$

2. Check students' graphs to see that the parabola is translated right 1 unit and up 2 units; $y - 2 = 2(x - 1)^2 + 3$

3. $O''(0, 8)$ and $P''(3, 10)$; translation up 8 units; $(x, y) \mapsto (x, y + 8)$

4. Yes, for instance by a composition of reflections over two intersecting lines; Answers may vary. Sample: In the coordinate plane, a reflection over the x-axis followed by a reflection over the y-axis is equivalent to a 180° rotation around the origin.

5. Answers may vary. Sample: Lengths and angle measures are preserved.

6. The composition of two reflections is a translation or a rotation; the composition of three reflections is either a reflection or a transformation that reflects figures across a line and translates them parallel to the line of reflection; the composition of four reflections is a translation or a rotation.

7. $A'(2, 1)$, $B'(-2, 3)$, $C'(2, 3)$

Investigation Overview

This investigation provides an introduction to coordinates in two and three dimensions. The Getting Started lesson is ideal for a class not yet familiar with coordinates. However, the lesson includes different-level exercises that you can use to gauge how comfortable your students may already be in working with the Cartesian coordinate system. These lessons include the midpoint and distance formulas, subscript notation, collinearity of points, and comparing slopes of parallel and perpendicular lines. The investigation ends with a lesson about coordinates in three dimensions.

You may wish to assign Questions 1–3 for students to think and write about during the investigation.

Learning Goals

- Calculate the distance between two points with given coordinates.
- Calculate the coordinates of the midpoint of a segment when you know the coordinates of the endpoints of the segment.
- Prove algebraically that three points are or are not collinear.
- Find and compare coefficients in equations of lines and recognize when two lines are parallel or perpendicular.
- Plot points in three dimensions and find the distance between them.

Habits and Skills

- Plot points with given coordinates in two and three dimensions.
- Describe the location of a point in the coordinate plane in terms of the quadrant in which it lies.
- Write equations of lines with given characteristics.
- Use subscript notation.
- Write proofs combining geometric and algebraic ideas.

Investigation 7B

Geometry in the Coordinate Plane

In *Geometry in the Coordinate Plane,* you will use coordinates in one, two, and three dimensions. You will learn the Midpoint Formula and the Distance Formula, and you will use these formulas in a variety of proofs.

By the end of this investigation, you will be able to answer questions like these:

1. How can you tell by examining the coordinates of two points whether they lie on a horizontal line? On a vertical line?
2. How do you calculate the distance between two points?
3. A box has dimensions 3 in. by 5 in. by 4 in. What is the length of a diagonal?

You will learn how to

- calculate the distance between two points with given coordinates
- calculate the coordinates of the midpoint of a segment
- prove algebraically that three points are or are not collinear
- recognize when two lines are parallel or perpendicular
- plot points in three dimensions and find the distance between them

You will develop these habits and skills:

- Plot points with given coordinates in two and three dimensions.
- Describe the location of a point on a coordinate plane.
- Write equations of lines with given characteristics.
- Use subscript notation.
- Write proofs combining geometric and algebraic ideas.

The boxes are 11 in. by $8\frac{1}{2}$ in. by $5\frac{1}{2}$ in. and $13\frac{5}{8}$ in. by $11\frac{7}{8}$ in. by $3\frac{3}{8}$ in. What is the longest rose you could ship in one of these boxes?

Investigation Road Map

LESSON 7.5, *Getting Started,* provides a basic review of the Cartesian coordinate plane.

LESSON 7.6, *Midpoint and Distance Formulas,* has students discover how to find the distance between two points on the coordinate plane by using the Pythagorean Theorem. This lesson also introduces subscript notation.

LESSON 7.7, *Parallel Lines and Collinear Points,* develops collinearity of points. It also develops the coefficients (slopes) of parallel lines.

LESSON 7.8, *Perpendicular Lines,* develops the relationship between coefficients (slopes) of perpendicular lines.

LESSON 7.9, *Coordinates in Three Dimensions,* begins with how to plot ordered triples in three dimensions. Students then extend the distance formula to three dimensions.

Getting Started

Activating Prior Knowledge
Exploring New Ideas

The coordinate plane allows you to make connections between geometry and algebra.

You have been working with polygons and circles geometrically, proving results through logic and reasoning. Now you can use your algebra skills to investigate some of these geometric ideas in the coordinate plane.

For example, coordinates locate points, so they are helpful for locating special parts, such as the midpoint of a line segment. Since coordinates involve numbers, you can use them to calculate lengths and distances exactly rather than relying on approximate measurements.

For You to Explore

1. The coordinates of three vertices of a rectangle are given. Find the coordinates of the points described below.

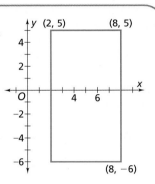

   a. the fourth vertex

   b. four points that are inside the rectangle

   c. four points that are outside the rectangle

   d. four more points that lie on the rectangle

   e. How can you tell whether a point is inside the rectangle just by looking at its coordinates?

2. Suppose $A(2, 5)$ and $B(2, 396)$.

   a. What is the distance between A and B?

   b. Find the coordinates of the midpoint of $\overline{AB}$.

3. a. How many vertical lines contain the point $(-1, 9)$?

   b. Name the coordinates of the intersection I of a horizontal line through $T(3, -5)$ and a vertical line through $R(-1, 9)$.

   c. Plot the points T, R, and I. Find the lengths of all three sides of $\triangle TRI$.

4. Suppose that $F(-1, 4)$ and $G(-3, -2)$.

   a. Find the coordinates of the midpoint of $\overline{FG}$.

   b. Find the length of $\overline{FG}$.

Go Online
Video Tutor
PHSchool.com

Web Code: bee-0705

Lesson Overview

GOAL
- Warm up to the ideas of the investigation.

Algebra 1 introduced students to the Cartesian coordinate plane. Use the For You to Explore problems to gauge how familiar your students are with the coordinate system. If you would like students to review the coordinate plane in more detail, use Blackline Master 7.5 as homework or as a one-day lesson.

FOR YOU TO EXPLORE	HOMEWORK
• Core: 1, 2, 3, 4	• Core: 5, 7, 8
	• Optional: 6, 11
MATERIALS	• Extension: 9, 10
• graph paper	
• straightedges	
• Blackline Master MC13 and 7.5	

Launch

Begin this lesson by assigning the four For You to Explore problems.

Explore

Discuss students' answers to the For You to Explore problems.

Wrap Up

Assign some On Your Own exercises if there is extra time.

Answers

For You to Explore

1. **a.** $(2, -6)$

   b. Check students' work. For each point, the x-coordinate should be between 2 and 8, and the y-coordinate should be between -6 and 5.

   c. Check students' work. For each point with coordinates (x, y), $2 \leq x \leq 8$ or $-6 \leq y \leq 5$ should be false.

   d. Check students' work. For a point with coordinates (x, y) to be on the rectangle, one of the following four conditions must be met:
   (1) $2 \leq x \leq 8$ and $y = 5$,
   (2) $x = 2$ and $-6 \leq y \leq 5$,
   (3) $x = 8$ and $-6 \leq y \leq 5$,
   (4) $2 \leq x \leq 8$ and $y = -6$.

   e. See the answer for part (b).

2. **a.** 391   **b.** $(2, 200.5)$

3. **a.** one   **b.** $(-1, -5)$

   c. Check students' diagrams; $RI = 14$, $IT = 4$, $RT = 2\sqrt{53}$

4. **a.** $(-2, 1)$ **b.** $2\sqrt{10}$

Exercises

HOMEWORK
- Core: 5, 7, 8
- Optional: 6, 11
- Extension: 9, 10

On Your Own

EXERCISE 6 Assign this exercise if you want to test your students' knowledge of the midpoint formula or if you want to listen to students' ideas about a process for finding the coordinates of the midpoint of a segment. If students are not familiar with the formula or not yet comfortable in the coordinate plane, do not assign this exercise.

Exercises Practicing Habits of Mind

On Your Own

5. Find the coordinates of the midpoint of the segment at the right. Describe the method you used.

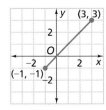

6. Suppose $C(-5, -7)$, $D(12, -7)$, and $E(12, 3)$.

   a. Find the distance between C and D.

   b. Find the coordinates of the midpoint of $\overline{CD}$.

   c. Find the distance between D and E.

   d. Find the coordinates of the midpoint of $\overline{DE}$.

   e. Find the distance between C and E.

   f. Find the coordinates of the midpoint of $\overline{CE}$.

7. In the diagram, m is a vertical line. Find each of the following.

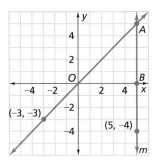

   a. the coordinates of A and B

   b. the length of $\overline{AB}$

   c. the coordinates of the midpoint of $\overline{AB}$

   d. the area of $\triangle AOB$

   e. the length of $\overline{AO}$

   f. the coordinates of the midpoint of $\overline{AO}$

Answers

Exercises

5. (1, 1); Answers may vary. Sample: I found the average of the x-coordinates of the given points and then the average of the y-coordinates.

6. a. 17   b. (3.5, −7)

   c. 10   d. (12, −2)

   e. $\sqrt{389}$ f. (3.5, −2)

7. a. A(5, 5), B(5, 0)

   b. 5   c. (5, 2.5)

   d. 12.5   e. $5\sqrt{2}$

   f. (2.5, 2.5)

8. List coordinates of points to make a connect-the-dots puzzle that draws your initials. Give it to a friend to try.

9. Take It Further How many quadrants in the coordinate plane does each line pass through?

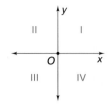

a. a vertical line through the origin

b. a vertical line not through the origin

c. a nonvertical, nonhorizontal line through the origin

d. a nonvertical, nonhorizontal line not through the origin

10. Take It Further Is it possible for a line to pass through only one quadrant? Is it possible for a line to pass through all four quadrants? Is there any slanting (nonvertical, nonhorizontal) line that passes through only two quadrants and does not contain the origin?

Maintain Your Skills

11. a. Copy and complete the table below.

A	B	C	D	E	F	G
$(x + y)$	$(x + 3, y)$	$(-x, y)$	$(x, -y)$	$(2x, 2y)$	$\left(\frac{x}{2}, \frac{y}{2}\right)$	$(-y, x)$
$(2, 1)$	▢	▢	▢	▢	$\left(1, \frac{1}{2}\right)$	▢
$(-4, 0)$	$(-1, 0)$	▢	▢	▢	▢	▢
$(-5, 4)$	▢	$(5, 4)$	▢	▢	▢	$(-4, -5)$

b. On a piece of graph paper, plot the three points in Column A and connect them to form triangle A. Plot the three points in Column B and connect them to form a triangle B. Describe how the two triangles differ.

c. On a new section of graph paper, draw triangles A and C. Describe how they differ.

d. Use clean graph paper each time. Pair triangle A with each of triangles D, E, F, and G. Each time describe how the two triangles differ.

Habits of Mind

Look for patterns. List any conjectures you come up with.

EXERCISE 9 Provide students with Blackline Master MC13 so that they can draw and experiment with different lines in the coordinate plane.

EXERCISE 11 Blackline Master 7.5 provides a table for students to complete.

8. Check students' work.

9. a. 0 **b.** 2 **c.** 2 **d.** 3

10. no; no; no

11. a–d. See back of book.

Lesson Overview

GOALS

- Calculate the distance between two points with given coordinates.
- Calculate the coordinates of the midpoint of a segment when you know the coordinates of the endpoints of the segment.

You should take two days to complete this lesson unless your students are already very comfortable with the distance and midpoint formulas. See the Daily Planner at the beginning of the chapter for one way to divide this lesson.

This lesson introduces and proves the distance formula for points in the coordinate plane and the formula for finding the coordinates of the midpoint of a given segment. The lesson also introduces subscript notation for general coordinates.

CHECK YOUR UNDERSTANDING	HOMEWORK
• Core: 1, 3, 4	• Core: 6, 7, 10, 12, 13, 14, 17, 19
• Optional: 2, 5, 8, 9	• Optional: 11, 15, 16, 18, 20, 21, 22, 23, 24
MATERIALS	
• Blackline Master 7.6	**VOCABULARY**
	• slope
	• subscript
	• (x_n, y_n)

Launch

Begin this lesson by assigning the In-Class Experiment.

Here is some very convenient notation.

When only a few points need names, you can call them A, B, C, and so on, and name their coordinates (a, b), (c, d), (e, f), and so on. If you have too many points, however, you can run out of letters. Since you can never run out of numbers, the convention is to use numbers as subscripts. For example, you could name the vertices of a decagon A_1, A_2, A_3, ..., A_{10}. You could name the vertices of an n-gon B_1, B_2, B_3, ..., B_n.

In-Class Experiment

Copy and complete the table below. Then answer the questions that follow.

Assume that point V_1 has coordinates (x_1, y_1), point V_2 has coordinates (x_2, y_2), and so on.

i	Coordinates of V_i	x_i	y_i
1	(■, ■)	■	■
2	(■, ■)	−2	■
3	(−4, −2)	−4	−2
4	(■, ■)	2	■

1. Here is a claim about the coordinates of the vertices of square $V_1V_2V_3V_4$.
   $$x_i = y_{i+1}$$
   Is the claim true when $i = 1$? That is, is it true that $x_1 = y_2$? Is the claim true when $i = 2$? When $i = 3$? When $i = 4$?

2. Here is another claim about the vertices of square $V_1V_2V_3V_4$.
   If V_i has coordinates (x_i, y_i), then V_{i+1} has coordinates $(−y_i, x_i)$.
   a. When $i = 2$, the claim says, "If V_2 has coordinates (x_2, y_2), then V_3 has coordinates $(−y_2, x_2)$." Look at the table and decide whether this is true.
   b. Find a value of i for which the statement does not make sense.

3. Name the vertices of the square for which it is true that $y_i = \frac{1}{2}x_i$.

4. Here is a rule for deriving a new set of points Q_i from the points V_1, V_2, V_3, and V_4.
   If $V_i = (x_i, y_i)$, then $Q_i = (−3 + x_i, 4 + y_i)$.
   a. The rule is written in algebraic symbols. Explain the rule in words.
   b. Find the new points Q_1, Q_2, Q_3, and Q_4 and plot them.

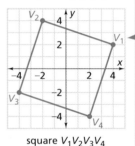

For example, is it true that $x_1 = y_{1+1} = y_2$?

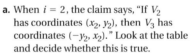
square $V_1V_2V_3V_4$

Answers

In-Class Experiment

i	Coordinates of V_i	x_i	y_i
1	(4, 2)	4	2
2	(−2, 4)	−2	4
3	(−4, −2)	−4	−2
4	(2, −4)	2	−4

1. true for $i = 1$, 2, 3 but not for $i = 4$

2. a. true for $i = 1$, 2, 3 but not for $i = 4$
   b. $i = 4$

3. V_1 and V_3

4. a. Answers may vary. Sample: For each vertex of the original figure, add −3 to its x-coordinate and 4 to its y-coordinate to get the coordinates of a vertex of the new figure. (The effect is to translate the original figure left 3 units and up 4 units.)

5. If $P_1 = (x_1, y_1)$, and you know that P_2 is a second point on the same horizontal line, how can you write its coordinates?

6. Let $P_i = (x_i, y_i)$, $x_i = i + 3$, and $y_i = x_i - 4$. Plot P_i as i goes from 1 to 8. Describe the result.

Minds in Action   episode 32

Hannah and Darren are trying to write a formula for finding the distance between two points. They are given

$$G = (x_1, y_1), \quad H = (x_2, y_2)$$

Hannah Well, the distance between two points on a vertical or horizontal line is easy to find. Just subtract the unlike coordinates. Say G is $(3, 4)$ and H is $(3, 90)$. Then the distance between G and H is $90 - 4 = 86$.

Darren But we don't know that G and H are on a horizontal or vertical line. They're just *any* two points.

We used the Pythagorean Theorem to help us find the distance between two points that weren't on the same horizontal or vertical line before. Let's try that here.

Hannah Don't we need three points to make a triangle so we can use the Pythagorean Theorem?

Darren Watch! I'll make a third point:

Before you ask, I know that the third point is (x_1, y_2). In my picture I had to go over as far as the (x_1, y_1) point—that's where I got the x_1—and up as far as the (x_2, y_2) point—that's where I got the y_2.

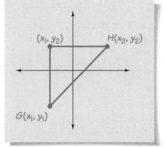

Hannah Great! Now let's use the Pythagorean Theorem to find the length of the hypotenuse of that triangle.

$$(y_2 - y_1)^2 + (x_2 - x_1)^2 = GH^2$$

So,

$$GH = \sqrt{(y_2 - y_1)^2 + (x_2 - x_1)^2}$$

---

b. $Q_1(1, 6)$, $Q_2(-5, 8)$, $Q_3(-7, 2)$, $Q_4(-1, 0)$

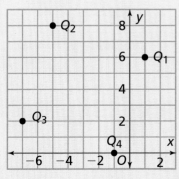

5. (x_2, y_1)

6. Answers may vary. Sample: eight equally spaced points along the line with equation $y = x - 4$, starting with $(4, 0)$ and ending with $(11, 7)$

Explore

Minds in Action

EPISODE 32 The dialog between Hannah and Darren provides a proof of the distance formula. Read through this episode with your class and write on the board the formula that the dialog presents. As part of your discussion of the distance formula, use points with a combination of positive and negative x and y coordinates, such as those in the For You to Do section. Ask, "Given the formula described in Theorem 7.2, does it matter which point you choose to be (x_1, y_1)?"

You may want to provide students with Blackline Master 7.6. They can fill in the table and draw on the graph.

Wrap Up

Use the For You to Do problems, on this page and on the following page, to check students' understanding.

Assessment Resources

Darren and Hannah's explanation is a proof of the following theorem.

Theorem 7.2 Distance Formula

The distance between two points (x_1, y_1) and (x_2, y_2) can be found using the Pythagorean Theorem. It is the square root of the sum of the square of the difference in the *x*-coordinates and the square of the difference in the *y*-coordinates.

Habits of Mind

Use facts you know. If you remember how you found it, you do not have to remember the Distance Formula. You can figure it out just by remembering the Pythagorean Theorem.

For You to Do

Find the distance between each pair of points.

7. $(1, 1)$ and $(-1, -1)$

8. $(1, 1)$ and $(4, 5)$

9. $(2, 4)$ and $(-4, -2)$

When you found the midpoint of a segment in the previous lesson, you may have used a method like this:

The *x*-coordinate is equal to the average of the *x*-coordinates of the endpoints. The *y*-coordinate is equal to the average of the *y*-coordinates of the endpoints.

Or, you can write it algebraically.

$$\left(\frac{x_1 + x_2}{2}, \frac{y_1 + y_2}{2} \right)$$

You can use Darren's diagram from Minds in Action to help justify this method for finding the midpoint.

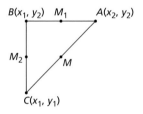

Theorem 7.3 Midpoint Formula

Each coordinate of the midpoint of a line segment is equal to the average of the corresponding coordinates of the endpoints of the line segment.

Answers

For You to Do

7. $2\sqrt{2}$

8. 5

9. $6\sqrt{2}$

Proof First, find the midpoint M_1 of $\overline{AB}$. This segment is horizontal, so every point on it has the same y-coordinate. You also know that $\frac{x_1 + x_2}{2}$ is the number halfway between x_1 and x_2. This means that the coordinates of M_1 are $\left(\frac{x_1 + x_2}{2}, y_2\right)$.

You can show that the distance from M_1 to A is the same as the distance from B to M_1 by looking at the difference in the x-coordinates of these points, since they are all on the same horizontal line.

$$M_1 \text{ to } A: x_2 - \left(\frac{x_1 + x_2}{2}\right) = \frac{x_2 - x_1}{2}$$

$$B \text{ to } M_1: \frac{x_1 + x_2}{2} - x_1 = \frac{x_1 + x_2}{2} - \frac{2x_1}{2} = \frac{x_2 - x_1}{2}$$

The same reasoning shows that the midpoint M_2 of the segment with coordinates (x_1, y_1) and (x_1, y_2) has coordinates $\left(x_1, \frac{y_1 + y_2}{2}\right)$. In this case, the three points are on a vertical line, so they must all have the same x-coordinate.

Now you need to find the coordinates of M, the midpoint of $\overline{AC}$. The Midline Theorem (Theorem 2.11) says that the segment joining the midpoints of two sides of a triangle is parallel to the third side. Also, its measure is equal to half the measure of the third side.

This means that if you draw a line through M_1 and M (wherever it is), that line must be parallel to $\overline{BC}$. And that means that the line through M_1 and M is vertical. Because you know that on a vertical line all points have the same x-coordinate, you know that the x-coordinate of M is $\frac{x_1 + x_2}{2}$.

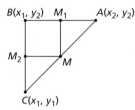

Similarly, if you draw a line through M_2 and M, that line will be parallel to $\overline{AB}$. It will be horizontal and will have the same y-coordinate as M_2, namely $\frac{y_1 + y_2}{2}$.

So the coordinates of M are $\left(\frac{x_1 + x_2}{2}, \frac{y_1 + y_2}{2}\right)$.

About halfway between Penzance and Land's End is the hamlet of Crows-an-wra. About how far, and in what direction, is the hamlet from this marker?

For You to Do

10. Find the midpoint of the segment with endpoints $(1327, 94)$ and $(-668, 17)$.

11. Find the midpoint of the segment with endpoints $(1776, 13)$ and $(2000, 50)$.

For You to Do

10. $(329.5, 55.5)$

11. $(1888, 31.5)$

Exercises

Exercises Practicing Habits of Mind

Check Your Understanding

1. Points A and B are endpoints of a diameter of a circle. Point C is the center of the circle. Find the coordinates of C given the following coordinates for A and B.

   a. $(-79, 687)$, $(13, 435)$

   b. $(x, 0)$, $(5x, y)$

2. Points A through G lie on a circle of radius 10, as shown in the figure. Find their missing coordinates.

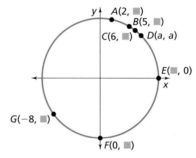

3. The vertices of $\triangle ABC$ are $A(2, 1)$, $B(4, 8)$, and $C(6, -2)$.

   a. Find the lengths of the three sides of the triangle.

   b. Find the length of the three medians of the triangle.

4. Consider the six points $A(5, 1)$, $B(10, -2)$, $C(8, 3)$, $A'(2, 3)$, $B'(7, 0)$, and $C'(5, 5)$. Show that $\triangle ABC \cong \triangle A'B'C'$.

5. Consider the six points $A(-800, -500)$, $B(160, 12)$, $C(-737, -484)$, $A'(0, 0)$, $B'(3840, 2048)$, and $C'(252, 64)$. Show that $\triangle ABC \sim \triangle A'B'C'$.

6. **Write About It** Explain how to tell whether two triangles are congruent by doing calculations on the coordinates of their vertices.

7. **Write About It** Explain how to tell whether two triangles are similar by doing calculations on the coordinates of their vertices.

Answers

Exercises

1. a. $(-33, 561)$ b. $\left(3x, \dfrac{y}{2}\right)$

2. $A(2, 4\sqrt{6})$, $B(5, 5\sqrt{3})$, $C(6, 8)$, $D(5\sqrt{2}, 5\sqrt{2})$, $E(10, 0)$, $F(0, -10)$, $G(-8, -6)$

3. a. $AB = \sqrt{53}$, $BC = 2\sqrt{26}$, $AC = 5$

   b. length of median from $A = \sqrt{13}$, length of median from $B = 8.5$, length of median from $C = \dfrac{\sqrt{205}}{2}$

4. $AB = A'B' = \sqrt{34}$, $BC = B'C' = \sqrt{29}$, $AC = A'C' = \sqrt{13}$, so $\triangle ABC \cong \triangle A'B'C'$ by SSS.

5. See back of book.

6. Answers may vary. Sample: Use the Distance Formula to calculate the side lengths of each triangle. If the side lengths for the two triangles are the same, then the triangles are congruent by SSS.

7. Answers may vary. Sample: Use the Distance Formula to calculate the

8. Quadrilateral *STAR* has vertices $S(-2, 8)$, $T(8, 2)$, $A(0, -4)$, and $R(-2, 0)$. Find the coordinates of the midpoint of the four sides of quadrilateral *STAR*. These points determine a new quadrilateral. Show that this new quadrilateral is a parallelogram.

9. Pick any four points that form a quadrilateral in the coordinate plane. Find the midpoints of all four sides. Show that if you connect the midpoints in order, you get a parallelogram.

> One way to show that a quadrilateral is a parallelogram is to show that opposite sides are parallel. What is another way?

On Your Own

10. Three vertices of a square are $(-1, 5)$, $(5, 3)$, and $(3, -3)$.

    a. Find the center of the square.

    b. Find the fourth vertex.

11. Three vertices of a square are $(-114, 214)$, $(186, 114)$, and $(-214, -86)$.

    a. Find the center of the square.

    b. Find the fourth vertex.

12. $\overline{DE}$ has midpoint $F(4.5, 17)$. If $D(2, 16)$, what are the coordinates of the other endpoint, E?

13. $\overline{AB}$ and $\overline{CD}$ bisect each other. If $A(110, 15)$, $B(116, 23)$, and $C(110, 23)$, find E, the point of bisection. Also, find the coordinates of D.

> **Remember...**
>
> Two segments bisect each other if they intersect at each other's midpoint.

14. A segment has length 25. Give possible coordinates for the endpoints of this segment in each case below.

    a. The segment is on a horizontal line.

    b. The segment is on a vertical line.

    c. The segment is neither horizontal nor vertical.

15. A segment has its midpoint at $(8, 10)$. List four possibilities for the coordinates of its endpoints.

16. A segment has one endpoint at $(-7, -2)$ and its midpoint at $(-2, 1.5)$. What are the coordinates of the other endpoint?

---

side lengths of each triangle. If the side lengths of one triangle are proportional to those of the other triangle, then the triangles are similar by SSS Similarity.

8. See back of book.

9. Check students' work.

10. a. $(1, 1)$ b. $(-3, -1)$

11. a. $(-14, 14)$ b. $(86, -186)$

12. $(7, 18)$

13. $E(113, 19)$, $D(116, 15)$

14. a. Answers may vary. Sample: $(21, 7)$ and $(46, 7)$

    b. Answers may vary. Sample: $(-16, -13)$ and $(-16, 12)$

    c. Answers may vary. Sample: $(0, 0)$ and $(15, 20)$

15. Answers may vary. Sample: $(6, 10)$ and $(10, 10)$, $(8, 0)$ and $(8, 20)$, $(7, 9)$ and $(9, 11)$, $(7, 7)$ and $(9, 13)$

16. $(3, 5)$

Additional Resources

PRINTED RESOURCES
- Texas Instruments Activities Workbook
- Cabrilog Activities
- Teaching Resources
- Practice Workbook
- Assessment Resources

TECHNOLOGY
- TeacherExpress CD-ROM
- **Exam**View CD-ROM
- **PHSchool.com**
  - Homework Help
  - Video Tutors
  - Multiple Choice
  - Crosswords

Additional Practice

For Exercises 1 and 2, points *A* and *B* are endpoints of a diameter of a circle. Point *C* is the center of the circle. Find the length of the diameter and the coordinates of *C*.

1. $A(-9, 12)$, $B(17, 21)$　　　　**2.** $A(-2x, 3y)$, $B(5x, -4y)$

3. One endpoint of a diameter of a circle is $(5, 12)$. The center of the circle is $(3, -5)$. Find the other endpoint of the diameter.

4. The vertices of parallelogram *ABCD* are $A(1, -2)$, $B(3, 3)$, $C(9, 3)$, and $D(7, -2)$.
　a. Find the length of each side.
　b. Find length of each diagonal.

5. If you know the coordinates of the vertices of two triangles, explain how you can determine if the triangles are congruent, rather than similar.

6. Three vertices of a rhombus are $M(3, 13)$, $A(0, 14)$, and $T(2, 16)$.
　a. Find the fourth vertex *H*.
　b. Find the center of the rhombus.

7. A segment has midpoint $(9, -12)$ and length 17. Give the coordinates for the endpoints of the segment in each case.
　a. The segment is on a horizontal line.
　b. The segment is on a vertical line.
　c. Give possible coordinates if the segment is neither horizontal nor vertical.

8. Which of the following pairs of lines are parallel? Explain.
　A. $3x - 2y = 8$
　　　$-3x + 2y = 9$
　B. $x + \frac{3}{2}y = 6$
　　　$2x - 6y = 12$
　C. $2x - 8 = 4$
　　　$5x + 12 = 17$
　D. $4x + y = 12$
　　　$-2x + \frac{1}{2}y = 14$

9. Find a point that is collinear with $J(3, -7)$ and $K(11, -5)$. Explain your method.

10. One diagonal of a parallelogram has endpoints $(3, -2)$ and $(8, 4)$. Give the coordinates of the other two vertices if the parallelogram is a rectangle.

11. Draw two lines ℓ and m with the following characteristics.
　• Line ℓ passes through $(0, 3)$ and $(-3, 0)$.
　• Line m passes through $(-4, 4)$ and $(4, 4)$.
　Find the coordinates of the point at which they intersect.

Practice: For Lesson 7.6, assign Exercises 1–7.

---

17. **Standardized Test Prep** Julio is planning to swim across the lake at his summer camp. On a map, the coordinates of his starting point are $(-2 \text{ cm}, 3.5 \text{ cm})$. The dock to which he will swim has coordinates $(14 \text{ cm}, -8.5 \text{ cm})$. The scale on the map is 1 cm : 100 m. What distance will Julio have to swim?

　A. 1200 meters　　　　　　**B.** 1300 meters
　C. 1600 meters　　　　　　**D.** 2000 meters

18. Point $P(5, 0)$ and $Q(15, 0)$.
　a. Find six points that are just as far from *P* as they are from *Q*.
　b. Find six points that are closer to *P* than they are to *Q*.
　c. How can you tell if a point is equidistant from *P* and *Q* just by looking at its coordinates?

19. The endpoints of a line segment are the midpoints of two sides of a triangle. Show that the length of this segment is one half the length of the third side of that triangle. Show that this is true for any triangle. (Use subscript notation.)

Maintain Your Skills

Find the slope between each pair of points.

20. $(3, 85)$ and $(0, 124)$

21. $(0, 124)$ and $(4, 72)$

22. $(4, 72)$ and $(-111, 1567)$

23. $(-111, 1567)$ and $(2, 98)$

24. $(2, 98)$ and $(3, 85)$

Habits of Mind

Use a symbol. You could use d_s for the length of a side of the triangle. You must show that d_m, the distance between the midpoints, is $\frac{1}{2}d_s$. But think ahead. Would it be helpful to use $2d_s$ for the length of a side?

Remember...

You find slope by calculating the ratio between the change in *y*-coordinates and the change in *x*-coordinates.

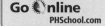
Go Online
PHSchool.com

For additional practice, go to **Web Code: bea-0706**

Answers

17. D

18. **a.** Any six points with *x*-coordinate 10 will do.
　b. Any six points with *x*-coordinate less than 10 will do.
　c. A point is equidistant from *P* and *Q* if and only if its *x*-coordinate is 10.

19. See back of book.

20. -13　　　　**21.** -13
22. -13　　　　**23.** -13
24. -13

7.7 Parallel Lines and Collinear Points

This In-Class Experiment should help you remember what you learned in Algebra 1 about the equations of lines.

In-Class Experiment

1. Plot several points with y-coordinates that have each property.

   a. 1 more than the x-coordinate

   b. 2 more than the x-coordinate

   c. 1 less than the x-coordinate

   For each property, draw a picture that shows all the points with that property.

2. Plot several points with y-coordinates that have each property.

   a. twice the x-coordinate

   b. three times the x-coordinate

   c. four times the x-coordinate

   For each property, draw a picture that shows all the points with that property.

3. Some of the lines you drew have points with coordinates of the form $(x, x + \text{something})$.

   a. What do those lines have in common?

   b. Write the equations of those lines in the form $ax + by = c$.

   c. What do these equations have in common?

4. Some other lines you drew have points with coordinates of the form $(x, x \times \text{something})$.

   a. What do those lines have in common?

   b. Write the equations of those lines in the form $ax + by = c$.

   c. What do these equations have in common?

In Algebra 1, you proved the following theorem.

Theorem 7.4

Two lines are parallel if and only if they have the same slope.

Habits of Mind

Experiment. You can work backward to find what must be true about the coeffients for the lines to be coincident (the same line). Try it and share your findings.

Lesson Overview

GOALS

- Prove algebraically that three points are or are not collinear.

- Find and compare coefficients in equations of lines and recognize when two lines are parallel.

This lesson contains a proof of Theorem 7.5, which students may have learned in Algebra 1. This theorem states that three points A, B, and C are collinear if and only if the slope between A and B is the same as the slope between B and C.

CHECK YOUR UNDERSTANDING	HOMEWORK
• Core: 1, 2	• Core: 6, 7, 9, 10
• Optional: 3, 4	• Optional: 5, 8, 11
	• Extension: 12
MATERIALS	**VOCABULARY**
• graph paper	• collinear
• straightedges	

Launch

Begin this lesson by assigning the In-Class Experiment. You might choose to divide your students into groups and have them work together.

Answers

In-Class Experiment

1. Check students' work.

2. Check students' work.

3. a. Answers may vary. Sample: The lines have the same slope (1). The lines have points in both quadrants I and III.

   b. Answers may vary. Sample:
   $x - y = -1$, $x - y = -2$, $x - y = 1$

   c. Answers may vary. Sample: The coefficient of x is 1, and the coefficient of y is -1

4. a. Answers may vary. Sample: The lines pass through the origin.

   b. Answers may vary. Sample:
   $2x - y = 0$, $3x - y = 0$, $4x - y = 0$

   c. Answers may vary. Sample: The coefficient of y is -1, and the value of c is 0.

Explore

Here are some notes for the proof of the first half of Theorem 7.5.

- In Step 1, $m\angle ABC = 180°$.
- In Steps 2 and 3, you know that the intersection points exist and that the angles with vertices at those points are right angles because any line parallel to the y-axis is perpendicular to any line parallel to the x-axis.
- In Step 4, $m\angle ABQ + m\angle AQB + m\angle BAQ = 180°$ because the sum of the angle measures of any triangle is $180°$. By substituting measures you already know, you can show that $m\angle ABQ + m\angle BAQ = 90°$.
- In Step 5, you can use the diagram to see that $m\angle ABQ + m\angle QBP + m\angle CBP = m\angle ABC$. By substituting measures you already know, you can show that $m\angle ABQ + m\angle CBP = 90°$. From this and the result of Step 4, you can conclude that $m\angle BAQ = \angle CBP$.
- In Step 6, AA shows that $\triangle AQB$ and $\triangle BPC$ are similar. From this you know that corresponding lengths are proportional, so $\frac{BQ}{QA} = \frac{CP}{PB}$. You also know that $m(A, B) = \frac{BQ}{QA}$ and $m(B, C) = \frac{CP}{PB}$, so $m(A, B) = m(B, C)$.

The proof of Theorem 7.4 depends on the Collinearity Postulate from Algebra 1. You can now prove this postulate.

Theorem 7.5

> Let A, B, and C be three points, no two of which are in line vertically. Points A, B, and C are collinear if and only if the slope between A and B, $m(A, B)$, is the same as the slope between B and C, $m(B, C)$. In symbols:
>
> $$A, B, \text{ and } C \text{ are collinear} \Leftrightarrow m(A, B) = m(B, C).$$

Points that lie in a line are **collinear**.

Proof Without affecting the generality of the argument, you can choose to name the three points so that A is the point with the smallest x-coordinate, B is the point with the next-largest x-coordinate, and C is the point with the largest x-coordinate.

Step 1 Suppose that A, B, and C are collinear. Then you know $m\angle ABC$.

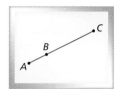

Step 2 Through points B and C, draw lines parallel to the y-axis. Through points A and B, draw lines parallel to the x-axis. By the Parallel Postulate, these lines are unique. You also know that any line parallel to the x-axis is perpendicular to any line parallel to the y-axis.

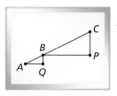

How do you treat the case in which the line containing A, B, and C is horizontal?

Assign the name P to the intersection of the horizontal line from B and the vertical line from C. Assign Q to the intersection of the horizontal line from A and the vertical line from B.

Step 3 Show that $m\angle AQB = m\angle QBP = m\angle BPC = 90°$.

Step 4 Show that $m\angle ABQ + m\angle BAQ = 90°$.

Step 5 Look at the three angles with vertex B ($\angle ABQ$, $\angle QBP$, and $\angle PBC$). From their relationship and from Step 4, you can conclude that $m\angle BAQ = m\angle CBP$.

Step 6 Use your previous results to show $\triangle AQB \sim \triangle BPC$. Then conclude that $\frac{BQ}{QA} = \frac{CP}{PB}$. This relationship tells you that $m(A, B)$ (the slope between points A and B) is equal to $m(B, C)$.

You have just proven half of Theorem 7.5!

Answers

For You to Do

5. If the slopes of $\overline{AB}$ and $\overline{BC}$ are equal and positive, then use the triangles shown in the text for the first part of the proof of Theorem 7.5. slope $\overline{AB} =$ slope $\overline{BC}$ means that $\frac{BQ}{AQ} = \frac{CP}{BP}$.

   Since $\angle AQB \cong \angle BPC$ (both are right angles), it follows that $\triangle AQB \sim \triangle BPQ$ (SAS Similarity).

But the two acute angles that have vertex B are complementary. So $m\angle ABQ + m\angle QBP + m\angle PBC = 180°$. From this it follows that $\overrightarrow{BA}$ and $\overrightarrow{BC}$ are opposite rays and hence that A, B, and C are collinear.

If the slopes of $\overline{AB}$ and $\overline{BC}$ are negative, then reflect $\overline{AB}$ and $\overline{BC}$ across the y-axis and use the argument above to conclude that A, B, and C are collinear and hence that A, B, and C are collinear.

Tony seems a bit puzzled.

Tony   Okay, so I understand how we proved that

A, B, and C are collinear $\Rightarrow m(A, B) = m(B, C)$.

But how can we prove the other direction?

Sasha   Well, it shouldn't be too hard. Somehow we have to reverse the steps. We want to start at the end of the proof we just did and work back to the beginning.

Tony   That reminds me of the reverse-list strategy.

Sasha   Yeah, it sounds pretty easy, and if it works we will have proved the rest of the theorem.

For You to Do

5. Use Tony's idea to prove the rest of Theorem 7.5.

A, B, and C are collinear $\Leftarrow m(A, B) = m(B, C)$

Developing Habits of Mind

Visualize. Here is another way to think about three collinear points, and this way has a bonus result! Think of points A, B, and C as vertices of a triangle. Also, think of B as moving continuously closer and closer to $\overline{AC}$.

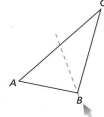
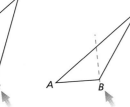

The triangle inequality says that $AB + BC > AC$. As B gets closer and closer to $\overline{AC}$, $AB + BC$ gets closer and closer to AC. When B is on $\overline{AC}$, $AB + BC$ is no longer greater than AC. In fact, $AB + BC = AC$.

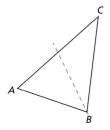

If the slopes of $\overline{AB}$ and $\overline{BC}$ are 0, then the y-coordinates of the three points are equal. This implies that the points all lie on the same horizontal line and hence that the points are collinear.

Developing Habits of Mind

This is a classic example of reasoning by continuity. Students visualize a known situation, the $\triangle ABC$ and push it to an extreme. They imagine what happens to the triangle inequality $AB + BC > AC$ as B gets closer and closer to $\overline{AC}$. Eventually, when B is actually on $\overline{AC}$, the triangle inequality will no longer hold and $AC = AB + BC$. This gives students another test for the collinearity of three points.

Students see this test applied in the Example, and then try it for themselves in the For You to Do problems.

Wrap Up

Assign the Check Your Understanding exercises for in-class work.

Assessment Resources

Now, suppose you are given three points, A, B, and C. Would knowing that $AC = AB + BC$ be enough to prove that the three points are collinear?

Yes, it would be enough, because if B was not in line with A and C, then A, B, and C would be the vertices of a triangle. The three segment lengths would satisfy the triangle inequality. But the segment lengths do not satisfy the triangle inequality, so the points cannot be the vertices of a triangle. The points have to be collinear.

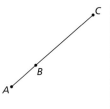

Example

Problem Decide whether the following three points are collinear.

$$A(1, 5) \quad B(0, 1) \quad C(3, 13)$$

Solution Use the triangle inequality.

$$AB = \sqrt{(1 - 0)^2 + (5 - 1)^2} \quad = \sqrt{1 + 16} \quad = \sqrt{17}$$
$$BC = \sqrt{(3 - 0)^2 + (13 - 1)^2} = \sqrt{9 + 144} = 3\sqrt{17}$$
$$AC = \sqrt{(3 - 1)^2 + (13 - 5)^2} = \sqrt{4 + 64} \quad = 2\sqrt{17}$$

For the three lengths, $AC + AB = 2\sqrt{17} + \sqrt{17} = 3\sqrt{17} = BC$. This means that A, B, and C are collinear, with A between B and C.

> **Habits of Mind**
>
> **Check your work.**
> You can use another method—namely Theorem 7.5—to check the result in the Example.

For You to Do

Use the triangle inequality or Theorem 7.5 to decide whether the three points are collinear. Use the other method to check your result.

6. $A\left(\frac{2}{7}, 0\right)$ $B(0, 2)$ $C(1, 9)$

7. $A\left(\frac{1}{25}, 2\right)$ $B(1, 26)$ $C(7, 0)$

8. $A(2, 2)$ $B(3, 3)$ $C(5, 9)$

9. $A(2, 4)$ $B(0, 0)$ $C(3, 6)$

10. $A(-1, 3)$ $B(-2, 2)$ $C(2, 6)$

Answers

For You to Do

6. collinear

7. not collinear

8. not collinear

9. collinear

10. collinear

Exercises *Practicing Habits of Mind*

Check Your Understanding

1. Are the two lines with the given equations parallel? Explain.

   a. $2x + 3y = 0$ $2x + 3y = 4$

   b. $x + \frac{1}{3}y = 7$ $3x + y = 1$

   c. $x + \frac{1}{3}y = 7$ $3x + y = 21$

   d. $\sqrt{2}x + 4y = 0$ $2x + 4y = 0$

   e. $2\sqrt{2}x + 4y = 1$ $x + \sqrt{2}y = 3$

2. Find a point that is collinear with $A(5, 1)$ and $B(8, -3)$. Explain your method.

3. Give a set of instructions for finding points that are collinear with $A(5, 1)$ and $B(8, -3)$. Explain why your method works.

4. Is $P(-4, -14)$ collinear with $R(-40, -30)$ and $S(80, 20)$? Explain.

On Your Own

5. Suppose $A(4, 1)$, $B(8, -2)$, $C(7, 1)$, and $D(3, 4)$.

   a. Show that the diagonals of quadrilateral $ABCD$ bisect each other.

   b. What does this tell you about what kind of quadrilateral $ABCD$ is? Explain.

6. Two vertices of an equilateral triangle are at $(1, 0)$ and $(9, 0)$. Find coordinates for the third vertex.

7. For each possible pairing of lines, tell whether the lines

   - are parallel
   - meet at the origin
   - intersect elsewhere
   - are the same line

   How many possible pairs are there to consider?

   ℓ: The y-coordinates are $\frac{1}{2}$ their x-coordinates.

   m: The y-coordinates are 3 more than their x-coordinates.

   n: The y-coordinates are 2 less than their x-coordinates.

   p: The y-coordinates are -2 times their x-coordinates.

   q: The y-coordinates are 5 times their x-coordinates.

   r: The y-coordinates are $\frac{1}{3}$ their x-coordinates.

8. Is $(110, 9)$ collinear with $(60, 10)$ and $(10, 11)$? Explain.

Exercises

HOMEWORK
- Core: 6, 7, 9, 10
- Optional: 5, 8, 11
- Extension: 12

On Your Own

EXERCISE 5 recalls students' earlier work with proof in geometry and asks then to verify results in the coordinate plane. You may wish to remind students that even though they are working with numbers and calculations, the theorems they have worked to prove can still provide insight.

Exercises

1. See back of book.

2. Answers may vary. Sample: $C(6.5, -1)$; find the coordinates of the midpoint of $\overline{AB}$.

3. See back of book.

4. No; Answers may vary. Sample: The slope of $\overline{PR}$ is $\frac{4}{9}$, but the slope of $\overline{RS}$ is $\frac{5}{12}$. By Theorem 7.5, the points are not collinear.

5. a. By the Midpoint Formula, the midpoint of each diagonal has coordinates $(5.5, 1)$.

   b. parallelogram

6. $\left(5, 4\sqrt{3}\right)$ or $\left(5, -4\sqrt{3}\right)$

7. Lines m and n are parallel. Lines ℓ, p, q, and r meet at the origin.

8. Yes; the segments joining two points at these locations all have slope $-\frac{1}{50}$. By Theorem 7.5, the points are collinear.

Maintain Your Skills

EXERCISE 12 is a Take It Further exercise only in the sense that the algebraic manipulation involved is extremely difficult, requiring accuracy and strict attention to detail. For most students, this exercise will not extend their understanding of the geometric ideas. It is an excellent exercise to assign, however, if you want to provide an algebraic challenge.

Additional Resources

PRINTED RESOURCES
- Texas Instruments Activities Workbook
- Cabrilog Activities
- Teaching Resources
- Practice Workbook
- Assessment Resources

TECHNOLOGY
- TeacherExpress CD-ROM
- **Exam***View* CD-ROM
- **PHSchool.com**
  - Homework Help
  - Video Tutors
  - Multiple Choice
  - Crosswords

Additional Practice

For Exercises 1 and 2, points *A* and *B* are endpoints of a diameter of a circle. Point *C* is the center of the circle. Find the length of the diameter and the coordinates of *C*.

1. $A(-9, 12)$, $B(17, 21)$

2. $A(-2x, 3y)$, $B(5x, -4y)$

3. One endpoint of a diameter of a circle is $(5, 12)$. The center of the circle is $(3, -5)$. Find the other endpoint of the diameter.

4. The vertices of parallelogram *ABCD* are $A(1, -2)$, $B(3, 3)$, $C(9, 3)$, and $D(7, -2)$.
   a. Find the length of each side.
   b. Find the length of each diagonal.

5. If you know the coordinates of the vertices of two triangles, explain how you can determine if the triangles are congruent, rather than similar.

6. Three vertices of a rhombus are $M(3, 13)$, $A(0, 14)$, and $T(2, 16)$.
   a. Find the fourth vertex *H*.
   b. Find the center of the rhombus.

7. A segment has midpoint $(9, -12)$ and length 17. Give the coordinates for the endpoints of the segment in each case.
   a. The segment is on a horizontal line.
   b. The segment is on a vertical line.
   c. Give possible coordinates if the segment is neither horizontal nor vertical.

8. Which of the following pairs of lines are parallel? Explain.
   A. $3x - 2y = 8$
   $-3x + 2y = 9$
   B. $x + \frac{3}{2}y = 6$
   $2x - 6y = 12$
   C. $2x - 8 = 4$
   $5x + 12 = 17$
   D. $4x + y = 12$
   $-2x + \frac{1}{2}y = 14$

9. Find a point that is collinear with $J(3, -7)$ and $K(11, -5)$. Explain your method.

10. One diagonal of a parallelogram has endpoints $(3, -2)$ and $(8, 4)$. Give the coordinates of the other two vertices if the parallelogram is a rectangle.

11. Draw two lines ℓ and *m* with the following characteristics.
   • Line ℓ passes through $(0, 3)$ and $(-3, 0)$.
   • Line *m* passes through $(-4, 4)$ and $(4, 4)$.
   Find the coordinates of the point at which they intersect.

Practice: For Lesson 7.7, assign Exercises 8–11.

---

9. **Standardized Test Prep** The coordinates of point *A* are $(3, 4)$. The coordinates of point *B* are $(5, -1)$. Which point is NOT collinear with *A* and *B*?

A. $(2, -5)$ **B.** $(1, 9)$

C. $(0, 11.5)$ **D.** $(4.6, 0)$

10. Draw two lines, *a* and *b*, with the following characteristics, on the coordinate plane.

   • Line *a* passes through $(0, 1)$ and $(1, 0)$.

   • Line *b* passes through the origin and makes a 45° angle with the axes as it enters Quadrant I.

   Find the coordinates of the point where lines *a* and *b* intersect.

Maintain Your Skills

11. Use the triangle inequality to test whether points lie on $\overline{RS}$ with endpoints $R(-40, -30)$ and $S(80, 20)$. Test some points that are collinear with *R* and *S* and some that are not.

12. **Take It Further** Now generalize your method. Suppose $R(r_1, r_2)$ and $S(s_1, s_2)$ are two points. Write an equation that has to be true if and only if a third point $P(p_1, p_2)$ lies on $\overline{RS}$. Simplify your equation until you come to a form like this.

$$(a - b) \cdot (c - d) = (e - f) \cdot (g - h)$$

(*Hint:* If an equation contains a square root, isolate it on one side and then square each side. You can repeat this step if necessary.)

Besides having the same slope, parallel lines are everywhere the same distance apart.

Habits of Mind

Establish a process. When you see that an expression becomes complex, take time to organize your work. This slows you down at first, but it will save you time in the end.

Go Online
PHSchool.com

For additional practice, go to **Web Code: bea-0707**

Answers

9. A

10.

The lines intersect at the point with coordinates $\left(\frac{1}{2}, \frac{1}{2}\right)$.

11. Answers may vary. Sample:
$P(20, -5)$ is on $\overleftrightarrow{RS}$ since $RP + PS = 65 + 65 = 130$ and $RS = 130$. $Q(20, 20)$ is not on $\overleftrightarrow{RS}$. $RS = 130$, $SQ = 20\sqrt{10}$, and $RQ = 30\sqrt{5}$, but no one of these lengths is equal to the sum of the other two.

12. Check students' work.

7.8 Perpendicular Lines

The slopes of two perpendicular lines have a special relationship.

In-Class Experiment

Study the diagram.

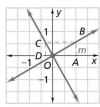

- $\overleftrightarrow{OB}$ and $\overleftrightarrow{OC}$ are perpendicular.
- Quadrilateral $ABCD$ has sides $\overline{AB}$ and $\overline{CD}$ parallel to the y-axis.
- Its other sides $\overline{BC}$ and $\overline{AD}$ are parallel to the x-axis.
- $AB = m$ and $OA = 1$.

1. Find CD and DO.

2. What is the slope of $\overleftrightarrow{OB}$?

3. What is the slope of $\overleftrightarrow{OC}$?

4. What is the product of the two slopes you found in Problems 2 and 3?

You just proved part of a very important theorem.

Theorem 7.6

Two lines are perpendicular if and only if the product of their slopes is -1.

Also, any horizontal line is perpendicular to any vertical line.

Lesson Overview

GOAL

- Find and compare the relationship that exists between the slopes in equations of lines and recognize when two lines are perpendicular.

This lesson is about the relationship that exists between, the slopes of perpendicular lines. It contains Theorem 7.6, which states that the slope of a line is m if and only if the slope of any line perpendicular to it is $\frac{1}{m}$.

CHECK YOUR UNDERSTANDING
- Core: 1, 3
- Optional: 2, 4

MATERIALS
- graph paper
- straightedges

HOMEWORK
- Core: 5, 6, 7, 9
- Optional: 8, 10, 11, 12, 13

Launch

Begin this lesson by assigning the In-Class Experiment.

Explore

Discuss students' results to the In-Class Experiment. Then present Theorem 7.6 and have students read the Minds in Action dialog on the following page.

Answers

In-Class Experiment

1. $CD = m$, $DO = m^2$
2. m
3. $-\frac{1}{m}$
4. -1

Minds in Action

EPISODE 34 The dialog between Tony and Sasha contains another proof of part of Theorem 7.6. You might ask students to summarize and rewrite the proof in their own words.

Tony wonders whether he has just seen a special case.

Tony   Hey Sasha, suppose the lines don't intersect at the origin. Is Theorem 7.6 still true?

Sasha   Well, Theorem 7.6 doesn't say anything about the lines having to intersect at the origin. But I agree that we have proved one direction of the theorem only for lines like that. Let's try to prove it for lines that could intersect anywhere.

Tony   Let's try to avoid a lot of work. Why don't we just try translating?

Sasha   That should work. The proof we came up with in the In-Class Experiment didn't really use the fact that the lines were through the origin. Look!

Sasha draws a diagram. She labels the rectangle like the one in the In-Class Experiment. She uses E instead of O for the intersection of the lines because it is no longer at the origin.

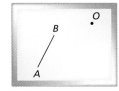

Tony   Wow, that's true! Everything is the same as before:

$$AB = CD = m$$

$$EA = 1$$

and

$$CB = DA = 1 + DE$$

Knowing that $\overleftrightarrow{EB}$ and $\overleftrightarrow{EC}$ are perpendicular and that $\angle EAB$ and $\angle EDC$ are right angles, we know that $\triangle EAB$ and $\triangle EDC$ are similar. So

$$CD : EA = DE : AB$$

This means that $DE = \dfrac{BA \cdot CD}{EA} = \dfrac{m^2}{1} = m^2$.

Sasha   Good, Tony! You really got it! So what are the slopes of the $\overleftrightarrow{EB}$ and $\overleftrightarrow{EC}$?

Tony   That's easy! The slope of $\overleftrightarrow{EB}$ is m, just as before. The slope of $\overleftrightarrow{CE}$ is

$$-\frac{CD}{DE} = -\frac{m}{m^2} = -\frac{1}{m}$$

So the product of the slopes is $m \cdot -\frac{1}{m} = -1$.

For Discussion

Now prove the second part of Theorem 7.6: *If the product of the slopes of two lines is* -1, *then the lines are perpendicular.*

Look at the figure below, where $m \geq 0$.

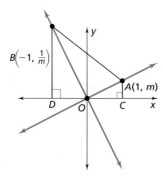

5. Find the slopes of $\overleftrightarrow{OA}$ and $\overleftrightarrow{OB}$. Show that the product of the slopes is -1.

6. Find BD, DO, OC, and AC.

7. Prove $\triangle BDO \sim \triangle OCA$.

8. Provide a justification for each step of the following proof.

Given $\triangle BDO \sim \triangle OCA$

Proof $m\angle DBO = m\angle COA$

$m\angle DBO + m\angle DOB = 90°$
$m\angle COA + m\angle DOB = 90°$
$m\angle BOA = 90°$

You can use Theorem 7.6 to find the distance between a point and a line.

For You to Do

9. Find an equation of the line through $P(3, 5)$ that is perpendicular to line ℓ with equation $2x + y = 9$.

10. Find the point of intersection Q of line ℓ and the perpendicular line you found.

11. What is the distance from P to ℓ?

Remember...

The distance from a point to a line is the shortest segment from the point to the line. This segment is perpendicular to the line.

Answers

For Discussion

5. slope of $\overleftrightarrow{OA} = m$

slope of $\overleftrightarrow{OB} = \frac{-1}{m}$

$m \cdot \frac{-1}{m} = -1$

6. $BD = \frac{1}{m}$; $OC = 1$; $DO = 1$, $AC = m$

7. $\triangle BDO$ and $\triangle OCA$ are right triangles and sides are in

proportion; $\frac{\frac{1}{m}}{1} = \frac{1}{m}$, therefore

$\triangle BDO \cong \triangle OCA$.

8. Since $\angle BDO$ is a right angle, the other two angles of the triangle must be supplementary to $\angle BDO$. $180 - 90 = 90°$.

For You to Do

9. $x - 2y = -7$

10. $(2.2, 4.6)$

11. $\frac{2\sqrt{5}}{5}$

Exercises

HOMEWORK
- Core: 5, 6, 7, 9
- Optional: 8, 10, 11, 12, 13

On Your Own

EXERCISE 8 Having to find the area of a triangle in the coordinate plane provides a reason for students to learn how to find the distance from a point to a line. To find the area of a triangle, you must find the length of one side and the length of the altitude to that side. Students have their choice of sides to use as the base of the triangle. The calculations will differ based on that choice.

Exercises *Practicing Habits of Mind*

Check Your Understanding

1. Write equations for two different lines that are perpendicular to the line with equation $x + y = 3$. Are there other possibilities?

2. Write an equation of the line through point $(1, 0)$ and perpendicular to the line with equation $x + 2y = 4$.

3. Find the distance from P to s in the figure below.

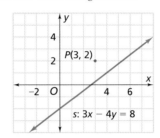

4. A circle has its center at the origin and radius 1. Find equations of two tangents to the circle through the point $(3, 0)$.

> **Remember...**
> What is the distance from a tangent to the center of the circle?

On Your Own

5. Write an equation for at least one line perpendicular to the line with each equation.

   a. $x + y = 2$
   b. $x - y + 2 = 0$
   c. $19x + 3y = 17$
   d. $y = 3 + 4x$

6. Write an equation of the line through the given point and perpendicular to the line with the given equation.

   a. $(0, 0), 2x - 3y = 14$
   b. $(0, -3), y = -x + 2$
   c. $(-4, -3), 2x + y + 6 = 0$
   d. $(1, 2), 2x - 3y + 1 = 0$

7. Find the distance from the given point to the given line.

   a. $(1, -2)$ to the line with equation $3x - y = -5$
   b. $(-1, 0)$ to the line with equation $y = 5x - 1$
   c. $(2, 2)$ to the line through points $(3, 1)$ and $(7, 4)$
   d. $(1, 2)$ to the line with equation $20x - 21y = 58$

Answers

Exercises

1. Answers may vary. Sample: $y = x$, $y = x + 1$; yes, infinitely many

2. Answers may vary. Sample: $2x - y = 2$

3. $\frac{7}{5}$

4. Answers may vary. Sample: $(\sqrt{2})x + 4y = 3\sqrt{2}$ and $(\sqrt{2})x - 4y = 3\sqrt{2}$

5. Answers may vary. Samples are given.
   a. $x - y = 0$
   b. $x - y = 0$
   c. $3x - 19y = 0$
   d. $x + 4y = 0$

6. Answers may vary. Samples are given.
   a. $3x + 2y = 0$
   b. $x - y = 3$
   c. $x - 2y = 2$
   d. $3x + 2y = 7$

8. Find the area of the triangle with the given vertices.

   a. $A(1, 1)$, $B(4, 5)$, $C(13, -4)$ **b.** $A(1, 1)$, $B(4, 2)$, $C(2, 3)$

9. **Standardized Test Prep** What is the equation of the line that is perpendicular at the point $(4, 1)$ to the line with equation $y = -\frac{1}{2}x + 3$?

   A. $y = \frac{1}{2}x - 1$ **B.** $y = 2x + 7$

   C. $-x + y = -3$ **D.** $2x - y = 7$

10. Graph quadrilateral $ABCD$ with vertices $A(\sqrt{2}, 4)$, $B(3, 3)$, $C(-\sqrt{2}, -4)$, and $D(-3, -3)$. How many right angles does it have? Prove your answer.

11. a. Draw $\triangle ABC$ on the coordinate plane, with vertices $A(1, 1)$, $B(5, 1)$, and $C(3, 6)$.

   b. Write an equation for the line containing the triangle's altitude relative to $\overline{AB}$.

   c. Find the coordinates of H, the point of intersection of the altitude in part (b) and the base $\overline{AB}$.

   d. Show algebraically that H is the midpoint of $\overline{AB}$.

12. a. Draw $\triangle ABC$ on the coordinate plane, with vertices $A(2, 3)$, $B(2, 7)$, $C(8, 5)$.

   b. Find the coordinates of the midpoint M of $\overline{AB}$.

   c. Find an equation of the line through M and C.

   d. Show algebraically that the line through M and C is perpendicular to $\overline{AB}$.

To do this, you should write an equation for $\overleftrightarrow{AB}$.

Maintain Your Skills

13. Line r has equation $2x + 3y = 4$. Line s has equation $ax + by = c$.

   a. Find the distance of $(1, 2)$ from r.

   b. Find the distance of (x_p, y_p) from r as a function of x_p and y_p.

   c. Find the distance of $(1, 2)$ from s as a function of a, b, and c.

   d. Find the distance of (x_p, y_p) from s as a function of x_p, y_p, a, b, and c.

Go Online
PHSchool.com

For additional practice, go to Web Code: **bea-0708**

A pier generally is built to be perpendicular to the shoreline. Why might this be so?

7. a. $\sqrt{10}$ **b.** $\dfrac{3\sqrt{26}}{13}$ **c.** $\dfrac{7}{5}$

   d. $\dfrac{80}{29}$

8. a. 31.5   **b.** 2.5

9. D

10. Four; slope $\overline{AB} = \dfrac{1}{-3 + \sqrt{2}}$, slope $\overline{BC} = \dfrac{7}{3 + \sqrt{2}}$, slope $\overline{CD} = \dfrac{1}{-3 + \sqrt{2}}$, and slope $\overline{DA} = \dfrac{7}{3 + \sqrt{2}}$. Since opposite sides of $ABCD$ have equal slopes, they are parallel. Hence $ABCD$ is a parallelogram. (slope $\overline{AB}$)·(slope $\overline{BC}$) $= -1$, so $\overline{AB}$ and $\overline{BC}$ are perpendicular. Hence $\angle B$ is a right angle. Therefore $ABCD$ is a rectangle and hence has four right angles.

11. See back of book.

12. See back of book.

13. See back of book.

Maintain Your Skills

EXERCISE 13 Students may think it very difficult to find the distance from a point P to a line ℓ. First they have to find the equation of the line perpendicular to ℓ through P. Then they have to find the intersection of that line with ℓ by solving a system of two equations in two variables. Then they have to find the distance between that intersection point and P. The numbers are often quite "messy."

This exercise shows students that it would be much more of a challenge to try to use a formula to find the distance from a point to a line.

First, they find the distance between a known point and a known line. They can then contrast this with the more difficult tasks of finding the distance between an unknown point and a known line, a known point and an unknown line, and, finally, an unknown point and an unknown line.

This is excellent practice with difficult algebraic manipulation and requires strict attention to detail. In any of the cases involving an unknown, the formula that results is so complex that students should all agree that they would rather just go through the process rather than try to memorize a formula.

Additional Resources

Additional Practice

Write an equation of a line perpendicular to the given line.

   1. $2x - y = 12$ **2.** $x - 3y = 15$ **3.** $y = -4x + 5$

   4. $x - 5 = 0$ **5.** $12x - 16y = 20$

Write an equation of the line through the given point and perpendicular to the given line.

   6. $(0, 0)$; $2x - 3y = 12$ **7.** $(1, 4)$: $x - 5y = 15$ **8.** $(0, -2)$; $y = 2x + 5$

   9. $(5, 6)$; $y - 3 = 0$ **10.** $(4, 0)$; $5x - 10y = 20$

For Exercises 11–14, find the distance from the given point to the given line.

   11. $(-1, 3)$; the line with equation $-3x - y = 9$

   12. $(0, 6)$; the line with equation $4x - 5y = 20$

   13. $(8, 5)$; the line through points $(4, 2)$ and $(-1, 5)$

   14. $(2, -3)$; the line with equation $y = -3x + 6$

   15. Imagine that a classroom is on a three-dimensional coordinate system, as shown below.

      a. Describe the location of the origin.

      b. Estimate the ordered triples of the four corners of the door.

      c. Estimate the ordered triples of the four corners of the desk. (Assume the desk has no height.)

      d. Estimate the ordered triples of the four corners of the whiteboard.

   16. Find the midpoint of the segment with the given endpoints.

      a. $A(4, 0, 2)$ and $C(0, 6, 2)$

      b. $D(0, 0, 2)$ and $F(4, 6, 0)$

      c. $B(4, 6, 2)$ and $G(0, 6, 0)$

   17. One of the vertices of a cube with side length 5 is $(0, 0, 0)$. What is the length of a diagonal of the cube?

Practice: For Lesson 7.8, assign Exercises 1–14.

Lesson Overview

GOAL

- Plot points in three dimensions and find the distance between them.

This is an optional lesson.

Understanding the three-dimensional coordinate system and learning how to plot points in three dimensions can take some students a bit of time. You may wish to spend two days working through this lesson and the accompanying exercises.

Note that although there are many ways to place the *x*-, *y*-, and *z*-axes to set up a three-dimensional coordinate system, in this course, the positive *x*-axis "comes out of the paper," the positive *y*-axis points to the right, and the positive *z*-axis points up. This makes the first octant—the section of three-dimensional space where all three coordinates are positive—show up at the front, right, and top of the space with respect to the axes.

This setup of the axes also follows the "right-hand rule." This means that if you point the fingers of your right hand in the direction of the positive *x*-axis and curl them in the direction of the positive *y*-axis to make a fist, your thumb will point in the direction of the positive *z*-axis. This "right-hand" orientation is a convention in mathematics. To avoid confusion, you may want to adopt this convention in your own drawings of three-dimensional coordinates.

CHECK YOUR UNDERSTANDING

- Core: 1, 2
- Optional: 3, 4, 5, 6

MATERIALS

- straightedges
- Blackline Master 7.9

HOMEWORK

- Core: 7, 8, 9, 10, 11, 13
- Optional: 12, 14, 15, 16, 18, 19, 20, 21, 22
- Extension: 17

VOCABULARY

- ordered triple
- *z*-axis
- *z*-coordinate

Launch

You may want to begin this lesson by modeling the three-dimensional coordinate system so your students can get a better idea of what it looks like. Blackline Master 7.9 provides a blank coordinate space. Try one of the demonstrations described in the Wrap Up.

Explore

Lead your students through the Example. Then have them try to plot some ordered triples they name in the For You to Do problems on page 586. If you choose to spend two class periods on this lesson, you can stop here on day 1 and assign Check Your Understanding Exercise 1 and On Your Own Exercises 7 and 10a.

In the Cartesian coordinate plane, you describe the location of any point with an ordered pair (x, y). In three-dimensional space, you describe the location of a point with an **ordered triple** (x, y, z).

In mathematics, the conventional way to extend Cartesian coordinates to three dimensions is to show a third coordinate axis. It is perpendicular to the other two.

> *Conventional* here means that most people do it or write it this way.

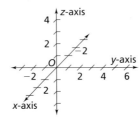

In this picture, the *x-y* coordinate plane lies flat, like the surface of your desk, and "face down." The new third axis—the **z-axis**—pierces the desk vertically and allows you to locate points above and below the *x-y* plane.

In this picture, *B* lies in plane and has coordinates $(3, 4, 0)$. Point *A* lies above the *x-y* plane and has coordinates $(3, 4, 2)$.

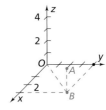

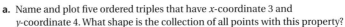

Example

Problem

a. Name and plot five ordered triples that have *x*-coordinate 3 and *y*-coordinate 4. What shape is the collection of all points with this property?

b. Name and plot five ordered triples that have *z*-coordinate 3. Describe where you find every point with *z*-coordinate 3.

Habits of Mind

Extend the description. You use an ordered pair for a point in two dimensions. You use an ordered triple for a point in three dimensions.

Solution

a. Here are five points that have the form $(3, 4, z)$.

$(3, 4, 0)$ $(3, 4, -2)$ $(3, 4, 2)$ $(3, 4, 4)$ $(3, 4, 6)$

All such points form a line that is parallel to the z-axis.

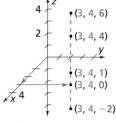

b. Here are five points that have the form $(x, y, 3)$.

$(0, 0, 3)$ $(0, 3, 3)$ $(-2, -3, 3)$ $(-2, 3, 3)$ $(4, 0, 3)$

It may not look like these points have anything in common, but every point with z-coordinate 3 lies on the plane that is three units above the x-y plane.

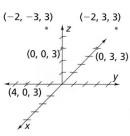

Developing Habits of Mind

Visualize. It is difficult to picture a three-dimensional figure, such as a plane, on a two-dimensional sheet of paper.

The diagram at the right might help you visualize three different planes in space. It looks like a corner of a room with no windows.

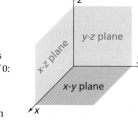

The x-y plane is the floor. All ordered triples that lie on this plane have a z-coordinate of 0: $(1, 2, 0)$, $(3, 5, 0)$, $(8, -2, 0)$, and so on.

The y-z plane is the wall at the back. All ordered triples that lie on this plane have an x-coordinate of 0: $(0, 1, 2)$, $(0, 3, 5)$, $(0, -2, 8)$, and so on.

The x-z plane is the wall at the left. All ordered triples that lie on this plane have a y-coordinate of 0: $(3, 0, 2)$, $(1, 0, 5)$, $(-12, -2, 0)$, and so on.

For You to Do

These problems give students a chance to characterize lines that are parallel to each axis.

The remainder of this lesson leads students through a way to find distance between two points in coordinate space when the two points are neither on a horizontal nor a vertical line.

For You to Do

Name five ordered triples that have each property. Then describe what the collection of all points with this property looks like.

1. x-coordinate 2 and y-coordinate -3

2. x-coordinate 2 and z-coordinate -3

3. y-coordinate 2 and z-coordinate -3

4. x-coordinate 2

For the diagram below, Tony had to find these lengths: AE, EF, GF, EG, AE, and AG.

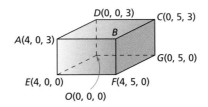

Here is Tony's work.

$AE = 3$ because $\overline{AE}$ is parallel to the z-axis.

$EF = 5$ because $\overline{EF}$ is parallel to the y-axis.

$GF = 4$ because $\overline{GF}$ is parallel to the x-axis.

$EG = \sqrt{41}$ because of the Pythagorean Theorem.

$AG = \sqrt{50}$ because of the Pythagorean Theorem.

For Discussion

5. Explain each of Tony's steps in the work above.

Tony's work leads to a formula for the distance between two points in three dimensions.

$$d = \sqrt{(x_2 - x_1)^2 + (y_2 - y_1)^2 + (z_2 - z_1)^2}$$

Answers

For You to Do

1. Any five points represented by ordered triples of the form $(2, -3, z)$ will do; a line through $(2, -3, 0)$ and perpendicular to the x-y plane

2. Any five points represented by ordered triples of the form $(2, y, -3)$ will do; a line through $(2, 0, -3)$ and perpendicular to the x-z plane

3. Any five points represented by ordered triples of the form $(x, 2, -3)$ will do; a line through $(0, 2, -3)$ and perpendicular to the y-z plane

4. Any five points represented by ordered triples of the form $(2, y, z)$ will do; a line through $(2, 0, 0)$ and parallel to the y-z plane

roof This proof uses two successive applications of the Pythagorean Theorem. (See Tony's work above.)

Let $K = (x_1, y_1, z_1)$ and $M = (x_2, y_2, z_2)$.

You can form a right triangle by drawing $\overline{KN}$, a diagonal of the base of the box below.

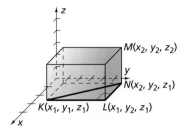

Apply the Pythagorean Theorem to get

$$KN^2 = KL^2 + LN^2$$

You can form right $\triangle KNM$ by drawing $\overline{KM}$, a diagonal of the box.

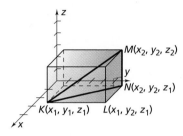

$$KM^2 = KN^2 + MN^2$$

Substituting $LN^2 + KL^2$ for KN^2 gives

$$KM^2 = LN^2 + KL^2 + MN^2$$

So $KM^2 = (x_2 - x_1)^2 + (y_2 - y_1)^2 + (z_2 - z_1)^2$.

The filaments of a dandelion suggest the points of a sphere in three dimensions.

For Discussion

5. For the first three lengths, the segments are parallel to an axis. To find the length of a segment parallel to the z-axis, find the absolute value of the difference of the z-coordinates of the endpoints. Use a similar approach for segments parallel to other axes. To find EG, use the Pythagorean Theorem to find the length of a diagonal of the rectangle $EFGO$. To find AG, use the Pythagorean

Theorem to find the length of the hypotenuse of $\triangle AEG$.

Wrap Up

End the lesson with a summarizing discussion:

- How do you find the distance between two points on a line parallel to an axis? (Answers may vary. Sample: Two of the coordinates of one point will match the corresponding coordinates of the other point. To find the distance between the points, find the difference of their nonmatching coordinates.)

- How do you find the midpoint of a horizontal or a vertical segment? (Answers may vary. Sample: Find the average of the nonmatching coordinates. For example, (3, 117) and (−21, 117) are the endpoints of a horizontal segment. The average of the nonmatching coordinates is $\frac{3 + (-21)}{2} =$ −9. The point (−9, 117) is the midpoint of the segment, because it is 12 units from either endpoint and lies on the line through the endpoints, which has equation $y = 117$.)

- How do you find the distance between two points if the two points are not on a vertical or a horizontal line? (Answers may vary. Sample: Think of the segment with these two points as endpoints of the hypotenuse of a right triangle. The length of one of the legs of this right triangle will be the difference of the x-coordinates of these two points. The length of the other leg will be the difference of their y-coordinates. Then, use the Pythagorean Theorem to find the length of the hypotenuse—the distance between the two points.)

Before assigning the On Your Own exercises, make sure your students are comfortable using the Pythagorean Theorem. They will need to use it often in the exercises.

Assessment Resources

Lesson Quiz 7.9

1. Find the coordinates of the midpoint of the segment with the given endpoints.
   a. $A(2, 0, 8)$ and $C(0, 2, 8)$
   b. $B(2, 2, 8)$ and $G(0, 2, 0)$

2. A cube has a vertex at the origin and side length 5 along the axes. Its vertices have no negative coordinates.
   a. What are the other vertices of the cube?
   b. What is the length of the diagonal of the cube?

3. $\triangle JLK$ has vertices $J(5, 0, 2)$, $L(5, 0, 0)$, and $K(0, 0, 2)$.
   a. Find the length of each side of $\triangle JLK$.
   b. Classify $\triangle JLK$.

Exercises

HOMEWORK
- Core: 7, 8, 9, 10, 11, 13
- Optional: 12, 14, 15, 16, 18, 19, 20, 21, 22
- Extension: 17

Exercises *Practicing Habits of Mind*

Check Your Understanding

1. Imagine that this room in your home is on a three-dimensional coordinate system.

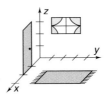

   a. Describe where the origin is.

   Estimate the ordered triples that describe each of the following.

   b. the four corners of the door

   c. the four corners of the window

   d. the four corners of the rug

2. Here is the picture that Tony was working with earlier. Find the coordinates of the midpoint for each segment with the endpoints listed.

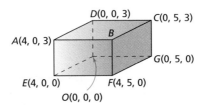

   a. $A(4, 0, 3)$ and $C(0, 5, 3)$

   b. $A(4, 0, 3)$ and $E(4, 0, 0)$

   c. $O(0, 0, 0)$ and $A(4, 0, 3)$

   d. $A(4, 0, 3)$ and $G(0, 5, 0)$

Answers

Exercises

1. Answers may vary. Samples are given.
   a. the corner of the room where the floor intersects the two walls shown in the diagram
   b. $(1, 0, 0)$, $(2, 0, 0)$, $(2, 0, 3)$, and $(1, 0, 3)$
   c. $(0, 1, 2)$, $(0, 2, 2)$, $(0, 2, 3)$, and $(0, 1, 3)$
   d. $(3, 1, 0)$, $(3, 3, 0)$, $(1, 3, 0)$, and $(1, 1, 0)$

2. **a.** $(2, 2.5, 3)$ **b.** $(4, 0, 1.5)$
   c. $(2, 0, 1.5)$ **d.** $(2, 2.5, 1.5)$

3. **a.** right triangle
   b. 13   **c.** $\sqrt{178}$

4. **a.** Answers may vary. Sample:
   $(0, \sqrt{5})$, $(-\sqrt{5}, 0)$, $(1, 2)$, $(2, 1)$, $(-2, -1)$, $(-2, 1)$, $(1, -2)$, and $\left(\frac{\sqrt{19}}{2}, \frac{1}{2}\right)$
   b. a circle of radius $\sqrt{5}$ with center at the origin
   c. Answers may vary. Sample:
   $(0, \sqrt{13})$, $(\sqrt{13}, 0)$, $(3, 2)$, $(3, -2)$, $(-3, 2)$, $(-3, -2)$, $(2, 3)$, $(1, 2\sqrt{3})$

3. The diagonal $\overline{AH}$ of the box shown here is one side of $\triangle ABH$.

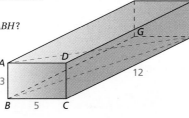

a. What kind of triangle is $\triangle ABH$?

b. What is BH?

c. What is AH?

4. Here is a recipe to perform on points in the plane: square each coordinate and add the results.

a. Find eight points that produce 5 when you apply the recipe to them.

b. What figure do you see if you look at all the points that produce 5?

Find eight points that produce each result.

c. 13   **d.** 625   **e.** 100

f. 169   **g.** 1

Developing Habits of Mind

Consider more than one strategy. One way to find a point that produces 5 in Exercise 4a is to use a calculator. Just decide, for example, that one coordinate of the point is 1.5. Then square 1.5, subtract the result from 5, and take the square root of what is left.

Another way is to think about sums of square integers. Can you express every integer as the sum of two squares? Can you express 5 as the sum of two squares?

5. a. If you draw a picture of all the points in the plane that are 13 units from the point (0, 0), what figure do you get?

b. Find the coordinates of eight points that are 13 units from the point (0, 0). How can you tell if some new point (a, b) is on this figure by doing a quick calculation on its coordinates?

c. If you draw a picture of all the points in the plane that are 13 units from the point (4, −1), what figure do you get?

d. Find the coordinates of eight points that are 13 units from the point (4, −1). How can you tell if some new point (a, b) is on this figure by doing a quick calculation on its coordinates?

---

d. Answers may vary. Sample:
(0, 25), (15, 20), (−20, 15),
$(5, 10\sqrt{6})$, $(5\sqrt{21}, 10)$,
$(9, 4\sqrt{34})$, $(17, 4\sqrt{21})$,
$(18, \sqrt{301})$

e. (0, 10), (0, −10), (−10, 0),
(6, 8), (−8, −6), $(2, 4\sqrt{6})$,
$(2\sqrt{21}, 4)$, $(−5, 5\sqrt{3})$

f. (0, 13), (0, −13), (12, 5)
(12, −5), (−12, −5),
(−12, 5), $(8, \sqrt{105})$,
$(3, 4\sqrt{10})$

g. (0, 1), (0, −1), (0.6,
0.8), (0.6, −0.8),
(−0.8, 0.6), $(0.2, 0.4\sqrt{6})$,

$(−0.2, −0.4\sqrt{6})$
$(0.5\sqrt{2}, 0.5\sqrt{2})$

5. a. a circle of radius 13 with center at the origin

b. Answers may vary. Sample: See the answer for Exercise 4c; find the sum of the squares of the coordinates of the point.

c. a circle of radius 13 with center at (4, −1)

5. d. See back of book.

6. Suppose you apply the following recipe to points in three dimensions: take each coordinate, square it, and add the results.

a. Find eight points that produce 81 when you apply the recipe. What do you get if you look at all points that produce 81?

b. What do you get if you look at all points in three dimensions that are 7 units from the origin? Find the coordinates of three points that are 7 units from the origin.

On Your Own

Use the diagram for Exercises 7–9.

7. Find the coordinates of each vertex of the box.

8. Find the length of each segment.

    a. $\overline{OE}$ **b.** $\overline{OB}$

    c. $\overline{AE}$ **d.** $\overline{FC}$

9. Name another segment with the same length as the given segment.

    a. $\overline{OE}$ **b.** $\overline{OB}$

    c. $\overline{AE}$ **d.** $\overline{FC}$

10. A cube has a vertex at the origin and sides of length 1 along the axes.

    a. What are the other vertices of the cube?

    b. What is the length of a diagonal of the cube?

11. $\triangle LMN$ has vertices $L(1, 0, 0)$, $M(0, 1, 0)$, and $N(0, 0, 1)$.

    a. Sketch $\triangle LMN$.

    b. Find the perimeter of $\triangle LMN$.

    c. Find the midpoints of each side of $\triangle LMN$.

12. $\triangle ABC$ has vertices $A(2, -1, 7)$, $B(4, 0, 5)$, and $C(0, 0, 5)$.

    a. Find the perimeter of $\triangle ABC$.

    b. Find the midpoints of each side of $\triangle ABC$.

    c. Find the perimeter of the triangle formed by connecting the midpoints of the sides of $\triangle ABC$.

Answers

6. a. Answers may vary. Sample:
$(0, 0, -9)$, $(4, 4, 7)$,
$(-3, -6, -6)$, $(-3, 6\sqrt{2}, 0)$,
$(-3, -5, \sqrt{47})$,
$(3, 4, 2\sqrt{14})$, $(1, 2, \sqrt{76})$,
and $(5, 6, \sqrt{20})$; a sphere of
radius 9 with center at the origin

    b. a sphere of radius 7 with center
at the origin; Answers may
vary. Sample: $(-2, -3, -6)$,
$(2\sqrt{2}, 4, 5)$, and $(0, 0, 7)$

7. $O(0, 0, 0)$, $A(0, 0, 3)$, $B(0, 3, 3)$,
$C(0, 3, 0)$, $D(3, 3, 0)$, $E(3, 0, 0)$,
$F(3, 0, 3)$, $G(3, 3, 3)$

8. a. 3   **b.** $3\sqrt{2}$

    c. $3\sqrt{2}$ **d.** $3\sqrt{3}$

9. a. Any other edge of the box
will do.

    b. Any other diagonal of a face of
the box will do.

    c. Any other diagonal of a face of
the box will do.

    d. Any of these: $\overline{GO}$, $\overline{BE}$, $\overline{AD}$

13. Standardized Test Prep A dowel is a long, straight rod with a small diameter. You want to ship a dowel in a rectangular box. The dimensions of four boxes are listed. Which dimensions allow for the longest dowel if the dowel extends from one corner to the opposite corner of the box?

A. 44 inches by 24 inches by 12 inches

B. 40 inches by 30 inches by 4 inches

C. 35 inches by 35 inches by 2 inches

D. 27 inches by 27 inches by 27 inches

14. Name six points in three dimensions that fit the rule: the sum of the coordinates is 30. What shape does this rule produce if you look at all of the points that fit it?

15. In a two-dimensional coordinate system, a square with a one-unit side length has one vertex at the origin. Two of its sides lie along the axes. Its vertices have no negative coordinates.

a. What are the coordinates of the vertex farthest from the origin?

b. How far is that vertex from the origin?

16. In a three-dimensional coordinate system, a cube with a one-unit side length sits with one vertex at the origin. Three of its edges lie along the axes. Its vertices have no negative coordinates.

a. What are the coordinates of the vertex farthest from the origin?

b. How far is that vertex from the origin?

17. Take It Further Two vertices of an equilateral triangle lie in the Cartesian plane at $(1, 0)$ and $(9, 0)$.

a. Find coordinates for the third vertex.

b. Embed the three points from part (a) in three dimensions. The coordinates become $(1, 0, 0)$, $(9, 0, 0)$, and $(a, b, 0)$, where (a, b) is your answer to part (a). Find the coordinates of the fourth vertex of a regular tetrahedron that has these three points as vertices.

Habits of Mind

Visualize. The four faces of a regular tetrahedron are equilateral triangles. The fourth vertex is the same distance from the other three vertices as they are from each other.

Maintain Your Skills

Points $(0, 0, 2)$, $(0, 1, 3)$, and $(0, 1, 2)$ are the vertices of a triangle. Describe the triangle that results if you apply each rule to the coordinates.

18. Multiply each coordinate by 4.

19. Multiply each coordinate by $\frac{1}{3}$.

20. Add 3 to the z-coordinates.

21. Add 3 to the y-coordinates.

22. Subtract 3 from the z-coordinates.

Go Online
PHSchool.com

For additional practice, go to **Web Code: bea-0709**

Additional Practice

Write an equation of a line perpendicular to the given line.

1. $2x - y = 12$ **2.** $x - 3y = 15$ **3.** $y = -4x + 5$

4. $x - 5 = 0$ **5.** $12x - 16y = 20$

Write an equation of the line through the given point and perpendicular to the given line.

6. $(0, 0); 2x - 3y = 12$ **7.** $(1, 4); x - 5y = 15$ **8.** $(0, -2); y = 2x + 5$

9. $(5, 6); y - 3 = 0$ **10.** $(4, 0); 5x - 10y = 20$

For Exercises 11–14, find the distance from the given point to the given line.

11. $(-1, 3)$; the line with equation $-3x - y = 9$

12. $(0, 6)$; the line with equation $4x - 5y = 20$

13. $(8, 5)$; the line through points $(4, 2)$ and $(-1, 5)$

14. $(2, -3)$; the line with equation $y = -3x + 6$

15. Imagine that a classroom is on a three-dimensional coordinate system, as shown below.

a. Describe the location of the origin.
b. Estimate the ordered triples of the four corners of the door.
c. Estimate the ordered triples of the four corners of the desk. (Assume the desk has no height.)
d. Estimate the ordered triples of the four corners of the whiteboard.

16. Find the midpoint of the segment with the given endpoints.
a. $A(4, 0, 2)$ and $C(0, 6, 2)$
b. $D(0, 0, 2)$ and $F(4, 6, 0)$
c. $B(4, 6, 2)$ and $G(0, 6, 0)$

17. One of the vertices of a cube with side length 5 is $(0, 0, 0)$. What is the length of a diagonal of the cube?

Practice: For Lesson 7.9, assign Exercises 15–17.

---

10. a. Answers may vary. Sample: $(0, 0, 0)$, $(1, 0, 0)$, $(0, 1, 0)$, $(1, 1, 0)$, $(0, 0, 1)$, $(1, 0, 1)$, $(1, 1, 1)$, $(0, 1, 1)$

b. $\sqrt{3}$

11. See back of book.

12. See back of book.

13. A

14. Answers may vary. Sample: $(30, 0, 0)$, $(15, 15, 0)$, $(0, 15, 15)$, $(10, 10, 10)$, $(20, 5, 5)$, $(10, 20, 0)$; a plane

15. a. $(1, 1)$ **b.** $\sqrt{2}$

16. a. $(1, 1, 1)$ **b.** $\sqrt{3}$

17. See back of book.

18. The triangle is dilated by a factor of 4 with respect to the origin.

19. The triangle is dilated by a factor of $\frac{1}{3}$ with respect to the origin.

20. The triangle moves 3 units parallel to the x-axis in the positive direction.

21. The triangle moves 3 units parallel to the y-axis in the positive direction.

22. The triangle moves 3 units parallel to the z-axis in the negative direction.

Mathematical Reflections

EXERCISES 6–8: At the start of the Investigation, you may have assigned these as Questions 1–3 for students to think and write about.

Mathematical 7B Reflections

In this investigation, you learned how to calculate the midpoint and length of a segment, write equations of lines with given characteristics, and prove whether three points are collinear. These questions will help you summarize what you have learned.

1. For $A\left(-3, \frac{1}{2}\right)$ and $B\left(\frac{2}{3}, \frac{1}{4}\right)$, find the distance of A from the origin O and the distance of A from B.

2. Calculate the coordinates of the midpoint of $\overline{JK}$ with endpoints $J(0, 3)$ and $K(-4, -6)$.

3. Are the following points collinear? Explain.

$$\left(0, \frac{1}{2}\right), \left(-1, -\frac{5}{2}\right), \left(\frac{1}{2}, 2\right)$$

4. Write an equation for the line through the origin and perpendicular to the line with equation $2x + 3y = 0$.

5. Here is a box in three dimensions.

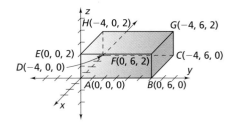

Find the length of its diagonal $\overline{EC}$.

6. How can you tell by examining the coordinates of two points whether they lie on a horizontal line? On a vertical line?

7. How do you calculate the distance between two points?

8. A box has dimensions 3 in. by 5 in. by 4 in. What is the length of a diagonal?

Vocabulary and Notation

In this investigation, you saw these terms and this symbol. Make sure you understand what each one means and how to use it.

- collinear
- ordered triple
- z-axis
- V_1 (V sub 1)

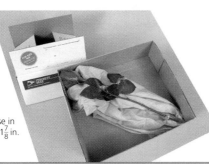

You can ship an 18-inch rose in the box that is $13\frac{5}{8}$ in. by $11\frac{7}{8}$ in. by $3\frac{3}{8}$ in.

Mathematical Reflections

1. $AO = \dfrac{\sqrt{37}}{2}$, $AB = \dfrac{\sqrt{1945}}{12}$

2. $\left(-2, -\dfrac{3}{2}\right)$

3. Yes; Answers may vary. Sample: All the points are on the line with equation $6x - 2y = -1$.

4. $3x - 2y = 0$

5. $2\sqrt{14}$

6. Two points lie on the same horizontal line if and only if their y-coordinates are equal; two points lie on the same vertical line if and only if their x-coordinates are equal.

7. Find the sum of the squares of the differences of corresponding coordinates. Then find the square root of the sum.

8. $5\sqrt{2}$

Chapter 7

Mid-Chapter Test

Go Online
PHSchool.com

For a mid-chapter test,
go to Web Code: **bea-0752**

Multiple Choice

1. Graph quadrilateral *ABCD* with vertices
   A(2, 4), *B*(6, 4), *C*(6, −4), and *D*(2, −4). Graph
   its image *A′B′C′D′* after a reflection over the
   x-axis. Which statement about *ABCD* and
   A′B′C′D′ is true?

   A. *ABCD* and *A′B′C′D′* are not congruent.

   B. *ABCD* and *A′B′C′D′* are not identical.

   C. *ABCD* and *A′B′C′D′* are not parallelograms.

   D. *ABCD* and *A′B′C′D′* are not squares.

2. Three vertices of a square are (−1, −3), (−1, 5),
   and (7, 5). What are the coordinates of the center
   of the square?

   A. (3, 1)

   B. ($\sqrt{3}$, 1)

   C. (3, $\sqrt{3}$)

   D. (1, 1)

3. A rectangular prism has three vertices (0, 0, 0),
   (3, 5, 0), and (3, 5, 4). Which must be the
   coordinates of a fourth vertex?

   A. (3, 0, 4)

   B. (3, 0, 5)

   C. (0, 5, 3)

   D. (4, 5, 0)

Open Response

4. Graph the line with equation $4x + 2y = 3$. Write
   an equation of its image after a reflection over
   the *y*-axis.

5. Copy $\overline{AB}$ and point *O*. Then rotate $\overline{AB}$ around *O*
   by 60° in the counterclockwise direction.

   O

   A •————————• *B*

6. Find the coordinates of the midpoint of $\overline{AB}$ with
   endpoints *A*(−3, 7) and *B*(4, −9).

7. The five vertices of a pentagon are given.

   - *A*(1, 2)

   - *B*(6, 1)

   - *C*(5, −5)

   - *D*(−8, −4)

   - *E*(−6, 1)

   Graph the pentagon. Find its perimeter without
   using a ruler.

8. Point *A* has coordinates (8, 6). Line ℓ has
   equation $3x − 5y = 2$. Write an equation for
   the line through *A* and parallel to ℓ.

9. Point *B* has coordinates (−8, 3). Line *m* has
   equation $2x − 5y = 1$. Write an equation for
   the line through *B* and perpendicular to *m*.

10. The coordinates of two points in three-
    dimensional coordinate space are given.

    - *A*(1, −3, 12)

    - *B*(−5, −9, 10)

    Calculate the length of $\overline{AB}$.

Additional Resources

Mid-Chapter Test

1. Reflect $\overline{AB}$ with endpoints *A*(0, 2) and *B*(5, 10) over the *y*-axis. Write the
   coordinates of the new endpoints.

2. Graph the line with equation $x − y = 5$. Write an equation of its image
   after a reflection over the *x*-axis.

3. Rotate $\overline{AB}$ about *P* by 30° in the counterclockwise direction.

   • *P*

   A •————• *B*

4. $\overline{AB}$ has endpoints *A*(20, −34) and *B*(−5, −8). Find the coordinates of the
   midpoint of $\overline{AB}$.

5. Points *A, B, C, D, E,* and *F* are the vertices of a hexagon. Plot each vertex
   and connect the points in order. Then find the perimeter of the hexagon
   without using a ruler.

   | *A*(1, 1) | *B*(4, −1) | *C*(4, −3) |
   | *D*(1, −6) | *E*(−1, −5) | *F*(−2, −2) |

6. Write an equation of the line through (4, 6) and parallel to the line with
   equation $23x − 5y = 21$.

7. Write an equation for the line through (8, −15) and perpendicular to the
   line with equation $4x − 35y = 1$.

8. For *J*(3, 12, −1) and *K*(4, 0, −4), two points in three-dimensional
   coordinate space, find the length of $\overline{JK}$.

Also available: Form B

Mid-Chapter Test

1. D

2. A

3. C

4. $4x − 2y = −3$

5. See back of book.

6. $\left(\frac{1}{2}, −1\right)$

7. See back of book.

8. $3x − 5y = −6$

9. $5x + 2y = −34$

10. $2\sqrt{19}$

Investigation Overview

In this investigation, students use points in the coordinate plane as algebraic objects to which they can add and also multiply by any real number. Students study vectors as ordered pairs of numbers and use vectors to find a new form for the equation of a line. Depending on how much time you have and how deeply you want to treat these topics, you can choose to stop after Lesson 7.11 (Introduction to Vectors) or continue through the remaining two lessons on the vector equation of a line.

You may wish to assign Questions 1–3 for students to think and write about during the investigation.

Learning Goals

- Add points and multiply points by any real number and write the results both algebraically and geometrically.
- Work with vectors.
- Write a vector equation for any line in the coordinate plane.

Habits and Skills

- See mathematical objects from a different perspective.
- Operate on points and vectors as algebraic objects.
- Use a vectors to write equations of lines.

Investigation 7C
Connections to Algebra

In *Connections to Algebra,* you will use points on the coordinate plane as algebraic objects. In other words, you will think of points as things that you can add or that you can multiply by any real number. Since points are also geometric objects, you will see the corresponding geometric consequences of these operations.

By the end of this investigation, you will be able to answer questions like these.

1. What are vectors?
2. How can you tell whether two vectors are equivalent?
3. Find the vector equation for the line through $A(1, 2)$ and $B(3, -4)$.

You will learn how to

- add points and multiply points by any real number and write the results both algebraically and geometrically
- work with vectors
- write a vector equation for any line on the coordinate plane

You will develop these habits and skills:

- See mathematical objects from a different perspective.
- Operate on points and vectors as algebraic objects.
- Use vectors to write equations of lines.

Geese stay in the V formation by flying with equivalent velocity vectors.

Investigation Road Map

LESSON 7.10, *Getting Started,* gets students used to working with points as algebraic objects. It asks them to predict the results of various algebraic operations on the points in a graph.

LESSON 7.11, *Introduction to Vectors,* is a two-day lesson that introduces vectors as ordered pairs of numbers. Students discover the Head-Minus-Tail Test and how to find the sum of two vectors both algebraically and geometrically. This lesson also includes Theorem 7.9 about scaling points.

LESSON 7.12, *The Vector Equation of a Line,* introduces a new way of writing equations of lines, the vector equation of a line.

LESSON 7.13, *Using the Vector Equation of a Line,* helps students understand, through an In-Class experiment, how to use the vector equations of lines to find the point of intersection of two lines.

To help prepare for the study of vectors, you need to know how to multiply a point by a number and how to add two points. To multiply a point by a number (scale a point), you simply multiply each of its coordinates by that number. To add two points, you simply add the corresponding coordinates.

or You to Explore

1. Use one coordinate grid for parts (a)–(g). For each exercise, graph A and cA on the coordinate point plane. How is the location of cA related to the location of A?

> cA is the point you get when you *scale A* by c.

a. $A(5, 1)$, $c = 2$

b. $A(5, 1)$, $c = \frac{1}{2}$

c. $A(3, 4)$, $c = 3$

d. $A(3, 4)$, $c = \frac{1}{2}$

e. $A(3, 4)$, $c = -1$

f. $A(3, 4)$, $c = -2$

g. $A(3, 4)$, $c = -\frac{1}{2}$

What happens if, instead of scaling one point by many different numbers, you take many collinear points and scale them by the same number? The next few exercises ask you to look at that question.

2. Draw a picture of what you get if you scale each of the collinear points below by 2. Describe in words what you get.

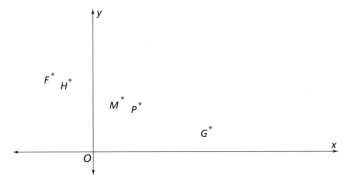

Lesson Overview

GOALS
- Warm up to the ideas of the investigation.
- Add points and multiply points by any real number, and write the results both algebraically and geometrically.

Use this lesson to assess your students' knowledge and understanding of point addition and multiplication of a point by a real number.

FOR YOU TO EXPLORE
- Core: 1, 2, 4, 6
- Optional: 3, 5

HOMEWORK
- Core: 7, 10, 11, 12
- Optional: 8, 9, 13, 14, 15, 16, 17

MATERIALS
- graph paper
- straightedges
- Blackline Master 7.10

Launch

Begin this lesson by assigning For You to Explore Problems 1, 2, 4, and 6.

Explore

For You to Explore

PROBLEMS 1–3 The first three problems ask students to scale points by multiplying the coordinates by real numbers. If your students have any questions about how this works, show them an example. Blackline Master 7.10 may be helpful here.

Wrap Up

Before assigning homework, allow students some time to discuss and summarize their findings.

Answers

For You to Explore

1. Check students' diagrams. The coordinates for cA for parts (a)–(g) are as follows:

a. $(10, 2)$ **b.** $\left(\frac{5}{2}, \frac{1}{2}\right)$

c. $(9, 12)$ **d.** $\left(\frac{3}{2}, 2\right)$

e. $(-3, -4)$ **f.** $(-6, -8)$

g. $\left(-\frac{3}{2}, -2\right)$

In parts (a)–(d), where each value of c is positive, CA is on $\overrightarrow{OA}$ and is c times as far from O as point A. In parts (e)–(g), where each value of c is negative, CA is on the ray opposite to $\overrightarrow{OA}$ and is $|c|$ times as far from O as point A.

2. The new set of points is also collinear, but each of the new points is twice as far from the origin as the original point.

3. Think of a circle with radius 6 and center at the origin. What do you get if you scale all the points on the circle by 2? By $\frac{1}{2}$? By $-\frac{1}{2}$?

You may want to sketch a picture on graph paper.

4. Use a separate coordinate grid for each part. On each grid, show O (the origin), A, B, and $A + B$.

   a. $A(5, 1)$ $B(3, 6)$

   b. $A(4, -2)$ $B(0, 6)$

   c. $A(4, -2)$ $B(-3, -5)$

   d. $A(4, -2)$ $B(-4, 2)$

   e. $A(4, -2)$ $B(-1, 4)$

   f. $A(3, 1)$, $B(6, 2)$

Remember...

To add points, you add their corresponding coordinates. For example, $(-2, 7) + (4, 1) = (2, 8)$.

5. Suppose $A(3, 5)$ and $B(6, -1)$.

   a. Plot B, $2B$, $0.5B$, $-1B$, $4B$, $-\frac{18}{5}B$, and three other multiples of B.

   b. What does the graph look like if you plot every possible multiple of B?

   c. Add A to each of the points you plotted in part (a). Plot the results on the same coordinate grid.

   d. What would your picture look like if you plotted the sum of A and each possible multiple of B?

6. Draw a polygon (like the one shown here if you like) on a coordinate grid. Apply each rule below to the vertices of the polygon. Draw the resulting polygon. Describe how each resulting polygon is related to the original.

   a. $(x, y) \mapsto (x + 8, y + 5)$

   b. $(x, y) \mapsto (x - 8, y + 5)$

   c. $(x, y) \mapsto (3x, 3y)$

   d. $(x, y) \mapsto \left(\frac{x}{2}, \frac{y}{2}\right)$

   e. $(x, y) \mapsto \left(\frac{x}{2} + 7, \frac{y}{2} + 10\right)$

   f. $(x, y) \mapsto (-x, y + 2)$

   g. $(x, y) \mapsto (2x, y + 2)$

Habits of Mind

Look for patterns. Can you make connections between the rules in Problem 6 and adding and scaling points?

Answers

3. a circle of radius 12 centered at the origin; a circle of radius 3 centered at the origin; a circle of radius 3 centered at the origin

4. See back of book.

5. **a.** See back of book
   b. The points would form a line.

c.

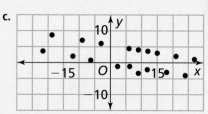

d. The points would form a line parallel to the line from part (b).

6. See back of book.

Exercises *Practicing Habits of Mind*

On Your Own

7. Write About It Suppose A is a point and c is some real number. Describe geometrically how cA is related to A. How can you tell someone how to locate $2A$ if that person knows where point A is, but you do not? How are the coordinates of cA related algebraically to the coordinates of A?

8. Write About It Why do you think *scaling* is a better term than *multiplying* when you refer to the operation that gives you cA?

9. Draw a picture of what you get if you scale each point shown by $\frac{1}{2}$. Describe what you get in words.

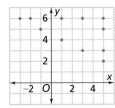

10. Draw what you get if you scale every point on the rectangle by -1. Then draw what you get if you scale each point by $\frac{5}{3}$.

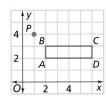

11. Plot the sum of $P(1, 4)$ and each point on the rectangle below.

> **Habits of Mind**
>
> **Visualize.** Of course, you cannot add P to every point of the rectangle, but what would you get if you could?

Exercises

7. See back of book.

8. Answers may vary. Sample: If you are working with a figure in the coordinate plane and multiply the coordinates of all its points by the same nonzero number, then the resulting figure is a scaled copy of the original figure.

9.

The original figure has been dilated with respect to the origin by a factor of $\frac{1}{2}$.

10. See back of book.

11. See back of book.

On Your Own

EXERCISES 7 AND 8 ask students to express in writing their thoughts about the geometric and algebraic meanings of the process of multiplying a point by a number (scaling).

12. For each of the diagrams, write a rule that transforms the vertices of polygon $JKLM$ to the vertices of polygon $J'K'L'M'$. (Use the $\mapsto$ notation.)

a.
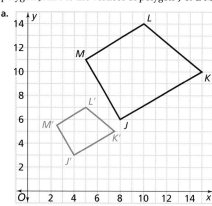

b.
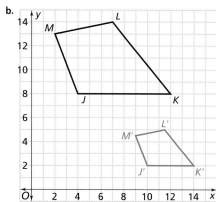

13. Jorge and Yutaka are both asked to transform $\triangle ABC$ with vertices $A(3, 6)$, $R(9, 6)$, and $C(9, 3)$. They are to scale it by $\frac{1}{4}$ and translate it 16 units to the right, but they are not told in which order to perform the transformations. Jorge chooses to scale the triangle first and then translate it. Yutaka translates first and then does the scaling.

a. Pick two vertices of $\triangle ABC$. Follow Jorge's and Yutaka's methods for each vertex. Write down where the images are.

b. Do both methods end up with a same image triangle?

c. The two algebraic statements below describe Jorge's and Yutaka's methods. Which is Jorge's? Which is Yutaka's?
- $(x, y) \mapsto \frac{1}{4}(x, y) + (16, 0)$
- $(x, y) \mapsto \frac{1}{4}(x + 16, y)$

Answers

12. a. $(x, y) \mapsto \left(\frac{1}{2}x, \frac{1}{2}y\right)$

   b. $(x, y) \mapsto \left(\frac{1}{2}x + 8, \frac{1}{2}y - 2\right)$

13. a. Jorge: $A'(16.75, 1.5)$, $B'(18.25, 1.5)$, $C'(18.25, 0.75)$; Yutaka: $A'(4.75, 1.5)$, $B'(6.25, 1.5)$, $C'(6.25, 0.75)$

   b. no

   c. Jorge used $(x, y) \mapsto \frac{1}{4}(x, y) + (16, 0)$, and Yutaka used $(x, y) \mapsto \frac{1}{4}(x + 16, y)$.

14. a. First, translate left 3 units and up 4 units. Next, dilate by a factor of $\frac{1}{2}$ with respect to the origin. Finally, translate right 5 units and up 2 units.

   b. $(a, b) \mapsto \left(\frac{1}{2}a + \frac{7}{2}, \frac{1}{2}b + 4\right)$; First, dilate by a factor of $\frac{1}{2}$ with respect to the origin. Then translate right $\frac{7}{2}$ units and up 4 units.

15. a. First, translate left 4 units and up 3 units. Next, dilate by a

14. Here is a complicated rule.

$$(a, b) \mapsto \left(\tfrac{1}{2}(a - 3) + 5, \tfrac{1}{2}(b + 4) + 2\right)$$

  a. Describe in words what this rule does.

  b. Simplify the algebra of the rule. Describe in words what your new (but equivalent) rule does.

15. Here is another complicated rule.

$$(x, z) \mapsto \left(\tfrac{1}{2}(2(x - 4) + 6), \tfrac{1}{2}(2(z + 3) - 4)\right)$$

  a. Describe in words what this rule does.

  b. Simplify the algebra of the rule. Describe in words what your new (but equivalent) rule does.

Habits of Mind

Check your work.
Apply your rule to some points on a specific picture to check that your description is right.

16. Compare $(x, y) \mapsto 2(x, y) + (2, 3)$ and $(x, y) \mapsto 2((x, y) + (1, 2))$. Do these rules give the same result?

17. Pick a point. Think about the following rule.

  Add $(2, 3)$.

  Scale by 3.

  Subtract $(1, 2)$.

  Now answer the following questions.

  a. If you start with $(4, 5)$, where do you end?

  b. If you start with $(-1, 3)$, where do you end?

  c. If you end with $(7, 1)$, where did you start?

  d. If you end with $(4, 6)$, where did you start?

  e. What simple rule is equivalent to the one above?

Maintain Your Skills

EXERCISES 14–17 are about "rules" that transform coordinates of points into coordinates of other points. By simplifying the algebraic expressions, students should be able to give a simple explanation of how one set of coordinates gets mapped onto another set of coordinates.

factor of 2 with respect to the origin. Then translate right 6 units and down 4 units. Finally, dilate by a factor of $\frac{1}{2}$ with respect to the origin.

  b. $(x, z) \mapsto (x - 1, z + 1)$;
  Translate left 1 unit and up 1 unit.

16. no

17. a. $(17, 22)$ **b.** $(2, 16)$

  c. $\left(\frac{2}{3}, -2\right)$ **d.** $\left(-\frac{1}{3}, -\frac{1}{3}\right)$

  e. $(a, b) \mapsto (3a + 5, 3b + 7)$

Lesson Overview

GOAL

• Work with vectors.

This lesson should take two class periods to complete. Refer to the Daily Planner at the beginning of the chapter for one way to divide this lesson.

This lesson introduces students to vectors as ordered pairs of points. Students learn the Head-Minus-Tail Test as a method for identifying equivalent vectors. If students are familiar with the concept of *vector* or have already seen this method, you might review the proof of the Head-Minus-Tail Test and continue onto Theorem 7.8.

CHECK YOUR UNDERSTANDING
• Core: 1, 2, 3, 4, 5, 6

MATERIALS
• straightedges
• graph paper
• Blackline Master 7.11

HOMEWORK
• Core: 7, 11, 12, 14, 15, 16
• Optional: 8, 9, 10, 13, 17, 18, 19

VOCABULARY
• direction
• equivalent vectors
• head
• Head-Minus-Tail Test
• orientation
• tail
• vector

Launch

Begin this lesson by explaining the concept of vector, as in the opening paragraphs. Make sure students understand the definition of vector. Minds in Action episode 35 and the For You to Do section that follows might help.

Explore

Use the Developing Habits of Mind section on page 603 to discuss equivalent vectors. Then have students do In-Class Experiment Problems 9–14 and For You to Do Problems 15 and 16, all on page 604, to lead into a discussion of Theorems 7.8 and 7.9.

Wrap Up

End this lesson by assigning Problems 17–20 in the last For You to Do section on page 605. Then work through a general proof of Theorem 7.9 with the whole class.

7.11 Introduction to Vectors

In Lesson 7.10, you saw some geometric effects of adding and scaling points. There is a very convenient language for using these concepts. It involves the notion of a vector.

In physics, people distinguish speed (such as 30 mi/h) from velocity. Velocity has a **direction** as well as a size, so that 30 mi/h northeast is different from 30 mi/h due south. You can model this idea on a coordinate system by thinking about line segments that have a direction.

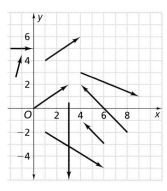

Each arrow in this figure can stand for a velocity. The length of the arrow is the speed. The direction of the arrow tells you which way the velocity is directed. The arrows are often called *vectors*. If A and B are points, the "vector from A to B" can be thought of as the arrow that starts at A and ends at B.

For navigators, vectors might stand for trips or currents or wind velocities.

Definition

Given two points A and B, the **vector** from A to B is the ordered pair of points (A, B). Point A is the **tail** of the vector and point B is the **head.**

You can write the vector from A to B as $\overrightarrow{AB}$.

Minds in Action   episode 35

Tony has seen vectors before and is a bit confused by this definition.

Tony   Hmm . . . I thought that two vectors with the same size and direction were the same, even with different heads and tails. According to this definition they aren't.

Sasha   If two vectors have the same size and direction, but different heads and tails, they are **equivalent vectors**.

Answers

For You to Do

1. $\overrightarrow{AB}$ and $O(B - A)$, $\overrightarrow{CD}$ and $\overrightarrow{BA}$, $\overrightarrow{OA}$ and $B(A + B)$, $\overrightarrow{OB}$ and $A(A + B)$

2. Each of the vectors $\overrightarrow{AB}$ and $O(B - A)$ has a direction opposite to the direction of each of the vectors $\overrightarrow{CD}$ and $\overrightarrow{BA}$.

3. $\overrightarrow{AB}$, $\overrightarrow{CD}$, $\overrightarrow{BA}$, and $O(B - A)$; $\overrightarrow{OA}$ and $B(A + B)$; $\overrightarrow{OB}$ and $A(A + B)$

4. $\overrightarrow{AB}$, $\overrightarrow{OB}$, and $A(A + B)$; $\overrightarrow{BA}$, $\overrightarrow{OA}$, and $B(A + B)$

5. $\overrightarrow{AB}$, $\overrightarrow{AC}$, and $A(A + B)$; $\overrightarrow{BA}$ and $B(A + B)$; $\overrightarrow{OA}$, $\overrightarrow{OB}$, and $O(B - A)$

For You to Do

Let $A(5, 1)$, $B(-2, 5)$, $C(9, -2)$, and $D(16, -6)$. On a coordinate system, draw each vector.

- $\overrightarrow{AB}$
- $\overrightarrow{CD}$
- $\overrightarrow{AC}$
- $\overrightarrow{BA}$
- $\overrightarrow{OA}$
- $\overrightarrow{OB}$
- $\overrightarrow{B(A + B)}$
- $\overrightarrow{A(A + B)}$
- $\overrightarrow{O(B - A)}$

1. Which vectors that you drew have the same direction?

2. Which have opposite directions?

3. Which have the same size?

4. Which have the same head?

5. Which have the same tail?

$\overrightarrow{B(A + B)}$ means the vector with tail B and head $A + B$.

In-Class Experiment

Suppose you are working on the coordinate plane.

6. If $A(5, 3)$ and $B(8, 7)$, find a vector with tail at the origin and the same size and direction as $\overrightarrow{AB}$.

7. If $A(3, 5)$ and $B(8, 1)$, find two points C and D (neither at the origin) such that the vector from A to B is equivalent to the vector from C to D. Find another point E such that the vector from the origin to E is equivalent to $\overrightarrow{AB}$ and $\overrightarrow{CD}$.

8. Two vectors are shown below. Find a way to tell whether the two vectors are equivalent just by looking at their coordinates (and doing some calculations with them).

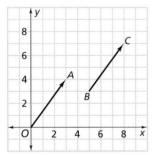

Assessment Resources

Lesson Quiz 7.11

1. Let $A(2, 5)$ and $B(8, 11)$. Find the head of a vector that starts at the origin, has the same direction as $\overrightarrow{AB}$, and is three times as long as $\overrightarrow{AB}$.

2. Let $P(4, 8)$ and $S(7, 14)$. Find the head of a vector that starts at $(5, -3)$ and is equivalent to the vector from P to S.

3. Use the figure.
   a. Name the four vectors shown.
   b. Use the head-minus-tail method to show that $\overrightarrow{A(A + B)}$ is equivalent to $\overrightarrow{OB}$ and that $\overrightarrow{OA}$ is equivalent to $\overrightarrow{B(A + B)}$.

4. Let $J(4, 7)$ and $K(7, 9)$. Calculate head minus tail for $\overrightarrow{JK}$.

Here is a test you can use for deciding whether two vectors are equivalent.

Theorem 7.7 The Head-Minus-Tail Test

Two vectors are equivalent if and only if head minus tail for one vector gives the same result as head minus tail for the other. In symbols: $\overrightarrow{AB}$ is equivalent to $\overrightarrow{CD}$ if and only if $B - A = D - C$.

Proof In general, you can write the coordinates of A, B, C, and D this way.

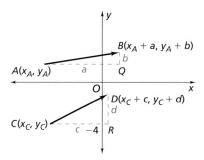

If $\overrightarrow{AB}$ and $\overrightarrow{CD}$ are equivalent, then $\overrightarrow{AB}$ is parallel to and congruent to $\overrightarrow{CD}$. Since the segments are parallel, the lines containing them have the same slope, so

$$\frac{b}{a} = \frac{d}{c}$$

This means that right $\triangle ABQ$ and right $\triangle CDR$ are similar. But the fact that $\overline{AB} \cong \overline{CD}$ implies that the two triangles are congruent. So, in particular, their corresponding legs are congruent.

$$(a, b) = (c, d), \text{ so } B - A = D - C$$

Conversely, if $B - A = D - C$, then $(a, b) = (c, d)$. So the legs of the two right triangles are congruent. This implies that $\overrightarrow{AB} \parallel \overrightarrow{CD}$ and that they have the same orientation. It also means that $AB = \sqrt{a^2 + b^2} = \sqrt{c^2 + d^2} = CD$. As a corollary, you have the following.

Corollary 7.7.1

If A and B are points, the vector from O to $B - A$ is equivalent to the vector from A to B.

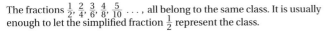

Look for relationships. To think about a class of equivalent objects, it is often enough to think of only one member of the class. Fractions provide a good example.

The fractions $\frac{1}{2}, \frac{2}{4}, \frac{3}{6}, \frac{4}{8}, \frac{5}{10} \ldots$, all belong to the same class. It is usually enough to let the simplified fraction $\frac{1}{2}$ represent the class.

Vectors provide another example. Because of Corollary 7.7.1, any vector in the coordinate plane is equivalent to a vector with its tail at the origin. So, you can think of any vector with its tail at the origin as a representative of a whole class of equivalent vectors. If you think of it this way, the collection of all vectors with tails at the origin represents all the vectors in the coordinate plane!

Twenty-two vectors are shown here. How many classes of equivalent vectors are there?

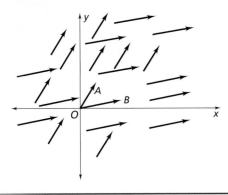

Corollary 7.7.1 lets you identify any vector with a point in the coordinate plane. Think of point A as $\overrightarrow{OA}$, for example. To add vectors, you add points as you did in the Getting Started lesson. Vectors, however, give this addition a geometric flavor. If A and B are points (and vectors), how can you locate $A + B$ using geometry?

Vectors must have the same direction and magnitude to be equivalent.

- For each pair of points *A* and *B* given below, plot the following four points: the origin *O*, *A*, *B*, and the sum *A* + *B*.

- Describe how *A* + *B* is located with respect to the other three points.

- Draw segments connecting *O* to *A* and *B*. Draw segments connecting *A* + *B* to *A* and *B*. What kind of figure do you get in each case?

9. $A(-3, 5)$, $B(5, 1)$

10. $A(2, 3)$, $B(5, 1)$

11. $A(-2, -2)$, $B(0, 6)$

12. $A(-3, 3)$, $B(5, -5)$

13. $A(-3, 5)$, $B2(5, 1)$

14. $A(-3, 5)$, $B\frac{1}{2}(5, 1)$

The In-Class Experiment suggests a theorem.

Theorem 7.8

If $A = (a_1, a_2)$ and $B = (b_1, b_2)$, then $A + B$ is the fourth vertex of the parallelogram that has *A*, *O*, and *B* as three of its vertices and $\overline{OA}$ and $\overline{OB}$ as two of its sides.

Habits of Mind

Use your own words. State the theorem in a way that makes the most sense for you.

Basically, you want to show that the quadrilateral with vertices *O*, *A*, *A* + *B*, and *B* is a parallelogram. One strategy is to show that the opposite sides are parallel.

Let $A = (a_1, a_2)$ and $B = (b_1, b_2)$.

Let $P = A + B = (a_1 + b_1, a_2 + b_2)$.

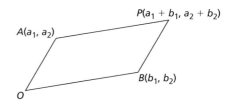

For You to Do

15. Prove that $\overline{OA}$ is parallel to $\overline{BP}$ and that $\overline{OB}$ is parallel to $\overline{AP}$.

16. Does Theorem 7.8 hold if *O*, *A*, and *B* are collinear? For example, where is the parallelogram if $A(9, -1)$ and $B(18, -2)$?

Identifying vectors with points in the coordinate plane also gives the scaling of points a geometric flavor.

Answers

In-Class Experiment

For Problems 9–11, 13, and 14, points *O*, *A*, *B*, and *A* + *B* are the vertices of a parallelogram. For Problem 12, these points are collinear.

9–14. See back of book.

For You to Do

15. We can assume *O*, *A*, and *B* are noncollinear.

CASE 1 Suppose $\overline{OA}$ is vertical. Then $a_1 = 0$, and hence $P = (0 + b_1, a_2 + b_2) = (b_1, a_2 + b_2)$. Also, $\overline{OB}$ is not vertical, since *O*, *A*, and *B* are noncollinear. This implies that $b_1 \neq 0$. It follows that $\overline{BP}$ is vertical (the *x*-coordinates of the endpoints are equal) and thus that $\overline{OA}$ and $\overline{BP}$ are parallel. $\overline{AP}$ and $\overline{OB}$ are parallel since each has slope $\frac{b_2}{b_1}$. Therefore, *OAPB* is a parallelogram.

Theorem 7.9

Suppose A is a point, c is a number greater than or equal to 1, and $B = cA$. Then,

- B is collinear with A and the origin.
- B is c times as far from the origin as A.

For $c > 1$, part 2 of the theorem implies that A is between O and B.

For You to Do

For each point A and value c given below, let $B = cA$. Then, show that the two statements in Theorem 7.9 are true. That is, show

a. $OA + AB = OB$
b. $OB = cOA$

17. $A(3, 4)$, $c = 3$
18. $A(-5, 12)$, $c = 2$

19. $A(6, 8)$, $c = 1.5$
20. $A(3, 8)$, $c = 4$

Exercises *Practicing Habits of Mind*

Check Your Understanding

1. Let $A(5, 3)$ and $B(8, 7)$. Find a vector that starts at the origin, has the same direction as $\overrightarrow{AB}$, and is twice as long as $\overrightarrow{AB}$.

2. Let $R(7, 2)$ and $S(15, 6)$. Find the head of a vector that starts at $(4, -3)$ and is equivalent to the vector from R to S.

3. True or false: If A and B are any points, the vector from O to B is equivalent to the vector from A to $A + B$. Explain.

4. Let $A(8, 15)$, $B(-4, 3)$, and $P = A + B$. Draw a picture of O, A, B, and P. Show that $OA = BP$ and $OB = AP$.

5. Let $A(8, 6)$, $B(3, 1)$, and $P = A + B$. Draw a picture of O, A, B, and P. Show that $OA = BP$ and $OB = AP$.

6. For $A(3, 2)$ and $P(4, 5)$, locate each of the following.

a. $P + A$
b. $P + 2A$
c. $P + 3A$
d. $P + 4A$

e. $P + \frac{1}{2}A$
f. $P + \frac{1}{3}A$
g. $P + \frac{1}{4}A$

CASE 2 Suppose $\overline{OB}$ is vertical. An argument similar to that for Case 1 shows that again $OAPB$ is a parallelogram.

CASE 3 If neither $\overline{OA}$ nor $\overline{OB}$ is vertical, then $a_1 \neq 0$ and $b_1 \neq 0$. Since $\overline{OA}$ and $\overline{BP}$ both have slope $\frac{a_2}{a_1}$, they are parallel. Since $\overline{OB}$ and $\overline{AP}$ both have slope $\frac{b_2}{b_1}$, they are parallel. Therefore, $OAPB$ is a parallelogram.

16. No; the points O, A, B, and P are collinear, so $OAPB$ is not a parallelogram.

For You to Do

17–20. See back of book.

Exercises

1. $\overrightarrow{OA}$, with $O = (0, 0)$ and $A = (6, 8)$

2. $(12, 1)$

3–6. See back of book.

Check Your Understanding

EXERCISES 1–5 give students a chance to practice finding equivalent vectors and understanding vector notation.

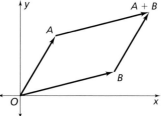

On Your Own

7. Here is a pair of fancy sentences: $\overrightarrow{A(A + B)}$ is equivalent to $\overrightarrow{OB}$, and $\overrightarrow{O(A + B)}$ is one diagonal of the parallelogram with vertices O, A, $A + B$, and B. Also, $\overrightarrow{OA}$ is equivalent to $\overrightarrow{B(A + B)}$.

   Copy the figure shown here. Label the five vectors that are mentioned in the sentences above. Use $A(3, 5)$ and $B(8, 2)$ to show that $\overrightarrow{A(A + B)}$ is equivalent to $\overrightarrow{OB}$. Also, show that $\overrightarrow{OA}$ is equivalent to $\overrightarrow{B(A + B)}$. Use the head-minus-tail method.

8. Suppose T is the function that maps a point X to the point $X + (10, 5)$. Pick two points A and B. Draw the vectors from A to $T(A)$ and from B to $T(B)$. Show that these vectors are equivalent.

9. For $A(3, 4)$, $B(5, -12)$, and $P = A + B$, draw a picture of O, A, B, and P. Show that $OA = BP$ and $OB = AP$.

10. Let A, B, and C be any three points. Show that the quadrilateral with vertices B, C, $C + A$, and $B + A$ is a parallelogram by showing that opposite sides are congruent. Draw a picture.

   Corollary 7.7.1 says that $\overrightarrow{AB}$ is equivalent to the vector from O to $B - A$. Some people think of this as moving $\overrightarrow{AB}$ so its tail is at the origin. They say, "To move $\overrightarrow{AB}$ to the origin, just draw the vector from O to $B - A$."

   Other people say it this way: "To move a vector to the origin, just subtract the tail from the head." The next exercises show you how you can apply this technique to the geometry of vectors.

11. Point A has coordinates $(1, 6)$. Point B has coordinates $(7, 8)$.

   a. Calculate head minus tail for $\overrightarrow{AB}$. Draw a diagram that shows both $\overrightarrow{AB}$ and $\overrightarrow{O(A + B)}$. You have moved $\overrightarrow{AB}$ to the origin.

   b. Now take the vector anchored at the origin. Move it to $P(3, -2)$ by adding P to the head and to the tail. Draw this new vector. What are the coordinates of its head and tail?

12. Prove the following theorem.

Theorem 7.10

Adding the same point to the tail and to the head of a vector produces an equivalent vector.

Remember...

This means that, for example, $T((4, 2)) = (4, 2) + (10, 5) = (14, 7)$.

Habits of Mind

Check the theorem. Use specific values to test this generalization. Draw a picture in the coordinate plane.

Answers

7. For $A(\overrightarrow{A + B})$, $(A + B) - A = (11, 7) - (3, 5) = (8, 2)$.

   For $\overrightarrow{OB}$, $B - O = (8, 2) - (0, 0) = (8, 2)$.

   So $A(\overrightarrow{A + B})$ is equivalent to $\overrightarrow{OB}$. For $\overrightarrow{OA}$, $A - O = (3, 5) - (0, 0) = (3, 5)$.

   For $B(\overrightarrow{A + B})$, $(A + B) - B = (11, 7) - (8, 2) = (3, 5)$. So $\overrightarrow{OA}$ is equivalent to $B(\overrightarrow{A + B})$.

8. The points chosen for A and B may vary. Check students' diagrams; regardless of the choices for A and B, $T(A) - A = (10, 5)$ and $T(B) - B = (10, 5)$. Therefore, by the Head Minus Tail Test, $A\overrightarrow{T(A)}$ is equivalent to $B\overrightarrow{T(B)}$.

9–14. See back of book.

15. $\frac{1}{3}B + \frac{2}{3}A$; the point $\frac{1}{3}$ of the way from A to B is $A + \frac{1}{3}(B - A)$. Simplify $A + \frac{1}{3}(B - A)$ to obtain $\frac{1}{3}B + \frac{2}{3}A$.

13. Show that if A and B are points, the midpoint of $\overline{AB}$ is $\frac{1}{2}(A + B)$.

14. Mathematical convention usually assigns

- capital-letter names to points
- lowercase names early in the alphabet to constants (numbers you know)
- lowercase names late in the alphabet to variables or unknowns (numbers you do not know yet, or numbers that can vary)

In the expressions below, A, B, C, X, Y, and Z are names of points. O is the name of a special point, the origin. The letters c, k, and x are names for numbers. Classify each expression as a *point*, a *number*, or just plain *meaningless*.

a. cB **b.** $c + A$ **c.** AB **d.** $c(AB)$ **e.** $k(OA)$

f. $A(BC)$ **g.** xX **h.** XX **i.** Bc **j.** $A + B$

k. $c(A + B)$ **l.** $A(c + B)$ **m.** cZ **n.** $c(XY)$ **o.** $c(X + Y)$

p. $A(X + Y)$ **q.** AX **r.** $X + Y$ **s.** $M(C + X)$

15. Given two points A and B, how can you find a point that is on $\overleftrightarrow{AB}$ and one third of the way from A to B? Explain.

16. **Standardized Test Prep** Equivalent vectors have the same magnitude and direction. Which vector is equivalent to $\overrightarrow{EF}$? (Point O is the origin.)

A. $\overrightarrow{FE}$ **B.** $\frac{1}{2}\overrightarrow{O(E + F)}$ **C.** $\overrightarrow{O(E - F)}$ **D.** $\overrightarrow{O(F - E)}$

17. Suppose A, B, C, and D are the vertices of a quadrilateral.

a. Express the midpoints of the sides of the quadrilateral in terms of A, B, C, and D.

b. Show that the quadrilateral formed by joining the midpoints from part (a) is a parallelogram.

Maintain Your Skills

18. Use $\overrightarrow{AB}$ from Exercise 11. Find (and draw) vectors equivalent to $\overrightarrow{AB}$ with the following properties.

a. tail at $C(8, 3)$ **b.** tail at $J(-8, 3)$

c. tail at $K(0, 3)$ **d.** head at O

e. head at $C(8, 3)$ **f.** tail at B

19. Suppose $A(3, 4)$, $B(9, 0)$, $C(-1, 2)$, and $D(5, -2)$. Show that $\overrightarrow{AB}$ is equivalent to $\overrightarrow{CD}$ by moving both vectors to the origin. Show also that $\overrightarrow{AC}$ is equivalent to $\overrightarrow{BD}$.

Go Online
Video Tutor
PHSchool.com

Web Code: bee-0711

Go Online
PHSchool.com

For additional practice, go to **Web Code: bea-0711**

Additional Practice

1. Let $A(4, 6)$ and $B(9, 11)$. Find the head of a vector that starts at the origin, has the same direction as $\overrightarrow{AB}$, and is three times as long as $\overrightarrow{AB}$.

2. Let $P(2, 5)$ and $S(6, 9)$. Find the head of a vector that starts at $(3, -2)$ and is equivalent to the vector from P to S.

3. Decide whether each statement is *true* or *false*.
  a. $\overrightarrow{AB}$ and $\overrightarrow{CD}$ are congruent vectors if they have the same direction and length.
  b. $\overrightarrow{AB}$ is equivalent to $\overrightarrow{CD}$ if and only if $B - A = D - C$.

4. Let $J(3, 4)$, $K(5, 1)$, and $L = J + K$. Draw a picture of O, J, K, and L. Show that $OJ = KL$ and $OK = JL$.

5. For $T(4, 5)$ and $R(5, 8)$, locate each of the following.
  a. $T + R$ **b.** $T + 2R$ **c.** $T + 3R$
  d. $T + \frac{1}{2}R$ **e.** $T + \frac{1}{3}R$

6. Use the figure.
  a. Name the four vectors shown.
  b. Use the head-minus-tail method to show that $\overrightarrow{A(A + B)}$ is equivalent to $\overrightarrow{OB}$ and that $\overrightarrow{OA}$ is equivalent to $\overrightarrow{B(A + B)}$.

7. Let $J(1, 9)$ and $K(4, 12)$.
  a. Calculate head minus tail for $\overrightarrow{JK}$.
  b. Take $\overrightarrow{JK}$ anchored at the origin. Move it to $L(4, -3)$ by adding L to the head and to the tail. What are the coordinates of its new head and tail?

8. In the expressions below, capital letters are points, c, k, and x are constants, and O represents the origin. Classify each expression as a *point*, a *number*, or just plain *meaningless*.
  a. xA **b.** cO **c.** $A + C$
  d. $cB + A$ **e.** AD **f.** $kB - A$
  g. $x(GH)$ **h.** $B(k - A)$ **i.** $A(B - C)$
  j. $k(CD)$ **k.** $kX + cH$ **l.** $V(D + C)$

Practice: For Lesson 7.11, assign Exercises 1–8.

---

16. D

17. a. $\dfrac{A + B}{2}$, $\dfrac{B + C}{2}$, $\dfrac{C + D}{2}$, and $\dfrac{A + D}{2}$

b. The segment with endpoints $\dfrac{A + B}{2}$ and $\dfrac{B + C}{2}$ is parallel to and has the same length as the segment with endpoints $\dfrac{A + D}{2}$ and $\dfrac{C + D}{2}$ since $\dfrac{B + C}{2} - \dfrac{A + B}{2} = \dfrac{C - A}{2} = \dfrac{C + D}{2} - \dfrac{A + D}{2}$. Therefore, the midpoint quadrilateral is a parallelogram.

18. a. the vector from $(8, 3)$ to $(14, 5)$
b. the vector from $(-8, 3)$ to $(-2, 5)$
c. the vector from $(0, 3)$ to $(6, 5)$
d. the vector from $(-6, -2)$ to $(0, 0)$
e. the vector from $(2, 1)$ to $(8, 3)$
f. the vector from $(7, 8)$ to $(13, 10)$

19. $\overrightarrow{AB}$ and $\overrightarrow{CD}$ are equivalent to the vector from O to $(6, -4)$ and hence are equivalent to each other. $\overrightarrow{AC}$ and $\overrightarrow{BD}$ are equivalent to the vector from O to $(-4, -2)$ and hence are equivalent to each other.

Lesson Overview

Theorem 7.11 begins this lesson and summarizes the main results from the previous lesson. Then the Minds in Action dialog has Tony and Sasha work out a way to find the vector equation of a line through two points. If you plan to teach Lesson 7.13, assign the In-Class Experiment and teach Theorem 7.12, both on page 610. Otherwise, you may stop after the first For You to Do section.

Launch

Have students read Theorem 7.11 and act out (or simply read) Minds in Action episode 36. You might also ask your students to summarize the results contained in the dialog.

Explore

For Discussion

Students will need to use part of Theorem 7.9 to prove Theorem 7.12 on page 610.

Wrap Up

End this lesson by assigning some Check Your Understanding exercises.

7.12 The Vector Equation of a Line

Theorem 7.9 in the previous lesson describes points that are on the line containing the vector from the origin to a point A. You can generalize this theorem to describe the line through the origin and A.

Theorem 7.11

If A is a point different from the origin, the set of all multiples of A is the line through the origin and A.

You might remember from Algebra 1 words such as *slope*, *y-intercept*, and *point-slope equation*. These terms had to do with equations of lines. In this lesson, you will revisit these terms and connect them with vectors.

Suppose $A(3, 1)$ and $B(8, -2)$ determine a line conveniently called $\overleftrightarrow{AB}$. How do you know if point $P(13, -5)$ or point $Q(13, -6)$ lies on $\overleftrightarrow{AB}$?

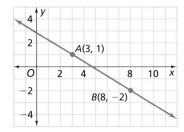

Minds in Action   episode 36

Tony seems perplexed.

Tony   I guess we are going to have to use Theorem 7.11, but I don't have the faintest idea how!

Sasha   Well, what would happen if P were on $\overleftrightarrow{AB}$? If we moved everything to the origin O by subtracting A, then $P - A$ would be on the line through O and $B - A$.

Tony   Stop! You're giving me a headache! Let me try to understand what you are saying with a picture. I calculated $B - A$ in my head, so . . .

Remember...
Sasha is using the technique from Exercise 11a in the previous lesson.

Answers

For You to Do

1. Answers may vary. Sample:
   $X = (3, 5) + k(-4, 10)$; Answers may vary. Sample points are given. Points that satisfy the equation: $(-5, -15)$, $(7, 15)$, and $(11, 25)$; the equation: $(-6, 10)$, $(4, 3)$, and $(11, 26)$

2. Answers may vary. Sample:
   $X = (8, -1) + k(-7, 8)$;
   Answers may vary. Sample points are given. Points that satisfy the equation: $(22, -17)$, $(-13, 23)$, and $(-9.5, 19)$; points that do not satisfy the equation: $(22, -15)$, $(-13, 20)$, and $(-9.5, 20)$

3. Answers may vary. Sample:
   $X = (6, 7) + k(-4, -10)$;
   Answers may vary. Sample points are given. Points that satisfy the equation: $(12, 22)$, $(0, -8)$, and $(-4, -18)$; points that do not satisfy the equation: $(12, 20)$, $(0, -9)$, and $(-4, 18)$

Tony draws a diagram showing his calculations.

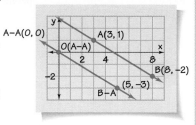

Sasha Good! Do you see it now? $P - A = (10, -6)$. Thanks to Theorem 7.11, we know that the point $P - A$ is on the line through $B - A$ and O only if $(10, -6)$ is a multiple of $(5, -3)$.

Tony And it is! So now we can move everything back and know that P lies on $\overleftrightarrow{AB}$. Hurray!

Sasha Okay, now it's your turn to see if Q is on $\overleftrightarrow{AB}$.

Tony $Q - A = (10, -7)$. I can't find any number k such that $(10, -7) = k(5, -3)$. It looks like Q isn't on $\overleftrightarrow{AB}$, because Theorem 7.11 says that otherwise there would be such a number k.

Sasha Good work, Tony!

So, in general, if a point X is on a line $\overleftrightarrow{AB}$, $X - A$ is a multiple of $B - A$. That is, there is a number k such that $X - A = k(B - A)$. So X lies on $\overleftrightarrow{AB}$ if

$$X = A + k(B - A)$$

This is a vector equation in X and k.

The converse is also true. If $X = A + k(B - A)$ for some number k, then X lies on $\overleftrightarrow{AB}$.

For You to Do

Find a vector equation of the line containing the two given points. Give three more points that satisfy each equation and three that do not.

1. $A(3, 5)$, $B(-1, -5)$

2. $P(8, -1)$, $Q(1, 7)$

3. $R(6, 7)$, $S(2, -3)$

4. $T(3, 5)$, $U(11, 11)$

Assessment Resources

Lesson Quiz 7.12

1. Suppose $A(-2, 3)$, $B(5, 7)$, $C(-6, 2)$, and $D(8, 10)$. Prove that $\overleftrightarrow{AB} \parallel \overleftrightarrow{CD}$.

2. Let $A(5, -3)$ and $B(9, -7)$.
   a. What multiple of $\overrightarrow{AB}$ has its head on the line $y = 3$?
   b. What multiple of $\overrightarrow{AB}$ has its head on the line $x = 6$?

3. For $B(5, 2)$ and $C(2, 4)$, find a vector equation of the line through B and parallel to $\overrightarrow{OC}$.

4. For $A(3, -4)$ and $B(6, 5)$, find C if B is the midpoint of $\overline{AC}$.

---

4. Answers may vary. Sample:
$X = (3, 5) + k(8, 6)$; Answers may vary. Sample points are given. Points that satisfy the equation: $(-21, -13)$, $(27, 23)$, and $(7, 8)$; points that do not satisfy the equation: $(20, -12)$, $(0, 3)$, and $(-1, 5)$

You can describe parallel lines using vectors. This In-Class Experiment will help you gather ideas about parallel vectors.

In-Class Experiment

Here are some vectors.

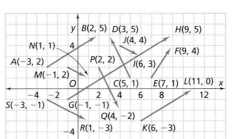

5. Which vectors are parallel?

6. Which are parallel in the same direction?

7. Which are parallel in opposite directions?

8. Which are equivalent?

9. Find a rule that uses head minus tail to tell you when two vectors are
- parallel in the same direction
- parallel in opposite directions

You can summarize the results of the In-Class Experiment in one general theorem.

Theorem 7.12

Two vectors $\vec{AB}$ and $\vec{CD}$ are parallel if and only if there is a number k such that

$$B - A = k(D - C)$$

If $k > 0$, the vectors have the same direction. If $k < 0$, the vectors have opposite directions. If $k = 1$, the vectors are equivalent.

For Discussion

10. Write a proof for Theorem 7.12.

Answers

In-Class Experiment

5. $\vec{AB}$, $\vec{GH}$, and $\vec{KL}$; $\vec{JI}$, $\vec{MN}$, and $\vec{RS}$; $\vec{CD}$ and $\vec{PQ}$

6. $\vec{AB}$, $\vec{GH}$, and $\vec{KL}$; $\vec{JI}$ and $\vec{MN}$

7. $\vec{JI}$ and $\vec{RS}$, $\vec{MN}$ and $\vec{RS}$, $\vec{CD}$ and $\vec{PQ}$

8. $\vec{AB}$ and $\vec{KL}$, $\vec{JI}$ and $\vec{MN}$

9. See Theorem 7.12.

For Discussion

10. Suppose $\vec{AB}$ and $\vec{CD}$ are parallel. By Corollary 7.1, the vectors are equivalent to $\vec{O(B - A)}$ and $\vec{O(D - C)}$, respectively. Since $\vec{O(B - A)}$ and $\vec{O(D - C)}$ both have the same slope or are both vertical, it follows that $D - C$ is on the ray that has endpoint O and passes through $B - A$. This means that $B - A$ is the dilation image of $D - C$ for a dilation that has center O. If the scale factor

For You to Do

11. Now prove the following theorem.

Theorem 7.13

If A and B are points, then the segment from O to $B - A$ is parallel and congruent to $\overline{AB}$.

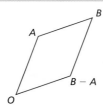

Exercises *Practicing Habits of Mind*

Check Your Understanding

1. Suppose $A(4, 1)$, $B(9, 5)$, $C(3, -1)$, and $D(13, 7)$. Prove that $\overleftrightarrow{AB} \parallel \overleftrightarrow{CD}$.

2. Show that if P and A are points and t is a number, the segment from P to $P + tA$ is parallel to the segment from O to A.

> For Exercise 2, refer to Exercise 6 from Lesson 7.10.

3. For $A(4, 4)$ and $B(8, -4)$, look at $\triangle OAB$. Let M be the midpoint of $\overline{OA}$ and N be the midpoint of $\overline{OB}$. Show that $\overline{MN} \parallel \overline{AB}$ and $MN = \frac{1}{2} AB$.

4. Show that Theorem 7.13 holds for $A(3, 5)$ and $B(7, 9)$.

> Exercise 3 shows a special case of the Midline Theorem.

On Your Own

5. Let $A(-1, 3)$ and $B(2, 6)$.

  a. What multiple of $\overrightarrow{AB}$ has its head on the line $y = 2$?

  b. What multiple of $\overrightarrow{AB}$ has its head on the line $x = -3$?

6. For $A(3, 2)$, $B(-4, 5)$, and $C(7, 4)$, show that $\triangle ABC \cong \triangle O(B - A)(C - A)$. Draw a picture.

---

is k, then $B - A = k(D - C)$. A positive value for k indicates that $\overrightarrow{AB}$ and $\overrightarrow{CD}$ have the same direction, and a negative value for k indicates that the vectors have opposite directions. In the special case $k = 1$, the vectors are equivalent (Theorem 7.7).

This argument can easily be reversed to show that if $B - A = k(D - C)$ for some nonzero number k, then $\overrightarrow{AB}$ and $\overrightarrow{CD}$ are parallel.

For You to Do

11. Theorem 7.13 follows immediately from Corollary 7.1 and the definition of equivalent vectors.

Exercises

1–6. See back of book.

Exercises

HOMEWORK
- Core: 5, 8, 10, 11, 12
- Optional: 6, 7, 9, 13, 14, 15, 16

Check Your Understanding

EXERCISE 4 Showing that a theorem holds in a specific numerical case can help students understand the statement of a theorem in a more concrete way. They can better see what the theorem means and in which situations the theorem may be helpful.

On Your Own

EXERCISES 6 AND 7 In Exercise 6, students work through a numerical exercise. In Exercise 7, they generalize their results from Exercise 6 to cover any three points. The steps they take in the numerical exercise give them a model to follow when they prove the general result.

EXERCISES 13 AND 14 Proving familiar theorems in a vector context helps students remember the theorems they know and, perhaps, learn something new about them as they deepen their understanding of vectors.

Maintain Your Skills

EXERCISES 15 AND 16 You can assign these two exercises separately.

Continued on page 612

continued from p. 611

In Exercise 15, some students may want to move straight to the general result rather than working each specific example, while others may find the practice with the specific examples necessary in order to write the proof of the general case.

For Exercise 16, encourage students to look at the task graphically. The goal is to approach the target point using steps that are multiples of the two given vectors. In the figure below, (5, 6) is the target point.

You can see two "$\overrightarrow{OA}$ steps" and one "$\overrightarrow{OB}$ step."

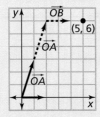

One more half step with $\overrightarrow{OB}$ and you are at (5, 6) using visualization rather than extensive calculations.

Additional Resources

PRINTED RESOURCES
- Texas Instruments Activities Workbook
- Cabrilog Activities
- Teaching Resources
- Practice Workbook
- Assessment Resources

TECHNOLOGY
- TeacherExpress CD-ROM
- **Exam**View CD-ROM
- PHSchool.com
  - Homework Help
  - Video Tutors
  - Multiple Choice
  - Crosswords

Additional Practice

1. Suppose $A(5, 6)$, $B(7, 9)$, $C(4, 6)$, and $D(8, 12)$. Prove that $\overrightarrow{AB} \parallel \overrightarrow{CD}$.

2. Let $A(4, 6)$ and $B(5, -3)$.
   a. Draw $\triangle OAB$.
   b. Find and label the coordinates of M, the midpoint of $\overrightarrow{OA}$, and N, the midpoint of $\overrightarrow{OB}$.
   c. Show that $\overrightarrow{MN} \parallel \overrightarrow{AB}$ and $MN = \frac{1}{2}AB$.

3. Let $A(-2, 5)$ and $B(4, 9)$.
   a. What multiple of $\overrightarrow{AB}$ has its head on the line $y = 4$?
   b. What multiple of $\overrightarrow{AB}$ has its head on the line $x = -1$?

4. Use the graph of point B and $\overrightarrow{OC}$. Find a vector equation of the line through B and parallel to $\overrightarrow{OC}$.

5. For $A(7, 10)$ and $B(4, 13)$, find C if B is the midpoint of $\overrightarrow{AC}$.

6. What point on $\overrightarrow{AB}$ is $\frac{2}{3}$ of the way from A to B?

7. a. Plot points $A(5, 2)$, $B(3, 6)$, and $C(8, 4)$ on the coordinate plane and connect them to form $\triangle ABC$.
   b. Translate $\triangle ABC$ to the origin by subtracting A from each vertex. Call the new vertices A_0 (origin), B_0, and C_0. Find midpoints M, N, and K of sides $\overline{A_0B_0}$, $\overline{B_0C_0}$, and $\overline{A_0C_0}$, respectively.
   c. Write vector equations for $\overrightarrow{A_0N}$ and $\overrightarrow{B_0K}$. Do these lines intersect? If so, find the point of intersection.

8. Given $A(-5, 12)$, how can you find the coordinates of a point B, such that $\overrightarrow{OA} \perp \overrightarrow{OB}$?

9. Find a vector equation of a line through $A(3, 5)$ and perpendicular to $\overrightarrow{OA}$.

Practice: For Lesson 7.12, assign Exercises 1–6.

---

7. Show that if A, B, and C are any three points, $\triangle ABC \cong \triangle O(B - A)(C - A)$.

8. The coordinates of P and A are given in the figure. Find a vector equation of the line through P and parallel to $\overrightarrow{OA}$.

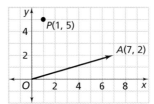

9. Show that the point $\frac{2}{3}A + \frac{1}{3}B$ is on $\overrightarrow{AB}$ $\frac{1}{3}$ of the way from A to B.

10. What point is on $\overrightarrow{AB}$ $\frac{1}{4}$ of the way from A to B?

11. For $A(3, 5)$ and $B(7, 1)$, find C if B is the midpoint of $\overline{AC}$.

12. **Standardized Test Prep** Points G and H have coordinates $(1, 3)$ and $(6, 5)$, respectively. Which point is NOT on $\overleftrightarrow{GH}$?
    A. $J(-4, 1)$ B. $K(-9, -1)$
    C. $L(0, 2.6)$ D. $M(-6, 0)$

13. Find vector equations of the three medians of $\triangle ABC$ with vertices $A(-1, 5)$, $B(5, -2)$, and $C(3, 5)$.

> What points of $\triangle ABC$ lie on its medians?

14. In the coordinate plane, draw $\triangle AOB$ with vertices $A(3, 6)$, $B(8, 1)$, and O, the origin. Find the midpoint M of $\overline{OA}$ and N of $\overline{OB}$. Prove that $\overline{MN}$ is parallel to $\overline{AB}$ and that the size of $\overline{MN}$ is half the size of $\overline{AB}$.

Maintain Your Skills

15. Suppose A and B are points. Using vectors, explain how to locate each point.
    a. $\frac{1}{3}A + \frac{2}{3}B$ b. $\frac{2}{3}A + \frac{1}{3}B$
    c. $\frac{1}{4}A + \frac{3}{4}B$ d. $\frac{3}{4}A + \frac{1}{4}B$
    e. $\frac{3}{5}A + \frac{2}{5}B$ f. $kA + (1 - k)B$ for $0 \leq k \leq 1$

16. The head of $\overrightarrow{OA}$ is $(1, 3)$. The head of $\overrightarrow{OB}$ is $(2, 0)$.
    Find x and y such that $x\overrightarrow{OA} + y\overrightarrow{OB}$ equals each of the following.
    a. $(2, 1)$ b. $(4, 3)$ c. $(11, 1)$
    d. $(5, 6)$ e. $(0, 8)$ f. $(1, -10)$

Habits of Mind

Visualize. Draw the two vectors on graph paper. For each point, sketch how you could get from the origin to that point if you could travel only in the directions allowed by the two vectors.

Answers

7. Note that if you translate each of the noncollinear points A, B, and C using the distance and direction indicated by $\overrightarrow{AO}$, you get the points O, $B - A$, and $C - A$, respectively. Since translations preserve distance, $\triangle ABC \cong \triangle O(B - C)(C - A)$.

8. $X = (1, 5) + t(7, 2)$

9. The point $\frac{1}{3}$ of the way from A to B is $A + \frac{1}{3}(B - A)$. Simplify $A + \frac{1}{3}(B - A)$ to obtain $\frac{1}{3}B + \frac{2}{3}A$.

10. $\frac{1}{4}B + \frac{3}{4}A$

11. $C = (11, -3)$

12. D

13–16. See back of book.

Using the Vector Equation of a Line

In this lesson, you use vector equations of lines to find the point of intersection of two lines, when it exists. You also learn how to tell whether a point of intersection exists just by looking at the equations of the lines. Then you will see how to prove that the medians of a triangle are concurrent by using vector equations of lines.

In-Class Experiment

Use point $A(1, 2)$, point $B(-2, 6)$, and the origin O.

1. Plot line ℓ with equation $P = A + p(-3, 4)$ and line s with equation $Q = B + q(1, 1)$.

2. Explain how you can find the point of intersection of ℓ and s. Then find it.

3. Now plot the line r with equation $T = O + m(1, 1)$. Can you find the point of intersection for ℓ and r? The point of intersection for s and r?

4. Plot line t with equation $H = (3, 5) + v(4, 4)$. Can you find the point of intersection for ℓ and t? For s and t? For r and t? Make conjectures about when it is possible to find the point of intersection and when it is not. Can you tell by simply looking at the vector equation?

For Discussion

5. Discuss with your class your results to the In-Class Experiment above. Write a summary of what you discovered in your notebook.

Answers

In-Class Experiment

The figure shows the lines for Problems 1, 3, and 4.

1. See back of book.

2. Answers may vary. Sample: Write the equations for ℓ and s as $P = (1, 2) + p(-3, 4)$ and $Q = (-2, 6) + q(1, 1)$, respectively. Rewrite these as $P = (1 - 3p, 2 + 4p)$ and $Q = (-2 + q, 6 + q)$ Set the x-coordinates equal and the y-coordinates equal to get a system of two equations in two variables:

$$1 - 3p = -2 + q$$
$$2 + 4p = 6 + q$$

Solve the system to get $p = 1$, $q = 0$. Substitute either of these values in the appropriate vector equation to find the point of intersection.

3. Lines ℓ and r intersect at $\left(\frac{10}{7}, \frac{10}{7}\right)$. Lines s and r do not intersect.

4. See back of book.

Lesson Overview

GOALS

- Work with vectors.
- Write a vector equation for any line in the coordinate plane.

This lesson is a continuation of Lesson 7.12. It includes an explanation of how to find the point of intersection (if one exists) of two lines with equations in vector-equation form.

CHECK YOUR UNDERSTANDING	HOMEWORK
• Core: 1, 2	• Core: 5, 6, 8, 9
• Optional: 3, 4	• Optional: 7, 10, 11, 12, 13, 14

MATERIALS
- straightedges

Launch

Begin this lesson by assigning the In-Class Experiment.

Explore

Use the For Discussion Section to summarize the results of the In-Class Experiment. Then present For You to Do Problem 6 and go over the Example, both on the following page.

Wrap Up

Assign and go over Check Your Understanding Exercises 1 and 2. Then assign Exercises 3 and 4 if there is time.

Assessment Resources

Lesson Quiz 7.13

1. Given $A(-2, 6)$, how can you find the coordinates of a point B, such that $\overline{OA} \perp \overline{OB}$?

2. Find a vector equation of a line through $A(4, 8)$ and perpendicular to $\overrightarrow{OA}$.

3. a. Plot points $A(1, 2)$, $B(2, 5)$, $C(6, 5)$, and $D(5, 2)$ on the coordinate plane.
   b. Translate the figure to the origin by subtracting A from each vertex. Label the new vertices A_0, B_0, C_0, and D_0.
   c. Write vector equations for the two diagonals of $A_0B_0C_0D_0$.
   d. Do these diagonals intersect? If so, find the point of intersection.

6. **What's Wrong Here?** Tony tried to solve the following problem, but got an inconsistent answer. Help him find his mistake.

Problem Write a vector equation of the line through $A(-1, 4)$ and $B(2, 6)$. Also, write a vector equation of the line through $C\left(\frac{1}{2}, 3\right)$ and $D(5, -1)$. Do the two lines intersect? If they do, find the point of intersection.

Solution Since $\overrightarrow{AB} = (2 - (-1), 6 - 4) = (3, 2)$, $\overrightarrow{CD} = \left(5 - \frac{1}{2}, -1 - 3\right) = \left(\frac{9}{2}, -4\right)$ and for any k

$$(3, 2) \neq k\left(\frac{9}{2}, -4\right)$$

the two lines intersect.

A vector equation for $\overleftrightarrow{AB}$ is

$$P = A + t(B - A)$$
$$P = (-1, 4) + t(3, 2)$$

A vector equation for $\overleftrightarrow{CD}$ is

$$Q = C + t(D - C)$$
$$Q = \left(\frac{1}{2}, 3\right) + t\left(\frac{9}{2}, -4\right)$$

So the value of t that gives the point of intersection can be found by solving the following system of equations.

$$-1 + 3t = \frac{1}{2} + \frac{9}{2}t$$
$$4 + 2t = 3 - 4t$$

The first equation has solution $t = -1$. The second equation has solution $t = -\frac{1}{6}$. This means the system has no solution. But the lines do intersect. What is wrong here?

There is a variation of the point-tester rule from Algebra 1 that works for vector equations of lines.

Example

Problem Does point $P(8, 9)$ lie on the line ℓ with vector equation $Q = (3, 5) + q(1, 2)$?

Solution If P lies on ℓ, then the following two equations would be satisfied for the same value of q.

$$8 = 3 + 1q$$
$$9 = 5 + 2q$$

Why is this the case?

The first equation has solution $q = 5$, but the second equation has solution $q = 2$. Therefore, P does not lie on ℓ.

Answers

For Discussion

5. Check students' work.

For You to Do

6. It is not correct that $(3, 2) = k\left(\frac{9}{2}, -4\right)$ implies that the lines do not intersect. The lines do not intersect, but the pertinent fact is that $\frac{2}{3} \neq \frac{-4}{\frac{9}{2}}$.

When Tony tried to set up a system of equations to find the point of intersection, he should have used t in one of the vector equations but a different variable, say u, in the other vector equation. He needs a system of two equations in two variables.

Exercises

1.

$$A_0 = O = (0, 0), B_0 = O = (2, 1),$$
$$C_0 = (4, 6), M = \left(1, \frac{1}{2}\right),$$
$$N = \left(3, \frac{7}{2}\right), K = (2, 3)$$

Exercises Practicing Habits of Mind

Check Your Understanding

In Chapter 6, you proved that the three medians of a triangle are concurrent and that the point of intersection is $\frac{2}{3}$ of the way from a vertex to the midpoint of the opposite side. You can use vector equations to check it out.

1. Plot points $A(3, 1)$, $B(5, 2)$, and $C(7, 7)$ on the coordinate plane and connect them to form $\triangle ABC$. Translate the triangle to the origin by subtracting A from each vertex. Call the new vertices $A_0 = O$, B_0, and C_0. Find the midpoints M, N, and K of sides $\overline{A_0 B_0}$, $\overline{B_0 C_0}$, and $\overline{C_0 A_0}$, respectively.

> What does translating the triangle to the origin change in the results?

2. Use the figure you drew for Exercise 1 and write vector equations for $\overleftrightarrow{C_0 M}$ and $\overleftrightarrow{B_0 K}$. Do these lines intersect? Explain. If they do, find their point of intersection and label it G_0.

3. Refer to the figure you drew for Exercise 1 and write the vector equation of line $\overleftrightarrow{A_0 N}$. Does G_0 lie on $\overleftrightarrow{A_0 N}$?

4. Refer to Exercises 1–3. What are the values of the parameters in the vector equations of lines $\overleftrightarrow{A_0 N}$, $\overleftrightarrow{B_0 K}$, and $\overleftrightarrow{C_0 M}$ that give point G_0? What does this result mean geometrically?

On Your Own

5. You are given point $A(-3, 4)$. How can you find the coordinates of a point B such that $\overrightarrow{OA}$ is perpendicular to $\overrightarrow{OB}$?

6. Find a vector equation of a line through $A(2, 4)$ and perpendicular to $\overrightarrow{OA}$.

7. Use vectors to show that the diagonals of a parallelogram bisect each other.

> **Habits of Mind**
>
> **Simplify the problem.** Assume that one vertex of the parallelogram is the origin O. If A, O, and B are consecutive vertices, the fourth vertex is $A + B$.

Exercises

HOMEWORK

- Core: 5, 6, 8, 9
- Optional: 7, 10, 11, 12, 13, 14

Check Your Understanding

EXERCISES 1–4 If you assign all four exercises, students will have the opportunity to work through a complete numerical example showing that the medians of a triangle are concurrent and intersect at a point that is $\frac{2}{3}$ of the way along each median.

---

2. For $\overleftrightarrow{C_0 M}$, an equation is
$$P = (4, 6) + t\left(-3, -\frac{11}{2}\right).$$
For $\overleftrightarrow{B_0 K}$, an equation is
$$Q = (2, 1) + k(0, 2).$$ You can see from the equations that $\overleftrightarrow{C_0 M}$ is not vertical, that $\overleftrightarrow{B_0 K}$, is vertical, and hence that the lines must intersect. The point of intersection is $\left(2, \frac{7}{3}\right)$.

3. $F = (0, 0) + q\left(3, \frac{7}{2}\right)$; yes

4. $t = \frac{2}{3}$, $k = \frac{2}{3}$, $q = \frac{2}{3}$; The point of intersection of the medians is two thirds of the way from each vertex to the corresponding midpoint.

5. Answers may vary. Sample: Interchange the coordinates of $(-3, 4)$ to get $(4, -3)$, then change the sign of the second coordinate of $(4, -3)$ to get $(4, 3)$. Use $(4, 3)$ for B.

6–7. See back of book.

Maintain Your Skills

EXERCISES 11–14 Students who work through these four exercises will have a complete numerical example showing that the altitudes of a triangle are concurrent.

Additional Resources

PRINTED RESOURCES
- Texas Instruments Activities Workbook
- Cabrilog Activities
- Teaching Resources
- Practice Workbook
- Assessment Resources

TECHNOLOGY
- TeacherExpress CD-ROM
- **Exam***View* CD-ROM
- **PHSchool.com**
  - Homework Help
  - Video Tutors
  - Multiple Choice
  - Crosswords

Additional Practice

1. Suppose $A(5, 6)$, $B(7, 9)$, $C(4, 6)$, and $D(8, 12)$. Prove that $\overleftrightarrow{AB} \parallel \overleftrightarrow{CD}$.

2. Let $A(4, 6)$ and $B(5, -3)$.
   a. Draw $\triangle OAB$.
   b. Find and label the coordinates of M, the midpoint of $\overline{OA}$, and N, the midpoint of $\overline{OB}$.
   c. Show that $\overline{MN} \parallel \overline{AB}$ and $MN = \frac{1}{2}AB$.

3. Let $A(-2, 5)$ and $B(4, 9)$.
   a. What multiple of $\overrightarrow{AB}$ has its head on the line $y = 4$?
   b. What multiple of $\overrightarrow{AB}$ has its head on the line $x = -1$?

4. Use the graph of point B and $\overrightarrow{OC}$. Find a vector equation of the line through B and parallel to $\overrightarrow{OC}$.

5. For $A(7, 10)$ and $B(4, 13)$, find C if B is the midpoint of $\overline{AC}$.

6. What point on $\overline{AB}$ is $\frac{2}{3}$ of the way from A to B?

7. a. Plot points $A(5, 2)$, $B(3, 6)$, and $C(8, 4)$ on the coordinate plane and connect them to form $\triangle ABC$.
   b. Translate $\triangle ABC$ to the origin by subtracting A from each vertex. Call the new vertices A_o (origin), B_o, and C_o. Find midpoints M, N, and K of sides $\overline{A_oB_o}$, $\overline{B_oC_o}$, and $\overline{A_oC_o}$, respectively.
   c. Write vector equations for $\overleftrightarrow{A_oN}$ and $\overleftrightarrow{B_oK}$. Do these lines intersect? If so, find the point of intersection.

8. Given $A(-5, 12)$, how can you find the coordinates of a point B, such that $\overline{OA} \perp \overline{OB}$?

9. Find a vector equation of a line through $A(3, 5)$ and perpendicular to $\overrightarrow{OA}$.

Practice: For Lesson 7.13, assign Exercises 7–9.

---

8. George has a way to find the population center for three cities of the same size. He puts the cities on a coordinate system, adds the coordinates of the three cities, and scales by $\frac{1}{3}$. In what sense is George's point the population center?

9. Martha extends George's method to allow for cities of different sizes. She first draws coordinates on the map and scales the coordinates of each city by its population. Next she adds the results, and then she divides the resulting point by the sum of the populations of all three cities. In what sense is Martha's point the population center?

10. **Standardized Test Prep** Which point is on the line with vector equation $F = (-2, 3) + r(1, -2)$?
    A. $A(3, -7)$
    B. $B(2, -3)$
    C. $C(-3, 6)$
    D. $D(1, 3)$

Maintain Your Skills

Exercises 11–13 will guide you through a proof of the fact that the three altitudes of a triangle are concurrent. Use $\triangle OAB$, with $A(9, 2)$, $B(1, 8)$, and the origin O.

11. Write vector equations for the lines $\overleftrightarrow{OA}$, $\overleftrightarrow{OB}$, and $\overleftrightarrow{AB}$. Find three vectors, each perpendicular to one of these lines.

12. Write vector equations for the line that contains B and is perpendicular to $\overleftrightarrow{OA}$, the line that contains A and is perpendicular to $\overleftrightarrow{OB}$, and the line that contains O and is perpendicular to $\overleftrightarrow{AB}$. These lines contain the three altitudes of the triangle.

13. Find the intersection point of the altitude through A and the altitude through B. Check to see whether this point lies on the altitude through O.

14. **Write About It** Think about how you proved that both the medians and the altitudes of a triangle are concurrent.
    a. Write general steps you can use to prove that three lines are concurrent.
    b. Prove that the three perpendicular bisectors of a triangle are concurrent. You can use $\triangle OAB$.

Go Online
PHSchool.com

For more information about vectors, go to Web Code: bee-9031

Go Online
PHSchool.com

For additional practice, go to Web Code: bea-0713

Answers

8. A reasonable definition for the "center of population" is to imagine the cities as weights at three points on a uniform board. If we think of each person (in each city) as a weight of equal size, all of these forces balance at the point George describes.

9. Scaling the coordinates amounts to weighting the three cities by their respective populations. Martha's point has the property that it would balance a triangle with these weights at the vertices.

10. B

11. For $\overleftrightarrow{OA}$, an equation is $P = t(9, 2)$. For $\overleftrightarrow{OB}$, an equation is $T = q(1, 8)$. For $\overleftrightarrow{AB}$, an equation is $R = (9, 2) + s(8, -6)$. Sample vectors with tail at O and perpendicular to $\overleftrightarrow{OA}$, $\overleftrightarrow{OB}$, and $\overleftrightarrow{AB}$ are, respectively, $\overline{O(2, -9)}$, $\overline{O(8, -1)}$, and $\overline{O(6, 8)}$.

12–14. See back of book.

In this investigation, you learned how to identify characteristics of vectors, add points and multiply them by any real number, and write a vector equation for any line on the coordinate plane. These questions will help you summarize what you have learned.

1. Let O be the origin, $A(-1, 5)$, and $B(6, 2)$. What are the coordinates of M if $\overrightarrow{OM}$ is equivalent to $\overrightarrow{AB}$?

2. Let $A(-6, 8)$, $B(2, 7)$, $C(-3, 3.5)$, and $D(1, 3)$. Are $\overrightarrow{AB}$ and $\overrightarrow{CD}$ equivalent?

3. Let $A(-2, 1)$, $B(1, 6)$, $C(1, 1)$, and $D(7, 11)$. Compare $\overrightarrow{AB}$ and $\overrightarrow{CD}$.

4. Let $A(-1, -1)$ and $B(2, 3)$. Write coordinates for a point C such that $\overrightarrow{OC}$ is three times as long as $\overrightarrow{AB}$ and parallel to $\overrightarrow{AB}$.

5. Find a vector equation for the line through $A\left(\frac{2}{3}, 1\right)$ and $B(0, 4)$.

6. What are vectors?

7. How can you tell whether two vectors are equivalent?

8. Find a vector equation for the line through $A(1, 2)$ and $B(3, -4)$.

Vocabulary and Notation

In this investigation, you learned these terms and symbols. Make sure you understand what each one means and how to use it.

- direction
- equivalent vectors
- head
- tail
- vector ($\overrightarrow{AB}$)

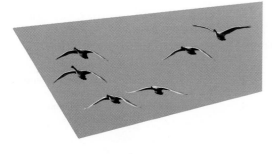

By flying behind and slightly higher than another goose, a goose faces less wind resistance. In this way, it uses less energy to maintain its velocity vector.

Mathematical Reflections

EXERCISES 6–8: At the start of the Investigation, you may have assigned these as Questions 1–3 for students to think and write about.

Mathematical Reflections

1. $(7, -3)$

2. no

3. $\overrightarrow{CD}$ has twice the magnitude of $\overrightarrow{AB}$ and the same direction as $\overrightarrow{AB}$.

4. $(9, 12)$ or $(-9, -12)$

5. $T = \left(\frac{2}{3}, 1\right) + t\left(-\frac{2}{3}, 3\right)$

6. Answers may vary. Sample: A vector is an ordered pair of points.

7. See if Head minus Tail is the same for the two vectors.

8. $X = (1, 2) + k(2, -6)$

Project

Use this project if you want to give your students a broader exposure to analytic geometry. This project will help students write an equation of a circle in the coordinate plane. They will use the equation to find the coordinates of the points of intersection of a line and a circle.

EXERCISE 3 The solution for this exercise involves solving a system of equations. You might want to go through this exercise in class with your students and then assign similar ones, such as Exercise 5, for homework.

EXERCISE 13 asks students to write an equation of a circle with a given center and radius. They can use the technique described in Steps 1 though 3.

Project: Using Mathematical Habits

Equations of Circles

A circle is the set of points that are a fixed distance from one particular point, called the circle's center. You can use equations to represent circles in a coordinate plane, such as the circles below.

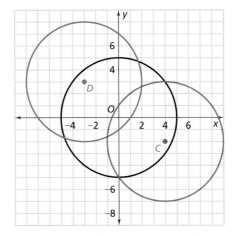

1. How can you tell if a point is on the circle O?

2. Find any points on O that are also on the vertical line through $(4, -9)$.

3. Find the intersection(s) of O with the vertical line through $(3, 2)$.

4. Find any points on O that are also on the horizontal line through $(8, 0)$.

5. Find the intersection(s) of O with the horizontal line through $(8, 3)$.

6. Find any points on O that are 13 units from the origin.

7. Find any points on O that are 11 units from $(0, 16)$.

Circle O is the set of all points (x, y) that are 5 units from the center, the origin $(0, 0)$. You can use the distance formula to write an equation for the circle.

Step 1 Use the distance formula.

$$\sqrt{(x - 0)^2 + (y - 0)^2} = 5$$

Step 2 Square both sides to get rid of the radical.

$$(x - 0)^2 + (y - 0)^2 = 5^2$$

Remember that equations are point testers, so all the points on the circle should satisfy this equation.

Step 3 Simplify.

$$x^2 + y^2 = 5^2, \text{ or } 25$$

Suppose, though, that you want to write an equation for a circle with center somewhere other than the origin. To do that, you have to go back to the distance formula. Consider circle C above, and answer these questions.

8. Find any points on C that are also on the vertical line through $(4, -9)$.

9. Find the intersection(s) of C with the horizontal line through $(8, 3)$.

10. **a.** What point is the center of circle C?

    b. What is the radius of the circle?

    c. Copy and complete the distance formula below to write an equation for circle C. Use the steps above to simplify your equation.

$$\sqrt{(x - \blacksquare)^2 + (y - \blacksquare)^2} = \blacksquare^2$$

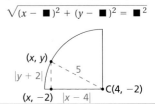

Answers

Project

1. Calculate the distance from the point to the origin to see if it is 5.

2. $(4, 3)$ and $(4, -3)$

3. $(3, 4)$ and $(3, -4)$

4. $(5, 0)$ and $(-5, 0)$

5. $(4, 3)$ and $(-4, 3)$

6. There are no such points.

7. $(0, 5)$

8. $(4, 3)$, $(4, -3)$

9. $(4, 3)$, $(-4, 3)$

10. **a.** $(0, 0)$

    b. 5

    c. $\sqrt{(x - 4)^2 + (y + 2)^2} = r^2$
    $(x - 4)^2 + (y + 2)^2 = 25$
    $x^2 - 8x + 16 + y^2 + 4y + 4 = 25$

Another way to write an equation for circle C is to use a translation.

You can translate circle C left 4 and up 2—a translation of $(-4, 2)$—to move its center to the origin.

Point $P(p_1, p_2)$ on circle C translates to point $P'(p_1 - 4, p_2 + 2)$. This point is a solution to the equation for circle O, $x^2 + y^2 = 25$.

$$x^2 + y^2 = 25, \text{ so}$$

$$(p_1 - 4)^2 + (p_2 + 2)^2 = 25$$

11. Expand and simplify the following equation.

$$(p_1 - 4)^2 + (p_2 + 2)^2 = 25$$

Compare this equation to the equation you wrote for circle C in Problem 10c above.

12. Write an equation for circle D above.

13. Write an equation for a circle with center $(0, 2)$ and radius 3 units.

14. **Take It Further** Consider the equation

$$\frac{x^2}{4} + \frac{y^2}{25} = 1.$$

a. **Write About It** How is the equation similar to the equation of a circle? How is it different?

b. Graph the equation on a coordinate plane. What shape do you have?

If the center axle of this double Ferris wheel is at the origin, equations for the circles would be $(x - a)^2 + (y - b)^2 = r^2$ and $(x + a)^2 + (y + b)^2 = r^2$.

11. $p_1^2 + 8p_1 + 16 + p_2^2 + 4p_2 + 4 = 25$

Equations are the same except for the variables.

12. $(x + 3)^2 + (y - 3)^2 = 25$

13. $x^2 + (y - 2)^2 = 9$

14. a. Answers may vary. Sample: The equations are the same since they each have an x^2 term, a y^2 term equal to a square number. The equations are different because the coefficients are fractions.

b.

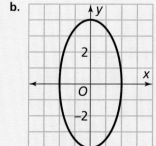

ellipse

Go Online
PHSchool.com

For vocabulary review, go to **Web Code: bej-0751**

In **Investigation 7A,** you learned to

- use multiple methods for reflecting a figure over a line
- rotate a figure on the plane given a center and angle of rotation
- apply transformations to figures and the graphs of functions in the coordinate plane

The following questions will help you check your understanding.

1. Graph the line with equation $2x + y = 4$ Write an equation for its image after a reflection over the x-axis.

2. The point $Q'(-1, -3)$ is the reflection image of point $Q(3, 1)$. What is the reflection line? Explain how you know.

3. Copy the figure below. Draw its lines of symmetry.

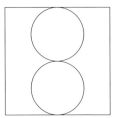

4. Copy the figure below. Draw the image of $\triangle ABC$ after a rotation of $70°$ around O in the counterclockwise direction.

In **Investigation 7B,** you learned to

- plot points in two and three dimensions
- calculate the coordinates of the midpoint of the segment and find the length of the segment given the coordinates of its endpoints
- write equations of lines with given characteristics
- prove whether three points are collinear

Answers

Chapter Review

1. $2x - y = 4$

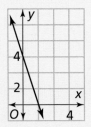

2. $y = -x$

3. See back of book.

4.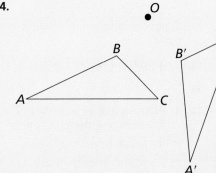

The following questions will help you check your understanding.

5. Find the length and the coordinates of the midpoint of $\overline{AB}$ where $A(-1, 1)$ and $B(3, 4)$

6. Find the midpoint of the line segment with endpoints $(-2.5, 3.1)$ and $(6.7, -3.3)$.

7. Are the three points collinear?

   a. $\left(2, \frac{1}{2}\right)$, $\left(0, \frac{3}{2}\right)$, $(1, 1)$
   b. $(0, 5)$, $(1, 12)$, $(-1, 1)$
   c. $(-7, 20)$, $(7, 6)$, $(3, 10)$

8. Quadrilateral $ABCD$ has coordinates $A(-3, -3)$, $B(4, -1)$, $C(3, 7)$, and $D(-1, 1)$. Find the coordinates of the midpoints of each side of the quadrilateral. Prove that these four points form a parallelogram.

9. Are the lines with equations $4x - 6y = 24$ and $4x + 6y = 24$ parallel? Explain.

10. Write an equation of the line through $P(5, 6)$ and perpendicular to the line through $A(-3, 4)$ and $B(4, -2)$.

11. What is the slope of all lines perpendicular to the line with equation $3x + 7y = 42$?

12. Plot points $A(3, 4, 5)$ and $B(0, 1, -6)$ on a three-dimensional coordinate system. Calculate the length of $\overline{AB}$.

In **Investigation 7C,** you learned to

- identify characteristics of vectors
- add points and multiply them by any real number, and write the results both algebraically and geometrically
- write a vector equation for any line on the coordinate plane

The following questions will help you check your understanding.

13. Let $A(4, 5)$ and $B(-3, 8)$. Point O is the origin. What are the coordinates of the tail of $O(A + B)$?

14. Answer the following questions for $\overline{AB}$ and $\overline{CD}$ in parts (a)–(c) below.

    - Are $\overline{AB}$ and $\overline{CD}$ parallel?
    - Are they oriented in the same direction?
    - Are they oriented in opposite directions?
    - Are they equivalent?

    a. $A(1, 4)$, $B(4, 7)$ and $C(2, 3)$, $D(-1, 0)$
    b. $A(-5, 3)$, $B(-2, 4)$ and $C(5, 7)$, $D(8, 6)$
    c. $A(1, -6)$, $B(-2, 3)$ and $C(3, -9)$, $D(0, 0)$

15. Write a vector equation for the line through point A with coordinates $(2, 3)$ and parallel to $\overline{OB}$, where $B(6, 1)$.

16. Line m has vector equation

    $$E = (-6, -1) + s(4, -1)$$

    Line n has vector equation

    $$H = (7, -1) + t(5, 2)$$

    What are the coordinates of the intersection of lines m and n?

---

5. $AB = 5$, midpoint: $\left(1, \frac{5}{2}\right)$

6. $(2.1, -0.1)$

7. **a.** yes   **b.** no   **c.** yes

8. See back of book.

9. No, the lines are not parallel because they have different slopes.

10. $7x - 6y = -1$

11. $\dfrac{7}{3}$

12. $AB = \sqrt{139}$

13. $T = (2, 3) + t(6, 1)$

14. **a.** parallel; not oriented in the same direction; oriented in opposite directions; not equivalent

    b. not parallel; not oriented in the same direction; not oriented in opposite directions; not equivalent

    c. parallel; oriented in the same direction; not oriented in opposite directions; equivalent

15. $X = (2, 3) + t(6, 1)$

16. $(5, -1)$

Chapter

7

Test

Go Online
PHSchool.com

For a chapter test,
go to Web Code: bee-0753

Multiple Choice

1. Which line is the reflection of $2x + y = -4$ over the y-axis?

   A. $y = 2x - 4$

   B. $y = -2x - 4$

   C. $y = 2x + 4$

   D. $y = -2x + 4$

2. $\overline{FG}$ has endpoints $F(-1, 0)$ and $G(2, 3)$. It is reflected first over the y-axis (as $\overline{F'G'}$) and then over the x-axis (as $\overline{F''G''}$). What are the coordinates of F'' and G''?

   A. $F''(1, 0)$ and $G''(-2, 3)$

   B. $F''(1, 0)$ and $G''(-2, -3)$

   C. $F''(-1, 0)$ and $G''(2, -3)$

   D. $F''(-1, 0)$ and $G''(-2, -3)$

3. Which rule translates $A(-2, 4)$ to $A'(-7, -3)$?

   A. $(x, y) \to (x - 5, y - 3)$

   B. $(x, y) \to (x - 5, y - 7)$

   C. $(x, y) \to (x + 5, y - 7)$

   D. $(x, y) \to (x + 5, y - 1)$

4. $\overline{XY}$ has endpoints $X(-4, -2)$ and $Y(2, 3)$. What are the coordinates of the midpoint of $\overline{XY}$?

   A. $\left(-1, \dfrac{1}{2}\right)$

   B. $\left(-1, \dfrac{3}{2}\right)$

   C. $\left(3, -\dfrac{1}{2}\right)$

   D. $\left(3, \dfrac{5}{2}\right)$

5. What is the distance between $G(-3, 5)$ and $H(-1, -3)$?

   A. 8.2

   B. 4.4

   C. 2.8

   D. 2.4

6. Three vertices of a square are $(-3, 5)$, $(6, 5)$, and $(6, -3)$. What are the coordinates of the center of the square?

   A. $(-3, -3)$

   B. $(\sqrt{3}, \sqrt{3})$

   C. $(2, 1)$

   D. $\left(1\dfrac{1}{2}, 1\right)$

7. Which point is NOT collinear with $(15, 5)$ and $(60, 20)$?

   A. $(-18, 6)$

   B. $(-3, -1)$

   C. $(0, 2)$

   D. $(24, 8)$

8. A cube has a vertex at the origin and sides of length 4 along the axes. What is the length of a diagonal of the cube?

   A. 2

   B. $4\sqrt{2}$

   C. 4

   D. $4\sqrt{3}$

9. For $A(-3, 2)$ and $B(-3, -5)$, what is $\overrightarrow{AB}$?

   A. $\overrightarrow{AB} = (-6, -3)$

   B. $\overrightarrow{AB} = (-6, -5)$

   C. $\overrightarrow{AB} = (9, -10)$

   D. $\overrightarrow{AB} = (9, -7)$

Answers

Chapter Test

1. A
2. B
3. B
4. A
5. A
6. D
7. C
8. D
9. A
10. B
11. D
12. The endpoints of the image are $A = (1, -2)$ and $B = (6, -8)$.
13. The slope of line s is $-\dfrac{3}{4}$, and the slope of line r is $\dfrac{4}{3}$. Since $-\dfrac{3}{4}$ is the opposite of the reciprocal of $\dfrac{4}{3}$, the lines are perpendicular.
14. $AB = \sqrt{929}$
15–16. See back of book.

10. For $G(-2, 10)$ and $K(3, -10)$, what is $G + 3K$?

   A. $(9, -30)$

   B. $(7, -20)$

   C. $(7, 20)$

   D. $(1, 0)$

11. For $X(-2, 4)$ and $Y(3, 2)$, what multiple of $\overrightarrow{XY}$ has its head on the line $y = -4$?

   A. $3\overrightarrow{XY}$

   B. $4\overrightarrow{XY}$

   C. $-3\overrightarrow{XY}$

   D. $-4\overrightarrow{XY}$

Open Response

12. Plot the points $A(1, 2)$ and $B(6, 8)$. Reflect $\overline{AB}$ over the x-axis. Write the coordinates of the images of its endpoints.

13. Here are equations of two lines.

   $s: 3x + 4y = 3$ $r: 16x - 12y = 28$

   Prove that $s \perp r$.

14. Here are the coordinates of two points in three-dimensional coordinate space.

   • $A(3, -13, 15)$ • $A(3, -13, 15)$

   Calculate the length of $\overline{AB}$.

15. Point A has coordinates $A(3, 8)$. Point B has coordinates $B(6, -3)$. O is the origin. Draw each vector on a coordinate plane.

   a. $\overrightarrow{AB}$ **b.** $\overrightarrow{OA}$

   c. $\overrightarrow{OB}$ **d.** $\overrightarrow{BA}$

   What is $\overrightarrow{AB} + \overrightarrow{BO} + \overrightarrow{OA}$?

16. Write the coordinates of the heads and tails of two vectors that are

   a. are parallel

   b. are parallel and oriented in the same direction

   c. are parallel and oriented in opposite directions

   Check your answers and explain why they are correct.

17. Quadrilateral $OACB$ is a parallelogram with vertices $A(4, 5)$, $C(3, 6)$, and O the origin. What are the coordinates of B?

18. For $P(1, 4)$ and $S(8, 12)$, find the vector that is equivalent to $\overrightarrow{PS}$ with its head at $(4, -3)$.

19. Line ℓ has a vector equation $T = t(3, 4)$, where T is a point on the line and t is any real number. Write a vector equation of the line through $A(-3, 5)$ and parallel to line ℓ.

20. Write a vector equation of the line through $A(0, -4)$ and $B(13, 20)$.

21. Find a vector equation of the line that passes through $A(5, 8)$ and is perpendicular to $\overrightarrow{OA}$.

22. For $A(6, 12)$ and $B(-2, 8)$, find C if B is the midpoint of $\overline{AC}$.

23. Find the intersection, if it exists, of the following pair of lines. If the point of intersection does not exist, explain why not.

$$S = (3, 4) + s(-3, 2)$$
$$R = (15, 3) - r(9, -6)$$

---

17. $(-1, 1)$

18. $X = (1, 4) + 4(7, 8)$

19. $S = (-3, 5) + s(3, 4)$

20. $R = (0, -4) + r(13, 24)$

21. Answers may vary. Sample:
$P = (5, 8) + t(5, 3)$

22. $(-10, 4)$

23. There is no point of intersection.

Both lines have slope $-\frac{2}{3}$, but the first line intersects the y-axis at $(0, 6)$ and the second line intersects the y-axis at $(0, 13)$.

Chapter 8
Optimization

Optimization problems—finding a maximum or minimum—are traditionally reserved for calculus. While you can indeed solve most of the problems in this chapter with calculus, you may be surprised by how approachable they are with geometric methods. These problems help students get at the big ideas behind optimization. Students will think about extreme cases and boundary conditions and use deduction, experimentation, and reasoning by continuity. Thus, optimization provides the context for the kind of thinking that teachers of mathematics want from their students.

Chapter Overview

- Investigation 8A, *Making the Least of a Situation,* introduces optimization and asks students to find the shortest path between two points, given a variety of restrictions.
- Investigation 8B, *Making the Most of a Situation,* explores the areas of various shapes, given a certain perimeter.
- Investigation 8C, *Contour Lines,* introduces topographic, temperature, and other contour plots. Students revisit the burning tent problem in this context.
- Investigation 8D, *Advanced Optimization,* further develops the Isoperimetric Problem, its solution, and a proof.

For more information on the investigations, see

- Chapter Road Map, p. 624
- Investigation Road Maps, pp. 626, 642, 658, 678

PROJECT The Project near the end of the chapter is optional. You can assign the Project at any time during the chapter depending on how often and how long you feel students should work on it.

Pacing Suggestions and Materials

Investigation 8A *Making the Least of a Situation*

DAY	LESSON	HOMEWORK
1	8.1 Getting Started Core: 3, 4 Optional: 1, 2	Core: 6, 7 Optional: 5, 8, 11, 12; Extension: 9, 10
2	8.2 Finding the Shortest Path Core: 1 Optional: 2, 3	Core: 4, 5, 8 Optional: 6, 7, 9, 10, 11, 12, 13, 14
3	8.3 Reflecting to Find Shortest Paths Core: 1 Optional: 2, 3	Core: 4, 6, 10 Optional: 5, 7, 8, 9, 11, 12, 13

Investigation 8B *Making the Most of a Situation*

DAY	LESSON	HOMEWORK
1	8.4 Getting Started Core: 1, 3 Optional: 2, 4	Core: 6, 7, 12 Optional: 5, 8, 9, 10, 11, 13, 14, 15, 16, 17
2	8.5 Maximizing Areas, Part I Core: 1, 3 Optional: 2	Core: 4, 6, 8 Optional: 5, 7, 9, 10, 11, 12, 13, 15, 16; Extensio
3	8.6 Maximizing Areas, Part 2 Core: 2, 3 Optional: 1	Core: 4, 5, 8, 9 Optional: 6, 7, 10, 11, 12, 13, 14, 15

Investigation 8C *Contour Lines*

DAY	LESSON	HOMEWORK
1	8.7 Getting Started Core: 1, 2 Optional: 3, 4	Core: 5 Optional: 6, 7, 8
2	8.8 Drawing Contour Plots Core: 1 Optional: 2, 3	Core: 4, 7, 8, 10 Optional: 5, 6, 9, 11, 12
3	8.9 Contour Lines and Functions Core: 1, 2, 3 Optional: 4	Core: 5, 7, 9, 12 Optional: 8, 13; Extension: 6, 10, 11
4	8.10 Revisiting the Burning Tent Core: 1 Optional: 2, 3	Core: 4, 5, 6 Optional: 7, 10, 11, 12, 13; Extension: 8, 9

NOTES	MATERIALS
	• rulers • Blackline Masters 8.1A, 8.1B, 8.1C
	• graph paper • protractors • rulers • Blackline Master 8.2
	• graph paper • protractors • rulers • Blackline Masters 8.3A, 8.3B, 8.3C

NOTES	MATERIALS
	• graph paper • protractors • rulers • Blackline Master MC 14
	• graphing calculators • rulers
	• rulers • Blackline Master 8.6

NOTES	MATERIALS
	• Blackline Master 8.7
	• protractors • rulers • Blackline Masters 8.8A, 8.8B, 8.8C
	• protractors • rulers • string • thumb tacks
	• compasses • protractors • rulers • Blackline Master 8.10

Mathematics Background

GEOMETRIC OPTIMIZATION Optimization problems are ubiquitous in mathematics and the sciences. They are one of the motivations for the development of calculus. However, there is also a long tradition of using purely geometric methods to solve optimization problems. General principles such as the shortest distance between two points is a straight line, and methods such as reflection over a line, form a coherent toolbox that you can use on many optimization problems.

In solving optimization problems, students will develop an understanding that will serve them well as they continue to study mathematics. They will gain practice relating geometric representations to graphical ones. They will notice that what goes up and then comes down has a maximum at some point. Students will learn the value of concretely looking at boundary conditions. For example, when restricted by a property line, you cannot always build a dog run with greatest possible area given a certain amount of fencing.

CONTOUR PLOTS Many optimization problems are embedded in the behavior of a function where the input is a point. You can visualize them on the coordinate plane using surface plots and contour lines. Contour lines are lines or curves drawn to show where a function takes on particular values. By using surface plots and contour lines, it becomes easier to visualize and describe a function's behavior. In the case of optimization problems, you can draw in any boundary conditions on the contour plot and see the maximum and minimum value for the function within those restrictions.

Think of the coordinate plane as a level floor. Picture a large piece of cloth positioned so that its height from the floor at any point is equal to the value of this function. This cloth is a surface plot of the function, and the maximum and minimum are identifiable.

THE ISOPERIMETRIC CONJECTURE One of the most famous optimization problems is to maximize the area enclosed by a given perimeter, or conversely, to minimize perimeter for a given area. This text treats this class of problems in the context of the isoperimetric problem. Students discover that for a given perimeter, the rectangle of greatest area is always a square. They generalize this result to see that for a given perimeter, the n-sided polygon of greatest area is always the regular n-gon. Students experiment and find that for a given perimeter, the more sides a regular polygon has, the greater the area it can enclose. They use visualization, deductive reasoning, and thought experiments to extend this result and eventually make a conjecture that the circle is the shape that encloses the greatest area for a given perimeter. Students also follow the arguments in a formal proof of the Isoperimetric Conjecture.

Pacing Suggestions and Materials

Investigation 8D *Advanced Optimization*

DAY	LESSON	HOMEWORK
1	8.11 Getting Started Core: 1, 2 Optional: 3, 4	Core: 6 Optional: 5, 7, 8, 9, 10, 11
2	8.12 Reasoning by Continuity Core: 2 Optional: 1, 3	Core: 4, 6, 7 Optional: 5, 8, 9, 10
3	8.13 Proving Rich's Function Is Constant Core: 1 Optional: 2, 3	Core: 4, 7, 8 Optional: 5, 6, 9, 13, 14, 15; Extension: 10, 11,
4	8.14 The Isoperimetric Problem Core: 2, 3 Optional: 1	Core: 4, 5, 7 Optional: 6, 8, 9, 10, 12, 13, 14, 15; Extension:
5	8.15 The Question of Existence Core: 2 Optional: 1	Core: 3, 4, 5 Optional: 7, 8, 9, 10, 11; Extension: 6
6	8.16 Solving the Isoperimetric Problem Core: 1, 2 Optional: 3, 4	Core: 5, 6, 9 Optional: 7, 8, 10, 12, 13, 14; Extension: 11

NOTES	MATERIALS
	• rulers • Blackline Master 8.11
	• rulers
	• rulers • Blackline Master 8.13
	• compasses • protractors • rulers
	• compasses • graph paper • protractors • rulers • Blackline Master 8.15
	• compasses • protractors • rulers

Developing Students' Mathematical Habits

In this chapter, students exercise most of the habits of mind that they have seen in this course. The following list outlines how this chapter develops certain mathematical habits of mind.

- Reasoning by continuity: In the Burning Tent problem, students see that the length of the path decreases and then begins to increase as the point at which they fill the bucket slides along the shoreline. Reasoning by continuity will lead them to conclude that the minimum value must be somewhere between the last decrease and the first increase.

- Performing thought experiments: When solving problems about building a fence that encloses the greatest possible area, students perform a thought experiment. A wall of a house must be one side of the pen. By reflecting the pen over that wall and looking at the original pen and its reflected image together, the problem becomes one that students have already solved.

- Looking for invariants: Lesson 8.12 presents a situation where Rich is trying to answer a multiple-choice question on a standardized test. Rich decides that one of the answer choices must be correct. Since the question involves a measurement, and no measuring tools are allowed, he then decides that the measurement he is looking for must be invariant. This leads him to a solution of the problem. Your students can model the situation described in this problem and experiment to verify Rich's conclusion.

Investigations at a Glance

- **8A** Making the *Least* of a Situation
- **8B** Making the *Most* of a Situation
- **8C** Contour Lines
- **8D** Advanced Optimization

Chapter Road Map

INVESTIGATION 8A, *Making the* Least *of a Situation,* introduces optimization in a real-world setting. In everyday life, students have probably tried to minimize the length of a path. For example, when faced with a series of errands, you plan the order of those errands to minimize the amount of time spent backtracking. One technique in this investigation is the use of reflection to form a straight line rather than using a path made of a series of segments.

INVESTIGATION 8B, *Making the* Most *of a Situation,* has students maximize quantities rather than minimize them. They maximize area under different restrictions on shape, perimeter, and angles, and through this work, they begin to explore the isoperimetric problem. Usually, you use calculus techniques to solve some of these problems. Here, students use reflection, experimentation, and graphing to find a maximum.

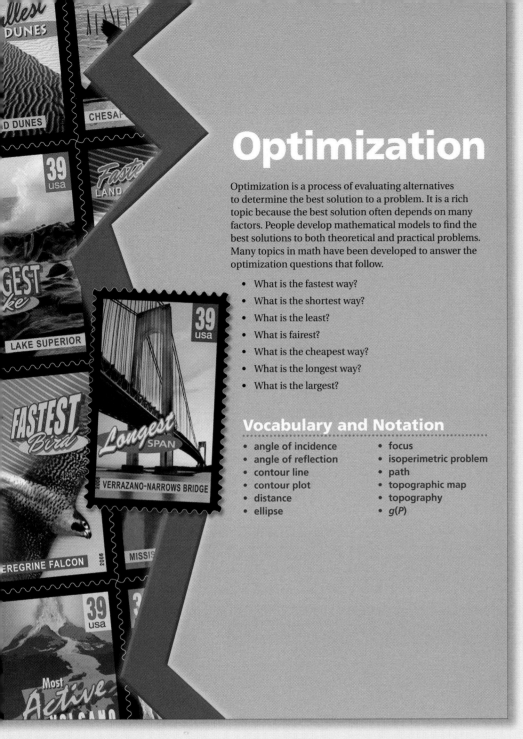

Optimization

Optimization is a process of evaluating alternatives to determine the best solution to a problem. It is a rich topic because the best solution often depends on many factors. People develop mathematical models to find the best solutions to both theoretical and practical problems. Many topics in math have been developed to answer the optimization questions that follow.

- What is the fastest way?
- What is the shortest way?
- What is the least?
- What is fairest?
- What is the cheapest way?
- What is the longest way?
- What is the largest?

Vocabulary and Notation

- angle of incidence
- angle of reflection
- contour line
- contour plot
- distance
- ellipse
- focus
- isoperimetric problem
- path
- topographic map
- topography
- $g(P)$

INVESTIGATION 8C, *Contour Lines,* introduces a new way of thinking about functions. You can think of a function that has a value for each point on a plane as a contour plot. The function's output determines the height of the terrain at each point. Large positive values are peaks, and negative values are valleys. This gives students a new way to visualize algebraic functions that is particularly helpful when trying to optimize those functions.

INVESTIGATION 8D, *Advanced Optimization,* brings together many threads of the course and develops some very complex mathematical ideas and proofs. Students investigate a function that returns the sum of the distances to the sides of a triangle for any point in the triangle. They also continue their work with the isoperimetric problem. In both cases, students must work to understand someone else's mathematical argument and to consider the implications of new theorems in related situations.

Chapter Vocabulary and Notation

The following list gives the key vocabulary and notation used in the chapter. Selected new vocabulary and notation items are shown in boldface on the student page.

- angle of incidence, p. 637
- angle of reflection, p. 637
- contour line, p. 662
- contour plot, p. 662
- distance, p. 627
- ellipse, p. 673
- Fermat point, p. 704
- focus, p. 673
- grid polygon, p. 643
- isoperimetric problem, p. 690
- level curve, p. 662
- maximum, p. 642
- maximize, p. 642
- minimum, p. 627
- minimize, p. 627
- optimization, p. 625
- path, p. 627
- Rich's function, p. 682
- topographic map, p. 659
- topography, p. 659
- $g(P)$, p. 667

Chapter Technology

Support for the use of technology is available in the Technology Handbook. See p. 712.

INVESTIGATION 8A *Geometry Software*

- **LESSON 8.3** Check that you found the best drop-off and pickup points, p. 639.

INVESTIGATION 8B *Graphing Calculator*

- **LESSON 8.5** Graph a function to find its maximum, p. 649.

INVESTIGATION 8C *Geometry Software*

- **LESSON 8.8** Experiment with the measures of kicking angles across a soccer field, p. 662.
- **LESSON 8.9** Define $f(P) = PA + PB$. Drag P around and observe the contour lines, p. 666.
- **LESSON 8.10** Pick a total path length, experiment, and determine the contour line, p. 672.

INVESTIGATION 8D *Geometry Software*

- **LESSON 8.13** Construct a scalene triangle to see if your visualization is correct, p. 688. For all triangles, build a sketch that computes S (the sum of the distances from a point inside a triangle to each side), p. 687.
- **LESSON 8.14** Experiment to come up with a conjecture about the isoperimetric problem, p. 694.

PROJECT *Geometry Software*

- Develop a model to explore the airport problem, pp. 703–705.

Investigation Overview

This investigation introduces optimization by asking students to find the minimum possible length for a path given various restrictions. Students learn to distinguish between distance and the length of a path. Students experiment to find the point for a minimum path, and then make broader conjectures about the location of such a point. Finally, students use reflection to change a path composed of several segments into one straight line.

You may wish to assign Questions 1–3 for students to think and write about during the investigation.

Learning Goals

- Find the length of a path under given restrictions.
- Choose points that result in a minimum length for a path.
- Compute lengths and distances on the coordinate plane.

Habits and Skills

- Distinguish between distance and the length of a path.
- Draw conclusions from trends in experimental data.
- Visualize reflections that will help minimize a path.
- Recognize key problem situations and choose techniques based on experience.

Investigation 8A

Making the *Least* of a Situation

In *Making the* Least *of a Situation,* you will minimize things. You minimize quantities in architecture, computer programming, economics, engineering, and medicine. This is because real-world optimization often involves making something as small as possible. You can minimize a rate, time, distance, area, volume, or angle measure.

By the end of this investigation, you will be able to answer questions like these:

1. What is the difference between the length of a path from one point to another and the distance between the points?

2. When and how can reflection help you find the shortest path for a situation?

3. In the following figure, $\overline{AS}$ and $\overline{BF}$ are perpendicular to $\overleftrightarrow{AB}$. $AS = 54$ ft, $BF = 27$ ft, and $AB = 84$ ft.

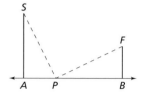

Describe the location of P on $\overline{AB}$ such that the path from S to P to F is as short as possible.

You will learn how to

- find the length of a path under given restrictions
- choose points that result in a minimum length for a path
- compute lengths and distances on the coordinate plane

You will develop these habits and skills:

- Distinguish between distance and the length of a path.
- Draw conclusions from trends in experimental data.
- Visualize reflections that will help minimize a path.
- Recognize key problem situations and choose techniques based on experience.

In this game, the least number of turns possible for moving one peg across the board is 1.

Investigation Road Map

LESSON 8.1, *Getting Started,* acquaints students with the types of problems in this investigation and describes the distinction between distance and the length of a path.

LESSON 8.2, *Finding the Shortest Path,* explores possible locations of a point on a line given a path that must touch the line. Students use reflection to visualize the location of such a point.

LESSON 8.3, *Reflecting to Find Shortest Paths,* extends the work of Lesson 8.2 to situations that require more than one reflection to see the solution as a straight line.

Activating Prior Knowledge
Exploring New Ideas

The **distance** between two fixed points is the length of the segment that contains them as endpoints. The distance is fixed. You cannot minimize or maximize it. A **path** between two points can be as long as you would like. A path between two points cannot be shorter than the distance between the points.

In the real world, the shortest possible path between two points may not be the segment containing them as endpoints. There may be obstacles in the way, or there may be an intermediate destination. In this investigation, you will find the shortest path from one point to another given a set of restrictions.

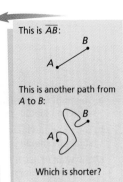

This is $\overline{AB}$:

This is another path from A to B:

Which is shorter?

For You to Explore

1. Suppose you and a friend are at a corner of a parking lot and it is raining hard. All the spaces are taken and you want to get to your car by the shortest way possible. You can run around the cars or between them. What route minimizes the length of your path to the car? Is there more than one best route to the car?

your car

you

2. This time, suppose you are standing in a courtyard with regularly spaced columns.

```
 o    o    o    o    o

 o   •F   o    o    o

 o    o    o    o    o

 o    o    o    o   o•S
```

Find the shortest path you can from S to F. Did you use a different technique than you did in Problem 1? Explain.

Habits of Mind

Visualize. Would it be possible to travel along the segment with endpoints at New York and Tokyo?

Lesson Overview

GOALS

- Warm up to the ideas of the investigation.
- Find the length of a path under given restrictions.

In this lesson, students start working on optimization problems that involve finding the shortest path between two points given a variety of restrictions. Make sure that your students understand the distinction between the distance between two points and the shortest path between two points. Ask them to think carefully about the restrictions in the problems and exercises you assign.

FOR YOU TO EXPLORE
- Core: 3, 4
- Optional: 1, 2

MATERIALS
- rulers
- Blackline Masters 8.1A, 8.1B, 8.1C

HOMEWORK
- Core: 6, 7
- Optional: 5, 8, 11, 12
- Extension: 9, 10

VOCABULARY
- distance
- minimize
- minimum
- optimization
- path

Launch

Begin this lesson by having students read the introductory paragraph about *distance* and *path* and assign some of the For You To Explore problems. Blackline Master 8.1A depicts the cars and columns art, so students can trace paths without having to copy the figures.

Answers

For You to Explore

1. Use the word "aisle" to refer to the horizontal and vertical strips of space between rows and columns of cars. One route that minimizes the distance you must walk goes to the third vertical aisle from your starting point and then up to the horizontal aisle between the top two rows. There are several other paths that have the same length as this one.

2. Check students' diagrams. The diagram below shows two paths, one of which is a "staircase" path similar to the ones that work for Ex. 1. The other path shown is clearly a shorter path, though it is not necessarily the shortest.

```
 o    o    o    o    o

F•
 o   o    o    o    o
       shorter path
 o    o    o   o    o

 o    o    o   o  o•S
```

Explore

Go over a few problems with your students and make sure they consider the effects of the various restrictions in Problems 3 and 4.

For You to Explore

PROBLEM 3 asks students to consider different kinds of restrictions and their effect on the optimum path.

PROBLEM 4 Part (b) is an optimization problem that has no solution. You can see that the best path would pass near point *N*, but since the path cannot actually touch point *N*, there is always a point closer to *N*. For any path there is always a shorter path that passes closer to *N*. This distinction is important if you plan to work through Investigation 8D. Otherwise, it is fine to allow students to consider an approximate solution.

3. You are lounging on the beach at *L*. You want to run to the shoreline and swim out to your friends at *K*.

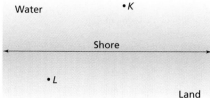

This run-and-swim problem will be referenced later in the chapter.

a. You want the swim to be as short as possible. To what point on the shoreline should you run to minimize the path you swim? Explain.

b. You want the run to be as short as possible. At what point on the shoreline should you enter the water now? Explain.

c. You want to reach *K* in the least possible total distance. Now where should you enter the water? Explain.

4. Use the following figure to answer parts (a) and (b).

a. Find the distance from $A(-2, 3)$ to $B(5, 7)$.

b. Add the restriction that no path from *A* to *B* may intersect $\overline{MN}$. Now find the length of the shortest path.

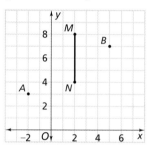

Answers

3. a. the point where the line through *K* perpendicular to the shoreline intersects the shoreline; the shortest segment from the point to the line is the segment perpendicular to the line.

b. the point where the line through *L* perpendicular to the shoreline intersects the shoreline; same reason as in part (a)

c. the point where $\overline{LK}$ intersects the shoreline; the shortest distance from *L* to *K* is along $\overline{LK}$.

4. a. $\sqrt{65}$

b. There is no shortest path.

Exercises *Practicing Habits of Mind*

On Your Own

5. How do you measure the distance between two points when you are not in math class? How do you measure the distance between two points on the coordinate plane?

6. How do you measure the distance from a point to a line outside of math class? On the coordinate plane? Describe the process you would go through, rather than giving a formula.

For Exercises 7–10, use this new way to think about a coordinate grid. Imagine that the coordinate grid is actually a wire mesh set in a vertical plane, and an ant walks on it. There are wires at each whole-number value for *x* and *y*. The ant can walk only horizontally or vertically along the wires. The distance between two adjacent horizontal or vertical wires is 1 unit.

7. **a.** Describe the ant's path from *A* to *B*.

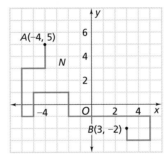

b. What is the length of this path?

c. Describe three different paths that an ant could take from *A* to *B* and give the length for each.

d. What is the length of the shortest possible path of an ant from *A* to *B*? Explain your answer.

e. Is the shortest path of an ant from *A* to *B* unique? If not, what do all the shortest paths from *A* to *B* have in common?

Wrap Up

You may want to assign students to do the On Your Own exercises with a partner in class; otherwise, assign these exercises as homework.

Exercises

HOMEWORK
- Core: 6, 7
- Optional: 5, 8, 11, 12
- Extension: 9, 10

On Your Own

EXERCISES 7–10 ask students to suppose that the coordinate grid is a wire mesh. An ant can walk only along a wire, so the path of an ant involves a series of 90° left and right turns. Blackline Master 8.1B depicts the graph used in Exercise 7. Take It Further Exercises 9 and 10 extend this work by asking students to generalize and draw conclusions.

Exercises

5. Answers may vary. Sample: You can use a ruler or odometer readings on a car. On the coordinate plane, you can use the Distance Formula.

6. See back of book.

7. **a.** The following description uses L, R, U, and D for the words *left, right, up,* and *down,* respectively: D2L2D4R1U2R3D2R7D2L2U1.

   b. 28 units

   c. Answers may vary. Sample: R7D7 has length 14 units, D7R7 has length 14 units, and R1D8L1U1R7 has length 18 units.

   d. 14 units; To get from *A* to *B* with no backtracking, the horizontal moves must always be to the right, and the vertical moves must always be down. Since *B* is 7 units below and 7 units to the right of *A*, nothing less than 14 units will do. The first two sample paths in part (c) show that paths 14 units long are possible.

   e. no; See the answer for part (d).

EXERCISES 11 AND 12 are an introduction to the burning tent problem of Lesson 8.2 and Investigation 8C. Blackline Master 8.1C depicts the graph used in Exercise 11.

8. Find the distance between each pair of points on the coordinate plane. Then find the length of a shortest path of an ant between them.

a. $(-1, 3)$ and $(3, -1)$

b. $(2, 4)$ and $(-1, -5)$

c. $(4, 0)$ and $(-3, 8)$

Go Online
Video Tutor
PHSchool.com

Web Code: bee-0801

9. **Take It Further** Name several pairs of points for which the distance between them is the same as the length of a shortest path of an ant. What relationship must the two points have for this to be true?

10. **Take It Further** Write a formula that gives the length of the shortest path of an ant from (x_1, y_1) to (x_2, y_2). Check that your formula works for points in any quadrant.

Maintain Your Skills

11. In the following graph, A, B, S, and F are fixed and P can be anywhere along $\overleftrightarrow{AB}$.

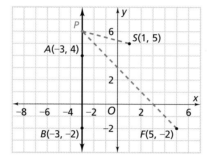

Find the length of the path from S to P to F for the following coordinates of P.

a. $P(-3, 6)$ b. $P(-3, 4)$ c. $P(-3, 2)$

d. $P(-3, 0)$ e. $P(-3, -2)$ f. $P(-3, -4)$

12. Refer to the information in Exercise 11.

a. What is the distance from S to F?

b. What location of P makes the length of the path from S to P to F the shortest possible? Explain.

c. What is the length of the shortest path from S to P to F?

Answers

8. a. $4\sqrt{2}$; 8
   b. $3\sqrt{10}$; 12
   c. $\sqrt{113}$; 15

9. Answers may vary. Sample: $(-1, 3)$ and $(-1, -1)$, $(-1, 3)$ and $(3, 3)$, $(2, -5)$ and $(-1, -5)$; The two points must be on the same vertical or horizontal line.

10. $L = |x_1 - x_2| + |y_1 - y_2|$, where L is the minimal length of an ant path from (x_1, y_1) to (x_2, y_2).

11. a. $\sqrt{17} + 8\sqrt{2}$
    b. $\sqrt{17} + 10$
    c. $5 + 4\sqrt{5}$
    d. $\sqrt{41} + 2\sqrt{17}$
    e. $\sqrt{65} + 8$
    f. $\sqrt{97} + 2\sqrt{17}$

12. a. $\sqrt{65}$
    b. See back of book.
    c. $\sqrt{193}$

As you saw in Lesson 8.1, you cannot always take the shortest path between two points. There may be something in the way, or you may have an intermediate stop.

Imagine that you are motorboating on a river and you need fuel. First you must drop a passenger off on one river bank. Then you must refuel at a station on the other river bank.

Below are some pictures of the situation. The boat is at *A*. After you drop the passenger off at *P*, you will refuel at *B*. You can choose the location for *P* anywhere along the south bank. Because you are low on fuel, you want to minimize the length of the path you travel.

Remember...

In the parking lot problem, cars were in the way.

Should you land here?

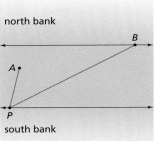

north bank

south bank

. . . or here?

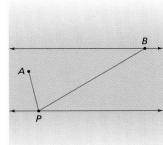

. . . or maybe here?

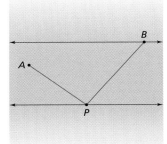

Lesson Overview

GOALS

- Choose points that result in a minimum length for a path.
- Compute lengths and distances on the coordinate plane.

In this lesson, students work on the refueling problem. All paths start at a point in a river, touch a riverbank (a line), and then end at a refueling station, which is represented by another point along the river. Students will learn how to simplify this problem with reflection.

CHECK YOUR UNDERSTANDING	**HOMEWORK**
• Core: 1	• Core: 4, 5, 8
• Optional: 2, 3	• Optional: 6, 7, 9, 10, 11, 12, 13, 14

MATERIALS
- graph paper
- protractors
- rulers
- Blackline Master 8.2

Launch

Begin this lesson by reading the introductory paragraph or describing the refueling problem. If you like, have two students act out the dialog between Tony and Sasha. Make sure students understand the scenario by assigning the For You to Do problems.

Explore

Check students' understanding of the For You to Do problems to assess their understanding of the refueling problem. Then read Developing Habits of Mind and have students do the For Discussion problem.

Tony and Sasha think about the refueling problem.

Sasha   If you are traveling downstream, there's no way that you'd go back upstream from A to drop off the passenger before refueling.

Tony   And you'd never go farther downstream than the fuel station at B.

Sasha   So the best solution has to be somewhere downstream from A and upstream from B.

Tony   Let's try some different places for P. We can measure to see what happens to the total distance traveled as we move P from left to right.

Possible drop-off points fall between the two vertical lines.

possible drop-off points

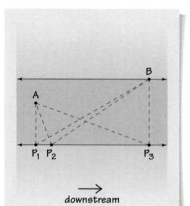

downstream

Sasha   The path through P_1 directly below A is about 63 mm. The path through P_3 directly below B is about 68 mm. The path through P_2 measures 59 mm. The best path has to be somewhere between P_1 and P_3.

For You to Do

Here are some questions about the refueling problem. Keep a record of any conjectures you make, and justify your conclusions.

1. What happens to AP as P moves downstream? What happens to PB?

2. How does the sum $AP + PB$ change as P moves downstream?

3. Visualize, or draw, a sketch in which you hold A constant, but widen the river and move B farther away. Does the best location for P move to the left or right?

Answers

For You to Do

It is assumed that P is between the points labeled P_1 and P_3 in the diagram just above For You to Do.

1. AP increases and PB decreases.

2. It decreases and then increases.; $AP + PB$ changes in a continuous way, so it is reasonable that it actually achieves a minimum value.

3. to the left

Visualize. Here is another way to think about the refueling problem. When you look into a mirror, an object's reflection appears to be the same distance from the mirror as the real object. However, the reflection appears to be on the opposite side of the mirror from the real object. This makes the image and the real object symmetric with respect to the mirror.

Picture a mirror along the south bank of the river. You are standing on the north bank looking across the river.

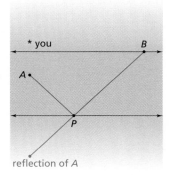

You can make the path from the *reflection of A* to *B* as short as possible by connecting the two points with a line segment. The point where this path crosses the south bank is also the point that minimizes the trip from *A* to *P* to *B*.

> **Remember...**
>
> In Chapter 7, you found that the mirror line is the perpendicular bisector of the segment joining a point and its reflected image.

For Discussion

4. The length of the path from the *reflection of A* to *P* to *B* is the same as the length of the path from *A* to *P* to *B*. Explain. Make a sketch using reflection to solve the refueling problem. Does it matter whether *A* or *B* is reflected? Explain.

For Discussion

4. If *M* is the point where the segment from *A* to its reflection image *A'* intersects the bottom shoreline, then $\overline{AM} \cong \overline{A'M}$. But $\overline{MP} \cong \overline{MP}$. So $\triangle AMP$ and $\triangle A'MP$ are congruent right triangles. It follows that $AP = A'P$ and hence that $AP + PB = A'P + PB$.

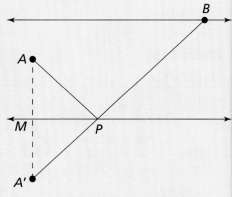

It does not matter whether you reflect *A* or *B*.

Wrap Up

End this lesson by assigning the first of the Check Your Understanding exercises.

Assessment Resources

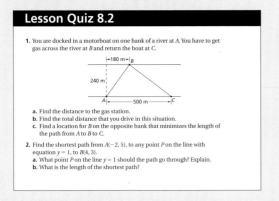

Lesson Quiz 8.2

1. You are docked in a motorboat on one bank of a river at *A*. You have to get gas across the river at *B* and return the boat at *C*.

   a. Find the distance to the gas station.
   b. Find the total distance that you drive in this situation.
   c. Find a location for *B* on the opposite bank that minimizes the length of the path from *A* to *B* to *C*.

2. Find the shortest path from $A(-2, 5)$, to any point *P* on the line with equation $y = 1$, to $B(4, 3)$.
   a. What point *P* on the line $y = 1$ should the path go through? Explain.
   b. What is the length of the shortest path?

Exercises

HOMEWORK
- Core: 4, 5, 8
- Optional: 6, 7, 9, 10, 11, 12, 13, 14

Check Your Understanding

EXERCISE 2 explores other points that result in the same-length path as *P*. This exercise previews the idea of a contour line—the set of all points that return the same value for a function. Students will explore contour lines in more detail in Investigation 8C. The idea of contour lines also gives students another way to approach minimization. If there are two points that are equally "bad," the optimum solution may be between them.

 Exercises *Practicing Habits of Mind*

Check Your Understanding

Use the figure below for Exercises 1–3.

You are in a rowboat, docked on the south bank of a river at *D*. You have to drop off a passenger on the north bank and then return the boat at *F*.

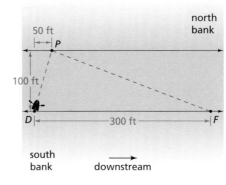

1. Find the total distance you have to row if the drop-off point *P* is 50 feet downstream from *D*. Assume that you can row in a straight line in spite of the river's current.

   If *P* were *x* feet downstream, what would be the length of the path?

2. In the figure above, *P* is 50 feet downstream from *D*. Describe the location of *Q* on the north bank if the path from *D* to *Q* to *F* has the same length as the path from *D* to *P* to *F*. Explain how you know the length is the same without calculating it. Where would *Q* be if *P* were *x* feet downstream from *D*?

3. Refer again to the figure above. Use reflection to find a location on the north bank for *P* that minimizes the length of the path from *D* to *P* to *F*. How far downstream is *P*? Is there another point on the north bank that has a path equal in length to the path from *D* to *P* to *F*?

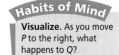

Habits of Mind

Visualize. As you move *P* to the right, what happens to *Q*?

Answers

Exercises

1. $50\left(\sqrt{5} + \sqrt{29}\right)$ ft $\approx$ 381 ft;
   $\left(\sqrt{x^2 + 100^2} + \sqrt{(300 - x)^2 + 100^2}\right)$ ft

2. *Q* is 200 ft downstream from *P'*. *Q* would be $(300 - 2x)$ ft downstream from *P*.

3.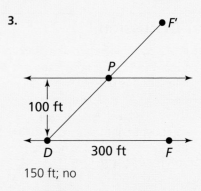

   150 ft; no

On Your Own

4. Write About It Returning from picking berries near a campground, you find your tent on fire. Luckily, the river is nearby. You must quickly empty your berry bucket and figure out at which point P you should fill your bucket with water to minimize the distance you travel. Write about methods you could use to find the shortest path from where you are, to the river, and then to the tent.

> This "burning-tent" problem will appear later in the text.

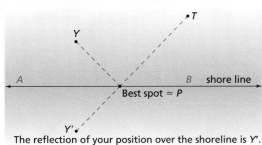

The reflection of your position over the shoreline is Y'.

5. Find the shortest path from $A(-4, 3)$ through any point P on the line $3x - 2y = 0$, to $B(4, -1)$.

   a. Sketch a graph of the situation.

   b. What point P on the line $3x - 2y = 0$ should the path go through? Explain.

   c. What is the length of the shortest path?

6. Find the shortest path from $A(-4, 3)$ to any point P on the line $y = 5$, to $B(4, -1)$.

   a. Sketch a graph of the situation.

   b. What point P on the line $y = 5$ should the path go through? Explain.

   c. What is the length of the shortest path?

7. Line ℓ has equation $2x - y = 0$. Because ℓ can also be written in the form $y = 2x$, points in ℓ are of the form $(x, 2x)$. Find a function that will give the distance between $(1, 2)$ and any other point on ℓ. For what value of x is this function at a minimum?

8. Standardized Test Prep Points $D(0, 1)$, $E(9, 13)$, and $F(25, 1)$ are the vertices of $\triangle DEF$, as shown at the right. Point $C(10, 6)$ is the intersection of the angle bisectors of $\triangle DEF$. $\overline{CH} \perp \overline{DE}$. What are the coordinates of point H? What is CH?

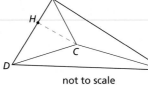

not to scale

A. $H(4.5, 7); CH = \frac{5\sqrt{5}}{2}$ **B.** $H\left(5, \frac{23}{3}\right); CH = \frac{5\sqrt{10}}{3}$

C. $H(5.25, 8); CH = \frac{5\sqrt{17}}{4}$ **D.** $H(6, 9); CH = 5$

---

4. Answers may vary. Sample: Model the situation with geometry software.

5. a.
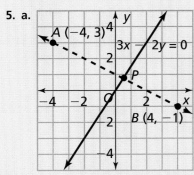

b. $P\left(\frac{1}{2}, \frac{3}{4}\right)$; an equation for $\overleftrightarrow{AB}$ is $x + 2y = 2$. Solve the system $x + 2y = 2$ and $3x - 2y = 0$ to find the coordinates of P.

c. $4\sqrt{5} \approx 8.9$

6. See back of book.

7. $D = \sqrt{5}|x - 1|; x = 1$

8. D

On Your Own

EXERCISES 5 AND 6 Make sure that students consider the situation before they begin to work. When the two points are on opposite sides of a line, the shortest path between them that touches the line is the segment connecting them. You can use reflection when the two points are on the same side of the line that the path must touch.

EXERCISE 7 gives students a chance to look at an algebraic interpretation of a minimization problem. However, students who use a graph gain the advantage of seeing that the point in question is actually on the line in question.

EXERCISE 9 Blackline Master 8.2 depicts the swimming pool in this exercise, so students do not have to copy the figure. Students will revisit this exercise in Investigation 8C.

Maintain Your Skills

EXERCISES 11–14 In this series of exercises, students see that at the point *P* that is part of the shortest path, the measure of the angle of the path's approach to the riverbank is equal to the measure of its angle leaving the riverbank. This result may be familiar to your students from their study of reflection in mathematics or in physics. The next lesson further discusses this result.

Additional Resources

PRINTED RESOURCES
- Texas Instruments Activities Workbook
- Cabrilog Activities
- Teaching Resources
- Practice Workbook
- Assessment Resources

TECHNOLOGY
- TeacherExpress CD-ROM
- **Exam***View* CD-ROM
- **PHSchool.com**
  - Homework Help
  - Video Tutors
  - Multiple Choice
  - Crosswords

Additional Practice

1. You are docked in a motorboat on one bank of a river at *A*. You have to get gas across the river at *B* and then return the boat at *C*.

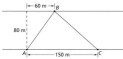

   a. Find the distance to the gas station.
   b. Find the total distance that you drive in this situation.
   c. Find a location for *B* on the opposite bank that minimizes the length of the path from *A* to *B* to *C*.

2. Returning from a hike, you see that your tent is on fire. A stream is nearby, but you want to be sure to get water at the spot that minimizes the total distance you travel from your current location, to the stream, to the tent. Explain how the reflection method helps you determine this spot.

3. Find the shortest path from *A*(−6, 4), to any point *P* on the line with equation −2*x* + 3*y* = 6, to *B*(−1, −2).
   a. Sketch a graph of the situation.
   b. What point *P* on the line −2*x* + 3*y* = 6 should the path go through? Explain.
   c. What is the length of the shortest path?

4. Find the shortest path from *A*(−5, 3) to any point *P* on the line with equation *y* = −3, to *B*(−1, −1).
   a. Sketch a graph of the situation
   b. What point *P* on the line *y* = −3 should the path go through? Explain.
   c. What is the length of the shortest path?

5. Line *m* has equation *y* = 3*x*.
   a. Points on line *m* are all of the form _____.
   b. Find a function that will give the distance between the point (1, 3) and any point on *m*.
   c. For what value of *x* is this function at a minimum?

Practice: For Lesson 8.2, assign Exercises 1–8.

---

9. You are at an arbitrary point *M* in a swimming pool with many sides. Describe the shortest path out of the pool. Is the path to a corner or to a side?

10. Draw a new pool and a position for *M* such that the shortest path is to a corner.

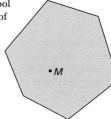

Maintain Your Skills

In Exercises 11–14, you will examine the burning-tent problem with trigonometry. This figure shows the coordinates of the starting point and the location of the burning tent. The *x*-axis is the riverbank.

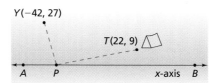

11. For each proposed location of *P*, the place you fill up your bucket, find the total length of the path.

   a. (−42, 0)   b. (−30, 0)
   c. (−15, 0)   d. (−3, 0)
   e. (10, 0)   f. (22, 0)

12. For each proposed location of *P*, find and compare the approximate measures of ∠*SPA* and ∠*FPB*.

   a. (−42, 0)   b. (−30, 0)
   c. (−15, 0)   d. (−3, 0)
   e. (10, 0)   f. (22, 0)

13. Analyze your data from Exercise 11. The point *P* with the shortest path falls between which two points? Analyze your data from Exercise 12. What happens to ∠*SPA* and ∠*FPB* as you approach this location for *P*?

14. Find the approximate location for the point *P* with the shortest path. Use your reasoning from Exercise 13.

Go Online
PHSchool.com

For additional practice, go to **Web Code: bea-0802**

Answers

9. The shortest path is the shortest perpendicular segment from *M* to a side; to a side.

10. See back of book.

11. a. $27 + \sqrt{4177} \approx 91.63$
    b. $3\sqrt{97} + \sqrt{2785} \approx 82.32$
    c. $27\sqrt{2} + 5\sqrt{58} \approx 76.26$
    d. $15\sqrt{10} + \sqrt{706} \approx 74.00$
    e. $\sqrt{3433} + 15 \approx 73.59$
    f. $5\sqrt{193} + 9 \approx 78.46$

12. See back of book.

13. between (−3, 0) and (22, 0); as you go from (−42, 0) to (22, 0), $m\angle SPA$ decreases, and $m\angle FPB$ increases. As you approach this location, $m\angle SPA$ approaches $m\angle FPB$.

14. (6, 0)

Reflecting to Find Shortest Paths

When you used reflection in the burning-tent and boating problems, you may have noticed similarities. Think about the angles at which the minimum-length paths intersect the riverbank. The situation is similar to the game of pool. The angle at which a ball hits the bumper is the same as the angle at which it ricochets off the bumper.

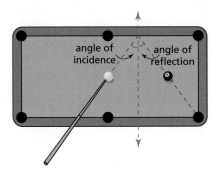

The **angle of incidence** is the angle between the incoming ball and the line perpendicular to the bumper at the collision point. The **angle of reflection** is the angle between the ball and the perpendicular line as the ball leaves the bumper.

For Discussion

1. Does this relationship hold for the minimum path length in the burning-tent problem? Is the angle at which you approach the river the same as the angle at which you leave the river? Does the reflection method guarantee this result? Explain.

In pool, friction affects the ball, and the ball's collision with the bumper is not perfectly elastic. This means that the measure of its angle of reflection is only approximately equal to the measure of its angle of incidence. In this lesson, imagine an ideal pool table, with no friction and perfectly elastic collisions.

Example

Problem Your goal is to hit the white ball in the figure off the top bumper, the right bumper, and then knock the black ball into the bottom center pocket.

Find the point on the top bumper where the white ball should hit.

For Discussion

1. yes; yes; yes; The following figure shows how you would use the reflection method to find the shortest path from A to B via a point on line ℓ.

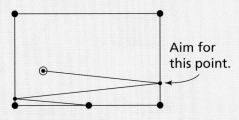

Aim for this point.

A′ is reflection of A, so ∠1 ≅ ∠2. But ∠2 and ∠3 are vertical angles, so ∠2 ≅ ∠3. Since congruence of angles is transitive, ∠1 ≅ ∠3.

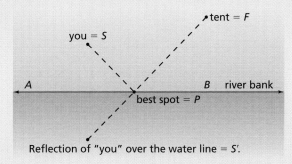

Wrap Up

End this lesson by assigning some of the Check Your Understanding exercises.

Solution You want to make a straight line through the top bumper of the table, the right bumper, and the target pocket. Reflect the pool table over its top edge. Reflect it again over its right edge. Now you can draw the straight line you want, as in the figure below. (The word *pool* is in the figure to help you visualize the reflections.)

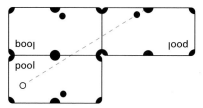

You should aim for the point where this line crosses the top edge of the table. Here is a sketch of the path the white ball will take.

For You to Do

2. Use the figure from the Example for the starting point of the white ball. This time, you want the white ball to hit the right bumper, the left bumper, and then go into the bottom center pocket. Find the point you should aim for and sketch the path of the ball.

Exercises *Practicing Habits of Mind*

Check Your Understanding

1. Your goal is to hit the white ball off the top bumper, the bottom bumper, and then knock the black ball into the top left corner pocket.

   Locate the point you should aim for and sketch the path you expect the ball to take.

Answers

For You to Do

2.

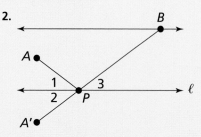

Exercises

1.

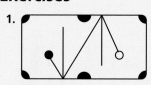

2. Design your own pool-shot problem involving at least two bumpers. Solve the problem yourself. Then give your problem to a classmate and compare your solutions.

3. A canoe is at *R* in the figure at the right. First, a passenger must be let off on the west bank. Then a passenger must be picked up on the east bank and dropped off at island *S*. Find the drop-off and pickup points that minimize the total distance traveled. Explain your reasoning. Check your answer with a ruler and string, or geometry software.

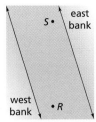

On Your Own

4. **Write About It** You are given line ℓ and two points *S* and *F* that are not on the line. Describe a strategy for finding *P* on ℓ that minimizes the length of the path from *S* to *P* to *F*.

5. You are in a rectangular swimming pool at *K*, out of reach of the sides of the pool. Before swimming to *L*, you want to swim to a side of the pool to put down your sunglasses.

Explain how to find the place to put your sunglasses that minimizes the length of the path you swim.

6. A path on the coordinate plane must go from *P*(3, −1) to point *L* on line ℓ with equation *x* = −1. Then the path goes to point *M* on line *m* with equation *x* = 7, and finally to *Q*(3, 8). Graph the shortest path and find the coordinates of *L* and *M*.

7. In Exercise 6, *P* is exactly halfway between lines ℓ and *m*.

a. If *P* moves closer to line ℓ than to line *m*, how does the path from *P* to ℓ, to *m*, and then to *Q* change?

b. Check your prediction in part (a) by solving the problem again, but with *P*(0, −1).

Assessment Resources

Lesson Quiz 8.3

1. For each of the following pool shots, locate the point you should aim for and sketch the path you expect the ball to take.
   a. Hit the ball off the top bumper and into the bottom left corner pocket.
   b. Hit the ball off the bottom bumper and into the top middle pocket.

2. A path on the coordinate plane must go from *A*(2, 5) to point *C* on line ℓ with equation *x* = 1. Then the path goes to point *D* on line *m* with equation *x* = 4, and finally to *B*(3, −3).
   a. Find the coordinates of *C* and *D*.
   b. Suppose *A* is farther from line ℓ than from line *m*. Describe how the path from *A* to ℓ, to *m*, to *B* changes.

Exercises

HOMEWORK
- Core: 4, 6, 10
- Optional: 5, 7, 8, 9, 11, 12, 13

Check Your Understanding

EXERCISE 1 Blackline Master 8.3A depicts the pool table so that students do not have to copy the figure.

EXERCISE 3 Blackline Master 8.3B depicts the river scene so that students do not have to copy the figure when checking their answer.

On Your Own

EXERCISE 5 Blackline Master 8.3C depicts the swimming pool, in case students want to sketch possible paths.

EXERCISE 7 asks students to determine how a change in the setup of the exercise will change the optimum path.

---

2. Check students' work.

3. Refer to the following figure.

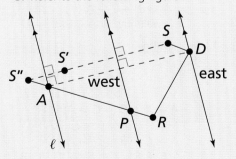

Line ℓ and S′ result from reflecting east bank and S across west bank.

S″ results from reflecting S′ across line ℓ. Draw $\overline{S''R}$. Reflect *A* across west bank to get *P*. The points *D* and *P* are the drop-off and pickup points, respectively.

4. See back of book.

5. Answers may vary. Sample: Find the best place on each side of the pool, then measure each path to find the shortest one.

6. See back of book.

7. See back of book.

EXERCISE 9 asks students to predict how the minimization of a different segment changes the optimum path.

Maintain Your Skills

EXERCISES 11–13 give students practice calculating distances and an opportunity to think about shortest closed paths for a set of vertices. Students see how quickly the number of paths becomes too great to check one by one, because with only 5 points there are already 12 possible paths. When there are 5 vertices the minimum possible path is not convex, but it is as close as possible to a convex polygon. Students who graph the points will see that no self-crossing path is ever the shortest. Encourage students to look at the graph of the points in question to make sense of their results.

Additional Resources

PRINTED RESOURCES
- Texas Instruments Activities Workbook
- Cabrilog Activities
- Teaching Resources
- Practice Workbook
- Assessment Resources

TECHNOLOGY
- TeacherExpress CD-ROM
- **Exam**_View_ CD-ROM
- **PHSchool.com**
  - Homework Help
  - Video Tutors
  - Multiple Choice
  - Crosswords

Additional Practice

1. For each of the following pool shots, locate the point you should aim for and sketch the path you expect the ball to take.

    a. Hit the ball off the top bumper and into the bottom right corner pocket.
    b. Hit the ball off the bottom bumper and into the top left corner pocket.
    c. Hit the ball off the top bumper, the bottom bumper, and into the top middle pocket.
    d. Hit the ball off the left bumper and into the top right corner pocket.

2. You are given line m and two points A and B that are not on the line. Describe a method for finding a point P on line m that minimizes the total length of the path from A to P to B.

3. A path on the coordinate plane must go from $A(5, 4)$ to point C on line ℓ with equation $x = 1$. Then the path goes to point D on line m with equation $x = 6$, and finally to $B(3, -4)$.
    a. Graph the shortest path.
    b. Find the coordinates of C and D.
    c. Suppose A is closer to line ℓ than to line m. Describe how the path from A to ℓ, to m, to B changes.

4. A path on the coordinate plane must go from $A(5, 4)$ to point C on line ℓ with equation $y = 2$. Then the path goes to point D on line m with equation $y = 7$, and finally to $B(-2, 4)$.
    a. Graph the shortest path.
    b. Find the coordinates of C and D.
    c. Suppose A is closer to line ℓ than to line m. Describe how the path from A to ℓ, to m, to B changes.

Practice: For Lesson 8.3, assign Exercises 1–5.

---

8. You are running a race at a July Fourth party. There are water troughs all along the left and right sides of the course.

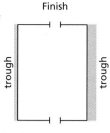

    The goal is to run to the left trough to fill up a pitcher, run to the right trough to empty it, and then cross the finish line. You want to minimize the distance you run. Where should you fill and empty the pitcher?

9. The race in Exercise 8 is too easy. Now, instead of a pitcher, you have to carry the water in a shallow bowl and you will get penalties for any water you spill. Find a new route that minimizes the distance you have to carry the water-filled bowl.

10. **Standardized Test Prep** The measure of the angle at which a ray of light hits a mirror is 30°. What is the measure of the angle at which the ray of light reflects off the mirror?

    A. 30°   **B.** 60°   **C.** 90°   **D.** 150°

Maintain Your Skills

You have been minimizing lengths of paths that go through only two or three points. In this next series of problems, you will explore situations with more stopping points. In Exercises 11–13, you have $A(-3, -2)$, $B(1, 3)$, and $C(4, -1)$. A path is defined as follows.

- The path must start and end at A.
- It must pass through each of the other given points once and only once.
- For two paths to be considered different, one must contain at least one point that is not on the other path.

Answer the following questions for each of the given situations.

a. How many different paths meet the requirements?

b. Find the length of each path that fits the requirements. Which path is the shortest?

11. A path in this situation is made up of segments having A, B, and C as endpoints. (A path must pass through B and C once and only once.)

12. Include a fourth point $D(-2, 0)$ in the situation. Now the path consists of segments having A, B, C, and D as endpoints.

13. Include a fifth point $E(0, 5)$ in the situation. Now the path consists of segments having A, B, C, D, and E as endpoints.

For additional practice go to **Web Code:** bea-0803

---

8. Let d be the distance from the start point to the finish point. The point for the left trough is $\frac{d}{4}$ units above the start line. The point for the right trough is $\frac{d}{4}$ units below the finish line.

9. Go to the midpoint of the left trough to fill the bowl, go straight to the right trough (along a segment perpendicular to the troughs) to empty the bowl, and then go to the finish point.

10. A

11. **a.** 1 path
    b. $\sqrt{41} + 5 + 5\sqrt{2}$
    ; $A \to B \to C \to A$ (or, equivalently, $A \to C \to B \to A$)

12. **a.** 3 paths
    b.
    $A \to B \to C \to D \to A$: $\sqrt{41} + \sqrt{37} + \sqrt{5} + 5$ (≈ 19.722)
    $A \to B \to D \to C \to A$: $\sqrt{41} + \sqrt{37} + 8\sqrt{2}$ (≈ 23.800)
    $A \to C \to B \to D \to A$: $\sqrt{5} + 8\sqrt{2} + 5$ (≈ 18.550)

13. See back of book.

Mathematical 8A Reflections

In this investigation, you learned to distinguish between path and distance, and find the length of a path under given restrictions. These questions will help you summarize what you have learned.

1. Describe this ant's path from *A* to *B* and find the path's length.

   Is this the shortest possible path between *A* and *B*? Explain your answer.

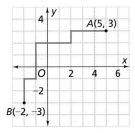

In Exercises 2 and 3, a path must lead from $(-3, 2)$, to the *x*-axis, and then to $(5, 2)$.

2. One path touches the *x*-axis at $(2, 0)$. Find the length of the path.

3. Find a different path that has the same length as the path in Exercise 2.

4. A path must lead from $(3, 5)$, to the line $2x + y = 4$, and then to $(1, 1)$. Where does the shortest path cross the line?

5. Find the path of minimum length that goes from $(-1, 4)$, to the line $y = 5$, to the line $y = -2$, and ends at $(2, 2)$. Your solution should include a graph and the coordinates of any significant points.

6. What is the difference between the length of a path from one point to another and the distance between the points?

7. When and how can reflection help you find the shortest path for a situation?

It's your turn. Can you move one peg across the board?

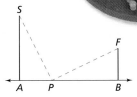

8. In the figure, $\overline{AS}$ and $\overline{BF}$ are perpendicular to $\overleftrightarrow{AB}$. $AS = 54$ ft, $BF = 27$ ft, and $AB = 84$ ft.

   Describe the location of *P* on $\overleftrightarrow{AB}$ so that the path from *S* to *P* to *F* is as short as possible.

Vocabulary

In this investigation, you saw these terms for the first time. Make sure you understand what each one means and how to use it.

- angle of incidence
- angle of reflection
- distance
- path

Mathematical Reflections

EXERCISES 6–8 At the start of the Investigation, you may have assigned these as Questions 1–3 for students to think and write about.

Mathematical Reflections

1. Move left 3 units, down 1 unit, left 3 units, down 3 units, left 1 unit, and down 2 units.; yes, because the ant travels only left and down

2. $\sqrt{29} + \sqrt{13}$

3. from $(-3, 2)$ to $(0, 0)$ to $(5, 2)$

4. $\left(\frac{5}{4}, \frac{3}{2}\right)$

5. See back of book.

6. A path from a point *A* to a point *B* may or may not be straight. If it is straight, then the path is $\overline{AB}$ and is the shortest path from *A* to *B*. Otherwise, the length of the path will be greater than *AB*.

7. Answers may vary. Sample: When stopping off at intermediate destinations or other restrictions require a path composed of several segments with endpoints that can move along a line, reflection can show a way to view that sequence of segments as a straight line.

8. *P* is 56 ft from *A*.

Investigation Overview

In this investigation, students maximize area under different restrictions. As in calculus, when students are faced with a maximization problem, they often have to consider boundary conditions. If the function's local maxima occur outside the allowed boundaries for the problem, then the maximum solution will be at a boundary. Because area is the quantity most often maximized in this investigation, your students will also begin to explore the *isoperimetric problem*: of all closed curves with the same perimeter, which one encloses the most area? This is a very complex problem. Investigation 8D, *Advanced Optimization*, will address it more fully.

You may wish to assign Questions 1–3 for students to think and write about during the investigation.

Learning Goals

- Find grid polygons with a given area or perimeter.
- Maximize area for a triangle or rectangle under given conditions.
- Find the maximum area for a shape with a given perimeter.

Habits and Skills

- Draw conclusions from trends in experimental data.
- Visualize reflections that will help maximize area.
- Reason by continuity to find maximums.

Making the *Most* of a Situation

In *Making the* Most *of a Situation*, you will maximize things—make things as large as possible. In general, people want to maximize food production, profit, gas mileage, fun, or comfort. In geometry, area, angles, and height are often maximized.

By the end of this investigation, you will be able to answer questions like these:

1. Describe some characteristics of a rectangle that has maximum perimeter for a given area. Describe some characteristics of a rectangle that has maximum area for a given perimeter.

2. Describe several situations in which reflection can help you find the maximum area for a figure.

3. You want to build a rectangular garden against one wall of your house. You have 29 feet of border fencing. What are the area and dimensions of the greatest possible garden you can build?

You will learn how to

- find grid polygons with a given area or perimeter
- maximize area for a triangle or rectangle under given conditions
- find the maximum area for a shape with a given perimeter

You will develop these habits and skills:

- Draw conclusions from trends in experimental data.
- Visualize reflections that will help maximize area.
- Reason by continuity to find maximums.

In-car monitors help you get the most miles per gallon.

Investigation Road Map

LESSON 8.4, *Getting Started,* introduces grid polygons, which are polygons made using only the grid lines on a sheet of graph paper. Students will develop their understanding of the relationship between perimeter and area. Finding polygons with maximum area for a given perimeter will prepare them for further exploration of the isoperimetric problem.

LESSON 8.5, *Maximizing Areas, Part I,* continues the study of optimization as students maximize the areas of triangles and rectangles. They will learn about which shapes maximize area under a variety of restrictions.

LESSON 8.6, *Maximizing Areas, Part II,* has students maximize areas of other polygons and learn the Regular Polygon Theorem, which they will prove in Investigation 8D.

Activating Prior Knowledge
Exploring New Ideas

Area and perimeter seem as though they should be related to each other. For example, if one fence encloses a greater area than another, it seems that the walk around the first fence should be longer. However, it does not always work that way. Here are two fields entirely enclosed by fences. You have to check the fences to see if they are in good repair.

Field A   Field B

Which field has more acreage? Which field has more fence for you to check?

> An acre is a unit of area equal to 43,560 square feet.

For You to Explore

1. Use only the grid lines on a sheet of graph paper. Draw several polygons with area 8 square units. Find the perimeter of each one. What are the greatest and least possible perimeters for grid polygons of this area?

2. Use only the grid lines on a sheet of graph paper. Draw several polygons with perimeter 12 units. Find the area of each one. What are the greatest and least possible areas for grid polygons of this perimeter?

3. Use only $1 \times 1 \times 1$ unit cubes joined face to face. Build and sketch several three-dimensional shapes with volume 8 cubic units. Find the surface area of each structure. What are the greatest and least possible surface areas for cube structures of this volume?

4. Use only $1 \times 1 \times 1$ unit cubes joined face to face. Build and sketch several three-dimensional shapes with surface area 22 square units. Find the volume of each structure. What are the greatest and least possible volumes for cube structures that have this surface area?

> **Habits of Mind**
>
> **Find another way.** You do not need a formula to find the surface area of your structures. Just count the exposed cube faces on the top, bottom, and sides of your structure. What is the area of each cube face?

Lesson Overview

GOAL
- Find grid polygons with a given area or perimeter.

In this lesson, students begin to characterize shapes with a large perimeter for a given area or a large area for a given perimeter. By working with grid polygons, students are often in a position to try all the possible shapes for a given situation. This is because when boundaries are restricted to grid lines, the number of possible shapes is kept to a manageable number. Students will also explore three-dimensional shapes that are made by attaching cubes to each other.

FOR YOU TO EXPLORE
- Core: 1, 3
- Optional: 2, 4

MATERIALS
- graph paper
- protractors
- rulers
- Blackline Master MC14

HOMEWORK
- Core: 6, 7, 12
- Optional: 5, 8, 9, 10, 11, 13, 14, 15, 16, 17

VOCABULARY
- grid polygon
- maximize
- maximum

Launch

Begin this lesson by asking your students to read the introductory paragraph. Assign some of the For You To Explore problems.

Explore

Go over the problems you assigned with your students to assess their level of understanding.

Wrap Up

End this lesson by assigning homework exercises.

Answers

For You to Explore

1. greatest: 18 units; least: 12 units
2. greatest: 9 unit^2; least: 5 unit^2
3. greatest: 34 unit^2; least: 24 unit^2
4. greatest: 6 unit^3; least: 5 unit^3

Exercises

HOMEWORK
• Core: 6, 7, 12
• Optional: 5, 8, 9, 10, 11, 13, 14, 15, 16, 17

On Your Own

EXERCISE 6 shows all the possible cases of adding one square to the area of a grid polygon. The new square could cover 1 edge of the old perimeter and show 3 new edges, cover 2 and show 2, cover 3 and show 1, or cover 4 and show no new edges. Students determine the effect each of these cases has on perimeter and area.

In the last case, the starting figure is not actually a polygon because it has a hole in the middle. A polygon must always be a simple closed curve, which means that you must be able to draw its entire boundary without lifting your pen (or crossing your own path). This case is included so that every possible effect on the perimeter of a figure from adding a square of area is shown.

EXERCISE 8 is similar to Exercise 6. It addresses all of the possible cases of adding one cube to a cube polyhedron. The new cube could cover 1 face of the old surface area and show 5 new faces, cover 2 and show 4, and so on until the last case when it covers 6 faces of the old surface area and shows no new faces. Students determine the effect each of these cases has on surface area and volume.

In the last two cases, the starting shape is not actually a polyhedron, because polyhedra must have polygonal faces. There is a hole in at least one face of these shapes.

Exercises *Practicing Habits of Mind*

On Your Own

5. Describe several situations in which maximizing area would help in making food or money, saving time, or providing other benefits.

6. Each of the following grid polygons is changing. One square unit of area will be added to the polygon in the location shown. Find the perimeter and area for both the original and the new polygon.

> In part (d), the original figure is not a polygon. The new figure is a polygon. The square with the missing center is included for the sake of completeness.

a.

b.

c.

d.

7. Change this grid polygon by adding as many square units to the polygon as you can without changing its perimeter. Show each step you take and check that the perimeter is unchanged. What is the greatest area you can get?

8. Each cube structure is changing. One cubic unit of volume will be added to the structure in the location shown. Find the surface area and volume of both the original and the new structures.

a.

b.

c.

d.

Answers

Exercises

5. Answers may vary. Sample: Maximizing area of farmable land can increase crop production.

6. **a.** old perimeter = 12, new perimeter = 14, old area = 5, new area = 6
   b. old perimeter = 12, new perimeter = 12, old area = 5, new area = 6
   c. old perimeter = 16, new perimeter = 12, old area = 8, new area = 6
   d. old perimeter = 16, new perimeter = 14, old area = 8, new area = 9

7. See back of book.

8. **a.** old surface area = 18, new surface area = 22, old volume = 4, new volume = 5
   b. old surface area = 24, new surface area = 26, old volume = 6, new volume = 7

Parts (e) and (f) may be difficult to visualize. Each figure is shown with an exploded view that shows the floors of the structure separately.

Original Structure

e. top floor: 8 cubes

 bottom floor: 9 cubes

f. Defining the surface area of the original structure is difficult because the structure has a hollow space in the middle. Count any square face that is touched by air as part of the surface area.

Original Structure

 top floor: 9 cubes

 middle floor: 8 cubes   The added cube fills in the hollow space.

 bottom floor: 9 cubes

9. Change this cube structure by adding as many cubic units as you can without changing its surface area. Show each step you take and check that the surface area is unchanged. What is the greatest volume you can get?

10. Write About It Describe the characteristics of grid polygons that have maximum perimeter for a given area. What do they look like? What features *don't* they have?

11. Write About It Describe the characteristics of grid polygons that have minimum perimeter for a given area. What do they look like? What features *don't* they have?

c. old surface area = 32,
new surface area = 32,
old volume = 10,
new volume = 11

d. old surface area = 42,
new surface area = 40,
old volume = 15,
new volume = 16

e. old surface area = 46,
new surface area = 42,
old volume = 17,
new volume = 18

f. old surface area = 60,
new surface area = 54,

old volume = 26,
new volume = 27

9. See back of book.

10. Answers may vary. Sample: Grid polygons are long and skinny. Maximum perimeter grid polygons will not contain a square that shares more than two sides with other squares of the polygon.

11. Answers may vary. Sample: Grid polygons will be clumped together and avoid jagged edges.

EXERCISES 13–17 provide students with a chance to practice trigonometry and to investigate the perimeters of regular polygons inscribed in a circle. Blackline Master MC 14 offers a quick review of try ratios. As the number of sides of the regular polygon increase, the polygon's shape approaches that of the circle. Its perimeter approaches the circumference of the circle. This exercise prepares students for the work they will do in Investigation 8D when proving the Regular Polygon Theorem.

12. Find four polygons with area 12 square units. Each must meet one of the following criteria.
    - It is a grid polygon that has maximum perimeter.
    - It is a grid polygon that has minimum perimeter.
    - It is a polygon of any type that has a greater perimeter than the maximum for grid polygons. (This polygon is not restricted to grid lines on graph paper.)
    - It is a polygon of any type that has a perimeter less than the minimum for grid polygons.

Maintain Your Skills

For Exercises 13–16, the regular polygon is inscribed in a circle of radius 1.
- Find the measure of the central angle θ, which intersects two adjacent vertices of the polygon.
- Find the length of one side of the polygon.
- Find the perimeter of the polygon.

13.

14.

15.

16.

17. Look at your results for Exercises 13–16. Describe any patterns that allow you to predict results for inscribed polygons with more sides.

Answers

12. max. perimeter = 26 units; min. perimeter = 14 units; check students' work.

13. 120°; side length = $\sqrt{3}$, perimeter = $3\sqrt{3}$

14. 90°; side length = $\sqrt{2}$, perimeter = $4\sqrt{2}$

15. 72°; side length = $\dfrac{\sqrt{10 - 2\sqrt{5}}}{2}$, perimeter = $\dfrac{5\sqrt{10 - 2\sqrt{5}}}{2}$
(Note: In Exercise 18 of Lesson 6.7, the exact value of cos 72° was calculated to be $\dfrac{\sqrt{5} - 1}{4}$.)

16. 60°; side length = 1, perimeter = 6

17. As the number of sides of the inscribed regular polygon increases, the measure of θ decreases, the length of an individual side decreases, and the perimeter increases. The perimeters approach the circumference of the circle (2π).

In Lesson 8.4, you were able to find maximums by trial and error. You were
working in a restricted environment, so you could try each of the possible
structures that met the given requirements. Now, you are going to prove
some results about maximum area using familiar shapes.

Minds in Action   episode 38

Sasha and Derman are working on the following problem.

Suppose you want to build a house with a rectangular base. The most
expensive part of the house to frame is the exterior walls. You decide
you can afford a house with a base (or floor) that has a total perimeter of
128 feet. What dimensions should you choose for the base if you want to
maximize the floor area?

Derman After working with the grid polygons, we know it has to be a
square. So it's a square with sides 32 feet long.

Sasha Well, we *think* it has to be a square. We haven't proven
anything yet.

Derman Okay, I'll take a stab at it. The 32×32 square is better than
a 40×24 rectangle. The area of the square is 1024 ft^2, while the
area of the 40×24 rectangle is only 960 ft^2.

Sasha True, but that's just one case. We have to show that the square
has a greater area than any rectangle we could choose. Let's
draw a picture.

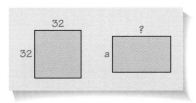

Derman Okay, the width of the rectangle is a, which is supposed to be less
than 32 feet. How can we find the length of the rectangle?

Is this a good example?
(What is the perimeter of
a 40×24 rectangle?)

Habits of Mind

Strategize. Use
the perimeter.

Lesson Overview

GOALS

• Maximize area for a triangle or rectangle under
given conditions.

• Find the maximum area for a shape with a given
perimeter.

In this lesson, students prove that the rectangle
with the maximum area for a given perimeter is a
square. They use the geometric dissection ideas from
Chapter 3 to visualize the proof. Students also solve
a common maximization problem from calculus
using both algebraic and geometric methods.
In the algebraic method, they write a quadratic
function that returns the area of the dog pen. In the
geometric method, they reflect the dog pen over a
line and then maximize the area of a rectangle with
the given perimeter. In the exercises, students will
find other maxim including some that require
them to consider the boundary conditions the
exercise imposes.

CHECK YOUR
UNDERSTANDING
• Core: 1, 3
• Optional: 2

MATERIALS
• graphing calculators
• rulers

HOMEWORK
• Core: 4, 6, 8
• Optional: 5, 7, 9, 10,
11, 12, 13, 15, 16
• Extension: 14

Launch

Begin this lesson by having students read or act out
the dialog between Derman and Sasha.

Explore

Have students work on the For You to Do problems with a partner or in small groups. Read through the Example as a class.

Wrap Up

End this lesson by assigning some Check Your Understanding exercises.

Assessment Resources

Sasha   We can try a cutting proof like the ones we used in Chapter 3. The length of the rectangle has to be greater than 32. Our rectangle has a width a and a length greater than 32 feet, so we can cut off a rectangle a feet by 32 feet.

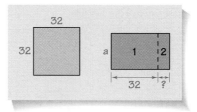

Derman   Then we can fit both pieces inside the square like this!

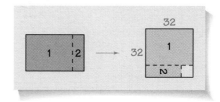

Sasha   Great. Now you can see that the area of the rectangle is less than the area of the square.

For You to Do

There are some details missing in the dialog above.

1. Find the length of a rectangle with perimeter 128 feet and width a feet. Your answer should be in terms of a.

2. If the width a of Sasha's rectangle is less than 32 feet, how does she know its length is greater than 32 feet?

3. When Sasha cut off the $32 \times a$ rectangle, what were the dimensions of the little rectangle that was left?

4. Do both pieces of the rectangle really fit into the square as Derman said they would? Explain.

5. Write out a proof of Sasha's cutting argument in your own words. Prove that any nonsquare rectangle with a perimeter of 128 feet has less area than a square with the same perimeter.

Answers

For You to Do

1. $(64 - a)$ ft

2. If the length were less than or equal to 32 ft, then the perimeter would be less than 128 ft.

3. $a \times (32 - a)$

4. yes

5. Refer to the shaded rectangles inside Derman's final diagram of the 32-ft by 32-ft square. The sum of their areas is the area of the original shaded rectangle. The shaded parts leave uncovered a piece of the 32-ft by 32-ft square that has an area of $(32 - a)^2$ ft^2 (a positive quantity). So the original shaded rectangle has an area less than the area of the 32-ft by 32-ft square.

Problem You want to fence in a rectangular exercise run for your dog. You have 36 feet of fencing material. You decide that to enclose more area, you will use a wall of your house as the fourth side of the run. What are the dimensions of the greatest area you can enclose?

Solution This figure shows a run with width a and length b.

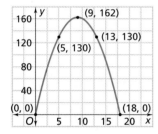

The total amount of fencing is 36 feet, so the perimeter equation is as follows.

$$2a + b = 36$$

You want to maximize A_{run}, which is the area of the run. The formula follows.

$$A_{run} = ab$$

Rewrite this formula in terms of one variable, say a, using the previous perimeter equation.

$$A_{run} = a(36 - 2a)$$
$$= 36a - 2a^2$$

Graph A_{run} as a function of a on a coordinate grid, either by hand or with a graphing calculator.

The graph is a parabola opening downward. The maximum value for A_{run} occurs at $a = 9$ feet. The dimensions of the run with the greatest area are 9 feet by 18 feet. Its area is 162 square feet.

Exercises

HOMEWORK
- Core: 4, 6, 8
- Optional: 5, 7, 9, 10, 11, 12, 13, 15, 16
- Extension: 14

Developing Habits of Mind

Use another method. Another way to approach the rectangular dog run problem is to use reflection. Reflect the dog run over the line of the house wall. Now you have a problem that you know how to solve.

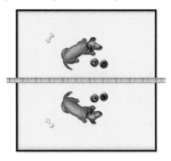

The new rectangle has a perimeter of 72 feet. You want to maximize the area. The maximum area will occur when the rectangle is a square with a side length of 18 feet. The real dog run is half of that square, so it measures 9 feet by 18 feet.

Exercises *Practicing Habits of Mind*

Check Your Understanding

1. Find the area of the triangle described in parts (a)–(c). In each case, the triangle is isosceles with a perimeter of 15 inches. Then answer part (d).

   a. base = 4 in.   **b.** base = 5 in.   **c.** base = 6 in.

   d. Make a conjecture about which isosceles triangle of a given perimeter will enclose the most area.

2. A triangle has a perimeter of 36 cm, and one side is 10 cm long. What should the lengths of the other two sides be to maximize the area of the triangle? Experiment and make a conjecture about the maximum area for this triangle.

   > You will prove your conjecture in Exercise 7.

3. Of all the rectangles with a given perimeter, which one has the greatest area? Explain.

Answers

Exercises

1. **a.** 10.247 in.^{2}
   (exact area: $\sqrt{105}$ in.^{2})
   b. 10.825 in.^{2}
   (exact area: $\frac{25\sqrt{3}}{4}$ in.^{2})
   c. 10.062 in.^{2} (exact area: $\frac{9\sqrt{5}}{2}$ in.^{2})
   d. For a given perimeter, an equilateral triangle encloses the maximum area.

2. 13 cm and 13 cm; 60 cm^2

3. a square ; the argument in the For You to Do questions can easily be generalized to work not just for the perimeter 128 but for any given perimeter p.

On Your Own

4. Standardized Test Prep Ned draws a rectangle such that its length is twice its width, and its perimeter is half its area. What is the area of Ned's rectangle?

A. 8 units^2 **B.** 18 units^2 **C.** 32 units^2 **D.** 72 units^2

5. Refer back to the cutting method used in this lesson's Minds in Action. Show that an $a \times b$ nonsquare rectangle has less area than a square with the same perimeter. (This is not the same problem as in Minds in Action. Here the perimeter is fixed, but you do not know what it is.)

6. Suppose as in the Example you have 36 ft of fencing. You want to build a rectangular dog run against a barn wall that is 13 ft long. Again, you plan to use the barn as one side of the run. What size rectangle maximizes the area of the run now?

7. Triangles of many different shapes may have one side of length 5 in. and one of length 6 in. Which of these triangles encloses the most area? Explain.

8. In Exercise 2, you studied triangles with one side 10 cm and perimeter 36 cm. You may have conjectured that the triangle with maximum area is isosceles. It would have two 13-cm sides. The conjecture is true. In this exercise, you will prove it.

Suppose the height you conjectured is not the maximum. So there is another point that gives a greater height for the triangle. Therefore, the two unknown sides are not equal. One must be greater than 13 cm and one must be less by the same amount. Also, the perpendicular from the third vertex of the triangle does not intersect the 10-cm side at its midpoint. The point of intersection is closer to one side.

This scenario is shown in the figure.

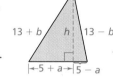

a. Write equations relating a, b, and h for each of the small right triangles in the figure. Use the Pythagorean Theorem.

b. Expand and simplify each side of the equation. Subtract one equation from the other. Find an expression for a in terms of b.

c. Using either of the two equations you wrote in part (a), write an equation for h in terms of b.

d. Show that the value of h is greatest when $b = 0$ and the triangle is isosceles.

9. A triangle has one side that measures s cm and a total perimeter of p cm. What lengths for the other two sides will maximize its area?

10. Out of all the triangles with perimeter 18 cm, which has the greatest area? Explain.

11. Find the maximum area for a triangle with perimeter 24 in. Now, find the maximum area for a rectangle with perimeter 24 in. Which is greater?

On Your Own

EXERCISE 5 addresses an important concept that students will use in the next lesson to show that for a given perimeter, the quadrilateral with the greatest area is a square. At this point, they have just shown that for a given perimeter, the *rectangle* with the greatest area is a square.

EXERCISE 6 In this exercise, the wall is not long enough to build the optimal rectangular dog run for the amount of fencing you have. This means that the boundary condition—the length of the given wall—comes into play. The Solution Manual explains why extending that wall with your fence does not result in a dog run with greater area than just using the wall as one full side. Exercises 8 and 12–15 in the next lesson examine this concept in greater detail.

EXERCISE 8 shows that the triangle with a given base and perimeter that encloses the most area must be isosceles. This result will be critical in the proof of the Regular Polygon Theorem, which the next lesson cites, but which students will not prove until Investigation 8D.

---

4. D

5. See back of book.

6. 13 m by 11.5 m

7. a right triangle with legs of lengths 5 in. and 6 in.

8. a. $h^2 + (5 + a)^2 = (13 + b)^2$,
    $h^2 + (5 - a)^2 = (13 - b)^2$

  b. $a = 2.6b$

  c. $h = \sqrt{144 - 5.76b^2}$

  d. h is greatest when $144 - 5.76b^2$ is greatest, and this occurs when $b = 0$. But when $b = 0$, both $13 + b$ and

$13 - b$ equal 13, which means that the triangle is isosceles.

9. $\left(\dfrac{p - s}{2}\right)$ cm

10. an equilateral triangle with sides of length 6 cm

11. $16\sqrt{3}$ in.^{2}; 36 in.^{2}; the area of the rectangle

Maintain Your Skills

EXERCISES 12–15 may seem very similar to Exercises 13–17 in the previous lesson, but there is an important difference that will be critical in the proof of the Regular Polygon Theorem. In the previous lesson, all the regular polygons were inscribed in a circle with a given radius. As the number of sides in the polygons increased, their perimeters increased. Here, the perimeters of the polygons are held constant as the number of sides increases. As the number of sides increases, the area that the polygon encloses also increases. Note that if this series of regular polygons were inscribed in circles, the radius of the circle would actually *decrease* as the number of sides increased.

Additional Resources

PRINTED RESOURCES
- Texas Instruments Activities Workbook
- Cabrilog Activities
- Teaching Resources
- Practice Workbook
- Assessment Resources

TECHNOLOGY
- TeacherExpress CD-ROM
- **Exam*View*** CD-ROM
- **PHSchool.com**
  - Homework Help
  - Video Tutors
  - Multiple Choice
  - Crosswords

Practice: For Lesson 8.5, assign Exercises 1–9.

Maintain Your Skills

12. Find the area of a regular triangle (an equilateral triangle) with perimeter 60 cm.

13. Find the area of a regular quadrilateral (a square) with perimeter 60 cm.

14. Take It Further

  a. This regular pentagon is inscribed in a circle and cut into 5 congruent isosceles triangles.

  Find the measurements of all three angles in one of the triangles.

  b. Here is one of the triangles by itself.

  Use the tangent function to find an approximation for h in terms of b.

  c. Find the area of a regular pentagon with perimeter 60 cm.

15. a. This regular hexagon is inscribed in a circle and cut into 6 congruent isosceles triangles.

  Find the measurements of all three angles in one of the triangles.

  b. Here is one of the triangles by itself.

  Use the tangent function to find an approximation for h in terms of base b.

  c. Find the area of a regular hexagon with perimeter 60 cm.

16. Refer to Exercises 12–15. Make some conjectures about what kind of shape will have the maximum area for a given perimeter.

Go Online
Video Tutor
PHSchool.com

Web Code: bee-0805

Go Online
PHSchool.com

For additional practice, go to **Web Code: bea-0805**

Answers

12. $100\sqrt{3}$ cm^2

13. 225 cm^2

14. a. $72°, 54°, 54°$

  b. $h \approx 0.688b$

  c. 247.749 cm^2

15. a. $60°, 60°, 60°$

  b. $h = \dfrac{b\sqrt{3}}{2}$

  c. $150\sqrt{3}$ cm$^2 \approx 259.8$ cm^2

16. Answers may vary. Sample: A polygon with a given perimeter has maximum area when it is a regular polygon.

8.6 Maximizing Areas, Part 2

In Lesson 8.5, you explored problems in which the perimeter of a polygon is fixed. You discovered that the triangle with the greatest area is equilateral. The rectangle with the greatest area is a square. These two results may have led you to a conjecture similar to the following theorem.

Theorem 8.1 The Regular Polygon Theorem

Of all the polygons having a given perimeter and a given number of sides, the regular polygon has the greatest area.

You will work toward a proof of this theorem in the exercises for this lesson and in Investigation 8D.

In Exercise 11 of the previous lesson, an equilateral triangle and a square have the same perimeter. The area of the square is greater. Exercises 12–15 support the conjecture that for a fixed perimeter, the more sides a regular polygon has, the greater is its area.

For Discussion

Suppose for now that Theorem 8.1 is true, even though you have not seen it proven. Also suppose that for a given perimeter, a regular polygon with more sides encloses more area than a polygon with fewer sides. Propose an answer to the following area-maximization problem.

1. For all shapes with the same perimeter, which has the greatest area?

> You will explore this question thoroughly in Investigation 8D.

Exercises *Practicing Habits of Mind*

Check Your Understanding

1. Which polygon has the greater area? Find a way to convince your teacher or someone else that your answer is correct.

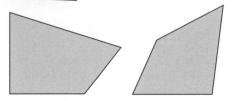

> **Habits of Mind**
>
> **Consider more than one strategy.** Could you trace and then cut up the polygons to compare the parts? What else might you do?

For Discussion

1. a circle

Exercises

1. The first polygon. Answers may vary. Sample: Cut up the second triangle and show that it fits inside the first triangle with some left over.

Lesson Overview

GOAL

- Find the maximum area for a shape with a given perimeter.

This lesson introduces the Regular Polygon Theorem, an important theorem about maximizing the areas of regular polygons.

CHECK YOUR UNDERSTANDING	HOMEWORK
• Core: 2, 3 • Optional: 1	• Core: 4, 5, 8, 9 • Optional: 6, 7, 10, 11, 12, 13, 14, 15

MATERIALS
- rulers
- Blackline Master 8.6

Launch

Begin this lesson by reading or stating Theorem 8.1.

Explore

For Discussion

Your students will likely conjecture that the circle has the greatest area for a given perimeter. The proof is very subtle and will be more fully explored in Investigation 8D. Right now, challenge your students to think about how they could show that for a given perimeter, a polygon with more sides would have to enclose more area. They will realize that this is quite difficult, especially if they have completed Exercises 12–15 in the previous lesson. Although the area of the polygons increased as the number of sides increased, the radii of the circumscribed circles decreased. Showing that the area will continue to increase is not a trivial matter.

Wrap Up

End this lesson by assigning some Check Your Understanding exercises.

Assessment Resources

Exercises

HOMEWORK

- Core: 4, 5, 8, 9
- Optional: 6, 7, 10, 11, 12, 13, 14, 15

Check Your Understanding

EXERCISE 1 may seem simplistic at first. It is meant to remind students of the definition of area and how they have compared and developed formulas for area in the past. Blackline Master 8.6 depicts the two polygons in case students want to cut and reconfigure the shapes.

EXERCISES 2 AND 6 are necessary preliminaries to the proof of the Isoperimetric Conjecture in Investigation 8D. Blackline Master 8.6 depicts the polygon in Exercise 2.

2. Consider the polygon at the right. Describe a way to make a polygon with the same side lengths, but with greater area.

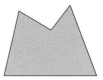

3. Consider all the parallelograms with side lengths 20, 30, 20, and 30. Which one encloses the most area? Explain.

On Your Own

4. **Standardized Test Prep** Suppose you have four regular polygons: a triangle, a quadrilateral, a pentagon, and a hexagon. The perimeters of the polygons are the same. Which polygon has the greatest area?

   A. triangle   **B.** quadrilateral   **C.** pentagon   **D.** hexagon

5. Consider all the quadrilaterals of a given perimeter. Prove that the one that encloses the most area is a rhombus. You might draw a diagonal that cuts the quadrilateral into two triangles. How can you guarantee that the triangles both have maximum area? What do you find if you draw the other diagonal?

6. Show that the n-gon of a given perimeter that encloses the most area must be equilateral. Use your reasoning from Exercise 5.

7. Prove that the rhombus of a given perimeter that encloses the most area is a square.

8. Use Theorem 8.1 to solve the following problem, which is similar to the example in Lesson 8.5.

   Suppose you want to build a four-sided pen that is not necessarily a rectangle. You plan to use a stone wall as one side of the pen. The other three walls will be built with 840 feet of fencing. What shape and dimensions maximize the area of the pen?

9. Explain why the hypotenuse is always the longest side of a right triangle.

10. A typical juice box contains about 250 milliliters (mL) of juice. It measures $10.5 \text{ cm} \times 6.5 \text{ cm} \times 4 \text{ cm}$.

    a. What is the volume of this box in cubic centimeters?

    b. Is this the best box size? Suppose the manufacturer wants to maximize profit by reducing packaging costs. What size rectangular box will hold 250 mL and use the least cardboard?

    c. Design a container (of any shape) that holds 250 mL of juice, using the least cardboard. (Be sure that it can be held comfortably by a child and can be assembled and stacked.) Explain your choice with enough information to convince a packaging engineer that it is the best shape.

Remember...

The hypotenuse of a right triangle is the side opposite the right angle.

Answers

2. Label the polygon as *ABCDE* starting with the bottom left vertex and ending with the bottom right vertex. Draw $\overleftrightarrow{BD}$ and reflect point *C* across $\overleftrightarrow{BD}$ to *C′*. Draw *ABC′DE*.

3. See back of book.

4. D

5–7. See back of book.

8. A trapezoid formed by dividing a regular hexagon in half by a line through two opposite vertices gives the maximum area. The sides made with fencing will each be 280 ft long, and the side along the stone wall will be 560 ft long.

9. Answers may vary. Sample: One reason is that the legs are perpendicular. The perpendicular is the shortest path from a point to a line, so any other path must be longer.

10. a. 273 cm^3

    b. a cube of edge length $\sqrt[3]{250}$ cm

    c. Check students' work.

11. Cut wood is often sold by the cord. A cord is a stack that measures 4 feet × 4 feet × 8 feet. This picture shows one way to stack a cord of 8-foot logs, all with the same diameter.

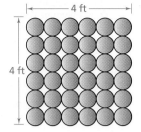

Jamal is ordering a cord of wood stacked this way. Suppose he can choose the diameter of the logs he buys. (In reality, there are many different diameters in a cord of wood.) What diameter should Jamal choose if he wants to maximize the amount of wood in the stack? (He wants to minimize the amount of air he buys.) Should Jamal buy one big log or many small logs?

Maintain Your Skills

Use the following description for Exercises 12–15.

Danae wants to build a rectangular dog run for her beagle, Bruiser. She has 48 feet of fencing to use. One wall of her house will serve as a side of the run. She wants Bruiser to have the maximum area possible.

12. What are the dimensions and area of the run she should build?

13. You tell Danae that the rectangular dog run is not the best possible 4-sided run. Instead, her run should be half of a regular hexagon. Give Danae directions (including lengths and angles) and the area of this dog run.

14. The wall of Danae's house is only 20 feet long. She cannot build the optimal rectangular run or the optimal half-hexagonal run. Find the new best rectangular run. Find the new best hexagonal run.

15. Danae has another problem. If she builds more than 9 feet from the house, she will run into the neighbor's property line. She has two possible solutions. Find the dimensions and the area of the best run of each type described below.

a. The run is a 9-foot wide rectangle. The 20-foot wall is part of one side.

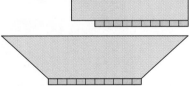

b. The run is a 9-foot-wide isosceles trapezoid. The 20-foot wall is one complete base of the trapezoid.

Go Online
PHSchool.com

For additional practice, go to **Web Code: bea-0806**

c. Which run should Danae choose?

Additional Practice

1. Describe a way to make a polygon with the same side lengths as the polygon in the figure, but with greater area.

2. a. What type of parallelogram, with fixed perimeter, encloses the most area?
b. What type of parallelogram encloses the most area if the side lengths are 12, 12, 24, and 24?

3. a. A quadrilateral has perimeter 40 meters. Prove that to maximize the area, the figure must be a square.
b. A regular pentagon has perimeter 50 meters. Find the area of the pentagon.
c. Show that an n-gon of a given perimeter must be regular to maximize the area it encloses.

4. A farmer has 300 meters of fencing to make a rectangular corral. A barn wall will border one length of the corral. The width of the corral is w.
a. Express the length and the area of the corral in terms of w.
b. What dimensions maximize the area of the corral?

5. a. Draw a rectangle.
b. Construct a square with equal area.
c. Compare their perimeters.

6. An equilateral triangle, a square, a regular hexagon, and a circle each have perimeter 30 meters.
a. Find the side length (radius for the circle) and area of each figure.
b. Make a conjecture about your results.

7. A rubber ball manufacturer wants to minimize costs on packaging. The company plans to package 1000 rubber balls, with diameters of 2 cm, in each box. What dimensions for the box minimize the amount of cardboard needed?

8. A pencil manufacturer wants to minimize costs on packaging. The company plans to package 20 pencils, with dimensions shown below, in each box. What dimensions for the box minimize the amount of cardboard needed?

Practice: For Lesson 8.6, assign Exercises 1–9.

---

11. It doesn't matter what diameter he chooses.

12. 12 ft by 24 ft; 288 ft^2

13. Use an isosceles trapezoid $ABCD$ with $AB = BC = CD = 16$ ft, $AD = 32$ ft, $m\angle A = m\angle D = 60°$, and $m\angle B = m\angle C = 120°$. The area will be $192\sqrt{3} \approx 332.6$ ft^2.

14. The new best rectangle is 20 ft by 14 ft for an area of 280 ft^2. The new best hexagonal run will be an isosceles trapezoid

$ABCD$ with $AD = 20$ ft and $AB = BC = CD = 16$ ft for an area of $256 + 12\sqrt{7} \approx 287.7$ ft^2.

15. a. 25 ft by 9 ft; 225 ft^2

b. isosceles trapezoid with height 9 ft, legs of length $\frac{227}{28} \approx 9.9$ ft, bases of lengths 20 ft and $\frac{395}{14} \approx 28.2$ ft, area = $\frac{6075}{28} \approx 217.0$ ft^2

c. the rectangular run

Mathematical Reflections

EXERCISES 6–8 At the start of the Investigation, you may have assigned these as Questions 1–3 for students to think and write about.

Mathematical Reflections 8B

In this investigation, you learned how to find grid polygons with a given area or perimeter, and to maximize the area for a shape with certain restrictions. These questions will help you summarize what you have learned.

1. Use only the grid lines on a sheet of graph paper. Find the polygon that has area 8 square units with the maximum perimeter possible.

2. Use only the grid lines on a sheet of graph paper. Find the polygon that has perimeter 12 units with the maximum area possible.

3. Several triangles have one side of length 7 cm and one side of length 5 cm. Which of these triangles encloses the most area? What is its perimeter?

4. Find the maximum possible area for a triangle with perimeter 24 in.

5. Find the maximum possible area for a quadrilateral with perimeter 24 in.

6. Describe some characteristics of a rectangle that has maximum perimeter for a given area. Describe some characteristics of a rectangle that has maximum area for a given perimeter.

7. Describe several situations in which reflection can help you find the maximum area for a figure.

8. You want to build a rectangular garden against one wall of your house. You have 29 feet of border fencing. What are the area and dimensions of the greatest possible garden you can build?

HOV lanes help move the most people per gallon.

Answers

Mathematical Reflections

1. Answers may vary. Sample: A rectangle 8 by 1 has perimeter 18.

2. A square with sides of length 3 has area 9.

3. a right triangle with legs of lengths 7 cm and 5 cm; $(12 + \sqrt{74})$ cm.

4. $16\sqrt{3}$ in^2.

5. 36 in.^{2}

6. long and thin; has adjacent sides whose lengths are equal or nearly equal

7. Answers may vary. Sample: Suppose you are given a certain amount of fencing and want to build a rectangular pen along a straight wall that uses the wall as one side of the pen. You can use a reflection to find the dimensions that will maximize the area.

8. 105.125 ft^2, 14.5 ft by 7.25 ft

Chapter 8

Mid-Chapter Test

Go Online
PHSchool.com

For a mid-chapter test, go to **Web Code: bea-0852**

Multiple Choice

1. Recall from Lesson 8.1 that an ant can only travel on the wire mesh of a coordinate grid. If an ant travels from $A(1, 4)$ to $B(-4, 0)$, what is the length of the shortest possible path?

A. 6 units   **B.** 9 units

C. 12 units   **D.** 15 units

2. Suppose a square is inscribed in a circle of radius 3 cm. Find the area of the square.

A. 9 cm^2 **B.** 18 cm^2

C. $6\sqrt{18} \text{ cm}^2$ **D.** 36 cm^2

Open Response

3. Trace these lines and draw the shortest path from A to B.

4. Trace these lines. Draw the shortest path from A to B through some point P on line m. Label P.

5. Describe and draw the shortest path from X to the polygon $ABCDEFG$.

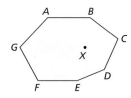

In Exercises 6 and 7, a path must lead from $(4, 5)$, to the y-axis, and then to $(4, -4)$.

6. One path touches the y-axis at $(0, -3)$. Find the length of the path.

7. Find a different path that follows the rules and has the same length as the path in Exercise 6.

8. A town ordinance says you must have a fence around your swimming pool. You can afford 36 meters of fence to enclose a rectangle around your pool.

a. What dimensions maximize the area of this rectangle if all four sides are made from your fencing?

b. Suppose you want to enclose an even greater area. You decide to build against your neighbor's existing 20-meter fence. The 36 meters of fencing will be used for the other three sides. What dimensions maximize the area of this rectangle?

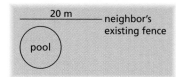

9. Suppose you have a group of 16 pictures, each 6 inches by 6 inches. You want to arrange them edge to edge and then frame the group. The frame store charges $2 per foot of frame.

a. How should you arrange your 16 pictures to minimize the cost? What is the cost? Draw a picture and explain your answer.

b. What is the most expensive arrangement? What is the cost? Draw a picture and explain your answer.

Assessment Resources

Mid-Chapter Test

1. Find the shortest path from $A(2, 6)$, to any point P on the line with equation $x = -3$, to $B(1, -3)$.
  a. What point P on the line $x = -3$ should the path go through? Explain.
  b. What is the length of the shortest path?

2. For the pool shot below, locate the point you should aim for and sketch the path you expect the ball to take.
  Hit the ball off the left bumper, the top bumper, and into the bottom middle pocket.

3. Find the maximum possible area for a triangle with perimeter 48 centimeters.

4. Locate a point P on line ℓ such that the path from A, to P, to B is the shortest possible path. Explain your method.

5. $\overline{AB}$ has endpoints $A(4, 4)$ and $B(4, -5)$. Describe the shortest path from $P(1, 2)$ to $Q(8, -4)$, such that the path does not intersect $\overline{AB}$. Estimate the length of this path.

6. You have 36 feet of fencing to enclose a rectangular dog kennel in your backyard. You plan to use a side of the house as one of the sides of the kennel. What dimensions maximize the area of the dog kennel?

Also available: Form B

Mid-Chapter Test

1. B

2. B

3. See back of book.

4. See back of book.

5. The shortest path from X to the polygon is the shortest segment from X perpendicular to a side of the polygon.

6. $4\sqrt{5} + \sqrt{17}$

7. the path from $(4, 5)$ to $(0, 4)$ to $(4, -4)$

8. a. 9 m by 9 m
  b. 9 m by 18 m

9. a. Use a 4-picture by 4-picture arrangement.
  b. To maximize the perimeter, use a 16-picture by 1-picture arrangement.

Investigation Overview

In this investigation, students think about mathematical functions in a new way. They are used to graphing functions by using a number as an input and evaluating the function to find the corresponding output. Together, the input and output are the coordinates of a point on the graph.

This investigation explores functions where a *point* is the input. For example, in the burning tent problem, the point *P* where you fill your bucket is the input. This point *P* determines the entire length of the path from your starting point, to *P*, and then to the tent. That total distance is the output value that the function returns for the input *P*.

One way to visualize functions like this is to think of the outputs as heights or altitudes. Then, as you travel from point to point on the plane, you are traveling over a terrain of different heights as the value of the function changes. To represent a three-dimensional environment like this on a two-dimensional piece of paper, you can use a *contour plot*, showing a series of *contour lines*. Along any contour line, the function returns the same value. By looking at this kind of a plot, you can spot likely locations for maximums and minimums, which makes it possible to solve optimization problems.

You may wish to assign Questions 1–3 for students to think and write about during the investigation.

Learning Goals

- Read and understand topographic maps and temperature maps.
- Interpret contour plots.
- Draw contour lines to make contour plots and solve optimization problems.

Habits and Skills

- Draw contour lines to visualize a possible solution for an optimization problem.
- See a contour line as the set of points for which a function takes on a single value.
- Recognize a pattern in the contour lines of a function.

Investigation 8C

Contour Lines

In *Contour Lines*, you will explore functions on the plane. You will draw pictures that show where a function takes on specific values. You will use these drawings to find minimum values for functions under certain restrictions. Then you will use the new techniques to revisit the burning-tent problem.

By the end of this investigation, you will be able to answer questions like these:

1. Describe how a contour plot can help you solve the burning-tent problem.

2. Can two contour lines of a contour plot intersect? Explain.

3. Below is a contour plot showing depth in feet of a lake. You drop your keys into the deepest part of the lake. How far down will you have to swim to get them?

You will learn how to

- read and understand topographic maps and temperature maps
- interpret contour plots
- draw contour lines to make contour plots and solve optimization problems

You will develop these habits and skills:

- Draw contour lines to visualize a possible solution for an optimization problem.
- See a contour line as the set of points for which a function takes on a single value.
- Recognize a pattern in the contour lines of a function.

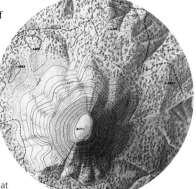

Each contour line marks a 20-ft change in height. What is it that is pictured here?

Investigation Road Map

LESSON 8.7, *Getting Started,* introduces topographic maps. You can use this lesson to assess students' ability to interpret maps. Students should understand that contour lines can never intersect, and the value of the function between contour lines is unknown.

LESSON 8.8, *Drawing Contour Plots,* introduces the idea of drawing a contour plot for a function. Students explore functions where each point on the plane returns a value, and they draw curves that show all the locations where the function takes on a particular value.

LESSON 8.9, *Contour Lines and Functions,* further explores contour lines. Students learn to visualize contour lines and solve optimization problems.

LESSON 8.10, *Revisiting the Burning Tent,* has students solve the burning tent problem using contour lines and reflection.

Activating Prior Knowledge
Exploring New Ideas

Have you ever seen a topographic map? A **topographic map** is a type of *contour plot* that usually depicts land elevations or sea depths. Curves or lines represent points of the same elevation.

Here is a map of a mountain. Each closed curve, or *contour line*, indicates a change of 200 feet. The lowest height marked on this map is 2000 feet.

> **Topograghy** is a precise detailed study of the surface features of a region. It comes from the Greek words *topos* (place) and *grafein* (to write).

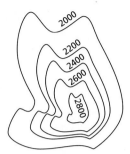

This diagram shows only closed curves. Other maps may include open (partial) curves. It depends on the size and scale of the map. For example, look at the following map that shows temperatures across Europe.

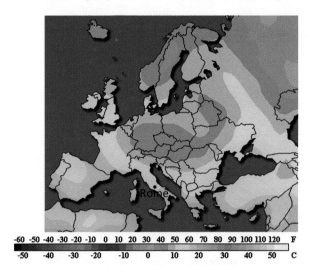

> Each color indicates an interval of temperatures. So, the temperature of Rome is between 55°F and 60°F.

Lesson Overview

GOALS

- Read and understand topographic maps and temperature maps.
- Interpret contour plots.

This lesson helps you assess your students' skills in interpreting topographic maps, temperature maps, and other contour plots. Make sure students think closely about the properties of these maps and how they relate to optimization.

FOR YOU TO EXPLORE
- Core: 1, 2
- Optional: 3, 4

MATERIALS
- Blackline Master 8.7

HOMEWORK
- Core: 5
- Optional: 6, 7, 8

VOCABULARY
- topographic map
- topography

Launch

Begin this lesson by reading the introductory paragraph and explaining how to interpret the first two maps.

Explore

Make sure you fully assess your students' skills in interpreting maps and contour plots. You might ask the following questions.

LEADING QUESTIONS

- On a temperature map, can you determine the exact temperature at any point? (Answer: No, the color of a region on the map indicates a range of temperatures.)

- On a topographic map, can you determine the exact altitude at any point? (Answer: Yes, points on a contour line of the map have the altitude associated with that line. However, you can only determine a range of possible altitudes for points between contour lines.)

- How could you use one of these maps to find a maximum or minimum? (Answer: The maps identify areas within which the maximum or minimum point will occur—they narrow down your search.)

For You to Explore

PROBLEMS 3 AND 4 An important distinction gets lost in looking at the contour plot for something like bleachers or a staircase and the contour plot for something like a hillside. The bleachers rise in discrete steps, whereas a hill exhibits a more continuous change in height. In later exercises, you will see how a surface plot reveals these differences better than a contour plot.

Wrap Up

End this lesson by assigning some On Your Own exercises.

Exercises

HOMEWORK
- Core: 5
- Optional: 6, 7, 8

For You to Explore

1. How high might the peak of the mountain in the Getting Started map be? What is its maximum possible height?

2. Here are two paths to get to the peak of the mountain.

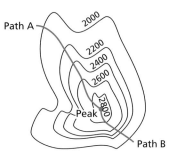

Suppose it is equally easy to get to the start of Path A and to the start of Path B at an altitude of 2000 feet. Which path would you choose? Explain.

3. Make a contour plot of your school's gym.

4. Make a contour plot of an outdoor amphitheater (such as the Hollywood Bowl).

Exercises *Practicing Habits of Mind*

On Your Own

5. Here is the topographic map for two neighboring peaks. There is an increase of 100 feet between contour lines.

    a. The lowest outermost line on the map represents areas that are 1000 feet above sea level. Sketch the areas on the map that are at least 1600 feet above sea level.

    b. The two summits are unmarked here. What is the maximum elevation that they could be? Which one must be higher? Explain.

    c. How can you find the steepest part of the mountains? Explain.

Answers

For You to Explore

1. between 2800 ft and 3000 ft

2. Answers may vary. Sample: Path A; Path A is longer than Path B, but not as steep as Path B.

3. Contour plots may vary. Check students' work.

4. See back of book.

Exercises

5. a. Check students' sketches. Any place inside the seventh contour line is above 1600 ft.

   b. The peak on the left is at some elevation at least 2200 but less than 2300 ft above sea level. The peak on the right is at some elevation at least 1900 but less than 2000 ft above sea level.

   c. Answers may vary. Sample: The steepest areas are where contour lines are most closely packed together.

6. Make a contour plot of a local sports stadium (include the stands).

7. The map at the right is of a pond for which the outer contour line represents the edge of the water. Each contour line represents an increase in depth of 5 feet. A camp has rights to the property bounded by the quadrilateral. The director wants to rope off a swimming area with water no deeper than 7 feet. Trace the map and sketch a proposal for such a roped-off area.

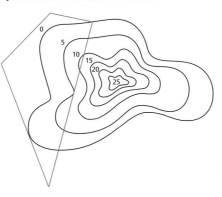

Maintain Your Skills

8. Use the contour plot of temperatures in the United States to answer the questions below.

a. Which areas are the hottest? What is the range of their temperatures?

b. You are in Washington, D.C. You want to get to an area where the temperature is at most 80° F. In which direction should you go so that you travel the shortest distance? (Assume there are straight routes to any location.)

c. You are at the point on the map marked you in Montana. You wish to get to an area where the temperature is at least 70° F. In which direction should you go so that you travel the shortest distance? (Assume there are straight routes to any location.)

On Your Own

EXERCISE 7 Blackline Master 8.7, the contour plot of the lake, is supplied so that students do not have to copy the figure.

6. Check students' work.

7. The roped-off area can be anywhere within the shaded region shown below.

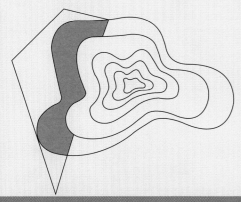

8. a. The hottest areas are the purple ones in the Southeast. Their temperatures are between 90°F and 95°F.

b. northwest

c. southeast

Lesson Overview

GOALS

- Interpret contour plots.
- Draw contour lines to make contour plots and solve optimization problems.

In this lesson, students begin to understand contour lines in a mathematical context. They extend their knowledge of contour plots such as topographic and temperature maps to develop a new way to visualize mathematical functions.

The lesson begins with an exploration of the kicking angle from different positions on a soccer field. There is a particular kicking angle for each point on the field. By looking at the set of locations that all have the same kicking angle, students can describe strategies to maximize a player's kicking angle under various restrictions. The concept of a contour plot for a mathematical function is fundamental because it provides a new way to visualize functions and to solve optimization problems. This concept is core in the following lessons of this chapter.

CHECK YOUR UNDERSTANDING
- Core: 1
- Optional: 2, 3

MATERIALS
- protractors
- rulers
- Blackline Masters 8.8A, 8.8B, 8.8C

HOMEWORK
- Core: 4, 7, 8, 10
- Optional: 5, 6, 9, 11, 12

VOCABULARY
- contour line
- contour plot
- level curve

Launch

Begin this lesson by defining *contour line*. Then work through the Example as a class.

Contour plots provide a new way to visualize functions. They can often be used to solve optimization problems. Topographic maps and temperature maps are examples of contour plots.

The individual curves in a contour plot are called contour lines or level curves. A **contour line** is a curve that shows where a particular feature is invariant. Sometimes contour lines make shapes that you recognize such as circles or polygons. You may be able to use the geometry of those shapes to solve optimization problems.

> **Habits of Mind**
>
> **Look for relationships.** Why would people use the words *contour* and *level* to describe these paths?

Example

Problem Suppose you are running straight down a soccer field toward the goal. You are off to the side because of the other team's defense. As you run, you have various openings to score a goal. From what position should you shoot if you want the widest angle between the goal posts?

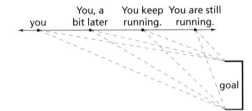

> **Habits of Mind**
>
> **Experiment.** Geometry software is an ideal tool for experimenting with this problem.

Solution The kicking angle is the angle from one goal post, to you, to the other goal post. You want to maximize this angle. To understand the situation, you might sketch a circle through the goal posts and you. (See the figure at the right.)

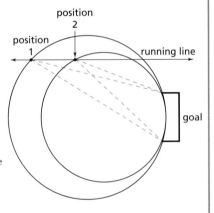

Recall from Chapter 5 that all angles inscribed in a circle with a given arc have the same degree measure. Therefore, each circle is a contour line that shows the set of points that have the same kicking angle.

As you try different kicking positions, the circle and angle change. The angle is greatest when the circle is tangent to the kicking line. This is because any other point on the kicking line is outside this tangent circle. It would make a lesser angle with the goal posts than the angle that has the tangent point as its vertex.

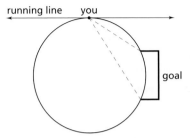

For You to Do

1. Imagine that you are running along a line parallel to the goal. You want to maximize your kicking angle. Where should you stop along that line to kick the ball?

Suppose your coach wants you to learn how to find the best kicking spots for scoring. This is a complicated skill, so first you look at some simple cases. Complete the following In-Class Experiment. Discuss your results with the class.

In-Class Experiment

The coach draws a line parallel to the goal and lines the team up on it.

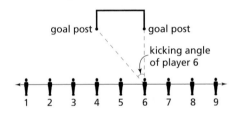

2. Which player has the maximum kicking angle?

3. How does the angle vary from player to player across the field?

> The player's position is the vertex of the kicking angle and each goal post is on a side of the angle.

4. Which players have a kicking angle that is approximately 5° less than the maximum?

5. Are there any players on the line with a kicking angle of 1°? Approximately where are they?

Explore

Students can work through the In-Class Experiment in groups. Blackline Master 8.8A depicts the figure showing the players spread across the field.

Wrap Up

End this lesson by assigning some Check Your Understanding exercises.

Assessment Resources

Lesson Quiz 8.8

1. Use the diagram of a soccer field.
  a. Suppose you start at *A* and run toward the goal on the path indicated. Where along your path is the best location to take a shot? Label it *P*.
  b. Suppose you start at *B* and run parallel to the goal on the path indicated. Where along your path is the best location to take a shot? Label it *Q*.

2. You are in an art museum looking at a mural that is 10 feet tall and 20 feet wide. Your eye level is 5 feet. The bottom of the mural is 3 feet above the ground. How far from the mural should you stand for the maximum viewing angle?

Answers

For You to Do

1. at the point where the line intersects the perpendicular bisector of the segment connecting the goal posts

In-Class Experiment

2. player 5

3. As you go from player 1 to 5, the kicking angles increase. As you go from player 5 to player 9, the kicking angles decrease.

4. 7 players; the positions labeled 1, 2, 3 and 6, 7, 8, 9

5. no

Exercises

HOMEWORK
- Core: 4, 7, 8, 10
- Optional: 5, 6, 9, 11, 12

Check Your Understanding

EXERCISE 1 is about the set of points that form a kicking angle of a certain measure. Have your students think about the properties of circles that cause the contour lines in the kicking angle problems to all be circular. In a circle, all of the angles that inscribe the same arc have the same measure. So contour lines that map constant angle measures are circular.

EXERCISE 2 Blackline Master 8.8B depicts the figure showing the penalty box and contour lines.

On Your Own

EXERCISE 4 Blackline Master 8.8C depicts the figure showing the building and your position on the street.

Exercises *Practicing Habits of Mind*

Check Your Understanding

1. Suppose you are on the soccer field from the In-Class Experiment. Sketch where the players should stand on the field to have a kicking angle of 40°.

   > Your sketch will show a contour line for a kicking angle of 40°.

2. Here is a contour map for the kicking angles in the penalty box of a soccer field.

   a. What shape are the contours? Explain.

   b. Copy the figure. Label the contour lines on your map with the measures of the kicking angles.

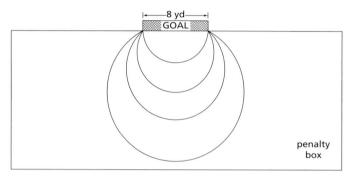

3. **Write About It** Describe the shape of the contour as you move away from the soccer goal. Explain from where on the field a player has the best chance to score.

On Your Own

4. You are driving through the country on a straight road. A building to your left has a beautiful façade that you wish to photograph. As shown in the figure, you are currently as close to the building as it is possible to be while on this road. Because the building is not set parallel to the road, you think you will get a better angle farther along the road. What is the best viewing position along the road?

   > *Façade* is a French word that means the face or front of a building.

Answers

Exercises

1. Players can be anywhere on the arc shown below.

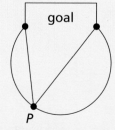

2. See back of book.

3. Answers may vary. Sample: More and more it resembles a full circle. A player is most likely to score if he or she is close to the goal posts and not too far from the perpendicular bisector of the segment that joins the base points of the goal posts.

4. Let A and B be the points at the front corners of the house, and let X be your location on the highway. Consider the circle through A, B, and X. The location of X that makes the circle tangent to your straight-line path is the best viewing position.

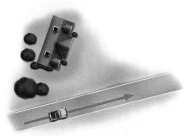

5. Write About It Find at least two ways in which weather forecasters use contour plots. You may have to contact a local weather service for help.

6. Write About It Are the constraints in this lesson's In-Class Experiment realistic? Explain.

In Exercises 7 and 8, a player with the ball is crossing the field in a straight line, but not parallel to the goal line.

7. Draw such a line on your contour map.

8. Determine the spot on the line from which the player has the greatest kicking angle. Use the map in your explanation.

9. You are in a gallery looking at a picture that is 4 feet tall and 6 feet wide. Your eye level is 5 feet. The bottom of the picture is 5.5 feet above the ground. How far from the wall should you stand for the maximum viewing angle? Is this likely to be the best place to stand?

10. Standardized Test Prep A topographic map of a mountain contains contour lines labeled in 50-foot increments. What do you think the contour lines represent?

A. temperature   **B.** elevation   **C.** humidity   **D.** air pressure

> You have to think about the angle from the top of the picture, to you, to the bottom of the picture. You also have to think about the angle from the left side of the picture, to you, to the right side of the picture.

Maintain Your Skills

11. Which of the two marked angles is greater? Explain.

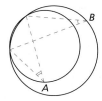

12. In the Example, you are running perpendicular to the goal. Now, suppose you are dribbling a soccer ball along a line that is *not* perpendicular to the goal. Describe how to locate the spot that maximizes your kicking angle.

Go Online
PHSchool.com

For additional practice, go to **Web Code:** bea-0808

---

5. Check students' work.

6. only insofar as it relates the size of the kick angle to various positions in the field

7. See back of book.

8. The point where the line is tangent to a curve is the smallest contour line it will cross, which creates the maximum angle.

9. about 1.5 ft from the wall; no, not if you face the wall directly, since you have a good view only of the bottom part of the picture.

10. B

11. $\angle A$; the arcs that the angles intercept have the same endpoints, but $\angle A$ is inscribed in a smaller circle than $\angle B$.

12. Draw the circle that passes through the base points of the goal posts and is tangent to the line of the runner. The point of tangency is the point in question.

Maintain Your Skills

Maintain Your Skills

EXERCISE 11 You may choose to explain to your class that circles provide a way to compare angle measures of intersecting angles. First, find the points of intersection for each of the corresponding rays of the angles. Construct a circle through these two points and the vertex of one of the angles you want to compare. The vertex of the other angle may be on this circle, in which case the angles are congruent. Or it may be inside the circle, indicating that its angle is larger. If it is outside, its angle is smaller.

Additional Resources

PRINTED RESOURCES
- Texas Instruments Activities Workbook
- Cabrilog Activities
- Teaching Resources
- Practice Workbook
- Assessment Resources

TECHNOLOGY
- TeacherExpress CD-ROM
- **Exam***View* CD-ROM
- **PHSchool.com**
  - Homework Help
  - Video Tutors
  - Multiple Choice
  - Crosswords

Additional Practice

1. Use the diagram of the soccer field.
  a. Suppose you start at *A* and run toward the goal on the path indicated. Where along your path is the best location to take a shot? Label it *P*.
  b. Suppose you start at *B* and run toward the goal on the path indicated. Where along your path is the best location to take a shot? Label it *Q*.
  c. Suppose you start at *C* and run parallel to the goal line on the path indicated. Where along your path is the best location to take a shot? Label it *R*.

2. You are in a museum of natural history. There is a dinosaur skeleton on display. The skeleton sits on a platform that is 10 feet wide and 4 feet high. The skeleton is 20 feet tall. Your eye level is 5 feet. Sketch a picture of the situation. Then use your sketch to determine where you should stand for the maximum viewing angle.

3. A hockey player skates across the ice on the path indicated. At what point along the path should the player shoot at the goal?

4. Suppose *A* is fixed in a plane. Function *f* determines all points in the plane that are equidistant to *A*.
  a. Make a contour plot for *f*.
  b. Label each contour line with the appropriate number.
  c. What shape is each contour?

5. Suppose $\overline{AC}$ is fixed in a plane. Function *g* determines a point's distance from $\overline{AC}$.
  a. Make a contour plot for *g*.
  b. What shape is each contour?
  c. How would the contours for *g* change if you look at all the points in space (not just in the plane)?

6. Suppose *C* and *D* are fixed the plane. Function *f* is defined so that $f(A) = AC + 3AD$. Make an approximate contour plot for *f* by hand.

Practice: For Lesson 8.8, assign Exercises 1–4.

Lesson Overview

This lesson formalizes the idea of a contour line as the set of points for which a function assigns values that are all the same. Make sure your students understand this way of interpreting contour lines, because it will be useful throughout the chapter.

Launch

Begin this lesson by having your class read through Developing Habits of Mind. You may choose to present the Facts and Notation information to the entire class.

8.9 Contour Lines and Functions

A contour plot assigns a number to each point on the plane. The number could represent any of the following.

- temperature
- barometric pressure
- height above sea level
- depth of water
- distance from a point to a pool's edge
- measure of a kicking angle

A contour line is a set of points (a curve of some type) with assigned values that are all the same. A contour plot is a collection of contour lines.

To understand a contour plot, you must be given information about the values of points that are between the lines.

Developing Habits of Mind

Visualize. The process of assigning a number to each point on a plane is an example of a function. In this new context, think of P moving around the plane carrying a little calculator on its back.

The calculator is programmed to do only one calculation, such as measure the kicking angle. The calculation is dependent on P's current location. As P travels along a contour line, the calculator produces the same value. A contour line is just the set of all points for which the calculator produces the same value.

Remember...

You met functions in *Algebra 1*. Those functions took in a number and gave out another number. The functions in this chapter take in a point and give out a number.

In-Class Experiment

Use geometry software. Define three points A, B, and P. Consider the function f that calculates the sum $PA + PB$.

1. Measure $PA + PB$.

2. Drag P around. As the lengths change, the sum will change. In other words, the value of your function will change.

3. Tape a transparency over the screen. Mark enough points to draw in a few contour lines for f.

Answers

In-Class Experiment

Check students' work. All but one of the contour lines are ellipses.

Now you are ready for a more formal presentation.

Facts and Notation

You can name functions. Call the one that determines $PA + PB$ g. The value of g for any P is written $g(P)$.

The notation $g(P)$ is pronounced "g of P" and means the "value of g at P." If you think of g as a calculating machine, $g(P)$ is the number produced by the machine when it is "fed" P. When P is the input, $g(P)$ is the output.

Minds in Action   episode 39

Sasha is fascinated by this new notation and decides to experiment with her drawing.

Sasha   Look, Tony. I placed the cursor on P and dragged it around. I watched the value of $f(P)$ and tried to keep it equal to 5.8.

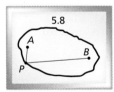

$f(P) = PA + PB$
$PA + PB = 5.80 \text{ cm}$

> Since Sasha's contour line was formed by dragging, there is some error. Not every point on the contour line has a value of h exactly equal to 5.8.

Tony   Oh, I see.

Sasha   Since $f(P)$ is 5.8 for any point on this contour line, I'll label the whole line 5.8.

Tony   Nice! Let me see what happens if A and B coincide. I'll use just one point, C. I'll define a new function h that determines the distance from C to any point P in the plane.

Explore

Have students read the Minds in Action dialog. Then have them do the For Discussion problem.

Wrap Up

End this lesson by assigning some Check Your Understanding exercises.

Assessment Resources

Lesson Quiz 8.9

For Exercises 1–4, suppose points C and D are fixed points in a plane and suppose f is the function defined by $f(X) = CX + DX$ for any point X.

1. Sketch a contour plot for f.

2. Label each contour line with an appropriate number.

3. What shape is each contour?

4. How would the contours for f change if f is defined in space rather than in a plane?

5. Describe the contours for each of the following.
   a. a fixed point A on a plane where the function f is defined by all points that are equidistant to A
   b. a fixed point B in space where the function f is defined by all points that are equidistant to B
   c. two fixed points C and D on a plane where the function f is defined by all points equidistant to C and D

For Discussion

4. A contour line for Tony's function is below. Draw a few more contour lines for Tony's function. What shape is each contour line? Give a proof.

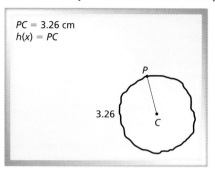

PC = 3.26 cm
h(x) = PC

P

3.26

C

Exercises *Practicing Habits of Mind*

Check Your Understanding

Suppose ℓ is some fixed line in a plane. Suppose f is the function that determines the distance from ℓ to a point in the plane.

1. Make a contour plot for f.

2. What shape is each contour? Give a proof.

3. Label each contour line with the appropriate number.

4. What would the contours for f look like for all points in space (not just in the plane)? That is, what is the set of points in space that are a fixed distance from a given line ℓ?

Answers

For Discussion

4. All of the contour lines that correspond to numbers greater than 0 are circles with center C. This follows from the definition of a circle.

Exercises

1–3. See back of book.

4. The contour corresponding to the number 0 is the line ℓ. There are no contours for negative numbers. The contour for a positive number k is an infinitely long cylinder with line ℓ as its axis.

On Your Own

5. Suppose E and F are fixed in the plane. Function f is defined so that $f(Z) = ZE + 2ZF$ for any Z.

   a. Make a contour plot for f. Label it appropriately.

   b. Draw a straight line on your contour plot. Explain how to locate the point on the line that minimizes the value of f.

6. **Take It Further** Suppose A, B, and C are fixed in the plane. Function j is defined to measure the sum of the distances from P to A, B, and C.

$$j(P) = PA + PB + PC$$

   Make a labeled contour plot for j.

> **Habits of Mind**
>
> **Experiment.** Try to invent a gadget using string that will help you draw the contour lines for j.

7. **Write About It** A function is defined on the points in a plane. Explain how to draw a contour plot for this function. Illustrate with examples.

Use points A and B for Exercises 8 and 9.

Suppose A and B are fixed. P moves around the plane and can be on either side of $\overleftrightarrow{AB}$. Define h as follows.

$$h(P) = m\angle APB$$

8. **a.** Make a labeled contour plot for h.

   b. Are any points in the plane on every contour line in your plot? Are there any points that could not be on any contour line in any contour plot for h? (That is, are there points on the plane for which h produces no number?) Explain.

> **Habits of Mind**
>
> **Represent with color.** You could use color coding to explain certain aspects of your map.

9. **a.** Place P above $\overleftrightarrow{AB}$ so that $m\angle APB = 90°$. Describe the contour line P traces.

   b. Describe $m\angle APB$ if P is inside this contour line and still above $\overleftrightarrow{AB}$.

   c. Describe $m\angle APB$ if P is outside this contour line.

10. **Take It Further** Suppose ℓ is a fixed line. E is a fixed point not on ℓ. Function f assigns a numerical value to each P as follows.

    • f finds the distance from P to E.
    • f finds the distance from P to ℓ.
    • f adds the results and assigns that number to P.

    Make a contour plot for f. Label your contour lines with the appropriate values determined by f.

On Your Own

5. See back of book.

6. See back of book.

7. To draw a contour plot of a function defined on points in the plane, you calculate the value of the function for lots of points and then connect with curves the points that output the same values.

8. **a.** See back of book.

8. **b.** No; yes, the points on $\overleftrightarrow{AB}$ that are not between A and B are excluded.

9. a semicircle minus its endpoints; $m\angle APB$ will be greater than 90° but less than 180°; $m\angle APB$ will be less than 90°.

10.

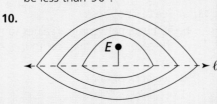

On Your Own

EXERCISES 5–6 Exercise 5 is core. For both exercises, students may sketch the contour plots by hand or by using the slider point method with computer software. Students can use Exercise 6 to generate figures other than circles. The set of possible loci that students can build depends on the available primitives. Students will need a dynamic geometry program with built in conic sections as primitives to do Exercise 6 with software.

EXERCISE 8 An important but subtle point is that because $h(A)$ and $h(B)$ are not defined points, you cannot include A and B on the contour plot. When P coincides with A or B, $\angle APB$ does not have a natural definition. You cannot use a limiting argument to assign an unambiguous meaning to it.

Additional Resources

PRINTED RESOURCES
• Texas Instruments Activities Workbook
• Cabrilog Activities
• Teaching Resources
• Practice Workbook
• Assessment Resources

TECHNOLOGY
• TeacherExpress CD-ROM
• **Exam***View* CD-ROM
• **PHSchool.com**
  – Homework Help
  – Video Tutors
  – Multiple Choice
  – Crosswords

Additional Practice

1. Use the diagram of the soccer field.
   a. Suppose you start at A and run toward the goal on the path indicated. Where along your path is the best location to take a shot? Label it P.
   b. Suppose you start at B and run toward the goal on the path indicated. Where along your path is the best location to take a shot? Label it Q.
   c. Suppose you start at C and run parallel to the goal line on the path indicated. Where along your path is the best location to take a shot? Label it R.

2. You are in a museum of natural history. There is a dinosaur skeleton on display. The skeleton sits on a platform that is 10 feet wide and 4 feet high. The skeleton is 20 feet tall. Your eye level is 5 feet. Sketch a picture of the situation. Then use your sketch to determine where you should stand for the maximum viewing angle.

3. A hockey player skates across the ice on the path indicated. At what point along the path should the player shoot at the goal?

4. Suppose A is fixed in a plane. Function f determines all points in the plane that are equidistant to A.
   a. Make a contour plot for f.
   b. Label each contour line with the appropriate number.
   c. What shape is each contour?

5. Suppose $\overline{AC}$ is fixed in a plane. Function g determines a point's distance from $\overline{AC}$.
   a. Make a contour plot for g.
   b. What shape is each contour?
   c. How would the contours for g change if you look at all the points in space (not just in the plane)?

6. Suppose C and D fixed the plane. Function f is defined so that $f(A) = AC + 3AD$. Make an approximate contour plot for f by hand.

Practice: For Lesson 8.9, assign Exercises 5–7.

11. Take It Further Define O as a fixed point in space. Suppose function g is defined in three-dimensional space. It determines the distance between any point in space and O.

   a. Describe the shape formed by all P such that $g(P) = 1$.

   b. Describe the two-dimensional picture (similar to a contour plot) formed by this function.

12. Standardized Test Prep Suppose P is a fixed point in the plane. Suppose f is the function that determines the distance between P and another point in the plane. What does the contour plot for f look like?

   A. parallel lines

   B. intersecting lines

   C. concentric circles

   D. intersecting circles

Maintain Your Skills

13. Place A, B, and X on a plane. The function f assigns $XA + XB$ to any X. Make a contour plot for f.

   a. Label each contour line with the appropriate number.

   b. Your contour plot cannot show every contour line. Count your smallest contour line as the first. Picture a new contour line between your second and third contour lines. What range of numbers could belong to the new contour line?

   c. Draw a line across your contour plot. Explain how to locate the point on that line for which f produces the least value.

   d. On your contour plot, draw a circle that contains A and B in its interior. Explain how to locate the point or points on the circle for which f produces the least value.

   e. Can any number be a value for some contour line? Explain your answer. If your answer is no, give an example of a number that could never be a value for f.

> To find the value that f assigns to X, measure the distance from X to A and the distance from X to B. Then add.

Go Online
PHSchool.com

For additional practice, go to **Web Code: bea-0809**

Contour plowing minimizes slope of rain runoff. This helps minimize soil erosion.

Answers

11. a. a sphere with center O and radius 1

   b. the point O and a set of concentric spheres with center O

12. C

13. a. See back of book.

   b. numbers between the values for the second and third contour lines

   c. See back of book.

   d. Check students' drawings. A point where one of the contour lines is tangent to the circle will yield the least value for f. If there are two contour lines tangent to the circle, choose the smaller contour line and then select a point of tangency.

   e. No; for example, $\frac{1}{2} AB$ cannot be a value for f.

Revisiting the Burning Tent

Sometimes you can find patterns in incorrect answers. The patterns, in turn, may help you find the correct answer.

episode 40

Tony explains how he used incorrect answers to reach the correct answer.

Tony   Hey Derman, do you remember the burning tent problem from Lesson 8.2?

Derman   Yes, we tried to find the best spot to fill the bucket in the river to minimize the total distance traveled.

Tony   Well, I was thinking we could solve it by looking at some wrong answers, like this point *P*.

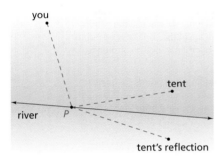

Why is point *P* not the best spot?

Derman   Why would we do that?

Tony   There are other points for which the length of the path is the same as the path above. We can call them equally bad points. To find them, I cut a piece of string equal to the total length above. I kept one end of the string at the tent and the other end at you. The paths through *B* and *C* are equally bad paths.

Lesson Overview

GOALS

- Interpret contour plots.
- Draw contour lines to make contour plots and solve optimization problems.

In this lesson, students re-examine the burning tent problem. Instead of experimenting to find an optimum solution to the problem, they look at the contour lines of the function of the total length of the path. They will apply their new skills and gain further insight into this problem.

Launch

Begin this lesson by having students act out the dialog between Tony and Derman. You might want to ask your students to explain the solution in their own words.

CHECK YOUR UNDERSTANDING
- Core: 1
- Optional: 2, 3

MATERIALS
- compasses
- protractors
- rulers
- Blackline Master 8.10

HOMEWORK
- Core: 4, 5, 6
- Optional: 7, 10, 11, 12, 13
- Extension: 8, 9

VOCABULARY
- ellipse
- focus

Explore

In-Class Experiment

The ellipse tangent to the river with foci at you and the tent is the contour line containing the optimal point. All the points on this ellipse give the same output value as this best point, which is the minimum total distance from your starting point, to the river, to the tent. The function that calculates the total distance between these three points produces a larger output value for all other points on the riverbank. The contour lines for those points will be larger ellipses and will not be tangent to the riverbank but will intersect it.

The smaller the total distance k, where $k = AP + BP$, the flatter the ellipse. The larger k is, the more the curve resembles a circle. A way to think about this is to consider two extreme cases. Very large values of k dwarf the distance between the two foci. Thus, the curve is more or less the set of all points k distance from that one place, which is a circle. Very small values of k generate a line segment between the two foci.

Tony's Picture

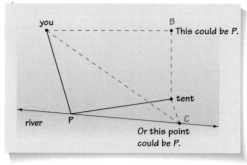

The three paths shown from you to the tent have the same length.

I think there's a pattern for the equally bad points. Many of the equally bad points are not on the riverbank, but the lengths from you to the point P and then to the tent are equal. If we can find that pattern, I think we'll have a way to find the equally good points.

Derman Oh, I get it! All of the points that have a certain path length are equally bad if that path length is too long. We can use the pattern to find a set of equally good points. One of the equally good points is the point we want to find on the riverbank. It's the solution to the burning-tent problem.

Tony We have to start by finding all the equally bad points for one bad point on the river bank. What does the set of points look like that are some constant total distance from you and from the tent?

In-Class Experiment

Help answer Tony's question. Pick a total path length, experiment, and determine the contour line. This contour line is the locus for all the points that share a given path length. You can use geometry software or a compass and ruler.

- Draw two points A and B.

- Construct a segment that has a path length greater than AB.

- Place P on the segment. This splits the segment into two parts d_1 and d_2. If you are using software, construct these two parts as separate segments.

- Construct a circle centered at A with radius d_1. Construct a circle centered at B with radius d_2.

You might want to hide the circles to neaten your sketch.

If you use software, do the following.

- Construct the intersections of these circles.

- Trace these points.

- You will get a contour line as you move *P* along the segment.

If you use a compass and ruler, do the following:

- Mark the intersections of these circles.

- Move *P* so that you have new lengths d_1 and d_2.

- Construct circles with these new radii. Mark their intersections.

- Repeat the last two steps for at least five points *P*. You should recognize the contour line that emerges.

1. Repeat the process with different path lengths. You should recognize a pattern to the contour lines.

The contour lines you have been drawing are called *ellipses*.

Definition

Begin with *A* and *B* and a positive number *k*. The set of all *P* for which PA + PB = k is called an **ellipse**. *A* and *B* are called the *foci* of the ellipse. *A* is one **focus** and *B* is the other *focus*.

Or you can define an ellipse as a contour line.

Definition

An **ellipse** with foci *A* and *B* is a contour line for the function *f*, which is defined by the following calculation.

$$f(P) = PA + PB$$

For Discussion

2. Are these two definitions of an ellipse equivalent? Explain.

Remember...

Two definitions A and B are equivalent if A implies B and B implies A.

Minds in Action   episode 41

Tony is still trying to explain his idea to Derman.

Tony   Look at the following figures. If there are points on the riverbank inside the ellipse, there is a shorter path. In the figure where *k* = 3.7, the runner never reaches the river, so that doesn't work, either. So we want to find the ellipse with only one point on the river. That will be the solution point.

Answers

In-Class Experiment

1. Check students' sketches. The contour lines should be ellipses.

For Discussion

2. Yes; the second definition simply uses "*f(P)*" and "contour line" in place of "*k*" and "set of all points *P*."

Wrap Up

End this lesson by assigning some Check Your Understanding exercises.

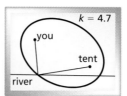

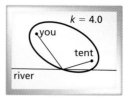

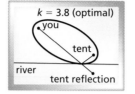

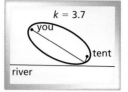

Derman Oh, now I see! The best path is the one that touches the river in exactly one point. We have to find an ellipse that is tangent to the river in a point. That happens when $k = 3.8$.

For Discussion

3. Do you see why the figure in which $k = 3.8$ is optimal? Describe its geometric characteristics.

Exercises *Practicing Habits of Mind*

Check Your Understanding

To construct elliptical shapes, builders can drive nails in at the two foci of the ellipse. Then they tie each end of a piece of string around the nails. With a pencil, they trace around the nails, keeping the string taut.

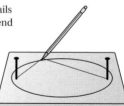

Answers

3. The contour line for $K = 3.8$ is the only one that intersects the line for the river at exactly one point.

1. Explain how this setup guarantees that all of the points the pencil passes through are the same total distance from the two nails.

2. **Write About It** Draw a contour plot for the burning-tent problem. Explain how and why the contour lines are used to solve the problem.

3. Draw a circle and a line tangent to the circle. Which point on the tangent line is closest to the center of the circle? Draw a radius from the point of contact to the center of the circle. How are this radius and the tangent line related?

On Your Own

4. Tony's little sister, Yeon, is celebrating her third birthday. This is a picture of her birthday cake. Each layer is 2 inches tall and the candles rise 3 inches above the top layer. Pretend you are looking at it from the top. Draw a contour plot of the cake.

5. Ellipses have some very interesting properties. One is the following tangent property.

Suppose an ellipse has foci A and B and $\overline{ST}$ is tangent to the ellipse at P. Then $m\angle SPA = m\angle TPB$.

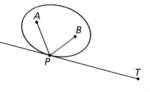

Suppose you place a ball at each focus of an elliptical billiard table. Shoot one of the balls in any direction. If you use enough force, it will hit the other ball after just one bounce off the elliptical cushion. Within this context, prove that the above tangent property is true for any ellipse.

6. **Standardized Test Prep** In isosceles right triangle ABC, the coordinates of A, B, and C are $(1, 0)$, $(0, 1)$, and $(0, 0)$, respectively. Which point on the bisector of the right angle minimizes the sum of the distances to the vertices of the triangle?

A. (0.292893, 0.292893)   B. (0.5, 0.5)

C. (0.211325, 0.211325)   D. C (0, 0)

Exercises

HOMEWORK
- Core: 4, 5, 6
- Optional: 7, 10, 11, 12, 13
- Extension: 8, 9

On Your Own

EXERCISE 4 is different from finding a contour plot for a function. All of the heights in the cake are defined, and there are only steep drop offs between those heights. Although the top layer of the cake is 6 inches from the table, and the tops of the candles are 9 inches from the table, there is no contour line for 7 inches or 8 inches between them. These heights do not change continuously as will the values of most functions your students encounter.

Exercises

1. The sum of the lengths of the segments from the pencil point to the nails is always equal to the length of the string.

2. See back of book.

3. Check students' drawings.; the point of tangency; perpendicular

4. See back of book.

5. The point of tangency P is the point on $\overline{ST}$ for which the sum of the differences to A and B is least. This should be the same point that is found by using the reflection method to find the shortest path from A to B via $\overline{ST}$. With the reflection method, you could reflect B across $\overline{ST}$ and connect A to B'. $\overline{AB'}$ will intersect $\overline{ST}$ at P. But $\angle TPB \cong \angle TPB'$ since B' is the image of B across $\overline{ST}$, and $\angle TPB' \cong \angle SPA$ since these are vertical angles. Therefore, $\angle TPB \cong \angle SPA$. This implies that $m\angle SPA = m\angle TPB$.

6. B

EXERCISE 9 Blackline Master 8.10 depicts the wildlife refuge so that students do not have to copy the figure.

Additional Resources

PRINTED RESOURCES
- Texas Instruments Activities Workbook
- Cabrilog Activities
- Teaching Resources
- Practice Workbook
- Assessment Resources

TECHNOLOGY
- TeacherExpress CD-ROM
- **Exam**View CD-ROM
- **PHSchool.com**
  - Homework Help
  - Video Tutors
  - Multiple Choice
  - Crosswords

Additional Practice

1. Place two thumbtacks on a piece of cardboard. The thumbtacks represent the foci of an ellipse. Tie a string in a loop so that when you pull the loop taut, the loop is 5 inches long. Place the loop around the thumbtacks and around a pencil. Trace around the thumbtacks keeping the string taut. Explain why this method guarantees that you draw an ellipse.

2. A playground is surrounded by an elliptical walkway.

Suppose that the swings are at *A* and the sandbox is at *B*. You walk from the swings, to the sandbox, to any point on the walkway. Then you walk back to the swings. Is there a point on the walkway that will minimize your total distance?

3. A builder uses ellipses to build a new building. The builder stacks the ellipse-shaped floors one on top of another so that the area of each floor decreases as the height of the building increases. Each floor is 10 feet tall and the building has 4 floors. Draw a contour plot of the building. Imagine you are looking down from the top.

4. You are on a camping trip and your tent catches on fire again. This time, your bucket is with your supplies. You must get the bucket, then get the water, and then put out the tent fire. Find the point along the river where you should go to minimize your path to put out the fire.

5. A city has two matching monuments with a road going between them. The city council wants to build a raised walkway to go over the road and both monuments. An engineer makes a plan that creates a path such that the sum of the distances between each monument and the walkway remains constant. Sketch a picture of what you believe the engineer has in mind.

Practice: For Lesson 8.10, assign Exercises 1–8.

In mathematics, relief maps are called surface plots. Surface plots are supposed to be three-dimensional. In this lesson, you saw two-dimensional drawings of surface plots.

7. **a.** **Write About It** Investigate topographic maps and relief maps. Describe how they are different.

   b. Suppose *O* is a fixed point and *f* is defined so that $f(X) = OX$. What would a relief map for *f* look like?

   c. Let *A* and *B* be fixed. Let *g* be defined so that $g(X) = AX + BX$. Describe *g*'s relief map.

8. **Take It Further** Review the burning-tent problem. This time, consider the fact that you run more slowly with a full bucket than with an empty bucket. Where should you fill the bucket to minimize the time it takes to reach the tent? Justify your answer.

9. **Take It Further** Here is a problem and a proposed solution. Read both carefully. Then critique the problem and support or refute the solution. There are some ambiguities in the problem and some weaknesses in the solution.

Problem Cities *A* and *B* are separated by a wildlife refuge. The taxpayers decide to pool their resources and build a recreation center. The new center cannot be located in the refuge. Traffic generated by the center cannot cross the refuge. New roads must be built. Where should the center be placed to minimize cost?

Solution To do the least road building, the road should be along $\overline{AB}$. However, that is not an option, because $\overline{AB}$ crosses the refuge. So, the total road length will be greater than $\overline{AB}$. All the locations that involve a certain road length lie on an ellipse. The best locations lie on the smallest ellipse that has foci at *A* and *B* and does not cross the refuge.

Maintain Your Skills

Equilateral $\triangle ABC$ is plotted on the coordinate plane. Vertices *A* and *C* have the coordinates indicated. In Exercises 10–12, what is the sum of the distances from *P* to each of the triangle's sides?

10. $P\left(\frac{1}{2}, \frac{1}{2}\right)$ 11. $P(1, 0)$

12. $P\left(1, -\frac{1}{2}\right)$

13. Compare your answers for Exercises 10–12. Which sum is the least? Can you find another point *P* for which the sum of the distances to the sides is even less? Explain.

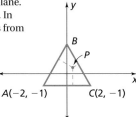

Go Online
Video Tutor
PHSchool.com
Web Code: bee-0810

Go Online
PHSchool.com
For additional practice, go to **Web Code: bea-0810**

Answers

7. **a.** Answers may vary. Sample: Topographical maps are two-dimensional while relief maps are three-dimensional.

   b. a cone

   c. suggestive of a cone but with horizontal cross sections that are elliptical

8. Get the water at a point of tangency of the river line and a contour line in a plot for a function that expresses the time it takes to

make the trip from where you are when you notice the fire (*A*) to a point on the river (*X*) to the tent (*B*).

9. See back of book.

10. $2\sqrt{3}$

11. $2\sqrt{3}$

12. $2\sqrt{3}$

13. no

8C Mathematical Reflections

In this investigation, you learned how to read topographic maps and how to interpret and draw contour plots. These questions will help you summarize what you have learned.

1. The contour plot at the right represents a mountain. You have to climb from the starting point to the peak on path A, B, or C. Which one is the shortest? Which one is the least steep?

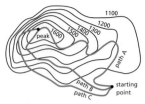

2. **a.** Graph the equation $2x - y = 0$. Label the graph ℓ.

   b. Find a function that gives the distance from any point to ℓ.

   c. Draw and label a contour plot for this function.

3. P falls in the interior of the rectangle. Write a function that calculates the sum of the distances from any point P to the sides of the rectangle.

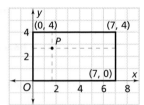

4. Write a function that determines the sum of the distances from point P to the vertices of the rectangle.

5. Consider two fixed points A and B on the plane. What shape are the contour lines that represent various values of $f(P) = PA + PB$?

6. Describe how a contour plot can help you solve the burning-tent problem.

7. Can two contour lines of a contour plot intersect? Explain.

8. At the right is a contour plot showing depth in feet of a lake. You drop your keys into the deepest part of the lake. How far down will you have to swim to get them?

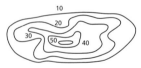

What might a contour map look like for Devils Tower in Wyoming?

Vocabulary

In this investigation, you saw these terms for the first time. Make sure you understand what each one means and how to use it.

- **contour line**
- **contour plot**
- **ellipse**
- **focus (plural foci)**
- **level curve**
- **topographic map**

Mathematical Reflections

EXERCISES 6–8 At the start of the Investigation, you may have assigned these as Questions 1–3 for students to think and write about.

Mathematical Reflections

1. path B; path A

2. See back of book.

3. $f(P) = 11$, where P has coordinates (x, y) with $0 < x < 7$ and $0 < y < 4$

4. $f(P) = \sqrt{x^2 + y^2} + \sqrt{x^2 + (4 - y)^2} + \sqrt{(7 - x)^2 + y^2} + \sqrt{(7 - x)^2 + (4 - y)^2}$, where P has coordinates (x, y) with $0 < x < 7$ and $0 < y < 4$

5. One contour line is $\overline{AB}$. All the other contour lines are ellipses with foci A and B.

6. See back of book.

7. No; Assuming the contour plot is the plot for a function, none of the contour lines can intersect, otherwise the function would have more than one value at each point of intersection, and a function has a single value at each point in its domain.

8. more than 50 ft but less than 60 ft

Investigation Overview

In this investigation, students use their new optimization techniques to explore the proofs of some fairly complex theorems. By looking at situations from different perspectives, students gain further understanding of the process of mathematical proof. In their proof of Rich's Theorem, students reason by continuity, examine extreme cases, and look at area in two different ways. In their proof of the Isoperimetric Conjecture, students learn that the circle is the figure that encloses the most area for a given perimeter. They then use critical properties of circles and polygons to prove the circle encloses the most area. There is an assumption made in the course of the proof. So students learn about the role of assumption in mathematical proof—when it can be useful and the type of difficulties that can arise from an assumption.

You may wish to assign Questions 1–3 for students to think and write about during the investigation.

Learning Goals

- Write functions and use them to solve optimization problems.
- Discuss the important variables of a problem, choose a subset of them, and find an optimal solution.
- Understand and explain a proof of the isoperimetric problem.

Habits and Skills

- Reason by continuity.
- Use special cases and models to look for solutions of more general problems.
- Understand that a proof comes through careful thinking, experience, and the use of mathematical habits of mind.

Investigation 8D

Advanced Optimization

In *Advanced Optimization*, you will work through proofs that at first seem fairly simple. By looking at the logical difficulties you encounter in proving these conjectures, you will come to understand more about the nature of optimization in geometry. For example, sometimes a maximum or minimum for an optimization problem does not exist.

By the end of this investigation, you will be able to answer questions like these.

1. For what point P is the sum of the distances from P to the sides of $\triangle ABC$ the least? Explain.

2. Give an example of an optimization problem that has no solution. Explain your reasoning.

3. What curve encloses the most area for a given perimeter? Explain.

You will learn how to

- write functions and use them to solve optimization problems
- discuss the important variables of a problem, choose a subset of them, and find an optimal solution
- understand and explain a proof of the isoperimetric problem

You will develop these habits and skills:

- Reason by continuity.
- Use special cases and models to look for solutions of more general problems.
- Understand that a proof comes through careful thinking, experience, and the use of mathematical habits of mind.

When the bubble floats free, surface tension minimizes the surface area needed to contain the air within. What is the shape that is formed?

Investigation Road Map

LESSON 8.11, *Getting Started,* previews the following lesson.

LESSON 8.12, *Reasoning by Continuity,* develops different ways to think about the sum of the distances from a point to the sides of an equilateral triangle.

LESSON 8.13, *Proving Rich's Function Is Constant,* proves that the sum of the distances from a point to the sides of an equilateral triangle is constant.

LESSON 8.14, *The Isoperimetric Problem,* introduces the isoperimetric problem.

LESSON 8.15, *The Question of Existence,* leads to the Isoperimetric Conjecture.

LESSON 8.16, *Solving the Isoperimetric Problem,* contains steps that lead to a proof of the Isoperimetric Conjecture, although the proof is incomplete.

 Activating Prior Knowledge
Exploring New Ideas

The distance from a point to a line is defined as the length of the perpendicular segment from the point to the line. The sum of the distances from P, a point inside a polygon, to the sides of the polygon depends on the location of P.

For You to Explore

Problems 1–4 refer to $\triangle ABC$, where $AB = 10$, $CB = 8$, $CA = 6$, $AH = 4$, $HB = 6$, and $PA = 5$.

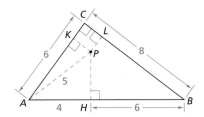

1. Find the sum of the distances from P to each side of the triangle. If you want an exact answer, use a system of two equations in LP and KP. For an approximate answer, trace the triangle and the segments inside the triangle. Carefully measure the distances from P to the sides.

2. What is the sum of the distances from P to the vertices of $\triangle ABC$?

3. Find the sum of the distances from P to the vertices for each case.

   a. P coincides with the vertex C.

   b. P coincides with the vertex A.

   c. P coincides with the vertex B.

4. Find a point where the sum of the distances from the vertices is less than 13.

Lesson Overview

GOAL

• Warm up to the ideas of the investigation.

This lesson contains problems that you should use to assess your students' knowledge about the sum of the distances from a point to the sides or vertices of a triangle or square. This will prepare students for Lesson 8.12, which introduces them to a conjecture about these distances in equilateral triangles.

FOR YOU TO EXPLORE
• Core: 1, 2
• Optional: 3, 4

HOMEWORK
• Core: 6
• Optional: 5, 7, 8, 9, 10, 11

MATERIALS
• rulers
• Blackline Master 8.11

Launch

Begin this lesson by assigning some or all of the For You to Explore problems. Blackline Master 8.11 depicts the right triangle, so students do not have to trace the figure.

Explore

Have students discuss their work on the For You to Explore problems you assigned.

Answers

For You to Explore

1. $\dfrac{28}{5}$

2. $5 + 3\sqrt{5} + \dfrac{\sqrt{85}}{5}$

3. a. 14
   b. 16
   c. 18

4. not possible

Wrap Up

End this lesson by assigning homework from On Your Own and Maintain Your Skills.

Exercises

HOMEWORK
- Core: 6
- Optional: 5, 7, 8, 9, 10, 11

On Your Own

EXERCISE 6 is a nice preview of Lesson 8.12. If students compare work on this exercise, they may be able to independently develop the conjecture introduced in the following lesson. In any case, they will have some experimental data to back up Rich's conjecture.

Exercises *Practicing Habits of Mind*

On Your Own

5. *M* is the midpoint of $\overline{DE}$. Find the sum of the distances from *M* to the sides of $\triangle DEF$.

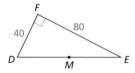

   P is on the side of $\triangle DEF$. Find *P* where the sum of the distances from *P* to the sides of the triangle is less than the sum of the distances from *M* to the sides of the triangle.

   For Exercises 6 and 7, you are given an equilateral triangle with side length 2 cm. *P* is inside the triangle.

6. Calculate (or measure) the sum of the distances from *P* to the sides of the triangle. If possible, find a point *P* that minimizes this sum.

7. Calculate (or measure) the sum of the distances from *P* to the vertices of the triangle. If possible, find a point *P* that minimizes this sum.

Maintain Your Skills

Find the sum of the distances from *P* to the sides of the square.

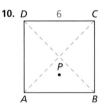

11. Does the placement of *P* within the square affect the sum? What is the sum if *P* is placed on a side of the square? Explain.

Answers

Exercises

5. 60; Answers may vary. Sample: point *D*

6. The sum of the distances is $\sqrt{3}$. *P* is not unique.

7. It appears that the sum is at its minimum $2\sqrt{3}$ when *P* is at the intersection of the medians.

8. 12

9. 12

10. 12

11. no; no, the sum is still 12.

Reasoning by Continuity

Rich answered the following problem on a standardized multiple-choice test.

Given an equilateral triangle with side length 10 units, find $DR + DQ + DP$. This is the sum of the lengths of the distances from a point inside the triangle D to the sides of the triangle.

A. 10 units

B. $5\sqrt{3}$ units

C. 30 units

D. 8.6 units

For Discussion

1. Think about the problem above and find a strategy to solve it. Discuss your ideas with the rest of the class. Remember that the distance from a point to a line means the length of the shortest path. In the diagram, $\overline{DR} \perp \overline{AB}$, $\overline{DQ} \perp \overline{AC}$, and $\overline{DP} \perp \overline{BC}$.

> **Habits of Mind**
>
> **Find another way.**
> Rich had no ruler and no computer. See what you can do without those tools.

Rich developed a function that calculates the sum of the distances from an interior point to the sides of an equilateral triangle. In the spirit of professional mathematicians, the students in the class refer to it as "Rich's Function."

Perhaps the writers of the test question above intended to find out if the students knew a particular theorem. Rich did not know it, but he demonstrated the ability to solve a problem through deduction, experimentation, and reasoning by continuity. Here is Rich's train of thought.

First, Rich decided that one of the four numbers listed had to be right.

Then he imagined D at different spots inside the triangle and compared the sums of the distances. That is when Rich realized that the problem did not say anything specific about where D is located. Rich realized that no matter where D is placed, the sum of the distances from D to the sides must be the same.

After drawing this conclusion, Rich got another idea. He placed D very close to a vertex to see how that affects the three distances.

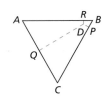

> Why is that a logical conclusion?
>
>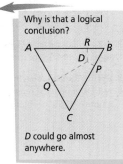
>
> D could go almost anywhere.

For Discussion

1. Answers will vary.

Lesson Overview

GOAL

• Discuss the important variables of a problem, choose a subset of them, and find an optimal solution.

In this lesson, students analyze a specific problem from a multiple-choice test and the reasoning that led a student, Rich, to the right solution. The habit of mind that is used here, reasoning by continuity, is very important as is Rich's use of extreme cases to develop his conjecture.

CHECK YOUR UNDERSTANDING	HOMEWORK
• Core: 2	• Core: 4, 6, 7
• Optional: 1, 3	• Optional: 5, 8, 9, 10

MATERIALS
• rulers

VOCABULARY
• Rich's function

Launch

Begin this lesson by reading the question from the multiple-choice test. Make sure your students understand it.

Explore

For Discussion

Your students may notice that the location of D in the triangle is not specified. This might lead some of them to assume that the problem is not solvable. Others may work from the list of answers and relate them to the triangle in the question.

Wrap Up

End this lesson by assigning some Check Your Understanding exercises.

Assessment Resources

Lesson Quiz 8.12

1. Use the given side length of an equilateral triangle. Find the sum of the distances from point *A* inside the triangle to the sides of the triangle.
   a. 14 cm
   b. 9 m

2. Two vertices of an equilateral triangle are *A*(−4, 0) and *B*(0, 3).
   a. Find the coordinates of the third vertex.
   b. Find the sum of the distances from *P*(0, 0) to each side of the triangle.
   c. Find the height of the triangle.

3. Describe three properties of equilateral triangles that are not true of isosceles triangles.

Exercises

HOMEWORK

- Core: 4, 6, 7
- Optional: 5, 8, 9, 10

Check Your Understanding

EXERCISE 3 Reasoning by continuity is a critical mathematical habit of mind. It involves visualization and transformation, and can be very helpful in finding the solutions to complex problems.

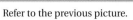 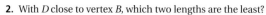 

Refer to the previous picture.

2. With *D* close to vertex *B*, which two lengths are the least?

3. Can you make those two lengths even less? Explain.

4. What is the least you can make them?

5. You previously used notation → to show something getting very close to a value. Fill in these blanks for *D* → *B*.

   a. *DP* → _____   b. *DR* → _____

6. As *DP* and *DR* decrease, what happens to *DQ*? *DQ* approaches the length of what part of the triangle?

Rich then made the following conjecture.

The sum of the distances from *any* point inside an equilateral triangle to the sides of the triangle is equal to the length of an altitude of the triangle. As a function, $f(P) = \frac{\sqrt{3}}{2}s$ where *P* is a point inside the triangle and *s* is the side length.

Exercises *Practicing Habits of Mind*

Check Your Understanding

1. Refer to Rich's standardized test question that is presented at the start of the lesson. Solve it using Rich's reasoning, your knowledge of equilateral triangles, and the Pythagorean Theorem.

2. An equilateral triangle has side length 8 cm, and *G* is inside the triangle. What is the sum of the distances from *G* to the sides of the triangle?

3. **Write About It** Teachers who followed Rich's reasoning through this lesson said that he used reasoning by continuity. Explain what this means in the context of the problem.

Remember...

The altitude of an equilateral triangle bisects the base.

Answers

In-Class Experiment

2. *DR* and *DP*

3. yes; move *D* closer to *B*.

4. There are no smallest values for *DR* and *DP* so long as *D* remains in the interior of the triangle, but you can make both lengths less than any small positive number you choose.

5. a. 0
   b. 0

6. It gets very close to the length of an altitude of the triangle.; $\overline{DQ}$ gets closer to the altitude from *B* to $\overline{AC}$.

Exercises

1. B

2. $4\sqrt{3}$

3. Answers may vary. Check students' explanations.

On Your Own

4. Standardized Test Prep *EFGH* is a rectangle inscribed in a circle with radius *r*. Which of the following is NOT true?

A. The area of *EFGH* is greatest when the length and width of *EFGH* are equal.

B. The length of each diagonal of *EFGH* is 2*r*.

C. The perimeter of *EFGH* is greatest when the length of *EFGH* is twice its width.

D. Each diagonal of *EFGH* is a diameter of the circle in which *EFGH* is inscribed.

5. An equilateral triangle with side length 2 is plotted on the coordinate plane. One vertex is $(-2, 1)$ and another is $(0, 1)$. What are possible coordinates of the third vertex? Choose the third vertex so that $P\left(-\frac{1}{2}, \frac{3}{2}\right)$ is inside the triangle. Calculate the sum of the distances from *P* to the sides of the triangle.

6. List as many facts as you can about equilateral triangles. Separate your list into facts that are true for all triangles, for some triangles, and just for equilateral triangles. Find a way to clearly present the information to other students.

7. The vertices of an isosceles triangle are $(-2, -1)$, $(1, -1)$, and $(-0.5, 3)$. Find the sum of the distances from $P(-1, 1)$ to each side of the triangle.

8. The term *function* has appeared many times in this lesson and in Algebra 1. Since this term has not been officially defined in this course, write what you understand it to mean. If you can, give some examples. Write any questions or describe any confusion that you have about the term.

Maintain Your Skills

9. The circles have center *O*, chords $\overline{AP}$ and $\overline{PB}$, and radius $AO = 2$ cm. In the circle on the left, *P* is moved along the circle to draw the figure below. As you drag *P* clockwise, *AP* changes but the size of the circle does not.

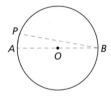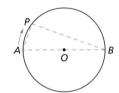

For (a)–(i) on the following page, determine whether the measure is *constant* or *changing* as *P* moves clockwise from *A* to *B*.

- For each measure that is constant, state what the constant value is or how it can be found.

- For each measure that is changing, explain how it is changing with a graph or a written explanation.

On Your Own

EXERCISES 5 AND 7 supply practice working in the coordinate plane. These skills are key to success in Algebra 2.

Maintain Your Skills

EXERCISE 9 exemplifies reasoning by continuity. Because they are not taking measurements, students must visualize what will happen to various quantities as point *P* moves along the circle.

Additional Resources

PRINTED RESOURCES
- Texas Instruments Activities Workbook
- Cabriˡog Activities
- Teaching Resources
- Practice Workbook
- Assessment Resources

TECHNOLOGY
- TeacherExpress CD-ROM
- **Exam***View* CD-ROM
- **PHSchool.com**
  - Homework Help
  - Video Tutors
  - Multiple Choice
  - Crosswords

Additional Practice

1. Use the given side length of an equilateral triangle. Find the sum of the distances from point *A* inside the triangle to the sides of the triangle.
  a. 12 cm   **b.** 20 m   **c.** 9 in.

2. For each property, list the type(s) of triangle(s), *equilateral, isosceles,* or *scalene,* that has the given property.
  a. The sum of the measures of the interior angles is 180°.
  b. The altitude at a vertex intersects the midpoint of the opposite side.
  c. A midline is parallel to and half the measure of the third side.
  d. Base angles are congruent.
  e. The height is equivalent to the length of any of the altitudes.

3. The vertices of a triangle are $A(-2, 4)$, $B(3, 4)$, and $C(0, 0)$.
  a. Classify the triangle as *equilateral, isosceles,* or *scalene.*
  b. Find the sum of the distances from $P(1, 3)$ to each side of the triangle.
  c. Find the height of the triangle.

4. A triangle has vertices $(-2, -2)$, $(3, 3)$, and $(6, 0)$. A function *F* is defined as the sum of the distances from point *Q* to the sides of the triangle.
  a. For $Q(3, 2)$, find the value of *F*.
  b. For what coordinates of *Q* does *F* have its least value?
  c. For what coordinates of *Q* does *F* have its greatest value? What is the greatest value of *F*?

5. Triangle *JLK* is right and isosceles, where $JL = LK$ and $\overline{JP}$, $\overline{LN}$, and $\overline{KM}$ are angle bisectors. Choose the correct symbol from =, >, <, or NG (not enough information given) to compare the relative measures of each given pair.
  a. *JN* ___ *NK*
  b. *LM* ___ *LP*
  c. *JM* ___ *JN*
  d. *KN* + *NL* ___ *JN* + *NL*
  e. area of △*JMK* ___ area of △*KPJ*
  f. *m∠MOL* ___ *m∠POL*
  g. area of △*JNL* ___ area of △*KNL*
  h. *KM* ___ *KL*
  i. *LN* ___ *LK*

Practice: For Lesson 8.12, assign Exercises 1–3.

---

4. C

5. $\left(-1, 1+\sqrt{3}\right)$ or $\left(-1, 1-\sqrt{3}\right)$

6. Check students' work.

7. $2 + \dfrac{12\sqrt{73}}{73}$

8. Answers may vary. Sample definition: A function is a rule that assigns a unique value to each element of a set.

9. a. constant (if *P* is not at *A* or *B*); 90°, since ∠*APB* intercepts a semicircle

b. constant; 2, since $\overline{PO}$ is a radius of the circle

c. changes; When *P* is at *A* or *B*, there is no △*APB*. For *P* on the top semicircle but not at *A* or *B*, the perimeter is $4 + AP + \sqrt{16 - AP^2}$. The values of this expression are always greater than 8 but less than or equal to $4 + 4\sqrt{2}$.

9. d–i. See back of book.

Measures:

a. $m\angle APB$
b. the distance from P to O

c. the perimeter of $\triangle APB$
d. the area of $\triangle APB$

e. the ratio of the circumference of the circle to the diameter of the circle

f. the sum of the distances $AP + PB$ g. the ratio of AP to BA

h. the ratio of AP to PB

i. MN, where M is the midpoint of $\overline{AP}$ and N is the midpoint of $\overline{PB}$

10. In $\triangle ABC$, $\angle A = 90°$, $AB = 12$, and $AC = 5$. Let $P(x, y)$ be inside $\triangle ABC$.

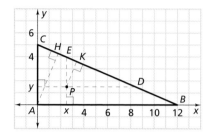

a. Find the height of $\triangle ABC$ relative to base $\overline{BC}$.

b. What are the side lengths of $\triangle PDE$ in terms of x and y? Compare corresponding side lengths to prove that $\triangle PDE$ is similar to $\triangle ABC$.

c. Find the length of $\overline{PK}$ as a function of x and y by solving the following proportion.

$$PD : AB = PK : AH$$

d. Write a function in x and y that finds the sum of the distances from P to the sides of $\triangle ABC$. Call the function $f(x, y)$. Check your function with $P_1(5, 1)$ and $P_2(6, 2)$.

Why is the proportion true?

Go Online

PHSchool.com

For additional practice, go to Web Code: **bea-0812**

Answers

10. a. $\frac{60}{13}$

 b. $PD = 12 - \frac{12}{5}y - x$,

 $PE = 5 - \frac{5}{12}x - y$,

 $ED = 13 - \frac{13}{5}y - \frac{13}{5}y -$

 $\frac{13}{12}x$; $\angle CAB$ and $\angle EPD$ are right angles and hence congruent. Corresponding angles formed by two parallel lines and a transversal are congruent, so $\angle EDP \cong \angle CBA$.

So $\triangle PDE \sim \triangle ABC$ (AA Similarity).

c. $\frac{60}{13} - \frac{12}{13}y - \frac{5}{13}x$

d. $\frac{60}{13} + \frac{1}{13}y + \frac{8}{13}x$; the results check for both P_1 and P_2.

Proving Rich's Function Is Constant

Rich's conjecture about the altitudes of equilateral triangles was made during a test. He did not have time to prove it true.

One possible proof calculates the area of $\triangle ABC$ twice. First, it is calculated as one large triangle and then as the sum of the areas of three small triangles.

Before you read through the proof, make sure you understand the idea behind these two area formulas.

$$\text{area}(\triangle ABC) = \tfrac{1}{2}bh$$

$$\text{area}(\triangle ABC) = \text{area}(\triangle ADC) + \text{area}(\triangle CDB) + \text{area}(\triangle BDA)$$

 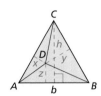

Here is the proof, using the diagrams above.

$$
\begin{aligned}
\tfrac{1}{2}bh &= \text{area}(\triangle ABC) \\
&= \text{area}(\triangle ADC) + \text{area}(\triangle CDB) + \text{area}(\triangle BDA) \\
&= \tfrac{1}{2}bx + \tfrac{1}{2}by + \tfrac{1}{2}bz \\
&= \tfrac{1}{2}b(x + y + z)
\end{aligned}
$$

Since $\tfrac{1}{2}bh = \tfrac{1}{2}b(x + y + z)$ and $b \neq 0$, then $h = x + y + z$.

For You to Do

1. Look back at the proof. Describe how you use the fact that the triangle is equilateral.

Now, rather than just a conjecture, Rich's class finally has a theorem.

Theorem 8.2 Rich's Theorem

The sum of the distances from any point inside an equilateral triangle to the sides of the triangle is equal to the length of the altitude of the triangle.

This theorem can be used to establish some inequalities.

For You to Do

1. We used the fact that $\triangle ABC$ is equilateral when we wrote expressions for the areas of $\triangle ADC$, $\triangle CDB$, and $\triangle BDA$. We used b as the length of the base of each triangle.

Lesson Overview

GOALS

- Write functions and use them to solve optimization problems.
- Discuss the important variables of a problem, choose a subset of them, and find an optimal solution.

This lesson contains the proof to Rich's Theorem.

CHECK YOUR UNDERSTANDING
- Core: 1
- Optional: 2, 3

MATERIALS
- rulers
- Blackline Master 8.13

HOMEWORK
- Core: 4, 7, 8
- Optional: 5, 6, 9, 13, 14, 15
- Extension: 10, 11, 12

Launch

Begin this lesson by having your students restate Rich's conjecture.

Explore

Assign the For You to Do problems. Blackline Master 8.13 depicts equilateral triangle *EFG* so students do not have to copy the figure.

Wrap Up

Assign some of the Check Your Understanding exercises to finish the lesson.

Assessment Resources

Lesson Quiz 8.13

1. A triangle has vertices $(-7, 2)$, $(5, 2)$, and $(5, -3)$. A function is defined as the sum of the distances from point Q to the sides of the given triangle.
   a. For $Q(-1, 1)$, find the value of the function.
   b. For what coordinates of Q does the function have its least value?
   c. For what coordinates of Q does the function have its greatest value? What is the greatest value of the function?

2. Triangle JLK is scalene where $m\angle JLK > m\angle LJK > m\angle JKL$. $\overline{JP}$, $\overline{LM}$, and $\overline{KN}$ are medians that intersect at point O. Choose the correct symbol from $=$, $>$, $<$, or NG (not enough information given) to compare the relative measures of each pair.
   a. KP ___ KO
   b. LM ___ LP
   c. JM ___ JN
   d. $KN + NL$ ___ $JP + PL$
   e. area of $\triangle JMO$ ___ area of $\triangle JNO$
   f. $\angle MOJ$ ___ $\angle POL$
   g. area of $\triangle MLK$ ___ area of $\triangle KNL$
   h. KM ___ JP
   i. MN ___ MP

For You to Do

2. Equilateral $\triangle EFG$ contains D and W, two points that do not coincide. $\overline{DA}$, $\overline{DB}$, and $\overline{DC}$ are perpendicular to the sides of the triangle. Show that the inequality $WA + WB + WC > DA + DB + DC$ is true.

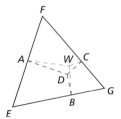

Hint: Draw perpendiculars to the sides from W, too.

Exercises *Practicing Habits of Mind*

Check Your Understanding

1. Rewrite the proof of Rich's Theorem in your own words. Try not to refer back to the text.

2. There are other ways to prove Rich's Theorem. Study the following pictures and try to make sense of what is going on from one step to the next.

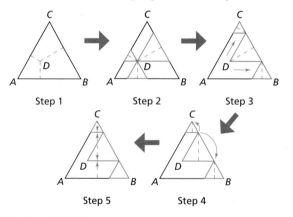

Step 1   Step 2   Step 3

Step 5   Step 4

Answers

2. Draw $\overline{WM}$ perpendicular to $\overline{EF}$ at M, $\overline{WQ}$ perpendicular to $\overline{EG}$ at Q, and $\overline{WP}$ perpendicular to $\overline{FG}$ at P. The segments $\overline{WM}$, $\overline{WQ}$, and $\overline{WP}$ are the shortest segments from W to the sides of $\triangle EFG$ since they are the perpendiculars to the sides. So $WA > WM$, $WB > WQ$, and $WC > WF$. Add to get $WA + WB + WC > WM + WQ + WF$. But $WM + WQ + WF = DA + DB + DC$ since each sum is equal to the height of $\triangle EFG$ (Theorem 8.2). Therefore, $WA + WB + WC > DA + DB + DC$.

Exercises

1. Check students' work.

2. See back of book.

For each step, write down exactly what changed from the previous step. Supply reasons that explain why each step is valid. For Step 1, you might write the following: *ABC* is an equilateral triangle with *D* in the interior. Perpendiculars have been drawn from *D* to the sides of the triangle.

3. Look back at the two proofs of Rich's Theorem in Exercises 1 and 2. For each proof, describe where you use the fact that the triangle is equilateral.

On Your Own

4. Suppose a triangle is not equilateral. Will the sum of the distances from a point to the sides still be equal to the height of the triangle? To answer this question, look back at Exercises 1 and 2. What goes wrong in these proofs when the triangle is not equilateral?

5. If the triangle is not equilateral, Rich's function is no longer constant on the triangle's interior. Different points *P* produce different values.

   Let *S* be the function that determines the sum of the distances from any *P* to the sides of a triangle.

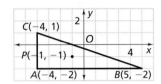

   There is a way that you can figure this out without any measuring at all.

   a. Calculate $S(P)$ for point $P(-1, -1)$ in the triangle.

   b. If *P* can be in the interior or on the sides of the triangle, where is *S* the least?

   c. If *P* can be in the interior or on the sides of the triangle, where is *S* the greatest?

   d. If *P* is in the interior (but not on the sides) of the triangle, can you find a minimum value for *S*? Explain.

   e. If *P* is in the interior (but not on the sides) of the triangle, can you find a maximum value for *S*? Explain.

6. In Exercise 5, you found the minimum and maximum value of *S* for the given triangle.

   a. Build a sketch with geometry software that computes *S* for all triangles.

   b. Describe the triangles in which the maximum value equals the minimum value.

Exercises

HOMEWORK
- Core: 4, 7, 8
- Optional: 5, 6, 9, 13, 14, 15
- Extension: 10, 11, 12

On Your Own

EXERCISE 4 This is another facet of proofs. By studying what goes wrong with a proof when you change what is given, you can often find new results. Students can develop a conjecture for this exercise by experimenting. However, by looking at the previous proofs and what goes wrong with them, students may actually see a way to prove the conjecture.

---

3. For the first proof, see the answer for Exercise 1, For You to Do. For the second proof, Step 4 uses the fact that the small triangles are equilateral, and their being equilateral stems from the fact that △*ABC* is equilateral.

4. no

5. a. $4 + \dfrac{\sqrt{73}}{10}$

   b. at *B*

   c. at *A*

   d. No; $S(A) < S(P)$ for all points *P* in the interior of the triangle.

   But as *P* approaches *A*, $S(P)$ gets closer and closer to $S(A)$.

   e. No; $S(B) > S(P)$ for all points *P* in the interior of the triangle. But as *P* approaches *B*, $S(P)$ gets closer and closer to $S(B)$.

6. a. Check students' work.

   b. equilateral triangles

c. What is the nature of the function for the subset of triangles with equal minimum and maximum values?

7. **Standardized Test Prep** In right triangle *GHI*, the coordinates of *G*, *H*, and *I* are (0, 0), (12, 0), and (0, 6), respectively. A rectangle is inscribed in △*GHI* so that one endpoint of one of the rectangle's diagonals is (0, 0). What are coordinates of the other endpoint of the diagonal when the area of the rectangle is maximized?

   A. (4, 4)   **B.** (5, 3.5)   **C.** (6, 3)   **D.** (8, 2.5)

8. Triangle *FGH* is isosceles, with *GF* = *HF*. $\overline{GK}$ and $\overline{HJ}$ are medians.

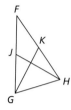

Choose the correct symbol to compare the relative measures of each pair of objects named. You may use =, >, ≥, <, ≤, or NG (not enough information given).

   a. *GJ* _?_ *FJ*   **b.** *GJ* _?_ *GH*   **c.** *KF* _?_ *JF*

   d. *FJ* + *JH* _?_ *FK* + *KH*   **e.** area(△*GHJ*) _?_ area(△*GHK*)

   f. ∠*KHG* _?_ ∠*JGK*   **g.** area(△*FKG*) _?_ area(△*HKG*)

   h. distance from *G* to *K* _?_ distance from *G* to $\overline{FH}$

   i. *JK* _?_ *GH*

9. Suppose △*FGH* is scalene with medians $\overline{GK}$ and $\overline{HJ}$. Which of the relationships in Exercise 8 would stay the same and which would change? Write *same* if the relationship stays the same, or choose the correct new symbol if the relationship changes.

   Try to do this exercise without drawing. Instead, visualize the scalene triangle. When you have finished, you can sketch or use geometry software to see if you are right.

10. **Take It Further** Find the length of $\overline{BN}$ if *AB* = 5 and *BC* = 12. Use the strategy of calculating area in more than one way.

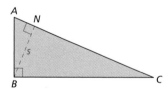

Answers

6. **c.** The function is constant.

7. C

8. **a.** =
   b. NG
   c. =
   d. >
   e. =
   f. >
   g. =
   h. ≥
   i. <

9. **a.** same
   b. same
   c. NG
   d. same
   e. same
   f. NG
   g. same
   h. same
   i. same

10. $\frac{60}{13}$

11. Take It Further Find the length of $\overline{ST}$ if $AB = 5$, $BC = 12$, and $SB = 4$. Use the strategy of calculating area in more than one way without using similar triangles. Recall that the area of a trapezoid is half the product of the height and the sum of the bases.

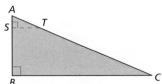

> Do you know another way to find the length of $\overline{ST}$?

12. Take It Further Let P be any point on an equilateral triangle except for the vertices. Use a sketch to show that the sum of the lengths of the perpendiculars from P to the sides of the triangle is equal to the height of the triangle. Your sketch should be a proof without words.

Maintain Your Skills

13. You are given $\triangle ABC$ with $m\angle A > m\angle B$. Construct the altitudes $\overline{AD}$ and $\overline{BE}$, and show that $AD < BE$.

14. In $\triangle ABC$, D is somewhere on $\overline{AB}$. The distance from D to $\overline{AC}$ is a. The distance from D to $\overline{BC}$ is b. Assume $\triangle ABC$ is not obtuse. Answer the following questions.

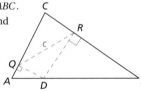

a. What position for D maximizes $a + b$?

b. What is the maximum value of $a + b$?

c. What position for D minimizes $a + b$?

d. What is the minimum value of $a + b$?

15. D lies somewhere on $\overline{AB}$ of nonobtuse $\triangle ABC$. Perpendiculars are drawn from D to $\overline{AC}$ and $\overline{BC}$. Let c be the length of $\overline{QR}$.

a. What position of D minimizes the value of c?

b. What is that minimum value?

c. What position of D maximizes the value of c?

d. What is that maximum value?

Go Online
PHSchool.com
For additional practice, go to **Web Code: bea-0813**

EXERCISE 14 One important point about this exercise is subtle. The function is still constant when the triangle is equilateral, but now it is also constant when the triangle is isosceles and $\overline{AC} \cong \overline{BC}$.

Additional Resources

PRINTED RESOURCES
- Texas Instruments Activities Workbook
- Cabrilog Activities
- Teaching Resources
- Practice Workbook
- Assessment Resources

TECHNOLOGY
- TeacherExpress CD-ROM
- **Exam**View CD-ROM
- **PHSchool.com**
  - Homework Help
  - Video Tutors
  - Multiple Choice
  - Crosswords

Additional Practice

1. Use the given side length of an equilateral triangle. Find the sum of the distances from point A inside the triangle to the sides of the triangle.
  a. 12 cm   **b.** 20 m   **c.** 9 in.

2. For each property, list the type(s) of triangle(s), *equilateral, isosceles,* or *scalene,* that has the given property.
  a. The sum of the measures of the interior angles is 180°.
  b. The altitude at a vertex intersects the midpoint of the opposite side.
  c. A midline is parallel to and half the measure of the third side.
  d. Base angles are congruent.
  e. The height is equivalent to the length of any of the altitudes.

3. The vertices of a triangle are $A(-2, 4)$, $B(3, 4)$, and $C(0, 0)$.
  a. Classify the triangle as *equilateral, isosceles,* or *scalene.*
  b. Find the sum of the distances from $P(1, 3)$ to each side of the triangle.
  c. Find the height of the triangle.

4. A triangle has vertices $(-2, -2)$, $(3, 3)$, and $(6, 0)$. A function F is defined as the sum of the distances from point Q to the sides of the triangle.
  a. For $Q(3, 2)$, find the value of F.
  b. For what coordinates of Q does F have its least value?
  c. For what coordinates of Q does F have its greatest value? What is the greatest value of F?

5. Triangle JLK is right and isosceles, where $JL = LK$ and $\overline{JP}$, $\overline{LN}$, and $\overline{KM}$ are angle bisectors. Choose the correct symbol from $=, >, <$, or NG (not enough information given) to compare the relative measures of each given pair.
  a. JN ___ NK
  b. LM ___ LP
  c. JM ___ JN
  d. $KN + NL$ ___ $JN + NL$
  e. area of $\triangle JMK$ ___ area of $\triangle KPJ$
  f. $m\angle MOL$ ___ $m\angle POL$
  g. area of $\triangle JNL$ ___ area of $\triangle KNL$
  h. KM ___ KL
  i. LN ___ LK

Practice: For Lesson 8.13, assign Exercises 4–7.

---

11. $\dfrac{12}{5}$

12.

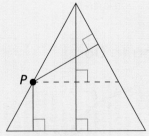

13. Check students' work.

14. a. D at the vertex of the smaller of $\angle A$ and $\angle B$

b. the height of $\triangle ABC$ as measured from the vertex of the smaller of $\angle A$ and $\angle B$

c. D at the vertex of the larger of $\angle A$ and $\angle B$

d. the height of $\triangle ABC$ as measured from the vertex of the larger of $\angle A$ and $\angle B$

15. a. D at the foot of the altitude from C to $\overline{AB}$

b. $h \sin \angle ACB$, where h is the height of $\triangle ABC$ as measured from vertex C

15. c–d. See back of book.

Lesson Overview

GOALS

- Discuss the important variables of a problem, choose a subset of them, and find an optimal solution.
- Understand and explain a proof of the isoperimetric problem.

This lesson re-introduces the Isoperimetric Problem—finding the closed curve that encloses the most area for a given perimeter. Students might remember it from the dialog between Sasha and Derman in Lesson 8.5.

CHECK YOUR UNDERSTANDING
- Core: 2, 3
- Optional: 1

MATERIALS
- compasses
- protractors
- rulers

HOMEWORK
- Core: 4, 5, 7
- Optional: 6, 8, 9, 10, 12, 13, 14, 15
- Extension: 11

VOCABULARY
- isoperimetric problem

Launch

Begin this lesson by restating the main points of the dialog in Lesson 8.5.

Explore

Have students work through the For Discussion and the first For You to Do problems. Then explain the Example before having them do For You to Do Problems 2–4.

8.14 The Isoperimetric Problem

In Lesson 8.5, Sasha and Derman look for the greatest floor area for a rectangular house with perimeter 128 feet. This is an isoperimetric problem. In general, **isoperimetric problems** involve geometric figures of a certain type with the same perimeter. You want to find the one that encloses the most area.

Remember...
The house with the greatest floor area was a square.

Suppose you have a rope of some fixed length, and you join the ends to make a loop. You can put the loop on the floor and form many shapes. The polygons, curves, and figure eights you can make all have the same perimeter. Which has the greatest area? This is the most general and most famous isoperimetric problem. It allows you to consider any shape.

The Isoperimetric Problem Of all closed curves with the same perimeter, which encloses the most area?

The word *isoperimetric* comes from three Greek words.
Iso- means "equal," as in *isosceles, isobars,* and *isometric.*
Peri- means "around," as in *pericardium* and *peripheral.*
Metri- means "measurement," as in *metric system.*

Theorem 8.1 from Lesson 8.6 is a good place to start. Even if the solution to the isoperimetric problem is not a polygon, proving the Regular Polygon Theorem will help.

Theorem 8.1 The Regular Polygon Theorem

Of all the polygons having a given perimeter and a given number of sides, the regular polygon has the greatest area.

For Discussion

1. You have already done some work that will contribute to the proof of this theorem. Explain how you know that the polygon that encloses the greatest area for a given perimeter must be convex and equilateral.

To prove the theorem, it is not enough to know that the polygon is convex and equilateral. You also need to show that the polygon is equiangular. One way to do this is to show that all the vertices of the polygon that encloses the greatest area must lie on a circle.

It turns out that it is much easier to do this if the polygon has an even number of sides. That case previews the key methods that you will use to solve the general isoperimetric problem, so it is the only one considered in this lesson. (You will learn more about the case of an odd number of sides in a later course.)

For You to Do

Justify the following claim.

If all the vertices of an equilateral polygon lie on a circle, all the angles of the polygon are congruent. (The polygon is *regular.*)

Answers

For Discussion

1. If a polygon is not convex, there is at least on pair of vertices such that the segment connecting them lies entirely outside the polygon. Reflect all the sides of the polygon between these two vertices across this segment. The result is polygon with the same perimeter as the original that clearly has a greater area. It has already been shown that a convex polygon with fixed perimeter that has the greatest area is equilateral.

For You to Do

2.

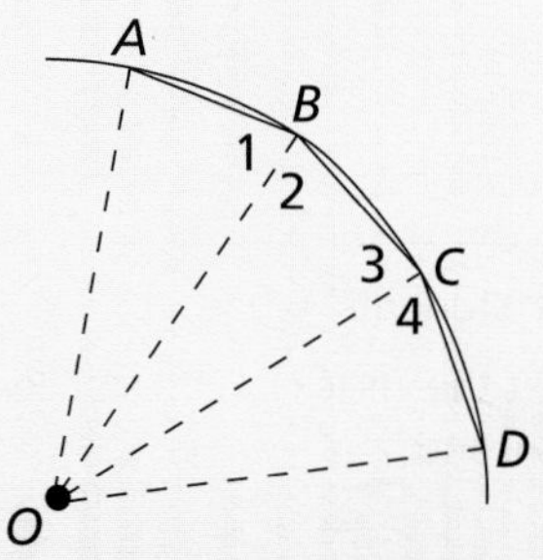

Example 1

Problem You are given an octagon. It encloses the maximum possible area for a fixed perimeter. Show that all of its vertices must lie on a circle.

Solution First, show that if a line cuts the perimeter of the polygon in half, it must also cut the area in half. Draw a line that passes through two vertices and divides the octagon into two polygons, I and II. See the polygon below at the left.

> This may seem like a strange place to start, but keep reading and it will make more sense.

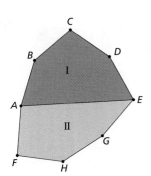
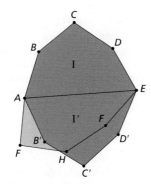

Both I and II have the same perimeter. Less obvious is that they also have the same area. To see this, suppose $\overline{AE}$ *does not* cut the area of the octagon in half—say, for example, that the area of I is greater than the area of II. You could reflect I over $\overline{AE}$ to create a new octagon with greater area and the same perimeter as shown above at the right.

But this contradicts the given fact that you started with an octagon of fixed perimeter that encloses the *maximum possible area* already. Therefore, $\overline{AE}$ must cut the area of the octagon in half.

Now work with a polygon that is half of the original octagon. If you can show that all of its vertices lie on a semicircle, you will be done.

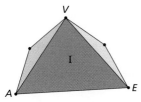

Look at $\angle AVE$, where V is any vertex of the half octagon except A or E. If $m\angle AVE = 90°$, then all V are on the semicircle with diameter $\overline{AE}$ and you are done. If $m\angle AVE$ does not equal 90°, then you have more work to do.

> Imagine you are squeezing and stretching the polygon to find the measure for $\angle AVE$ that guarantees that the area of the polygon is maximized.

In the figures at the top of the next page, the shaded regions labeled α are congruent, and the shaded regions labeled β are congruent. The half octagons have been altered so that $\angle AVE$ is acute in the first figure and obtuse in the second.

$OA = OB = OC = OD$ and
$AB = BC = CD$. Therefore,
$\triangle AOB \cong \triangle BOC \cong \triangle COD$ and
$\angle 1 \cong \angle 2$ and $\angle 3 \cong \angle 4$. So
$\angle ABC \cong \angle BCD$, and polygon
$\triangle ABCD \dots$ is equiangular.

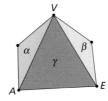
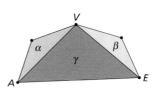

Remember that $\triangle AVE$ is part of the half octagon with maximized area. Therefore, the area of $\triangle AVE$ must be maximized as well. The lengths of $\overline{AV}$ and $\overline{VE}$ cannot change because that would alter the areas of the shaded regions.

Recall Exercise 7 in Lesson 8.5. You found the triangle with maximum area given two fixed side lengths. It is the right triangle with legs that measure the two given lengths. Therefore, the maximum-area triangle with sides $\overline{AV}$ and $\overline{VE}$ is the triangle in which $m\angle AVE = 90°$. You have shown that all vertices V of the half octagon lie on a semicircle. So all of the vertices V of the original octagon lie on a circle.

For You to Do

2. For the octagon, $\overline{AE}$ connected the "first" vertex A to the fifth vertex E. If the polygon had 10 sides, which vertex would be connected to A (if A is the first)? Which vertex would be connected to A if the polygon had 12 sides? If it had $2n$ sides?

3. Carry out the argument in the Example for a general polygon with an even number of sides (that is, for a $2n$-gon).

4. Explain how you know that if $m\angle AVB = 90°$ for some point V, it must lie on the same circle as any other point V for which that is true. In other words, explain why it cannot lie on a different circle.

You have now shown that Theorem 8.1 is true for polygons with an even number of sides.

- First, you showed that the polygon enclosing the maximum area must be convex and equilateral.

- Then, you showed that a polygon with an even number of sides encloses the most area when its vertices lie on a circle.

- You also explained why the vertices of this maximum-area polygon lie on the same circle.

The fact that the vertices all lie on a circle shows that the equilateral polygon is also equiangular. This is because you can divide the polygon into congruent triangles by connecting the center of the circle to each vertex. All the triangles formed are congruent and isosceles. The base angles are congruent, so when combined, they form congruent angles of the polygon.

You have shown that given a perimeter and number of sides of a polygon, the regular polygon encloses the greatest area. This is an important step on the path to solving the isoperimetric problem.

Answers

For You to Do

2. 6th vertex; 7th; $n + 1$

3. We have shown that a $2n$-gon with a given perimeter whose area is maximal is convex and equilateral and has all its vertices on the same circle. This means that the $2n$-gon is regular. Suppose the vertices of a regular $2n$-gon are $V_1, V_2, V_3, \ldots, V_{2n}$. Then the polygon $V_1V_3\ldots V_{2n-1}$ is an n-gon. We know that all the vertices of the $2n$-gon lie on the same circle. So all the vertices of the n-gon are on this same circle, and both the polygons are regular. From the fact that the area of the $2n$-gon is maximal for its perimeter, it follows that the area of the n-gon is maximal for its perimeter.

4. If V is a point such that $m\angle AVB = 90°$, then $\triangle AVB$ is a right triangle with hypotenuse $\overline{AB}$. The midpoint M of $\overline{AB}$ is equidistant from A, B, and V. So V is on the circle with center M and diameter $\overline{AB}$.

Exercises *Practicing Habits of Mind*

Check Your Understanding

1. When you were proving Theorem 8.1, you probably did not consider any self-intersecting polygons. Consider the one below.

   Explain why a self-intersecting polygon could not have maximum area for its perimeter. Describe a way to draw a simple polygon (one that does not cross itself) that has the same perimeter as the self-intersecting polygon but that encloses more area.

2. Find the area of the greatest 6-sided polygon with a perimeter of 36 inches. Then find another figure with a perimeter of 36 inches that encloses more area.

3. Find the least possible perimeter for a 5-sided polygon with area 30 square centimeters. Then find another figure that has area 30 square centimeters but a smaller perimeter.

On Your Own

4. **Write About It** Prove the even case of Theorem 8.1 in your own words. Explain how this theorem could affect a proof of the isoperimetric problem.

5. Work through the following sequence of steps. Develop a formula that will approximate the area of a regular polygon with n sides and perimeter p.

   a. Visualize your regular polygon inscribed in a circle. Draw segments connecting each vertex to the center of the circle. This process forms a number of congruent triangles. Sketch one of the triangles. Label the angle measures and side lengths you know in terms of n and p.

   b. Define h as the height of the triangle with respect to the triangle side that is also a side of the polygon. Use trigonometry to approximate h.

   c. Write an expression in terms of n and p for the area of a single triangle and for the total area of the polygon.

> **Remember...**
> The height h is the apothem of the polygon.

6. You want to build a five-sided dog run against a wall of your house. You have 84 feet of fence. From similar problems, you know that the best possibility will be half of some regular polygon. (You can see the whole polygon if you reflect your dog run over the line of the wall.)

   a. Reflect your five-sided dog run over the line of the wall. How many sides does the resulting polygon have? Consider all possible cases.

   b. For each of the possibilities, work out the area of the resulting best dog run.

Wrap Up

End this lesson by assigning some Check Your Understanding exercises.

Assessment Resources

Lesson Quiz 8.14

1. Find the area of the largest 8-sided polygon with perimeter 32 meters. Then find another figure with perimeter 32 meters that encloses more area.

2. Find the least possible perimeter for a 6-sided polygon with area 78 square inches. Then find another figure with area 78 square inches that has a smaller perimeter.

3. Find the area of each regular figure with perimeter 72 inches.
   a. triangle
   b. square
   c. hexagon

Exercises

HOMEWORK
- Core: 4, 5, 7
- Optional: 6, 8, 9, 10, 12, 13, 14, 15
- Extension: 11

Check Your Understanding

EXERCISE 2 challenges students to find a figure that encloses a greater area, given a certain perimeter. Students who have not yet conjectured that the circle is the solution to the isoperimetric problem may choose a polygon with more than six sides.

Exercises

1. See back of book.

2. $54\sqrt{3}$ in.^{2}; Answers may vary.
   Sample: a circle of radius $\frac{18}{\pi}$ in.

3. ≈ 20.8788 cm (exact: $10\sqrt{6} \cdot \sqrt[4]{5 - 2\sqrt{5}}$ cm); Answers may vary. Sample: a circle of radius $\frac{\sqrt{30\pi}}{\pi}$ cm

4. Check students' proofs. The theorem tells us that of all the polygons with a given number of sides, n, and a given perimeter, a regular polygon has the maximum area. The vertices of a regular polygon all lie on the same circle. This suggests that of all closed plane curves having a given perimeter, the curve of maximum area will be a circle.

5. See back of book.

6. See back of book.

On Your Own

EXERCISE 12 Here is another way to visualize what is happening. Picture a closed loop of rope lying on a flat surface in no particular shape. Suppose that you pour some liquid into the center of the loop, and the liquid pushes the rope out as far as it can go. Once the liquid pushes the rope into the shape of a circle, it cannot push the rope outward any farther.

Maintain Your Skills

EXERCISES 13–15 have students informally investigate limits as they practice calculating with fractions and complex fractions.

Additional Resources

PRINTED RESOURCES
- Texas Instruments Activities Workbook
- Cabrilog Activities
- Teaching Resources
- Practice Workbook
- Assessment Resources

TECHNOLOGY
- TeacherExpress CD-ROM
- **Exam***View* CD-ROM
- **PHSchool.com**
  - Homework Help
  - Video Tutors
  - Multiple Choice
  - Crosswords

Additional Practice

1. a. Find the area of the largest 6-sided polygon with perimeter 48 meters.
 b. Find another figure with perimeter 48 meters that encloses more area.

2. a. Find the area of the largest 8-sided polygon with perimeter 80 meters.
 b. Find another figure with perimeter 80 meters that encloses more area.

3. a. Find the least possible perimeter for a 6-sided polygon with area 120 square inches.
 b. Find another figure with area 120 square inches that has a smaller perimeter.

4. a. Find the least possible perimeter for a 5-sided polygon with area 96 square centimeters.
 b. Find another figure with area 96 square centimeters that has a smaller perimeter.

5. Each figure described below is inscribed in a circle. Form congruent triangles by drawing a segment from the center of the figure to each vertex. Then use trigonometry to find the area of each individual triangle.
 a. a pentagon with perimeter 60 m
 b. an octagon in a circle of radius 5 in.
 c. a 10-sided figure with perimeter 65 cm

6. Find the area of each regular figure with perimeter 36 inches.
 a. triangle
 b. square
 c. hexagon
 d. dodecagon

7. You have 120 feet of fencing to build a dog kennel alongside a barn. You plan to use the barn wall for one side of the kennel. For each given number of sides, find the maximum area of the dog kennel.
 a. 4 sides
 b. 5 sides
 c. 6 sides

Practice: For Lesson 8.14, assign Exercises 1–8.

---

7. Standardized Test Prep Sarah and Zoey want to build a pen for their puppy. They have 2 m of fencing, and they plan to use the side of the garage as one side of the pen. Which shape pen has the greatest area?

A. an equilateral triangle
B. a square with $\frac{2}{3}$-m sides
C. a 1m-by-$\frac{1}{2}$ m rectangle
D. cannot be determined

8. What's Wrong Here? Tony says, "I think I know where we are going with all this regular polygon stuff. Think about a regular polygon inscribed in a circle. If you double the number of sides, of course you increase the area. If you keep doubling, the area increases, but it cannot become greater than the area of the circumscribed circle."

Find the areas of the following regular polygons inscribed in a circle of radius 1.
 a. triangle
 b. hexagon
 c. dodecagon (a 12-sided polygon)

 d. Sasha says, "Hold on a minute! The perimeter isn't staying the same for all of your polygons. You're enclosing more area, but you're also increasing the perimeter." Is Sasha right?

9. Find the perimeter of Tony's polygons from Exercise 8.

10. Find the area of a regular triangle, hexagon, and dodecagon, each with perimeter 12 cm.

11. Take It Further Your evidence shows that for a given perimeter, polygons with more sides enclose more area. Can you prove this conjecture? Explain.

12. Make a conjecture about the isoperimetric problem. Use any tool to convince yourself that your conjecture is true. Explain in detail what you did.

Maintain Your Skills

13. To prepare for Exercise 6 in Lesson 8.15, evaluate $x + \frac{1-x}{2}$ for the following values of x. Express your answer as an exact fraction.
 a. $x = \frac{9}{10}$
 b. $x = \frac{99}{100}$
 c. $x = \frac{999}{1000}$
 d. $x = \frac{9999}{10000}$

14. In Exercise 13, the values of x are all of the form $\frac{n-1}{n}$. As n increases, does $\frac{n-1}{n}$ increase or decrease? Is x approaching some value?

15. In Exercise 14, you describe the behavior of x as n increases. If x continues to change in this way, does the expression $x + \frac{1-x}{2}$ increase or decrease? Does it approach some value?

Go Online
Video Tutor
PHSchool.com
Web Code: bee-0814

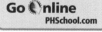

Go Online
PHSchool.com

For additional practice, go to **Web Code: bea-0814**

Answers

7. C

8. a. $\frac{3}{4}\sqrt{3}$ unit^2
 b. $\frac{3}{2}\sqrt{3}$ unit^2
 c. 3 unit^2
 d. yes

9. perimeter of triangle $= 3\sqrt{3}$, perimeter of hexagon $= 6$, perimeter of dodecagon $= 12\sqrt{2 - \sqrt{3}}$ (or $6\sqrt{6} - 6\sqrt{2}$)

10. area of triangle $= 4\sqrt{3}$, area of hexagon $= 6\sqrt{3}$, area of dodecagon $= 6 + 3\sqrt{3}$

11. Check students' work.

12. A circle encloses the greatest area for a given perimeter.

13. a. $\frac{19}{20}$
 b. $\frac{199}{200}$
 c. $\frac{1999}{2000}$
 d. $\frac{19,999}{20,000}$

14. The value of $\frac{n-1}{n}$ increases; yes, 1

15. increase; yes, 1

The Question of Existence

You have had some practice finding the polygon that encloses the most area for a given perimeter and number of sides. Now you can return to the isoperimetric problem.

Example

Problem Is the figure that encloses the most area for a given perimeter a polygon? Explain how you know.

Solution No, it is not. Consider a square of side length a. Cut off the lower right corner of the square. Call the lengths of the sides of the resulting triangle r, s, and t.

 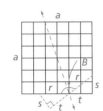 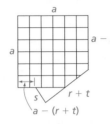

Now reflect the triangle about the angle bisector of $\angle B$. Line up its longest side r with the base of the square. You now have a hexagon with the same area and perimeter as the original square. The area is unchanged since you just cut off a piece of the square and taped it back on. To show that the perimeter is the same, add up the lengths of the six sides. Start at the top and proceed clockwise.

$$a + (a - s) + (r + t) + s + [a - (r + t)] + a = 4a$$

Call this new hexagon C for curve. The important fact about C is that it has the same area and perimeter as the original square, but it is concave. This means that there is another curve with the same perimeter as C that encloses more area. So the figure with this perimeter that encloses the maximum area is not a square.

Using this method, you can always draw a concave polygon with the same area and perimeter as any given polygon. You also can transform any concave polygon to increase its area without increasing its perimeter. Therefore, it is impossible that any polygon could be the solution to the isoperimetric problem.

Habits of Mind

Develop your understanding. This argument can be generalized to any polygon. The right angle that was cut off the square was not used in the proof, so you could cut off the corner of any polygon and reflect it this way.

Lesson Overview

GOALS

- Discuss the important variables of a problem, choose a subset of them, and find an optimal solution.

- Understand and explain a proof of the isoperimetric problem.

This lesson presents the Isoperimetric Conjecture, which states that of all closed curves with the same perimeter, the circle encloses the most area. Students see that the solution could not be a polygon through a method of transforming any convex polygon into a concave polygon with the same area.

CHECK YOUR UNDERSTANDING
- Core: 2
- Optional: 1

MATERIALS
- compasses
- graph paper
- protractors
- rulers
- Blackline Master 8.15

HOMEWORK
- Core: 3, 4, 5
- Optional: 7, 8, 9, 10, 11
- Extension: 6

Launch

Begin this lesson by having your students work through the Example. It answers whether the curve that encloses the most area for a given perimeter could be a polygon. Have students cut out a square and follow the process in the Example.

Explore

For Discussion

The curve that will eventually solve the isoperimetric problem must be simple (it cannot intersect itself), closed, and convex. It cannot be a polygon. Students may also suggest that any line that bisects the perimeter of the optimal curve must also bisect its area, using an argument parallel to that in the Example in Lesson 8.14. Many students will conjecture that the circle is the curve that solves the Isoperimetric Problem.

Wrap Up

End this lesson by assigning some Check Your Understanding exercises.

Assessment Resources

For Discussion

1. Summarize everything you know about the curve that will eventually solve the isoperimetric problem. Share any conjectures you have made, and record any characteristics that the best curve must have.

Through experiments and visualization, you may know the solution to the isoperimetric problem. To make a conjecture about which shape solves the problem is a good start. Now, you must prove your conjecture.

From your experiments, you may have decided a circle is the best shape.

Conjecture 8.1 The Isoperimetric Conjecture

Of all closed curves with the same perimeter, the circle encloses the most area.

In this lesson and the next, you will study one plan for a proof. You will look at a sequence of partial results that imply the conjecture is a theorem. You will establish all but one of these partial results. Then you will have a good idea of how the isoperimetric conjecture is proven.

Here are the main steps in the plan you will study.

Step 1 For a fixed perimeter, show that there is at least one curve that encloses the most area.

Step 2 You are given a curve that encloses the most area. Show that any line that cuts its perimeter in half must also bisect its area. Call such a line a diameter of the curve.

Step 3 You are given a curve that encloses the most area and one of its diameters. Pick any point *P* on the curve that is not on the diameter. Draw segments from *P* to the endpoints of the diameter. The angle formed at *P* is always a right angle.

> This particular plan follows the one described in Courant and Robbins "What is Mathematics" (1941).

Remember...

How do you define *diameter* in a circle?

For Discussion

2. How do the three steps above imply that a circle encloses the most area for a given perimeter?

As it turns out, the first step in this plan is the toughest. It cannot be proved using the methods developed in this text. In other words, you cannot prove that there is a curve of given perimeter that encloses the most area.

How could there not be a solution to an optimization problem? In the following exercises, you will see several examples of optimization problems that do not have solutions.

Answers

For Discussion

1. Check students' work.
2. They imply that if there is a closed curve that encloses the maximum area for a given perimeter, then all points of the curve lie on a circle.

Exercises *Practicing Habits of Mind*

Check Your Understanding

1. **Write About It** The isoperimetric problem asks which curve encloses the most area. Could there be more than one best curve? Give an example of an optimization problem that has several solutions. That is, find a situation for which there is more than one way to maximize or minimize something.

2. Trace the figure below, including *A* and *B*. Take turns with a partner trying to draw the shortest path in the plane from *A* to *B* that does not touch the circle. Is there a shortest path? Explain.

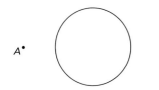

On Your Own

3. Describe how you would draw a regular polygon with *n* sides and perimeter *p*.

4. Look back at Steps 2 and 3 of the plan for establishing the isoperimetric conjecture. Point out the places where these steps assume that there is a best curve. Why is this assumption necessary?

5. **Standardized Test Prep** You cut an 80-cm wire into two pieces. You fold one piece into a square and the other piece into an equilateral triangle. Which wire lengths will produce the greatest total area of the square and equilateral triangle?

   A. square: 40 cm; triangle: 40 cm

   B. square: 45.7 cm; triangle: 34.3 cm

   C. square: 34.8 cm; triangle: 45.2 cm

   D. square: 50 cm; triangle: 30 cm

Check Your Understanding

EXERCISE 2 Blackline Master 8.15 depicts the circle and points *A* and *B* so students do not have to trace the figure.

On Your Own

EXERCISE 3 You do not have to worry about the existence of a regular polygon with *n* sides and perimeter *p* because you can always construct one. Students may decide this means that they do not have to worry about the existence of an optimal curve because they already know that the optimal curve is a circle. You can always construct a circle for a given perimeter. However, you will need to remind them that they do not yet know that the circle is the solution. It is still only a conjecture. If they assume that the solution is a circle, they can construct the circle for the given perimeter and its existence is guaranteed. However, they have made a different assumption and have actually assumed the result they want to prove. This is a common pitfall and very difficult for students to spot themselves.

Exercises

1. Answers may vary. Sample: Suppose a city has streets that run only north-south or east-west and that all blocks are the same length. Suppose you want to travel along the streets from a point *A* at one street intersection to a point *B* at an intersection 10 blocks east and 10 blocks south. There are many possible routes of minimum length even though the length of each such route will be 20 blocks.

2. There is no shortest path.

3. See back of book.

4. The existence of a best curve is assumed in the opening words of each step: "Given a curve that encloses the most area."

5. C

EXERCISE 6 contains a good review of algebraic reasoning and provides an example of a proof that begins with an incorrect assumption.

Maintain Your Skills

EXERCISES 8–11 provide practice in algebraic skills that your students will need for Algebra 2, and present optimization in a new context.

Additional Resources

PRINTED RESOURCES
- Texas Instruments Activities Workbook
- Cabrilog Activities
- Teaching Resources
- Practice Workbook
- Assessment Resources

TECHNOLOGY
- TeacherExpress CD-ROM
- **Exam***View* CD-ROM
- **PHSchool.com**
  - Homework Help
  - Video Tutors
  - Multiple Choice
  - Crosswords

Additional Practice

1. a. Use a compass to draw a circle.
  b. Use the same compass setting as in part (a). Mark six congruent chords in the circle.
  c. Explain why this process works to construct a regular hexagon.

2. a. Use a compass to draw a circle.
  b. Use a compass setting that is half the length of the setting in part (a). Mark 12 congruent chords in the circle.
  c. Find the difference in area of the circle and the dodecagon.

3. What do you assume to be true to prove the Isoperimetric Conjecture? Why is this assumption necessary?

4. Is it possible to find the polygon with perimeter 48 inches that encloses the most area? Explain.

5. Consider circle P with diameter $\overline{AB}$.
  a. Find the measures of $\angle ACB$, $\angle ADB$, and $\angle AEB$.
  b. Make a conjecture about the measure of such angles in relation to any diameter.
  c. How does your conjecture relate to the Isoperimetric Conjecture?

6. C is a closed curve that encloses the maximum area for a perimeter. Find the area C encloses for each given perimeter.
  a. 6π meters
  b. 16π inches
  c. 20π centimeters

7. A rose garden has a stone wall along one of its sides. You want to surround the remainder of the garden with a walkway that maximizes the area of the garden.
  a. Describe the shape of the walkway that encloses the most area.
  b. The perimeter of the walkway is 40 feet. Find the area of the maximized rose garden.

Practice: For Lesson 8.15, assign Exercises 1–6.

---

6. Take It Further Many positive numbers are less than 1. Examples include $\frac{1}{2}$, $\frac{3}{4}$, $\sqrt{2} - 1$, and 0.897. What is the greatest positive number less than 1? Here is an argument, a proof by contradiction, that shows such a number does not exist.

Suppose there is a greatest number less than 1. Call it x.

  a. Explain how you know that $1 - x$ is a positive number.
  b. Begin with the assumption that x is the greatest number less than 1. What can you conclude about $\frac{1-x}{2}$? Give an argument that $x + \frac{1-x}{2}$ must be greater than or equal to 1.
  c. Draw a number line showing 0 and 1. Show possible locations for x and $x + \frac{1-x}{2}$.
  d. Use algebra to solve this inequality.

$$x + \frac{1-x}{2} \geq 1$$

Does your solution agree with your definition of x at the beginning of the exercise?

  e. How does this argument show that the optimization problem of finding the greatest number less than one does not have a solution?

7. Explain why the following optimization problem has no solution.

Find the polygon with perimeter 24 inches that encloses the greatest area.

Maintain Your Skills

8. Factor each of the following quadratic expressions.
  a. $-x^2 - 6x + 16$
  b. $-x^2 + 2x + 3$
  c. $x^2 - 3x - 10$

9. Use your factorizations from Exercise 8 to solve the following equations.
  a. $-x^2 - 6x + 16 = 0$
  b. $-x^2 + 2x + 3 = 0$
  c. $x^2 - 3x - 10 = 0$

10. Use your solutions from Exercise 9 to sketch the graph of each function.
  a. $y = x^2 + 6x - 16$
  b. $y = x^2 - 2x - 3$
  c. $y = -x^2 + 3x + 10$

11. Find the maximum value for y in each graph in Exercise 10. If a maximum does not exist, explain why.

Habits of Mind

Use an indirect proof. This is one of those exercises where you have to read and understand a proof, so read carefully.

If something exists, you can name it anything you like.

Go Online
PHSchool.com

For additional practice, go to **Web Code:** bea-0815

Answers

6. See back of book.

7. Answers may vary. Sample: We do not seem to have enough to give a proof of this result. However, the formula for the area of a regular n-gon of perimeter p (developed in Lesson 8.14, Ex. 5(c)) seems to produce a sequence of numbers that approach but never reach a limiting maximum value when $p = 24$ and n increases without limit.

8. a. $-(x - 2)(x + 8)$
  b. $-(x - 3)(x + 1)$
  c. $(x + 2)(x - 5)$

9. a. 2, -8
  b. 3, -1
  c. 5, -2

10. See back of book.

11. In part (a), the maximum is 25. In part (b), the maximum is 4. There is no maximum in part (c) because the parabola opens upward.

Solving the Isoperimetric Problem

A plan for proving the isoperimetric problem is presented in Lesson 8.15. You learned you are unable to prove its first step. However, you can assume the first step is true and continue with the proof. This situation is fairly common in mathematics and can be addressed as follows.

Postulate 8.1 The Existence Hypothesis

For any given perimeter, there is a closed curve that encloses the greatest area.

You can assume the existence of a best-possible curve, which is Step 1 of the plan. That assumption can be used to prove Steps 2 and 3.

Developing Habits of Mind

Use a different process. Once you assume that there is a best possible curve, you can figure out some of its properties. You want to prove that the best possible curve must be a circle. Little by little, you will rule out curves that are not circles. You have already ruled out polygons, self-crossing curves, and concave curves. You are like a detective, on the hunt for a mystery curve. You will figure out what it is by nailing down its properties.

Maybe you will not prove the existence hypothesis today or even this year. It would be satisfying if you could prove it someday.

Even if you do not prove it now, it is important to note that it is possible to prove the existence hypothesis. Avoid assuming existence and then determining properties based on that assumption. It results in serious consequences in math and in other fields such as social sciences.

The solution of the isoperimetric problem that you are studying took centuries to evolve. When reading a plan like this, many people might say, "I'd never think of that." They might assume that mathematical ideas and proofs are only discovered by extremely gifted people. This is not true.

The truth is that mathematics is developed by a community of people. Each person contributes small insights and occasional breakthroughs. The three-step plan was not developed by one person. It emerged from the work of dozens of mathematicians over the centuries.

An important part of mathematics is reading and understanding discussions, such as this presentation of the isoperimetric problem. Think of the proof as a sophisticated machine that you can study.

Lesson Overview

GOALS

- Discuss the important variables of a problem, choose a subset of them, and find an optimal solution.

- Understand and explain a proof of the isoperimetric problem.

This lesson completes the proof of the Isoperimetric Conjecture with the assumption of the Existence Hypothesis. Students see that with the Existence Hypothesis, the proof is very similar to that of the Regular Polygon Theorem.

CHECK YOUR UNDERSTANDING
- Core: 1, 2
- Optional: 3, 4

MATERIALS
- compasses
- protractors
- rulers

HOMEWORK
- Core: 5, 6, 9
- Optional: 7, 8, 10, 12, 13, 14
- Extension: 11

Launch

Begin this lesson by reviewing the plan outlined in Lesson 8.15.

Explore

Discuss the Existence Hypothesis with your class. Talk about what it would mean for the validity of your Isoperimetric Conjecture proof if this hypothesis was never proven, or was invalid.

Wrap Up

End this lesson by assigning some Check Your Understanding exercises.

Assessment Resources

Exercises

HOMEWORK
- Core: 5, 6, 9
- Optional: 7, 8, 10, 12, 13, 14
- Extension: 11

Check Your Understanding

EXERCISE 2 Looking at half of the geometric figure for which you want to maximize the area is the same technique used for several problems in Lesson 8.5. Recall the dog run problems that used a wall of the house as a reflection line. If you want to maximize the area of a five-sided pen in which one of the sides is a stonewall, it suffices to look at the four sides as half of a larger figure to be maximized. The largest five-sided pen is half of a regular octagon. Similarly, if the circle is the shape that maximizes area for a given perimeter, the semicircle whose diameter lies along the reflection line is the shape that maximizes area.

Exercises Practicing Habits of Mind

Check Your Understanding

1. Prove Step 2 of the plan. Assume that curve C is the curve that encloses the greatest area for its perimeter. Show that any line that bisects the perimeter of C must also bisect its area.

2. Now that you have proved Step 2 of the plan, the isoperimetric conjecture has been reduced to the following.

Conjecture 8.2 The Reduced Isoperimetric Conjecture

> Take line ℓ. Of all the curves that have two points on ℓ and have the same perimeter, the one that encloses the most area is a semicircle with diameter that lies along ℓ.

Explain why proving this restricted conjecture is enough to prove the isoperimetric conjecture.

3. Because of the restricted isoperimetric conjecture, you now only have to consider half of a curve. Assume that any angle formed by a point on the half curve and the endpoints of a diameter is a right angle. (This is the condition for Step 3 of the plan.) Can you guarantee that the curve is a semicircle? Explain.

4. Curve C is your candidate for the best curve. Draw diameter $\overline{AB}$ and connect its endpoints to some point P on C. How can you guarantee that $\angle APB$ is a right angle? Remember, C encloses the greatest area for its perimeter.

On Your Own

5. **Standardized Test Prep** Suppose you construct a semicircular fence with 2 m of curved fence. What is the radius r of the fence? What is the area enclosed by the fence?

   A. $r = \frac{1}{2\pi}$ m; area $= 0.628$ m^2
   B. $r = \frac{1}{\pi}$ m; area $= \frac{1}{\pi}$ m^2
   C. $r = \frac{2}{\pi}$ m; area $= \frac{2}{\pi}$ m^2
   D. $r = \frac{2}{\pi}$ m; area $= \frac{4}{\pi}$ m^2

Answers

Exercises

1. See back of book.

2. If a closed curve with fixed perimeter encloses the maximum area, then a line ℓ cuts the perimeter in half will also cut the area in half. So if you can prove that ℓ and the portion of the curve on one side of ℓ determine a semicircular region, the entire curve will be a circle.

3. yes; If the conclusion of Step 3 is true, then any point P not on a diameter $\overline{AB}$ of the curve is the vertex of a right angle whose sides pass through the endpoints of $\overline{AB}$. The midpoint of $\overline{AB}$ is equidistant from A, B, and P. So P is on a semicircle whose diameter is $\overline{AB}$.

4. See back of book.

5. C

6. See back of book.

6. In Exercise 1, you show that a line that cuts the perimeter of the curve in half must also cut the area in half. How do you know there is a line that cuts the perimeter of the best possible curve in half? Describe a method for constructing such a line.

7. Write About It State the existence hypothesis in your own words. Why do you need to assume it in order to establish the isoperimetric conjecture? Again, answer in your own words.

8. Write About It You used the detective method when you searched for a mystery curve by discovering its properties. It is a different approach than the one used to solve other optimization problems, such as the burning-tent problem. Describe the differences between the two approaches.

9. In Lesson 8.5 Developing Habits of Mind, you solved the rectangular-dog-run problem with a certain method. Can the same method be used to solve the restricted isoperimetric problem? Explain.

10. Write About It If you assume the existence hypothesis, you can now prove the isoperimetric conjecture. Write out a careful proof in your own words. Use examples and pictures and explain each step.

11. Take It Further The isoperimetric conjecture also can be proved with Theorem 8.1 and limits, a topic you will study in calculus. Think about a collection of regular polygons, each one having more vertices than the previous polygon. All the polygons have the same perimeter. What happens to the area of these polygons as the number of vertices increases? Sketch a proof of the isoperimetric conjecture using the idea of limits.

Go Online
PHSchool.com

For more information about optimization, go to **Web Code: bee-9031**

Maintain Your Skills

In Exercises 12–14, C is a closed curve of perimeter 4π cm that encloses the maximum area for that perimeter.

12. How much area does C enclose?

13. If C contains the points $(-1, 5)$, $(-3, 3)$, and $(1, 3)$, find an equation for C on the coordinate plane.

14. Name at least two other points on C.

Go Online
PHSchool.com

For additional practice, go to **Web Code: bea-0816**

On Your Own

EXERCISE 9 In Developing Habits of Mind in Lesson 8.5, students maximized the area of a rectangular run built against a wall. They reflected the image of the run over the wall and saw that the area was maximized when the figure was a square. They found that the best pen would be half of a square. However, students already knew that the best figure would be a square. They had solved the isoperimetric problem for quadrilaterals earlier, and they used that solution to solve the dog run problem.

EXERCISE 11 If you assign this exercise, explain that some limits are more straightforward than others. For example, the limit of the function $y = \frac{1}{x}$ as x approaches infinity is zero. You are dividing 1 by greater and greater numbers, which makes the quotient decrease without bound, but it will always be positive. The graph will never intersect the x-axis and $\frac{1}{x}$ will never actually equal zero. If you choose a great enough value for x, you can make $\frac{1}{x}$ as close to zero as you want.

Additional Resources

PRINTED RESOURCES	TECHNOLOGY
• Texas Instruments Activities Workbook	• TeacherExpress CD-ROM
• Cabrilog Activities	• Exam*View* CD-ROM
• Teaching Resources	• PHSchool.com
• Practice Workbook	– Homework Help
• Assessment Resources	– Video Tutors
	– Multiple Choice
	– Crosswords

Additional Practice

1. a. Use a compass to draw a circle.
  b. Use the same compass setting as in part (a). Mark six congruent chords in the circle.
  c. Explain why this process works to construct a regular hexagon.

2. a. Use a compass to draw a circle.
  b. Use a compass setting that is half the length of the setting in part (a). Mark 12 congruent chords in the circle.
  c. Find the difference in area of the circle and the dodecagon.

3. What do you assume to be true to prove the Isoperimetric Conjecture? Why is this assumption necessary?

4. Is it possible to find the polygon with perimeter 48 inches that encloses the most area? Explain.

5. Consider circle P with diameter $\overline{AB}$.
  a. Find the measures of $\angle ACB$, $\angle ADB$, and $\angle AEB$.
  b. Make a conjecture about the measure of such angles in relation to any diameter.
  c. How does your conjecture relate to the Isoperimetric Conjecture?

6. C is a closed curve that encloses the maximum area for a perimeter. Find the area C encloses for each given perimeter.
  a. 6π meters
  b. 16π inches
  c. 20π centimeters

7. A rose garden has a stone wall along one of its sides. You want to surround the remainder of the garden with a walkway that maximizes the area of the garden.
  a. Describe the shape of the walkway that encloses the most area.
  b. The perimeter of the walkway is 40 feet. Find the area of the maximized rose garden.

---

7. The existence hypothesis states that of all closed, non-self crossing curves that have a fixed perimeter, there is at least one that has the maximum possible area. You need this to proceed through Steps 2 and 3 of the proof plan.

8. The "detective method" is different from the method used in the earlier optimization problems in that the earlier problems used algorithms to construct a figure with the measure you wished to optimize.

9. No, because the fence problem used the established fact that of all rectangles with a given perimeter, the one with maximum area is a square.

10. See back of book.

11. Check students' work.

12. 4π cm^2

13. $(x + 1)^2 + (y - 3)^2 = 4$

14. Answers may vary. Sample:
$(0, 3 + \sqrt{3})$, $(0, -3 - \sqrt{3})$,
$(-2, 3 + \sqrt{3})$, $(-2, 3 - \sqrt{3})$.

Practice: For Lesson 8.16, assign Exercises 7–10.

Mathematical Reflections

EXERCISES 7–9 At the start of the Investigation, you may have assigned these as Questions 1–3 for students to think and write about.

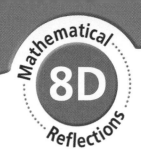

Mathematical Reflections 8D

In this investigation, you learned how to write functions and use them to find an optimal solution, and you learned how to understand a proof of the isoperimetric problem. These questions will help you summarize what you have learned.

1. Let P be any point inside the square. Write a function $f(x, y)$ that finds the sum of the distances from P to the vertices of the square.

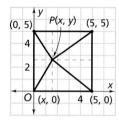

2. Use the function from Exercise 1 to calculate $f(2, 2)$, $f(1, 1)$, and $f(3, 3)$. Which P on a diagonal of the square gives the least value of f?

3. In the figure, $\triangle ABC$'s area is 45 and $AB = 5$. What is CH?

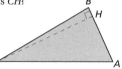

4. The centroid of an equilateral triangle divides each median into two segments. Use Rich's Theorem to prove that one of the segments is twice as long as the other.

5. There are many hexagons of perimeter 27 cm. Find the dimensions and area of the one that encloses the greatest possible area.

6. The interior of a triangle contains P. Consider the sum of the distances from P to each of the sides. Is this sum constant for any P or does it depend on the kind of triangle? Explain with examples.

7. For what P is the sum of the distances from P to the sides of $\triangle ABC$ the least? Explain.

8. Give an example of an optimization problem that has no solution. Explain your reasoning.

9. What curve encloses the greatest area for a given perimeter? Explain.

Vocabulary

In this investigation, you saw this term for the first time. Make sure you understand what it means and how to use it.

• **isoperimetric problem**

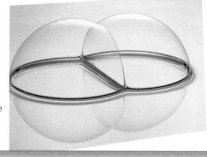

What shape do you think the joined bubbles had before they landed on this mirror?

Answers

Mathematical Reflections

1. $f(x, y) = 10$

2. 10, 10, 10; a point P inside the square and on a diagonal gives the smallest value, 10.

3. 18

4. The medians of an equilateral $\triangle ABC$ are also angle bisectors. Every point on the bisector of an angle is equidistant from the sides of the angle. The angle bisectors are concurrent at a point O.

   So, by Rich's Theorem, $OK = OH = OJ = \frac{1}{3}$ CH. Therefore $OC = \frac{2}{3} CH$. Hence $\overline{OC}$ is twice as long as $\overline{OH}$.

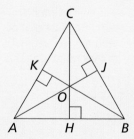

5. All sides have length $\frac{9}{2}$ cm, all angles have measure 120°, and the area is $\frac{243}{8}\sqrt{3}$ cm².

6. The sum is constant if the triangle is equilateral, otherwise it is not. Check students' examples.

7. P can be any point in the interior of the triangle (Theorem 8.2).

8. Answers may vary. Sample: Find the length of the longest segment on a number line that has one endpoint at the origin and its other endpoint between 0 and 1. The answer for Ex. 5 of Lesson 8.15 shows that this problem has no solution.

9. a circle (Theorem 8.1)

Project: Using Mathematical Habits

The Airport Problem

Three neighboring cities, all about the same size, decide to share the cost of building a new airport. They hire your group as consultants to find a location for the airport.

The three cities decide that they want the location to be environmentally friendly and practical. They state their request to your group in the following way.

The Airport Problem Let A, B, and C be the locations of the cities. Let D be the location of the airport such that $DA + DB + DC$ is the least sum possible.

Models

Sometimes a model can help you experiment with a system. If you already have a conjecture, a model can help you test it. If you do not have a conjecture, a physical or computer model may help you come up with one.

Make a physical model to explore the airport problem. Take a flat piece of wood and pound nails into it, more or less in a circle.

Use a small metal ring to represent the airport and strong string to represent the roads to the cities. You will need twice as much string as the length of the roads because the string must be double-looped around the nails. The following sketch shows how the thread is passed through the ring and is looped around the nails.

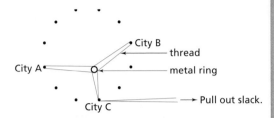

1. Explain how this device can be used to locate the best airport location for the three cities. Why does it work?

2. Use the model to explore several arrangements of the three cities. Place a piece of paper inside the circle of nails. Record each experiment by tracing out the roads to the best airport location for each arrangement.

3. For a given set of three cities, can there be more than one spot where the sum of the distances to the cities is the least possible? Explain.

4. Use the string, ring, and nails to make a contour plot for the sum of the distances from the airport to the cities. Use your contour plot to defend your answer to Exercise 3.

You can also use geometry software to model the airport problem. Build a dynagraph, like the one below, that lets you see the airport function both numerically and geometrically.

THE MODEL The length of the string represents twice the distance to the cities. If there is any slack in the string, you should pull it out. By pulling out the slack, you are using the shortest bit of string possible and the roads are the least possible length. The ring will then be at the best location for the airport.

Chapter Project

1. Answers may vary. Sample: By pulling the slack, you are using the shortest bit of string possible to model the roads to the airport.

2. Check students' work.

3. Yes; for example, if the three cities are at the vertices of an equilateral triangle, the sum of the distances is constant no matter where the airport is.

4. Check students' work.

THE AIRPORT CONJECTURE Hoffman's conjecture applies the strategy outlined in the burning tent problem but with a few more complications. Hoffman's work was designed to prove that the best airport location within the triangle will have 120° angles between the roads around it. It also provides a method for finding that point, without hunting around for it.

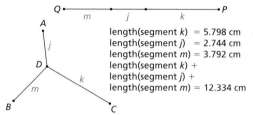

length(segment k) = 5.798 cm
length(segment j) = 2.744 cm
length(segment m) = 3.792 cm
length(segment k) +
length(segment j) +
length(segment m) = 12.334 cm

As you move D around, the total distance increases and decreases. The length QP is the value of the airport function for D. You are trying to minimize this length.

5. Have the software trace the locus of P. As you move D, what happens to P when you minimize the total distance?

6. Use your geometry software to draw the contour lines for the sum of the distances from the airport to the cities.

7. Use your computer to keep track of the angles in the airport problem. Make some conjectures about the patterns you find.

Hoffman's Construction

Since you have been thinking about the airport problem, the following conjecture may seem reasonable to you.

The Airport Conjecture Three cities are arranged in a triangle. If no angle of the triangle is too great, then the best place for the airport is where the roads form 120° angles with each other.

The Fermat point of a triangle is the point that forms three 120° angles when you connect it with the vertices of the triangle.

In 1929, the German mathematician J. E. Hoffman found an ingenious way to construct the Fermat point of a triangle.

Step 1 Start with △ABC. Rotate $\overline{AB}$ 60° counterclockwise around B.

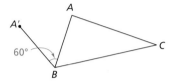

Step 2 Connect A' and C. Draw a line through B that intersects $\overline{A'C}$ in D so that $m\angle A'DB = 60°$. Then $m\angle BDC = 120°$.

So D is a good candidate for the Fermat point. For it to be the Fermat point, all you have to prove is that $m\angle ADB = 120°$.

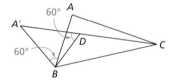

Step 3 Rotate $\overline{BD}$ 60° counterclockwise around B.

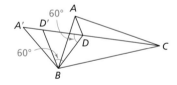

8. Prove that D' lies on $\overline{A'C}$.

Answers

5–8. Check students' work.

Go Online
PHSchool.com

For more information
about the Airport Problem,
go to Web Code: bed-0861

Since A, D', and D are collinear, and $\triangle BDD'$ is equilateral, $m\angle A'D'B = 180° - m\angle BD'D = 180° - 60° = 120°$. You can show that $\triangle A'BD'$ is congruent to $\triangle ABD$, so $m\angle ADB = 120°$. This proves that D is the Fermat point of $\triangle ABC$.

Proving the Conjecture

To be sure that the Airport Conjecture is true, you need to think of a proof. There are different ways of proceeding. Start with a triangle and inside it, choose point D, which is not the Fermat point.

You will prove that the sum of the distances from any D to the vertices is greater than the sum from the Fermat point to the vertices.

9. Use Hoffman's construction to find the Fermat point F of $\triangle ABC$.

10. Draw the line perpendicular to $\overline{BF}$ through B, the line perpendicular to $\overline{FC}$ through C, and the line perpendicular to $\overline{AF}$ through A. Prove that $\triangle EGH$ is equilateral.

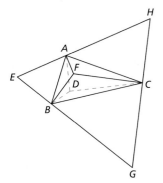

11. Prove that $DA + DB + DC > FA + FB + FC$. Refer to Rich's Function and the fact that the hypotenuse of a triangle is greater than either of the legs.

You have proved the following theorem.

Theorem 8.3

The best place to put the airport is where the roads make 120° angles with one another, unless there is no such place inside the triangle.

9–11. Check students' work.

In **Investigation 8A** you learned how to

- distinguish between distance and the length of a path
- use reflection to make a straight path from a segmented path
- find the shortest path between two points if you must pass through a third point

The following questions will help you check your understanding.

1.

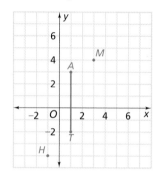

a. Find the distance from $M(3, 4)$ to $H(-1, -4)$.

b. Now find the shortest path from M to H if your path cannot intersect $\overline{AT}$.

2. Let A and B fall on opposite sides of a line. Explain how to find P on the line so that $AP + PB$ is a minimum. Include a sketch.

3. Let X and Y be on the same side of a line. Explain how to use reflection to find P on the line so that $XP + PY$ is a minimum. Include a sketch.

In **Investigation 8B** you learned how to

- find grid polygons with a given area or perimeter
- find the triangle or rectangle that maximizes area for a given perimeter
- find the polygon that maximizes area for a given perimeter

The following questions will help you check your understanding.

4. Use only grid lines on a sheet of graph paper. Find the maximum perimeter possible for a grid polygon with an area of 12 square units.

5. Find the maximum area for a triangle with perimeter 36 in.

6. The perimeter of a rectangle is 80 cm and its length is 32 cm. What is its area?

7. Find the area of each regular polygon, given that its perimeter is 52 in.

a. a triangle
b. a square
c. a hexagon
d. a dodecagon

8. You want to build a dog kennel along an outer wall of a barn. You have 200 feet of fencing. What is the maximum area of the dog kennel for each number of sides?

a. 4 sides
b. 5 sides
c. 6 sides

Answers

Chapter Review

1. a. $4\sqrt{5} \approx 8.94$
   b. There is no shortest path under the stated conditions.

2. Draw $\overline{AB}$. The point P where $\overline{AB}$ intersects the given line is the desired point.

3. Reflect X across the given line to get X'. Draw $\overline{X'Y}$ and mark the point P where the segment intersects the line. P is the desired point.

4. 26

5. $36\sqrt{3}$ in.^{2}

6. 256 cm^2

7. a. $\frac{676}{9}\sqrt{3}$

   b. 169 in^2

c. $\frac{338}{3}\sqrt{3}$ in^2

d. $\frac{676}{12}\sqrt{3}$ in^2

8. a. $4444\frac{4}{9}$ ft^2

   b. $\frac{4 \cdot 25^2}{\tan(22.5)}$ ft$^2 \approx 6036$ ft^2

   c. $\frac{5 \cdot 20^2}{\tan(18)}$ ft$^2 \approx 6155$ ft^2

9. Tony and Sasha will probably want to hike up a path that is the least steep. Although it will take longer, if there is a rise of 20 ft between contour lines,

hiking a longer distance to travel this 20-ft rise will be easier while carrying all of their equipment. If the rise is only 10 ft, hiking a shorter distance will not be too bad. Below is one example of such a path. The rise between the first and second contour lines is 20 ft, but it is spread out over more of a distance, so it will be easier to hike.

In **Investigation 8C** you learned how to

- draw and interpret contour plots
- define an ellipse
- use ellipses to solve optimization problems

The following questions will help you check your understanding.

9. This contour plot is of a hill where Tony and Sasha pick blueberries. The contour lines show height in feet. Since they carry a picnic basket and blueberry buckets, they are looking for the easiest hike up the hill. Draw a path that you think Tony and Sasha might take. Explain why you think this is the easiest hike.

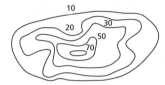

10. What is an ellipse? Mark *A* and *B* and draw an ellipse with those points as foci.

11. Solve Exercise 3 using contour lines.

12. Suppose points *C* and *D* are fixed points in a plane. Function *f* is defined so that $f(A) = 2AC + AD$. Make a contour plot for *f*. Label it appropriately.

In **Investigation 8D** you learned how to

- identify reasoning by continuity
- use Rich's Theorem
- state the isoperimetric problem and investigate related conjectures

The following questions will help you check your understanding.

13. State Rich's Theorem.

14. You have 24 cm of string to make different shapes.

  a. What is the area of the equilateral triangle with the greatest area?

  b. What is the area of the square with the greatest area?

  c. What is the area of the regular hexagon with the greatest area?

  d. Describe a shape that has a greater area than this triangle, square, and regular hexagon.

15. State the isoperimetric conjecture.

16. Explain why the following optimization problem has no solution.

  Find the polygon with perimeter 60 inches that encloses the most area.

17. C is a closed curve that encloses the maximum area for each of the following perimeters. What is the area of C for each perimeter?

  a. 9π m   **b.** 24π in.   **c.** π cm

17. a. 20.25π m^2
  b. 144π in.^{2}
  c. 0.25π cm^2

10. If *A* and *B* are two points, then an ellipse with foci *A* and *B* is the set of all points *P* for which $PA + PB = K$, where *k* is a positive constant greater than *AB*.

11. Draw a family of ellipses with foci at *X* and *Y*. One of these will be tangent to the given line ℓ. The point of tangency *P* is the desired point.

12. Check students' work.

13. The sum of the distances from any point inside an equilateral triangle to the sides of the triangle is constant and equal to the length of an altitude of the triangle.

14. a. $16\sqrt{3}$ cm^2

  b. 36 cm^2

  c. $24\sqrt{3}$ cm^2

  d. Answers may vary. Sample: a regular polygon with more than 6 sides

15. Of all closed curves with a given perimeter, the circle encloses the greatest area.

16. Check students' work.

Chapter Test

Assessment Resources

1. Below is a contour map for a mountain. The highest point of the mountain is at 1189 meters and the contour lines show the altitude from sea level in increments of 200 meters. Approximately how high is the mountain at point *P*? At point *Q*?

2. Which of the polygons described below has the greatest area? What is that area?
   I.   a right triangle with perimeter 64.8 centimeters
   II. a square with perimeter 64.8 centimeters
   III. a regular hexagon with perimeter 64.8 centimeters
   IV. an equilateral triangle with perimeter 64.8 centimeters

3. *C* is a closed curve that encloses the maximum area for a perimeter. Find the area *C* encloses for each given perimeter.
   a. 5π inches
   b. 8π centimeters
   c. 10π feet

4. What is the sum $HP + HQ + HZ$ in the equilateral triangle below with side length 32 centimeters?

Also available: Form B

Chapter

8   **Test**

Go Online
PHSchool.com

For a chapter test, go to
Web Code: bea-0853

Multiple Choice

1. Suppose you want to enclose a rectangular garden with 50 feet of fencing. A stone wall that is 20 feet long will serve as the border of the back of the garden. What are the dimensions of the rectangle that will maximize the area of the garden?
   A. 15 ft by 20 ft
   B. 12 ft by 13 ft
   C. 10 ft by 15 ft
   D. 7 ft by 18 ft

2. A company wants to minimize the costs associated with packaging a box of 30 markers. The length of each marker is 6.5 in., and the diameter of each marker is 0.5 in. What are the dimensions of the box that will minimize the costs?
   A. 0.5 in. by 15 in. by 6.5 in.
   B. 1 in. by 7.5 in. by 6.5 in.
   C. 1.5 in. by 5 in. by 6.5 in.
   D. 2.5 in. by 3 in. by 6.5 in.

Suppose you want to find the shortest path from $A(-2, 3)$ to any point *P* on the line $y = -1$ to $B(1, 2)$.

3. What point *P* on the line $y = -1$ should the path pass through?
   A. $(0, -1)$
   B. $\left(-\frac{2}{7}, -1\right)$
   C. $\left(-\frac{7}{3}, -1\right)$
   D. $\left(-\frac{5}{3}, -1\right)$

4. What is the length of the shortest path? Round your answer to the nearest hundredth.
   A. 7.61   B. 7.63
   C. 8.03   D. 8.50

A square and a rectangle have the same area. The rectangle has a perimeter of 212.

5. The length of the rectangle is 36. What is the perimeter of the square, rounded to the nearest tenth?
   A. 50.2
   B. 200.8
   C. 212
   D. 2520

6. If you maximize the area of the rectangle, what is the perimeter of the square?
   A. 50.2
   B. 200.8
   C. 212
   D. 2520

Open Response

7. Which has the greatest area? Explain.
   • an equilateral triangle with perimeter 120 cm
   • a square with perimeter 120 cm
   • any nonsquare rectangle with perimeter 120 cm

8. This is a contour map for a pond at Camp Pascal. The greatest depth is 6.5 meters at the center of the pond. Each contour line represents a rise of 1.5 meters. Approximately how deep is the pond at *X*? At *Y*?

Answers

Chapter Test

1. C
2. C
3. B
4. A
5. B
6. C
7. The square; of all rectangles having a given perimeter, the square has the greatest area. The square has a greater area than the equilateral triangle (since both are regular polygons), the perimeters are equal, but the square has the greater number of sides.
8. between 2 and 3.5 m; between 5 and 6.5 m

9. Below is a contour map for kicking angles on a soccer field. List the players in order from the player with the greatest kicking angle to the player with the least kicking angle.

10. The equilateral triangle has side length 6 cm. Find $RH + IH + CH$.

11. Given equilateral $\triangle PQR$ and altitude $\overline{PT}$, fill in each blank with $>$, $<$, or $=$.

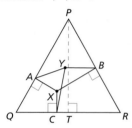

a. $AX + XB + XC \underline{} AY + BY + CY$

b. $AX + XB + XC \underline{} PT$

c. $PT \underline{} QR$

d. $AY + BY + CY \underline{} PT$

12. Two cities want to build a park. The park must be built along an exisiting road. The amount of new road built to the park must be minimized. For each sketch below, determine where the park should be built. Explain your reasoning.

a.

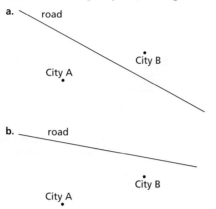

road

City B

City A

b.

road

City B

City A

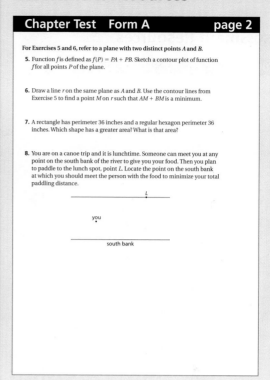
9. Jamal, Guy, Sandy, Tim

10. $3\sqrt{3}$

11. a. $<$
   b. $=$
   c. $<$
   d. $>$

12. a. The best spot is at the intersection of $\overline{AB}$ and the road.
   b. To find the best spot, the best idea is to use contour lines. Find a family of ellipses with the two cities as foci. One of the ellipses will be tangent to the road. The point of tangency is the best spot.

Cumulative Review

Assessment Resources

Review

Cumulative Review

1. a. $A'(1, -6), B'(-2, -5), C'(4, -2)$
b. $A'(3, 5), B''(6, 3), C'(0, 0)$

2. See back of book.

3. Check students' work.

4. See back of book.

5. $(2, -10)$

6. Answers may vary. Sample: $(5, 7)$, $(5 - \sqrt{5}, 2)$, $(5 + \sqrt{5}, 2)$

7. Answers may vary. Sample: $(19, 3)$

8. a. $(2.5, -3), (9.5, -3)$
b. $(6, 0.5), (6, -6.5)$
c. Answers will vary. Sample: $(7, -2)$ and $(5, -4)$

---

1. In $\triangle ABC$, $A(1, 5)$, $B(-2, 3)$, and $C(4, 0)$.
a. If you reflect $\triangle ABC$ over the line $y = -1$, what are the coordinates of the vertices of $\triangle A'B'C'$?
b. If you reflect $\triangle A'B'C'$ over the line $x = 2$, what are the coordinates of the vertices of $\triangle A''B''C''$?

2. For each figure below, do the following.
- Draw all lines of symmetry.
- Tell whether the figure has rotational symmetry. If so, give the angle of rotation.

a.   **b.**   **c.**

3. You are on another camping trip and your new tent catches on fire. This time, your bucket is with your supplies. You must get the bucket first and then get the water from the river, and then put out the fire. What point along the river will minimize your path? Explain.

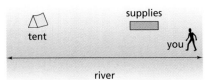

tent   supplies   you

river

4. Copy each figure and point P on a separate piece of paper. Draw the image of each figure for the given rotation about P.
a. 60°   **b.** $-45°$ **c.** 150°

5. One endpoint of a circle's diameter is $(8, -2)$. If the center of the circle is $(5, -6)$, what are the coordinates of the other endpoint of the diameter?

6. The center of a certain equilateral triangle is $(5, 4)$. Give two sets of coordinates that could be the vertices of the triangle.

7. Find the coordinates of a point that is collinear with $J(5, -9)$ and $K(12, -3)$. Explain your reasoning.

8. The midpoint of a segment that is 7 units long is $(6, -3)$. For each condition below, give the coordinates of the endpoints of this segment.
a. The segment is horizontal.
b. The segment is vertical.
c. The segment is neither horizontal nor vertical.

9. Determine whether the following statements are *true* or *false*. If a statement is false, give a counterexample.
a. If two nonvertical lines are parallel, then their slopes are equal.
b. The product of the slopes of two nonvertical perpendicular lines is -1.

10. Write an equation of the line that is perpendicular to each line through the given point.
a. $3x - 2y = 12$; $(0, 0)$
b. $-x + 6y = 9$; $(2, 3)$

11. Find the following distances.
a. from $(2, 0)$ to $4x - 6y = 24$
b. from $(-4, 5)$ to the line through $(6, 2)$ and $(-3, 5)$

12. Suppose that you have points $J(3, 5)$ and $K(5, 11)$. Find a point that is collinear with J and K.

9. a. True
b. True

10. a. $y = -\dfrac{2}{3}x$
b. $y = -6x + 15$

11. a. $\sqrt{\dfrac{1202}{117}} \approx 2.61$ units
b. $\dfrac{113\sqrt{2}}{5} \approx 31.96$

12. Answers will vary. Sample: $(1, -1)$

13. A parallelogram has a length of 20 inches and a height of 12 inches. You dilate the parallelogram by the factor 2.5. What are the length and width of each resulting parallelogram?

14. Find the coordinates of the midpoint of each segment.

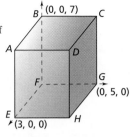

a. $\overline{AC}$

b. $\overline{DF}$

c. $\overline{BG}$

15. A cube has a side length of 8. One vertex of the cube is at the origin.

a. Draw a picture that illustrates this situation.

b. What is the length of a diagonal of the cube?

16. Given $A(2, 3)$ and $B(5, 10)$, find a vector that meets the following requirements.

- starts at the origin
- has the same direction as $\overrightarrow{AB}$
- is three times longer than $\overrightarrow{AB}$

17. Suppose that you have points $A(-5, 5)$ and $B(4, 8)$.

a. What multiple of $\overrightarrow{AB}$ has its head on the line $y = 3$?

b. What multiple of $\overrightarrow{AB}$ has its head on the line $x = -2$?

18. You are given points $J(2, 6)$ and $K(5, 9)$.

a. Calculate head minus tail for $\overrightarrow{JK}$. Draw a diagram that shows both $\overrightarrow{JK}$ and $O\overrightarrow{(J + K)}$. You have moved $\overrightarrow{JK}$ to the origin.

b. Move the vector anchored at the origin to $L(3, -1)$ by adding L to the head and to the tail. Draw this new vector. What are the coordinates of its head and tail?

19. Returning from a hike, you see that your tent is on fire. The stream is nearby, but you want to be sure you go to the point in the stream that minimizes the total distance you travel. Explain how you can use the reflection method to find this point.

20. Given: $\overline{AB} \parallel \overline{CD}$; $\overline{AB} \cong \overline{CD}$

Prove: E is the midpoint of $\overline{AD}$ and $\overline{BC}$.

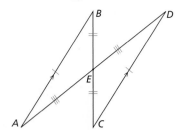

21. The vertices of $\triangle ABC$ are $A(-3, 5)$, $B(3, 5)$, and $C(0, 0)$.

a. Is $\triangle ABC$ equilateral, isosceles or scalene? Explain.

b. The coordinates of point P are $(1, 3)$. Find the sum of the distances from P to each *side* of the triangle.

c. Find the height of $\triangle ABC$.

22. A path on the coordinate plane must go from $A(3, 4)$, to line ℓ with equation $x = 1$, to line m with equation $x = 6$, to $B(5, -4)$.

a. Graph the shortest path.

b. Suppose C is the point where the path intersects ℓ, and D is the point where the path intersects m. What are the coordinates of C and D?

c. If point A was closer to ℓ than to m, how would the shortest path differ? Explain.

23. a. Construct a square.

b. Construct a rectangle, such that the area of the rectangle is equal to the area of the square.

c. How does the perimeter of the square compare to the perimeter of the rectangle?

24. a. Describe a situation in which there is more than one way to maximize a certain area.

b. Describe a situation in which there is more than one way to minimize a certain area.

13. Length $= 50$ in. and width $= 30$ in.

14. a. $(1.5, 2.5, 0)$

   b. $(1.5, 2.5, 3.5)$

   c. $(0, 2.5, 3.5)$

15. a.

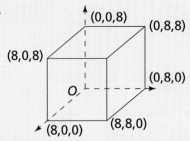

   b. $8\sqrt{2}$

16. Check students' work.

17. a. 2

   b. 2

18. a–b. Check students' work.

19. Check students' work.

20. Answers may vary. Sample: $\overline{AB} \parallel \overline{CD}$; $\overline{AB} \cong \overline{CD}$ (given). $\angle B \cong \angle C$ and $\angle A \cong \angle D$ (PAI Theorem). $\triangle AEB \cong \triangle DEB$ (ASA). $\overline{BE} \cong \overline{CE}$ and $\overline{AE} \cong \overline{DE}$ (CPCTC). E is the midpoint of $\overline{AD}$ and $\overline{BC}$ (definition of midpoint)

21. a. isosceles; $AC = BC$ and $AC \neq AB$

   b. 5   **c.** 5

22. a.

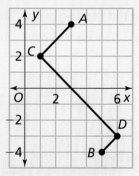

   b. $C(1, 2)$, $D(6, -3)$

   c. Check students' work.

23. a. Check students' work.

   b. Check students' work.

   c. The perimeter of the rectangle is greater.

24. a. Check students' work.

   b. Check students' work.

Placing a Point on an Object

1. Choose the **Point On** option in the **Points & Lines** menu.

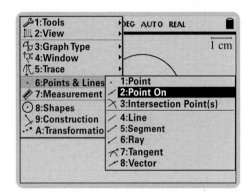

2. Position the pointer on the object. Press 🌑.

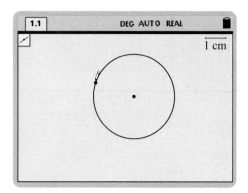

Constructing a Line Through Two Points

1. Choose the **Line** option in the **Points & Lines** menu.

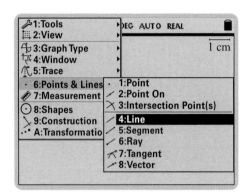

2. Position the pointer on a point. Press 🌑. Position the pointer on the other point. Press 🌑.

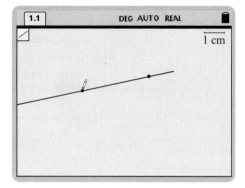

Constructing a Ray Through Two Points

1. Choose the **Ray** option in the **Points & Lines** menu.

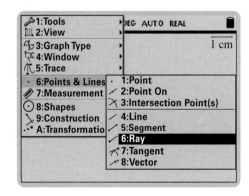

2. Position the pointer on the endpoint of the ray. Press 🌑. Position the pointer on the other point and press 🌑.

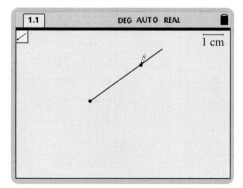

Dragging an Object

1. Position the cursor on the object. Press **ctrl** ✱.

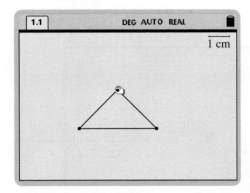

2. Drag the object to the desired location. Press ✱.

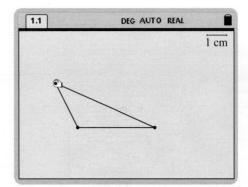

Hiding/Showing an Object

1. Select **Hide/Show** from the **Tools** menu. Position the pointer on the object. Press ✱.

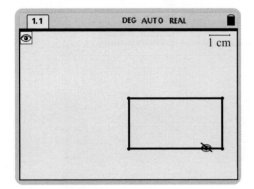

2. Select **Hide/Show** from the **Tools** menu. Position the pointer on the hidden object. Press ✱.

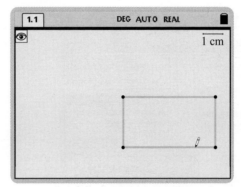

Deleting an Object

1. Position the pointer anywhere on the object. Press ✱ ⬅.

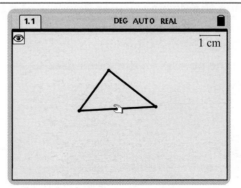

Constructing a Line Perpendicular to a Given Line Through a Given Point

1. Choose the **Perpendicular** option in the **Construction** menu.

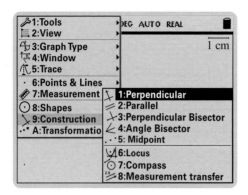

2. Position the pointer on the given line. Press 🟢. Position the pointer on the given point. Press 🟢.

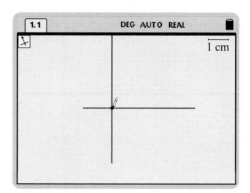

Constructing a Line Parallel to a Given Line Through a Given Point

1. Choose the **Parallel** option in the **Construction** menu.

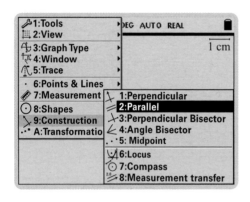

2. Position the pointer on the given line. Press 🟢. Position the pointer on the given point. Press 🟢.

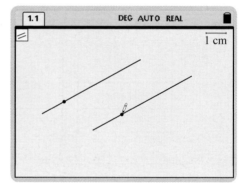

Constructing the Perpendicular Bisector of a Segment

1. Choose the **Perpendicular Bisector** option in the **Construction** menu.

2. Position the pointer on the segment. Press 🟢.

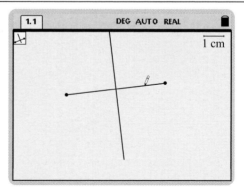

Constructing a Regular Polygon

1. Choose the **Regular Polygon** option in the **Shapes** menu.

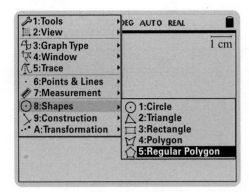

2. Press 🟦 to set the center of the regular polygon. Move the pointer away from the center. Press 🟦 to set a vertex.

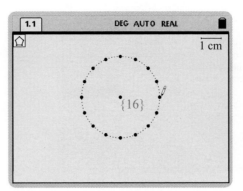

3. To reduce the number of sides, move the pointer clockwise around the polygon. When the polygon has the desired number of sides, press 🟦.

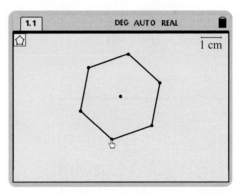

Constructing an Irregular Polygon

1. Choose the **Polygon** option in the **Shapes** menu. Move the pointer and press 🟦 to set each vertex.

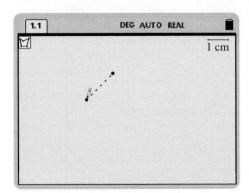

2. Press 🟦 🟦 to set the last vertex of the polygon.

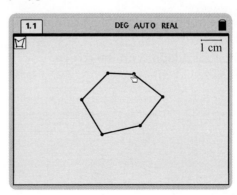

Constructing a Circle with a Given Center Through a Given Point

1. Choose the **Circle** option in the **Shapes** menu.

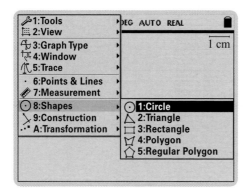

2. Position the pointer on the given center. Press ⊛. Position the pointer on the given point. Press ⊛.

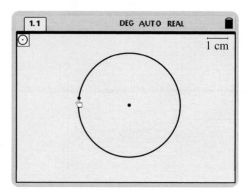

Constructing a Circle with a Given Center and Radius Length

1. Use the **Text** tool in the **Tools** menu. Write the radius.

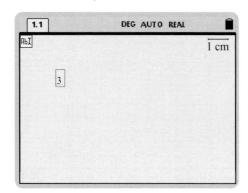

2. Choose the **Compass** option in the **Construction** menu.

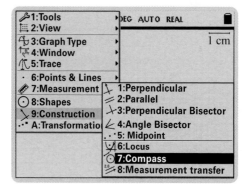

3. Position the pointer on the given center. Press ⊛.

4. Select the radius length on the screen. Press ⊛.

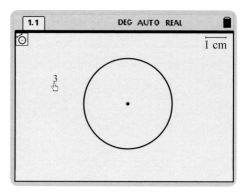

Finding the Intersection(s) of Two Objects

1. Choose the **Intersection Point(s)** option in the **Points & Lines** menu.

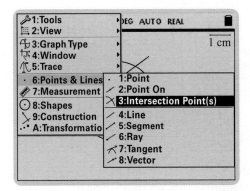

2. Position the pointer on the first object. Press ✸. Position the pointer on the second object. Press ✸.

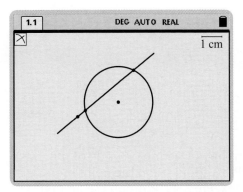

Finding the Area of a Polygon

1. Choose the **Area** option in the **Measurement** menu.

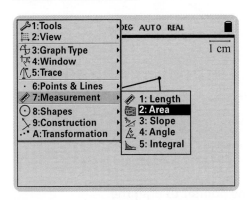

2. Place the pointer on the polygon. Press ✸.

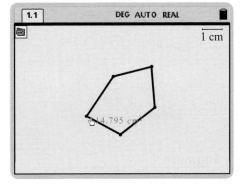

3. Move the pointer to drag the area value. Press ✸ to anchor it.

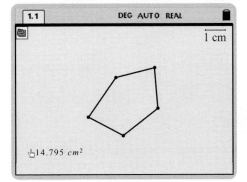

Measuring an Angle (in degrees)

1. Check that the system settings show degree mode.

2. Choose the **Angle** option in the **Measurement** menu.

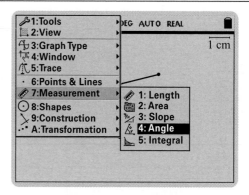

3. Position the pointer on one side of the angle. Press 🕹. Position the pointer on the vertex. Press 🕹. Position the pointer on the other side of the angle. Press 🕹.

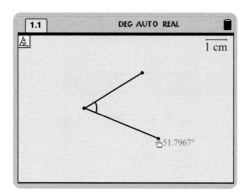

4. Move the pointer to drag the measurement. Press 🕹 to anchor it.

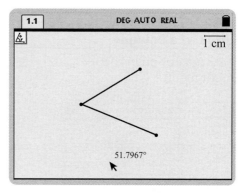

Measuring a Segment

1. Choose the **Length** option in the **Measurement** menu. Position the pointer on the segment. Press 🕹.

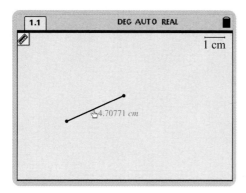

2. Move the pointer to drag the measurement. Press 🕹 to anchor it.

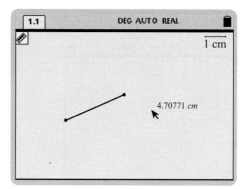

Translating an Object by a Given Vector

1. Choose the **Translation** option in the **Transformation** menu.

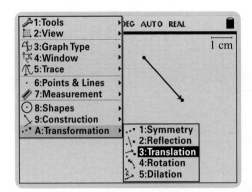

2. Position the pointer on the object. Press ⊛.

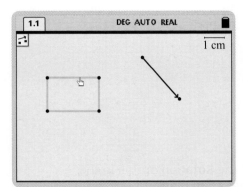

3. Position the pointer on the given vector. Press ⊛.

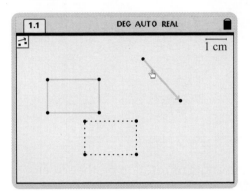

Reflecting an Object Over a Line

1. Choose the **Reflection** option in the **Transformation** menu. Position the pointer on the line. Press ⊛.

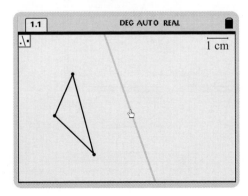

2. Position the pointer on the object. Press ⊛.

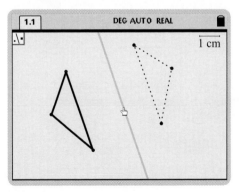

Rotating an Object About a Point by a Given Number of Degrees

1. Check that the system settings show degree mode.

2. Use the **Text** tool in the **Tools** menu. Write the given number of degrees.

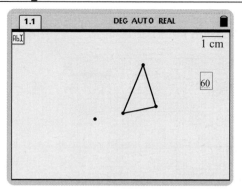

3. Choose the **Rotation** option in the **Transformation** menu.

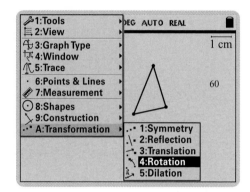

4. Place the pointer on the center of rotation. Press ⊛.

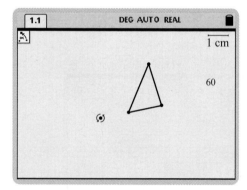

5. Place the pointer on the object. Press ⊛.

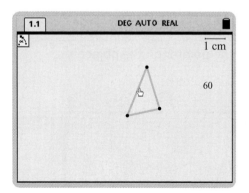

6. Select the angle of rotation on the screen. Press ⊛.

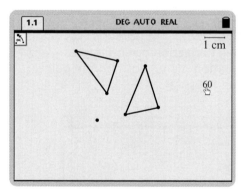

Finding the Coordinates of a Point (Graphing View Only)

1. Choose the **Coordinates and Equations** option in the **Tools** menu.

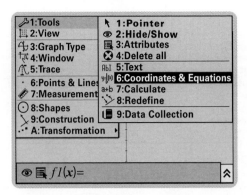

2. Position the pointer on the point. Press ⊙. Press ⊙.

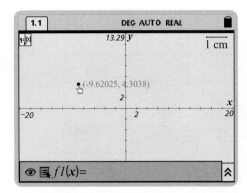

Graphing an Equation (Graphing View Only)

1. Use the **Text** tool in the **Tools** menu. Write the equation.

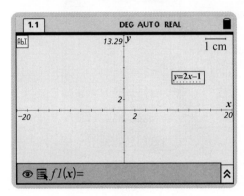

2. Drag the equation to the *x*-axis or the *y*-axis. Press ⊙.

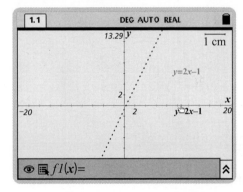

Graphing a Function (Graphing View Only)

1. Tab down to the entry line at the bottom of the screen. Type an expression in *x*.

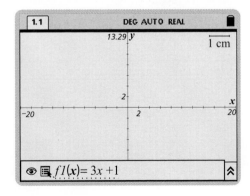

2. Press **enter**.

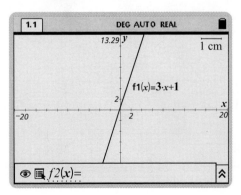

Scaling a Figure

1. Use **Rectangle** in the **Shapes** menu. Construct a rectangle

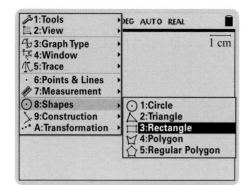

2. Use **Text** in the **Actions/Measurement** menu. Label the rectangle.

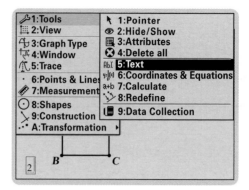

3. Use **Text** again. Write the scale factor on the screen.

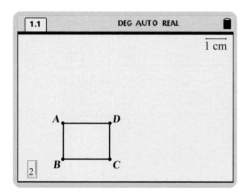

4. Choose **Dilation** in the **Transformation** menu.

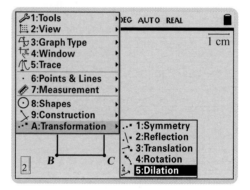

5. Select the scale factor on the screen. Then select the rectangle to set the scaled rectangle. Press 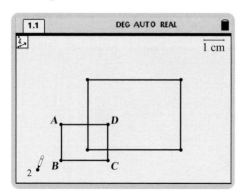 to anchor the scaled rectangle.

Finding a Dilation—The Ratio Method

1. Choose **Triangle** from the **Shapes** menu. Position the pointer. Press ✹ to anchor one vertex of the triangle. Type **Ⓐ** to label vertex *A*. Anchor and label vertices *B* and *C* in a similar way.

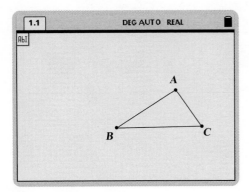

2. Choose **Point** in the **Points & Lines** menu. Position the pointer outside the triangle. Press ✹. Type **Ⓗ** to label point *H*.

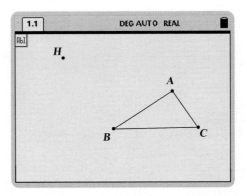

3. Use **Ray** in the **Points & Lines** menu. Draw rays *HA*, *HB*, and *HC*.

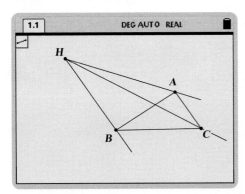

4. Use **Text** in the **Actions/Measurement** menu. Write the scale factor 0.5.

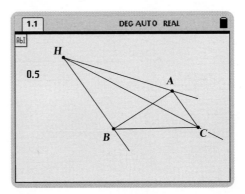

5. Choose **Dilation** in the **Transformation** menu. Click point *H*, point *A*, and the scale factor. The dilated point appears on ray *HA*. Label the dilated point *A'*. Scale points *B* and *C* in a similar way.

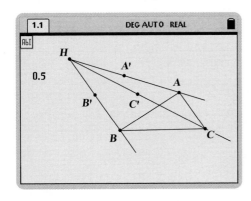

6. Use **Segment** in the **Points & Lines** menu to join points *A'*, *B'*, and *C'*. The dilation of △*ABC* by the factor 0.5 is △*A'B'C'*.

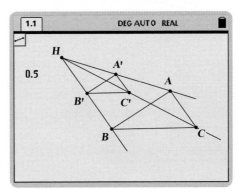

Tables

Table 1 Math Symbols

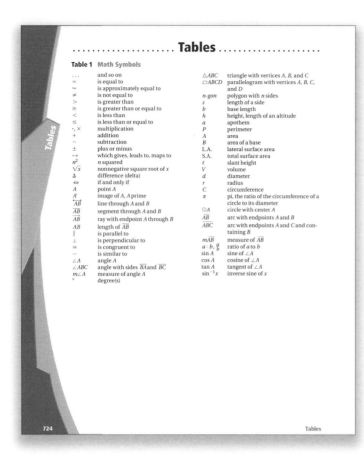

...	and so on	△ABC	triangle with vertices A, B, and C
=	is equal to	▱ABCD	parallelogram with vertices A, B, C, and D
≈	is approximately equal to	n-gon	polygon with n sides
≠	is not equal to	s	length of a side
>	is greater than	b	base length
≥	is greater than or equal to	h	height, length of an altitude
<	is less than	a	apothem
≤	is less than or equal to	P	perimeter
·, ×	multiplication	A	area
+	addition	B	area of a base
−	subtraction	L.A.	lateral surface area
±	plus or minus	S.A.	total surface area
↦	which gives, leads to, maps to	ℓ	slant height
n^2	n squared	V	volume
$\sqrt{x}$	nonnegative square root of x	d	diameter
Δ	difference (delta)	r	radius
⇔	if and only if	C	circumference
A	point A	π	pi, the ratio of the circumference of a circle to its diameter
A′	image of A, A prime	⊙A	circle with center A
$\overleftrightarrow{AB}$	line through A and B	$\overparen{AB}$	arc with endpoints A and B
$\overline{AB}$	segment through A and B	$\overparen{ABC}$	arc with endpoints A and C and containing B
$\overrightarrow{AB}$	ray with endpoint A through B		
AB	length of $\overline{AB}$	$m\overparen{AB}$	measure of $\overparen{AB}$
∥	is parallel to	$a:b, \frac{a}{b}$	ratio of a to b
⊥	is perpendicular to	sin A	sine of ∠A
≅	is congruent to	cos A	cosine of ∠A
~	is similar to	tan A	tangent of ∠A
∠A	angle A	$\sin^{-1}x$	inverse sine of x
∠ABC	angle with sides $\overrightarrow{BA}$ and $\overrightarrow{BC}$		
m∠A	measure of angle A		
°	degree(s)		

Table 2 Formulas

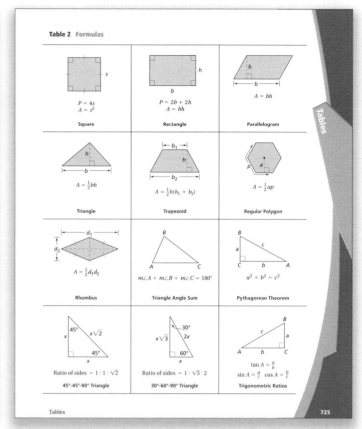

Square
$P = 4s$
$A = s^2$

Rectangle
$P = 2b + 2h$
$A = bh$

Parallelogram
$A = bh$

Triangle
$A = \frac{1}{2}bh$

Trapezoid
$A = \frac{1}{2}h(b_1 + b_2)$

Regular Polygon
$A = \frac{1}{2}ap$

Rhombus
$A = \frac{1}{2}d_1d_2$

Triangle Angle Sum
$m\angle A + m\angle B + m\angle C = 180°$

Pythagorean Theorem
$a^2 + b^2 = c^2$

45°-45°-90° Triangle
Ratio of sides = $1 : 1 : \sqrt{2}$

30°-60°-90° Triangle
Ratio of sides = $1 : \sqrt{3} : 2$

Trigonometric Ratios
$\tan A = \frac{a}{b}$
$\sin A = \frac{a}{c} \quad \cos A = \frac{b}{c}$

724

Tables

Tables

725

T724

Tables

Table 2 Formulas (continued)

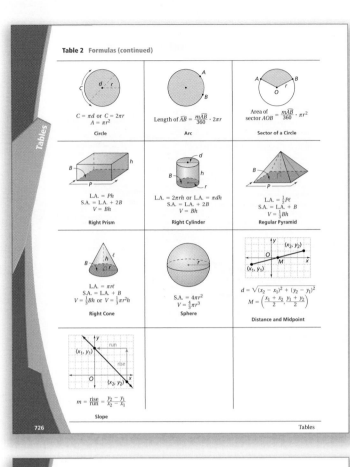

$C = \pi d$ or $C = 2\pi r$
$A = \pi r^2$
Circle

Length of $\widehat{AB} = \frac{m\widehat{AB}}{360} \cdot 2\pi r$
Arc

Area of sector $AOB = \frac{m\widehat{AB}}{360} \cdot \pi r^2$
Sector of a Circle

L.A. $= Ph$
S.A. $= $ L.A. $+ 2B$
$V = Bh$
Right Prism

L.A. $= 2\pi rh$ or L.A. $= \pi dh$
S.A. $= $ L.A. $+ 2B$
$V = Bh$
Right Cylinder

L.A. $= \frac{1}{2}P\ell$
S.A. $= $ L.A. $+ B$
$V = \frac{1}{3}Bh$
Regular Pyramid

L.A. $= \pi r\ell$
S.A. $= $ L.A. $+ B$
$V = \frac{1}{3}Bh$ or $V = \frac{1}{3}\pi r^2 h$
Right Cone

S.A. $= 4\pi r^2$
$V = \frac{4}{3}\pi r^3$
Sphere

$d = \sqrt{(x_2 - x_1)^2 + (y_2 - y_1)^2}$
$M = \left(\frac{x_1 + x_2}{2}, \frac{y_1 + y_2}{2}\right)$
Distance and Midpoint

$m = \frac{\text{rise}}{\text{run}} = \frac{y_2 - y_1}{x_2 - x_1}$
Slope

Table 3 Measures

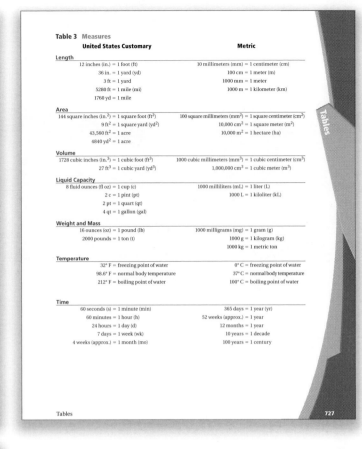

United States Customary	Metric
Length	
12 inches (in.) = 1 foot (ft)	10 millimeters (mm) = 1 centimeter (cm)
36 in. = 1 yard (yd)	100 cm = 1 meter (m)
3 ft = 1 yard	1000 mm = 1 meter
5280 ft = 1 mile (mi)	1000 m = 1 kilometer (km)
1760 yd = 1 mile	
Area	
144 square inches (in.^{2}) = 1 square foot (ft^2)	100 square millimeters (mm^2) = 1 square centimeter (cm^2)
9 ft^2 = 1 square yard (yd^2)	10,000 cm^2 = 1 square meter (m^2)
43,560 ft^2 = 1 acre	10,000 m^2 = 1 hectare (ha)
4840 yd^2 = 1 acre	
Volume	
1728 cubic inches (in.^{3}) = 1 cubic foot (ft^3)	1000 cubic millimeters (mm^3) = 1 cubic centimeter (cm^3)
27 ft^3 = 1 cubic yard (yd^3)	1,000,000 cm^3 = 1 cubic meter (m^3)
Liquid Capacity	
8 fluid ounces (fl oz) = 1 cup (c)	1000 milliliters (mL) = 1 liter (L)
2 c = 1 pint (pt)	1000 L = 1 kiloliter (kL)
2 pt = 1 quart (qt)	
4 qt = 1 gallon (gal)	
Weight and Mass	
16 ounces (oz) = 1 pound (lb)	1000 milligrams (mg) = 1 gram (g)
2000 pounds = 1 ton (t)	1000 g = 1 kilogram (kg)
	1000 kg = 1 metric ton
Temperature	
32° F = freezing point of water	0° C = freezing point of water
98.6° F = normal body temperature	37° C = normal body temperature
212° F = boiling point of water	100° C = boiling point of water
Time	
60 seconds (s) = 1 minute (min)	365 days = 1 year (yr)
60 minutes = 1 hour (h)	52 weeks (approx.) = 1 year
24 hours = 1 day (d)	12 months = 1 year
7 days = 1 week (wk)	10 years = 1 decade
4 weeks (approx.) = 1 month (mo)	100 years = 1 century

Table 4 Properties of Real Numbers

Unless otherwise stated, a, b, c, and d are real numbers.

Identity Properties
Addition $a + 0 = a$ and $0 + a = a$
Multiplication $a \cdot 1 = a$ and $1 \cdot a = a$

Commutative Properties
Addition $a + b = b + a$
Multiplication $a \cdot b = b \cdot a$

Associative Properties
Addition $(a + b) + c = a + (b + c)$
Multiplication $(a \cdot b) \cdot c = a \cdot (b \cdot c)$

Inverse Properties
Addition
The sum of a number and its *opposite*, or *additive inverse*, is zero.
$a + (-a) = 0 = -a + a = 0$
Multiplication
The reciprocal, or multiplicative inverse, of a rational number $\frac{a}{b}$ is $\frac{b}{a}$ $(a, b \neq 0)$.
$a \cdot \frac{1}{a} = 1$ and $\frac{1}{a} \cdot a = 1$ $(a \neq 0)$

Distributive Properties
$a(b + c) = ab + ac$ $(b + c)a = ba + ca$
$a(b - c) = ab - ac$ $(b - c)a = ba - ca$

Properties of Equality
Addition   If $a = b$, then $a + c = b + c$.
Subtraction   If $a = b$, then $a - c = b - c$.
Multiplication If $a = b$, then $a \cdot c = b \cdot c$.
Division   If $a = b$ and $c \neq 0$, then $\frac{a}{c} = \frac{b}{c}$.
Substitution   If $a = b$, then b can replace a in any expression.
Reflexive $a = a$
Symmetric   If $a = b$, then $b = a$.
Transitive   If $a = b$ and $b = c$, then $a = c$.

Properties of Proportions
$\frac{a}{b} = \frac{c}{d}$ $(a, b, c, d \neq 0$ is equivalent to
(1) $ad = bc$ (2) $\frac{b}{a} = \frac{d}{c}$
(3) $\frac{a}{c} = \frac{b}{d}$ (4) $\frac{a + b}{b} = \frac{c + d}{d}$

Zero-Product Property
If $ab = 0$, then $a = 0$ or $b = 0$.

Properties of Inequality
Addition   If $a > b$ and $c \geq d$, then $a + c > b + d$.
Multiplication If $a > b$ and $c > 0$, then $ac > bc$.
If $a > b$ and $c < 0$, then $ac < bc$.
Transitive   If $a > b$ and $b > c$, then $a > c$.
Comparison   If $a = b + c$, then $c > 0$, then $a > b$.

Properties of Exponents
For any nonzero numbers a and b, any positive number c, and any integers m and n,
Zero Exponent $a^0 = 1$
Negative Exponent $a^{-n} = \frac{1}{a^n}$
Product of Powers $a^m \cdot a^n = a^{m+n}$
Quotient of Powers $\frac{a^m}{a^n} = a^{m-n}$
Power to a Power $(c^m)^n = c^{mn}$
Product to a Power $(ab)^n = a^n b^n$
Quotient to a Power $\left(\frac{a}{b}\right)^n = \frac{a^n}{b^n}$

Properties of Square Roots
For any nonnegative numbers a and b, and any positive number c,
Product of Square Roots $\sqrt{a} \cdot \sqrt{b} = \sqrt{ab}$
Quotient of Square Roots $\frac{\sqrt{a}}{\sqrt{c}} = \sqrt{\frac{a}{c}}$

Theorem 1.1
Perpendicular Bisector Theorem, p. 29
Each point on the perpendicular bisector of a segment is equidistant from the two endpoints of the segment.

Theorem 1.2
Concurrence of Perpendicular Bisectors, p. 60
In any triangle, the perpendicular bisectors of the sides are concurrent.

Theorem 1.3
Concurrence of Angle Bisectors, p. 60
In any triangle, the angle bisectors are concurrent.

Postulate 2.1
The Triangle Congruence Postulates, p. 84
If two triangles share the following triplets of congruent corresponding parts, the triangles are congruent.
• ASA   • SAS   • SSS

Theorem 2.1 Vertical Angles Theorem, p. 93
Vertical angles are congruent.

Theorem 2.2 AIP Theorem, p. 99
If two lines form congruent alternate interior angles with a transversal, then the two lines are parallel.

Postulate 2.2 Parallel Postulate, p. 105
If a point P is not on line ℓ, exactly one line through P exists that is parallel to ℓ.

Theorem 2.3 PAI Theorem, p. 105
If two parallel lines are cut by a transversal, then the alternate interior angles are congruent.

Theorem 2.4
Triangle Angle-Sum Theorem, p. 107
The sum of the measures of the angles in a triangle is 180°.

Theorem 2.5
Unique Perpendicular Theorem, p. 109
If a point P is not on line ℓ, there is exactly one line through P that is perpendicular to ℓ.

Theorem 2.6 Isosceles Triangle Theorem, p. 136
The base angles of an isosceles triangle are congruent.

Triangle Inequality Theorem, p. 140
In a triangle, the length of one side is less than the sum of the lengths of the other two sides.

Theorem 2.7, p. 151
Each diagonal of a parallelogram divides the parallelogram into two congruent triangles.

Theorem 2.8, p. 152
The diagonals of a parallelogram bisect each other.

Theorem 2.9, p. 156
If two opposite sides of a quadrilateral are congruent and parallel, then the figure is a parallelogram.

Theorem 2.10 Midline Theorem, p. 156
The segment that joins the midpoints of two sides of a triangle is parallel to the third side and half the length of the third side.

Theorem 3.1, p. 178
The segment joining the midpoints of the legs of a trapezoid is parallel to the bases. Its length is half the sum (the average) of the lengths of the bases.

Postulate 3.1 Congruence Postulate, p. 197
Congruent figures have the same area.

Postulate 3.2 Additivity Postulate, p. 197
If two polygons P and Q do not intersect (except possibly at a point or along an edge), then the area of the union of P and Q is the sum of the areas of P and Q.

Postulate 3.3 Rectangle Postulate, p. 199
The area of a rectangle with dimensions b and h (expressed in the same unit) is bh.

Postulate 3.4
Scissors-Congruence Postulate, p. 199
Two figures that are scissors-congruent have the same area.

Theorem 3.2 Pythagorean Theorem, p. 217
• In a right triangle, the square built on the longest side has area equal to the sum of the areas of the squares built on the other two sides.

Theorem 4.1
The Parallel Side-Splitter Theorem, p. 310
If a segment with endpoints on two sides of a triangle is parallel to the third side of the triangle, then

- the segment splits the sides it intersects proportionally
- the ratio of the length of the side of the triangle to the length of the parallel segment is the common ratio

Theorem 4.2
Proportional Side-Splitter Theorem, p. 311
If a segment with endpoints on two sides of a triangle splits those sides proportionally, then the segment is parallel to the third side.

Theorem 4.3 AAA Similarity Theorem, p. 331
If three angles of one triangle are congruent to three angles of another triangle, the triangles are similar.

Theorem 4.4 SAS Similarity Theorem, p. 332
If two triangles have two pairs of proportional side lengths, and the included angles are congruent, the triangles are similar.

Theorem 4.5 SSS Similarity Theorem, p. 333
If two triangles have all three pairs of side lengths proportional, the triangles are similar.

Theorem 4.6, p. 340
If you scale a polygon by some positive number r, then the ratio of the area of the scaled copy to the area of the original polygon is r^2.

Theorem 5.1, p. 368
The area A of a regular polygon is equal to half of the product of its perimeter P and its apothem a.
$$A = \tfrac{1}{2}Pa$$

Theorem 5.2, p. 370
The area of a circle is one half its circumference times its radius.
$$A = \tfrac{1}{2}Cr$$

Theorem 5.3, p. 377
If a circle is scaled by a positive number s, then its area is scaled by s^2.

Theorem 5.4, p. 377
If the area of a circle with radius 1 is k, then the area of a circle with radius r is kr^2.

Theorem 5.5, p. 378
The area of a circle of radius r is π times the radius squared.
$$A = \pi r^2$$

Theorem 5.6, p. 382
The circumference of a circle of radius r is 2π times the radius.
$$C = 2\pi r$$

Theorem 5.7, p. 394
Two chords are congruent if and only if their corresponding arcs are congruent.

Theorem 5.8, p. 400
A line through the center of a circle bisects a chord if it is perpendicular to the chord.

Theorem 5.9, p. 401
If a line through the center of a circle bisects a chord, then it is perpendicular to the chord.

Theorem 5.10, p. 401
The center of a circle lies on the line perpendicular to a chord if and only if the line bisects the chord.

Theorem 5.11, p. 401
The measure of an inscribed angle is equal to half the measure of its intercepted arc.

Corollary 5.11.1, p. 402
Inscribed angles are congruent if and only if they intercept the same arc or congruent arcs.

Corollary 5.11.2, p. 402
Any triangle inscribed in a semicircle is a right triangle.

Theorem 5.12, p. 407
If a line intersects a circle in one point (that is, the line is tangent to the circle), it is perpendicular to the radius r drawn to the point of contact.

Theorem 5.13, p. 408
A secant angle with vertex inside a circle is equal in measure to half of the sum of the measures of the arcs it intercepts.

Theorem 5.14, p. 409
A secant angle with vertex outside a circle is equal in measure to half of the difference of the measures of the arcs it intercepts.

Theorem 6.1, p. 454
In a right triangle, either leg is the geometric mean of its projection on the hypotenuse and the whole hypotenuse.

Theorem 6.2, p. 454
In a right triangle, the altitude relative to the hypotenuse is the geometric mean of the two segments of the hypotenuse.

Theorem 6.3 Cavalieri's Principle, p. 504
Two solids of the same height are cut by a plane so that the resulting cross sections have the same areas. If the solids also have cross-sectional areas equal to each other when cut by any plane parallel to the first, then they have the same volume.

Theorem 6.4, p. 511
The volume of a prism is equal to the product of the area of its base and its height.
$$V_{\text{prism}} = A_{\text{base}} \cdot h$$

Theorem 6.5, p. 512
The volume of a cylinder is equal to the product of the area of its base (a circle) and its height.
$$V_{\text{cylinder}} = A_{\text{base}} \cdot h$$

Theorem 6.6, p. 514
The volume of a pyramid is equal to one third of the product of the area of its base and its height.
$$V_{\text{pyramid}} = \frac{A_{\text{base}} \cdot h}{3}$$

Theorem 6.7, p. 515
The volume of a cone is equal to one third of the product of the area of its base (a circle) and its height.
$$V_{\text{cone}} = \frac{A_{\text{base}} \cdot h}{3}$$

Theorem 6.8, p. 521
The volume of a sphere with radius r is $\tfrac{4}{3}\pi r^3$.

Theorem 6.9, p. 521
The surface area of a sphere with radius r is $4\pi r^2$.

Theorem 7.1, p. 557
The composition of two reflections over intersecting lines produces a rotation. Its center is the intersection of the lines. The angle of rotation is equal to twice the measure of the angle formed by the two lines.

Theorem 7.2 Distance Formula, p. 568
The distance between two points (x_1, y_1) and (x_2, y_2) can be found using the Pythagorean Theorem. It is the square root of the sum of the square of the difference in the x-coordinates and the square of difference in the y-coordinates.

Theorem 7.3 Midpoint Formula, p. 568
Each coordinate of the midpoint of a line segment is equal to the average of the corresponding coordinates of the endpoints of the line segment.

Theorem 7.4, p. 573
Two lines are parallel if and only if they have the same slope.

Theorem 7.5, p. 574
Let A, B, and C be three points, no two of which are in line vertically. Points A, B, and C are collinear if and only if the slope between A and B, $m(A,B)$, is the same as the slope between B and C, $m(B,C)$.
A, B, and C are collinear $\Leftrightarrow m(A,B) = m(B,C)$.

Theorem 7.6, p. 579
Two lines are perpendicular if and only if the product of their slopes is -1.

Theorem 7.7 The Head-Minus-Tail Test, p. 602
Two vectors are equivalent if and only if head minus tail for one vector gives the same result as head minus tail for the other.
$\overrightarrow{AB}$ is equivalent to $\overrightarrow{CD}$ if and only if $B - A = D - C$.

Corollary 7.7.1, p. 602
If A and B are points, the vector from O to $B - A$ is equivalent to the vector from A to B.

Theorem 7.8, p. 604
If $A = (a_1, a_2)$ and $B = (b_1, b_2)$, then $A + B$ is the fourth vertex of the parallelogram that has A, O, and B as three of its vertices and $\overline{OA}$ and $\overline{OB}$ as two of its sides.

Theorem 7.9, p. 605
Suppose A is a point, c is a number greater than or equal to 1, and $B = cA$. Then,
- B is collinear with A and the origin.
- B is c times as far from the origin as A.

Theorem 7.10, p. 606
Adding the same point to the tail and to the head of a vector produces an equivalent vector.

Theorem 7.11, p. 608
If A is a point different from the origin, the set of all multiples of A is the line through the origin and A.

Theorem 7.12, p. 610
Two vectors, $\overrightarrow{AB}$ and $\overrightarrow{CD}$, are parallel if and only if there is a number k such that $B - A = k(D - C)$. If $k > 0$, the vectors have the same direction. If $k < 0$, the vectors have opposite directions. If $k = 1$, the vectors are equivalent.

Theorem 7.13, p. 611
If A and B are points, then the segment from O to $B - A$ is parallel and congruent to $\overline{AB}$.

Theorem 8.1 Regular Polygon Theorem, p. 653
Of all the polygons having a given perimeter and a given number of sides, the regular polygon has the greatest area.

Theorem 8.2 Rich's Theorem, p. 685
The sum of the distances from any point inside an equilateral triangle to the sides of the triangle is equal to the length of the altitude of the triangle.

Postulate 8.1 The Existence Hypothesis, p. 699
For any given perimeter, there is a closed curve that encloses the greatest area.

Theorem 8.3, p. 705
The best place to put the airport is where the roads make 120° angles with each other, unless there is no such place inside the triangle.

·············· Glossary ··············

A

acre (p. 643) An acre is a unit of area equal to 43,560 ft².

acute angle (p. 484) An acute angle is an angle whose measure is between 0° and 90°.

adjacent angles (p. 42) Adjacent angles are two coplanar angles that have a common side and a common vertex but no common interior points.

∠1 and ∠2 are adjacent.   ∠3 and ∠4 are *not* adjacent.

algorithm (p. 181) An algorithm is a set of steps to a completely determined result.

alternate exterior angles (p. 102) Alternate exterior angles are nonadjacent exterior angles that lie on opposite sides of a transversal.

∠1 and ∠2 are alternate exterior angles.

alternate interior angles (p. 99) Alternate interior angles are nonadjacent interior angles that lie on opposite sides of a transversal.

∠1 and ∠2 are alternate interior angles.

altitude *See* cone; cylinder; prism; pyramid; triangle.

angle bisector (p. 31) An angle bisector is a ray that divides an angle exactly in half, making two congruent angles.

angle bisector

angle of incidence (p. 637) The angle of incidence is the angle between an incoming ray and the line perpendicular to the surface at the point of arrival.

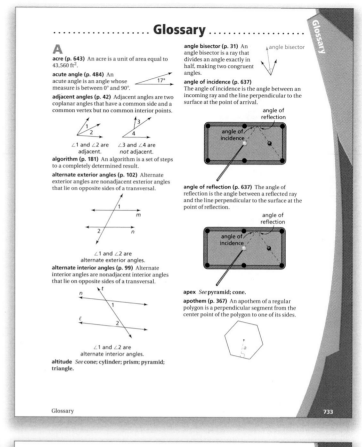

angle of reflection (p. 637) The angle of reflection is the angle between a reflected ray and the line perpendicular to the surface at the point of reflection.

apex *See* pyramid; cone.

apothem (p. 367) An apothem of a regular polygon is a perpendicular segment from the center point of the polygon to one of its sides.

---

arc (p. 392) An arc is the set of points on a circle that lie in the interior of a particular central angle.

$m\widehat{TY} = 70$
$m\widehat{TOY} = 290$

area (p. 197) Area is the number of square units contained within a figure.

The area of the rectangle is 12 square units, or 12 units².

arithmetic mean (p. 448) The arithmetic mean of two numbers a and b is $\frac{a+b}{2}$. The arithmetic mean is commonly referred to as the average.

assumption (p. 84) An assumption is a statement accepted without proof.

axiom (p. 91) An axiom is a conclusion accepted without proof.

B

base(s) *See* cone; prism; pyramid; cylinder; trapezoid; triangle.

base angles *See* isosceles trapezoid; isosceles triangle.

bisection (p. 46) A bisection is a dissection that results in two congruent parts.

△ABC is bisected by line ℓ.

C

center of dilation *See* dilation.

center of rotation *See* rotation.

central angle (p. 392) A central angle is an angle that has its vertex at the center of a circle.

∠AOB is a central angle.

centroid (p. 458) A centroid is the point of concurrency of the three medians of a triangle.

centroid

chord (p. 392) A chord is a segment that connects two points on a circle. Any chord through the center of a circle is a diameter.

$\overline{AB}$ is a chord.

circle (p. 16) A circle is the set of all points that are a given distance, the radius, from a given point, the center.

circumference (p. 241) The perimeter of a circle.

circumference = 8π units

$C = 2\pi r$
$= 2\pi(4)$
$= 8\pi$

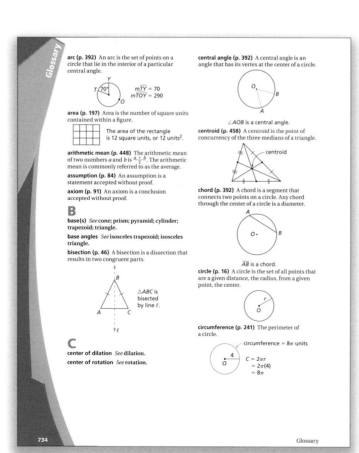

---

circumscribe (p. 361) A circle is circumscribed about a polygon if all of the vertices of the polygon are on the circle. A polygon is circumscribed about a circle if all of the sides of the polygon are tangent to the circle.

The circle is circumscribed about the octagon.

closed figure (p. 144) A figure is closed if you can "walk" its outer edges and get back to where you started.

closed   not closed

coincide (p. 281) Points or lines coincide if they take up the same place in space.

collinear points (p. 61) Collinear points exist on the same line.

Points A, B, and C are collinear.

common ratio *See* dilation.

composition (p. 547) Any translation is a composition of two reflections.

concave polygon (p. 145) A concave polygon has at least one diagonal that contains points outside the polygon.

diagonal outside the quadrilateral

concentric circles (p. 404) Concentric circles have the same center but not necessarily the same radius.

The two circles both have center D and are therefore concentric.

concurrent lines (p. 59) Concurrent lines are three or more lines that meet or intersect at one point.

Lines ℓ, m, and n are concurrent lines.

cone (p. 242) A cone is a solid with a circular *base* and a smooth curved *lateral surface* that comes to a point, the *apex*. The distance from the edge of the base to the apex is the *slant height* of the cone. The *altitude* of the cone is a perpendicular segment from the apex of the cone to the plane of its base. The length of the altitude is the *height* of the cone.

apex
height
lateral surface
slant height
base

congruent figures (p. 73) Two figures are congruent if they have the same size and shape regardless of location or orientation.

△ABC is congruent to △A′B′C′.

conjecture (p. 22) A conjecture is a conclusion reached by using inductive reasoning.

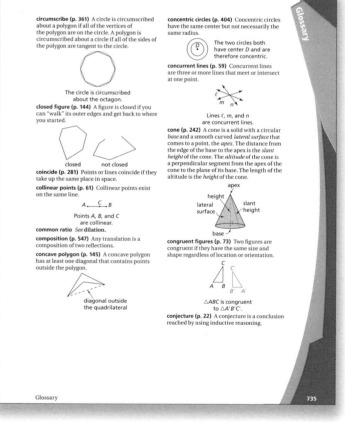

Page 736

consecutive angles (p. 99) Consecutive angles of a polygon are angles that have a common side.

In □JKLM, ∠J and ∠M are consecutive angles, as are ∠J and ∠K. ∠J and ∠L are *not* consecutive.

constant (p. 51) A constant is a numerical invariant.

constant-area-rectangle (p. 450) A constant-area-rectangle is a construction of a rectangle in which the area of the rectangle remains the same as the dimensions are changed.

construction (p. 27) A construction is a guaranteed recipe for drawing a figure with a specified set of tools.

The diagram shows the construction (in progress) of a line perpendicular to a line ℓ through a point P on ℓ.

contour line (p. 662) A contour line is a curve that shows where a particular quantity is invariant.

contour plot (p. 662) A contour plot is a collection of contour lines.

Contour plot showing height

converse (p. 30) The converse of the conditional "if p, then q" is the conditional "if q, then p."

convex polygon (p. 61) A polygon is convex if no diagonal of the polygon contains points outside the polygon.

convex | not convex (concave)

corollary (p. 100) A corollary is a consequence that follows from a theorem.

corresponding parts (p. 45) Corresponding parts are in the same relative position in congruent figures.

△ABC ≅ △DEF
∠A and ∠D are corresponding parts.
$\overline{BC}$ and $\overline{EF}$ are corresponding parts.

cosine *See* trigonometric ratios.

counterexample (p. 122) A counterexample is an example that proves that a statement is false.

CPCTC (p. 82) CPCTC is an abbreviation of "corresponding parts of congruent triangles are congruent."

△KLM ≅ △QPR by SAS.
By CPCTC, you also know that ∠L ≅ ∠P, ∠M ≅ ∠R, and $\overline{LM}$ ≅ $\overline{PR}$.

cross section (p. 35) A cross section is the intersection of a solid and a plane.

The blue regions are cross sections.

cyclic quadrilateral (p. 462) A cyclic quadrilateral is a quadrilateral inscribed in a circle.

Page 737

cylinder (p. 240) A cylinder is a solid with two congruent parallel circles as *bases*, joined by a curved smooth *lateral surface*. The *altitude* of the cylinder is a perpendicular segment from one base to the other. The *height* of the cylinder is the length of the altitude.

base
altitude
base

D

diagonal (p. 143) A diagonal is a segment that connects two nonconsecutive vertices of a polygon.

diameter (p. 392) A diameter is a chord that passes through the center of a circle.

$\overline{DM}$ is a diameter.

dilation (p. 289) A dilation is a nonrigid transformation that scales a figure from a *center of dilation* by a *scale factor*. The ratio of corresponding parts of the original figure to the scaled figure is the *common ratio*.

The scale factor of the dilation that maps △ABC to △A'B'C' is $\frac{1}{2}$.

dimensions (p. 265) The dimensions are measurements that indicate the size of a figure.

Rectangle ABCD has dimensions 3 ft by 5 ft.

disc (p. 61) A disc is a circle and its interior points.

discrete case (p. 425) A discrete case deals with finite numbers.

dissection (p. 174) A dissection is a process of cutting a polygon into two or more polygons.

distance (p. 627) The distance between two points is the length of the segment that connects the two points. The distance between a point and a line is the length of the perpendicular segment from the point to the line.

The distance from point P to line ℓ is PT.

E

ellipse (p. 68) An ellipse is a set of points P in a plane such that the sum of the distances from P to two fixed points F_1 and F_2 is a given constant k. F_1 and F_2 are the *foci* (plural of *focus*) of the ellipse.

foci

equiangular (p. 124) An equiangular polygon is a polygon with angles that are all congruent.

Each angle of the pentagon is a 108° angle.

equilateral triangle (p. 31) An equilateral triangle is a triangle whose sides are all congruent. Each angle measures 60°.

60° 60° 60°

Page 738

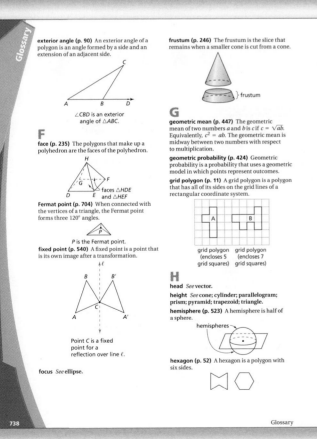

exterior angle (p. 90) An exterior angle of a polygon is an angle formed by a side and an extension of an adjacent side.

∠CBD is an exterior angle of △ABC.

F

face (p. 235) The polygons that make up a polyhedron are the faces of the polyhedron.

faces △HDE and △HEF

Fermat point (p. 704) When connected with the vertices of a triangle, the Fermat point forms three 120° angles.

P is the Fermat point.

fixed point (p. 540) A fixed point is a point that is its own image after a transformation.

Point C is a fixed point for a reflection over line ℓ.

focus *See* ellipse.

frustum (p. 246) The frustum is the slice that remains when a smaller cone is cut from a cone.

frustum

G

geometric mean (p. 447) The geometric mean of two numbers a and b is c if $c = \sqrt{ab}$. Equivalently, $c^2 = ab$. The geometric mean is midway between two numbers with respect to multiplication.

geometric probability (p. 424) Geometric probability is a probability that uses a geometric model in which points represent outcomes.

grid polygon (p. 11) A grid polygon is a polygon that has all of its sides on the grid lines of a rectangular coordinate system.

grid polygon (encloses 5 grid squares) | grid polygon (encloses 7 grid squares)

H

head *See* vector.

height *See* cone; cylinder; parallelogram; prism; pyramid; trapezoid; triangle.

hemisphere (p. 523) A hemisphere is half of a sphere.

hemispheres

hexagon (p. 52) A hexagon is a polygon with six sides.

Page 739

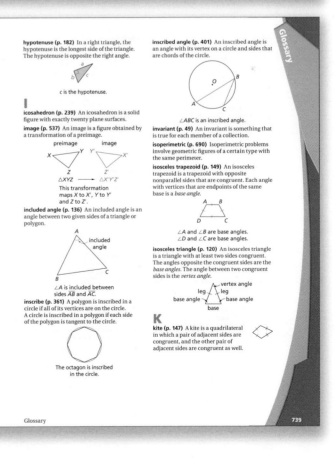

hypotenuse (p. 182) In a right triangle, the hypotenuse is the longest side of the triangle. The hypotenuse is opposite the right angle.

c is the hypotenuse.

I

icosahedron (p. 239) An icosahedron is a solid figure with exactly twenty plane surfaces.

image (p. 537) An image is a figure obtained by a transformation of a preimage.

preimage | image

△XYZ → △X'Y'Z'

This transformation maps X to X', Y to Y', and Z to Z'.

included angle (p. 136) An included angle is an angle between two given sides of a triangle or polygon.

included angle

∠A is included between sides $\overline{AB}$ and $\overline{AC}$.

inscribe (p. 361) A polygon is inscribed in a circle if all of its vertices are on the circle. A circle is inscribed in a polygon if each side of the polygon is tangent to the circle.

The octagon is inscribed in the circle.

inscribed angle (p. 401) An inscribed angle is an angle with its vertex on a circle and sides that are chords of the circle.

∠ABC is an inscribed angle.

invariant (p. 49) An invariant is something that is true for each member of a collection.

isoperimetric (p. 690) Isoperimetric problems involve geometric figures of a certain type with the same perimeter.

isosceles trapezoid (p. 149) An isosceles trapezoid is a trapezoid with opposite nonparallel sides that are congruent. Each angle with vertices that are endpoints of the same base is a *base angle*.

∠A and ∠B are base angles. ∠D and ∠C are base angles.

isosceles triangle (p. 120) An isosceles triangle is a triangle with at least two sides congruent. The angles opposite the congruent sides are the *base angles*. The angle between two congruent sides is the *vertex angle*.

vertex angle
leg | leg
base angle | base angle
base

K

kite (p. 147) A kite is a quadrilateral in which a pair of adjacent sides are congruent, and the other pair of adjacent sides are congruent as well.

L

lateral surface *See* **cone; cylinder.**

lateral surface area (p. 237) The lateral surface area of a polyhedron is the sum of the areas of every lateral face of the polyhedron but not the areas of the bases.

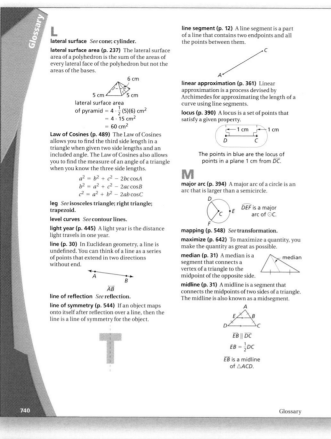

lateral surface area
of pyramid $= 4 \cdot \frac{1}{2}(5)(6)\ cm^2$
$= 4 \cdot 15\ cm^2$
$= 60\ cm^2$

Law of Cosines (p. 489) The Law of Cosines allows you to find the third side length in a triangle when given two side lengths and an included angle. The Law of Cosines also allows you to find the measure of an angle of a triangle when you know the three side lengths.

$$a^2 = b^2 + c^2 - 2bc\cos A$$
$$b^2 = a^2 + c^2 - 2ac\cos B$$
$$c^2 = a^2 + b^2 - 2ab\cos C$$

leg *See* **isosceles triangle; right triangle; trapezoid.**

level curves *See* **contour lines.**

light year (p. 445) A light year is the distance light travels in one year.

line (p. 30) In Euclidean geometry, a line is undefined. You can think of a line as a series of points that extend in two directions without end.

$\overleftrightarrow{AB}$

line of reflection *See* **reflection.**

line of symmetry (p. 544) If an object maps onto itself after reflection over a line, then the line is a line of symmetry for the object.

line segment (p. 12) A line segment is a part of a line that contains two endpoints and all the points between them.

linear approximation (p. 361) Linear approximation is a process devised by Archimedes for approximating the length of a curve using line segments.

locus (p. 390) A locus is a set of points that satisfy a given property.

The points in blue are the locus of points in a plane 1 cm from $\overline{DC}$.

M

major arc (p. 394) A major arc of a circle is an arc that is larger than a semicircle.

$\widehat{DEF}$ is a major arc of $\odot C$.

mapping (p. 548) *See* **transformation.**

maximize (p. 642) To maximize a quantity, you make the quantity as great as possible.

median (p. 31) A median is a segment that connects a vertex of a triangle to the midpoint of the opposite side.

midline (p. 31) A midline is a segment that connects the midpoints of two sides of a triangle. The midline is also known as a midsegment.

$\overline{EB} \parallel \overline{DC}$
$EB = \frac{1}{2}DC$
$\overline{EB}$ is a midline of $\triangle ACD$.

---

midpoint (p. 29) A midpoint is the point on a segment that is halfway between two endpoints. A midpoint on a coordinate grid is the average of the coordinates of the endpoints of the segment.

midpoint of $\overline{AB}$

midpoint quadrilateral (p. 192) A midpoint quadrilateral is a quadrilateral formed by connecting the midpoints of the sides of a quadrilateral with segments.

midpoint quadrilateral

midsegment *See* **midline.**

minimize (p. 626) To minimize a quantity, you make the quantity as small as possible.

minor arc (p. 394) A minor arc is an arc that is smaller than a semicircle.

$\widehat{KC}$ is a minor arc of $\odot S$.

Monte Carlo Method (p. 425) The Monte Carlo Method is a statistical simulation method that utilizes sequences of random numbers to perform a simulation.

N

nested triangles (p. 307) One triangle is nested in another triangle if it lies completely inside it.

n-gon (p. 119) An n-gon is a polygon with n sides, where n is a whole number greater than or equal to 3.

nonagon (p. 21) A nonagon is a nine-sided polygon.

O

oblique prism (p. 236) An oblique prism is a prism with lateral edges that are not perpendicular to the bases.

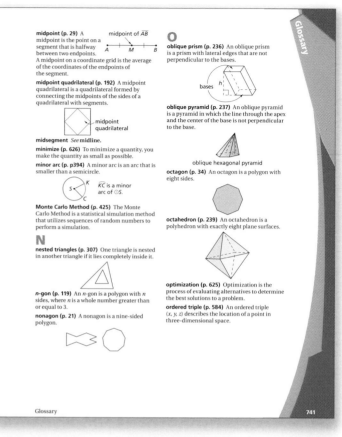

bases

oblique pyramid (p. 237) An oblique pyramid is a pyramid in which the line through the apex and the center of the base is not perpendicular to the base.

oblique hexagonal pyramid

octagon (p. 34) An octagon is a polygon with eight sides.

octahedron (p. 239) An octahedron is a polyhedron with exactly eight plane surfaces.

optimization (p. 625) Optimization is the process of evaluating alternatives to determine the best solutions to a problem.

ordered triple (p. 584) An ordered triple (x, y, z) describes the location of a point in three-dimensional space.

P

parallel lines (p. 12) Parallel lines are lines in the same plane that do not intersect.

two parallel lines

a plane (for example, a piece of paper)

parallel planes (p. 12) Parallel planes are planes in space that do not intersect.

two parallel planes

parallelepiped (p. 232) A parallelepiped is a prism in which every pair of opposite faces are congruent parallelograms.

parallelogram (p. 43) A parallelogram is a quadrilateral with two pairs of parallel sides.

pentagon (p. 52) A pentagon is a polygon with exactly five sides.

perimeter (p. 241) The perimeter is the length of the border of a two-dimensional figure.

$P = 4\ in. + 4\ in. + 5\ in. + 3\ in.$
$= 16\ in.$

perpendicular lines (p. 33) Perpendicular lines are lines that intersect to form right angles.

$m \perp n$

perpendicular bisector (p. 29) A perpendicular bisector is a line that is perpendicular to a segment at the segment's midpoint.

pi (p. 241) Pi, (π), is the ratio of the circumference of any circle to its diameter. Pi is the numerical value of the area of a circle with radius 1. Pi is an infinite nonrepeating decimal constant that begins with 3.14159.

planar figure (p. 145) A planar figure is a figure with all of its points in the same plane.

$\triangle ABC$ lies in plane Z.

plane (p. 12) A plane is a flat surface that has no thickness, contains many lines, and extends without end in the directions of its lines.

a plane

point (p. 68) A point is a location in space. It has no size.

point of tangency (p. 21) The point of tangency is the point of intersection of a tangent line and a circle.

P is the point of tangency of line ℓ and the circle.

polygon (p. 49) A polygon is a closed plane figure with at least three sides.

vertices
diagonal
sides
convex   concave

polyhedron (p. 235) A polyhedron is a solid with faces that are polygons.

polyominoes (p. 77) Polyominoes are shapes made up of congruent squares that meet edge to edge.

---

postulate (p. 84) A postulate is a statement accepted without proof.

power of a point (p. 418) The power of a point with respect to a circle is $(PA)(PB)$, where A and B are the points of intersection of a line through P and the circle.

preimage (p. 537) The preimage is the original figure before a transformation.

preimage   image

$\triangle XYZ$ $\triangle X'Y'Z'$

This transformation maps X to X', Y to Y' and Z to Z'.

prism (p. 232) A prism is a polyhedron with two congruent and parallel *faces*, called the *bases*. The other faces, which are parallelograms, are the *lateral faces*. An *altitude* of a prism is a perpendicular segment that joins the planes of the bases. The *height* of the prism is the length of its altitude.

lateral faces
base   base

triangular prism

projection (p. 455) A projection is the transformation of the points of a geometric figure onto the points of another figure. The projection of a point A onto a line ℓ is the intersection of ℓ with the line perpendicular to ℓ through A.

The projection of $\overline{AB}$ onto $\overline{CD}$ is $\overline{EF}$

proof (p. 94) A proof is an argument in which every statement is supported with a reason.

pyramid (p. 237) A pyramid is a polyhedron with one *base*. The base can be any polygon. The *lateral faces* are triangles that have a common vertex, the *apex* of the pyramid. An *altitude* of the pyramid is the perpendicular segment from the apex to the plane of the base. The *height* of the pyramid is the length of the altitude. The *slant height* of the pyramid is the height of a triangular face.

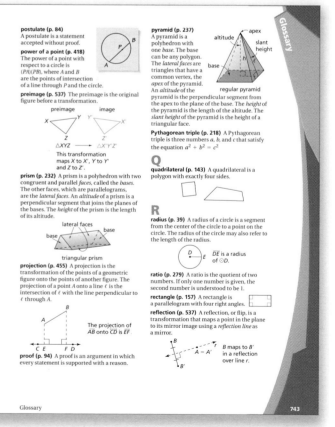

regular pyramid

Pythagorean triple (p. 218) A Pythagorean triple is three numbers a, b, and c that satisfy the equation $a^2 + b^2 = c^2$

Q

quadrilateral (p. 143) A quadrilateral is a polygon with exactly four sides.

R

radius (p. 39) A radius of a circle is a segment from the center of the circle to a point on the circle. The radius of the circle may also refer to the length of the radius.

$\overline{DE}$ is a radius of $\odot D$.

ratio (p. 279) A ratio is the quotient of two numbers. If only one number is given, the second number is understood to be 1.

rectangle (p. 157) A rectangle is a parallelogram with four right angles.

reflection (p. 537) A reflection, or flip, is a transformation that maps a point in the plane to its mirror image using a *reflection line* as a mirror.

B maps to B' in a reflection over line r.

regular polygon (p. 21) A regular polygon is a polygon that is both equiangular and equilateral.

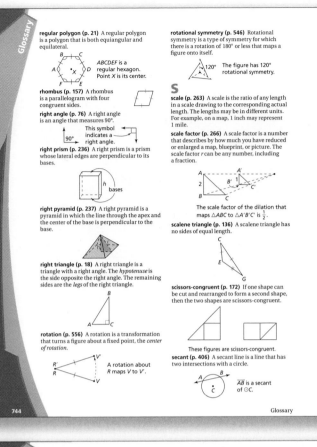

ABCDEF is a regular hexagon. Point *X* is its center.

rhombus (p. 157) A rhombus is a parallelogram with four congruent sides.

right angle (p. 76) A right angle is an angle that measures 90°.

This symbol indicates a right angle.

right prism (p. 236) A right prism is a prism whose lateral edges are perpendicular to its bases.

right pyramid (p. 237) A right pyramid is a pyramid in which the line through the apex and the center of the base is perpendicular to the base.

right triangle (p. 18) A right triangle is a triangle with a right angle. The *hypotenuse* is the side opposite the right angle. The remaining sides are the *legs* of the right triangle.

rotation (p. 556) A rotation is a transformation that turns a figure about a fixed point, the *center of rotation*.

A rotation about *R* maps *V* to *V'*.

rotational symmetry (p. 546) Rotational symmetry is a type of symmetry for which there is a rotation of 180° or less that maps a figure onto itself.

The figure has 120° rotational symmetry.

S

scale (p. 263) A scale is the ratio of any length in a scale drawing to the corresponding actual length. The lengths may be in different units. For example, on a map, 1 inch may represent 1 mile.

scale factor (p. 266) A scale factor is a number that describes by how much you have reduced or enlarged a map, blueprint, or picture. The scale factor *r* can be any number, including a fraction.

The scale factor of the dilation that maps △*ABC* to △*A'B'C'* is $\frac{1}{2}$.

scalene triangle (p. 136) A scalene triangle has no sides of equal length.

scissors-congruent (p. 172) If one shape can be cut and rearranged to form a second shape, then the two shapes are scissors-congruent.

These figures are scissors-congruent.

secant (p. 406) A secant line is a line that has two intersections with a circle.

$\overline{AB}$ is a secant of ⊙*C*.

744

---

secant angle (p. 407) A secant angle is an angle with sides that are two secants of a circle. A secant angle's vertex can be inside or outside the circle.

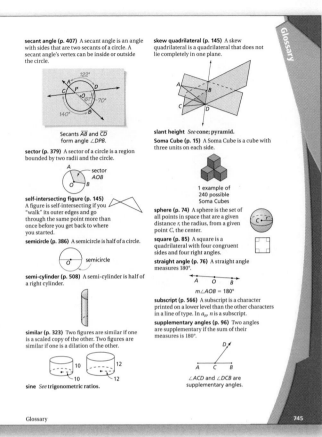

Secants $\overline{AB}$ and $\overline{CD}$ form angle ∠*DPB*.

sector (p. 379) A sector of a circle is a region bounded by two radii and the circle.

sector *AOB*

self-intersecting figure (p. 145) A figure is self-intersecting if you "walk" its outer edges and go through the same point more than once before you get back to where you started.

semicircle (p. 386) A semicircle is half of a circle.

semicircle

semi-cylinder (p. 508) A semi-cylinder is half of a right cylinder.

similar (p. 323) Two figures are similar if one is a scaled copy of the other. Two figures are similar if one is a dilation of the other.

sine *See* trigonometric ratios.

skew quadrilateral (p. 145) A skew quadrilateral is a quadrilateral that does not lie completely in one plane.

slant height *See* cone; pyramid.

Soma Cube (p. 15) A Soma Cube is a cube with three units on each side.

1 example of 240 possible Soma Cubes

sphere (p. 74) A sphere is the set of all points in space that are a given distance *r*, the radius, from a given point *C*, the center.

square (p. 85) A square is a quadrilateral with four congruent sides and four right angles.

straight angle (p. 76) A straight angle measures 180°.

m∠*AOB* = 180°

subscript (p. 566) A subscript is a character printed on a lower level than the other characters in a line of type. In a_n, *n* is a subscript.

supplementary angles (p. 96) Two angles are supplementary if the sum of their measures is 180°.

∠*ACD* and ∠*DCB* are supplementary angles.

745

---

surface area (p. 233) The surface area of a polyhedron is the sum of the areas of all the faces of the polyhedron.

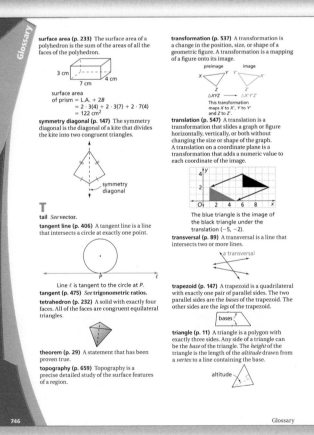

surface area of prism = L.A. + 2*B*
= 2 · 3(4) + 2 · 3(7) + 2 · 7(4)
= 122 cm²

symmetry diagonal (p. 147) The symmetry diagonal is the diagonal of a kite that divides the kite into two congruent triangles.

symmetry diagonal

T

tail *See* vector.

tangent line (p. 406) A tangent line is a line that intersects a circle at exactly one point.

Line ℓ is tangent to the circle at *P*.

tangent (p. 475) *See* trigonometric ratios.

tetrahedron (p. 232) A solid with exactly four faces. All of the faces are congruent equilateral triangles.

theorem (p. 29) A statement that has been proven true.

topography (p. 659) Topography is a precise detailed study of the surface features of a region.

transformation (p. 537) A transformation is a change in the position, size, or shape of a geometric figure. A transformation is a mapping of a figure onto its image.

This transformation maps *X* to *X'*, *Y* to *Y'* and *Z* to *Z'*.

translation (p. 547) A translation is a transformation that slides a graph or figure horizontally, vertically, or both without changing the size or shape of the graph. A translation on a coordinate plane is a transformation that adds a numeric value to each coordinate of the image.

The blue triangle is the image of the black triangle under the translation (−5, −2).

transversal (p. 89) A transversal is a line that intersects two or more lines.

a transversal

trapezoid (p. 147) A trapezoid is a quadrilateral with exactly one pair of parallel sides. The two parallel sides are the *bases* of the trapezoid. The other sides are the *legs* of the trapezoid.

bases

triangle (p. 11) A triangle is a polygon with exactly three sides. Any side of a triangle can be the *base* of the triangle. The *height* of the triangle is the length of the *altitude* drawn from a *vertex* to a line containing the base.

altitude

746

---

trigonometric ratios (p. 475) Trigonometric ratios are special ratios that compare the lengths of sides of right triangles. They are used to find missing side lengths and angle measures.

cosine　In a right triangle, cosine is the ratio of the length of the side adjacent to a given angle and the hypotenuse. Cosine is often abbreviate *cos*.

sine　In a right triangle, sine is the ratio of the length of the side opposite a given angle and the hypotenuse. Sine is often abbreviated *sin*.

tangent　In a right triangle, tangent is the ratio of the length of the side opposite a given angle to the side adjacent the given angle. Tangent is often abbreviated *tan*.

trisection (p. 155) A trisection is a dissection that results in three congruent parts.

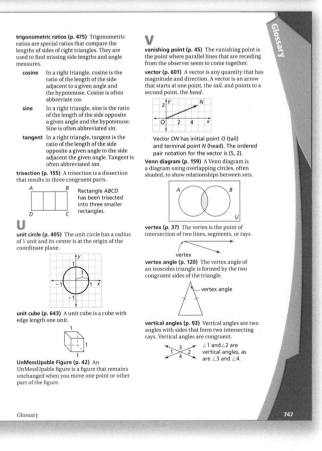

Rectangle *ABCD* has been trisected into three smaller rectangles.

U

unit circle (p. 405) The unit circle has a radius of 1 unit and its center is at the origin of the coordinate plane.

unit cube (p. 643) A unit cube is a cube with edge length one unit.

UnMessUpable Figure (p. 42) An UnMessUpable figure is a figure that remains unchanged when you move one point or other part of the figure.

V

vanishing point (p. 45) The vanishing point is the point where parallel lines that are receding from the observer seem to come together.

vector (p. 601) A vector is any quantity that has magnitude and direction. A vector is an arrow that starts at one point, the *tail*, and points to a second point, the *head*.

Vector *ON* has initial point *O* (tail) and terminal point *N* (head). The ordered pair notation for the vector is (5, 2).

Venn diagram (p. 159) A Venn diagram is a diagram using overlapping circles, often shaded, to show relationships between sets.

vertex (p. 37) The vertex is the point of intersection of two lines, segments, or rays.

vertex

vertex angle (p. 120) The vertex angle of an isosceles triangle is formed by the two congruent sides of the triangle.

vertex angle

vertical angles (p. 93) Vertical angles are two angles with sides that form two intersecting rays. Vertical angles are congruent.

∠1 and∠2 are vertical angles, as are ∠3 and ∠4.

747

volume (p. 247) Volume is a measure of the space a figure occupies.

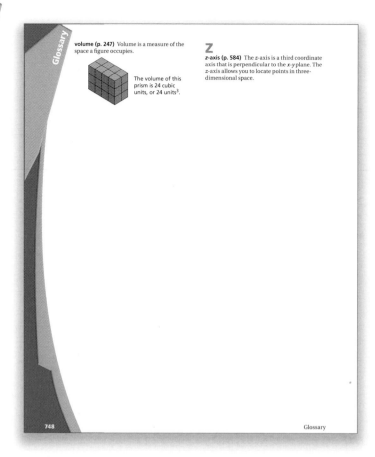

The volume of this prism is 24 cubic units, or 24 units^3.

Z

z-axis (p. 584) The z-axis is a third coordinate axis that is perpendicular to the x-y plane. The z-axis allows you to locate points in three-dimensional space.

Chapter 1
Lesson 1.1
5. Shapes 1, 2, and 8 can cast square shadows if the beams of light are parallel. Shapes 6 and 7 can cast square shadows if the beams of light are from a nearby point source. 7. The triangle and its shadow have the same shape, but the shadow is bigger.

9.

11.

Lesson 1.2
1. Answers may vary. Sample: Since the two bases are the same distance apart at all points, the connecting lines appear to be the same length. Since the points on the second base are translated in the same direction from the corresponding points on the first base, the connecting segments take on the same slope. This makes them appear parallel. 3. Answers may vary. Sample: The darkest regions sometimes appear to be upper parts of a three-dimensional figure. Then they suddenly switch to be right-hand parts of a different figure. 7. 15; 26 9. The figure on the left is a square whose top side and left side have both been divided into segments of lengths a and b. This allows you to divide the large rectangle into an a-by-a square, two a-by-b rectangles, and a b-by-b square. The area of the largest square is $(a + b)^2$. The areas of the four parts are a^2, ab, ab, and b^2. The area of the largest square is equal to the sum of the areas of the parts, so $(a + b)^2 = a^2 + 2ab + b^2$. The figure on the right is a rectangle divided into four smaller rectangles. The area of the largest rectangle is $(a + b)(c + d)$. This is equal to the sum of the areas of the parts. So $(a + b)(c + d) = ac + ad + bc + bd$.

11.

Lesson 1.3
1a. a rectangle b. north c. The assumption is that the right turn is a 90° right turn. This is reasonable because 90° turns are common in everyday experience.

5a.

b. Yes; the figure must be a square, though the size of the square can vary.

7.

9.   11.
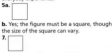

13. D
Lesson 1.4
1.

3. S 9a. square b. a right angle 11. Answers may vary. Sample: Draw an equilateral triangle. Mark the midpoints of the sides of the triangle. Connect the midpoints with segments.
13. Answers may vary. Sample: Start with the figure you obtained in Exercise 12. That figure contains three groups of triangles similar to the group of triangles for Exercise 12. Repeat the procedure used for Exercise 12 on each of these groups of small triangles.

Mathematical Reflections 1A
1. Answers may vary. Sample: A circle or an ellipse can cast a circular shadow. A square cannot cast a circular shadow. Its edges are straight, but a circle is curved. 3. 4; 2; only if the rectangle is a square 5. Answers may vary. Sample: Draw a 1-in. vertical segment. From the top endpoint of the segment, draw a 1-in. horizontal segment that extends to the right. Starting at the right and moving clockwise, draw a semicircle with radius 1 in. that starts at the bottom endpoint of the vertical segment.

Lesson 1.5
9. Comparing the results from Problem 6 shows that equal angles yield triangles that have the same shape, though they may be different sizes. Comparing results from Problem 2 shows that equal side lengths yield triangles that are both the same shape and same size.

Lesson 1.6
1a. Mark two points, A and B, on the given line. Construct the perpendicular bisector of $\overline{AB}$. b. Use the procedure from part (a) to construct a line perpendicular to the perpendicular bisector from part (a). 3a. Fold the square to make the left side match the right side. Fold the resulting rectangle so that the top side matches the bottom side. b. Open the folded sheet from part (a). Fold the corners of the large square inward to meet at the point of intersection of the crease lines. The new crease lines form a square with half the area of the large square. 5a. Answers may vary. Sample: Construct a circle

c. Answers may vary. Sample: pass to the length of the segment. Use that radius and construct the two circles that have centers at the endpoints of the segment. Select a point where the circles intersect and draw segments from that point to the endpoints of the segment. d. Answers may vary. Sample: Construct perpendicular lines through the endpoints of the given segment. Construct a circle having one of the endpoints as its center and passing through the other endpoint. Construct a line parallel to the original segment through one of the points of intersection of the circle and the line perpendicular to the original segment. 7a–c. Midpoints (the key to the constructions in parts (a) and (b) in the exercise) and angle bisectors have been constructed in earlier exercises. d. Answers may vary. Sample: Let the triangle be $\triangle ABC$. Construct a circle with center A that passes through B. If $\overline{BC}$ intersects the circle at another point, call this point D. If it does not, extend $\overline{BC}$ until it intersects the circle at D. Construct the midpoint of $\overline{BD}$ and call it E. The segment $\overline{AE}$ is an altitude of $\triangle ABC$. Construct the other two altitudes in a similar way. 9. Answers may vary. Sample: Construct the perpendicular bisectors of two sides of the equilateral $\triangle ABC$. The perpendicular bisectors intersect at a point X. Construct the circle that has center X and radius XA. 11. Answers may vary. Sample: Construct a circle. Draw a line through the center of the circle. Call the points of intersection A and B. Construct a circle with center A and radius AB. 13a. acute triangles b. right triangles c. obtuse triangles 15b. Construct the perpendicular bisectors of two of the sides of the triangle that has the bases of the saplings as vertices. Place the sprinkler at the point of intersection of the perpendicular bisectors.

Chapter 1
Lesson 1.1
5. Shapes 1, 2, and 8 can cast square shadows

Lesson 1.2
1. Answers may vary. Sample: Since the two bases are the same distance apart at all points, the connecting lines appear to be the same length. Since the points on the second base are translated in the same direction from the corresponding points on the first base, the connecting segments take on the same slope. This makes them appear parallel. 3. Answers may vary. Sample: The darkest regions sometimes appear to be upper parts of a three-dimensional figure. Then they suddenly switch to be right-hand parts of a different figure. 7. 15; 26 9. The figure on the left is a square whose top side and left side have both been divided into segments of lengths a and b. This allows you to divide the large rectangle into

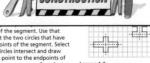

Page 752

Lesson 1.5

9. Comparing the results from Problem 6 shows that equal angles yield triangles that have the same shape, though they may be different sizes. Comparing results from Problem 2 shows that equal side lengths yield triangles that are both the same shape and same size.

Lesson 1.6

1a. Mark two points, *A* and *B*, on the given line. Construct the perpendicular bisector of $\overline{AB}$. **b.** Use the procedure from part (a) to construct a line perpendicular to the perpendicular bisector from part (a). **3a.** Fold the square to make the left side match the right side. Fold the resulting rectangle so that the top side matches the bottom side. **b.** Open the folded sheet from part (a). Fold the corners of the large square inward to meet at the point of intersection of the crease lines. The new crease lines form a square with half the area of the large square. **5a.** Answers may vary. Sample: Construct a circle ⎯ of the segment an⎯ radius. Draw anot⎯ the first. Draw the⎯ endpoints on the ⎯ Sample: Fold the s⎯ on the crease line⎯ original segment),⎯ that point to the e⎯ **c.** Answers may va⎯ pass to the length ⎯ radius and constru⎯ centers at the endpoints of the segment. Select a point where the circles intersect and draw segments from that point to the endpoints of the segment. **d.** Answers may vary. Sample: Construct perpendicular lines through the endpoints of the given segment. Construct a circle having one of the endpoints as its center and passing through the other endpoint. Construct a line parallel to the original segment through one of the points of intersection of the circle and the line perpendicular to the original segment. **7a–c.** Midpoints (the key to the constructions in parts (a) and (b) in the exercise) and angle bisectors have been constructed in earlier exercises. **d.** Answers may vary. Sample: Let the triangle be △*ABC*. Construct a circle with center *A* that passes through *B*. If $\overline{BC}$ intersects the circle at another point, call this point *D*. If it does not, extend $\overline{BC}$ until it intersects the circle at *D*. Construct the midpoint of

$\overline{BD}$ and call it *E*. The segment $\overline{AE}$ is an altitude of △*ABC*. Construct the other two altitudes in a similar way. **9.** Answers may vary. Sample: Construct the perpendicular bisectors of two sides of the equilateral △*ABC*. The perpendicular bisectors intersect at a point *X*. Construct the circle that has center *X* and radius *XA*. **11.** Answers may vary. Sample: Construct a circle. Draw a line through the center of the circle. Call the points of intersection *A* and *B*. Construct a circle with center *A* and radius *AB*. **13a.** acute triangles **b.** right triangles **c.** obtuse triangles **15b.** Construct the perpendicular bisectors of two of the sides of the triangle that has the bases of the saplings as vertices. Place the sprinkler at the point of intersection of the perpendicular bisectors.

Chapter 1

Lesson 1.1

5. Shapes 1, 2, and 8 can cast square shadows ⎯llel. Shapes 6 and ⎯the beams of light ⎯ce. **7.** The triangle ⎯e shape, but the

Lesson 1.2

1. Answers may vary. Sample: Since the two bases are the same distance apart at all points, the connecting lines appear to be the same length. Since the points on the second base are translated in the same direction from the corresponding points on the first base, the connecting segments take on the same slope. This makes them appear parallel. **3.** Answers may vary. Sample: The darkest regions sometimes appear to be upper parts of a three-dimensional figure. Then they suddenly switch to be right-hand parts of a different figure. **7.** 15; 26 **9.** The figure on the left is a square whose top side and left side have both been divided into segments of lengths *a* and *b*. This allows you to divide the large rectangle into

Page 753

an *a*-by-*a* square, two *a*-by-*b* rectangles, and a *b*-by-*b* square.

Lesson 1.5

9. Comparing the results from Problem 6 shows that equal angles yield triangles that have the same shape, though they may be different sizes. Comparing results from Problem 2 shows that equal side lengths yield triangles that are both the same shape and same size.

Lesson 1.6

1a. Mark two points, *A* and *B*, on the given line. Construct the perpendicular bisector of $\overline{AB}$. **b.** Use the procedure from part (a) to construct a line perpendicular to the perpendicular bisector from part (a). **3a.** Fold the square to make the left side match the right side. Fold the resulting rectangle so that the top side matches the bottom side. **b.** Open the folded sheet from part (a). Fold the corners of the large square inward to meet at the point of intersection of the crease lines. The new crease lines form a square ⎯ large square. **5a.** A⎯ Construct a circle ⎯ of the segment an⎯ radius. Draw anot⎯ the first. Draw the⎯ endpoints on the ⎯ Sample: Fold the s⎯ on the crease line⎯ original segment),⎯ that point to the e⎯ **c.** Answers may va⎯ pass to the length of the segment. Use that radius and construct the two circles that have centers at the endpoints of the segment. Select a point where the circles intersect and draw segments from that point to the endpoints of the segment. **d.** Answers may vary. Sample: Construct perpendicular lines through the endpoints of the given segment. Construct a circle having one of the endpoints as its center and passing through the other endpoint. Construct a line parallel to the original segment through one of the points of intersection of the circle and the line perpendicular to the original segment. **7a–c.** Midpoints (the key to the constructions in parts (a) and (b) in the exercise) and angle bisectors have been constructed in earlier exercises. **d.** Answers may vary. Sample: Let the triangle be △*ABC*. Construct a circle with center *A* that passes through *B*. If $\overline{BC}$ intersects the circle at another point, call this point *D*. If it does not, extend $\overline{BC}$ until it intersects the circle at *D*. Construct the midpoint of

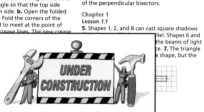

$\overline{BD}$ and call it *E*. The segment $\overline{AE}$ is an altitude of △*ABC*. Construct the other two altitudes in a similar way. **9.** Answers may vary. Sample: Construct the perpendicular bisectors of two sides of the equilateral △*ABC*. The perpendicular bisectors intersect at a point *X*. Construct the circle that has center *X* and radius *XA*. **11.** Answers may vary. Sample: Construct a circle. Draw a line through the center of the circle. Call the points of intersection *A* and *B*. Construct a circle with center *A* and radius *AB*. **13a.** acute triangles **b.** right triangles **c.** obtuse triangles **15b.** Construct the perpendicular bisectors of two of the sides of the triangle that has the bases of the saplings as vertices. Place the sprinkler at the point of intersection of the perpendicular bisectors.

Chapter 1

Lesson 1.1

5. Shapes 1, 2, and 8 can cast square shadows ⎯llel. Shapes 6 and ⎯the beams of light ⎯ce. **7.** The triangle ⎯e shape, but the

Lesson 1.2

1. Answers may vary. Sample: Since the two bases are the same distance apart at all points, the connecting lines appear to be the same length. Since the points on the second base are translated in the same direction from the corresponding points on the first base, the connecting segments take on the same slope. This makes them appear parallel. **3.** Answers may vary. Sample: The darkest regions sometimes appear to be upper parts of a three-dimensional figure. Then they suddenly switch to be right-hand parts of a different figure. **7.** 15; 26 **9.** The figure on the left is a square whose top side and left side have both been divided into segments of lengths *a* and *b*. This allows you to divide the large rectangle into an *a*-by-*a* square, two *a*-by-*b* rectangles, and a *b*-by-*b* square.

Page 754

Lesson 1.5

9. Comparing the results from Problem 6 shows that equal angles yield triangles that have the same shape, though they may be different sizes. Comparing results from Problem 2 shows that equal side lengths yield triangles that are both the same shape and same size.

Lesson 1.6

1a. Mark two points, *A* and *B*, on the given line. Construct the perpendicular bisector of $\overline{AB}$. **b.** Use the procedure from part (a) to construct a line perpendicular to the perpendicular bisector from part (a). **3a.** Fold the square to make the left side match the right side. Fold the resulting rectangle so that the top side matches the bottom side. **b.** Open the folded sheet from part (a). Fold the corners of the large square inward to meet at the point of intersection of the crease lines. The new crease lines form a square with half the area of the large square. **5a.** Answers may vary. Sample: Construct a circle ⎯ of the segment an⎯ radius. Draw anot⎯ the first. Draw the⎯ endpoints on the ⎯ Sample: Fold the s⎯ on the crease line⎯ original segment),⎯ that point to the e⎯ **c.** Answers may va⎯ pass to the length ⎯ radius and constru⎯ centers at the endpoints of the segment. Select a point where the circles intersect and draw segments from that point to the endpoints of the segment. **d.** Answers may vary. Sample: Construct perpendicular lines through the endpoints of the given segment. Construct a circle having one of the endpoints as its center and passing through the other endpoint. Construct a line parallel to the original segment through one of the points of intersection of the circle and the line perpendicular to the original segment. **7a–c.** Midpoints (the key to the constructions in parts (a) and (b) in the exercise) and angle bisectors have been constructed in earlier exercises. **d.** Answers may vary. Sample: Let the triangle be △*ABC*. Construct a circle with center *A* that passes through *B*. If $\overline{BC}$ intersects the circle at another point, call this point *D*. If it does not, extend $\overline{BC}$ until it intersects the circle at *D*. Construct the midpoint of

$\overline{BD}$ and call it *E*. The segment $\overline{AE}$ is an altitude of △*ABC*. Construct the other two altitudes in a similar way. **9.** Answers may vary. Sample: Construct the perpendicular bisectors of two sides of the equilateral △*ABC*. The perpendicular bisectors intersect at a point *X*. Construct the circle that has center *X* and radius *XA*. **11.** Answers may vary. Sample: Construct a circle. Draw a line through the center of the circle. Call the points of intersection *A* and *B*. Construct a circle with center *A* and radius *AB*. **13a.** acute triangles **b.** right triangles **c.** obtuse triangles **15b.** Construct the perpendicular bisectors of two of the sides of the triangle that has the bases of the saplings as vertices. Place the sprinkler at the point of intersection of the perpendicular bisectors.

Chapter 1

Lesson 1.1

5. Shapes 1, 2, and 8 can cast square shadows ⎯llel. Shapes 6 and ⎯the beams of light ⎯ce. **7.** The triangle ⎯e shape, but the

Lesson 1.2

1. Answers may vary. Sample: Since the two bases are the same distance apart at all points, the connecting lines appear to be the same length. Since the points on the second base are translated in the same direction from the corresponding points on the first base, the connecting segments take on the same slope. This makes them appear parallel. **3.** Answers may vary. Sample: The darkest regions sometimes appear to be upper parts of a three-dimensional figure. Then they suddenly switch to be right-hand parts of a different figure. **7.** 15; 26 **9.** The figure on the left is a square whose top side and left side have both been divided into segments of lengths *a* and *b*. This allows you to divide the large rectangle into

754   Selected Answers

Page 755

an *a*-by-*a* square, two *a*-by-*b* rectangles, and a *b*-by-*b* square.

Lesson 1.5

9. Comparing the results from Problem 6 shows that equal angles yield triangles that have the same shape, though they may be different sizes. Comparing results from Problem 2 shows that equal side lengths yield triangles that are both the same shape and same size.

Lesson 1.6

1a. Mark two points, *A* and *B*, on the given line. Construct the perpendicular bisector of $\overline{AB}$. **b.** Use the procedure from part (a) to construct a line perpendicular to the perpendicular bisector from part (a). **3a.** Fold the square to make the left side match the right side. Fold the resulting rectangle so that the top side matches the bottom side. **b.** Open the folded sheet from part (a). Fold the corners of the large square inward to meet at the point of intersection of the crease lines. The new crease lines form a square ⎯ large square. **5a.** A⎯ Construct a circle ⎯ of the segment an⎯ radius. Draw anot⎯ the first. Draw the⎯ endpoints on the ⎯ Sample: Fold the s⎯ on the crease line⎯ original segment),⎯ that point to the e⎯ **c.** Answers may va⎯ pass to the length of the segment. Use that radius and construct the two circles that have centers at the endpoints of the segment. Select a point where the circles intersect and draw segments from that point to the endpoints of the segment. **d.** Answers may vary. Sample: Construct perpendicular lines through the endpoints of the given segment. Construct a circle having one of the endpoints as its center and passing through the other endpoint. Construct a line parallel to the original segment through one of the points of intersection of the circle and the line perpendicular to the original segment. **7a–c.** Midpoints (the key to the constructions in parts (a) and (b) in the exercise) and angle bisectors have been constructed in earlier exercises. **d.** Answers may vary. Sample: Let the triangle be △*ABC*. Construct a circle with center *A* that passes through *B*. If $\overline{BC}$ intersects the circle at another point, call this point *D*. If it does not, extend $\overline{BC}$ until it intersects the circle at *D*. Construct the midpoint of

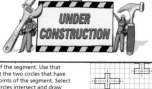

$\overline{BD}$ and call it *E*. The segment $\overline{AE}$ is an altitude of △*ABC*. Construct the other two altitudes in a similar way. **9.** Answers may vary. Sample: Construct the perpendicular bisectors of two sides of the equilateral △*ABC*. The perpendicular bisectors intersect at a point *X*. Construct the circle that has center *X* and radius *XA*. **11.** Answers may vary. Sample: Construct a circle. Draw a line through the center of the circle. Call the points of intersection *A* and *B*. Construct a circle with center *A* and radius *AB*. **13a.** acute triangles **b.** right triangles **c.** obtuse triangles **15b.** Construct the perpendicular bisectors of two of the sides of the triangle that has the bases of the saplings as vertices. Place the sprinkler at the point of intersection of the perpendicular bisectors.

Chapter 1

Lesson 1.1

5. Shapes 1, 2, and 8 can cast square shadows ⎯llel. Shapes 6 and ⎯the beams of light ⎯ce. **7.** The triangle ⎯e shape, but the

Lesson 1.2

1. Answers may vary. Sample: Since the two bases are the same distance apart at all points, the connecting lines appear to be the same length. Since the points on the second base are translated in the same direction from the corresponding points on the first base, the connecting segments take on the same slope. This makes them appear parallel. **3.** Answers may vary. Sample: The darkest regions sometimes appear to be upper parts of a three-dimensional figure. Then they suddenly switch to be right-hand parts of a different figure. **7.** 15; 26 **9.** The figure on the left is a square whose top side and left side have both been divided into segments of lengths *a* and *b*. This allows you to divide the large rectangle into an *a*-by-*a* square, two *a*-by-*b* rectangles, and a *b*-by-*b* square.

Selected Answers   755

Lesson 1.5

9. Comparing the results from Problem 6 shows that equal angles yield triangles that have the same shape, though they may be different sizes. Comparing results from Problem 2 shows that equal side lengths yield triangles that are both the same shape and same size.

Lesson 1.6

1a. Mark two points, *A* and *B*, on the given line. Construct the perpendicular bisector of $\overline{AB}$. **b.** Use the procedure from part (a) to construct a line perpendicular to the perpendicular bisector from part (a). **3a.** Fold the square to make the left side match the right side. Fold the resulting rectangle so that the top side matches the bottom side. **b.** Open the folded sheet from part (a). Fold the corners of the large square inward to meet at the point of intersection of the crease lines. The new crease lines form a square with half the area of the large square. **5a.** Answers may vary. Sample: Construct a circle

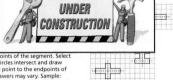

of the segment an[...] radius. Draw anot[...] the first. Draw the[...] endpoints on the [...] Sample: Fold the s[...] on the crease line[...] original segment),[...] that point to the e[...] **c.** Answers may va[...] pass to the length of the segment. Use that radius and construct the two circles that have centers at the endpoints of the segment. Select a point where the circles intersect and draw segments from that point to the endpoints of the segment. **d.** Answers may vary. Sample: Construct perpendicular lines through the endpoints of the given segment. Construct a circle having one of the endpoints as its center and passing through the other endpoint. Construct a line parallel to the original segment through one of the points of intersection of the circle and the line perpendicular to the original segment. **7a–c.** Midpoints (the key to the constructions in parts (a) and (b) in the exercise) and angle bisectors have been constructed in earlier exercises. **d.** Answers may vary. Sample: Let the triangle be △*ABC*. Construct a circle with center *A* that passes through *B*. If $\overline{BC}$ intersects the circle at another point, call this point *D*. If it does not, extend $\overline{BC}$ until it intersects the circle at *D*. Construct the midpoint of

$\overline{BD}$ and call it *E*. The segment $\overline{AE}$ is an altitude of △*ABC*. Construct the other two altitudes in a similar way. **9.** Answers may vary. Sample: Construct the perpendicular bisectors of two sides of the equilateral △*ABC*. The perpendicular bisectors intersect at a point *X*. Construct the circle that has center *X* and radius *XA*. **11.** Answers may vary. Sample: Construct a circle. Draw a line through the center of the circle. Call the points of intersection *A* and *B*. Construct a circle with center *A* and radius *AB*. **13a.** acute triangles **b.** right triangles **c.** obtuse triangles **15b.** Construct the perpendicular bisectors of two of the sides of the triangle that has the bases of the saplings as vertices. Place the sprinkler at the point of intersection of the perpendicular bisectors.

Chapter 1

Lesson 1.1

5. Shapes 1, 2, and 8 can cast square shadows [...]llel. Shapes 6 and [...]the beams of light [...]e. **7.** The triangle [...]e shape, but the

Lesson 1.2

1. Answers may vary. Sample: Since the two bases are the same distance apart at all points, the connecting lines appear to be the same length. Since the points on the second base are translated in the same direction from the corresponding points on the first base, the connecting segments take on the same slope. This makes them appear parallel. **3.** Answers may vary. Sample: The darkest regions sometimes appear to be upper parts of a three-dimensional figure. Then they suddenly switch to be right-hand parts of a different figure. **7.** 15; 26 **9.** The figure on the left is a square whose top side and left side have both been divided into segments of lengths *a* and *b*. This allows you to divide the large rectangle into

---

an *a*-by-*a* square, two *a*-by-*b* rectangles, and a *b*-by-*b* square.

Lesson 1.5

9. Comparing the results from Problem 6 shows that equal angles yield triangles that have the same shape, though they may be different sizes. Comparing results from Problem 2 shows that equal side lengths yield triangles that are both the same shape and same size.

Lesson 1.6

1a. Mark two points, *A* and *B*, on the given line. Construct the perpendicular bisector of $\overline{AB}$. **b.** Use the procedure from part (a) to construct a line perpendicular to the perpendicular bisector from part (a). **3a.** Fold the square to make the left side match the right side. Fold the resulting rectangle so that the top side matches the bottom side. **b.** Open the folded sheet from part (a). Fold the corners of the large square inward to meet at the point of intersection of the crease lines. The new crease lines form a square

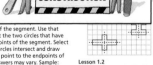

Construct a circle [...] of the segment an[...] radius. Draw anot[...] the first. Draw the[...] endpoints on the [...] Sample: Fold the s[...] on the crease line[...] original segment),[...] that point to the e[...] **c.** Answers may va[...] pass to the length of the segment. Use that radius and construct the two circles that have centers at the endpoints of the segment. Select a point where the circles intersect and draw segments from that point to the endpoints of the segment. **d.** Answers may vary. Sample: Construct perpendicular lines through the endpoints of the given segment. Construct a circle having one of the endpoints as its center and passing through the other endpoint. Construct a line parallel to the original segment through one of the points of intersection of the circle and the line perpendicular to the original segment. **7a–c.** Midpoints (the key to the constructions in parts (a) and (b) in the exercise) and angle bisectors have been constructed in earlier exercises. **d.** Answers may vary. Sample: Let the triangle be △*ABC*. Construct a circle with center *A* that passes through *B*. If $\overline{BC}$ intersects the circle at another point, call this point *D*. If it does not, extend $\overline{BC}$ until it intersects the circle at *D*. Construct the midpoint of

$\overline{BD}$ and call it *E*. The segment $\overline{AE}$ is an altitude of △*ABC*. Construct the other two altitudes in a similar way. **9.** Answers may vary. Sample: Construct the perpendicular bisectors of two sides of the equilateral △*ABC*. The perpendicular bisectors intersect at a point *X*. Construct the circle that has center *X* and radius *XA*. **11.** Answers may vary. Sample: Construct a circle. Draw a line through the center of the circle. Call the points of intersection *A* and *B*. Construct a circle with center *A* and radius *AB*. **13a.** acute triangles **b.** right triangles **c.** obtuse triangles **15b.** Construct the perpendicular bisectors of two of the sides of the triangle that has the bases of the saplings as vertices. Place the sprinkler at the point of intersection of the perpendicular bisectors.

Chapter 1

Lesson 1.1

5. Shapes 1, 2, and 8 can cast square shadows [...]llel. Shapes 6 and [...]the beams of light [...]e. **7.** The triangle [...]e shape, but the

Lesson 1.2

1. Answers may vary. Sample: Since the two bases are the same distance apart at all points, the connecting lines appear to be the same length. Since the points on the second base are translated in the same direction from the corresponding points on the first base, the connecting segments take on the same slope. This makes them appear parallel. **3.** Answers may vary. Sample: The darkest regions sometimes appear to be upper parts of a three-dimensional figure. Then they suddenly switch to be right-hand parts of a different figure. **7.** 15; 26 **9.** The figure on the left is a square whose top side and left side have both been divided into segments of lengths *a* and *b*. This allows you to divide the large rectangle into an *a*-by-*a* square, two *a*-by-*b* rectangles, and a *b*-by-*b* square.

Lesson 1.5

9. Comparing the results from Problem 6 shows that equal angles yield triangles that have the same shape, though they may be different sizes. Comparing results from Problem 2 shows that equal side lengths yield triangles that are both the same shape and same size.

Lesson 1.6

1a. Mark two points, *A* and *B*, on the given line. Construct the perpendicular bisector of $\overline{AB}$. **b.** Use the procedure from part (a) to construct a line perpendicular to the perpendicular bisector from part (a). **3a.** Fold the square to make the left side match the right side. Fold the resulting rectangle so that the top side matches the bottom side. **b.** Open the folded sheet from part (a). Fold the corners of the large square inward to meet at the point of intersection of the crease lines. The new crease lines form a square with half the area of the large square. **5a.** Answers may vary. Sample: Construct a circle

of the segment an[...] radius. Draw anot[...] the first. Draw the[...] endpoints on the [...] Sample: Fold the s[...] on the crease line[...] original segment),[...] that point to the e[...] **c.** Answers may va[...] pass to the length of the segment. Use that radius and construct the two circles that have centers at the endpoints of the segment. Select a point where the circles intersect and draw segments from that point to the endpoints of the segment. **d.** Answers may vary. Sample: Construct perpendicular lines through the endpoints of the given segment. Construct a circle having one of the endpoints as its center and passing through the other endpoint. Construct a line parallel to the original segment through one of the points of intersection of the circle and the line perpendicular to the original segment. **7a–c.** Midpoints (the key to the constructions in parts (a) and (b) in the exercise) and angle bisectors have been constructed in earlier exercises. **d.** Answers may vary. Sample: Let the triangle be △*ABC*. Construct a circle with center *A* that passes through *B*. If $\overline{BC}$ intersects the circle at another point, call this point *D*. If it does not, extend $\overline{BC}$ until it intersects the circle at *D*. Construct the midpoint of

$\overline{BD}$ and call it *E*. The segment $\overline{AE}$ is an altitude of △*ABC*. Construct the other two altitudes in a similar way. **9.** Answers may vary. Sample: Construct the perpendicular bisectors of two sides of the equilateral △*ABC*. The perpendicular bisectors intersect at a point *X*. Construct the circle that has center *X* and radius *XA*. **11.** Answers may vary. Sample: Construct a circle. Draw a line through the center of the circle. Call the points of intersection *A* and *B*. Construct a circle with center *A* and radius *AB*. **13a.** acute triangles **b.** right triangles **c.** obtuse triangles **15b.** Construct the perpendicular bisectors of two of the sides of the triangle that has the bases of the saplings as vertices. Place the sprinkler at the point of intersection of the perpendicular bisectors.

Chapter 1

Lesson 1.1

5. Shapes 1, 2, and 8 can cast square shadows [...]llel. Shapes 6 and [...]the beams of light [...]e. **7.** The triangle [...]e shape, but the

Lesson 1.2

1. Answers may vary. Sample: Since the two bases are the same distance apart at all points, the connecting lines appear to be the same length. Since the points on the second base are translated in the same direction from the corresponding points on the first base, the connecting segments take on the same slope. This makes them appear parallel. **3.** Answers may vary. Sample: The darkest regions sometimes appear to be upper parts of a three-dimensional figure. Then they suddenly switch to be right-hand parts of a different figure. **7.** 15; 26 **9.** The figure on the left is a square whose top side and left side have both been divided into segments of lengths *a* and *b*. This allows you to divide the large rectangle into

758 Selected Answers

---

an *a*-by-*a* square, two *a*-by-*b* square.

Lesson 1.5

9. Comparing the results from Problem 6 shows that equal angles yield triangles that have the same shape, though they may be different sizes. Comparing results from Problem 2 shows that equal side lengths yield triangles that are both the same shape and same size.

Lesson 1.6

1a. Mark two points, *A* and *B*, on the given line. Construct the perpendicular bisector of $\overline{AB}$. **b.** Use the procedure from part (a) to construct a line perpendicular to the perpendicular bisector from part (a). **3a.** Fold the square to make the left side match the right side. Fold the resulting rectangle so that the top side matches the bottom side. **b.** Open the folded sheet from part (a). Fold the corners of the large square inward to meet at the point of intersection of the crease lines. The new crease lines form a square

$\overline{BD}$ and call it *E*. The segment $\overline{AE}$ is an altitude of △*ABC*. Construct the other two altitudes in a similar way. **9.** Answers may vary. Sample: Construct the perpendicular bisectors of two sides of the equilateral △*ABC*. The perpendicular bisectors intersect at a point *X*. Construct the circle that has center *X* and radius *XA*. **11.** Answers may vary. Sample: Construct a circle. Draw a line through the center of the circle. Call the points of intersection *A* and *B*. Construct a circle with center *A* and radius *AB*. **13a.** acute triangles **b.** right triangles **c.** obtuse triangles **15b.** Construct the perpendicular bisectors of two of the sides of the triangle that has the bases of the saplings as vertices. Place the sprinkler at the point of intersection of the perpendicular bisectors.

Chapter 1

Lesson 1.1

5. Shapes 1, 2, and 8 can cast square shadows

Lesson 1.2

1. Answers may vary. Sample: Since the two bases are the same distance apart at all points, the connecting lines appear to be the same length. Since the points on the second base are translated in the same direction from the corresponding points on the first base, the connecting segments take on the same slope. This makes them appear parallel. **3.** Answers may vary. Sample: The darkest regions sometimes appear to be upper parts of a three-dimensional figure. Then they suddenly switch to be right-hand parts of a different figure. **7.** 15; 26 **9.** The figure on the left is a square whose top side and left side have both been divided into segments of lengths *a* and *b*. This allows you to divide the large rectangle into an *a*-by-*a* square, two *a*-by-*b* rectangles, and a *b*-by-*b* square.

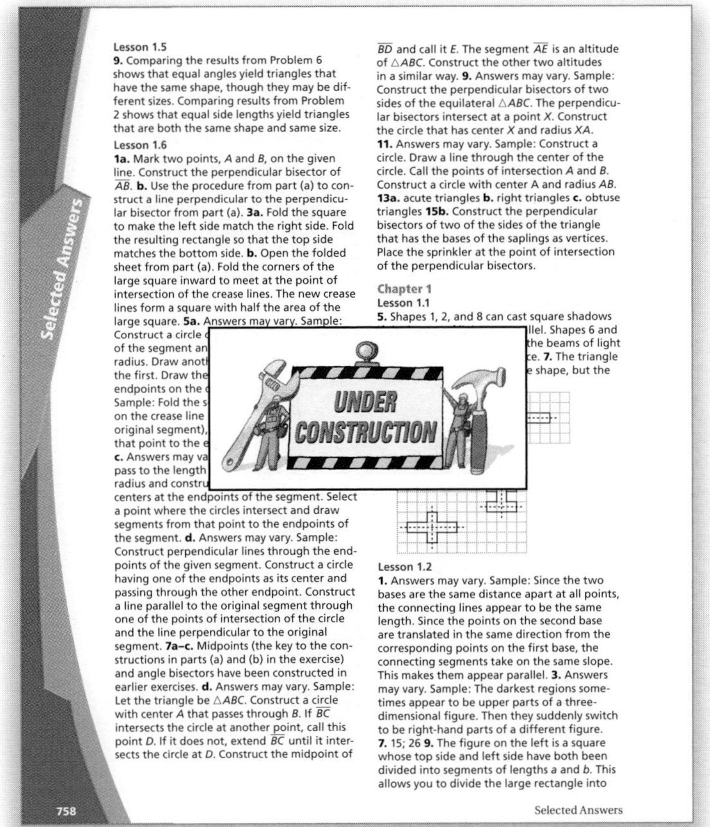

Selected Answers 759

Lesson 1.5
9. Comparing the results from Problem 6 shows that equal angles yield triangles that have the same shape, though they may be different sizes. Comparing results from Problem 2 shows that equal side lengths yield triangles that are both the same shape and same size.

Lesson 1.6
1a. Mark two points, A and B, on the given line. Construct the perpendicular bisector of $\overline{AB}$. **b.** Use the procedure from part (a) to construct a line perpendicular to the perpendicular bisector from part (a). **3a.** Fold the square to make the left side match the right side. Fold the resulting rectangle so that the top side matches the bottom side. **b.** Open the folded sheet from part (a). Fold the corners of the large square inward to meet at the point of intersection of the crease lines. The new crease lines form a square with half the area of the large square. **5a.** Answers may vary. Sample: Construct a circle 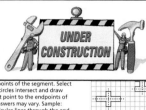 of the segment and radius. Draw anot the first. Draw the endpoints on the Sample: Fold the s on the crease line original segment), that point to the e **c.** Answers may va pass to the length radius and constru centers at the endpoints of the segment. Select a point where the circles intersect and draw segments from that point to the endpoints of the segment. **d.** Answers may vary. Sample: Construct perpendicular lines through the endpoints of the given segment. Construct a circle having one of the endpoints as its center and passing through the other endpoint. Construct a line parallel to the original segment through one of the points of intersection of the circle and the line perpendicular to the original segment. **7a–c.** Midpoints (the key to the constructions in parts (a) and (b) in the exercise) and angle bisectors have been constructed in earlier exercises. **d.** Answers may vary. Sample: Let the triangle be △ABC. Construct a circle with center A that passes through B. If $\overline{BC}$ intersects the circle at another point, call this point D. If it does not, extend $\overline{BC}$ until it intersects the circle at D. Construct the midpoint of

$\overline{BD}$ and call it E. The segment $\overline{AE}$ is an altitude of △ABC. Construct the other two altitudes in a similar way. **9.** Answers may vary. Sample: Construct the perpendicular bisectors of two sides of the equilateral △ABC. The perpendicular bisectors intersect at a point X. Construct the circle that has center X and radius XA. **11.** Answers may vary. Sample: Construct a circle. Draw a line through the center of the circle. Call the points of intersection A and B. Construct a circle with center A and radius AB. **13a.** acute triangles **b.** right triangles **c.** obtuse triangles **15b.** Construct the perpendicular bisectors of two of the sides of the triangle that has the bases of the saplings as vertices. Place the sprinkler at the point of intersection of the perpendicular bisectors.

Chapter 1
Lesson 1.1
5. Shapes 1, 2, and 8 can cast square shadows parallel. Shapes 6 and the beams of light ce. **7.** The triangle shape, but the

Lesson 1.2
1. Answers may vary. Sample: Since the two bases are the same distance apart at all points, the connecting lines appear to be the same length. Since the points on the second base are translated in the same direction from the corresponding points on the first base, the connecting segments take on the same slope. This makes them appear parallel. **3.** Answers may vary. Sample: The darkest regions sometimes appear to be upper parts of a three-dimensional figure. Then they suddenly switch to be right-hand parts of a different figure. **7.** 15; 26 **9.** The figure on the left is a square whose top side and left side have both been divided into segments of lengths a and b. This allows you to divide the large rectangle into

an a-by-a square, two a-by-b rectangles, and a b-by-b square.

Lesson 1.5
9. Comparing the results from Problem 6 shows that equal angles yield triangles that have the same shape, though they may be different sizes. Comparing results from Problem 2 shows that equal side lengths yield triangles that are both the same shape and same size.

Lesson 1.6
1a. Mark two points, A and B, on the given line. Construct the perpendicular bisector of $\overline{AB}$. **b.** Use the procedure from part (a) to construct a line perpendicular to the perpendicular bisector from part (a). **3a.** Fold the square to make the left side match the right side. Fold the resulting rectangle so that the top side matches the bottom side. **b.** Open the folded sheet from part (a). Fold the corners of the large square inward to meet at the point of intersection of the crease lines. The new crease lines form a square  large square. **5a.** A Construct a circle of the segment an radius. Draw anot the first. Draw the endpoints on the Sample: Fold the s on the crease line original segment), that point to the e **c.** Answers may va pass to the length of the segment. Use that radius and construct the two circles that have centers at the endpoints of the segment. Select a point where the circles intersect and draw segments from that point to the endpoints of the segment. **d.** Answers may vary. Sample: Construct perpendicular lines through the endpoints of the given segment. Construct a circle having one of the endpoints as its center and passing through the other endpoint. Construct a line parallel to the original segment through one of the points of intersection of the circle and the line perpendicular to the original segment. **7a–c.** Midpoints (the key to the constructions in parts (a) and (b) in the exercise) and angle bisectors have been constructed in earlier exercises. **d.** Answers may vary. Sample: Let the triangle be △ABC. Construct a circle with center A that passes through B. If $\overline{BC}$ intersects the circle at another point, call this point D. If it does not, extend $\overline{BC}$ until it intersects the circle at D. Construct the midpoint of

$\overline{BD}$ and call it E. The segment $\overline{AE}$ is an altitude of △ABC. Construct the other two altitudes in a similar way. **9.** Answers may vary. Sample: Construct the perpendicular bisectors of two sides of the equilateral △ABC. The perpendicular bisectors intersect at a point X. Construct the circle that has center X and radius XA. **11.** Answers may vary. Sample: Construct a circle. Draw a line through the center of the circle. Call the points of intersection A and B. Construct a circle with center A and radius AB. **13a.** acute triangles **b.** right triangles **c.** obtuse triangles **15b.** Construct the perpendicular bisectors of two of the sides of the triangle that has the bases of the saplings as vertices. Place the sprinkler at the point of intersection of the perpendicular bisectors.

Chapter 1
Lesson 1.1
5. Shapes 1, 2, and 8 can cast square shadows parallel. Shapes 6 and the beams of light ce. **7.** The triangle shape, but the

Lesson 1.2
1. Answers may vary. Sample: Since the two bases are the same distance apart at all points, the connecting lines appear to be the same length. Since the points on the second base are translated in the same direction from the corresponding points on the first base, the connecting segments take on the same slope. This makes them appear parallel. **3.** Answers may vary. Sample: The darkest regions sometimes appear to be upper parts of a three-dimensional figure. Then they suddenly switch to be right-hand parts of a different figure. **7.** 15; 26 **9.** The figure on the left is a square whose top side and left side have both been divided into segments of lengths a and b. This allows you to divide the large rectangle into an a-by-a square, two a-by-b rectangles, and a b-by-b square.

Lesson 1.5
9. Comparing the results from Problem 6 shows that equal angles yield triangles that have the same shape, though they may be different sizes. Comparing results from Problem 2 shows that equal side lengths yield triangles that are both the same shape and same size.

Lesson 1.6
1a. Mark two points, A and B, on the given line. Construct the perpendicular bisector of $\overline{AB}$. **b.** Use the procedure from part (a) to construct a line perpendicular to the perpendicular bisector from part (a). **3a.** Fold the square to make the left side match the right side. Fold the resulting rectangle so that the top side matches the bottom side. **b.** Open the folded sheet from part (a). Fold the corners of the large square inward to meet at the point of intersection of the crease lines. The new crease lines form a square with half the area of the large square. **5a.** Answers may vary. Sample: Construct a circle  of the segment an radius. Draw anot the first. Draw the endpoints on the Sample: Fold the s on the crease line original segment), that point to the e **c.** Answers may va pass to the length radius and constru centers at the endpoints of the segment. Select a point where the circles intersect and draw segments from that point to the endpoints of the segment. **d.** Answers may vary. Sample: Construct perpendicular lines through the endpoints of the given segment. Construct a circle having one of the endpoints as its center and passing through the other endpoint. Construct a line parallel to the original segment through one of the points of intersection of the circle and the line perpendicular to the original segment. **7a–c.** Midpoints (the key to the constructions in parts (a) and (b) in the exercise) and angle bisectors have been constructed in earlier exercises. **d.** Answers may vary. Sample: Let the triangle be △ABC. Construct a circle with center A that passes through B. If $\overline{BC}$ intersects the circle at another point, call this point D. If it does not, extend $\overline{BC}$ until it intersects the circle at D. Construct the midpoint of

$\overline{BD}$ and call it E. The segment $\overline{AE}$ is an altitude of △ABC. Construct the other two altitudes in a similar way. **9.** Answers may vary. Sample: Construct the perpendicular bisectors of two sides of the equilateral △ABC. The perpendicular bisectors intersect at a point X. Construct the circle that has center X and radius XA. **11.** Answers may vary. Sample: Construct a circle. Draw a line through the center of the circle. Call the points of intersection A and B. Construct a circle with center A and radius AB. **13a.** acute triangles **b.** right triangles **c.** obtuse triangles **15b.** Construct the perpendicular bisectors of two of the sides of the triangle that has the bases of the saplings as vertices. Place the sprinkler at the point of intersection of the perpendicular bisectors.

Chapter 1
Lesson 1.1
5. Shapes 1, 2, and 8 can cast square shadows parallel. Shapes 6 and the beams of light ce. **7.** The triangle shape, but the

Lesson 1.2
1. Answers may vary. Sample: Since the two bases are the same distance apart at all points, the connecting lines appear to be the same length. Since the points on the second base are translated in the same direction from the corresponding points on the first base, the connecting segments take on the same slope. This makes them appear parallel. **3.** Answers may vary. Sample: The darkest regions sometimes appear to be upper parts of a three-dimensional figure. Then they suddenly switch to be right-hand parts of a different figure. **7.** 15; 26 **9.** The figure on the left is a square whose top side and left side have both been divided into segments of lengths a and b. This allows you to divide the large rectangle into

762

an a-by-a square, two a-by-b rectangles, and a b-by-b square.

Lesson 1.5
9. Comparing the results from Problem 6 shows that equal angles yield triangles that have the same shape, though they may be different sizes. Comparing results from Problem 2 shows that equal side lengths yield triangles that are both the same shape and same size.

Lesson 1.6
1a. Mark two points, A and B, on the given line. Construct the perpendicular bisector of $\overline{AB}$. **b.** Use the procedure from part (a) to construct a line perpendicular to the perpendicular bisector from part (a). **3a.** Fold the square to make the left side match the right side. Fold the resulting rectangle so that the top side matches the bottom side. **b.** Open the folded sheet from part (a). Fold the corners of the large square inward to meet at the point of intersection of the crease lines. The new crease lines form a square 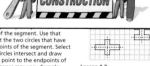 large square. **5a.** A Construct a circle of the segment an radius. Draw anot the first. Draw the endpoints on the Sample: Fold the s on the crease line original segment), that point to the e **c.** Answers may va pass to the length of the segment. Use that radius and construct the two circles that have centers at the endpoints of the segment. Select a point where the circles intersect and draw segments from that point to the endpoints of the segment. **d.** Answers may vary. Sample: Construct perpendicular lines through the endpoints of the given segment. Construct a circle having one of the endpoints as its center and passing through the other endpoint. Construct a line parallel to the original segment through one of the points of intersection of the circle and the line perpendicular to the original segment. **7a–c.** Midpoints (the key to the constructions in parts (a) and (b) in the exercise) and angle bisectors have been constructed in earlier exercises. **d.** Answers may vary. Sample: Let the triangle be △ABC. Construct a circle with center A that passes through B. If $\overline{BC}$ intersects the circle at another point, call this point D. If it does not, extend $\overline{BC}$ until it intersects the circle at D. Construct the midpoint of

$\overline{BD}$ and call it E. The segment $\overline{AE}$ is an altitude of △ABC. Construct the other two altitudes in a similar way. **9.** Answers may vary. Sample: Construct the perpendicular bisectors of two sides of the equilateral △ABC. The perpendicular bisectors intersect at a point X. Construct the circle that has center X and radius XA. **11.** Answers may vary. Sample: Construct a circle. Draw a line through the center of the circle. Call the points of intersection A and B. Construct a circle with center A and radius AB. **13a.** acute triangles **b.** right triangles **c.** obtuse triangles **15b.** Construct the perpendicular bisectors of two of the sides of the triangle that has the bases of the saplings as vertices. Place the sprinkler at the point of intersection of the perpendicular bisectors.

Chapter 1
Lesson 1.1
5. Shapes 1, 2, and 8 can cast square shadows parallel. Shapes 6 and the beams of light ce. **7.** The triangle shape, but the

Lesson 1.2
1. Answers may vary. Sample: Since the two bases are the same distance apart at all points, the connecting lines appear to be the same length. Since the points on the second base are translated in the same direction from the corresponding points on the first base, the connecting segments take on the same slope. This makes them appear parallel. **3.** Answers may vary. Sample: The darkest regions sometimes appear to be upper parts of a three-dimensional figure. Then they suddenly switch to be right-hand parts of a different figure. **7.** 15; 26 **9.** The figure on the left is a square whose top side and left side have both been divided into segments of lengths a and b. This allows you to divide the large rectangle into an a-by-a square, two a-by-b rectangles, and a b-by-b square.

Selected Answers   763

Lesson 1.5

9. Comparing the results from Problem 6 shows that equal angles yield triangles that have the same shape, though they may be different sizes. Comparing results from Problem 2 shows that equal side lengths yield triangles that are both the same shape and same size.

Lesson 1.6

1a. Mark two points, A and B, on the given line. Construct the perpendicular bisector of $\overline{AB}$. **b.** Use the procedure from part (a) to construct a line perpendicular to the perpendicular bisector from part (a). **3a.** Fold the square to make the left side match the right side. Fold the resulting rectangle so that the top side matches the bottom side. **b.** Open the folded sheet from part (a). Fold the corners of the large square inward to meet at the point of intersection of the crease lines. The new crease lines form a square with half the area of the large square. **5a.** Answers may vary. Sample: Construct a circle

of the segment an[…] radius. Draw anoth[…] the first. Draw the […] endpoints on the c[…] Sample: Fold the s[…] on the crease line […] original segment), […] that point to the e[…] **c.** Answers may va[ry] […] pass to the length of the segment. Use that radius and construct the two circles that have centers at the endpoints of the segment. Select a point where the circles intersect and draw segments from that point to the endpoints of the segment. **d.** Answers may vary. Sample: Construct perpendicular lines through the endpoints of the given segment. Construct a circle having one of the endpoints as its center and passing through the other endpoint. Construct a line parallel to the original segment through one of the points of intersection of the circle and the line perpendicular to the original segment. **7a–c.** Midpoints (the key to the constructions in parts (a) and (b) in the exercise) and angle bisectors have been constructed in earlier exercises. **d.** Answers may vary. Sample: Let the triangle be $\triangle ABC$. Construct a circle with center A that passes through B. If $\overline{BC}$ intersects the circle at another point, call this point D. If it does not, extend $\overline{BC}$ until it intersects the circle at D. Construct the midpoint of

$\overline{BD}$ and call it E. The segment $\overline{AE}$ is an altitude of $\triangle ABC$. Construct the other two altitudes in a similar way. **9.** Answers may vary. Sample: Construct the perpendicular bisectors of two sides of the equilateral $\triangle ABC$. The perpendicular bisectors intersect at a point X. Construct the circle that has center X and radius XA. **11.** Answers may vary. Sample: Construct a circle. Draw a line through the center of the circle. Call the points of intersection A and B. Construct a circle with center A and radius AB. **13a.** acute triangles **b.** right triangles **c.** obtuse triangles **15b.** Construct the perpendicular bisectors of two of the sides of the triangle that has the bases of the saplings as vertices. Place the sprinkler at the point of intersection of the perpendicular bisectors.

Chapter 1

Lesson 1.1

5. Shapes 1, 2, and 8 can cast square shadows […] parallel. Shapes 6 and […] the beams of light […] ce. **7.** The triangle […] e shape, but the

Lesson 1.2

1. Answers may vary. Sample: Since the two bases are the same distance apart at all points, the connecting lines appear to be the same length. Since the points on the second base are translated in the same direction from the corresponding points on the first base, the connecting segments take on the same slope. This makes them appear parallel. **3.** Answers may vary. Sample: The darkest regions sometimes appear to be upper parts of a three-dimensional figure. Then they suddenly switch to be right-hand parts of a different figure. **7.** 15; 26 **9.** The figure on the left is a square whose top side and left side have both been divided into segments of lengths a and b. This allows you to divide the large rectangle into an a-by-a square, two a-by-b rectangles, and a b-by-b square.

Lesson 1.5

9. Comparing the results from Problem 6 shows that equal angles yield triangles that have the same shape, though they may be different sizes. Comparing results from Problem 2 shows that equal side lengths yield triangles that are both the same shape and same size.

Lesson 1.6

1a. Mark two points, A and B, on the given line. Construct the perpendicular bisector of $\overline{AB}$. **b.** Use the procedure from part (a) to construct a line perpendicular to the perpendicular bisector from part (a). **3a.** Fold the square to make the left side match the right side. Fold the resulting rectangle so that the top side matches the bottom side. **b.** Open the folded sheet from part (a). Fold the corners of the large square inward to meet at the point of intersection of the crease lines. The new crease lines form a square with half the area of the large square. **5a.** Answers may vary. Sample: Construct a circle

7a–c. Midpoints (the key to the constructions in parts (a) and (b) in the exercise) and angle bisectors have been constructed in earlier exercises. **d.** Answers may vary. Sample: Let the triangle be $\triangle ABC$. Construct a circle with center A that passes through B. If $\overline{BC}$ intersects the circle at another point, call this point D. If it does not, extend $\overline{BC}$ until it intersects the circle at D. Construct the midpoint of

$\overline{BD}$ and call it E. The segment $\overline{AE}$ is an altitude of $\triangle ABC$. Construct the other two altitudes in a similar way. **9.** Answers may vary. Sample: Construct the perpendicular bisectors of two sides of the equilateral $\triangle ABC$. The perpendicular bisectors intersect at a point X. Construct the circle that has center X and radius XA. **11.** Answers may vary. Sample: Construct a circle. Draw a line through the center of the circle. Call the points of intersection A and B. Construct a circle with center A and radius AB. **13a.** acute triangles **b.** right triangles **c.** obtuse triangles **15b.** Construct the perpendicular bisectors of two of the sides of the triangle that has the bases of the saplings as vertices. Place the sprinkler at the point of intersection of the perpendicular bisectors.

Chapter 1

Lesson 1.1

5. Shapes 1, 2, and 8 can cast square shadows

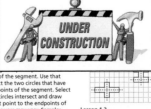

Lesson 1.2

1. Answers may vary. Sample: Since the two bases are the same distance apart at all points, the connecting lines appear to be the same length. Since the points on the second base are translated in the same direction from the corresponding points on the first base, the connecting segments take on the same slope. This makes them appear parallel. **3.** Answers may vary. Sample: The darkest regions sometimes appear to be upper parts of a three-dimensional figure. Then they suddenly switch to be right-hand parts of a different figure. **7.** 15; 26 **9.** The figure on the left is a square whose top side and left side have both been divided into segments of lengths a and b. This allows you to divide the large rectangle into an a-by-a square, two a-by-b rectangles, and a b-by-b square.

766   767   Selected Answers

Lesson 1.5

9. Comparing the results from Problem 6 shows that equal angles yield triangles that have the same shape, though they may be different sizes. Comparing results from Problem 2 shows that equal side lengths yield triangles that are both the same shape and same size.

Lesson 1.6

1a. Mark two points, A and B, on the given line. Construct the perpendicular bisector of $\overline{AB}$. b. Use the procedure from part (a) to construct a line perpendicular to the perpendicular bisector from part (a). 3a. Fold the square to make the left side match the right side. Fold the resulting rectangle so that the top side matches the bottom side. b. Open the folded sheet from part (a). Fold the corners of the large square inward to meet at the point of intersection of the crease lines. The new crease lines form a square with half the area of the large square. 5a. Answers may vary. Sample: Construct a circle

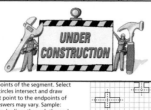

of the segment an... radius. Draw anoth... the first. Draw the... endpoints on the... Sample: Fold the s... on the crease line... original segment),... that point to the e... c. Answers may va... pass to the length... radius and constru... centers at the endpoints of the segment. Select a point where the circles intersect and draw segments from that point to the endpoints of the segment. d. Answers may vary. Sample: Construct perpendicular lines through the endpoints of the given segment. Construct a circle having one of the endpoints as its center and passing through the other endpoint. Construct a line parallel to the original segment through one of the points of intersection of the circle and the line perpendicular to the original segment. 7a–c. Midpoints (the key to the constructions in parts (a) and (b) in the exercise) and angle bisectors have been constructed in earlier exercises. d. Answers may vary. Sample: Let the triangle be $\triangle ABC$. Construct a circle with center A that passes through B. If $\overline{BC}$ intersects the circle at another point, call this point D. If it does not, extend $\overline{BC}$ until it intersects the circle at D. Construct the midpoint of

$\overline{BD}$ and call it E. The segment $\overline{AE}$ is an altitude of $\triangle ABC$. Construct the other two altitudes in a similar way. 9. Answers may vary. Sample: Construct the perpendicular bisectors of two sides of the equilateral $\triangle ABC$. The perpendicular bisectors intersect at a point X. Construct the circle that has center X and radius XA. 11. Answers may vary. Sample: Construct a circle. Draw a line through the center of the circle. Call the points of intersection A and B. Construct a circle with center A and radius AB. 13a. acute triangles b. right triangles c. obtuse triangles 15b. Construct the perpendicular bisectors of two of the sides of the triangle that has the bases of the saplings as vertices. Place the sprinkler at the point of intersection of the perpendicular bisectors.

Chapter 1
Lesson 1.1

5. Shapes 1, 2, and 8 can cast square shadows... parallel. Shapes 6 and... the beams of light... ce. 7. The triangle... shape, but the

Lesson 1.2

1. Answers may vary. Sample: Since the two bases are the same distance apart at all points, the connecting lines appear to be the same length. Since the points on the second base are translated in the same direction from the corresponding points on the first base, the connecting segments take on the same slope. This makes them appear parallel. 3. Answers may vary. Sample: The darkest regions sometimes appear to be upper parts of a three-dimensional figure. Then they suddenly switch to be right-hand parts of a different figure. 7. 15; 26 9. The figure on the left is a square whose top side and left side have both been divided into segments of lengths a and b. This allows you to divide the large rectangle into

an a-by-a square, two a-by-b rectangles, and a b-by-b square.

Lesson 1.5

9. Comparing the results from Problem 6 shows that equal angles yield triangles that have the same shape, though they may be different sizes. Comparing results from Problem 2 shows that equal side lengths yield triangles that are both the same shape and same size.

Lesson 1.6

1a. Mark two points, A and B, on the given line. Construct the perpendicular bisector of $\overline{AB}$. b. Use the procedure from part (a) to construct a line perpendicular to the perpendicular bisector from part (a). 3a. Fold the square to make the left side match the right side. Fold the resulting rectangle so that the top side matches the bottom side. b. Open the folded sheet from part (a). Fold the corners of the large square inward to meet at the point of intersection of the crease lines. The new crease lines form a square

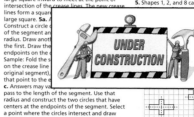

Construct a circle... of the segment an... radius. Draw anoth... the first. Draw the... endpoints on the... Sample: Fold the s... on the crease line... original segment),... that point to the e... c. Answers may va... pass to the length of the segment. Use that radius and construct the two circles that have centers at the endpoints of the segment. Select a point where the circles intersect and draw segments from that point to the endpoints of the segment. d. Answers may vary. Sample: Construct perpendicular lines through the endpoints of the given segment. Construct a circle having one of the endpoints as its center and passing through the other endpoint. Construct a line parallel to the original segment through one of the points of intersection of the circle and the line perpendicular to the original segment. 7a–c. Midpoints (the key to the constructions in parts (a) and (b) in the exercise) and angle bisectors have been constructed in earlier exercises. d. Answers may vary. Sample: Let the triangle be $\triangle ABC$. Construct a circle with center A that passes through B. If $\overline{BC}$ intersects the circle at another point, call this point D. If it does not, extend $\overline{BC}$ until it intersects the circle at D. Construct the midpoint of

$\overline{BD}$ and call it E. The segment $\overline{AE}$ is an altitude of $\triangle ABC$. Construct the other two altitudes in a similar way. 9. Answers may vary. Sample: Construct the perpendicular bisectors of two sides of the equilateral $\triangle ABC$. The perpendicular bisectors intersect at a point X. Construct the circle that has center X and radius XA. 11. Answers may vary. Sample: Construct a circle. Draw a line through the center of the circle. Call the points of intersection A and B. Construct a circle with center A and radius AB. 13a. acute triangles b. right triangles c. obtuse triangles 15b. Construct the perpendicular bisectors of two of the sides of the triangle that has the bases of the saplings as vertices. Place the sprinkler at the point of intersection of the perpendicular bisectors.

Chapter 1
Lesson 1.1

5. Shapes 1, 2, and 8 can cast square shadows... parallel. Shapes 6 and... the beams of light... ce. 7. The triangle... shape, but the

Lesson 1.2

1. Answers may vary. Sample: Since the two bases are the same distance apart at all points, the connecting lines appear to be the same length. Since the points on the second base are translated in the same direction from the corresponding points on the first base, the connecting segments take on the same slope. This makes them appear parallel. 3. Answers may vary. Sample: The darkest regions sometimes appear to be upper parts of a three-dimensional figure. Then they suddenly switch to be right-hand parts of a different figure. 7. 15; 26 9. The figure on the left is a square whose top side and left side have both been divided into segments of lengths a and b. This allows you to divide the large rectangle into an a-by-a square, two a-by-b rectangles, and a b-by-b square.

769

Lesson 1.5

9. Comparing the results from Problem 6 shows that equal angles yield triangles that have the same shape, though they may be different sizes. Comparing results from Problem 2 shows that equal side lengths yield triangles that are both the same shape and same size.

Lesson 1.6

1a. Mark two points, A and B, on the given line. Construct the perpendicular bisector of $\overline{AB}$. b. Use the procedure from part (a) to construct a line perpendicular to the perpendicular bisector from part (a). 3a. Fold the square to make the left side match the right side. Fold the resulting rectangle so that the top side matches the bottom side. b. Open the folded sheet from part (a). Fold the corners of the large square inward to meet at the point of intersection of the crease lines. The new crease lines form a square with half the area of the large square. 5a. Answers may vary. Sample: Construct a circle

of the segment an... radius. Draw anoth... the first. Draw the... endpoints on the... Sample: Fold the s... on the crease line... original segment),... that point to the e... c. Answers may va... pass to the length... radius and constru... centers at the endpoints of the segment. Select a point where the circles intersect and draw segments from that point to the endpoints of the segment. d. Answers may vary. Sample: Construct perpendicular lines through the endpoints of the given segment. Construct a circle having one of the endpoints as its center and passing through the other endpoint. Construct a line parallel to the original segment through one of the points of intersection of the circle and the line perpendicular to the original segment. 7a–c. Midpoints (the key to the constructions in parts (a) and (b) in the exercise) and angle bisectors have been constructed in earlier exercises. d. Answers may vary. Sample: Let the triangle be $\triangle ABC$. Construct a circle with center A that passes through B. If $\overline{BC}$ intersects the circle at another point, call this point D. If it does not, extend $\overline{BC}$ until it intersects the circle at D. Construct the midpoint of

$\overline{BD}$ and call it E. The segment $\overline{AE}$ is an altitude of $\triangle ABC$. Construct the other two altitudes in a similar way. 9. Answers may vary. Sample: Construct the perpendicular bisectors of two sides of the equilateral $\triangle ABC$. The perpendicular bisectors intersect at a point X. Construct the circle that has center X and radius XA. 11. Answers may vary. Sample: Construct a circle. Draw a line through the center of the circle. Call the points of intersection A and B. Construct a circle with center A and radius AB. 13a. acute triangles b. right triangles c. obtuse triangles 15b. Construct the perpendicular bisectors of two of the sides of the triangle that has the bases of the saplings as vertices. Place the sprinkler at the point of intersection of the perpendicular bisectors.

Chapter 1
Lesson 1.1

5. Shapes 1, 2, and 8 can cast square shadows... parallel. Shapes 6 and... the beams of light... ce. 7. The triangle... shape, but the

Lesson 1.2

1. Answers may vary. Sample: Since the two bases are the same distance apart at all points, the connecting lines appear to be the same length. Since the points on the second base are translated in the same direction from the corresponding points on the first base, the connecting segments take on the same slope. This makes them appear parallel. 3. Answers may vary. Sample: The darkest regions sometimes appear to be upper parts of a three-dimensional figure. Then they suddenly switch to be right-hand parts of a different figure. 7. 15; 26 9. The figure on the left is a square whose top side and left side have both been divided into segments of lengths a and b. This allows you to divide the large rectangle into

770 Selected Answers

an a-by-a square, two a-by-b rectangles, and a b-by-b square.

Lesson 1.5

9. Comparing the results from Problem 6 shows that equal angles yield triangles that have the same shape, though they may be different sizes. Comparing results from Problem 2 shows that equal side lengths yield triangles that are both the same shape and same size.

Lesson 1.6

1a. Mark two points, A and B, on the given line. Construct the perpendicular bisector of $\overline{AB}$. b. Use the procedure from part (a) to construct a line perpendicular to the perpendicular bisector from part (a). 3a. Fold the square to make the left side match the right side. Fold the resulting rectangle so that the top side matches the bottom side. b. Open the folded sheet from part (a). Fold the corners of the large square inward to meet at the point of intersection of the crease lines. The new crease lines form a square

Construct a circle... of the segment an... radius. Draw anoth... the first. Draw the... endpoints on the... Sample: Fold the s... on the crease line... original segment),... that point to the e... c. Answers may va... pass to the length of the segment. Use that radius and construct the two circles that have centers at the endpoints of the segment. Select a point where the circles intersect and draw segments from that point to the endpoints of the segment. d. Answers may vary. Sample: Construct perpendicular lines through the endpoints of the given segment. Construct a circle having one of the endpoints as its center and passing through the other endpoint. Construct a line parallel to the original segment through one of the points of intersection of the circle and the line perpendicular to the original segment. 7a–c. Midpoints (the key to the constructions in parts (a) and (b) in the exercise) and angle bisectors have been constructed in earlier exercises. d. Answers may vary. Sample: Let the triangle be $\triangle ABC$. Construct a circle with center A that passes through B. If $\overline{BC}$ intersects the circle at another point, call this point D. If it does not, extend $\overline{BC}$ until it intersects the circle at D. Construct the midpoint of

$\overline{BD}$ and call it E. The segment $\overline{AE}$ is an altitude of $\triangle ABC$. Construct the other two altitudes in a similar way. 9. Answers may vary. Sample: Construct the perpendicular bisectors of two sides of the equilateral $\triangle ABC$. The perpendicular bisectors intersect at a point X. Construct the circle that has center X and radius XA. 11. Answers may vary. Sample: Construct a circle. Draw a line through the center of the circle. Call the points of intersection A and B. Construct a circle with center A and radius AB. 13a. acute triangles b. right triangles c. obtuse triangles 15b. Construct the perpendicular bisectors of two of the sides of the triangle that has the bases of the saplings as vertices. Place the sprinkler at the point of intersection of the perpendicular bisectors.

Chapter 1
Lesson 1.1

5. Shapes 1, 2, and 8 can cast square shadows... parallel. Shapes 6 and... the beams of light... ce. 7. The triangle... shape, but the

Lesson 1.2

1. Answers may vary. Sample: Since the two bases are the same distance apart at all points, the connecting lines appear to be the same length. Since the points on the second base are translated in the same direction from the corresponding points on the first base, the connecting segments take on the same slope. This makes them appear parallel. 3. Answers may vary. Sample: The darkest regions sometimes appear to be upper parts of a three-dimensional figure. Then they suddenly switch to be right-hand parts of a different figure. 7. 15; 26 9. The figure on the left is a square whose top side and left side have both been divided into segments of lengths a and b. This allows you to divide the large rectangle into an a-by-a square, two a-by-b rectangles, and a b-by-b square.

771

Lesson 1.5

9. Comparing the results from Problem 6 shows that equal angles yield triangles that have the same shape, though they may be different sizes. Comparing results from Problem 2 shows that equal side lengths yield triangles that are both the same shape and same size.

Lesson 1.6

1a. Mark two points, A and B, on the given line. Construct the perpendicular bisector of $\overline{AB}$. **b.** Use the procedure from part (a) to construct a line perpendicular to the perpendicular bisector from part (a). **3a.** Fold the square to make the left side match the right side. Fold the resulting rectangle so that the top side matches the bottom side. **b.** Open the folded sheet from part (a). Fold the corners of the large square inward to meet at the point of intersection of the crease lines. The new crease lines form a square with half the area of the large square. **5a.** Answers may vary. Sample: Construct a circle ___ of the segment an___ radius. Draw anot___ the first. Draw the ___ endpoints on the ___ Sample: Fold the s___ on the crease line ___ original segment), ___ that point to the e___ **c.** Answers may va___ pass to the length ___ radius and constr___ centers at the endpoints of the segment. Select a point where the circles intersect and draw segments from that point to the endpoints of the segment. **d.** Answers may vary. Sample: Construct perpendicular lines through the endpoints of the given segment. Construct a circle having one of the endpoints as its center and passing through the other endpoint. Construct a line parallel to the original segment through one of the points of intersection of the circle and the line perpendicular to the original segment. **7a–c.** Midpoints (the key to the constructions in parts (a) and (b) in the exercise) and angle bisectors have been constructed in earlier exercises. **d.** Answers may vary. Sample: Let the triangle be $\triangle ABC$. Construct a circle with center A that passes through B. If $\overline{BC}$ intersects the circle at another point, call this point D. If it does not, extend $\overline{BC}$ until it intersects the circle at D. Construct the midpoint of

$\overline{BD}$ and call it E. The segment $\overline{AE}$ is an altitude of $\triangle ABC$. Construct the other two altitudes in a similar way. **9.** Answers may vary. Sample: Construct the perpendicular bisectors of two sides of the equilateral $\triangle ABC$. The perpendicular bisectors intersect at a point X. Construct the circle that has center X and radius XA. **11.** Answers may vary. Sample: Construct a circle. Draw a line through the center of the circle. Construct a circle with center A and radius AB. **13a.** acute triangles **b.** right triangles **c.** obtuse triangles **15b.** Construct the perpendicular bisectors of two of the sides of the triangle that has the bases of the saplings as vertices. Place the sprinkler at the point of intersection of the perpendicular bisectors.

Chapter 1
Lesson 1.1

5. Shapes 1, 2, and 8 can cast square shadows ___ llel. Shapes 6 and ___ the beams of light ___ ce. **7.** The triangle ___ e shape, but the ___

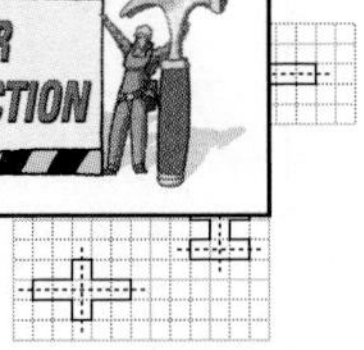

Lesson 1.2

1. Answers may vary. Sample: Since the two bases are the same distance apart at all points, the connecting lines appear to be the same length. Since the points on the second base are translated in the same direction from the corresponding points on the first base, the connecting segments take on the same slope. This makes them appear parallel. **3.** Answers may vary. Sample: The darkest regions sometimes appear to be upper parts of a three-dimensional figure. Then they suddenly switch to be right-hand parts of a different figure. **7.** 15; 26 **9.** The figure on the left is a square whose top side and left side have both been divided into segments of lengths a and b. This allows you to divide the large rectangle into

---

an a-by-a square, two a-by-b rectangles, and a b-by-b square.

Lesson 1.5

9. Comparing the results from Problem 6 shows that equal angles yield triangles that have the same shape, though they may be different sizes. Comparing results from Problem 2 shows that equal side lengths yield triangles that are both the same shape and same size.

Lesson 1.6

1a. Mark two points, A and B, on the given line. Construct the perpendicular bisector of $\overline{AB}$. **b.** Use the procedure from part (a) to construct a line perpendicular to the perpendicular bisector from part (a). **3a.** Fold the square to make the left side match the right side. Fold the resulting rectangle so that the top side matches the bottom side. **b.** Open the folded sheet from part (a). Fold the corners of the large square inward to meet at the point of intersection of the crease lines. The new crease lines form a square ___ large square. **5a.** ___ Construct a circle ___ of the segment an___ radius. Draw anot___ the first. Draw the ___ endpoints on the ___ Sample: Fold the s___ on the crease line ___ original segment), ___ that point to the e___ **c.** Answers may va___ pass to the length of the segment. Use that radius and construct the two circles that have centers at the endpoints of the segment. Select a point where the circles intersect and draw segments from that point to the endpoints of the segment. **d.** Answers may vary. Sample: Construct perpendicular lines through the endpoints of the given segment. Construct a circle having one of the endpoints as its center and passing through the other endpoint. Construct a line parallel to the original segment through one of the points of intersection of the circle and the line perpendicular to the original segment. **7a–c.** Midpoints (the key to the constructions in parts (a) and (b) in the exercise) and angle bisectors have been constructed in earlier exercises. **d.** Answers may vary. Sample: Let the triangle be $\triangle ABC$. Construct a circle with center A that passes through B. If $\overline{BC}$ intersects the circle at another point, call this point D. If it does not, extend $\overline{BC}$ until it intersects the circle at D. Construct the midpoint of

$\overline{BD}$ and call it E. The segment $\overline{AE}$ is an altitude of $\triangle ABC$. Construct the other two altitudes in a similar way. **9.** Answers may vary. Sample: Construct the perpendicular bisectors of two sides of the equilateral $\triangle ABC$. The perpendicular bisectors intersect at a point X. Construct the circle that has center X and radius XA. **11.** Answers may vary. Sample: Construct a circle. Draw a line through the center of the circle. Call the points of intersection A and B. Construct a circle with center A and radius AB. **13a.** acute triangles **b.** right triangles **c.** obtuse triangles **15b.** Construct the perpendicular bisectors of two of the sides of the triangle that has the bases of the saplings as vertices. Place the sprinkler at the point of intersection of the perpendicular bisectors.

Chapter 1
Lesson 1.1

5. Shapes 1, 2, and 8 can cast square shadows ___ llel. Shapes 6 and ___ the beams of light ___ ce. **7.** The triangle ___ e shape, but the ___

Lesson 1.2

1. Answers may vary. Sample: Since the two bases are the same distance apart at all points, the connecting lines appear to be the same length. Since the points on the second base are translated in the same direction from the corresponding points on the first base, the connecting segments take on the same slope. This makes them appear parallel. **3.** Answers may vary. Sample: The darkest regions sometimes appear to be upper parts of a three-dimensional figure. Then they suddenly switch to be right-hand parts of a different figure. **7.** 15; 26 **9.** The figure on the left is a square whose top side and left side have both been divided into segments of lengths a and b. This allows you to divide the large rectangle into an a-by-a square, two a-by-b rectangles, and a b-by-b square.

Lesson 1.5

9. Comparing the results from Problem 6 shows that equal angles yield triangles that have the same shape, though they may be different sizes. Comparing results from Problem 2 shows that equal side lengths yield triangles that are both the same shape and same size.

Lesson 1.6

1a. Mark two points, A and B, on the given line. Construct the perpendicular bisector of $\overline{AB}$. **b.** Use the procedure from part (a) to construct a line perpendicular to the perpendicular bisector from part (a). **3a.** Fold the square to make the left side match the right side. Fold the resulting rectangle so that the top side matches the bottom side. **b.** Open the folded sheet from part (a). Fold the corners of the large square inward to meet at the point of intersection of the crease lines. The new crease lines form a square with half the area of the large square. **5a.** Answers may vary. Sample: Construct a circle ___ of the segment an___ radius. Draw anot___ the first. Draw the ___ endpoints on the ___ Sample: Fold the s___ on the crease line ___ original segment), ___ that point to the e___ **c.** Answers may va___ pass to the length ___ radius and constr___ centers at the endpoints of the segment. Select a point where the circles intersect and draw segments from that point to the endpoints of the segment. **d.** Answers may vary. Sample: Construct perpendicular lines through the endpoints of the given segment. Construct a circle having one of the endpoints as its center and passing through the other endpoint. Construct a line parallel to the original segment through one of the points of intersection of the circle and the line perpendicular to the original segment. **7a–c.** Midpoints (the key to the constructions in parts (a) and (b) in the exercise) and angle bisectors have been constructed in earlier exercises. **d.** Answers may vary. Sample: Let the triangle be $\triangle ABC$. Construct a circle with center A that passes through B. If $\overline{BC}$ intersects the circle at another point, call this point D. If it does not, extend $\overline{BC}$ until it intersects the circle at D. Construct the midpoint of

$\overline{BD}$ and call it E. The segment $\overline{AE}$ is an altitude of $\triangle ABC$. Construct the other two altitudes in a similar way. **9.** Answers may vary. Sample: Construct the perpendicular bisectors of two sides of the equilateral $\triangle ABC$. The perpendicular bisectors intersect at a point X. Construct the circle that has center X and radius XA. **11.** Answers may vary. Sample: Construct a circle. Draw a line through the center of the circle. Construct a circle with center A and radius AB. **13a.** acute triangles **b.** right triangles **c.** obtuse triangles **15b.** Construct the perpendicular bisectors of two of the sides of the triangle that has the bases of the saplings as vertices. Place the sprinkler at the point of intersection of the perpendicular bisectors.

Chapter 1
Lesson 1.1

5. Shapes 1, 2, and 8 can cast square shadows ___ llel. Shapes 6 and ___ the beams of light ___ ce. **7.** The triangle ___ e shape, but the ___

Lesson 1.2

1. Answers may vary. Sample: Since the two bases are the same distance apart at all points, the connecting lines appear to be the same length. Since the points on the second base are translated in the same direction from the corresponding points on the first base, the connecting segments take on the same slope. This makes them appear parallel. **3.** Answers may vary. Sample: The darkest regions sometimes appear to be upper parts of a three-dimensional figure. Then they suddenly switch to be right-hand parts of a different figure. **7.** 15; 26 **9.** The figure on the left is a square whose top side and left side have both been divided into segments of lengths a and b. This allows you to divide the large rectangle into

774   Selected Answers

an a-by-a square, two a-by-b rectangles, and a b-by-b square.

Lesson 1.5

9. Comparing the results from Problem 6 shows that equal angles yield triangles that have the same shape, though they may be different sizes. Comparing results from Problem 2 shows that equal side lengths yield triangles that are both the same shape and same size.

Lesson 1.6

1a. Mark two points, A and B, on the given line. Construct the perpendicular bisector of $\overline{AB}$. **b.** Use the procedure from part (a) to construct a line perpendicular to the perpendicular bisector from part (a). **3a.** Fold the square to make the left side match the right side. Fold the resulting rectangle so that the top side matches the bottom side. **b.** Open the folded sheet from part (a). Fold the corners of the large square inward to meet at the point of intersection of the crease lines. The new crease lines form a square ___ large square. **5a.** ___ Construct a circle ___ of the segment an___ radius. Draw anot___ the first. Draw the ___ endpoints on the ___ Sample: Fold the s___ on the crease line ___ original segment), ___ that point to the e___ **c.** Answers may va___ pass to the length of the segment. Use that radius and construct the two circles that have centers at the endpoints of the segment. Select a point where the circles intersect and draw segments from that point to the endpoints of the segment. **d.** Answers may vary. Sample: Construct perpendicular lines through the endpoints of the given segment. Construct a circle having one of the endpoints as its center and passing through the other endpoint. Construct a line parallel to the original segment through one of the points of intersection of the circle and the line perpendicular to the original segment. **7a–c.** Midpoints (the key to the constructions in parts (a) and (b) in the exercise) and angle bisectors have been constructed in earlier exercises. **d.** Answers may vary. Sample: Let the triangle be $\triangle ABC$. Construct a circle with center A that passes through B. If $\overline{BC}$ intersects the circle at another point, call this point D. If it does not, extend $\overline{BC}$ until it intersects the circle at D. Construct the midpoint of

$\overline{BD}$ and call it E. The segment $\overline{AE}$ is an altitude of $\triangle ABC$. Construct the other two altitudes in a similar way. **9.** Answers may vary. Sample: Construct the perpendicular bisectors of two sides of the equilateral $\triangle ABC$. The perpendicular bisectors intersect at a point X. Construct the circle that has center X and radius XA. **11.** Answers may vary. Sample: Construct a circle. Draw a line through the center of the circle. Call the points of intersection A and B. Construct a circle with center A and radius AB. **13a.** acute triangles **b.** right triangles **c.** obtuse triangles **15b.** Construct the perpendicular bisectors of two of the sides of the triangle that has the bases of the saplings as vertices. Place the sprinkler at the point of intersection of the perpendicular bisectors.

Chapter 1
Lesson 1.1

5. Shapes 1, 2, and 8 can cast square shadows ___ llel. Shapes 6 and ___ the beams of light ___ ce. **7.** The triangle ___ e shape, but the ___

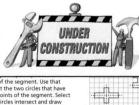

Lesson 1.2

1. Answers may vary. Sample: Since the two bases are the same distance apart at all points, the connecting lines appear to be the same length. Since the points on the second base are translated in the same direction from the corresponding points on the first base, the connecting segments take on the same slope. This makes them appear parallel. **3.** Answers may vary. Sample: The darkest regions sometimes appear to be upper parts of a three-dimensional figure. Then they suddenly switch to be right-hand parts of a different figure. **7.** 15; 26 **9.** The figure on the left is a square whose top side and left side have both been divided into segments of lengths a and b. This allows you to divide the large rectangle into an a-by-a square, two a-by-b square.

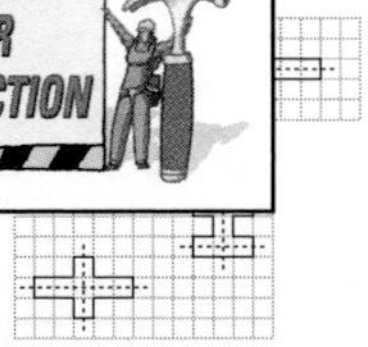

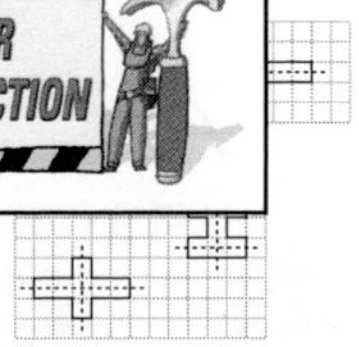

Selected Answers   775

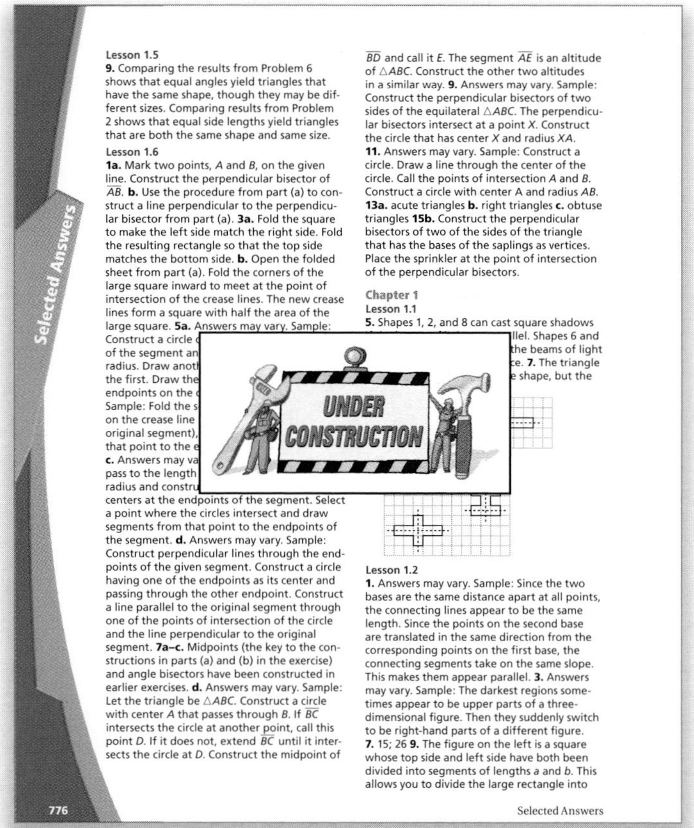

Page 776

Lesson 1.5

9. Comparing the results from Problem 6 shows that equal angles yield triangles that have the same shape, though they may be different sizes. Comparing results from Problem 2 shows that equal side lengths yield triangles that are both the same shape and same size.

Lesson 1.6

1a. Mark two points, A and B, on the given line. Construct the perpendicular bisector of $\overline{AB}$. **b.** Use the procedure from part (a) to construct a line perpendicular to the perpendicular bisector from part (a). **3a.** Fold the square to make the left side match the right side. Fold the resulting rectangle so that the top side matches the bottom side. **b.** Open the folded sheet from part (a). Fold the corners of the large square inward to meet at the point of intersection of the crease lines. The new crease lines form a square with half the area of the large square. **5a.** Answers may vary. Sample: Construct a circle [...] of the segment an[...] radius. Draw anot[...] the first. Draw the[...] endpoints on the [...] Sample: Fold the s[...] on the crease line [...] original segment),[...] that point to the e[...] **c.** Answers may va[...] pass to the length[...] radius and constru[...] centers at the endpoints of the segment. Select a point where the circles intersect and draw segments from that point to the endpoints of the segment. **d.** Answers may vary. Sample: Construct perpendicular lines through the endpoints of the given segment. Construct a circle having one of the endpoints as its center and passing through the other endpoint. Construct a line parallel to the original segment through one of the points of intersection of the circle and the line perpendicular to the original segment. **7a–c.** Midpoints (the key to the constructions in parts (a) and (b) in the exercise) and angle bisectors have been constructed in earlier exercises. **d.** Answers may vary. Sample: Let the triangle be $\triangle ABC$. Construct a circle with center A that passes through B. If $\overline{BC}$ intersects the circle at another point, call this point D. If it does not, extend $\overline{BC}$ until it intersects the circle at D. Construct the midpoint of

$\overline{BD}$ and call it E. The segment $\overline{AE}$ is an altitude of $\triangle ABC$. Construct the other two altitudes in a similar way. **9.** Answers may vary. Sample: Construct the perpendicular bisectors of two sides of the equilateral $\triangle ABC$. The perpendicular bisectors intersect at a point X. Construct the circle that has center X and radius XA.
11. Answers may vary. Sample: Construct a circle. Draw a line through the center of the circle. Call the points of intersection A and B. Construct a circle with center A and radius AB.
13a. acute triangles **b.** right triangles **c.** obtuse triangles **15b.** Construct the perpendicular bisectors of two of the sides of the triangle that has the bases of the saplings as vertices. Place the sprinkler at the point of intersection of the perpendicular bisectors.

Chapter 1
Lesson 1.1

5. Shapes 1, 2, and 8 can cast square shadows [...]allel. Shapes 6 and [...] the beams of light [...]ce. **7.** The triangle [...]e shape, but the

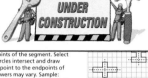

Lesson 1.2

1. Answers may vary. Sample: Since the two bases are the same distance apart at all points, the connecting lines appear to be the same length. Since the points on the second base are translated in the same direction from the corresponding points on the first base, the connecting segments take on the same slope. This makes them appear parallel. **3.** Answers may vary. Sample: The darkest regions sometimes appear to be upper parts of a three-dimensional figure. Then they suddenly switch to be right-hand parts of a different figure. **7.** 15; 26 **9.** The figure on the left is a square whose top side and left side have both been divided into segments of lengths a and b. This allows you to divide the large rectangle into

Selected Answers

776

Page 777

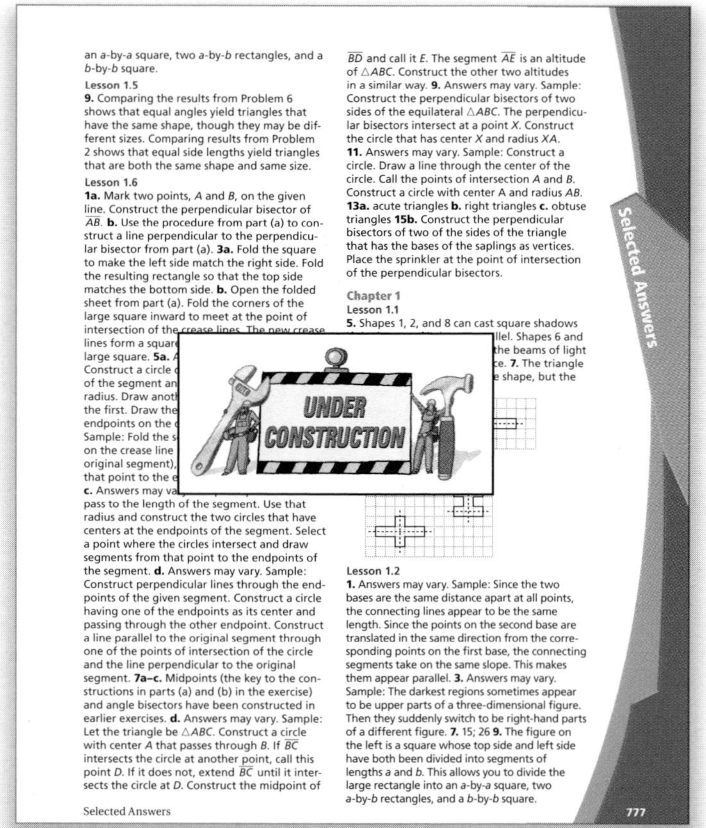

an a-by-a square, two a-by-b rectangles, and a b-by-b square.

Lesson 1.5

9. Comparing the results from Problem 6 shows that equal angles yield triangles that have the same shape, though they may be different sizes. Comparing results from Problem 2 shows that equal side lengths yield triangles that are both the same shape and same size.

Lesson 1.6

1a. Mark two points, A and B, on the given line. Construct the perpendicular bisector of $\overline{AB}$. **b.** Use the procedure from part (a) to construct a line perpendicular to the perpendicular bisector from part (a). **3a.** Fold the square to make the left side match the right side. Fold the resulting rectangle so that the top side matches the bottom side. **b.** Open the folded sheet from part (a). Fold the corners of the large square inward to meet at the point of intersection of the crease lines. The new crease lines form a squa[...] large square. **5a.** A[...] Construct a circle [...] of the segment an[...] radius. Draw anot[...] the first. Draw the[...] endpoints on the [...] Sample: Fold the s[...] on the crease line [...] original segment),[...] that point to the e[...] **c.** Answers may va[...] pass to the length of the segment. Use that radius and construct the two circles that have centers at the endpoints of the segment. Select a point where the circles intersect and draw segments from that point to the endpoints of the segment. **d.** Answers may vary. Sample: Construct perpendicular lines through the endpoints of the given segment. Construct a circle having one of the endpoints as its center and passing through the other endpoint. Construct a line parallel to the original segment through one of the points of intersection of the circle and the line perpendicular to the original segment. **7a–c.** Midpoints (the key to the constructions in parts (a) and (b) in the exercise) and angle bisectors have been constructed in earlier exercises. **d.** Answers may vary. Sample: Let the triangle be $\triangle ABC$. Construct a circle with center A that passes through B. If $\overline{BC}$ intersects the circle at another point, call this point D. If it does not, extend $\overline{BC}$ until it intersects the circle at D. Construct the midpoint of

$\overline{BD}$ and call it E. The segment $\overline{AE}$ is an altitude of $\triangle ABC$. Construct the other two altitudes in a similar way. **9.** Answers may vary. Sample: Construct the perpendicular bisectors of two sides of the equilateral $\triangle ABC$. The perpendicular bisectors intersect at a point X. Construct the circle that has center X and radius XA.
11. Answers may vary. Sample: Construct a circle. Draw a line through the center of the circle. Call the points of intersection A and B. Construct a circle with center A and radius AB.
13a. acute triangles **b.** right triangles **c.** obtuse triangles **15b.** Construct the perpendicular bisectors of two of the sides of the triangle that has the bases of the saplings as vertices. Place the sprinkler at the point of intersection of the perpendicular bisectors.

Chapter 1
Lesson 1.1

5. Shapes 1, 2, and 8 can cast square shadows [...]allel. Shapes 6 and [...] the beams of light [...]ce. **7.** The triangle [...]e shape, but the

Lesson 1.2

1. Answers may vary. Sample: Since the two bases are the same distance apart at all points, the connecting lines appear to be the same length. Since the points on the second base are translated in the same direction from the corresponding points on the first base, the connecting segments take on the same slope. This makes them appear parallel. **3.** Answers may vary. Sample: The darkest regions sometimes appear to be upper parts of a three-dimensional figure. Then they suddenly switch to be right-hand parts of a different figure. **7.** 15; 26 **9.** The figure on the left is a square whose top side and left side have both been divided into segments of lengths a and b. This allows you to divide the large rectangle into an a-by-a square, two a-by-b rectangles, and a b-by-b square.

Selected Answers

777

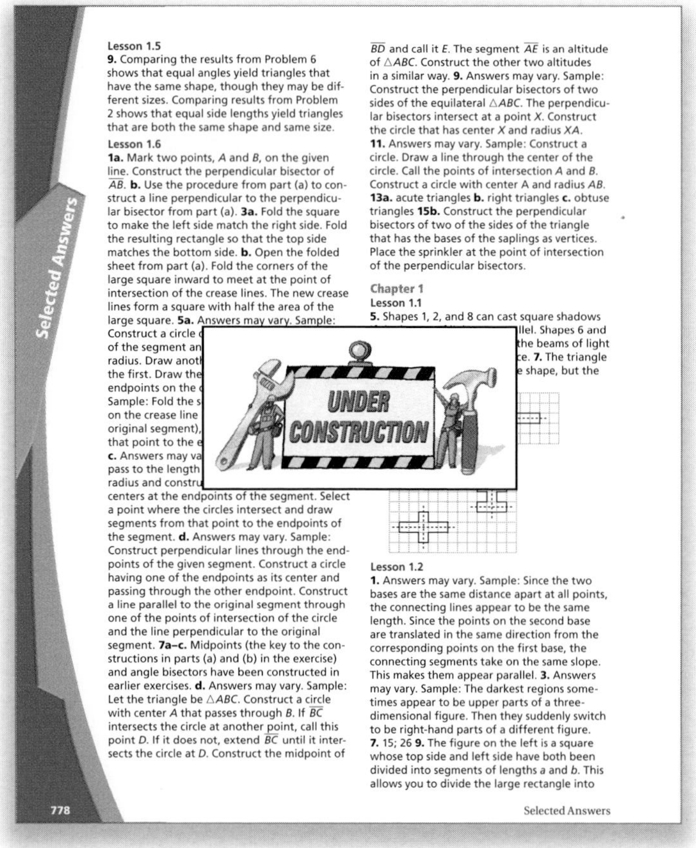

Page 778

Lesson 1.5

9. Comparing the results from Problem 6 shows that equal angles yield triangles that have the same shape, though they may be different sizes. Comparing results from Problem 2 shows that equal side lengths yield triangles that are both the same shape and same size.

Lesson 1.6

1a. Mark two points, A and B, on the given line. Construct the perpendicular bisector of $\overline{AB}$. **b.** Use the procedure from part (a) to construct a line perpendicular to the perpendicular bisector from part (a). **3a.** Fold the square to make the left side match the right side. Fold the resulting rectangle so that the top side matches the bottom side. **b.** Open the folded sheet from part (a). Fold the corners of the large square inward to meet at the point of intersection of the crease lines. The new crease lines form a square with half the area of the large square. **5a.** Answers may vary. Sample: Construct a circle [...] of the segment an[...] radius. Draw anot[...] the first. Draw the[...] endpoints on the [...] Sample: Fold the s[...] on the crease line [...] original segment),[...] that point to the e[...] **c.** Answers may va[...] pass to the length[...] radius and constru[...] centers at the endpoints of the segment. Select a point where the circles intersect and draw segments from that point to the endpoints of the segment. **d.** Answers may vary. Sample: Construct perpendicular lines through the endpoints of the given segment. Construct a circle having one of the endpoints as its center and passing through the other endpoint. Construct a line parallel to the original segment through one of the points of intersection of the circle and the line perpendicular to the original segment. **7a–c.** Midpoints (the key to the constructions in parts (a) and (b) in the exercise) and angle bisectors have been constructed in earlier exercises. **d.** Answers may vary. Sample: Let the triangle be $\triangle ABC$. Construct a circle with center A that passes through B. If $\overline{BC}$ intersects the circle at another point, call this point D. If it does not, extend $\overline{BC}$ until it intersects the circle at D. Construct the midpoint of

$\overline{BD}$ and call it E. The segment $\overline{AE}$ is an altitude of $\triangle ABC$. Construct the other two altitudes in a similar way. **9.** Answers may vary. Sample: Construct the perpendicular bisectors of two sides of the equilateral $\triangle ABC$. The perpendicular bisectors intersect at a point X. Construct the circle that has center X and radius XA.
11. Answers may vary. Sample: Construct a circle. Draw a line through the center of the circle. Call the points of intersection A and B. Construct a circle with center A and radius AB.
13a. acute triangles **b.** right triangles **c.** obtuse triangles **15b.** Construct the perpendicular bisectors of two of the sides of the triangle that has the bases of the saplings as vertices. Place the sprinkler at the point of intersection of the perpendicular bisectors.

Chapter 1
Lesson 1.1

5. Shapes 1, 2, and 8 can cast square shadows [...]allel. Shapes 6 and [...] the beams of light [...]ce. **7.** The triangle [...]e shape, but the

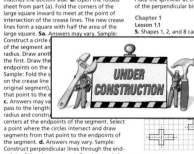

Lesson 1.2

1. Answers may vary. Sample: Since the two bases are the same distance apart at all points, the connecting lines appear to be the same length. Since the points on the second base are translated in the same direction from the corresponding points on the first base, the connecting segments take on the same slope. This makes them appear parallel. **3.** Answers may vary. Sample: The darkest regions sometimes appear to be upper parts of a three-dimensional figure. Then they suddenly switch to be right-hand parts of a different figure. **7.** 15; 26 **9.** The figure on the left is a square whose top side and left side have both been divided into segments of lengths a and b. This allows you to divide the large rectangle into

Selected Answers

778

Page 779

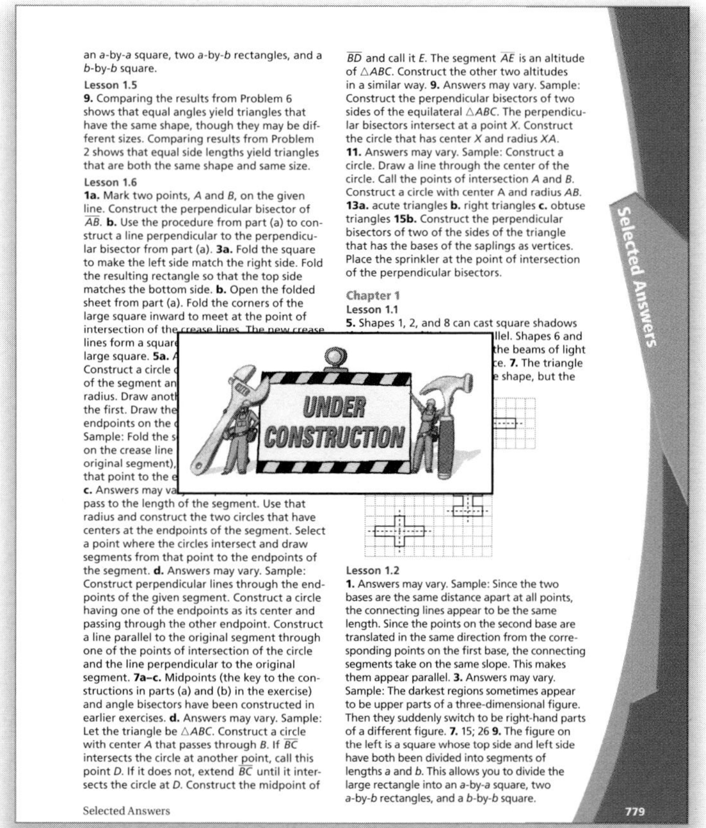

an a-by-a square, two a-by-b rectangles, and a b-by-b square.

Lesson 1.5

9. Comparing the results from Problem 6 shows that equal angles yield triangles that have the same shape, though they may be different sizes. Comparing results from Problem 2 shows that equal side lengths yield triangles that are both the same shape and same size.

Lesson 1.6

1a. Mark two points, A and B, on the given line. Construct the perpendicular bisector of $\overline{AB}$. **b.** Use the procedure from part (a) to construct a line perpendicular to the perpendicular bisector from part (a). **3a.** Fold the square to make the left side match the right side. Fold the resulting rectangle so that the top side matches the bottom side. **b.** Open the folded sheet from part (a). Fold the corners of the large square inward to meet at the point of intersection of the crease lines. The new crease lines form a squa[...] large square. **5a.** A[...] Construct a circle [...] of the segment an[...] radius. Draw anot[...] the first. Draw the[...] endpoints on the [...] Sample: Fold the s[...] on the crease line [...] original segment),[...] that point to the e[...] **c.** Answers may va[...] pass to the length of the segment. Use that radius and construct the two circles that have centers at the endpoints of the segment. Select a point where the circles intersect and draw segments from that point to the endpoints of the segment. **d.** Answers may vary. Sample: Construct perpendicular lines through the endpoints of the given segment. Construct a circle having one of the endpoints as its center and passing through the other endpoint. Construct a line parallel to the original segment through one of the points of intersection of the circle and the line perpendicular to the original segment. **7a–c.** Midpoints (the key to the constructions in parts (a) and (b) in the exercise) and angle bisectors have been constructed in earlier exercises. **d.** Answers may vary. Sample: Let the triangle be $\triangle ABC$. Construct a circle with center A that passes through B. If $\overline{BC}$ intersects the circle at another point, call this point D. If it does not, extend $\overline{BC}$ until it intersects the circle at D. Construct the midpoint of

$\overline{BD}$ and call it E. The segment $\overline{AE}$ is an altitude of $\triangle ABC$. Construct the other two altitudes in a similar way. **9.** Answers may vary. Sample: Construct the perpendicular bisectors of two sides of the equilateral $\triangle ABC$. The perpendicular bisectors intersect at a point X. Construct the circle that has center X and radius XA.
11. Answers may vary. Sample: Construct a circle. Draw a line through the center of the circle. Call the points of intersection A and B. Construct a circle with center A and radius AB.
13a. acute triangles **b.** right triangles **c.** obtuse triangles **15b.** Construct the perpendicular bisectors of two of the sides of the triangle that has the bases of the saplings as vertices. Place the sprinkler at the point of intersection of the perpendicular bisectors.

Chapter 1
Lesson 1.1

5. Shapes 1, 2, and 8 can cast square shadows [...]allel. Shapes 6 and [...] the beams of light [...]ce. **7.** The triangle [...]e shape, but the

Lesson 1.2

1. Answers may vary. Sample: Since the two bases are the same distance apart at all points, the connecting lines appear to be the same length. Since the points on the second base are translated in the same direction from the corresponding points on the first base, the connecting segments take on the same slope. This makes them appear parallel. **3.** Answers may vary. Sample: The darkest regions sometimes appear to be upper parts of a three-dimensional figure. Then they suddenly switch to be right-hand parts of a different figure. **7.** 15; 26 **9.** The figure on the left is a square whose top side and left side have both been divided into segments of lengths a and b. This allows you to divide the large rectangle into an a-by-a square, two a-by-b rectangles, and a b-by-b square.

Selected Answers

779

Additional Answers

Chapter 1
Lesson 1.0 pp. 4–7
In-Class Experiment
11. An octagon is the only shape listed that you cannot make by slicing a cube.

square: equilateral triangle:

nonsquare rectangle: nonequilateral triangle:

pentagon: hexagon:

trapezoid: nonrectangular parallelogram:

Mathematical Reflections p. 23
2.

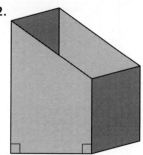

5. Answers may vary. Sample: Draw a 1-in. vertical segment. From the top endpoint of the segment, draw a 1-in. horizontal segment that extends to the right. Starting right and moving clockwise, draw a semicircle with radius 1 in. that starts at the bottom endpoint of the vertical segment. **6.** When you can fold a shape in half so that the two halves fit exactly on top of each

other, the shape is symmetric, and the line containing the fold is a line of symmetry. **7.** A prism is a 3-dimensional figure with two parallel and congruent polygonal faces. All the other faces are parallelograms. Segments joining corresponding vertices of the congruent faces are parallel. **8.** Answers may vary. Sample: When giving someone directions, you must make sure that the directions are precise and that the person you are giving them to understands all the terms you use.

Lesson 1.5 pp. 25–26
For You to Explore
5.

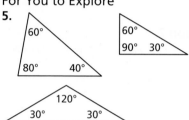

6a. Check students' work. **b.** 1.53; 2.00; 1.73 **c.** The triangles may vary in size; the ratios are the same. **d.** Answers may vary. Sample: If the angles of two triangles are the same, then the triangles have the same shape, even though the side lengths may vary. The length ratio for longest side to shortest side does not change from one triangle to the other.

Lesson 1.6 pp. 27–23
Exercises 7a–c. Midpoints (the key to the constructions in parts (a) and (b) in the exercise) and angle bisectors have been constructed in earlier exercises. **d.** Answers may vary. Sample: Let the triangle be $\triangle ABC$. Construct a circle with center A that passes through B. If $\overline{BC}$ intersects the circle at another point, call this point D. If it does not, extend $\overline{BC}$ until it intersects the circle at D. Construct the midpoint of $\overline{BD}$ and call it E. The segment $\overline{AE}$ is an altitude of $\triangle ABC$. Construct the other two altitudes in a similar way. **e.** Check students' work. **8.** Answers may vary. Sample: The diagonals of a square have the same length; each diagonal divides the square in half; the diagonals intersect at right angles; the diagonals cut the square into quarters.

Project p. 65
1–2. For all $\frac{m}{n} < 1$, you can construct a square with area $\frac{m}{n}$ using just folding techniques (assuming you start with a square paper of area 1). To show this, first note that you can n-sect the side of your square, so you can construct a length of $\frac{1}{n}$ for all $n \geq 1$. Folding the paper over on itself, though it works to bisect segments, is unworkable for general values of n. You can n-sect the side by using parallels. First, construct the diagonal of the square, and mark off n equal lengths along the diagonal (lengths are easily copied by folding). Connect the last endpoint to a vertex of the square not touching the chosen diagonal. Fold parallels to this segment from each mark along the diagonal. (You can fold parallels by folding perpendiculars of perpendiculars.) This will n-sect the side of the square. If you construct a right triangle with leg lengths of $\frac{1}{n}$ and $\frac{1}{n}$, we can use the Pythagorean Theorem to find the hypotenuse. $\left(\frac{1}{n}\right)^2 + \left(\frac{1}{n}\right)^2 = \frac{2}{n^2}$, so the hypotenuse has length $\frac{\sqrt{2}}{n}$. (It is easiest to do this by using paper folding techniques to transfer line segments to the edge of the square sheet of paper first.) Now you can construct a right triangle with leg lengths of $\frac{1}{n}$ and $\frac{\sqrt{2}}{n}$. Again, you can use the Pythagorean Theorem to find the hypotenuse. $\left(\frac{1}{n}\right)^2 + \left(\frac{\sqrt{2}}{n}\right)^2 = \frac{3}{n^2}$, so the hypotenuse has length $\frac{\sqrt{3}}{n}$. You can continue this process, as long as the lengths fit on the 1×1 square. In particular, you can form the length $\frac{\sqrt{n}}{n} = \frac{1}{\sqrt{n}}$ by repeating the process $n - 1$ times. A similar procedure allows you to construct a length of $\sqrt{\frac{m}{n}}$. First, construct the length $\sqrt{\frac{1}{n}}$ as described above. Next, construct a right triangle with both legs of that length. (You may need to transfer side lengths to the edge of the square.) Calculate the length of the hypotenuse: $\left(\sqrt{\frac{1}{n}}\right)^2 + \left(\sqrt{\frac{1}{n}}\right)^2 = \frac{2}{n}$. So, the hypotenuse has length $\sqrt{\frac{2}{n}}$. Now construct a right triangle with legs of

length $\sqrt{\frac{2}{n}}$ and $\sqrt{\frac{1}{n}}$. The hypotenuse has length $\sqrt{\frac{3}{n}}$. In this way, you can construct any length of $\sqrt{\frac{m}{n}}$, as long as it fits on the 1×1 square. Once you construct the length $\sqrt{\frac{m}{n}}$, simply copy that length to two adjacent sides of your square. Fold a square with that side length. Its area will be $\frac{m}{n}$.

4. Fold 0 determines the rectangle that you are going to "square." Here's how to fold the paper to find the square: Fold the lower left corner so that the left edge aligns with Fold 0. This determines point E. Fold the right side over along Fold 1 so that B matches up with E. This determines point F. Fold the lower left corner along Fold 3 so that point A lies on the right hand edge of the page at point G. Without unfolding Fold 3, make Fold 4 so that Fold 4 is perpendicular to the right hand side of the paper and passes through G. Fold the lower right corner so that the right hand edge lines up with Fold 4. This determines point H. Fold the left side of the paper through H so that the lower left edge and the lower right edge line up. Point J is the intersection of Fold 6 and Fold 4, and $BGJH$ is the required square. To see why this works, first note that the area of the rectangle is $AD \cdot AB$.

1. By construction, $AE = AD$.
2. Therefore,
$EB = AB - AE = AB - AD$.
3. By construction, $EF = \frac{EB}{2}$, so $EF = \frac{AB - AD}{2}$.
4. Since $AF = AE + EF$, we have
$AF = AD + \frac{AB - AD}{2} = \frac{AB + AD}{2}$
(by steps 1 and 3).

5. By construction, $FB = EF$, so
$FB = \frac{AB - AD}{2}$ (by step 3).
6. By construction, $GF = AF$.
7. $\triangle BFG$ is a right triangle, so by the Pythagorean Theorem $GF^2 = FB^2 + BG^2$, or $BG^2 = GF^2 - FB^2$.
8. But $GF^2 - FB^2 = AF^2 - EF^2$ (by steps 5 and 6). So $BG^2 = \left(\frac{AB + AD}{2}\right)^2 - \left(\frac{AB - AD}{2}\right)^2$, which simplifies to $AB \cdot AD$.
9. Since you constructed BG to be one side of a square, its area is $BG^2 = AB \cdot AD$. Therefore, $BGJH$ and $ABCD$ have the same area.

Chapter 2
Lesson 2.1   pp. 73–74
Exercises 5. Answers may vary. Sample: For two segments, use a ruler to compare their lengths. For two angles, use a protractor to compare their measures. For two triangles, try fitting one on top of the other to see if the fit is perfect. For rectangular solids, measure their edges to see if the solids have the same length, width, and height. For right cones, see whether the circular bases have equal radii and whether the cones have the same height. For right cylinders, use the same procedure as for cones.

Lesson 2.2   pp. 75–78
Exercises 6a. True; F and E are midpoints of segments that have the same length, so all the parts of those segments have the same length.
b. Nonsensical; two segments cannot be equal. They can only be congruent.
c. Nonsensical; a segment cannot equal a measurement. **d.** Nonsensical; an angle cannot equal a measurement. **e.** Nonsensical; triangles cannot be

equal. They can only be congruent.
f. True; $\overline{DC} \perp \overline{AB}$ and perpendicular segments form right angles. **g.** True; by part (a), $FA = BE$, therefore $\overline{FA} \cong \overline{BE}$.
h. False; $FA = \frac{1}{2}DA = \frac{1}{2}BD$.
i. Nonsensical; two angles cannot be equal. They can only have the same measure. **j.** True; if you fold along $\overline{DC}$, then $\overrightarrow{DA}$ and $\overrightarrow{DB}$ will coincide.
k. Nonsensical; two measurements cannot be congruent. **l.** True; if you fold along $\overline{DC}$, the angles match perfectly.
m. Nonsensical; a triangle cannot be congruent to an angle. **n.** Nonsensical; a triangle cannot be congruent to an angle.

Lesson 2.3   pp. 79–81
Exercises 9a. $\triangle ABC$, $\triangle DBC$, and $\triangle DEC$

b. 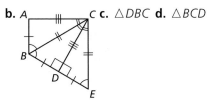   **c.** $\triangle DBC$ **d.** $\triangle BCD$

10a. $m\angle D = 90°$, $m\angle E = 50°$, $m\angle A = 80°$

b.
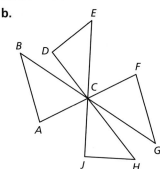

11. 10 pairs; sketches and statements may vary. Sample:
See Figure 1.

Figure 1

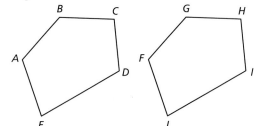

$ABCDE \cong FGHIJ$, $\overline{AB} \cong \overline{FG}$, $\overline{BC} \cong \overline{GH}$, $\overline{CD} \cong \overline{HI}$, $\overline{DE} \cong \overline{IJ}$, $\overline{EA} \cong \overline{JF}$, $\angle A \cong \angle F$, $\angle B \cong \angle G$, $\angle C \cong \angle H$, $\angle D \cong \angle I$, $\angle E \cong \angle J$

Lesson 2.4   pp. 82–86
In-Class Experiment

7. There are three such triangles possible.
See Figure 1.

Exercises

15a. No new triangles can be proved congruent. **b.** One new congruence statement is $\triangle ADE \cong \triangle ADF$ (by SAS). The initial information that $\overline{AD}$ is the perpendicular bisector of $\overline{BC}$ lets us prove $\triangle ADB \cong \triangle ADC$. You can use this, the new congruence statement $\triangle ADE \cong \triangle ADF$, and CPCTC to conclude that $AB = AC$ and $AE = EF$. Since $\overline{AD}$ is the perpendicular bisector of $\overline{BC}$ and $\overline{EF}$, it follows that $BE = FC$ and $BF = CE$. Use SSS to obtain two additional congruence statements: $\triangle AEB \cong \triangle AFC$ and $\triangle AEC \cong \triangle AFB$. **c.** $\triangle ADE \cong \triangle ADF$ by ASA. ($\angle EAD \cong \angle FAD$, $\overline{AD} \cong \overline{AD}$, and $\angle ADB \cong \angle ADC$.) As in part (b), once it is known that $\triangle ADE \cong \triangle ADF$, you can also prove $\triangle AEB \cong \triangle AFC$ and $\triangle AEC \cong \triangle AFB$. **16a.** Yes; $m\angle C = m\angle F = 180° - 72° - 47° = 61°$, so $\angle C \cong \angle F$, and $\triangle ABC \cong \triangle DEF$ by ASA. **b.** If two angles of a triangle are congruent to two angles of another, then the third angle of the two triangles are also congruent. Then you can use ASA to prove that the triangles are congruent.

Mathematical Reflections   p. 87

1a. ASA, SSS, and SAS **b.** ASA: If two angles and the included side of one triangle are congruent to two angles and the included side of a second triangle, then the triangles are congruent. SSS: If the three sides of one triangle are congruent to the three sides of a second triangle, then the triangles are congruent. SAS: If two sides and the included angle of one triangle are congruent to two sides and the included angle of a second triangle, then the triangles are congruent.

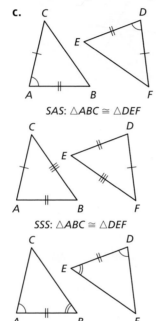

c.
SAS: $\triangle ABC \cong \triangle DEF$

SSS: $\triangle ABC \cong \triangle DEF$

ASA: $\triangle ABC \cong \triangle DEF$

2a. No; congruence relates geometric figures, not measurements; $MA = FL$ or $\overline{MA} \cong \overline{FL}$. **b.** yes **c.** yes **d.** yes **e.** No; angles can only be congruent, not equal; $m\angle AMT = m\angle LFO$, or $\angle AMT \cong \angle LFO$.

4. You can prove that $\angle AOC \cong \angle DOB$ and $\angle BOA \cong \angle COD$. Since $\overline{BO} \cong \overline{CO}$ and $\overline{OD} \cong \overline{OA}$, it follows by SAS that $\triangle AOC \cong \triangle DOB$. By CPCTC, $\overline{BD} \cong \overline{AC}$. Similarly, $\triangle AOB \cong \triangle DOC$, and hence $\overline{CD} \cong \overline{BA}$.

Lesson 2.5   pp. 89–90
For You to Explore

1.

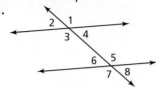

a. $\angle 1 \cong \angle 3 \cong \angle 5 \cong \angle 7$ and $\angle 2 \cong \angle 4 \cong \angle 6 \cong \angle 8$. **b.** The four numbered angles that have the same vertex have measures with a sum of 360°. Two numbered angles that have a common side (such as $\angle 1$ and $\angle 2$, or $\angle 5$ and $\angle 8$) have measures with a sum of 180°. There are many pairs of congruent angles, so there are many other pairs with measures that have a sum of 180°. For example, $m\angle 2 + m\angle 5 = 180°$ and $m\angle 3 + m\angle 6 = 180°$.

2.

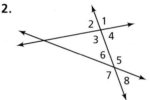

a. $m\angle 1 + m\angle 2 + m\angle 3 + m\angle 4 = 360°$; $m\angle 5 + m\angle 6 + m\angle 7 + m\angle 8 = 360°$ **b.** The invariants involving vertical angles and supplementary angles that you found in Problem 1b exist here as well. The sums $m\angle 3 + m\angle 6$ and $m\angle 2 + m\angle 5$ are also invariant, though in this case they do not equal 180°.

Figure 1

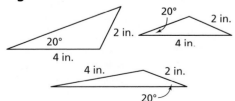

Exercises 4. Answers may vary. Sample: ∠AMR is a straight angle, so m∠AMC + m∠CMR = 180°. ∠BMC is a straight angle, so m∠BMR + m∠CMR = 180°. By algebra, m∠AMC = m∠BMR, and hence ∠AMC ≅ ∠BMR. But AM = MR (given) and BM = CM (M is the midpoint of $\overline{BC}$). $\overline{AM} ≅ \overline{MR}$ and $\overline{BM} ≅ \overline{CM}$. Therefore, △AMC ≅ △RMB (by SAS) and ∠C ≅ ∠MBR (by CPCTC). Since ∠MBR and ∠CBR are the same angle, m∠C = m∠CBR. **5.** Notice that the figure for this exercise is like the figure in Exercise 4, except the figure in Exercise 4 has the segment $\overline{AR}$ drawn through the midpoint M, and an additional segment $\overline{BR}$. By Exercise 5, you know that m∠C = m∠CBR. Since ∠CBD contains ∠CBR, m∠CBD is greater than m∠C. You can use a similar argument to show that m∠CBD is greater than m∠A. Use the figure for Exercise 5. Mark the midpoint N of $\overline{AB}$, extend $\overline{CB}$ through B to point O, and draw $\overline{PC}$ through N so that CN = NP. Prove that ∠A ≅ ∠NBP and use the fact that ∠ABO ≅ ∠CBD.

Lesson 2.6   pp. 91–97
Exercises
2. m∠COB + m∠BOA = 90° and m∠DOC + m∠COB = 90°, so m∠COB + m∠BOA = m∠DOC + m∠COB (transitive property of equality). Therefore m∠BOA = m∠DOC (basic rules of equations).

Lesson 2.7   pp. 98–104
Exercises
1.

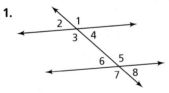

a. A pair of angles are alternate interior angles if they have different vertices, lie between the two lines cut by the transversal, and are on opposite sides of the transversal. ∠4 and ∠6 are alternate interior angles. **b.** A pair of angles are alternate exterior angles if they have different vertices, lie on opposite sides of the transversal, and are not between the two lines cut by the transversal. ∠2 and ∠8 are

alternate exterior angles. **c.** A pair of angles are corresponding angles if they have different vertices and lie on the same side of the transversal, with exactly one of them lying between the two lines cut by the transversal. ∠1 and ∠5 are corresponding angles. **d.** A pair of angles are consecutive angles if they have different vertices, lie on the same side of the transversal, and are both between the two lines cut by the transversal. ∠3 and ∠6 are consecutive angles.
2a. △PXU ≅ △UMP; SSS
b.

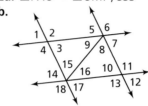

Angles congruent by CPCTC: ∠3 ≅ ∠10, ∠9 ≅ ∠16, ∠8 ≅ ∠15 Angles congruent because the parts of one are congruent to the parts of the other: ∠XUM ≅ ∠XPM Vertical angles: ∠1 ≅ ∠3, ∠2 ≅ ∠4, ∠5 ≅ ∠7, ∠6 ≅ ∠XUM, ∠10 ≅ ∠12, ∠11 ≅ ∠13, ∠14 ≅ ∠17, ∠18 ≅ ∠XPM
c. $\overleftrightarrow{XU} \parallel \overleftrightarrow{PM}$ and $\overleftrightarrow{XP} \parallel \overleftrightarrow{UM}$; AIP Theorem
4. Refer to the figure for parts (a), (b), and (e).

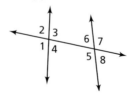

a. Yes; suppose ∠1 ≅ ∠5. ∠1 ≅ ∠3 (vertical angles). So ∠3 ≅ ∠5 (angles congruent to the same angle are congruent). Hence j ∥ k (AIP Theorem). **b.** Yes; suppose ∠1 ≅ ∠7. Since ∠1 ≅ ∠3 and ∠5 ≅ ∠7 (vertical angles), it follows that ∠3 ≅ ∠5. Hence j ∥ k (AIP Theorem). **c.** No; answers may vary. Sample: Let △PAB be an isosceles triangle with $\overline{PA} ≅ \overline{PB}$. If M is the midpoint of $\overline{AB}$, then △PMA ≅ △PMB by SSS. Hence ∠A ≅ ∠B. But $\overleftrightarrow{AB}$ is a transversal of intersecting lines $\overleftrightarrow{PA}$ and $\overleftrightarrow{PB}$. **d.** No; answers may vary. Sample: Consider

the situation described in the answer for part (c). For the transversal $\overleftrightarrow{AB}$ of $\overleftrightarrow{PA}$ and $\overleftrightarrow{PB}$, each pair of alternate exterior angles are supplementary, but $\overleftrightarrow{PA}$ and $\overleftrightarrow{PB}$ are not parallel. **e.** Yes; refer to the figure above the answer for part (a), and suppose ∠4 and ∠5 are supplementary. Since ∠4 and ∠3 are supplementary, it follows that ∠3 ≅ ∠5. Hence j ∥ k (AIP Theorem).
8. By the Triangle Angle-Sum Theorem, m∠OMP + m∠PMO + m∠MOP = m∠NOQ + m∠QON + m∠OQN. Since ∠MOP ≅ ∠NOQ by the Vertical Angle Theorem, m∠OMP + m∠PMO = m∠QON + m∠OQN by the basic moves of equations. Since △MOP and △NOQ are isosceles, m∠OMP = m∠PMO and m∠QON = m∠OQN. This means that 2m∠OMP = 2m∠OQN, and m∠OMP = m∠OQN. Therefore $\overline{NQ} \parallel \overline{MP}$ by AIP.

Lesson 2.8   pp. 105–111
Exercises
1a. m∠1 = 72°, m∠2 = 108°, m∠3 = 108°, m∠4 = 72°, m∠5 = 72°, m∠6 = 108°, m∠7 = 108°, m∠8 = 72°
b. m∠1 = 46°, m∠2 = 134°, m∠3 = 134°, m∠4 = 46°, m∠5 = 46°, m∠6 = 134°, m∠7 = 134°, m∠8 = 46°
c. m∠1 = x°, m∠2 = 180° − x°, m∠3 = 180° − x°, m∠4 = x°, m∠5 = x°, m∠6 = 180° − x°, m∠7 = 180° − x°, m∠8 = x°
d. m∠1 = 60°, m∠2 = 120°, m∠3 = 120°, m∠4 = 60°, m∠5 = 60°, m∠6 = 120°, m∠7 = 120°, m∠8 = 60°
e. m∠1 = 120°, m∠2 = 60°, m∠3 = 60°, m∠4 = 120°, m∠5 = 120°, m∠6 = 60°, m∠7 = 60°, m∠8 = 120°
7a. Answers may vary. Sample: ∠CBD ≅ ∠CDB and ∠DCE ≅ ∠DEC. **b.** No; suppose $\overline{BC} \parallel \overline{DE}$. Then ∠ACB ≅ ∠AED since they are corresponding angles. Since $\overline{BC} ≅ \overline{DE}$ and ∠A ≅ ∠A, you know that △ABC ≅ △ADE by AAS. Then $\overline{AC} ≅ \overline{AE}$ by CPCTC. But this last statement is impossible given the way the diagram was drawn. Therefore, the

assumption that $\overline{BC} \parallel \overline{DE}$ is wrong.
10. In the figure, $\ell \parallel m$ and $n \parallel m$. Draw a transversal of all the lines, as shown in the diagram.

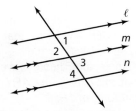

$\angle 1 \cong \angle 2$ (PAI Theorem) and $\angle 2 \cong \angle 3$ (Vertical Angles Theorem). But $\angle 3 \cong \angle 4$ (PAI), so by transitivity of $\cong$, $\angle 1 \cong \angle 4$. Hence $\ell \parallel m$ (AIP).

11. If the conditions of AAS are met by two triangles, then it follows that all three angles of the triangles are congruent. Hence the triangles meet the conditions in the ASA Postulate. So the triangles are congruent.

13a. Select a vertex of a given pentagon and draw the two diagonals from that vertex. The diagonals divide the pentagon into three triangles. The sum of the measures of the angles of these triangles is equal to the sum of the measures of the angles of the pentagon. By the Triangle Angle-Sum Theorem, this sum equals 3(180°), or 540°. **b.** Select a vertex of a given hexagon and draw the three diagonals from that vertex. The diagonals divide the hexagon into four triangles. The sum of the measures of the angles of these triangles is equal to the sum of the measures of the angles of the hexagon. By the Triangle Angle-Sum Theorem, this sum equals 4(180°), or 720°. **14a.** Impossible; if $m\angle 3 + m\angle 6 = 180°$, then $m\angle 4 = m\angle 6$ (since $\angle 3$ and $\angle 4$ are supplementary). It follows by AIP that $n \parallel p$. **b.** Possible; $n \parallel p$ implies $m\angle 4 = m\angle 6$ (PAI). $m\angle 4 = m\angle 6$ implies $n \parallel p$ (AIP). **c.** possible if and only if $q \perp n$ and $q \perp p$ **d.** Impossible; $m\angle 4 + m\angle 5 = m\angle 2 + m\angle 7$ since $m\angle 4 = m\angle 2$ (vertical angles) and $m\angle 5 = m\angle 7$ (vertical angles).

Mathematical Reflections p. 112

4. Draw a line m through P intersecting ℓ at a point A. Choose a point B, different from A, on ℓ. Construct $\angle APC$ congruent to $\angle PAB$ so that $\overrightarrow{AB}$ and $\overrightarrow{PC}$ are on opposite sides of m. The line PC is parallel to ℓ because $\angle APC$ and $\angle PAB$ are congruent alternate interior angles.

Mid-Chapter Test p. 113

5a. yes; SAS **b.** yes; AAS **c.** no **d.** no
6. Since $\overline{AD}$ bisects $\angle CAB$, $\angle MAD \cong \angle BAD$. Since $\overline{PM} \parallel \overline{AD}$, $\angle PMA \cong \angle MAD$ (PAI) and $\angle MPA \cong \angle BAD$ (congruent alternate interior angles implies congruent corresponding angles). Therefore, $\angle MPA \cong \angle PMA$. Since $\overline{MP} \cong \overline{PM}$, it follows by ASA that $\triangle MPA \cong \triangle PMA$, and hence (by CPCTC) that $\overline{PA} \cong \overline{MA}$. Hence $\triangle APM$ is isosceles.

Lesson 2.9   pp. 115–116
For You to Explore 2. Answers may vary. Sample: Divide each of two opposite sides of a square with side length a into 5 segments of equal length. Join corresponding points to get 5 rectangles, each with length a and width $\frac{a}{5}$.

Each of the rectangles has area $\frac{a^2}{5}$.

Together they have area $5\left(\frac{a^2}{5}\right)$, or a^2, which is the area of the original square. **3.** odd number **a.** Answers may vary. Sample: You can think of even numbers as being made out of pairs. Think of pairs of shoes. If every shoe has one partner to make a pair, you have an even number of shoes. Odd numbers are made out of pairs, too, but they also have one leftover shoe. When you add an even number to an odd number, you'll end up with some pairs and one leftover shoe from the odd number, so the sum has to be odd. **b.** Answers may vary. Sample: An even number can be represented by $2a$, where a is an integer. An odd number can be represented by $2b + 1$, where b is an integer. The sum of the numbers is $2a + (2b + 1)$, or $2(a + b) + 1$, which is an odd number.

Exercises 7. Since
$m\angle DAC + m\angle BAC = 180°$, and $m\angle BAC + m\angle B + m\angle C =$

180°, then by the basic moves of equations, $m\angle DAC = m\angle B + m\angle C$.

Lesson 2.11   pp. 123–124
Exercises

2a. Hypothesis: Two lines make congruent alternate interior angles with a transversal. Conclusion: The two lines are parallel. **b.** Hypothesis: n is a whole number; conclusion: $n^2 + n + 41$ is prime. **c.** Hypothesis: two sides and the included angle of one triangle are congruent to two sides and the included angle of another triangle; conclusion: The triangles are congruent. **d.** Hypothesis: two lines are both parallel to a third line; conclusion: the two lines are parallel to each other. True; proofs may vary. Sample: Select two alternate interior angles formed by the two lines and the transversal to which they are perpendicular. These angles are congruent since all the angles formed by perpendicular lines are right angles. By AIP, the lines perpendicular to the transversal are parallel.

6. False; the sketch of the hypothesis shown here provides a counterexample.
7. True; proofs may vary. Sample: If $\triangle ABC$ has $\angle B$ congruent to $\angle C$, then $\triangle ABC \cong \triangle ACB$ by SSS. It follows that $\overline{AB} \cong \overline{AC}$ and hence that $\triangle ABC$ is isosceles.
8. True; proofs may vary. Sample: Reasoning similar to that in the answer for Exercise 7 shows that if all angles of $\triangle ABC$ are congruent, then $\overline{AB} \cong \overline{AC} \cong \overline{BC}$.
9. False; the sketch of the hypothesis shown here provides a counterexample.
10. If $\triangle ABC$ is a right triangle with legs $\overline{AB}$ and $\overline{AC}$, and $AB = \frac{1}{2}AC$, then $CB = 5AB^2$. Proof: By the Pythagorean Theorem, $CB^2 = AB^2 + AC^2$. Since $AB =$

$\frac{1}{2}AC$, it follows that $AC = 2AB$. Hence $CB^2 = AB^2 + (2AB)^2$. Simplify to obtain $CB^2 = 5AB^2$.

Lesson 2.12   pp. 125–130
Exercises

2.

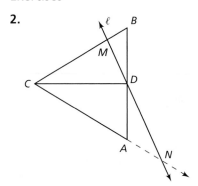

9. Since $\overline{VR}$ and $\overline{UQ}$ are medians to congruent segments, $\overline{TU} \cong \overline{TV}$. $\angle RTQ$ is common to $\triangle RTV$ and $\triangle QTU$. Hence $\triangle RTV \cong \triangle QTU$ by SAS. It follows by CPCTC that $\overline{RV} \cong \overline{QU}$. Thus $VR = UQ$. **10.** Let N be the midpoint of $\overline{LM}$. Since $\overline{LN} \cong \overline{MN}$, $\overline{PN} \cong \overline{PN}$, and $\angle PNL \cong \angle PNM$, it follows that $\triangle PLN \cong \triangle PMN$ by SAS. Therefore $\overline{PL} \cong \overline{PM}$ by CPCTC, and $PL = PM$. **11.** The line $x = 3$ is the perpendicular bisector of $\overline{OA}$, so B is equidistant from O and A. This implies $\overline{BA} \cong \overline{BO}$, and therefore $\triangle AOB$ is isosceles.

Lesson 2.13   pp. 131–134
Exercises 4. Let $\triangle ABC$ be isosceles with $\overline{AB} \cong \overline{AC}$ and $\overline{BE}$ and $\overline{CD}$ bisecting $\angle ABC$ and $\angle ACB$. Since $\angle ABC \cong \angle ACB$, you also know $\angle EBC \cong \angle DCB$. Therefore $\triangle ABE \cong \triangle ACD$ by ASA, and $\overline{BE} \cong \overline{CD}$ by CPCTC. **5.** Let $\triangle ABC$ have altitudes $\overline{BE}$ and $\overline{CD}$, with $\overline{BE} \cong \overline{CD}$. If the triangle is acute, the altitudes lie inside the triangle. Since $\angle A \cong \angle A$, $\overline{BE} \cong \overline{CD}$, and $\angle ADC \cong \angle AEB$ (because all right angles are congruent), you can conclude that $\triangle ADC \cong \triangle AEB$ by SAS. Therefore $\overline{AC} \cong \overline{AB}$, and $\triangle ABC$ is isosceles. If the triangle is a right triangle, the altitudes coincide with two of the sides of the triangle. And since the altitudes are congruent, the sides are congruent as well. Therefore, the triangle is

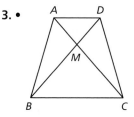

isosceles. If the riangle is obtuse, the altitudes $\overline{CD}$ and $\overline{BE}$ lie outside the triangle. $\angle AEB \cong \angle ADC$ (both are right angles) and $\angle EAB \cong \angle DAC$ (vertical angles). But $\overline{BE} \cong \overline{CD}$ (given). So $\triangle AEB \cong \triangle ADC$ (AAS). Hence $\overline{AB} \cong \overline{AC}$ (CPCTC), which means $\triangle ABC$ is isosceles. **6.** Let $\triangle ABC$ be isosceles with $\overline{AB} \cong \overline{AC}$ with altitudes $\overline{BE}$ and $\overline{CD}$. If $\triangle ABC$ is acute, the altitudes lie inside the triangle. Since $\angle ADC \cong \angle AEB$ (because right angles are congruent), $\overline{AB} \cong \overline{AC}$, and $\angle A \cong \angle A$, you can conclude that $\triangle ADC \cong \triangle AEB$ by AAS. Therefore, $\overline{DC} \cong \overline{EB}$ by CPCTC. If $\triangle ABC$ is a right triangle, the altitudes from B and C coincide with the legs of the isosceles triangle; therefore, they are congruent. If $\triangle ABC$ is obtuse, the altitudes lie outside the triangle. Since $\angle AEB \cong \angle ADC$, $\angle EAB \cong \angle DAC$, and $\overline{AB} \cong \overline{AC}$, you can conclude that $\triangle AEB \cong \triangle ADC$ by AAS. Therefore, $\overline{BE} \cong \overline{CD}$ by CPCTC. **7.** Since M and N are midpoints, $CM = \frac{1}{2}AC$ and $CN = \frac{1}{2}BC$. But $AC = BC$, so $\frac{1}{2}AC = \frac{1}{2}BC$. Hence $CM = CN$, which implies $\triangle CMN$ is isosceles. **8.** Since M and N are midpoints of congruent segments $\overline{CB}$ and $\overline{FE}$, respectively, $\overline{CM} \cong \overline{FN}$. Since $\overline{AC} \cong \overline{DF}$ and $\overline{AM} \cong \overline{DN}$, it follows that $\triangle ACM \cong \triangle DFN$ by SSS, and $\angle C \cong \angle F$ by CPCTC. Therefore, $\triangle ABC \cong \triangle DEF$ by SAS.

Lesson 2.14   pp. 135–140
Exercises

3. •

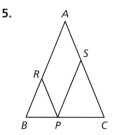

• $m\angle ABC = m\angle BCD = m\angle CDA = m\angle DAB = 90°$; $\overline{AB} \cong \overline{BC} \cong \overline{CD} \cong \overline{DA}$; $\overline{BE} \cong \overline{CF} \cong \overline{DG} \cong \overline{AH}$

• Because they are all supplementary to right angles, $m\angle GDH = m\angle HAE = m\angle EBF = m\angle FCG = 90°$. Because $\overline{AB} \cong \overline{BC} \cong \overline{CD} \cong \overline{DA}$ and $\overline{BE} \cong \overline{CF} \cong$

$\overline{DG} \cong \overline{AH}$, it is also true that $\overline{DH} \cong \overline{AE} \cong \overline{BF} \cong \overline{CG}$. Therefore, $\triangle HAE \cong \triangle EBF \cong \triangle FCG \cong \triangle GDH$ by SAS. This means that $\overline{GH} \cong \overline{HE} \cong \overline{EF} \cong \overline{FG}$ by CPCTC. Again by CPCTC, it follows that $\angle AHE \cong \angle BEF$, and hence that $m\angle AHE = m\angle BEF$. By the Triangle Angle-Sum Theorem, we know that $m\angle AHE + m\angle AEH = 90°$. Therefore, $m\angle HEF = m\angle BEF + m\angle AEH = m\angle AHE + m\angle AEH = 90°$. Similarly, $m\angle EFG = m\angle FGH = m\angle GHE = 90°$. Since the sides of $EFGH$ are all congruent, and all the angles of $EFGH$ are right angles, $EFGH$ is a square.

4.

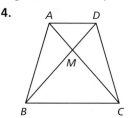

$\overline{AC} \cong \overline{BD}$; $\overline{AB} \cong \overline{DC}$ $\triangle ABC \cong \triangle DCB$ by SSS. Therefore $\angle MBC \cong \angle MCB$ by CPCTC. It then follows that $\triangle MBC$ is isosceles.

5.

• $\overline{AB} \cong \overline{AC}$; $\overline{AB} \parallel \overline{SP}$, $\overline{AC} \parallel \overline{RP}$

• First note that $\angle SCP \cong \angle RPB$ because they are corresponding angles formed by parallel lines cut by a transversal. Since $\triangle ABC$ is isosceles, $\angle RBP \cong \angle SCP$, and therefore, by transitivity, $\angle RBP \cong \angle RPB$. This means that $\triangle RBP$ is isosceles and $\overline{RB} \cong \overline{RP}$. Next, draw $\overline{RS}$. By PAI, $\angle RSP \cong \angle ARS$ and $\angle PRS \cong \angle ASR$. Since $\overline{RS} \cong \overline{RS}$, you can conclude that $\triangle SRA \cong \triangle RSP$ by ASA. So $PR = SA$ and $RA = PS$. It follows, by substitution, that perimeter $ARPS = PR + RA + AS + PS = BR + RA + BR + RA = 2(BR + RA) = 2BA$. **6.** There are six proofs involved. For the first five, refer to the following figure.

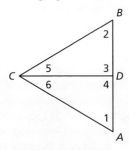

- Assume statements 1 and 2. Then $\overline{AC} \cong \overline{BC}$ and $\overline{DB} \cong \overline{DA}$. Since $\overline{CD} \cong \overline{CD}$, it follows that $\triangle ACD \cong \triangle BCD$. By CPCTC, $\angle 5 \cong \angle 6$. Hence $\overline{CD}$ bisects $\angle ACB$. Again by CPCTC, $\angle 3 \cong \angle 4$. Hence $\angle 3$ and $\angle 4$ are right angles, which implies $\overline{CD}$ is an altitude.
- Assume statements 1 and 3. Then $\overline{AC} \cong \overline{BC}$ and $\angle 3$ and $\angle 4$ are right angles. $\angle 1 \cong \angle 2$ by the Isosceles Triangle Theorem. Therefore, $\triangle ACD \cong \triangle BCD$ by AAS. By CPCTC, $\overline{DA} \cong \overline{DB}$. So $\overline{CD}$ is a median. Also by CPCTC, $\angle 5 \cong \angle 6$, and hence $\overline{CD}$ bisects $\angle ACB$. • Assume statements 1 and 4. Then $\overline{BC} \cong \overline{AC}$ and $\angle 5 \cong \angle 6$. But $\overline{CD} \cong \overline{CD}$, so $\triangle ACD \cong \triangle BCD$ by SAS. By CPCTC, $\overline{DA} \cong \overline{DB}$. So $\overline{CD}$ is a median. Also by CPCTC, $\angle 3 \cong \angle 4$. Hence $\overline{CD}$ is an altitude. • Assume statements 2 and 3. Then $\overline{DA} \cong \overline{DB}$ and $\overline{CD} \perp \overline{AB}$. It follows that $\overline{CD}$ is the perpendicular bisector of $\overline{AB}$ and hence, by the Perpendicular Bisector Theorem, $AC = BC$. Therefore $\triangle ABC$ is isosceles. Since $\overline{CD} \cong \overline{CD}$ and

$\angle 3 \cong \angle 4$, $\triangle ACD \cong \triangle BCD$ by SAS. By CPCTC, $\angle 5 \cong \angle 6$. Thus $\overline{CD}$ bisects $\angle ACB$. • Assume statements 3 and 4. Then $\angle 3 \cong \angle 4$ and $\angle 5 \cong \angle 6$. Since $\overline{CD} \cong \overline{CD}$, it follows that $\triangle ACD \cong \triangle BCD$ (ASA). By CPCTC, $\overline{AC} \cong \overline{BC}$ and $\overline{DA} \cong \overline{DB}$. Therefore, $\triangle ABC$ is isosceles and $\overline{CD}$ is a median. • Assume statements 2 and 4. Then $\overline{DB} \cong \overline{DA}$ and $\angle BCD \cong \angle ACD$. First we use an indirect proof that $\overline{AB} \perp \overline{CD}$. Suppose that $\overline{AB}$ is not perpendicular to $\overline{CD}$. Draw the line ℓ that is perpendicular to $\overline{CD}$ at D. Let M be the point where ℓ intersects $\overrightarrow{CB}$, and let N be the point where ℓ intersects $\overrightarrow{CA}$, as indicated in the figure below.

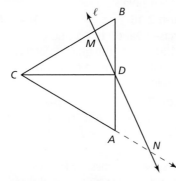

Since $\ell \perp \overline{CD}$, $\angle MDC$ and $\angle NDC$ are right angles and hence are congruent. But $\angle BCD \cong \angle ACD$ (given) and $\overline{CD} \cong \overline{CD}$. Hence $\triangle CMD \cong \triangle CND$ by AAS. By CPCTC, $\overline{DM} \cong \overline{DN}$. But $\overline{DB} \cong \overline{DA}$ (given) and $\angle BDM \cong \angle ADN$ (vertical angles).

Hence $\triangle BMD \cong \triangle AND$ by SAS. By CPCTC, $\angle BMD \cong \angle AND$. However, these are alternate interior angles for lines CB and CA and the transversal ℓ. The AIP Theorem implies that lines CB and CA are parallel. This contradicts the fact that lines CB and CA intersect at C. Since the assumption that $\overline{AB}$ is not perpendicular to $\overline{CD}$ has led to a contradiction, these segments are perpendicular. Hence $\overline{CD}$ is an altitude and the perpendicular bisector of $\overline{AB}$. By the Perpendicular Bisector Theorem, $CA = CB$. **7.** Answers may vary. Sample: $\triangle ACD \cong \triangle BCD$. **8a.** the set of all nonequilateral isosceles triangles **b.** There are no members of this set. **c.** the set of all equilateral triangles **16.** Yes; suppose you know two side lengths, a and c, and the measure of $\angle A$.

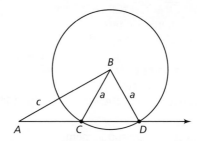

The third side must lie along $\overrightarrow{AC}$, which yields two possibilities for the placement of side a, as shown above. But if $\angle A$ has the largest measure of all the angles in the triangle, then a is the longest side, and the other two sides fall completely within the circle. See Figure 1

Figure 1

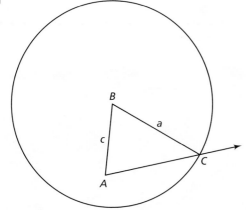

Because the circle intersects $\overrightarrow{AC}$, in only one place, there is only one possible placement for side a. This means that $\triangle ABC$ is uniquely determined, and that SSA is a valid congruence test, when the congruent angles are the largest angles in each triangle. **17.** No; consider the figure below, where $\angle A$ is the smallest angle of the triangle.

See Figure 1

The placement of side a is not uniquely determined, so SSA is not a valid congruence test. **18.** Draw lines through C and D perpendicular to $\overline{AB}$ at P and Q, respectively. Since $\overline{CP}$ and $\overline{DQ}$ are perpendicular to the same segment, they are parallel. If you draw $\overline{DP}$, you can use ASA to prove $\triangle DQP \cong \triangle PCD$. It follows that $\overline{CP} \cong \overline{QD}$ (CPCTC). The HL Congruence test shows that $\triangle ADQ \cong \triangle BCP$, and hence that $\angle A \cong \angle B$. It follows by the converse of the Isosceles Triangle Theorem that $\triangle ABE$ is isosceles.

Mathematical Reflections   p. 141

5. Let $m\angle ATC = x°$. Since $\angle ATC$ and $\angle CTB$ are supplementary, $m\angle CTB = 180° - x°$. The base angles of isosceles triangle ATC have measure $\frac{1}{2}(180 - x)°$ (Isosceles Triangle Theorem, Triangle Angle-Sum Theorem, and algebra). Similarly, the base angles of isosceles triangle CTB have measure $\frac{1}{2}x°$. Therefore, $m\angle A + m\angle B = 90°$.

By the Triangle Angle-Sum Theorem, $m\angle ACB = 90°$, which means that $\triangle ABC$ is a right triangle.

6. two-column proof, paragraph proof, flowchart, outline **7.** The Perpendicular Bisector Theorem is the theorem that states that each point on the perpendicular bisector of a segment is equidistant from the endpoints of the segment. **8.** Hypothesis: an object is a tree; conclusion: it is green.

Lesson 2.15   p. 143
Exercises 9. Answers may vary. Sample: Fold the paper so that the shorter side lines up evenly with the longer side. The point where this diagonal crease meets the longer side marks off a segment congruent to the shorter side on the longer side. Unfold the paper and then make a fold at this point parallel to the shorter side. The result is a square.

Lesson 2.16   pp. 144–146
Exercises 9a. 60 **b.** 60°, 60°, 120°, and 120° **c.** No; the quadrilateral is either a parallelogram or an isosceles trapezoid.

Lesson 2.17   pp. 147–150
Exercises 20. Let $ABCD$ be a kite with $\overline{AB} \cong \overline{BC}$ and $\overline{CD} \cong \overline{DA}$. Draw diagonals $\overline{BD}$ and $\overline{AC}$. $\triangle BCA$ and $\triangle DCA$ are isosceles triangles. By Exercise 19, $\overline{BD}$ bisects the vertex angles of these isosceles triangles. The bisector of the vertex angle of an isosceles triangle is an altitude of the triangle. It follows that $\overline{BD} \perp \overline{AC}$. **21.** false; a resident of Toronto **22.** true **23.** false; a 2-by-8 rectangle **24.** true **25.** true

Lesson 2.18   pp. 151–156
Exercises 6. Answers may vary. Sample: If a pair of consecutive angles of a parallelogram are congruent, then the

parallelogram is also a rectangle. To prove this, note that consecutive angles of a parallelogram are supplementary. Then each congruent angle must have measure 90°. The other two angles must then also have measure 90° since they are also consecutive with the first two angles considered. **7a.** Since a diagonal divides a parallelogram into two congruent triangles, opposite sides of the parallelogram are congruent by CPCTC. **b.** Since a diagonal divides a parallelogram into two congruent triangles, opposite angles of the parallelogram are congruent by CPCTC.
8. Let $ABCD$ be a parallelogram whose diagonals intersect at E,

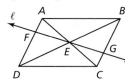

as shown in the diagram. Let ℓ be a line through E that does not contain a diagonal. (You can assume ℓ intersects $\overline{AD}$ and $\overline{BC}$, since you can easily modify the proof if ℓ intersects the other pair of parallel sides.) $\overline{AE} \cong \overline{CE}$ because the diagonals of a parallelogram bisect each other. $\angle EAF \cong \angle ECG$ because $\overline{AD}$ is parallel to $\overline{BC}$. Also, $\angle AEF \cong \angle CEG$ because they are vertical angles. Therefore, $\triangle AEF \cong \triangle CEG$ by AAS, and hence $\overline{EF} \cong \overline{EG}$.
9. always **10.** sometimes **11.** never
12. sometimes **13.** sometimes
14. sometimes **15.** sometimes
16. sometimes **17.** sometimes
18. never **19.** sometimes **20.** never
21. never **22.** always **23.** always
24. sometimes **25.** sometimes
26. sometimes **27.** never **28.** always

Figure 1

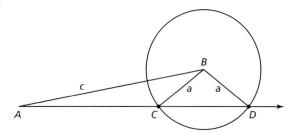

29. A **30a.** $\overline{XS} \parallel \overline{WT}$, $\overline{XS} \cong \overline{WT}$, $\overline{XW} \parallel \overline{ST}$, $\overline{XW} \cong \overline{ST}$ **b.** Parallelogram; since the two points marked on each side of *MNPQ* trisect the side and since opposite sides of *MNPQ* are congruent, it follows that $\overline{MS} \cong \overline{PW}$ and $\overline{MX} \cong \overline{PT}$. Also, $\angle M \cong \angle P$. Therefore, $\triangle XMS \cong \triangle TPW$ by SAS, and $\overline{XS} \cong \overline{TW}$ by CPCTC. A similar argument shows that $\triangle QXW \cong \triangle NTS$ and that $\overline{XW} \cong \overline{TS}$. Since both pairs of opposite sides of *STWX* are congruent, *STWX* is a parallelogram. **c.** They bisect each other. **33a.** If a person lives in New York City, then that person lives in New York State. **b.** true **c.** If a person lives in New York State, then that person lives in New York City. **d.** false

34a. If an animal is a lizard, then it is a reptile. **b.** true **c.** If an animal is a reptile, then it is a lizard. **d.** false

35a. If an animal is a bird, then it has feathers. **b.** true **c.** If an animal has feathers, then it is a bird. **d.** true

36a. If a person is a cowboy, then that person comes from Texas. **b.** false **c.** If a person comes from Texas, then that person is a cowboy. **d.** false

37a. If something is a piece of fruit, then it is an apple. **b.** false **c.** If something is an apple, then it is a piece of fruit. **d.** true

Lesson 2.19   **pp. 157–159**
Exercises 16. Let *ABCD* be a parallelogram with congruent diagonals $\overline{AC}$ and $\overline{DB}$. Opposite sides of a parallelogram are congruent, so $\overline{AD} \cong \overline{BC}$. A segment is congruent to itself, so $\overline{AB} \cong \overline{AB}$. Hence $\triangle DAB \cong \triangle CBA$ by SSS. The consecutive angles $\angle DAB$ and $\angle CBA$ of *ABCD* are supplementary and hence are right angles. From Exercise 15, it follows that *ABCD* is a rectangle.

17. Rhombus; let *ABCD* be a rectangle with *M*, *N*, *P*, and *Q* as the midpoints of $\overline{AB}$, $\overline{BC}$, $\overline{CD}$, and $\overline{DA}$, respectively. $\triangle AMQ \cong \triangle MBN \cong \triangle PCN \cong \triangle PDQ$ by SAS, so $\overline{QM} \cong \overline{MN} \cong \overline{NP} \cong \overline{PQ}$ by CPCTC.

18. Suppose *ABCD* has four congruent sides. *ABCD* is a parallelogram. Therefore, *ABCD* is a rhombus.

19. Since all sides of a rhombus are congruent, the two triangles formed by drawing a diagonal each have two congruent sides. **20.** A diagonal divides the rhombus into two isosceles triangles, by Exercise 19. Their base angles are congruent. Therefore, the diagonal bisects opposite sides of the rhombus. **21.** It follows from the converse of the Perpendicular Bisector Theorem that each diagonal of a rhombus is the perpendicular bisector of the other diagonal.

22. Let *ABCD* be a parallelogram that has perpendicular diagonals. Since the diagonals of a parallelogram bisect each other, the four right triangles into which *ABCD* is divided by its diagonals are congruent. By CPCTC, the hypotenuses of these right triangles are all congruent. Therefore *ABCD* is a rhombus. **23.** By PAI, all four angles formed by the diagonal are congruent, so each triangle is isosceles. Moreover, the triangles are also congruent, so all four sides of the parallelogram are congruent by CPCTC.

24.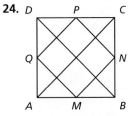

By Exercise 17, *MNPQ* is a rhombus. By Exercise 21, the diagonals $\overline{AC}$ and $\overline{BD}$ of *ABCD* are perpendicular. By the Midline Theorem, $\overline{PN} \parallel \overline{BD}$ and $\overline{MN} \parallel \overline{AC}$. It follows that $\overline{PN} \perp \overline{MN}$. By Exercise 15, *MNPQ* is a rectangle. Since *MNPQ* is a rhombus and a rectangle, it is a square. **25a.** squares **b.** squares **c.** kites

Mathematical Reflections   **p. 160**
3. A parallelogram has parallel opposite sides, and a rectangle is a parallelogram whose angles are right angles. **4.** Yes; a rhombus is both a kite and a parallelogram. **5.** If you construct the diagonal of a kite so that two of the congruent adjacent sides of the kite are sides of each triangle, then the triangles are isosceles. You can do this two ways only if the kite is also a rhombus. **6.** Answers may vary. Sample: Opposite sides of a parallelogram are congruent. Diagonals of a parallelogram divide the parallelogram into congruent triangles, and the two diagonals bisect each other. At least one diagonal of a kite is an axis of symmetry. The diagonals of a kite are perpendicular to one another. Trapezoids have exactly one pair of parallel sides. **7.** yes, because squares have two pairs of parallel sides; no, because a parallelogram need not have congruent sides or right angles **8.** not necessarily

Cumulative Review   **pp. 166–167**
12. The figure below shows why SSA cannot be used as a test for congruence.

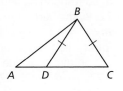

$\triangle ABC$ and $\triangle ABD$ have two congruent sides, and one congruent noninluded angle, but the two triangles are clearly not congruent.

13a.

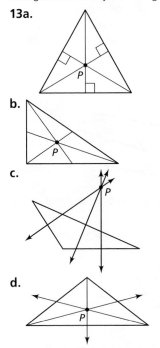

b.

c.

d.

14a. always **b.** always **c.** always
15. Two geometrical objects are congruent when you can superimpose one over the other with no overlap, possibly after flipping it over. Equality deals with measurements of geometric figures. **16.** Not all isosceles right triangles are congruent. Consider such a triangle with legs of length 1, and another with legs of length 2. They are the same shape, but the second

triangle is larger than the first.
17a. $\triangle ABC \cong \triangle ADC$ **b.** SSS
18a. $\triangle ABC \cong \triangle DEC$ **b.** ASA
19. Since M is the midpoint of $\overline{AB}$ and $\overline{CD}$, we have $\overline{DM} \cong \overline{MC}$ and $\overline{AM} \cong \overline{MB}$. And by the Vertical Angles Theorem, $\angle AMD \cong \angle BMC$. Therefore, $\triangle AMD \cong \triangle BMC$ by SAS. **20.** The two triangles will not necessarily be congruent. AAA is not a strong enough test for congruence. **21a.** alternate interior angles **b.** consecutive angles **c.** corresponding angles **d.** corresponding angles
22. By the Vertical Angles Theorem, $m\angle 1 = 140°$. By PAI, the angle formed by t and n supplementary to $\angle 2$ on the same side of t has measure $140°$. Therefore $m\angle 2 = 40°$.
23. $\overleftrightarrow{HK} \parallel \overleftrightarrow{IL}$ follows immediately from the Midline Theorem. **24.** Since $\overline{AB} \parallel \overline{CD}$, you know $\angle BAC \cong \angle DCA$ by the PAI Theorem. And since $\overline{AC} \cong \overline{AC}$ and $\overline{AB} \cong \overline{CD}$, you can conclude that $\triangle ABC \cong \triangle CDA$ by SSS. **25a.** The hypothesis is, "Two lines are parallel to a third line." The conclusion is, "The lines are parallel to each other."
b.

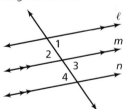

c. This statement is true. **d.** Refer to the diagram below.

Suppose $\ell \parallel m$ and $n \parallel m$. By PAI, $\angle 1 \cong \angle 2$. By the Vertical Angles Theorem, $\angle 2 \cong \angle 3$. By PAI, $\angle 3 \cong \angle 4$. By transitivity, $\angle 1 \cong \angle 4$. Finally, $\ell \parallel n$ by AIP. **26a.** The hypothesis is, "A parallelogram is equiangular." The conclusion is, "The parallelogram is a square."
b.

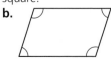

c. The statement is not true.
d. A nonsquare rectangle is an equiangular parallelogram.
27a. The hypothesis is, "Two angles are congruent and supplementary." The conclusion is, "The two angles are congruent."
b.

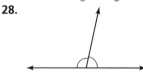

c. The statement is true. **d.** Suppose that $\angle 1 \cong \angle 2$ and that they are supplementary. Then $m\angle 1 = m\angle 2$ and $m\angle 1 + m\angle 2 = 180°$. This implies $m\angle 1 = m\angle 2 = 90°$. $\angle 1$ and $\angle 2$ are both right angles.
28.

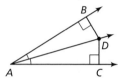

29. Refer to the figure below.

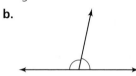

Need	$\overline{CD} \cong \overline{DB}$
Use	CPCTC
Need	congruent triangles: $\triangle ACD \cong \triangle ABD$
Use	ASA
Need	two congruent angles: $\angle BAD \cong \angle CAD$
Use	given
Need	two congruent angles: $\angle BDA \cong \angle CDA$
Use	Triangle Angle-Sum Theorem
Need	two congruent sides: $\overline{AD} \cong \overline{AD}$
Use	reflexivity of congruence

Proof: Because the point D lies on the angle bisector of $\angle CAB$, you know that $\angle BAD \cong \angle CAD$. By the Triangle Angle-Sum Theorem, $m\angle DCA + m\angle CAD + m\angle CDA = 180°$ and $m\angle DBA + m\angle BAD + m\angle BDA = 180°$, so $m\angle CDA = 180° - m\angle DCA - m\angle CAD$, and $m\angle BDA = 180° - m\angle DBA - m\angle BAD$. But $m\angle DCA = m\angle DBA$ and $m\angle CAD = m\angle BAD$, so $m\angle CDA = m\angle BDA$, and $\angle CDA \cong \angle BDA$. Therefore,

$\triangle ACD \cong \triangle ABD$ by ASA, and $\overline{CD} \cong \overline{DB}$ by CPCTC.
30. Refer to the figure below.

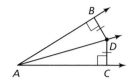

Need	$\angle BAD \cong \angle CAD$
Use	CPCTC
Need	congruent triangles: $\triangle ACD \cong \triangle ABD$
Use	HL
Need	two right angles: $m\angle DBA = m\angle DCA = 90°$
Use	given
Need	congruent legs: $\overline{CD} \cong \overline{DB}$
Use	given
Need	congruent hypotenuses: $\overline{AD} \cong \overline{AD}$
Use	reflexivity of congruence

Proof: $\triangle ACD \cong \triangle ABD$ by HL since $m\angle DBA = m\angle DCA = 90°$, $\overline{CD} \cong \overline{DB}$, and $\overline{AD} \cong \overline{AD}$. Then $\angle BAD \cong \angle CAD$ by CPCTC, and point D lies on the bisector of $\angle ABC$.

Chapter 3
Lesson 3.1   pp. 171–173
For You to Explore

1. Construct $\overline{AE}$ perpendicular to $\overline{DC}$. Cut along $\overline{AE}$ and slide the triangle to the right.

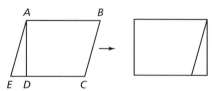

2. Cut along $\overline{MN}$, where M and N are the midpoints of $\overline{BC}$ and $\overline{AC}$, respectively. Rotate $\triangle MCN$ 180° about point M.

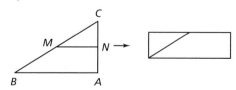

3. Cut along $\overline{MN}$, where M and N are the midpoints of $\overline{BC}$ and $\overline{AC}$ respectively. Rotate $\triangle MCN$ 180° about point N.

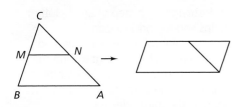

4. Construct $\overline{PQ}$, where P and Q are the midpoints of $\overline{AB}$ and $\overline{CB}$, respectively. Construct $\overline{BR}$ perpendicular to $\overline{PQ}$. Cut along $\overline{PQ}$ and $\overline{BR}$. Rotate $\triangle PRB$ and $\triangle QRB$ both 180°, about P and Q respectively.

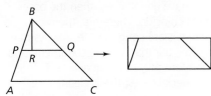

5. Construct $\overline{EF}$, where E and F are the midpoints of $\overline{AB}$ and $\overline{DC}$, respectively. Construct $\overline{BG}$ perpendicular to $\overline{EF}$. Cut along $\overline{EF}$ and $\overline{BG}$. Rotate $\triangle EGB$ and trapezoid $FGBC$ both 180°, about E and F respectively.

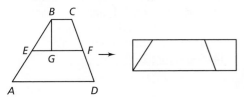

Exercises

8. There are 14 polygons in all.

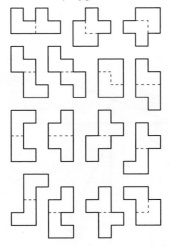

Lesson 3.2   pp. 174–180

Exercises 4a. Cut along a diagonal. Reflect one of the triangles along a horizontal line. Translate one of the triangles so that two congruent sides align. **b.** Find the midpoint of a side. Cut along the line from that midpoint to one of the endpoints of the opposite side. Rotate the resulting triangle 180° around the midpoint. **c.** Cut along a diagonal. Translate one of the triangles so that two congruent sides align. **d.** Use the procedure from part (b) to form a right triangle. The triangle is scalene unless one side of the rectangle is twice the length of the other. If so, choose the midpoint of the shorter side to start your dissection. **e.** Start with rectangle $ABCD$. Pick a point E on $\overline{BC}$ and a point F on $\overline{AD}$. Let G be the midpoint of $\overline{BE}$ and H be the midpoint of $\overline{EC}$. Draw $\overline{AG}$ and $\overline{FH}$. Rotate $\triangle ABG$ 180° about G and rotate trapezoid $FDCH$ 180° about H.

6.

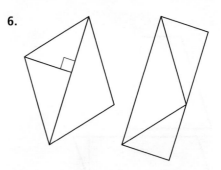

11. Cut along the median to the base of the isosceles triangle. Rotate one of the resulting triangles 90° so that the halves of the base of the original triangle align. The result is an isosceles triangle with two sides of length s. The new triangle is congruent to the old triangle if and only if the base angles measure 45°; if the base angles measure 45°, the angle opposite the base measures 90°. Since in an isosceles triangle the median to the base and the bisector of the angle opposite the base coincide, the new triangle also has angles of 45°, 45°, and 90°. And because they also have two pairs of congruent sides, the old triangle and the new one are congruent. If the base angles of the original triangle are anything other than 45°, the angles of the old and new triangles cannot be the same, and therefore the triangles cannot be congruent.

Lesson 3.3   pp. 181–183

Exercises 1a. • parallelogram

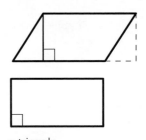

• triangle

See Figure 1

Figure 1

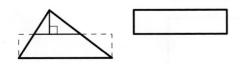

• trapezoid

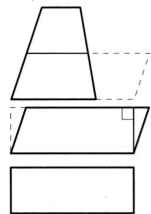

6. Answers may vary. Sample: Let *a*, *b*, and *c* be the digits (from left to right) of the three-digit number. Let *x* and *y* be the digits (from left to right) of the two-digit number. • Multiply *a* and *x* and append three zeros to the right side. • Multiply *a* and *y* and append two zeros to the right side. • Multiply *b* and *x* and append two zeros to the right side. • Multiply *b* and *y* and append one zero to the right side. • Multiply *c* and *x* and append one zero to the right side. • Multiply *c* and *y*. • Add all the sums to find the product.

Lesson 3.4   **pp. 184–188**
Exercises 14a. See Figure 1

b.

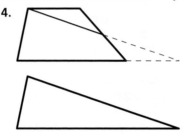

c.

Mathematical Reflections   **p. 193**

4.

6. An algorithm is a set of steps to follow to arrive at a desired outcome.

7. Justifying each step of an algorithm helps you to convince someone that the algorithm yields the desired outcome. **8.** The segment joining the midpoints of two sides of a triangle is parallel to the third side and is half as long as the third side.

Lesson 3.8   **pp. 205–213**
Exercises 7d. Always true; superimpose one angle on top of its congruent counterpart. Two of the pairs of sides coincide, and the bases of the triangles are parallel by AIP. But if the triangles also have equal areas, then the bases must coincide. Therefore, the two triangles are congruent. **e.** Always true; by SSS, the triangles are congruent, and therefore they have equal area. **f.** True for special cases; this is clearly true for congruent triangles, but a triangle with a base of length 6 and a height of length 3, and another triangle with base of length 9 and a height of length 2 have the same area, but none of the side lengths are equal. **g.** True for special cases; this is clearly true for congruent triangles, but an equilateral triangle with sides of length 1, and an equilateral triangle with sides of length 2 have equal angles, but different areas.
14. See Figure 2.

Figure 1

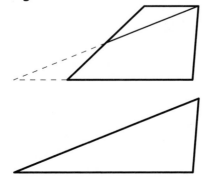

Figure 2

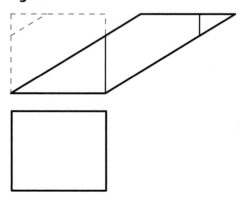

15. See Figure 1.

Mid-Chapter Test   p. 215

1a. Draw a midsegment joining the midpoints of two sides. The two segments used to get the midline have a common endpoint. Draw a segment from that endpoint to the midline and perpendicular to the midline. Two small triangles are formed, and each of these will have one of the midline endpoints as a vertex. Rotate each of these triangles around the corresponding midpoint to get a rectangle.

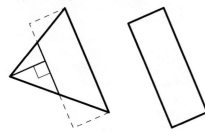

b. Cut along the midline between one leg and the hypotenuse. Rotate the smaller triangle 180° about the midpoint of the hypotenuse.

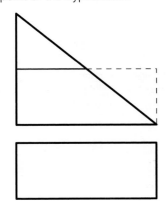

Lesson 3.9   pp. 217–218
For You to Explore
1. Answers may vary. Sample: In the first figure, call the length of the long leg of the right triangles a, the length of the short leg b, and the hypotenuse c. If you draw the vertical line in the first figure, as shown below, you can see that the total area is $a^2 + b^2$. By rearranging the pieces into the second figure, you can see that the total area is also equal to c^2.

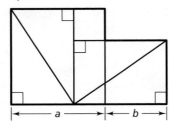

Lesson 3.11   pp. 224–228
Exercises

16. Answers may vary. Sample:

- $(0^2 + 0^2)^2 = (0^2 - 0^2)^2 + (2 \cdot 0 \cdot 0)^2$
  $$0^2 = 0^2 + 0^2$$
  $$0 = 0$$
- $(1^2 + 0^2)^2 = (1^2 - 0^2)^2 + (2 \cdot 1 \cdot 0)^2$
  $$1^2 = 1^2 + 0^2$$
  $$1 = 1$$
- $(0^2 + 1^2)^2 = (0^2 - 1^2)^2 + (2 \cdot 0 \cdot 1)^2$
  $$1^2 = (-1)^2 + 0^2$$
  $$1 = 1$$

- $(1^2 + 1^2)^2 = (1^2 - 1^2)^2 + (2 \cdot 1 \cdot 1)^2$
  $$2^2 = 0^2 + 2^2$$
  $$4 = 4$$
- $((-1)^2 + (-1)^2)^2 = ((-1)^2 - (-1)^2)^2 + (2 \cdot (-1) \cdot (-1))^2$
  $$2^2 = 0^2 + 2^2$$
  $$4 = 4$$

Lesson 3.12   pp. 231–234
For You to Explore

2.

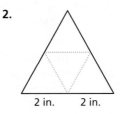

2 in.   2 in.

$4\sqrt{3}$ in.^{2}

Lesson 3.14   pp. 240–246
Exercises 8a. See Figure 2

Mathematical Reflections   p. 253

6. Answers may vary. Sample: A regular prism with a very large number of sides resembles a cylinder. If the radius of the polygonal base stays the same and the number of sides increases more and more, then the prism resembles a cylinder even more. A similar statement applies to regular pyramids and cones.

Figure 1

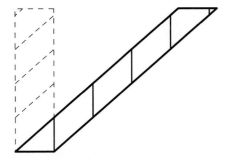

Figure 2

5 cm   5 cm

13 cm

Chapter Test p. 258

4a. See Figure 1

Chapter 5

Lesson 5.1 pp. 355–357

For You to Explore 2. Answers may vary. Sample: *Method 1.* Pick a starting point and mark several points that are spaced evenly around the entire border of the blob. Measure the segments that connect one point to the next until you return to the original point. Add all the lengths to estimate the perimeter. *Method 2.* Fit a piece of string along the border of the blob. Measure the length of the string.

Lesson 5.3 pp. 367–372

Exercises 10. Suppose a regular *n*-gon with sides of length *s* is inscribed in a circle of radius 1 whose center is *O*. If you draw the radii from *O* to the vertices of the *n*-gon, you divide the *n*-gon into *n* congruent isosceles triangles. If you draw the radii that are the perpendicular bisectors of the sides of the *n*-gon, you will have on the circle 2*n* points that are vertices of a regular inscribed 2*n*-gon. In the figure below, *A* and *C* are two consecutive vertices of the regular inscribed *n*-gon. *A*, *B*, and *C* are three consecutive vertices of the regular inscribed 2*n*-gon. We want to show that $AB = \sqrt{2 - \sqrt{4 - s^2}}$.

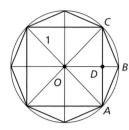

Use the Pythagorean Theorem with right $\triangle AOD$ to get $OD = \sqrt{1 - \frac{s^2}{4}}$. Since $OB = 1$, it follows that $BD = 1 - OD = 1 - \sqrt{1 - \frac{s^2}{4}}$. Use the Pythagorean Theorem with right $\triangle ADB$ to get

$AB = \sqrt{AD^2 + BD^2} = \sqrt{\frac{s^2}{4} + \left(1 - \sqrt{1 - \frac{s^2}{4}}\right)^2}$. Simplify to get $AB = \sqrt{2 - \sqrt{4 - s^2}}$.

11a. Check students' work.
b. $\angle BKO = 90°$ $\angle KOB = 30°$ $\angle OBK = 60°$ $\angle JON = 60°$ $\angle ONJ = 30°$ $\angle NJO = 90°$ **c.** The triangles are congruent by ASA. You have proved that all angles are congruent and $\overline{OB} \cong \overline{ON}$ because they are radii of the same circle. **d.** Since the triangles are congruent, all of their corresponding sides are congruent. In particular, $\overline{OK}$ corresponds with $\overline{NJ}$ and therefore they are congruent. **e.** The triangle's apothem is $\overline{OK}$. This is a side of one of the two congruent triangles. Its corresponding side is

$\overline{NJ}$, which is also half the side of the equilateral triangle inscribed in the circle. Therefore, the hexagon's apothem is half of the equilateral triangle's side.

Mathematical Reflections p. 373

1. Answers may vary. Sample: Mark several points that seem more or less evenly distributed along the whole curve. Start at one of these points and connect the points in order with segments until you come back to the point where you started. Measure all the segments and add their lengths. The sum is approximately equal to the perimeter of the curve. To get a better approximation, double the number of segments you use to get the approximate perimeter. An approximate perimeter for the curve shown in the exercise is 23 cm.

Lesson 5.4 pp. 375–376

For You to Explore

3a.

Number of Sides	perimeter apothem
4	8
6	6.928
8	6.627
16	6.365

b.

Number of Sides	perimeter apothem
32	6.303
64	6.288
128	6.284

c. yes; 2π

Figure 1

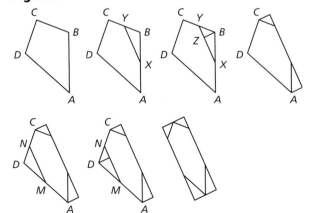

Exercises 4. about 9.1 cm²

Lesson 5.5 pp. 377–381

Exercises 9a. If $\pi = \dfrac{A}{r^2}$ is true for every circle of radius r, then it is true for a circle with $r = 1$. Hence the area A of a circle of radius 1 will be $1^2 \cdot \pi$, or π. If you scale a circle of radius 1 by a factor of r, then the area π of the circle will be multiplied by r^2; that is, $A = \pi r^2$, or $\pi = \dfrac{A}{r^2}$. **b.** Defining π to be $\dfrac{C}{2r}$ is equivalent to defining it to be $\dfrac{C}{d}$, because $d = 2r$. **c.** In Exercise 3 of Lesson 5.4, you saw evidence that $\dfrac{P}{2a}$ approaches $\dfrac{C}{2r}$ as the number of sides of a regular polygon inscribed in a circle increases without limit. **d.** If we accept the truth of $A = \frac{1}{2}Cr$, it is clear that saying "π is the area of a unit circle" is equivalent to saying "π is half the circumference of a unit circle". **e.** The statement in part (e) is equivalent to the statement in part (d) because scaling a unit circle by a factor of $\frac{1}{2}$ will result in a circumference $\frac{1}{2}$ as great as the circumference of the unit circle.

Lesson 5.7 pp. 389–391

For You to Explore 4. The two points where the circles intersect; the points described must be equidistant from A and B. We are only interested in points that lie on at least one of the circles, so any point that fits the description must lie on both the circles, since the radii of the circles are equal.

Exercises

6e.

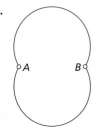

f.

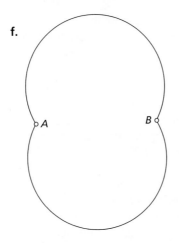

Lesson 5.8 pp. 392–399

Exercises 11b. Let $\overline{OH}$ be the altitude from O in isosceles $\triangle AOD$, and let $\overline{OK}$ be the altitude from O in isosceles $\triangle BOC$. Number angles as shown below.

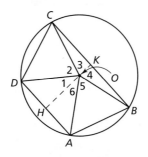

Since $\overline{OH}$ and $\overline{OK}$ are altitudes from the vertex angles of isosceles triangles, they bisect the vertex angles. Also, from part (a), $\angle 2 \cong \angle 5$. It follows that $m\angle 1 + m\angle 2 + m\angle 3 = m\angle 6 + m\angle 5 + m\angle 4$. But the sum of the measures of all six numbered angles is 360°, so $m\angle 1 + m\angle 2 + m\angle 3 = \frac{1}{2} \cdot 360° = 180°$. This implies that H, O, and K are collinear. Thus $\overline{AD}$ and $\overline{BC}$ are both perpendicular to $\overleftrightarrow{HK}$. Therefore, $\overline{AD} \parallel \overline{BC}$.

Lesson 5.9 pp. 400–405

For Discussion 3. Answers may vary. Sample proof of Theorem 5.9 given: Consider the line that contains $\overline{OK}$ through the center O of the circle, as in the figure in Theorem 5.8. Suppose the line bisects chord $\overline{AB}$. You have to prove that it is also perpendicular to $\overline{AB}$. $\triangle AOB$ is isosceles because $AO = r = OB$, where r is the length of the radius of the circle. Since $\overline{OK}$

bisects $\overline{AB}$, $\overline{AK} \cong \overline{BK}$. Since $\triangle AOB$ is isosceles, $\angle BAO \cong \angle ABO$. Therefore, $\triangle AKO \cong \triangle BKO$ by SAS. Since $\triangle AKO \cong \triangle BKO$, corresponding parts $\angle OKB$ and $\angle OKA$ are congruent. By the Angle Sum Theorem, $m\angle AKO + m\angle BKO = m\angle AKB$. Since points A, K, and B all lie on the same line, $m\angle AKB = 180°$, and $m\angle AKO + m\angle BKO = m\angle AKB = 180°$. Since $m\angle AKO \cong m\angle BKO$, each angle must measure $\frac{1}{2}(180°)$, or 90°. Therefore, the line that contains $\overline{OK}$ forms right angles with chord $\overline{AB}$, so it is perpendicular to the chord.

Exercises 2. If A is at the center of the circle, then all chords through A will have the same length and hence the shortest possible length. If A is not at the center and the center is O, the shortest chord through A will be the chord $\overline{XY}$ perpendicular to $\overline{OA}$ at A. To see why, note that $\overline{XY}$ is shorter than a diameter. Suppose $\overline{PQ}$ is any chord other than $\overline{XY}$ that passes through A. In $\triangle POQ$, let $\overline{OR}$ be the altitude from O. Since $\triangle OAR$ is a right triangle with its right angle at R, it follows that $OA > OR$ (the hypotenuse of a right triangle is longer than each of the legs). $\triangle XOY$ and $\triangle POQ$ are isosceles triangles with legs that are radii of the circle. It follows from the Pythagorean Theorem that the triangle with the greater altitude from O has the shorter base. Hence $XY < PQ$.

3. Check students' sketches. Sample:

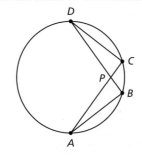

$\angle CAB \cong \angle BDC$, since they intercept the same arc. For the same reason, $\angle ABD \cong \angle DCA$. It is given that $\overline{AB} \cong \overline{CD}$, so $\triangle ABP \cong \triangle DCP$ by ASA. Since they are corresponding parts of congruent triangles, the two segments that form $\overline{AC}$ ($\overline{AP}$ and $\overline{PC}$) are congruent to the two segments that form $\overline{BD}$ ($\overline{DP}$ and $\overline{PB}$). Therefore, $\overline{AC} \cong \overline{BD}$. Similar reasoning applies for other possible diagrams. 4. uppose the adjacent chords are $\overline{AB}$ and $\overline{CB}$ and that $\overline{OB}$ is the radius with which they form congruent angles. $\triangle AOB$ and $\triangle COB$ are isosceles (two sides of each are radii). It is given that $\angle ABO \cong \angle CBO$. So the base angles of $\triangle AOB$ are congruent to the base angles of $\triangle COB$. Since the triangles have $\overline{OB}$ as a common side, $\triangle AOB \cong \triangle COB$ (by AAS). Therefore, $\overline{AB} \cong \overline{BC}$ (by CPCTC).

11. Answers may vary. Sample: Draw $\overline{OK}$ such that K is on $\overline{CD}$ and $\overline{OK} \perp \overline{CD}$. Since $\overline{OK}$ is the altitude from the vertex angle of each of the isosceles triangles $\triangle COD$ and $\triangle AOB$, it is the perpendicular bisector of $\overline{CD}$ and $\overline{AB}$. Hence $CK = KD$ and $AK = KB$. But $AK = AC + CK$ and $KB = KD + DB$. Therefore $AC = DB$, which means that $\overline{AC} \cong \overline{DB}$. **12a.** A diameter of a circle that is perpendicular to a chord bisects the chord (Theorem 5.8). $\overline{FZ}$ is perpendicular to $\overline{PQ}$ since it is perpendicular to $\overline{MN}$ and $\overline{MN} \parallel \overline{PQ}$. Hence $\overline{FZ}$ is the perpendicular bisector of $\overline{MN}$ and $\overline{PQ}$. **b.** 5 cm **c.** $5\sqrt{3}$ cm **d.** $\frac{5\sqrt{3}}{2}$ cm **e.** 90°

Lesson 5.10   **pp. 406–412**
For Discussion 11. By Theorem 5.11 and arc addition, $m\angle A = \frac{1}{2} m\widehat{BCD} = \frac{1}{2}(m\widehat{CB} + m\widehat{DC})$ $m\angle D = \frac{1}{2} m\widehat{ABC} = \frac{1}{2}(m\widehat{AB} + m\widehat{CB})$ By the Triangle Angle Sum Theorem, $m\angle APD = 180° - (m\angle A + m\angle D)$ $= \frac{1}{2}(m\widehat{AB} + 2m\widehat{CB} + m\widehat{DC})$ In this last equation, you can replace 180° with $\frac{1}{2}(m\widehat{AD} + m\widehat{AB} + m\widehat{CB} + m\widehat{DC})$. When you make the substitution and simplify, you get $m\angle APD = \frac{1}{2}(m\widehat{AD} + m\widehat{CB})$.

Exercises 3. Suppose the given circle has center O, and let the external point be P. Draw $\overline{OP}$. Construct the midpoint M of $\overline{OP}$. Draw the circle with center M and radius $\overline{MO}$. Let C and D be the points where this circle intersects the given circle. Draw $PCOD$. $\angle C$ and $\angle D$ both intercept a semicircle of the circle with center M. Therefore, $\angle C$ and $\angle D$ are right angles. Hence $\overline{PC}$ and $\overline{PD}$ are tangent to the original circle.
Exercises 5a. 14° **b.** 27.5°
c. Answers may vary. From part (b), $m\angle CAD = 27.5°$. By Theorem 5.14,
$m\angle ADC = \frac{1}{2}(m\widehat{CBF} - m\widehat{CE}) =$
$\frac{1}{2}[(180° + 14°) - 69°] = 62.5°$.
So $m\angle ACD = 180°$
$= 27.5° - 62.5° = 90°$. **9.** Check students' drawings. By Theorem 5.13,
$m\angle AMN = \frac{1}{2}(m\widehat{BP} + m\widehat{AQ})$ and
$m\angle ANM = \frac{1}{2}(m\widehat{AP} + m\widehat{CQ})$. But $\overline{BP} \cong \overline{AP}$ and $\overline{AQ} \cong \overline{CQ}$. Hence $m\angle AMN = m\angle ANM$. Therefore, $\triangle AMN$ is isosceles with legs $\overline{AM}$ and $\overline{AN}$, which means that $\overline{AM} \cong \overline{AN}$.
11a. Exercise 1 shows that $\overline{PA} \cong \overline{PB}$ and $\overline{PC} \cong \overline{PD}$. Radii of the same circle are congruent, so it follows that $PDOC$ and $PBOA$ are kites that have $\overline{PO}$ as a shared axis of symmetry. From this it follows easily that $\angle APC \cong \angle DPB$. **b.** Use the angle congruence proved in part (a) and the facts that $\overline{PA} \cong \overline{PB}$ and $\overline{PC} \cong \overline{PD}$ to conclude that $\triangle PAC \cong \triangle PBD$ (SAS). Hence $\overline{AC} \cong \overline{BD}$ by CPCTC. The diagonals of a kite are perpendicular and $\overline{PQ}$ is a shared diagonal of $PDOC$ and $PBOA$. Therefore $\overline{AB}$ and $\overline{CD}$ are both perpendicular to $\overline{PO}$. Hence $\overline{AB} \parallel \overline{CD}$.
12a–f. Check students' drawings. A sample figure is shown below, with the additional segment from the center of γ to C.

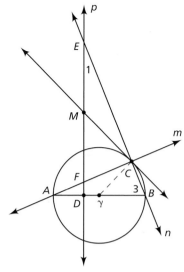

$\angle ACB$ intercepts a semicircle and hence is a right angle. This means that $\angle ECF$ is a right angle. By construction, $\angle EDB$ is a right angle. Since $\triangle FCE$ and $\triangle BDE$ share $\angle 1$ and a right angle, $\triangle FCE \sim \triangle BDE$ (AA Similarity). Since $\triangle BDE$ and $\triangle BCA$ share $\angle 3$, $\triangle BDE \sim \triangle BCA$ (AA Similarity). Therefore $\triangle FCE \sim \triangle BCA$ ($\sim$ is transitive). If you rotate $\triangle FCE$ and $\overline{CM}$ 90° about C to make the images of the legs of $\triangle FCE$ align with the legs of $\triangle BCA$, then the image of $\overline{CM}$ will align with $\overline{C\gamma}$, since $\angle MC\gamma$ is a right angle ($\overleftrightarrow{CM}$ is a tangent of the circle, and $\overline{C\gamma}$ is a radius drawn to the point of contact). From this it is easy to show that since $\overline{C\gamma}$ is a median of $\triangle BCA$, the image of $\overline{CM}$ must be a median of the image of $\triangle FCE$. The point M is therefore the midpoint of $\overline{EF}$. **13a.** If $\overline{AC}$ is a diameter and B is not at A or C, then $m\angle ABC$ is 90°. (If B is at A or C, then there is no angle ABC.) If $\overline{AC}$ is not a diameter, then A and C split the circle into a minor arc and a major arc. If $k°$ is the measure of the minor arc, then the measure of the major arc is $360° - k°$. If B is on the minor arc and not at A or C, then $m\angle ABC$ is $180° - \frac{1}{2}k°$. If B is on the major arc and not at A or C, then $m\angle ABC$ is $\frac{1}{2}k°$. **b.** There will be no line ℓ when B coincides with A, since you need more than one point to determine a line. The tangent line is the limiting position that ℓ is approaching before B finally arrives at A. **c.** When B coincides with A, no angle is formed by ℓ and $\overline{AC}$, since ℓ vanishes. But just before B gets to A, the arc is getting close to one of the arcs with A and C as endpoints. **d.** Answers may vary. Sample: The angle measures are equal, $k°$ or $(180 - k)°$, because a tangent angle is an angle that intercepts the same arc $(\overset{\frown}{AC})$ as all the angles $\angle ABC$, where B is a point on the circle.

Lesson 5.11   pp. 413–418
Exercises 1. Construct a circle and a point P inside it so that $\prod(P) = 12$. One such circle and point can be constructed by picking two numbers with a product of 12, such as 2 and 6. Draw a segment of length 8 (that is, $2 + 6$). Mark its midpoint. Then draw the circle that has the segment as a diameter. Mark P on the segment so that P is 2 units from one endpoint. Then $\prod(P) = 12$. Select a stick and place it so that it goes through P and has one end on the circle. Mark the place on the stick that corresponds to P. Cut off any excess part of the stick that is outside the circle at the other end. Cut the stick in two at the point corresponding to P. Cut another two pieces of these same lengths from another stick. Use the four pieces to build one rectangle. Repeat the process to get rectangles with other dimensions.
5. a. $\angle ABE \cong \angle DCE$ because they intercept the same arc $(\overset{\frown}{AD})$.
b. $\angle AEB \cong \angle DEC$ because they are vertical angles.
c. $\triangle ABE \sim \triangle DCE$ by AA Similarity.
d. $\frac{AE}{DE} = \frac{BE}{CE}$ because ratios of corresponding parts of similar triangles are equal. **e.** Answers may vary. Sample: $\angle ABE \cong \angle DCE$ because they intercept the same arc $(\overset{\frown}{AD})$. $\angle AEB \cong \angle DEC$ because they are vertical angles. $\triangle ABE \sim \triangle DCE$ by AA Similarity. $\frac{AE}{DE} = \frac{BE}{CE}$ because ratios of corresponding parts of similar triangles are equal. $(AE)(CE) = (BE)(DE)$ because cross products of a proportion are equal.

Mathematical Reflections   p. 419
5. Suppose $\angle ABC$ has all three of the points A, B, and C on the circle. Then A, C, and all points of the circle in the interior of $\angle ABC$ constitute a *minor arc*. The points of the circle that are not in the interior of $\angle ABC$ constitute a *major arc*. The endpoints of a diameter and all points of the circle on one side of the diameter are arcs and are called *semicircles*. A *chord* is a segment whose endpoints are on the circle. **6.** The inscribed angle is half as large as the central angle. (This assumes the inscribed angle is not obtuse.) **7.** If P is a point inside a circle, then the power $\prod(P)$ of the point is $PA \cdot PB$, where A and B are the endpoints of a chord that contains P. If P is on the circle, then $\prod(P) = 0$. If P is outside the circle and a line through P intersects the circle in two points A and B, then $\prod(P) = PA \cdot PB$.

Project   pp. 434–435
10. Answers may vary. Sample: Take a piece of string and tie it to two tacks so that there are a few centimeters of string between the tacks. Stick the tacks into a thick, flat piece of cardboard. Leave some slack in the string. Push the pencil firmly against the string. Keep the pencil point in contact with the cardboard and keep the string stretched to form an angle that has the pencil point as vertex and sides that pass through the points where the tacks are stuck into the cardboard. With the string tight against the pencil point, move the pencil around to draw a complete curve. The curve will be an ellipse.

Review   pp. 436–437
5. Answers may vary. Sample: A tangent to a circle is perpendicular to the radius drawn to the point of contact. Hence $\triangle PBC$ and $\triangle PAC$ are right triangles that have a common hypotenuse, $\overline{PC}$. $PB = PC$ since they are radii of the same circle. By the Pythagorean Theorem, it follows that $BC = AC$. Since both P and C are equidistant from A and B, $\overline{PC}$ is a perpendicular bisector of $\overline{AB}$.
9. Let R be the radius of the goldfish bowls. Then the area of the table top is $(3R)^2$, the area of table covered by

goldfish bowls is $9\pi R^2$, and the area of the openings is $\frac{1}{3} \cdot 9\pi R^2$, or $3\pi R^2$. The probability that Sam will take home a goldfish is $\frac{3\pi R^2}{(3R)^2} = \frac{3\pi R^2}{9R^2} = \frac{\pi}{3}$.

Test   pp. 438–439
6. A diameter of a circle is a segment that passes through the center of the circle and has its endpoints on the circle; proofs may vary. Sample: In a circle with center O, let $\overline{AB}$ be a chord that is not a diameter. Draw $\overline{BO}$ and extend it to intersect the circle in a second point, C. Draw $\overline{AC}$. Since $\angle CAB$ intercepts a semicircle, it is a right angle. So $\triangle CAB$ is a right triangle with hypotenuse $\overline{CB}$. Since the hypotenuse of a right triangle is longer than each leg, $CB > AB$. Therefore a diameter is longer than any chord that is not a diameter.

Chapter 6
Lesson 6.1   pp. 443–445
For You to Explore
4a.

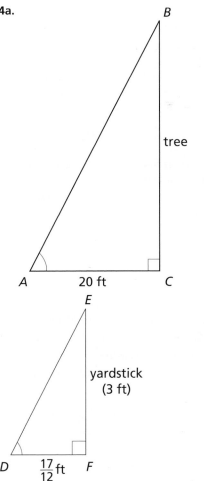

Exercises 12b. The altitudes of an equilateral triangle are medians and angle bisectors of the triangle. Since each angle of an equilateral triangle has a measure of 60°, it follows that each of the six small angles that have vertices at A, B, and C has measure 30° and that each of the six smallest angles at the point where the altitudes intersect has measure 60°. Therefore, the twelve right triangles in the figure are all similar (AAA Similarity). There are three isosceles triangles in the figure that have their vertex angles at the point in the center of $\triangle ABC$ where the altitudes of $\triangle ABC$ intersect. They are congruent by ASA and hence are similar. **c.** $\triangle AHC \sim \triangle ACB \sim \triangle CHB$ by the AA Similarity Test.
d. $\triangle ADE \sim \triangle ABC$ (AA Similarity Test: $\angle A$ is common to the triangles, and $\angle D \cong \angle B$ since these inscribed angles both intercept $\overarc{EC}$). The vertical angles formed by $\overline{BC}$ and $\overline{DE}$ are congruent; so if P is the point of intersection of $\overline{BC}$ and $\overline{DE}$, then $\triangle PDC \sim \triangle PBE$ (AA Similarity Test).

Lesson 6.3   pp. 452–457
Exercises 3. If $\overline{CB}$ is the diameter through B, then $\angle CAB$ intercepts a semicircle and hence is a right angle. Theorem 6.1 implies that AB^2 is the product of CB and the length of the projection of $\overline{AB}$ on $\overline{CB}$.

Lesson 6.4   pp. 458–462
Exercises 6. a. Check students' work.
b. $A_{\triangle APC} = A_{\triangle ACM} - A_{\triangle APM}$ and $A_{\triangle BPC} = A_{\triangle BCM} - A_{\triangle BPM}$, since the area of a polygon is the sum of the areas of its nonoverlapping parts. Note that since triangles with congruent altitudes and congruent bases have the same area, it follows that $A_{\triangle APC} = A_{\triangle BPC}$. **c.** The figure below shows a point P not on the median $\overline{CM}$ and on the same side of $\overline{CM}$ as A. The segment $\overline{AP}$ has been drawn and extended to intersect $\overline{CM}$ at K.

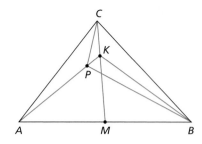

From the answer for part (b), you know that $A_{\triangle CKB} = A_{\triangle CKA}$. Thus
$A_{\triangle BPC} - A_{\triangle APC} =$
$(A_{\triangle CKB} + A_{\triangle CPK} + A_{\triangle PKB}) - (A_{\triangle CKA} - A_{\triangle CPK}) =$
$2A_{\triangle CPK} + A_{\triangle PKB}$. Since $2A_{\triangle CPK} + A_{\triangle PKB} > 0$, it follows that $A_{\triangle BPC} - A_{\triangle APC} \neq 0$ and hence that $A_{\triangle APC} \neq A_{\triangle BPC}$. A similar argument shows that when P is on the other side of $\overline{CM}$, it is again true that $A_{\triangle APC} \neq A_{\triangle BPC}$. **d.** The median $\overline{CM}$ is the set of points C, M, and all points P inside $\triangle ABC$ such that $A_{\triangle APC} = A_{\triangle BPC}$.

Mathematical Reflections   p. 463
7. An altitude of a triangle, such as BH, is the perpendicular segment from a vertex to the line containing the opposite side, $\overline{AC}$. It creates two right triangles. In Exercise 4, $\overline{BH} \perp \overline{AC}$, $\triangle ABC \sim \triangle AHB$, and $\triangle AHB \sim \triangle BHC$, therefore $\triangle ABC \sim \triangle BHC$ by the AAA Similarity Theorem.

Lesson 6.5   pp. 465–468
Exercises 13c. A: 1; B: $\frac{1}{2}$; C: $\frac{1}{3}$; D: $\frac{1}{4}$; E: $\frac{1}{5}$; the ratios decrease as the widths increase. **d.** A: $\frac{\sqrt{2}}{2}$; B: $\frac{\sqrt{5}}{5}$ C: $\frac{\sqrt{10}}{10}$; D: $\frac{\sqrt{17}}{17}$ E: $\frac{\sqrt{26}}{26}$; the ratios decrease as the widths increase.

Lesson 6.6   pp. 469–473
Exercises 3. $m\angle T = 30°$, $m\angle A = 60°$, and $m\angle R = 90°$; the converse of the Pythagorean Theorem tells you that the triangle is a right triangle, and the ratios of the lengths of the sides tell you that its acute angles are 30° and 60°. The larger acute angle is opposite the longer leg.
4. Such a triangle may be a 30-60-90 triangle, but it does not have to be. Answers may vary. Sample:

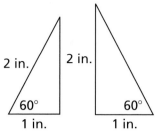

6. $m\angle P = m\angle G = 45°$, $m\angle I = 90°$; $\triangle PGI$ is a 45-45-90 triangle.
7. $m\angle E = 90°$, $m\angle O = 30°$, $EO = \frac{3}{2}$; $\triangle GOE$ is a 30-60-90 triangle.

11.

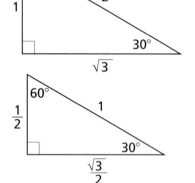

12.

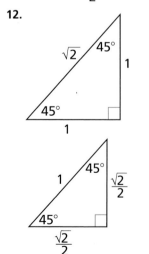

Lesson 6.7   pp. 474–480
Exercises

3a. $\sin A = \dfrac{\sqrt{5}}{5}$, $\cos A = \dfrac{2\sqrt{5}}{5}$,
$\tan A = \dfrac{1}{2}$ **b.** $\sin B = \dfrac{2\sqrt{5}}{5}$,
$\cos B = \dfrac{\sqrt{5}}{5}$, $\tan B = 2$

c. $\cos A = \sin B$, and
$\sin A = \cos B$; leg adjacent and
leg opposite switch roles when you
switch from $\angle A$ to $\angle B$. **10.** First
triangle: $\sin A = \dfrac{2\sqrt{5}}{5}$, $\cos A = \dfrac{\sqrt{5}}{5}$,
$\tan A = 2$, $\sin B = \dfrac{\sqrt{5}}{5}$, $\cos B =$
$\dfrac{2\sqrt{5}}{5}$, $\tan B = \dfrac{1}{2}$. Second triangle:
$\sin A = \dfrac{3}{4}$, $\cos A = \dfrac{\sqrt{7}}{4}$, $\tan A =$
$\dfrac{3\sqrt{7}}{7}$, $\sin B = \dfrac{\sqrt{7}}{4}$, $\cos B = \dfrac{3}{4}$,
$\tan B = \dfrac{\sqrt{7}}{3}$. **12.** $\sin 33° = \cos 57°$
and $\cos 33° = \sin 57°$ because in
a right triangle with acute angles of
33° and 57°, the leg opposite the
33° angle is the leg adjacent to the
57° angle, and the leg adjacent to
the 33° angle is the leg opposite the
57° angle. $\dfrac{\sin 33°}{\cos 33°} = \tan 33°$ because
$\dfrac{\text{length of leg adjacent to } 33°}{\text{length of hypotenuse}} =$
$\dfrac{\text{length leg opposite } 33°}{\text{length of hypoteneuse}} \div$
$\dfrac{\text{length of leg opposite } 33°}{\text{length of leg adjacent to } 33°}$. Similar
reasoning explains why $\dfrac{\sin 57°}{\cos 57°}$
$= \tan 57°$.

Lesson 6.9   pp. 488–495
Exercises 10. Use the Law of Cosines to
find the measures of two acute angles
of the triangle (the angles opposite the
two shortest sides). Then use the Triangle Angle Sum Theorem to compute the
measure of the third angle. Draw the
altitude from the vertex of the largest
angle. Compute its length by using the
definition of the sine function and what
you know about the side lengths and
angle measures. Use the formula for the
area of a triangle to compute the area
of the given triangle. **11.** Answers may
vary. Sample: Suppose sides of lengths
a and b form an angle of measure θ.
If $\theta < 90°$, use the Law of Cosines
to find the length of the third side.
Once you know the lengths of all three
sides, you can use the procedure in the
answer for Exercise 9. If $\theta = 90°$, use

the Pythagorean Theorem to find the
length of the hypotenuse. Then use the
procedure in the answer for Exercise 9.
If $\theta > 90°$, draw the altitude $\overline{BD}$ from
one endpoint of the side of length a to
the line that contains the side of length
b, as shown in the diagram below.

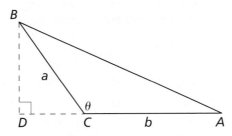

Since $m\angle BCD = 180° - \theta$, you
can use the right triangles ($\triangle BDC$
and $\triangle BDA$) to compute the needed
length and angle measures for $\triangle ABC$.
18. area of the pentagon on the
hypotenuse $= 2661.75$ area of the
pentagon on short leg $= 393.75$ area
of the pentagon on long leg $= 2223$
$393.75 + 2268 = 2661.75$.

Mathematical Reflections   p. 496
4. Answers may vary. Sample: A triangle
formed by drawing a diagonal of a
square with side length 1 is a 45-45-90
right triangle with legs of length 1
and hypotenuse of length $\sqrt{2}$. A right
triangle formed by drawing a median of
an equilateral triangle with side length
2 is a 30-60-90 right triangle. The
leg opposite the 30° angle has length
1, the leg opposite the 60° angle has
length $\sqrt{3}$, and the hypotenuse has
length 2. You can use this information
with the definitions of the trigonometric
functions to find the sine, cosine, and
tangent of 30°, 45°, and 60°.

Mid-Chapter Test   p. 497
9. $m\angle A = 135°$; $OM \approx 10.85$ cm;
$ON \approx 16.77$ cm

Lesson 6.12   pp. 511–518
Exercises 5. The cone and the pyramid
are the same height and are cut by a
plane, so the resulting cross sections have
the same area. The cone and the pyramid
also have cross-sectional areas that are
equal to each other when cut by any
plane parallel to the first, therefore the
cone and pyramid have the same volume.

Test   pp. 530–531
8. Yes; consider a plane parallel to the
bases and d cm below each apex. It will
make cross sections with areas $\left(\dfrac{d}{15}\right)^2$
times the areas of the bases. Since the
cross sections shown are parallel to the
bases and have equal areas, it follows
that the base of the pyramid has area
$40\,\text{cm}^2$. It also follows that all planes
below the apexes and parallel to the
bases determine cross sections of equal
area.; $V_{pyramid} = V_{cone} = \left(\dfrac{1}{3}\right) \cdot$
$40 \cdot 15\ \text{cm}^3 = 200\ \text{cm}^3$
11. Construct a segment m of length
$a + b$. Copy segment ℓ so that one
endpoint divides m into segments of
length a and b. Construct a circle that
passes through the endpoints of m and
ℓ (excluding the endpoint of ℓ that lies
on m). Extend ℓ so that it intersects the
circle in two places. The segment from
the intersection of m and ℓ to where
the extension of ℓ intersects the circle
is the desired segment.

Cumulative Review   pp. 532–533
1. Answers may vary. Sample: The
following answers assume that two grid
lines pass through the center of the
circle. **a.** inner area $= 8$ in.²; outer area
$= 12$ in.² **b.** inner area $= 11$ in.²;
outer area $= 14$ in.²
c. inner area $= 11.375$ in.²;
outer area $= 13.375$ in.²
d. inner area $= 11.75$ in.²;
outer area $= 13.2$ in.²

13a.

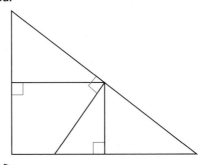

b.

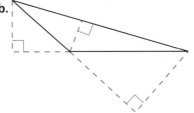

c.

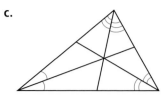

14. Answers may vary. Sample: ∠ADE ≅ ∠DBC, since they are both right angles. $\overline{DE} \parallel \overline{BC}$ because corresponding angles are congruent. Since $\overline{DE} \parallel \overline{BC}$ and $\overline{AD} \cong \overline{BD}$, $\overline{DE}$ is the mid-segment of △ABC. $\overline{AE} \cong \overline{EC}$ by the definition of mid-segment. Therefore, $\overline{BE}$ is a median, since E is the midpoint of $\overline{AC}$.

18a. See Figure 1 **21.** Answers may vary. Sample: $\overline{AC}$ and $\overline{DB}$ are perpendicular to $\overline{CD}$, since points C and D are on tangent $\overline{CD}$. ∠ACE and ∠BDE are 90° by the definition of perpendicular. ∠AEC ≅ ∠BED by the Vertical Angle Theorem. △ACE ~ △BDE by AA Similarity.

Chapter 7
Lesson 7.1   pp. 537–539
Exercises 8a. See Figure 2 **b.** Answers may vary. Sample using part (a): clockwise **c.** Answers may vary. Sample using part (a): See Figure 3 **d.** Answers may vary. Sample using part (a): counter-

clockwise **e.** Answers may vary. Sample using part (a): No, the direction of the preimage is clockwise. The direction of the reflection is counterclockwise.
11a. Answers may vary. Sample: Any fold line *l* that does not intersect △ABC will do. **b.** Answers may vary. Sample: Any fold line *l* that intersects △ABC at a vertex but nowhere else will do. **c.** Answers may vary. Sample: Any fold line *l* that passes through the interior of △ABC will do. **d.** Answers may vary. Sample: Any of the fold lines $\overleftrightarrow{AB}$, $\overleftrightarrow{AC}$, or $\overleftrightarrow{BC}$ will do.

Lesson 7.2   pp. 540–546
Exercises 1a. Always true; if you fold along the line of reflection, a segment in the preimage will coincide with the corresponding segment in the image. **b.** Always true; if you fold along the line of reflection, an angle in the preimage will coincide with the corresponding angle in the image. **c.** Always true; if you fold along the line of reflection, the image of a line is a line. **d.** Sometimes true; Answers may vary. Sample: Suppose the line of reflection is $y = x$. For A(2, 4) and B(5, 7), the image of $\overline{AB}$ is $\overline{A'B'}$ with A'(4, 2) and B'(7, 5). Both segments have slope 1. For C(5, 9) and C'(9, 5), the image of $\overline{AC}$ is $\overline{A'C'}$; but $\overline{AC}$ has slope $\frac{5}{3}$, and $\overline{A'C'}$

has slope $\frac{3}{5}$. **e.** Always true; Answers may vary. Sample: A transversal of two parallel segments in the preimage will form congruent corresponding angles with the segments. The angle measures will, by part (b), be preserved in the image. So the segments in the image will be parallel. **f.** Always true; Answers may vary. Sample: By part (b), angle measures are preserved. **6.** Use the diagram provided in the text, with the additional markings and the segments $\overline{BM}$ and $\overline{B'M}$ shown below.

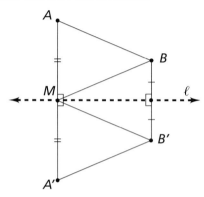

Since *l* is the perpendicular bisector of $\overline{BB'}$, △BMB' is isosceles and $\overline{MN}$ is the median from M to the base. $\overline{MB} \cong \overline{MB'}$ since every point on the perpendicular bisector of a segment is equidistant from the endpoints of

---

Figure 1

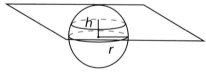

Figure 2

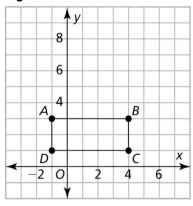

Figure 3

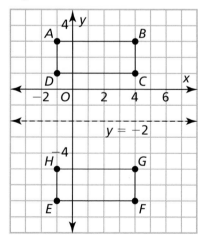

the segment. The median to the base of an isosceles triangle bisects the vertex angle. Thus $\angle BMN \cong \angle B'MN$. $\angle AMN$ and $\angle A'MN$ are right angles and hence are congruent. Hence $\angle AMB \cong \angle A'MB'$. It follows that $\triangle AMB \cong \triangle A'MB'$ (by SAS). Therefore, $\overline{AB} \cong \overline{A'B'}$ by CPCTC.

Lesson 7.3   pp. 547–554
Exercises

4a.

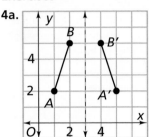

b.

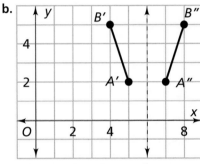

c. $A(5, 2)$, $B(4, 5)$, $A(7, 2)$, $B(8, 5)$
d. Yes; translation to the right 6 units
7. Graphs are shown after part (d).
a. $y = -x^2 - 4x - 3$; a translation to the left 3 units.

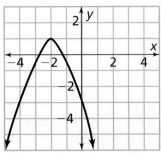

b. $y = -x^2 + 6x - 8$; a correct prediction is that the parabola will be translated to the right 2 units.

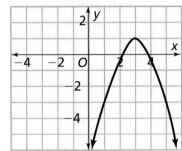

c. $y = -x^2 + 2x + 2$; a translation up 2 units.

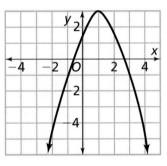

d. $y = -x^2 + 2x - 3$; a correct prediction is that the parabola will be translated down 3 units.

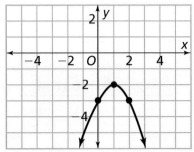

Lesson 7.4   pp. 555–560
Exercises 2. See Figure 1

3.

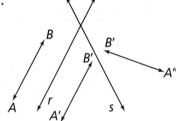

The point of intersection of r and s; about 115° counterclockwise; yes, by measuring one of the acute angles formed by r and s and doubling the result. **4.** See Figure 2

Figure 1

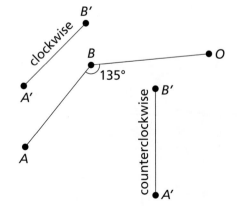

Figure 2

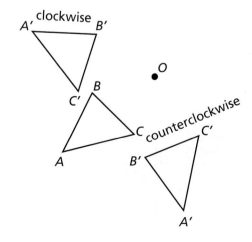

11. a–d. See Figures

· ·

11. a.

A	B	C	D	E	F	G
(x, y)	$(x + 3, y)$	$(-x, y)$	$(x, -y)$	$(2x, 2y)$	$\left(\frac{x}{2}, \frac{y}{2}\right)$	$(-y, x)$
$(2, 1)$	$(5, 1)$	$(-2, 1)$	$(2, -1)$	$(4, 2)$	$\left(1, \frac{1}{2}\right)$	$(-1, 2)$
$(-4, 0)$	$(-1, 0)$	$(4, 0)$	$(-4, 0)$	$(-8, 0)$	$(-2, 0)$	$(0, -4)$
$(-5, 4)$	$(-2, 4)$	$(5, 4)$	$(-5, -4)$	$(-10, 8)$	$(-2.5, 2)$	$(-4, -5)$

b.

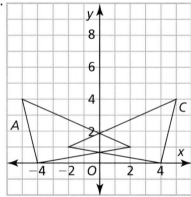

Triangle *B* is the result of translating triangle *A* to the right 3 units.

c.

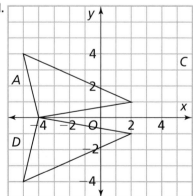

Triangle *C* is the reflection image of triangle *A* over the *y*-axis.

d.

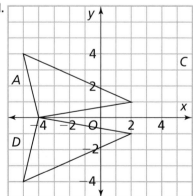

Triangle *D* is the reflection image of triangle *A* over the *x*-axis.

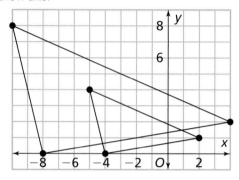

Triangle *E* is a dilation image of triangle *A* (center of dilation at (0, 0), scale factor 2).

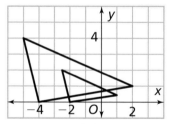

Triangle *F* is a dilation image of triangle *A* (center of dilation at (0, 0), scale factor $\frac{1}{2}$).

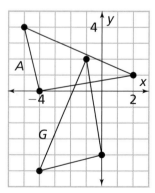

Triangle *G* is a rotation image of triangle *A* (90° counterclockwise around the origin).

Additional Answers

Lesson 7.6 — pp. 566–572

Exercises 5. $AB = \sqrt{960^2 + 512^2}$ and $A'B' = \sqrt{3840^2 + 2048^2}$, so $AB = \frac{1}{4}A'B'$ because

$\sqrt{3840^2 + 2048^2} = \sqrt{(4 \cdot 960)^2 + (4 \cdot 512)^2}$.

$BC = \sqrt{897^2 + 496^2}$ and $B'C' = \sqrt{3588^2 + 1984^2}$, so $BC = \frac{1}{4}B'C'$ because $\sqrt{3588^2 + 1984^2} = \sqrt{(4 \cdot 897)^2 + (4 \cdot 496^2)}$.

$AC = \sqrt{63^2 + 16^2}$ and $A'C' = \sqrt{252^2 + 64^2}$, so $AC = \frac{1}{4}A'C'$ because $\sqrt{252^2 + 64^2} = \sqrt{(4 \cdot 63)^2 + (4 \cdot 16)^2}$. The lengths of the sides of $\triangle ABC$ are $\frac{1}{4}$ the lengths of the corresponding sides of $\triangle A'B'C'$, so the triangles are similar (SSS Similarity). **8.** Answers may vary. Sample: Starting with $\overline{ST}$ and going clockwise, let the midpoints of the sides of $STAR$ be P, Q, V, and W. Use the Midpoint Formula to show that these are the points $P(3, 5)$, $Q(4, 1)$, $V(-1, -2)$, and $W(-2, 4)$. Use the Distance Formula to show that $PW = VQ = \sqrt{26}$ and $PQ = WV = \sqrt{37}$. Since the opposite sides of $PQVW$ are congruent, $PQVW$ is a parallelogram. **19.** Answers may vary. Sample: Let the vertices of the triangle be $A(x_1, y_1)$, $B(x_2, y_2)$, and $C(x_3, y_3)$. The following proof shows that if P and Q are the midpoints of $\overline{AB}$ and $\overline{BC}$, respectively, then $PQ = \frac{1}{2}AC$. The proofs for the other cases are exactly analogous. By the Midpoint Formula, the midpoint of $\overline{AB}$ is $P\left(\frac{x_1 + x_2}{2}, \frac{y_1 + y_2}{2}\right)$ and the midpoint of $\overline{BC}$ is $Q\left(\frac{x_2 + x_3}{2}, \frac{y_2 + y_3}{2}\right)$. The

Distance Formula gives

$PQ = \sqrt{\left(\frac{x_2 + x_3}{2} - \frac{x_1 + x_2}{2}\right)^2 + \left(\frac{y_2 + y_3}{2} - \frac{y_1 + y_2}{2}\right)^2}$

$= \sqrt{\left(\frac{x_3 - x_1}{2}\right)^2 + \left(\frac{y_3 - y_1}{2}\right)^2}$

$= \frac{1}{2}\sqrt{(x_3 - x_1)^2 + (y_3 - y_1)^2}$.

But $AC = \sqrt{(x_3 - x_1) + (y_3 - y_1)^2}$.

Therefore, $PQ = \frac{1}{2}AC$.

Lesson 7.7 — pp. 573–578

Exercises 1a. Parallel; the graphs of the lines are different and the ratios of corresponding coefficients are equal. **b.** Parallel; the graphs of the lines are different and the ratios of corresponding coefficients are equal. **c.** Not parallel; the lines are the same. **d.** Not parallel; the ratios of corresponding coefficients are not equal. **e.** Parallel; the graphs of the lines are different and the ratios of corresponding coefficients are equal. **3.** Answers may vary. Sample: Start with $B(8, -3)$. Add 3 to the x-coordinate and subtract 4 from the y-coordinate to get $(11, -7)$, the coordinates of a new point on $\overleftrightarrow{AB}$.

Do the same with the new point, and continue in this fashion to get still more points.; The slope of $\overleftrightarrow{AB}$ is $\frac{-4}{3}$, and the procedure gives new points that are collinear with A and B by Theorem 7.5.

Lesson 7.8 — pp. 579–583

Exercises

11a.

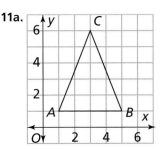

b. $x = 3$ **c.** (3, 1) **d.** By the Midpoint Formula, the coordinates of the midpoint of $\overline{AB}$ are $\left(\frac{1 + 5}{2}, \frac{1 + 1}{2}\right)$, or (3, 1).

12a.

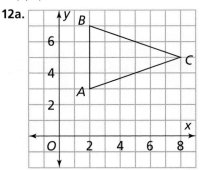

b. (2, 5) **c.** $y = 5$ **d.** The slope of $\overleftrightarrow{MC}$ is 0 and the slope of $\overline{AB}$ is undefined. This means that $\overleftrightarrow{MC} \perp \overline{AB}$.

13a. $\frac{4\sqrt{13}}{13}$ **b.** $\frac{|-2x_p - 3y_p + 4|}{\sqrt{13}}$ **c.** $\frac{|-a - 2b + c|}{\sqrt{a^2 + b^2}}$ **d.** $\frac{|-ax_p - by_p + c|}{\sqrt{a^2 + b^2}}$

Lesson 7.9 — pp. 584–591

Exercises 5d. Answers may vary. Sample: (4, 12), (17, −1), (4, −14), (−9, −1), (16, 4), (−8, −6), (16, −6), (−8, 4); If the point has coordinates (a, b), calculate $(a - 4)^2 + (b + 1)^2$ to see if the sum is 169.

11a. See Figure 1 **b.** $3\sqrt{2}$ **c.** midpoint of $\overline{LM}$: $\left(\frac{1}{2}, \frac{1}{2}, 0\right)$, midpoint of $\overline{MN}$: $\left(0, \frac{1}{2}, \frac{1}{2}\right)$, midpoint of $\overline{NL}$: $\left(\frac{1}{2}, 0, \frac{1}{2}\right)$

12a. 10 **b.** midpoint of $\overline{AB}$: $\left(3, -\frac{1}{2}, 6\right)$, midpoint of $\overline{BC}$: $(2, 0, 5)$, midpoint of $\overline{AC}$: $\left(1, -\frac{1}{2}, 6\right)$ **c.** 5 **17a.** $\left(5, 4\sqrt{3}\right)$ or $\left(5, -4\sqrt{3}\right)$ **b.** For the regular tetrahedron with three vertices at $(1, 0, 0)$, $(9, 0, 0)$, and $(5, 4\sqrt{3}, 0)$, the fourth vertex could be at $\left(5, \frac{4}{3}\sqrt{3}, \frac{8}{3}\sqrt{6}\right)$ or $\left(5, \frac{4}{3}\sqrt{3}, -\frac{8}{3}\sqrt{6}\right)$. For the regular tetrahedron with three vertices at $(1, 0, 0)$, $(9, 0, 0)$, and $(5, -4\sqrt{3}, 0)$, the fourth vertex could be at $\left(5, -\frac{4}{3}\sqrt{3}, \frac{8}{3}\sqrt{6}\right)$ or $\left(5, -\frac{4}{3}\sqrt{3}, -\frac{8}{3}\sqrt{6}\right)$

Mid-Chapter Test   **p. 593**

5.

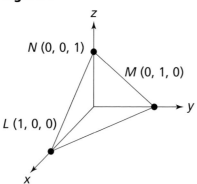

7.

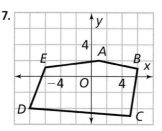

perimeter = $\sqrt{26} + \sqrt{37} + \sqrt{170} + \sqrt{29} + 5\sqrt{2}$

Lesson 7.9   **pp. 595–599**
For You to Explore

4a.

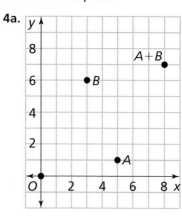

b.

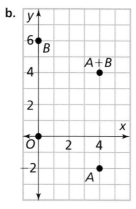

c.

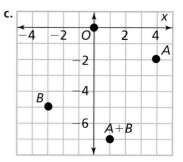

d.

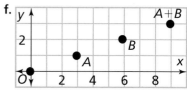

e.

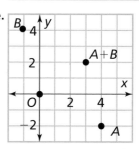

f.

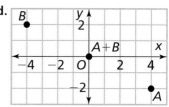

Figure 1

N $(0, 0, 1)$

M $(0, 1, 0)$

L $(1, 0, 0)$

5a. The additional points that were requested may vary. Samples are shown.

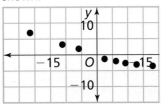

6a. The original polygon is translated right 8 units and up 5 units to obtain the image. **b.** The original polygon is translated left 8 units and up 5 units to obtain the image. **c.** The original polygon is dilated by a factor of 3 with respect to the origin to obtain the image. **d.** The original polygon is dilated by a factor of $\frac{1}{2}$ with respect to the origin to obtain the image. **e.** The image from part (d) is translated right 7 units and up 10 units to obtain the final image. **f.** This image is obtained by reflecting the original polygon across the y-axis and translating the resulting polygon up 2 units. **g.** This image is obtained by stretching the original polygon outward from the y-axis and then translating the resulting polygon up 2 units.

Exercises 7. If A has coordinates (0, 0), then cA has coordinates (0, 0) for all real numbers c, and this means that A and cA are the same point. If A does not have coordinates (0, 0), then cA is (0, 0) if and only if $c = 0$. If A does not have coordinates (0, 0) and $c < 0$,

then cA, O, and A are collinear, and O is between cA and A. cA is c times as far from O as A. If A does not have coordinates (0, 0) and $c > 0$, then cA, O, and A are collinear and cA is c times as far from O as A. If $C < 1$, then cA is between O and A. If $c = 1$, then cA is the same as A. If $c > 1$, then A is between O and cA. If A does not have coordinates (0, 0), then you can locate $2A$ by drawing $\overrightarrow{OA}$. On this ray, mark the point P on the opposite side of A from O such that $AP = OA$. The point P is $2A$. The coordinates of cA are c times the corresponding coordinates of A.
10. See Figure 1

11.

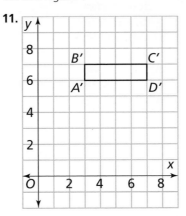

9. parallelogram

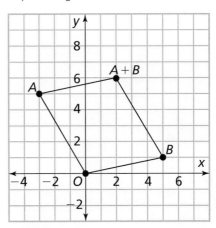

10. parallelogram

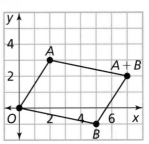

Figure 1

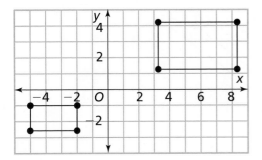

11. parallelogram

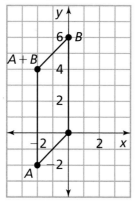

12. line

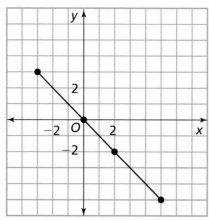

13. parallelogram
See Figure 1

14. parallelogram

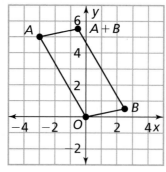

For You to Do 17. $A = (3, 4)$ and $B = (9, 12)$, so $OA = 5$, $AB = 10$, and $OB = 15$. Hence $OA + AB = OB$ and $OB = 3OA = cOA$.
18. $A = (-5, 12)$ and $B = (-10, 24)$, so $OA = 13$, $AB = 13$, and $OB = 26$. Hence $OA + AB = OB$ and $OB = 2OA = cOA$. **19.** $A = (6, 8)$ and $B = (9, 12)$, so $OA = 10$, $A = 10$, $AB = 5$, and $OB = 15$. Hence $OA + AB = OB$ and $OB = 1.5OA = cOA$. **20.** $A = (3, 8)$ and $B = (12, 32)$, so $OA = \sqrt{73}$, $AB = 3\sqrt{73}$, and $OB = 4\sqrt{73}$. Hence $OA + AB = OB$ and $OB = 4OA = cOA$.

Exercises 3. True; if $A = (a_1, a_2)$ and $B = (b_1, b_2)$, then $B - O = (b_1, b_2)$ and $(A + B) - A = (a_1 + b_1, a_2 + b_2) - (a_1, a_2) = (b_1, b_2)$. Since $B - O = (A + B) - A$, it follows from Theorem 7.7 that the vector from O to B is equivalent to the vector from A to $A + B$.

4.

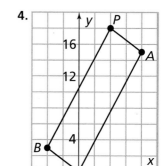

By the Distance Formula, $OA = 17$, $BP = 17$, $OB = 5$, and $AP = 5$. So $OA = BP$ and $OB = AP$. **5.** See Figure 2 By the Distance Formula, $OA = 10$, $BP = 10$, $OB = \sqrt{10}$, and $AP = \sqrt{10}$. So $OA = BP$ and $OB = AP$. **6. a.** (7, 7) **b.** (10, 9) **c.** (13, 11) **d.** (16, 13) **e.** $\left(\frac{11}{2}, 6\right)$ **f.** $\left(5, \frac{17}{3}\right)$ **g.** $\left(\frac{19}{4}, \frac{11}{2}\right)$

9.

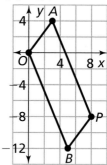

By the Distance Formula, $OA = 5$, $BP = 5$, $OB = 13$, and $AP = 13$. So $OA = BP$ and $OB = AP$.

Figure 1

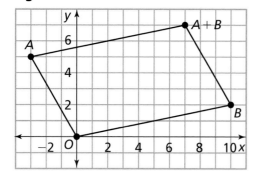

Figure 2

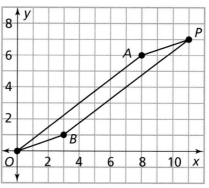

Additional Answers

10. See Figure 1 By Theorem 7.7, $B(\overrightarrow{B+A})$ and $\overrightarrow{OA}$ are equivalent, and $C(\overrightarrow{C+A})$ and $\overrightarrow{OA}$ are equivalent since $(B+A)-B=A-O=A$ and $(C+A)-C=A-O=A$. So $\overline{B(B+A)}\cong\overline{C(C+A)}$. $\overrightarrow{BC}$ and $(\overrightarrow{B+A})(C+A)$ are equivalent since $(C+A)-(B+A)=C-B$. So $\overline{(B+A)(C+A)}\cong\overline{BC}$. It fwollows that the quadrilateral with vertices B, C, $C+A$, and $B+A$ is a parallelogram.

11a.

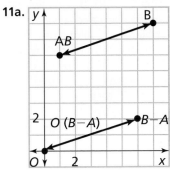

For $\overrightarrow{AB}$, $Head-Tail=(6,2)$ **b.** See Figure 2 The coordinates of the head of $P(\overrightarrow{B-A}+P)$ are $(9, 0)$, and the coordinates of the tail are $(3, -2)$.

12. For $\overrightarrow{AB}$, $Head-Tail=B-A$. For $(A+P)(B+P)$, $Head-Tail=(B-P)-(A+P)=B-A$. Therefore, $(A+P)(B+P)$ is equivalent to $\overrightarrow{AB}$ (Theorem 7.7).

13. If A and B are two different points, it follows immediately from Theorem

7.3 that the midpoint of $\overline{AB}$ is $\frac{1}{2}(A+B)$. **14a.** point **b.** meaningless **c.** number **d.** number **e.** number **f.** point **g.** point **h.** meaningless **i.** point **j.** point **k.** Point **l.** meaningless **m.** point **n.** number **o.** point **p.** number **q.** number **r.** point **s.** number

Lesson 7.12 pp. 608–612
Exercises 1. Answers may vary. Sample: $B-A=(5,4)$ and $D-C=(10,8)$. Hence $D-C=2(B-A)$. $\overrightarrow{AB}$ and $\overrightarrow{CD}$ are not collinear. It follows from Theorem 7.12 that $\overrightarrow{AB}$ and $\overrightarrow{CD}$ have the same direction and that $\overrightarrow{AB}$ and $\overrightarrow{CD}$ are parallel. **2.** Assume $A\neq O$, $t\neq 0$, and O, A, and P are not collinear. By Theorems 7.8 and 7.11, it follows that O, P, tA, and $P+tA$ are the vertices of a parallelogram. $\overline{O(tA)}$ and $\overline{P(P+tA)}$ are opposite sides of the parallelogram and hence are parallel. Since $\overline{OA}$ and $\overline{O(tA)}$ are collinear, it follows that $\overline{OA}$ and $\overline{P(P+tA)}$ are parallel. **3.** The midpoint M of $\overline{OA}$ is $\frac{1}{2}(O+A)=(2,2)$. The midpoint N of $\overline{OB}$ is $\frac{1}{2}(O+B)=(4,-2)$. The vectors $\overrightarrow{MN}$ and $\overrightarrow{AB}$ are noncollinear and $N-M=(2,-4)=\frac{1}{2}(B-A)$. By Theorem 7.12, it follows that $\overline{MN}\|\overline{AB}$. By the Distance Formula, $MN=2\sqrt{5}$ and $AB=4\sqrt{5}$. So $MN=\frac{1}{2}AB$. **4.** $B-A=(4,4)$, so the segment

from O to $B-A$ has slope 1 and length $4\sqrt{2}$. The segment from A to B also has slope 1 and length $4\sqrt{2}$. So $\overline{O(B-A)}$ is parallel to and congruent to $\overline{AB}$. **5a.** 1 **b.** $-\frac{2}{3}$

6.

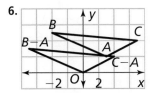

$B-A=(-7,3)$ and $C-A=(4,2)$. By the Distance Formula, $AB=\sqrt{58}$, $BC=\sqrt{122}$, $AC=2\sqrt{5}$, $O(B-A)=\sqrt{58}$, $(B-A)(C-A)=\sqrt{122}$, and $O(C-A)=2\sqrt{5}$. **13.** Line that contains the median through A: $X=(-1,5)+t\left(5,-\frac{7}{2}\right)$; line that contains the median through B: $X=(3,5)+t\left(-1,-\frac{7}{2}\right)$; line that contains the median through C: $X=(5,-2)+t(-4,7)$

14. $M=\left(\frac{3}{2},3\right)$ and $N=\left(4,\frac{1}{2}\right)$. For $\overrightarrow{MN}$, $N-M=\left(\frac{5}{2},-\frac{5}{2}\right)$. For $\overrightarrow{AB}$, $B-A=(5,-5)$. Since $B-A=2(N-M)$, it follows by Theorem 7.12 that $\overrightarrow{MN}$ and $\overrightarrow{AB}$ are parallel. The Midline Theorem implies that the magnitude of $\overrightarrow{MN}$ is half the magnitude of $\overrightarrow{AB}$. **15a.** Go to the point on $\overline{AB}$ that is $\frac{2}{3}$ of the way from

---

Figure 1

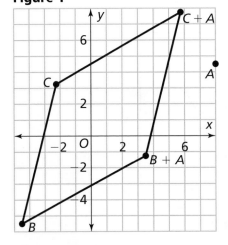

Figure 2

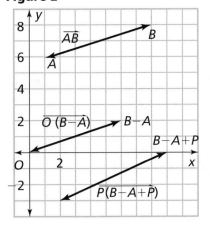

A to *B*. **b.** Go to the point on $\overline{AB}$ that is $\frac{1}{3}$ of the way from *A* to *B*. **c.** Go to the point on $\overline{AB}$ that is $\frac{3}{4}$ of the way from *A* to *B*. **d.** Go to the point on $\overline{AB}$ that is $\frac{1}{4}$ of the way from *A* to *B*. **e.** Go to the point on $\overline{AB}$ that is $\frac{2}{5}$ of the way from *A* to *B*. **f.** Go to the point on $\overline{AB}$ that is $1 - k$ of the way from *A* to *B*. **16a.** $x = \frac{1}{3}, y = \frac{5}{6}$

b. $x = 1, y = \frac{3}{2}$ **c.** $x = \frac{1}{3}, y = \frac{16}{3}$

d. $x = 2, y = \frac{3}{2}$ **e.** $x = \frac{8}{3}, y = -\frac{4}{3}$

f. $x = -\frac{10}{3}, y = \frac{13}{6}$

Lesson 7.13   **pp. 613–616**
In-Class Experiment
The figure shows the lines for Problems 1, 3, and 4. **1.** See Figure 1 **4.** Lines ℓ and *t* intersect at $\left(\frac{4}{7}, \frac{18}{7}\right)$. Lines *s* and *t* do not intersect. Lines *r* and *t* do not intersect. Consider lines *p* and *q* with vector equations $P = (a, b) + s(c, d)$ and $Q = (e, f) + t(g, h)$, respectively, where (a, b), (c, d), (e, f), and (g, h) are specific points and *s* and *t* are variables that range over the set of real numbers. *p* is vertical if $c = 0$, and *q* is vertical if $g = 0$. If one line is vertical and the other is not, there is one point of intersection. If both *p* and *q* are vertical, then they are parallel when $a \neq e$ and they coincide when $a = e$. If neither line is vertical, then compare $\frac{d}{c}$ and $\frac{h}{g}$. If $\frac{d}{c} \neq \frac{h}{g}$, then the lines have different slopes and have

one point of intersection. If $\frac{d}{c} = \frac{h}{g}$, then the lines have equal slopes, which means they are parallel or coincide. To decide which is the case, see whether the points where they intersect the *y*-axis are different or the same. To find this point of intersection for line *p*, compute $(a, b) + \left(-\frac{a}{c}\right)(c, d)$; for line *q*, compute $(e, f) + \left(-\frac{e}{g}\right)(g, h)$.

Exercises 6. Answers may vary. Sample: $P = (2, 4) + t(2, -1)$

7. Let *ABCD* be any parallelogram. If you translate the parallelogram to have the image of *A* at the origin, the vertices are $O, B - A, C - A,$ and $D - A$. But it follows from Theorem 7.8 that $C - A = (B - A) + (D - A)$. The midpoint of $\overline{O(C - A)}$ is therefore $\frac{1}{2}(B + D - 2A)$, or $\frac{1}{2}B + \frac{1}{2}D - A$. The midpoint of $\overline{(B - A)(D - A)}$ is also $\frac{1}{2}B + \frac{1}{2}D - A$. Since the diagonals of $O(B - A)(C - A)(D - A)$ bisect each other, so do the diagonals of the original parallelogram. **12.** If *M*, *N*, and *Q* are the midpoints of $\overline{OA}, \overline{AB},$ and $\overline{OB}$, respectively, then $M = \left(\frac{9}{2}, 1\right)$, $N = (5, 5)$, and $Q = \left(\frac{1}{2}, 4\right)$. An equation of the perpendicular bisector

of $\overline{OA}$ is $T = \left(\frac{9}{2}, 1\right) + n(2, -9)$. An equation of the perpendicular bisector of $\overline{OB}$ is $R = \left(\frac{1}{2}, 4\right) + f(8, -1)$. An equation of the perpendicular bisector of $\overline{AB}$ is $S = (5, 5) + g(6, 8)$.

13. $\left(\frac{55}{14}, \frac{25}{7}\right)$; $\left(\frac{55}{14}, \frac{25}{7}\right)$ is on the perpendicular bisector of $\overline{AB}$, since $(5, 5) + \left(-\frac{5}{28}\right)(6, 8) = \left(\frac{55}{14}, \frac{25}{7}\right)$.

14a. Answers may vary. Sample: Find vector equations of the three lines. Use the equations to check that no two of the lines are parallel or collinear. Find the point of intersection of a pair of the lines. Find the point of intersection of another pair. If the two points of intersection are the same, then the lines are concurrent. **b.** vector equation for the line containing the altitude through *O*: $J = q(6, 8)$; vector equation for the line containing the altitude through *A*: $I = (9, 2) + t(8, -1)$; vector equation for the line containing the altitude through *B*: $L = (1, 8) + n(2, -9)$; all pairs of these lines intersect at $\left(\frac{15}{7}, \frac{20}{7}\right)$, so the lines are concurrent.

Review   **pp. 620–621**

3. See Figure 2

Figure 1

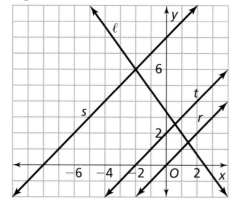

Figure 2

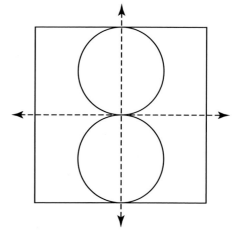

8. midpoint F of $\overline{AB}$: $\left(\frac{1}{2}, -2\right)$;

midpoint G of $\overline{BC}$: $\left(\frac{7}{2}, 3\right)$;

midpoint H of $\overline{CD}$: (1, 4); midpoint

I of $\overline{DA}$: (−2,−1); slope of

$\overline{FG}$ = slope of $\overline{HI}$ = $\frac{5}{3}$, and slope of

$\overline{HG}$ = slope of $\overline{IF}$ = $\frac{2}{5}$. Since opposite

sides of FGHI have equal slopes, they
are parallel. So FGHI is a parallelogram.

Test   **pp. 622–623**

15a.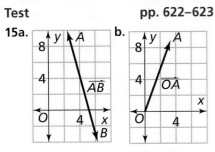

16. Answers may vary. Samples
are given. **a.** $\overrightarrow{AB}$ and $\overrightarrow{CD}$, with
A = (0, 2), B = (2, 4), C = (0, 0),
and D = (6, 6); The segments $\overline{AB}$ and
$\overline{CD}$ both have a slope of 1. **b.** same
vectors as in part (a); if you translate
$\overline{AB}$ down 2 units, then the image of
$\overline{AB}$ is contained in $\overline{CD}$. **c.** $\overrightarrow{AB}$ and
$\overrightarrow{CD}$, with A = (0, 2), B = (−2, 0),
C = (0, 0), and D = (6, 6); $\overline{AB}$
and $\overline{CD}$ have the same slope. If you
translate $\overline{AB}$ down 2 units, then the
image $\overline{A'B'}$ has A' = C, and $\overline{A'B'}$ and
$\overrightarrow{CD}$, are opposite rays.

Chapter 8
Lesson 8.1   **pp. 627–630**
Exercises 6. Answers may vary.
Sample: Find a straight path from the
point perpendicular to the line. Use
a ruler, tape measure, or some other
measuring device to find the length of
the path. For a point and a line in the
coordinate plane, find an equation for

the line. Then find an equation for the
line through the given point perpendicular to the given line. Solve a system
of equations to find the coordinates of
the point of intersection of the lines.
Use the Distance Formula to find the
distance from the point of intersection
to the given point.

12b. $\left(-3, \frac{8}{3}\right)$; Answers may vary.

Sample: Reflect S across $\overleftrightarrow{AB}$. The image
is S′(−7, 5). Write an equation for $\overleftrightarrow{S'F}$
and use it to show that $\overleftrightarrow{S'F}$ intersects
$\overleftrightarrow{AB}$ at $K\left(-3, \frac{8}{3}\right)$. $\overline{S'F}$ is the shortest
path from S′ to F, and so, by symmetry,
the path made up of the segments $\overline{SK}$
and $\overline{KF}$ is the shortest path from S to F
via a point on $\overleftrightarrow{AB}$.

Lesson 8.2   **pp. 631–636**
Exercises

6a.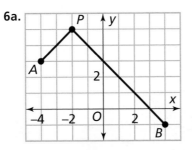

b. P(−2, 5); reflect A across the line
y = 5 to get A′(−2,7). The equation
of $\overleftrightarrow{A'B}$ is y = −x + 3. Solve the
system y = 5 and y = −x + 3 to get
P(−2,5). **c.** $8\sqrt{2} \approx 11.3$

10.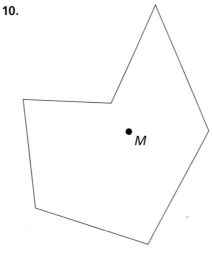

12a. $m\angle SPA = 90°, m\angle FPB \approx 8.00°$
b. $m\angle SPA \approx 66.04°, m\angle FPB \approx 9.82°$

c. $m\angle SPA = 45°, m\angle FPB \approx 13.67°$
d. $m\angle SPA \approx 34.70°,$
$m\angle FPB \approx 19.80°$
e. $m\angle SPA \approx 27.44°,$
$m\angle FPB \approx 36.87°$
f. $m\angle SPA \approx 22.87°, m\angle FPB = 90°$

Lesson 8.3   **pp. 637–640**
Exercises 4. There are two cases
to consider. **Case 1** S and F are on
opposite sides of line ℓ. In this case,
draw $\overline{SF}$. The point P where $\overline{SF}$
intersects ℓ is the desired point.
Case 2 S and F are on the same side of
line ℓ. In this case, reflect F across ℓ to
get F′. Draw $\overline{SF'}$. The point P where
$\overline{SF'}$ intersects ℓ is the desired point.
6. $L\left(-1, \frac{5}{4}\right), M\left(7, \frac{23}{4}\right)$

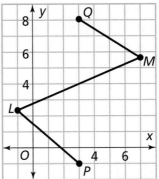

7a. If P stays on the line with equation
y = −1 as it moves closer to ℓ, then
you would expect both L and M to
move downward.
b. $L\left(-1, -\frac{4}{13}\right), M\left(7, \frac{68}{13}\right)$
13a. 12 paths
b. $A \to B \to C \to D \to E \to A$:
$\sqrt{41} + \sqrt{37} + \sqrt{58} + \sqrt{29} +$
$5(\approx 30.487)$
$A \to B \to C \to E \to D \to A$:
$\sqrt{41} + \sqrt{29} + 2\sqrt{13} + \sqrt{5} +$
$5(\approx 26.235)$
$A \to B \to D \to C \to E \to A$:
$\sqrt{58} + \sqrt{41} + \sqrt{37} + 2\sqrt{13} +$
$3\sqrt{2}(\approx 31.555)$
$A \to B \to D \to E \to C \to A$:
$\sqrt{41} + \sqrt{29} + 2\sqrt{13} +$
$8\sqrt{2}(\approx 30.313)$
$A \to B \to E \to C \to D \to A$:
$\sqrt{41} + \sqrt{37} + 2\sqrt{13} +$
$2\sqrt{5}(\approx 24.169)$
$A \to B \to E \to D \to C \to A$:
$\sqrt{41} + \sqrt{37} + \sqrt{29} + \sqrt{5} +$
$5\sqrt{2}(\approx 27.178)$

$A \rightarrow C \rightarrow B \rightarrow D \rightarrow E \rightarrow A$:
$\sqrt{58} + \sqrt{29} + 8\sqrt{2} +$
$5 \, (\approx 29.315)$
$A \rightarrow C \rightarrow B \rightarrow E \rightarrow D \rightarrow A$:
$\sqrt{29} + 2\sqrt{5} + 5\sqrt{2} +$
$5 \, (\approx 21.928)$
$A \rightarrow C \rightarrow D \rightarrow B \rightarrow E \rightarrow A$:
$\sqrt{58} + \sqrt{37} + \sqrt{5} +$
$8\sqrt{2} \, (\approx 27.248)$
$A \rightarrow C \rightarrow E \rightarrow B \rightarrow D \rightarrow A$:
$2\sqrt{13} + 2\sqrt{5} + 8\sqrt{2} \, (\approx 22.997)$
$A \rightarrow D \rightarrow B \rightarrow C \rightarrow E \rightarrow A$:
$\sqrt{58} + 2\sqrt{13} + \sqrt{5} + 3\sqrt{2} +$
$5 \, (\approx 26.306)$
$A \rightarrow D \rightarrow C \rightarrow B \rightarrow E \rightarrow A$:
$\sqrt{58} + \sqrt{37} + 2\sqrt{5} +$
$5 \, (\approx 23.171)$
The shortest path is
$A \rightarrow C \rightarrow B \rightarrow E \rightarrow D \rightarrow A$.

Mathematical Reflections   p. 641

5. The path goes from $(-1, 4)$ to $\left(-\frac{3}{4}, 5\right)$ to $(1, -2)$ to $(2, 2)$.

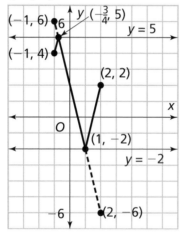

Lesson 8.4   pp. 643–646

Exercises 7. Answers may vary.
Sample: Add squares in the order indicated by the numbers.

		1	4
5			3
8	6		2
9	7		

The maximum area possible is 16 unit^2.
9. See Figure 1
The maximum volume possible is 22 unit^3.

Lesson 8.5   pp. 647–652

Exercises 5. The argument in For You to Do can be used, along with the final figure that Derman used. Replace 32 with $\frac{p}{4}$, where $p = 2(a + b)$ and $a < b$. In the final figure, the square has a square with sides of length $\frac{p}{4}$, and its interior is covered by the two pieces of the $a \times b$ rectangle except for a white square of area $\left(\frac{p}{4} - a\right)^2$.

Lesson 8.6   pp. 653–655

Exercises 3. a rectangle with side lengths 20, 30, 20, 30; suppose $ABCD$ is a parallelogram with $AB = 20$ and $AD = 30$. Let h be the length of the perpendicular segment from B to $\overleftrightarrow{AD}$. If $\angle A$ is acute, then $h = 20 \sin A$; so $h < 20$ since $\sin A < 1$. If $\angle A$ is obtuse, then $h = 20 \sin(180° - m\angle A)$; so $h < 20$ since $\sin(180° - m\angle A) < 1$. If $\angle A$ is a right angle, then $h = AB = 20$. In this last case, h has its maximum

possible value and the parallelogram has its maximum possible area.
5. Consider an arbitrary quadrilateral $ABCD$. Draw the diagonal $\overline{AC}$. You can maximize the areas of $\triangle ABC$ and $\triangle ADC$ while keeping the perimeter the same by making them isosceles triangles with base $\overline{AC}$. Now draw diagonal $\overline{BD}$. You can maximize the areas of $\triangle ABD$ and $\triangle CBD$ wile keeping the perimeter the same by making them isosceles triangles with base $\overline{BD}$. Since the side lengths of this new quadrilateral are all congruent, it is a rhombus. **6.** Suppose you are given an n-gon (convex) whose area is the greatest possible for a given perimeter p. Assume the polygon is not equilateral. Then there are two sides $\overline{AB}$ and $\overline{BC}$ with a common endpoint such that $AB \neq BC$. Find the point B' such that $\triangle AB'C$ is isosceles and has the same perimeter as $\triangle ABC$. Area $(\triangle AB'C) >$ Area $(\triangle ABC)$, so if you replace the vertex B of the original polygon with B', the new polygon has an area greater than that of the original. This contradicts what we were originally given. So the assumption that the given polygon is not equilateral must be false.
7. Suppose a rhombus of given perimeter has sides of length s and encloses the maximum possible area. Let $x°$ be the measure of the angle formed by a pair of adjacent sides of the rhombus. If $x = 90$, then the rhombus is a square and has area s^2. If $x \neq 90$, then the rhombus has height

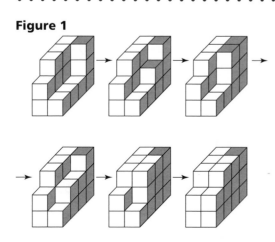

Figure 1

$h = s \sin x°$ or $h = s \sin (180 - x)°$.
In either case, $h < s$ since the value of the sine function is less than 1 for acute angles. As a result, the area of the rhombus is less than s^2 for $x \neq 90$. Hence the rhombus of maximum area for perimeter p is a square.

Chapter Test   **p. 657**
3. See Figure 1
4. The shortest path is from A to P to B. See Figure 2

Lesson 8.7   **pp. 659–661**
For You to Explore
4.

Lesson 8.8   **pp. 662–665**
Exercises 2a. circular arcs

b.

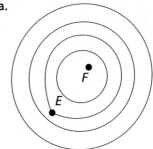

7.

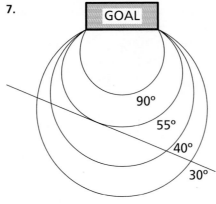

Lesson 8.9   **pp. 666–670**
Exercises 1. See Figure 3
2. Each contour is a pair of lines parallel with, and equidistant to, ℓ. To prove this, choose a coordinate system so that ℓ is the graph of the equation

$y = 0$. For any point $P(x, y)$, the distance between P and ℓ is $|y|$. So the set of all points a distance c from ℓ is the graph of the equation $|y| = c$. The equation $|y| = c$ is equivalent to $y = c$ or $y = -c$, so the locus of points a distance c from ℓ is the two horizontal lines that pass through $(0, c)$ and $(0, -c)$.
3. Check students' work. See Figure 4

5a.

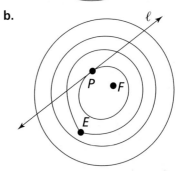

b.

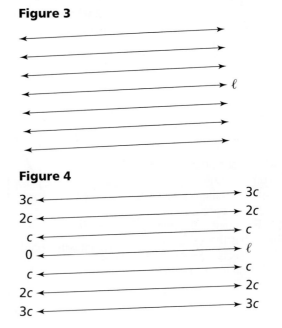

Figure 1

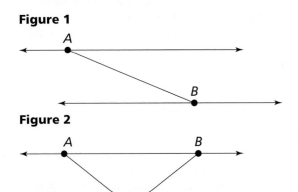

Figure 2

Figure 3

Figure 4

Find a contour that is tangent to the line ℓ. The point of tangency P is the point that minimizes the value of f.

6.

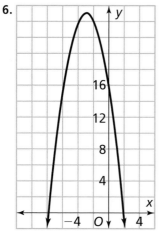

8a.

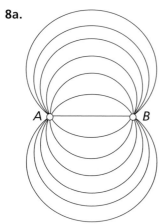

13a.

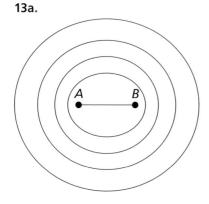

c. Check students' drawings. If the line ℓ drawn on the contour plot does not intersect $\overline{AB}$, then there will be a contour line that is tangent to ℓ at some point P. This point is the point on ℓ for which f has the least value possible. If ℓ intersects $\overline{AB}$, then the point of intersection yields the least value AB.

Lesson 8.10   pp. 671–676
Exercises

2.

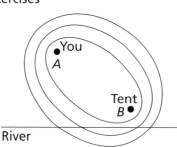

Only one contour line will be tangent to the river. The path from A to the point of tangency to B is the shortest.

4.

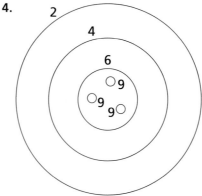

9. Answers may vary. Sample: Somewhere along an ellipse with A and B as foci seems reasonable, but there is no reason why the entire refuge should be inside the ellipse. Also, the location should probably be at approximately equal distances from A and B, not just anywhere on the portion of an arc that does not cross the refuge.

Mathematical Reflections   p. 677
Exercises

2a.

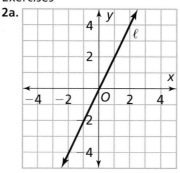

b. $f(P) = \dfrac{|2x - y|}{\sqrt{5}}$, where P is the point with coordinates (x, y)

c.

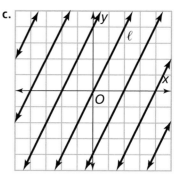

6. Contour lines that do not intersect the river indicate that you would not walk far enough to get to the river. Contour lines that intersect the river in more than one point indicate that you have walked too far. So select the contour line that is tangent to the riverbank, go to the point of tangency, and then go to the tent.

Lesson 8.12   pp. 681–684
Exercises 9d. changes; There is no triangle when P is at A or B. For all other points on the top semicircle, the area of $\triangle APB$ is $\frac{1}{2}AP\sqrt{16 - AP^2}$. All the values of this expression will be greater than 0 but less than or equal to 4. (The maximum value 4 is attained when $\triangle APB$ is isosceles.)
e. constant; π, since the circumference of a circle with diameter d is πd.
f. changes; The value of $AP + PB$ is $AP + \sqrt{16 - AP^2}$. The value of AP can vary from 0 to 4. The value of $AP + \sqrt{16 - AP^2}$ varies from 4 to $4\sqrt{2}$. **g.** changes; As P moves clockwise from A to B, AP varies from 0 to 4. Hence $\frac{AP}{BA}$ varies from 0 to 1.
h. changes; When P is at A, the ratio is 0. As P moves counterclockwise away from A and toward B, the value of the ratio increases more and more rapidly and without any limit, because AP is approaching 4 while PB is approaching 0. The ratio is undefined when P reaches B. **i.** constant; P cannot be at A or B. For all other positions of P, the distance from M to N is MN. By the Midsegment Theorem, this length is 2.

Lesson 8.13   pp. 685–689
Exercises 2. In Step 1, draw the segments perpendicular to the sides of equilateral $\triangle ABC$ from a point D in the interior of $\triangle ABC$. In Step 2,

draw segments through D parallel to the sides of $\triangle ABC$. Each of these segments should have its endpoints on the other two sides of the triangle. Three equilateral triangles will be formed, each having D as a vertex. The segments drawn in Step 1 will be altitudes of these triangles. To get the figure in Step 3, translate the small equilateral triangles from Step 2, along with their altitudes, so that you fit each into a corner of $\triangle ABC$, as shown. The fit will be perfect since the triangles you are translating are equilateral and equiangular and since perpendicular segments from one of two parallel segments to the other are congruent. To get from Step 3 to Step 4, replace the oblique altitudes of the image triangles with vertical altitudes. The new altitudes are congruent to the old ones because all altitudes of an equilateral triangle are congruent. To get from Step 4 to Step 5, use the fact that perpendicular segments from one of two parallel segments to the other are congruent. Translate the altitudes of the two small equilateral triangles at the bottom to align with the altitude of the small equilateral triangle at the top. The sum of the lengths of the three small altitudes is equal to the length of an altitude of $\triangle ABC$.

15c. D at A or B if $\triangle ABC$ is isosceles with $AC = BC$; if $AC \neq BC$, then D at A for $AC > BC$, and D at B for $AC < BC$ **d.** the greater of the two heights of $\triangle ABC$ as measured from A and from B

Lesson 8.14　　　　**pp. 690–694**

Exercises 1. The given figure is not convex and so cannot enclose the maximum area for its perimeter. In the first diagram below, $ABCDEF$ is the original figure given in the text. Perform reflections across the dashed lines in the first diagram to get a figure with the same perimeter and a greater area that does not cross itself. Perform reflections across the dashed lines in the second diagram to get a convex polygon with the same perimeter and a yet greater area.

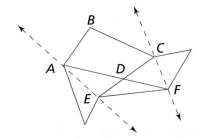

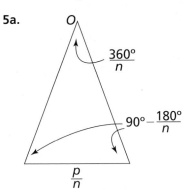

5a.

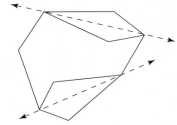

b. $h = \dfrac{p}{2n \tan\left(\frac{180°}{n}\right)}$.

c. Area of triangle $= \dfrac{p^2}{4n^2 \tan\left(\frac{180°}{n}\right)}$,

Area of polygon $= \dfrac{p^2}{4n \tan\left(\frac{180°}{n}\right)}$

6a. 6, 7, or 8 sides

b. area of run that is half of a regular hexagon $= \dfrac{168^2}{48 \tan 30°}$, area of run that is half of a regular heptagon $= \dfrac{168^2}{56 \tan\left(\frac{180°}{7}\right)}$, area of run that is half of a regular octagon $= \dfrac{168^2}{48 \tan 22.5°}$

Lesson 8.15　　　　**pp. 695–698**

Exercises 3. First draw isosceles $\triangle OAB$ with base angles at A and B of measure $90° - \dfrac{180°}{n}$ and base $\dfrac{p}{n}$ units long. Its vertex angle will have measure $\dfrac{360°}{n}$. Next, construct a triangle congruent to $\triangle OAB$ that has O as its vertex and shares leg $\overline{OB}$ with $\triangle OAB$. Continue attaching triangles congruent

to $\triangle OAB$ in this fashion until you have n triangles whose bases form the desired regular n-gon.

6a. We are assuming $x < 1$. Subtract x from each side of $x < 1$ to get $x - x < 1 - x$, or $0 < 1 - x$. Saying that $0 < 1 - x$ is the same as saying that $1 - x$ is positive. **b.** From part (a), $1 - x$ is positive, and this implies that $\dfrac{1-x}{2}$ is positive. But then $x + \dfrac{1-x}{2}$ is positive and greater than x. So $x + \dfrac{1-x}{2} \geq 1$, since we are assuming that x is the largest positive number less than 1. **c.** Answers may vary. Sample:

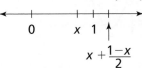

d. The solution is $x \geq 1$. This contradicts the original assumption that x is less than 1. **e.** It is an indirect proof that there is no greatest positive number less than 1.

10a.

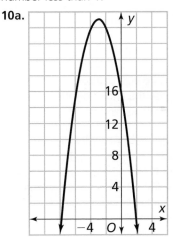

b.

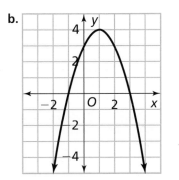

c.

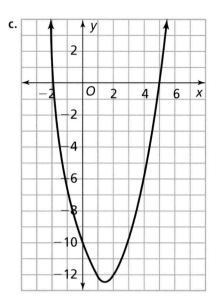

Lesson 8.16 pp. 699–701
Exercises 1. Suppose a line ℓ cuts the perimeter in half. If the part of the area on one side of the line is greater than the part on the other side, you can reflect the part of the curve on the side with the greater area across ℓ to get a curve with the original perimeter but a greater area. This contradicts the assumption that the area of the original curve was maximal. **4.** If this angle did not measure 90°, you could increase or decrease the angle to form a right triangle with larger area. This would create a new half-curve with the same perimeter as C, but enclosing more area, which would contradict your assumption that C is the best possible curve. **6.** Refer to the curve C in the answer for Ex. 4. Pick a point J on C. Move around the curve in one direction

until you have traveled a distance $\frac{p}{2}$ along the curve. Call the point you come to K. Then $\overset{\longleftrightarrow}{JK}$ intersects C in two points and cuts the perimeter in half.

10. We are given a non-self crossing curve C with a given perimeter p with the greatest area possible. (The existence hypothesis assumes that such a curve really exists.) The curve C is convex. To see why, suppose C is not convex. Then there would be two points X and y on C such that all points on $\overline{XY}$ between X and Y are in the exterior of C. Reflect the non-convex part of C bounded by X and Y across $\overline{XY}$. This would give a new curve C' with the same perimeter as C but with greater area than C. This contradicts the given information that C has the greatest possible area. Choose a line ℓ that intersects C in two points and divides the perimeter in half. (See the answer for Ex. 5.) This line divides the area of C in half, for if it did not, you could reflect the part on the side of ℓ with the greater area across ℓ to obtain a curve of perimeter p but with greater area than before. That would contradict the given information about C. Consider a region on one side of ℓ (bounded by ℓ and one of the halves of C). The reasoning in the answer for Ex. 4 shows that it is a semicircular region. But by the same reasoning, the region on the other side is semicircular, and the two regions share a diameter of C. Hence the curve C is a circle.

Cumulative Review pp. 710–710
2a. The teacup has a plane of symmetry, but no line of symmetry.

b.

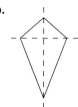

c. There is no line of symmetry, but the figure has 180° rotational symmetry.

Figure **c** has 180° rotational symmetry.

4a.

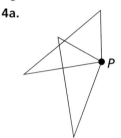

b.

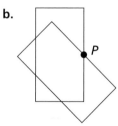

c.

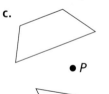

Staff Credits

The Pearson people on the CME Project team—representing curriculum design, editorial, editorial services, digital product development, publishing services, and technical operations—are listed below. Bold type denotes the core team members.

Ernest Albanese, Scott Andrews, Carolyn Artin, Margaret Banker, Beth Blumberg, Kerry Cashman, Carolyn Chappo, Gina Choe, Casey Clark, Jason Cuoco, Sheila DeFazio, **Frederick Fellows**, **Patti Fromkin**, Paul J. Gagnon, Ellen Welch Granter, Jonathan Kier, Jennifer King, Elizabeth Krieble, Sara Levendusky, Lisa Lin, Carolyn Lock, **Carolyn McGuire**, Rich McMahon, Eve Melnechuk, **Hope Morley**, **Jen Paley**, Linda Punskovsky, Marcy Rose, Rashid Ross, Carol Roy, Ted Smykal, Laura Smyth, Kara Stokes, Richard Sullivan, Tiffany Taylor-Sullivan, Catherine Terwilliger, Mark Tricca, Paula Vergith, **Joe Will**, **Kristin Winters**, Heather Wright, Allison Wyss

Additional Credits

Niki Birbilis, Robert Doron, Patty Fagan, Cynthia Metallides, Jill A. Ort, Deborah Savona, Jewel Simmons

Cover Design and Illustration
9 Surf Studio

Cover Photography
Jim Cummins/Corbis; **Inset**, Stockbyte/Getty Images, Inc.

Illustration
Kerry Cashman, Rich McMahon, Jen Paley, Rashid Ross, Ted Smykal

Maps
XNR Productions, Inc. p.180

Photography
Chapter 1: Pages 2–3, Randy Faris/Corbis; **8**, Jason Hawkes/Corbis; **21**, Thom Lang/Corbis; **23**, Kyodo News; **24**, Javier Pierini/Digital Vision/Getty Images, Inc.; **34**, Atlanpic/Alamy; **36**, Clement McCarthy/Alamy; **47**, Robert Estall photo agency/Alamy; **48**, Clement McCarthy/Alamy; **64 inset**, rubberball/Royalty Free; **65br**, Pablo San Juan/Corbis; **71 inset**, Mike McQueen/Corbis; **74**, AP Photo/Charlie Riedel; **83**, AP Photo/Austin Daily Herald, Eric Johnson.

Chapter 2: Pages 70–71, Getty Images, Inc.; **72**, Chris Daniels/Corbis; **74**, Lew Robertson/Corbis; **79**, Roger Ressmeyer/Corbis; **87**, Chris Daniels/Corbis; **98**, Jim Cummins/Corbis; **109**, Catherine Booker/Jupiter Images; **112**, Wikimedia; **114**, David Bergman/Corbis; **116**, Kara Stokes; **125**, AP Photo/Timothy D. Easley; **132**, Georgette Douwma/Getty Images, Inc.; **138t**, Elio Ciol/Corbis; **138b**, iStockphoto.com; **141**, David Bergman/Corbis; **142**, Swerve/Alamy; **160**, Rick Friedman/Corbis.

Chapter 3: Pages 168–169, Kirsty McLaren/Alamy; **170**, Siri Schwartzman; **189**, Steve Allen/Brand X/Corbis; **193**, Siri Schwartzman; **194**, Paul Gagnon; **201 inset**, Michele Falzone/JAI/Corbis; **201r**, Angelo Cavalli/Getty Images, Inc.; **206**, Christian Hoehn/Getty Images, Inc.; **214**, Paul Gagnon; **216**, MAPS.com/Corbis; **225**, Robert Daly/Getty Images, Inc.; **229 both**, Stephen Finn/Alamy; **230**, Scott Peterson/Getty Images; **232**, Kara Stokes; **233**, Kara Stokes; **237**, Larry Lee Photography/Corbis; **238**, Jose Fuste Raga/Corbis; **246**, Kara Stokes; **247**, Kara Stokes; **253**, Jeppe De Boer; **255**, Laurie Chamberlain/Corbis.

Chapter 4: Pages 260–261, JLImages/Alamy; **262**, Paul Ott; **268l**, Fernando Fernández/age fotostock; **268r**, K-PHOTOS/Alamy; **283 both**, Paul Gagnon; **287**, Paul Ott; **288**, Kavashkin Boris/ITAR-TASS/Corbis; **293**, Michael Newman/Photo Edit; **302**, Deb Nicholls; **304**, Deb Nicholls; **314**, SuperStock Inc.; **317**, Deb Nicholls; **319**, Enrique Algarra/age fotostock; **321**, Deb Nicholls; **322**, Deb Nicholls; **325**, Kara Stokes; **343**, Deb Nicholls.

Chapter 5: Pages 352–353 background, Robert Harding Picture Library Ltd/Alamy; **352–353 inset**, ScotStock/Alamy; **354**, AP Photo/POOL, Mark Wilson; **366**, Big Cheese Photo LLC/Alamy; **366 inset**, Garry Gay/Alamy; **373**, AP Photo/John Gaps III; **374**, Atmosphere Picture Library/Alamy; **385**, AP Photo/Matt Rourke; **386**, www.circlemakers.org; **388**, Allan Munsie/Alamy; **391**, Grigory Dukor/Reuters/Corbis; **399**, ACE STOCK LIMITED/Alamy; **419**, Allan Munsie/Alamy; **420**, Torleif Svensson/Corbis; **429**, Jeffrey Coolidge/Getty Images, Inc.; **433**, Richard S. Durrance/National Geographic/Getty Images, Inc.

Chapter 6: Pages 440–441, ER Productions/Corbis; **441 inset**, Stockbyte/Getty Images, Inc.; **442**, Artist painting a portrait over a grid for accurate proportion, printed Paris 1737 (engraving), Bosse, Abraham (1602–76) (after)/Private Collection, The Stapleton Collection/The Bridgeman Art Library; **446**, Paul Gagnon; **463**, Foto Marburg/Art Resource, NY; **464**, Ted Pink/Alamy; **466**, David R. Frazier Photolibrary, Inc./Alamy; **496**, Ted Pink/Alamy; **498**, Kara Stokes; **526**, Kara Stokes.

Chapter 7: Pages 534–535, David Parmenter/www.daveparm.com; **536**, image100/Alamy; **540**, image100/Alamy; **545**, Craig Tuttle/Corbis; **555**, Kara Stokes; **561**, image100/Alamy; **562**, Heather Wright; **569**, Adam Woolfitt/Corbis; **578**, Joel Day/Alamy; **583**, Bob Krist/Corbis; **587**, Fabrice Bettex/Alamy; **592**, Heather Wright; **594**, Redmond Durrell/Alamy; **603**, Comstock/Corbis; **617**, Frank Krahmer/zefa/Corbis; **619**, Steve Skjold/Alamy.

Chapter 8: Pages 624–625, USPS; **626**, Heather Wright; **641**, Heather Wright; **642**, AP Photo/Daily Southtown, Brett Roseman, File; **656**, David McNew/Getty Images, Inc.; **658**, University of Texas Libraries; **659**, Wunderground.com; **661**, Wunderground.com; **670**, Envision/Corbis; **677**, Panoramic Images/Getty Images, Inc.; **678**, Derek Mitchell/Alamy; **702**, Gusto/Photo Researchers, Inc.

Text Acknowledgments
412 (Exercise 12), From *Nuovi Elementi de Matematica* 1 by N. Dodero, P. Baroncini, and D. Trezzi. Copyright © 1996 Ghisetti e Corvi Editori, Milano. Used by permission.

Note: Every effort has been made to locate the copyright owner of the material reprinted in this book. Omissions brought to our attention will be corrected in subsequent editions.